Mathematics
For Winthrop University

A Second Custom Edition

Taken from:
*Mathematics with Applications in the Management,
Natural, and Social Sciences*, Eleventh Edition
by Margaret L. Lial, Thomas W. Hungerford,
John P. Holcomb, Jr. and Bernadette Mullins

Mathematical Ideas, Twelfth Edition
by Charles D. Miller, Vern E. Heeren, John Hornsby,
Margaret L. Morrow and Jill Van Newenhizen

Cover Art: Courtesy of PhotoDisc/Getty Images, brandXpictures.

Taken from:

Mathematics with Applications in the Management, Natural, and Social Sciences, Eleventh Edition
by Margaret L. Lial, Thomas W. Hungerford, John P. Holcomb, Jr. and Bernadette Mullins
Copyright © 2015, 2011, 2007, 2004 by Pearson Education, Inc.
Boston, Massachusetts 02116

Mathematical Ideas, Twelfth Edition
by Charles D. Miller, Vern E. Heeren, John Hornsby, Margaret L. Morrow and Jill Van Newenhizen
Copyright © 2012, 2008, 2004 by Pearson Education, Inc.
Published by Addison-Wesley
Boston, Massachusetts 02116

This special edition published in cooperation with Pearson Learning Solutions.

All trademarks, service marks, registered trademarks, and registered service marks are the property of
their respective owners and are used herein for identification purposes only.

Pearson Learning Solutions, 501 Boylston Street, Suite 900, Boston, MA 02116
A Pearson Education Company
www.pearsoned.com

Printed in the United States of America

2 3 4 5 6 7 8 9 10 V0UD 18 17 16 15 14

000200010271884121

SH

ISBN 10: 1-269-86581-1
ISBN 13: 978-1-269-86581-4

Contents

Taken from: *Mathematics with Applications in the Management, Natural, and Social Sciences*, Eleventh Edition by Margaret L. Lial, Thomas W. Hungerford, John P. Holcomb, Jr. and Bernadette Mullins

Taken from: *Mathematical Ideas*, Twelfth Edition by Charles D. Miller, Vern E. Heeren, John Hornsby, Margaret L. Morrow and Jill Van Newenhizen

Preface

Mathematics with Applications is an applications-centered text for students in business, management, and natural and social sciences. It covers the basics of college algebra, followed by topics in finite mathematics and concluding with a treatment of applied calculus. The text can be used for a variety of different courses, and the only prerequisite is a basic course in algebra. Chapter 1 provides a thorough review of basic algebra for those students who need it. The newly added Prerequisite Skills Test (for Chapters 1–4) and Calculus Readiness Test (for Chapters 11–14) at the front of the text can help determine where remediation is needed for students with gaps in their basic algebra skills.

It has been our primary goal to present sound mathematics in an understandable manner, proceeding from the familiar to new material and from concrete examples to general rules and formulas. There is an ongoing focus on real-world problem solving, and almost every section includes relevant, contemporary applications.

New to This Edition

With each revision comes an opportunity to improve the presentation of the content in a variety of ways. This revision is no exception as we have revised and added content, updated and added new applications, fine-tuned pedagogical devices, and evaluated and enhanced the exercise sets. In addition, both the functionality of MyMathLab and the resources within it have been greatly improved and expanded for this revision. These improvements were incorporated after careful consideration and much feedback from those who teach this course regularly. Following is a list of some of the more substantive revisions made to this edition.

- **Prerequisite Diagnostic Tests:** As a way to address the often weak algebra skills that students bring to this course, two diagnostic exams are provided just prior to Chapter 1. These two diagnostics can be used in a variety of ways, depending on the expectations and goals of the course. The Prerequisite Skills Test assesses student understanding of the core skills students should have prior to starting Chapter 1. The Calculus Readiness Test is designed to diagnose any missing prerequisite algebra skills prior to starting Chapter 11. Solutions are provided in the back of the text so students can self-remediate as needed, saving valuable class time. *Getting Ready* quizzes in MyMathLab are also available as automated versions of these diagnostics.

- **Additional Figures:** An additional six graphical figures were added to Section 2.2 to help illustrate slope as part of writing the equation of a line.

- **Quadratic Functions:** In the previous edition, there were two separate sections (3.4 and 3.5) for quadratic functions and applications of quadratic functions. These two sections have been consolidated into one section for ease of teaching.

- **Implicit Differentiation and Related Rates:** By popular demand, two sections have been added: implicit differentiation and related rates. These sections include step-by-step instructions for students to find the derivative of an implicitly defined function and to find a rate of change given that two quantities are related to each other and also changing over time. Examples and exercises include applications to business such as the rates of change of the number of employees and revenue of a corporation.

- **Case Studies:** The popular culminating activities at the end of every chapter have been expanded to provide options for **extended projects** for individual students or more extensive **group work.** In addition, three of the case studies are completely new and five have been updated significantly.

- A careful and thorough review of the **correlation between examples and exercises** has been completed to ensure that students have examples to refer to when working homework exercises. A table at the start of the answers for the Review Exercises (in the Answers to Exercises section in the back of the book) tells students in which section each of the review exercises is covered.

- The **MyMathLab** course that accompanies this text has been markedly improved and expanded to include even greater coverage of the topics in this course through more exercises, videos, animations, and PowerPoint slides. In addition, answer tolerance for exercises has been checked and adjusted when necessary, and prerequisite diagnostic tools are available for personalized assessment and remediation. See the Supplements portion of this preface for more details on MyMathLab.

- **Annotated Instructor's Edition**: An invaluable resource for instructors, the Annotated Instructor's Edition (AIE) contains answers to the exercises right on the exercise set page (whenever possible). In addition, *Teaching Tips* are included in the margins to provide helpful hints for less experienced instructors.

- **Graphing Calculator** screen shots have been updated to represent the newest TI calculator, the TI-84+ C. These visuals often prove valuable even to students not using graphing calculators.

- The **exercises** are now better paired so that the even exercises require similar knowledge as the corresponding odd exercise. In addition, approximately 21 percent of the 5,436 exercises in the text are new or updated.

- Approximately 22 percent of the 641 **examples** in the text are new or updated. Many examples and exercises are based on real-world data.

- **Student Learning Objectives** for every section of the text are provided at the back of the text. These objectives describe what students should understand and be able to do after studying the section and completing the exercises.

- An **Index of Companies, Products, and Agencies** is provided to increase student interest and motivation.

Continued Pedagogical Support

- **Balanced Approach**: Multiple representations of a topic (symbolic, numerical, graphical, verbal) are given when appropriate. However, we do not believe that all representations are useful for all topics, so effective alternatives are discussed only when they are likely to increase student understanding.

- **Strong Algebra Foundation:** The text begins with four thorough chapters of college algebra that can be used in a variety of ways based on the needs of the students and the goals of the course. Take advantage of the content in these chapters as needed so students will be more successful with later topics and future courses.

- **Real-Data Examples and Explanations:** Real-data exercises have long been a popular and integral aspect of this book. A significant number of new real-data examples and exercises have also been introduced into the text. Applications are noted with the type of industry in which they fall so instructors or students can focus on applications that are in line with students' majors. (See pages 190–192.)

- **The Checkpoint Exercises** (marked with icons such as) within the body of the text provide an opportunity for students to stop, check their understanding of the specific concept at hand, and move forward with confidence. Answers to Checkpoint Exercises are located at the end of the section to encourage students to work the problems before looking at the answers. (See pages 184, 192.)

- **Cautions** highlight common student difficulties or warn against frequently made mistakes. (See page 204.)

- **Exercises:** In addition to skill-based practice, conceptual, and application-based exercises, there are some specially marked exercises:
Writing Exercises (see page 216)

Connection Exercises ◗ that relate current topics to earlier sections (see pages 253 and 262)

Practice Exercises from previous CPA exams (see page 242), and

Technology Required Exercises ➚ (see page 263).

- **Example/Exercise Connection**: Selected exercises include a reference back to related example(s) within the section (e.g., "See Examples 6 and 7") to facilitate what students do naturally when they use a book—i.e., look for specific examples when they get stuck on a problem. Later exercises leave this information out and provide opportunities for mixed skill practice.

- End-of-chapter materials are designed to help students prepare for exams and include a **List of Key Terms and Symbols** and **Summary of Key Concepts**, as well as a thorough set of **Chapter Review Exercises**.

- **Case Studies** appear at the end of each chapter and offer contemporary, real-world and up-to-date applications of some of the mathematics presented in the chapter. Not only do these provide an opportunity for students to see the mathematics they are learning in action, but they also provide at least a partial answer to the question, "What is this stuff good for?" These have been expanded to include options for longer-term projects if the instructor should choose to use them.

Technology

In our text, we choose to support a variety of different technologies in a way that provides greater understanding and encourages exploration of the tools students have at their disposal. The technology that is supported by this text includes graphing calculators, spreadsheets, and a variety of resources within MyMathLab.

MyMathLab: This text is not just supported by MyMathLab (MML), but rather it is enriched and expanded upon within MML. Fortunately, today's students are well-equipped to take full advantage of resources beyond the text, and the MML course for this text is especially valuable to the typical student.

- Concepts that are difficult to describe in print can be shown dynamically through video or animation, providing a visual that students may otherwise miss.

- Topics that are particularly challenging to students can be practiced, assessed, reviewed, and practiced some more through algorithmically generated homework or videos.

- Prerequisite skills that students lack can be assessed and then addressed on an individual basis using quick, pre-built assessments and personalized homework.

Although use of MML with this text is completely optional, students stand a greater chance of success if they take advantage of the many resources available to them within MML. More details as to all that MML can do are provided in the Supplements portion of this preface.

Graphing Calculators and Spreadsheets: It is assumed that all students have a calculator that will handle exponential and logarithmic functions. Beyond that, however, graphing calculator and spreadsheet references are highlighted in the text so that those who use the technology can easily incorporate it and those who do not can easily omit it. Examples and exercises that require some sort of technology are marked with the icon ➚, making it obvious where technology is being included.

Instructors who routinely use technology in their courses will find more than enough material to satisfy their needs. Here are some of the features they may want to incorporate into their courses:

- **Examples and Exercises marked with** ➚ A number of examples show students how various features of graphing calculators and spreadsheets can be applied to the topics in this book. Exercises marked with the same icon give students a chance to practice particular skills using technology.

- **Technology Tips:** These are placed at appropriate points in the text to inform students of various features of their graphing calculator, spreadsheet, or other computer programs. Note that Technology Tips designed for TI-84+ C also apply to the TI-84+, TI-83, and TI-Nspire.

- **Appendix A: Graphing Calculators:** This appendix consists of a brief introduction to the relevant features of the latest TI-84+ C graphing calculator. An outline of the appendix is on page 859, and the full appendix is available online in MyMathLab and at www.mathstatsresources.com.
- A **Graphing Calculator Manual** and **Excel Spreadsheet Manual** are also available within MyMathLab. These manuals provide students with the support they need to make use of the latest versions of graphing calculators and Excel 2013.

Course Flexibility

The content of the text is divided into three parts:

- College Algebra (Chapters 1–4)
- Finite Mathematics (Chapters 5–10)
- Applied Calculus (Chapters 11–14)

This coverage of the material offers flexibility, making the book appropriate for a variety of courses, including:

- Finite Mathematics and Applied Calculus (one year or less). Use the entire book; cover topics from Chapters 1–4 as needed before proceeding to further topics.
- Finite Mathematics (one semester or two quarters). Use as much of Chapters 1–4 as needed, and then go into Chapters 5–10 as time permits and local needs require.
- Applied Calculus (one semester or quarter). Cover the precalculus topics in Chapters 1–4 as necessary, and then use Chapters 11–14.
- College Algebra with Applications (one semester or quarter). Use Chapters 1–8, with Chapters 7 and 8 being optional.

Pearson regularly produces custom versions of this text (and its accompanying MyMath-Lab course) to address the needs of specific course sequences. Custom versions can be produced for even smaller-enrollment courses due to advances in digital printing. Please contact your local Pearson representative for more details.

Chapter interdependence is as follows:

Chapter		*Prerequisite*
1	Algebra and Equations	None
2	Graphs, Lines, and Inequalities	Chapter 1
3	Functions and Graphs	Chapters 1 and 2
4	Exponential and Logarithmic Functions	Chapter 3
5	Mathematics of Finance	Chapter 4
6	Systems of Linear Equations and Matrices	Chapters 1 and 2
7	Linear Programming	Chapters 3 and 6
8	Sets and Probability	None
9	Counting, Probability Distributions, and Further Topics in Probability	Chapter 8
10	Introduction to Statistics	Chapter 8
11	Differential Calculus	Chapters 1–4
12	Applications of the Derivative	Chapter 11
13	Integral Calculus	Chapters 11 and 12
14	Multivariate Calculus	Chapters 11–13

Student Supplements

Student's Solutions Manual

- By Salvatore Sciandra, Niagara County Community College

- This manual contains detailed carefully worked out solutions to all odd-numbered section exercises and all Chapter Review and Case exercises.
ISBN 13: 978-0-321-92492-6
ISBN 10: 0-321-92492-4

Graphing Calculator Manual (downloadable)

- By Victoria Baker, Nicholls State University

- Contains detailed instruction for using the TI-83/TI-83+/TI-84+ C.

- Instructions are organized by topic.

- Available in MyMathLab.

Excel Spreadsheet Manual (downloadable)

- By Stela Pudar-Hozo, Indiana University—Northwest

- Contains detailed instructions for using Excel 2013.

- Instructions are organized by topic.

- Available in MyMathLab.

Instructor Supplements

Annotated Instructor's Edition

- The AIE contains answers to all exercises in the text on the exercise set page whenever possible.

- In addition, Teaching Tips are provided in the margin to give less-experienced instructors a cue as to where students typically struggle.
ISBN 13: 978-0-321-92961-7
ISBN 10: 0-321-92961-6

Instructor's Solutions Manual (downloadable)

- By Salvatore Sciandra, Niagara County Community College

- This manual contains detailed solutions to all text exercises, suggested course outlines, and a chapter interdependence chart.

- Available through www.pearsonhighered.com/irc or in MyMathLab.

Printable Test Bank (downloadable)

- By David Bridge, University of Central Oklahoma

- This test bank includes four alternate tests per chapter that parallel the text's Chapter Tests.

- Available through www.pearsonhighered.com/irc or in MyMathLab.

Media Supplements

MyMathLab® Online Course (access code required)

MyMathLab delivers **proven results** in helping individual students succeed.

- MyMathLab has a consistently positive impact on the quality of learning in higher education math instruction. MyMathLab can be successfully implemented in any environment—lab-based, hybrid, fully online, traditional—and demonstrates the quantifiable difference that integrated usage has on student retention, subsequent success, and overall achievement.

- MyMathLab's comprehensive online gradebook automatically tracks your students' results on tests, quizzes, homework, and in the study plan. You can use the gradebook to quickly intervene if your students have trouble, or to provide positive feedback on a job well done. The data within MyMathLab is easily exported to a variety of spreadsheet programs, such as Microsoft Excel. You can determine which points of data you want to export, and then analyze the results to determine success.

MyMathLab provides **engaging experiences** that personalize, stimulate, and measure learning for each student.

- **Continuously Adaptive:** Adaptive learning functionality analyzes student work and points them toward resources that will maximize their learning.

- **Exercises:** The homework and practice exercises in MyMathLab are correlated to the exercises in the textbook, and they regenerate algorithmically to give students unlimited opportunity for practice and mastery. The software offers immediate, helpful feedback when students enter incorrect answers.

- **Chapter-Level, Just-in-Time Remediation:** Students receive remediation only for those skills that they have not yet mastered through *Getting Ready* diagnostics and content, and personalized homework.

- **Multimedia Learning Aids:** Exercises include guided solutions, sample problems, animations, videos, and eText clips for extra help at point-of-use.
- **Expert Tutoring:** Although many students describe the whole of MyMathLab as "like having your own personal tutor," students using MyMathLab do have access to live tutoring from Pearson, from qualified math and statistics instructors who provide tutoring sessions for students via MyMathLab.

And, MyMathLab comes from a **trusted partner** with educational expertise and an eye on the future.

- Knowing that you are using a Pearson product means knowing that you are using quality content. That means that our eTexts are accurate and our assessment tools work.
- Whether you are just getting started with MyMathLab, or have a question along the way, we're here to help you learn about our technologies and how to incorporate them into your course.

To learn more about how MyMathLab combines proven learning applications with powerful assessment, visit www.mymathlab.com or contact your Pearson representative.

MyMathLab® Ready to Go Course (access code required)

These new Ready to Go courses provide students with all the same great MyMathLab features, but make it easier for instructors to get started. Each course includes pre-assigned homework and quizzes to make creating a course even simpler. In addition, these Ready to Go courses include a course-level "Getting Ready" diagnostic that helps pinpoint student weaknesses in prerequisite skills. Ask your Pearson representative about the details for this particular course or to see a copy of this course.

MathXL® Online Course (access code required)

MathXL® is the homework and assessment engine that runs MyMathLab. (MyMathLab is MathXL plus a learning management system.)

With MathXL, instructors can:

- Create, edit, and assign online homework and tests using algorithmically generated exercises correlated at the objective level to the textbook.
- Create and assign their own online exercises and import TestGen tests for added flexibility.
- Maintain records of all student work tracked in MathXL's online gradebook.

With MathXL, students can:

- Take chapter tests in MathXL and receive personalized study plans and/or personalized homework assignments based on their test results.
- Use the study plan and/or the homework to link directly to tutorial exercises for the objectives they need to study.
- Access supplemental animations and video clips directly from selected exercises.

MathXL is available to qualified adopters. For more information, visit our website at www.mathxl.com, or contact your Pearson representative.

New! Video Lectures with Optional Subtitles

The video lectures for this text are available in MyMathLab, making it easy and convenient for students to watch the videos from computers at home or on campus, or from their smart phones! The videos feature engaging chapter summaries and worked-out examples. The videos have **optional English subtitles;** they can easily be turned on or off for individual student needs.

PowerPoint® Lecture Slides

These slides present key concepts and definitions from the text. They are available in MyMathLab or at www.pearsonhighered.com/irc.

TestGen®

TestGen® (www.pearsoned.com/testgen) enables instructors to build, edit, print, and administer tests using a computerized bank of questions developed to cover all the objectives of the text. TestGen is algorithmically based, allowing instructors to create multiple but equivalent versions of the same question or test with the click of a button. Instructors can also modify test bank questions or add new questions. The software and testbank are available for download from Pearson Education's online catalog.

Acknowledgments

The authors wish to thank the following reviewers for their thoughtful feedback and helpful suggestions without which we could not continue to improve this text.

Hossein A. Abbasi, Bloomsburg University
Zachary J. Abernathy, Winthrop University
Sasha Anderson, Fresno City College
Sviatoslav Archava, East Carolina University
Peter Barendse, Boston University
Linda Estes Barton, Ball State University
Jaromir J. Becan, University of Texas at San Antonio
Shari Beck, Navarro College
Elizabeth Bowman, The University of Alabama in Huntsville
Dwayne C. Brown, University of South Carolina Lancaster
Priscilla Chaffe-Stengel, California State University, Fresno
Michelle Cook, Stephen F. Austin State University
Michael Dixon, Midland College
Edward D. Esparza, University of Texas at San Antonio
Mark Goldstein, West Virginia Community College
Ronald D. Hagan, The University of Tennessee
Timothy Huber, University of Texas–Pan American
Mary Jackson, Brookhaven College
Patricia Kan, Cleveland State University

Timothy Kohl, Boston University
Ronald E. Kutz, Western Connecticut State University
Gregory L. Macklin, Delaware Technical Community College
Marna Mozeff, Drexel University
Charles Odion, Houston Community College
Lindsay Packer, Metropolitan State University of Denver
David Rangel, Northeast Texas Community College
Aaron Rosenberg, Folsom Lake College
Sharon M. Saxton, Cascadia Community College
Zachary Sharon, The University of Texas at San Antonio
Robin Gayer Sirkis, Delaware Technical Community College
Pam Stogsdill, Bossier Parish Community College
Karel Stroethoff, University of Montana
Frank Viviano, Bossier Parish Community College
Cassandra Wright, Stephen F. Austin State University
Cong-Cong Xing, Nicholls State University
Xinyun Zhu, The University of Texas of the Permian Basin

A special thanks goes to Jason Stone for his help in developing the Prerequisite Skills Test. Additionally, we gratefully acknowledge Birmingham-Southern College and Cleveland State University for their whole-hearted suport of the Eleventh Edition.

We also wish to thank our accuracy checkers, who did an excellent job of checking both text and exercise answers: Paul Lorczak and Douglas Ewert. Thanks also to the supplements authors: Salvatore Sciandra, David Bridge, Victoria Baker, and Stela Pudar-Hozo.

We want to thank the staff of Pearson Education for their assistance with, and contributions to this book, particularly Greg Tobin, Deirdre Lynch, Jennifer Crum, Jeff Weidenaar, Sherry Berg, Sheila Spinney, Chere Bemelmans, Joanne Wendelken, Caitlin Crain, and Jean Choe. Finally, we wish to express our appreciation to Kelly Ricci of Aptara Corporation, who was a pleasure to work with.

Thomas W. Hungerford
John P. Holcomb, Jr.
Bernadette Mullins

To the Student

The key to succeeding in this course is to remember that *mathematics is not a spectator sport.* You can't expect to learn mathematics without *doing* mathematics any more than you could learn to swim without getting wet. You must take an active role, making use of all the resources at your disposal: your instructor, your fellow students, this book, and the supplements that accompany it. Following are some general tips on how to be successful in the course, and some specific tips on how to get the most out of this text and supplementary resources.

Ask Questions! Remember the words of the great Hillel: "The bashful do not learn." There is no such thing as a "dumb question" (assuming, of course, that you have read the book and your class notes and attempted the homework). Your instructor will welcome questions that arise from a serious effort on your part. So get your money's worth: Ask questions!

Read the Book Interactively! There is more to a math textbook than just the exercise sets. Each section introduces topics carefully with many examples—both mathematical and contextual. Take note of the "Caution" and "Note" comments, and bookmark pages with key definitions or formulas. After reading the example, try the *Checkpoint Exercise* that follows it in the margin to check your understanding of the concept. This will help you solidify your understanding or diagnose if you do not fully understand the concept. The answers to the Checkpoint exercises are right after the homework exercises in each section. Resist the temptation to flip to the answer until you've worked the problem completely!

Take Advantage of the Supplementary Material! Both within and outside the text, there are many resources at your disposal. Take the time to interact with them and determine which resources suit your learning style the best.

- If your instructor allows the use of graphing calculators and/or spreadsheets, work through the examples and exercises marked with the ⬈. Some instructors may make this material part of the course, whereas others will not require you to use technology. For those who use technology, there is a *Graphing Calculator Appendix* that covers the basics of calculator use and provides a number of helpful programs for working with some of the topics in the text. An outline of the appendix is on page 859, and the full appendix is available in MyMathLab. In addition, there are *Technology Tips* throughout the text that describe the proper menu or keys to use for various procedures on a graphing calculator. Note that Technology Tips for the TI-84+ C also apply to TI-83+, TI-Nspire, and usually TI-83.

- MyMathLab has a variety of types of resources at your disposal including videos and PowerPoints for every section of the text, example-level videos, animations to help visualize difficult concepts, unlimited practice and assessment on newly learned or prerequisite skills, and access to the *Student Solutions Manual, Graphing Calculator Manual* and *Excel Spreadsheet Manual,* a variety of helpful reference cards, and links to useful websites like Texas Instruments.

Do Your Homework! Whether it is paper/pencil homework or assigned online, you must practice what you have learned. Remember, math is not a spectator sport! This is your opportunity to practice those essential skills needed for passing this course, and for applying in future courses or your career.

We wish you the best in your efforts with this course, in future courses, and beyond school.

Algebra and Equations

1

Mathematics is widely used in business, finance, and the biological, social, and physical sciences, from developing efficient production schedules for a factory to mapping the human genome. Mathematics also plays a role in determining interest on a loan from a bank, the growth of traffic on websites, and the study of falling objects. See Exercises 61 and 67 on page 51 and Exercise 63 on page 59.

Algebra and equations are the basic mathematical tools for handling many applications. Your success in this course will depend on your having the algebraic skills presented in this chapter.

1.1 The Real Numbers

Only real numbers will be used in this book.* The names of the most common types of real numbers are as follows.

The Real Numbers

Natural (counting) numbers	$1, 2, 3, 4, \ldots$
Whole numbers	$0, 1, 2, 3, 4, \ldots$

---

*Not all numbers are real numbers. For example, $\sqrt{-1}$ is a number that is *not* a real number.

Integers	$\ldots, -3, -2, -1, 0, 1, 2, 3, \ldots$
Rational numbers	All numbers that can be written in the form p/q, where p and q are integers and $q \neq 0$
Irrational numbers	Real numbers that are not rational

As you can see, every natural number is a whole number, and every whole number is an integer. Furthermore, every integer is a rational number. For instance, the integer 7 can be written as the fraction $\frac{7}{1}$ and is therefore a rational number.

One example of an irrational number is π, the ratio of the circumference of a circle to its diameter. The number π can be approximated as $\pi \approx 3.14159$ ($\approx$ means "is approximately equal to"), but there is no rational number that is exactly equal to π.

Example 1 What kind of number is each of the following?

(a) 6

Solution The number 6 is a natural number, a whole number, an integer, a rational number, and a real number.

(b) $\dfrac{3}{4}$

Solution This number is rational and real.

(c) 3π

Solution Because π is not a rational number, 3π is irrational and real. ✓

✓ **Checkpoint 1**

Name all the types of numbers that apply to the following.

(a) -2

(b) $-5/8$

(c) $\pi/5$

Answers to Checkpoint exercises are found at the end of the section.

All real numbers can be written in decimal form. A rational number, when written in decimal form, is either a terminating decimal, such as .5 or .128, or a repeating decimal, in which some block of digits eventually repeats forever, such as $1.3333 \ldots$ or $4.7234234234 \ldots$.[†] Irrational numbers are decimals that neither terminate nor repeat.

When a calculator is used for computations, the answers it produces are often decimal *approximations* of the actual answers; they are accurate enough for most applications. To ensure that your final answer is as accurate as possible,

you should not round off any numbers during long calculator computations.

It is usually OK to round off the final answer to a reasonable number of decimal places once the computation is finished.

The important basic properties of the real numbers are as follows.

Properties of the Real Numbers

For all real numbers, a, b, and c, the following properties hold true:

Commutative properties	$a + b = b + a$ and $ab = ba.$
Associative properties	$(a + b) + c = a + (b + c)$ and $(ab)c = a(bc).$

---

[*]The use of Checkpoint exercises is explained in the "To the Student" section preceding this chapter.
[†]Some graphing calculators have a FRAC key that automatically converts some repeating decimals to fraction form.

Identity properties	There exists a unique real number 0, called the **additive identity,** such that

$$a + 0 = a \quad \text{and} \quad 0 + a = a.$$

There exists a unique real number 1, called the **multiplicative identity,** such that

$$a \cdot 1 = a \quad \text{and} \quad 1 \cdot a = a.$$

Inverse properties	For each real number a, there exists a unique real number $-a$, called the **additive inverse** of a, such that

$$a + (-a) = 0 \quad \text{and} \quad (-a) + a = 0.$$

If $a \neq 0$, there exists a unique real number $1/a$, called the **multiplicative inverse** of a, such that

$$a \cdot \frac{1}{a} = 1 \quad \text{and} \quad \frac{1}{a} \cdot a = 1.$$

Distributive property	$a(b + c) = ab + ac \quad \text{and} \quad (b + c)a = ba + ca.$

The next five examples illustrate the properties listed in the preceding box.

Example 2   The commutative property says that the order in which you add or multiply two quantities doesn't matter.

(a) $(6 + x) + 9 = 9 + (6 + x) = 9 + (x + 6)$ 　　**(b)** $5 \cdot (9 \cdot 8) = (9 \cdot 8) \cdot 5$

Example 3   When the associative property is used, the order of the numbers does not change, but the placement of parentheses does.

(a) $4 + (9 + 8) = (4 + 9) + 8$ 　　**(b)** $3(9x) = (3 \cdot 9)x$ ✅2

✓Checkpoint 2

Name the property illustrated in each of the following examples.

(a) $(2 + 3) + 9 = (3 + 2) + 9$

(b) $(2 + 3) + 9 = 2 + (3 + 9)$

(c) $(2 + 3) + 9 = 9 + (2 + 3)$

(d) $(4 \cdot 6)p = (6 \cdot 4)p$

(e) $4(6p) = (4 \cdot 6)p$

✓Checkpoint 3

Name the property illustrated in each of the following examples.

(a) $2 + 0 = 2$

(b) $-\dfrac{1}{4} \cdot (-4) = 1$

(c) $-\dfrac{1}{4} + \dfrac{1}{4} = 0$

(d) $1 \cdot \dfrac{2}{3} = \dfrac{2}{3}$

Example 4   By the identity properties,

(a) $-8 + 0 = -8$ 　　**(b)** $(-9) \cdot 1 = -9.$

✦ **TECHNOLOGY TIP** To enter -8 on a calculator, use the negation key (labeled $(-)$ or $+/-$), *not* the subtraction key. On most one-line scientific calculators, key in $8 \; +/-$. On graphing calculators or two-line scientific calculators, key in either $(-) \; 8$ or $+/- \; 8$.

Example 5   By the inverse properties, the statements in parts (a) through (d) are true.

(a) $9 + (-9) = 0$ 　　**(b)** $-15 + 15 = 0$

(c) $-8 \cdot \left(\dfrac{1}{-8} \right) = 1$ 　　**(d)** $\dfrac{1}{\sqrt{5}} \cdot \sqrt{5} = 1$

📄 **NOTE** There is no real number x such that $0 \cdot x = 1$, so 0 has no multiplicative inverse.

Example 6   By the distributive property,

(a) $9(6 + 4) = 9 \cdot 6 + 9 \cdot 4$

(b) $3(x + y) = 3x + 3y$

(c) $-8(m + 2) = (-8)(m) + (-8)(2) = -8m - 16$

(d) $(5 + x)y = 5y + xy.$ ✓4

✓ **Checkpoint 4**

Use the distributive property to complete each of the following.

(a) $4(-2 + 5)$

(b) $2(a + b)$

(c) $-3(p + 1)$

(d) $(8 - k)m$

(e) $5x + 3x$

Order of Operations

Some complicated expressions may contain many sets of parentheses. To avoid ambiguity, the following procedure should be used.

Parentheses

Work separately above and below any fraction bar. Within each set of parentheses or square brackets, start with the innermost set and work outward.

Example 7   Simplify: $[(3 + 2) - 7]5 + 2([6 \cdot 3] - 13)$.

Solution   On each segment, work from the inside out:

$$[(3 + 2) - 7]5 - 2([6 \cdot 3] - 13)$$
$$= [5 - 7]5 + 2(18 - 13)$$
$$= [-2]5 + 2(5)$$
$$= -10 + 10 = 0.$$

Does the expression $2 + 4 \times 3$ mean

$$(2 + 4) \times 3 = 6 \times 3 = 18?$$

Or does it mean

$$2 + (4 \times 3) = 2 + 12 = 14?$$

To avoid this ambiguity, mathematicians have adopted the following rules (which are also followed by almost all scientific and graphing calculators).

Order of Operations

1. Find all powers and roots, working from left to right.
2. Do any multiplications or divisions in the order in which they occur, working from left to right.
3. Finally, do any additions or subtractions in the order in which they occur, working from left to right.

If sets of parentheses or square brackets are present, use the rules in the preceding box within each set, working from the innermost set outward.

According to these rules, multiplication is done *before* addition, so $2 + 4 \times 3 = 2 + 12 = 14$. Here are some additional examples.

Example 8   Use the order of operations to evaluate each expression if $x = -2$, $y = 5$, and $z = -3$.

(a) $-4x^2 - 7y + 4z$

Solution   Use parentheses when replacing letters with numbers:

$$-4x^2 - 7y + 4z = -4(-2)^2 - 7(5) + 4(-3)$$
$$= -4(4) - 7(5) + 4(-3) = -16 - 35 - 12 = -63.$$

(b) $\dfrac{2(x - 5)^2 + 4y}{z + 4} = \dfrac{2(-2 - 5)^2 + 4(5)}{-3 + 4}$

$$= \dfrac{2(-7)^2 + 20}{1}$$

$$= 2(49) + 20 = 118. \quad \boxed{5}$$

✓ **Checkpoint 5**

Evaluate the following if $m = -5$ and $n = 8$.

(a) $-2mn - 2m^2$

(b) $\dfrac{4(n - 5)^2 - m}{m + n}$

Example 9   Use a calculator to evaluate

$$\frac{-9(-3) + (-5)}{3(-4) - 5(2)}.$$

Solution   Use extra parentheses (shown here in blue) around the numerator and denominator when you enter the number in your calculator, and be careful to distinguish the negation key from the subtraction key.

If you don't get -1 as the answer, then you are entering something incorrectly. $\boxed{6}$

✓ **Checkpoint 6**

Use a calculator to evaluate the following.

(a) $4^2 \div 8 + 3^2 \div 3$

(b) $[-7 + (-9)] \cdot (-4) - 8(3)$

(c) $\dfrac{-11 - (-12) - 4 \cdot 5}{4(-2) - (-6)(-5)}$

(d) $\dfrac{36 \div 4 \cdot 3 \div 9 + 1}{9 \div (-6) \cdot 8 - 4}$

Square Roots

There are two numbers whose square is 16, namely, 4 and -4. The positive one, 4, is called the **square root** of 16. Similarly, the square root of a nonnegative number d is defined to be the *nonnegative* number whose square is d; this number is denoted $\sqrt{d}$. For instance,

$$\sqrt{36} = 6 \text{ because } 6^2 = 36, \quad \sqrt{0} = 0 \text{ because } 0^2 = 0, \text{ and}$$
$$\sqrt{1.44} = 1.2 \text{ because } (1.2)^2 = 1.44.$$

No negative number has a square root that is a real number. For instance, there is no real number whose square is -4, so -4 has no square root.

Every nonnegative real number has a square root. Unless an integer is a perfect square (such as $64 = 8^2$), its square root is an irrational number. A calculator can be used to obtain a rational approximation of these square roots.

🖈 **TECHNOLOGY TIP**

On one-line scientific calculators, $\sqrt{40}$ is entered as 40 $\sqrt{\ }$. On graphing calculators and two-line scientific calculators, key in $\sqrt{\ }$ 40 ENTER (or EXE).

Example 10   Estimate each of the given quantities. Verify your estimates with a calculator.

(a) $\sqrt{40}$

Solution   Since $6^2 = 36$ and $7^2 = 49$, $\sqrt{40}$ must be a number between 6 and 7. A typical calculator shows that $\sqrt{40} \approx 6.32455532$.

Checkpoint 7

Estimate each of the following.

(a) $\sqrt{73}$

(b) $\sqrt{22} + 3$

(c) Confirm your estimates in parts (a) and (b) with a calculator.

Checkpoint 8

Draw a number line, and graph the numbers $-4, -1, 0, 1, 2.5,$ and $13/4$ on it.

(b) $5\sqrt{7}$

Solution $\sqrt{7}$ is between 2 and 3 because $2^2 = 4$ and $3^2 = 9$, so $5\sqrt{7}$ must be a number between $5 \cdot 2 = 10$ and $5 \cdot 3 = 15$. A calculator shows that $5\sqrt{7} \approx 13.22875656.$ ✓7

⚠ **CAUTION**   If c and d are positive real numbers, then $\sqrt{c + d}$ is *not* equal to $\sqrt{c} + \sqrt{d}$. For example, $\sqrt{9 + 16} = \sqrt{25} = 5$, but $\sqrt{9} + \sqrt{16} = 3 + 4 = 7$.

The Number Line

The real numbers can be illustrated geometrically with a diagram called a **number line.** Each real number corresponds to exactly one point on the line and vice versa. A number line with several sample numbers located (or **graphed**) on it is shown in Figure 1.1. ✓8

Figure 1.1

When comparing the sizes of two real numbers, the following symbols are used.

Symbol	Read	Meaning
$a < b$	a is less than b.	a lies to the *left* of b on the number line.
$b > a$	b is greater than a.	b lies to the *right* of a on the number line.

Note that $a < b$ means the same thing as $b > a$. The inequality symbols are sometimes joined with the equals sign, as follows.

Symbol	Read	Meaning
$a \leq b$	a is less than or equal to b.	either $a < b$ or $a = b$
$b \geq a$	b is greater than or equal to a.	either $b > a$ or $b = a$

 TECHNOLOGY TIP

If your graphing calculator has inequality symbols (usually located on the TEST menu), you can key in statements such as "5 < 12" or "−2 ≥ 3." When you press ENTER, the calculator will display 1 if the statement is true and 0 if it is false.

Only one part of an "either . . . or" statement needs to be true for the entire statement to be considered true. So the statement $3 \leq 7$ is true because $3 < 7$, and the statement $3 \leq 3$ is true because $3 = 3$.

Example 11   Write *true* or *false* for each of the following.

(a) $8 < 12$

Solution   This statement says that 8 is less than 12, which is true.

(b) $-6 > -3$

Solution   The graph in Figure 1.2 shows that -6 is to the *left* of -3. Thus, $-6 < -3$, and the given statement is false.

Figure 1.2

Checkpoint 9

Write *true* or *false* for the following.

(a) $-9 \leq -2$

(b) $8 > -3$

(c) $-14 \leq -20$

(c) $-2 \leq -2$

Solution   Because $-2 = -2$, this statement is true. ✓9

A number line can be used to draw the graph of a set of numbers, as shown in the next few examples.

Example 12   Graph all real numbers x such that $1 < x < 5$.

Solution   This graph includes all the real numbers between 1 and 5, not just the integers. Graph these numbers by drawing a heavy line from 1 to 5 on the number line, as in Figure 1.3. Parentheses at 1 and 5 show that neither of these points belongs to the graph. ✓

Figure 1.3

✓**Checkpoint 10**

Graph all real numbers x such that

(a) $-5 < x < 1$

(b) $4 < x < 7$.

A set that consists of all the real numbers between two points, such as $1 < x < 5$ in Example 12, is called an **interval.** A special notation called **interval notation** is used to indicate an interval on the number line. For example, the interval including all numbers x such that $-2 < x < 3$ is written as $(-2, 3)$. The parentheses indicate that the numbers -2 and 3 are *not* included. If -2 and 3 are to be included in the interval, square brackets are used, as in $[-2, 3]$. The following chart shows several typical intervals, where $a < b$.

Intervals

Inequality	Interval Notation	Explanation
$a \le x \le b$	$[a, b]$	Both a and b are included.
$a \le x < b$	$[a, b)$	a is included; b is not.
$a < x \le b$	$(a, b]$	b is included; a is not.
$a < x < b$	(a, b)	Neither a nor b is included.

Interval notation is also used to describe sets such as the set of all numbers x such that $x \ge -2$. This interval is written $[-2, \infty)$. The set of all real numbers is written $(-\infty, \infty)$ in interval notation.

Example 13   Graph the interval $[-2, \infty)$.

Solution   Start at -2 and draw a heavy line to the right, as in Figure 1.4. Use a square bracket at -2 to show that -2 itself is part of the graph. The symbol ∞, read "infinity," *does not* represent a number. This notation simply indicates that *all* numbers greater than -2 are in the interval. Similarly, the notation $(-\infty, 2)$ indicates the set of all numbers x such that $x < 2$. ✓

✓**Checkpoint 11**

Graph all real numbers x in the given interval.

(a) $(-\infty, 4]$

(b) $[-2, 1]$

Figure 1.4

Absolute Value

The **absolute value** of a real number a is the distance from a to 0 on the number line and is written $|a|$. For example, Figure 1.5 shows that the distance from 9 to 0 on the number line is 9, so we have $|9| = 9$. The figure also shows that $|-9| = 9$, because the distance from -9 to 0 is also 9.

Figure 1.5

The facts that $|9| = 9$ and $|-9| = 9 = -(-9)$ suggest the following algebraic definition of absolute value.

> ## Absolute Value
>
> For any real number a,
>
> $$|a| = a \qquad \text{if } a \geq 0$$
> $$|a| = -a \qquad \text{if } a < 0.$$

The first part of the definition shows that $|0| = 0$ (because $0 \geq 0$). It also shows that the absolute value of any positive number a is the number itself, so $|a|$ is positive in such cases. The second part of the definition says that the absolute value of a negative number a is the *negative* of a. For instance, if $a = -5$, then $|-5| = -(-5) = 5$. So $|-5|$ is positive. The same thing works for any negative number—that is, its absolute value (the negative of a negative number) is positive. Thus, we can state the following:

For every nonzero real number a, the number $|a|$ is positive.

✓ **Checkpoint 12**

Find the following.

(a) $|-6|$

(b) $-|7|$

(c) $-|-2|$

(d) $|-3 - 4|$

(e) $|2 - 7|$

Example 14   Evaluate $|8 - 9|$.

Solution   First, simplify the expression within the absolute-value bars:

$$|8 - 9| = |-1| = 1. \; \boxed{✓_{12}}$$

1.1 Exercises

In Exercises 1 and 2, label the statement true or false. (See Example 1.)

1. Every integer is a rational number.

2. Every real number is an irrational number.

3. The decimal expansion of the irrational number π begins 3.141592653589793 . . . . Use your calculator to determine which of the following rational numbers is the best approximation for the irrational number π:

$$\frac{22}{7}, \quad \frac{355}{113}, \quad \frac{103,993}{33,102}, \quad \frac{2,508,429,787}{798,458,000}.$$

Your calculator may tell you that some of these numbers are equal to π, but that just indicates that the number agrees with π for as many decimal places as your calculator can handle (usually 10–14). No rational number is exactly equal to π.

Identify the properties that are illustrated in each of the following. (See Examples 2–6.)

4. $0 + (-7) = -7 + 0$

5. $6(t + 4) = 6t + 6 \cdot 4$

6. $3 + (-3) = (-3) + 3$

7. $-5 + 0 = -5$

8. $(-4) \cdot \left(\frac{-1}{4}\right) = 1$

9. $8 + (12 + 6) = (8 + 12) + 6$

10. $1 \cdot (-20) = -20$

11. How is the additive inverse property related to the additive identity property? the multiplicative inverse property to the multiplicative identity property?

12. Explain the distinction between the commutative and associative properties.

Evaluate each of the following if $p = -2$, $q = 3$, and $r = -5$. (See Examples 7–9.)

13. $-3(p + 5q)$

14. $2(q - r)$

15. $\dfrac{q + r}{q + p}$

16. $\dfrac{3q}{3p - 2r}$

Business *The nominal annual percentage rate (APR) reported by lenders has the formula APR = 12r, where r is the monthly interest rate. Find the APR when*

17. $r = 3.8$ **18.** $r = 0.8$

Find the monthly interest rate r when

19. $APR = 11$ **20.** $APR = 13.2$

Evaluate each expression, using the order of operations given in the text. (See Examples 7–9.)

21. $3 - 4 \cdot 5 + 5$

22. $8 - (-4)^2 - (-12)$

23. $(4 - 5) \cdot 6 + 6$

24. $\dfrac{2(3 - 7) + 4(8)}{4(-3) + (-3)(-2)}$

25. $8 - 4^2 - (-12)$

26. $-(3 - 5) - [2 - (3^2 - 13)]$

27. $\dfrac{2(-3) + 3/(-2) - 2/(-\sqrt{16})}{\sqrt{64} - 1}$

28. $\dfrac{6^2 - 3\sqrt{25}}{\sqrt{6^2 + 13}}$

Use a calculator to help you list the given numbers in order from smallest to largest. (See Example 10.)

29. $\dfrac{189}{37}$, $\dfrac{4587}{691}$, $\sqrt{47}$, 6.735, $\sqrt{27}$, $\dfrac{2040}{523}$

30. $\dfrac{385}{117}$, $\sqrt{10}$, $\dfrac{187}{63}$, π, $\sqrt{\sqrt{85}}$, 2.9884

Express each of the following statements in symbols, using $<$, $>$, $\leq$, or $\geq$.

31. 12 is less than 18.5.

32. -2 is greater than -20.

33. x is greater than or equal to 5.7.

34. y is less than or equal to -5.

35. z is at most 7.5.

36. w is negative.

Fill in the blank with $<$, $=$, or $>$ so that the resulting statement is true.

37. -6 _____ -2 **38.** $3/4$ _____ .75

39. 3.14 _____ π **40.** $1/3$ _____ .33

Fill in the blank so as to produce two equivalent statements. For example, the arithmetic statement "a is negative" is equivalent to the geometric statement "the point a lies to the left of the point 0."

Arithmetic Statement	Geometric Statement
41. $a \geq b$	_____
42. _____	a lies c units to the right of b
43. _____	a lies between b and c, and to the right of c
44. a is positive	_____

Graph the given intervals on a number line. (See Examples 12 and 13.)

45. $(-8, -1)$ **46.** $[-1, 10]$

47. $(-2, 3]$ **48.** $[-2, 2)$

49. $(-2, \infty)$ **50.** $(-\infty, -2]$

Evaluate each of the following expressions (see Example 14).

51. $|-9| - |-12|$

52. $|8| - |-4|$

53. $-|-4| - |-1 - 14|$

54. $-|6| - |-12 - 4|$

In each of the following problems, fill in the blank with either $=$, $<$, or $>$, so that the resulting statement is true.

55. $|5|$ _____ $|-5|$

56. $-|-4|$ _____ $|4|$

57. $|10 - 3|$ _____ $|3 - 10|$

58. $|6 - (-4)|$ _____ $|-4 - 6|$

59. $|-2 + 8|$ _____ $|2 - 8|$

60. $|3| \cdot |-5|$ _____ $|3(-5)|$

61. $|3 - 5|$ _____ $|3| - |5|$

62. $|-5 + 1|$ _____ $|-5| + |1|$

Write the expression without using absolute-value notation.

63. $|a - 7|$ if $a < 7$ **64.** $|b - c|$ if $b \geq c$

65. If a and b are any real numbers, is it always true that $|a + b| = |a| + |b|$? Explain your answer.

66. If a and b are any two real numbers, is it always true that $|a - b| = |b - a|$? Explain your answer.

67. For which real numbers b does $|2 - b| = |2 + b|$? Explain your answer.

68. **Health** Data from the National Health and Nutrition Examination Study estimates that 95% of adult heights (inches) are in the following ranges for females and males. (Data from: www. cdc.gov/nchs/nhanes.htm.)

Females	63.5 ± 8.4
Males	68.9 ± 9.3

Express the ranges as an absolute-value inequality in which x is the height of the person.

Business *The Consumer Price Index (CPI) tracks the cost of a typical sample of a consumer goods. The following table shows the percentage increase in the CPI for each year in a 10-year period.*

Year	2003	2004	2005	2006	2007
% Increase in CPI	2.3	2.7	2.5	3.2	4.1

Year	2008	2009	2010	2011	2012
% Increase in CPI	0.1	2.7	1.5	3.0	1.7

Let *r* denote the yearly percentage increase in the CPI. For each of the following inequalities, find the number of years during the given period that *r* satisfied the inequality. (Data from: U.S. Bureau of Labor Statistics.)

69. $r > 3.2$

70. $r < 3.2$

71. $r \leq 3.2$

72. $r \leq 1.5$

73. $r \geq 2.1$

74. $r \geq 1.3$

Finance The table presents the 2012 percent change in the stock price for six well-known companies. (Data from: finance.yahoo.com.)

Company	Percent Change
American Express	+36.5
Coca-Cola	+3.4
ExxonMobil	+0.6
Hewlett-Packard	−46.5
IBM	+4.4
McDonald's	−10.8

Suppose that we wish to determine the difference in percent change between two of the companies in the table and we are interested only in the magnitude, or absolute value, of this difference. Then we subtract the two entries and find the absolute value. For example, the difference in percent change of stock price for American Express and McDonald's is $|36.5\% - (-10.8\%)| = 47.3\%$.

Find the absolute value of the difference between the two indicated changes in stock price.

75. Coca-Cola and Hewlett-Packard

76. IBM and McDonald's

77. ExxonMobil and IBM

78. American Express and ExxonMobil

79. McDonald's and Hewlett-Packard

80. IBM and Coca-Cola

Finance The following graph shows the per capita amount of disposable income (in thousands of dollars) in the United States. (Data from: U.S. Bureau of Economic Analysis.)

For each of the following, determine the years for which the expression is true where *x* is the per capita disposable income.

81. $|x - 35,000| > 1000$

82. $|x - 32,000| > 3500$

83. $|x - 36,500| \leq 2200$

84. $|x - 31,500| \leq 4400$

✓Checkpoint Answers

1. (a) Integer, rational, real
   (b) Rational, real
   (c) Irrational, real

2. (a) Commutative property
   (b) Associative property
   (c) Commutative property
   (d) Commutative property
   (e) Associative property

3. (a) Additive identity property
   (b) Multiplicative inverse property
   (c) Additive inverse property
   (d) Multiplicative identity property

4. (a) $4(-2) + 4(5) = 12$ (b) $2a + 2b$
   (c) $-3p - 3$ (d) $8m - km$
   (e) $(5 + 3)x = 8x$

5. (a) 30   (b) $\frac{41}{3}$

6. (a) 5   (b) 40
   (c) $\frac{19}{38} = \frac{1}{2} = .5$ (d) $-\frac{1}{4} = -.25$

7. (a) Between 8 and 9
   (b) Between 7 and 8
   (c) 8.5440; 7.6904

8. [number line]

9. (a) True   (b) True   (c) False

10. (a) [number line −5 to 1]   (b) [number line 4 to 7]

11. (a) [number line 4]   (b) [number line −2 to 1]

12. (a) 6   (b) −7
    (c) −2   (d) 7
    (e) 5

1.2   Polynomials

Polynomials are the fundamental tools of algebra and will play a central role in this course. In order to do polynomial arithmetic, you must first understand exponents. So we begin with them. You are familiar with the usual notation for squares and cubes, such as:

$$5^2 = 5 \cdot 5 \quad \text{and} \quad 6^3 = 6 \cdot 6 \cdot 6.$$

We now extend this convenient notation to other cases.

> If n is a natural number and a is any real number, then
>
> $$a^n \quad \text{denotes the product} \quad a \cdot a \cdot a \cdots a \ (n \text{ factors}).$$
>
> The number a is the **base,** and the number n is the **exponent.**

Example 1 4^6, which is read "four to the sixth," or "four to the sixth power," is the number

$$4 \cdot 4 \cdot 4 \cdot 4 \cdot 4 \cdot 4 = 4096.$$

Similarly, $(-5)^3 = (-5)(-5)(-5) = -125$, and

$$\left(\frac{3}{2}\right)^4 = \frac{3}{2} \cdot \frac{3}{2} \cdot \frac{3}{2} \cdot \frac{3}{2} = \frac{81}{16}.$$

Example 2   Use a calculator to approximate the given expressions.

(a) $(1.2)^8$

Solution   Key in 1.2 and then use the x^y key (labeled $\wedge$ on some calculators); finally, key in the exponent 8. The calculator displays the (exact) answer 4.29981696.

(b) $\left(\dfrac{12}{7}\right)^{23}$

Solution   Don't compute $12/7$ separately. Use parentheses and key in $(12/7)$, followed by the x^y key and the exponent 23 to obtain the approximate answer 242,054.822. ✓₁

> ⚠ **CAUTION**   A common error in using exponents occurs with expressions such as $4 \cdot 3^2$. The exponent of 2 applies only to the base 3, so that
>
> $$4 \cdot 3^2 = 4 \cdot 3 \cdot 3 = 36.$$
>
> On the other hand,
>
> $$(4 \cdot 3)^2 = (4 \cdot 3)(4 \cdot 3) = 12 \cdot 12 = 144,$$
>
> so
>
> $$4 \cdot 3^2 \neq (4 \cdot 3)^2.$$
>
> Be careful to distinguish between expressions like -2^4 and $(-2)^4$:
>
> $$-2^4 = -(2^4) = -(2 \cdot 2 \cdot 2 \cdot 2) = -16$$
> $$(-2)^4 = (-2)(-2)(-2)(-2) = 16,$$
>
> so
>
> $$-2^4 \neq (-2)^4. \ ✓₂$$

✓ **Checkpoint 1**

Evaluate the following.

(a) 6^3

(b) 5^{12}

(c) 1^9

(d) $\left(\dfrac{7}{5}\right)^8$

✓ **Checkpoint 2**

Evaluate the following.

(a) $3 \cdot 6^2$

(b) $5 \cdot 4^3$

(c) -3^6

(d) $(-3)^6$

(e) $-2 \cdot (-3)^5$

By the definition of an exponent,

$$3^4 \cdot 3^2 = (3 \cdot 3 \cdot 3 \cdot 3)(3 \cdot 3) = 3^6.$$

Since $6 = 4 + 2$, we can write the preceding equation as $3^4 \cdot 3^2 = 3^{4+2}$. This result suggests the following fact, which applies to any real number a and natural numbers m and n.

Multiplication with Exponents

To multiply a^m by a^n, *add* the exponents:

$$a^m \cdot a^n = a^{m+n}.$$

Example 3   Verify each of the following simplifications.

(a) $7^4 \cdot 7^6 = 7^{4+6} = 7^{10}$

(b) $(-2)^3 \cdot (-2)^5 = (-2)^{3+5} = (-2)^8$

(c) $(3k)^2 \cdot (3k)^3 = (3k)^5$

(d) $(m + n)^2 \cdot (m + n)^5 = (m + n)^7$ ✓₃

The multiplication property of exponents has a convenient consequence. By definition,

$$(5^2)^3 = 5^2 \cdot 5^2 \cdot 5^2 = 5^{2+2+2} = 5^6.$$

Note that $2 + 2 + 2$ is $3 \cdot 2 = 6$. This is an example of a more general fact about any real number a and natural numbers m and n.

Power of a Power

To find a power of a power, $(a^m)^n$, *multiply* the exponents:

$$(a^m)^n = a^{mn}.$$

Example 4   Verify the following computations.

(a) $(x^3)^4 = x^{3 \cdot 4} = x^{12}$.

(b) $[(-3)^5]^3 = (-3)^{5 \cdot 3} = (-3)^{15}$.

(c) $[(6z)^4]^4 = (6z)^{4 \cdot 4} = (6z)^{16}$. ✓₄

It will be convenient to give a zero exponent a meaning. If the multiplication property of exponents is to remain valid, we should have, for example, $3^5 \cdot 3^0 = 3^{5+0} = 3^5$. But this will be true only when $3^0 = 1$. So we make the following definition.

Zero Exponent

If a is any nonzero real number, then

$$a^0 = 1.$$

For example, $6^0 = 1$ and $(-9)^0 = 1$. Note that 0^0 is *not* defined.

✓ Checkpoint 3

Simplify the following.

(a) $5^3 \cdot 5^6$

(b) $(-3)^4 \cdot (-3)^{10}$

(c) $(5p)^2 \cdot (5p)^8$

✓ Checkpoint 4

Compute the following.

(a) $(6^3)^7$

(b) $[(4k)^5]^6$

✓ Checkpoint 5

Evaluate the following.

(a) 17^0

(b) 30^0

(c) $(-10)^0$

(d) $-(12)^0$

Polynomials

A **polynomial** is an algebraic expression such as

$$5x^4 + 2x^3 + 6x, \qquad 8m^3 + 9m^2 + \frac{3}{2}m + 3, \qquad -10p, \qquad \text{or} \qquad 8.$$

The letter used is called a **variable,** and a polynomial is a sum of **terms** of the form

(constant) $\times$ (nonnegative integer power of the variable).

We assume that $x^0 = 1$, $m^0 = 1$, etc., so terms such as 3 or 8 may be thought of as $3x^0$ and $8x^0$, respectively. The constants that appear in each term of a polynomial are called the **coefficients** of the polynomial. The coefficient of x^0 is called the **constant term.**

Example 5   Identify the coefficients and the constant term of the given polynomials.

(a) $5x^2 - x + 12$

Solution   The coefficients are 5, -1, and 12, and the constant term is 12.

(b) $7x^3 + 2x - 4$

Solution   The coefficients are 7, 0, 2, and -4, because the polynomial can be written $7x^3 + 0x^2 + 2x - 4$. The constant term is -4.

A polynomial that consists only of a constant term, such as 15, is called a **constant polynomial.** The **zero polynomial** is the constant polynomial 0. The **degree** of a polynomial is the *exponent* of the highest power of x that appears with a *nonzero* coefficient, and the nonzero coefficient of this highest power of x is the **leading coefficient** of the polynomial. For example,

Polynomial	Degree	Leading Coefficient	Constant Term
$6x^7 + 4x^3 + 5x^2 - 7x + 10$	7	6	10
$-x^4 + 2x^3 + \frac{1}{2}$	4	-1	$\frac{1}{2}$
x^3	3	1	0
12	0	12	12

The degree of the zero polynomial is *not defined*, since no exponent of x occurs with nonzero coefficient. First-degree polynomials are often called **linear polynomials.** Second- and third-degree polynomials are called **quadratics** and **cubics,** respectively.

✓ Checkpoint 6

Find the degree of each polynomial.

(a) $x^4 - x^2 + x + 5$

(b) $7x^5 + 6x^3 - 3x^8 + 2$

(c) 17

(d) 0

Addition and Subtraction

Two terms having the same variable with the same exponent are called **like terms;** other terms are called **unlike terms.** Polynomials can be added or subtracted by using the distributive property to combine like terms. Only like terms can be combined. For example,

$$12y^4 + 6y^4 = (12 + 6)y^4 = 18y^4$$

and

$$-2m^2 + 8m^2 = (-2 + 8)m^2 = 6m^2.$$

The polynomial $8y^4 + 2y^5$ has unlike terms, so it cannot be further simplified.

In more complicated cases of addition, you may have to eliminate parentheses, use the commutative and associative laws to regroup like terms, and then combine them.

Example 6   Add the following polynomials.

(a) $(8x^3 - 4x^2 + 6x) + (3x^3 + 5x^2 - 9x + 8)$

Solution $8x^3 - 4x^2 + 6x + 3x^3 + 5x^2 - 9x + 8$ Eliminate parentheses.

$= \underline{(8x^3 + 3x^3)} + \underline{(-4x^2 + 5x^2)} + \underline{(6x - 9x)} + 8$ Group like terms.

$= 11x^3 + x^2 - 3x + 8$ Combine like terms.

(b) $(-4x^4 + 6x^3 - 9x^2 - 12) + (-3x^3 + 8x^2 - 11x + 7)$

Solution

$-4x^4 + 6x^3 - 9x^2 - 12 - 3x^3 + 8x^2 - 11x + 7$ Eliminate parentheses.

$= -4x^4 + \underline{(6x^3 - 3x^3)} + \underline{(-9x^2 + 8x^2)} - 11x + \underline{(-12 + 7)}$ Group like terms.

$= -4x^4 + 3x^3 - x^2 - 11x - 5$ Combine like terms.

Care must be used when parentheses are preceded by a minus sign. For example, we know that

$$-(4 + 3) = -(7) = -7 = -4 - 3.$$

If you simply delete the parentheses in $-(4 + 3)$, you obtain $-4 + 3 = -1$, which is the wrong answer. This fact and the preceding examples illustrate the following rules.

Rules for Eliminating Parentheses

Parentheses preceded by a plus sign (or no sign) may be deleted.

Parentheses preceded by a minus sign may be deleted *provided that* the sign of every term within the parentheses is changed.

Example 7   Subtract: $(2x^2 - 11x + 8) - (7x^2 - 6x + 2)$.

Solution $2x^2 - 11x + 8 - 7x^2 + 6x - 2$ Eliminate parentheses.

$= (2x^2 - 7x^2) + (-11x + 6x) + (8 - 2)$ Group like terms.

$= -5x^2 - 5x + 6$ Combine like terms. ✓₇

Multiplication

The distributive property is also used to multiply polynomials. For example, the product of $8x$ and $6x - 4$ is found as follows:

$$8x(6x - 4) = 8x(6x) - 8x(4)$$ Distributive property

$$= 48x^2 - 32x$$ $x \cdot x = x^2$

Example 8   Use the distributive property to find each product.

(a) $2p^3(3p^2 - 2p + 5) = 2p^3(3p^2) + 2p^3(-2p) + 2p^3(5)$

$= 6p^5 - 4p^4 + 10p^3$

(b) $(3k - 2)(k^2 + 5k - 4) = 3k(k^2 + 5k - 4) - 2(k^2 + 5k - 4)$

$= 3k^3 + 15k^2 - 12k - 2k^2 - 10k + 8$

$= 3k^3 + 13k^2 - 22k + 8$ ✓₈

✓ **Checkpoint 7**

Add or subtract as indicated.

(a) $(-2x^2 + 7x + 9)$
$+ (3x^2 + 2x - 7)$

(b) $(4x + 6) - (13x - 9)$

(c) $(9x^3 - 8x^2 + 2x)$
$- (9x^3 - 2x^2 - 10)$

✓ **Checkpoint 8**

Find the following products.

(a) $-6r(2r - 5)$

(b) $(8m + 3) \cdot (m^4 - 2m^2 + 6m)$

Example 9 The product $(2x - 5)(3x + 4)$ can be found by using the distributive property twice:

$$\begin{aligned}
(2x - 5)(3x + 4) &= 2x(3x + 4) - 5(3x + 4) \\
&= \underbrace{2x \cdot 3x} + \underbrace{2x \cdot 4} + \underbrace{(-5) \cdot 3x} + \underbrace{(-5) \cdot 4} \\
&= 6x^2 \quad + \quad 8x \quad - \quad 15x \quad - \quad 20 \\
&= 6x^2 \quad - \quad\quad 7x \quad\quad - \quad 20
\end{aligned}$$

Observe the pattern in the second line of Example 9 and its relationship to the terms being multiplied:

$$(2x - 5)(3x + 4) = 2x \cdot 3x + 2x \cdot 4 + (-5) \cdot 3x + (-5) \cdot 4$$

First terms

$(2x - 5)(3x + 4)$ Outside terms

$(2x - 5)(3x + 4)$ Inside terms

$(2x - 5)(3x + 4)$ Last terms

This pattern is easy to remember by using the acronym **FOIL** (**F**irst, **O**utside, **I**nside, **L**ast). The FOIL method makes it easy to find products such as this one mentally, without the necessity of writing out the intermediate steps.

Example 10 Use FOIL to find the product of the given polynomials.

(a) $(3x + 2)(x + 5) = 3x^2 + 15x + 2x + 10 = 3x^2 + 17x + 10$

First Outside Inside Last

(b) $(x + 3)^2 = (x + 3)(x + 3) = x^2 + 3x + 3x + 9 = x^2 + 6x + 9$

(c) $(2x + 1)(2x - 1) = 4x^2 - 2x + 2x - 1 = 4x^2 - 1$ ✓9

✓ **Checkpoint 9**

Use FOIL to find these products.
(a) $(5k - 1)(2k + 3)$
(b) $(7z - 3)(2z + 5)$

Applications

In business, the *revenue* from the sales of an item is given by

Revenue = (price per item) × (number of items sold).

The *cost* to manufacture and sell these items is given by

Cost = Fixed Costs + Variable Costs,

where the fixed costs include such things as buildings and machinery (which do not depend on how many items are made) and variable costs include such things as labor and materials (which vary, depending on how many items are made). Then

Profit = Revenue − Cost.

Example 11 **Business** A manufacturer of scientific calculators sells calculators for $12 each (wholesale) and can produce a maximum of 150,000. The variable cost of producing x thousand calculators is $6995x - 7.2x^2$ dollars, and the fixed costs for the manufacturing operation are $230,000. If x thousand calculators are manufactured and sold, find expressions for the revenue, cost, and profit.

Solution If x thousand calculators are sold at $12 each, then

Revenue = (price per item) × (number of items sold)
$$R = 12 \times 1000x = 12{,}000x,$$

where $x \leq 150$ (because only 150,000 calculators can be made). The variable cost of making x thousand calculators is $6995x - 7.2x^2$, so that

$$\text{Cost} = \text{Fixed Costs} + \text{Variable Costs},$$

$$C = 230{,}000 + (6995x - 7.2x^2) \quad (x \leq 150).$$

Therefore, the profit is given by

$$P = R - C = 12{,}000x - (230{,}000 + 6995x - 7.2x^2)$$

$$= 12{,}000x - 230{,}000 - 6995x + 7.2x^2$$

$$P = 7.2x^2 + 5005x - 230{,}000 \quad (x \leq 150). \quad ✓_{10}$$

✓ **Checkpoint 10**

Suppose revenue is given by $7x^2 - 3x$, fixed costs are \$500, and variable costs are given by $3x^2 + 5x - 25$. Write an expression for

(a) Cost

(b) Profit

1.2 Exercises

Use a calculator to approximate these numbers. (See Examples 1 and 2.)

1. 11.2^6

2. $(-6.54)^{11}$

3. $(-18/7)^6$

4. $(5/9)^7$

5. Explain how the value of -3^2 differs from $(-3)^2$. Do -3^3 and $(-3)^3$ differ in the same way? Why or why not?

6. Describe the steps used to multiply 4^3 and 4^5. Is the product of 4^3 and 3^4 found in the same way? Explain.

Simplify each of the given expressions. Leave your answers in exponential notation. (See Examples 3 and 4.)

7. $4^2 \cdot 4^3$

8. $(-4)^4 \cdot (-4)^6$

9. $(-6)^2 \cdot (-6)^5$

10. $(2z)^5 \cdot (2z)^6$

11. $[(5u)^4]^7$

12. $(6y)^3 \cdot [(6y)^5]^4$

List the degree of the given polynomial, its coefficients, and its constant term. (See Example 5.)

13. $6.2x^4 - 5x^3 + 4x^2 - 3x + 3.7$

14. $6x^7 + 4x^6 - x^3 + x$

State the degree of the given polynomial.

15. $1 + x + 2x^2 + 3x^3$

16. $5x^4 - 4x^5 - 6x^3 + 7x^4 - 2x + 8$

Add or subtract as indicated. (See Examples 6 and 7.)

17. $(3x^3 + 2x^2 - 5x) + (-4x^3 - x^2 - 8x)$

18. $(-2p^3 - 5p + 7) + (-4p^2 + 8p + 2)$

19. $(-4y^2 - 3y + 8) - (2y^2 - 6y + 2)$

20. $(7b^2 + 2b - 5) - (3b^2 + 2b - 6)$

21. $(2x^3 + 2x^2 + 4x - 3) - (2x^3 + 8x^2 + 1)$

22. $(3y^3 + 9y^2 - 11y + 8) - (-4y^2 + 10y - 6)$

Find each of the given products. (See Examples 8–10.)

23. $-9m(2m^2 + 6m - 1)$

24. $2a(4a^2 - 6a + 8)$

25. $(3z + 5)(4z^2 - 2z + 1)$

26. $(2k + 3)(4k^3 - 3k^2 + k)$

27. $(6k - 1)(2k + 3)$

28. $(8r + 3)(r - 1)$

29. $(3y + 5)(2y + 1)$

30. $(5r - 3s)(5r - 4s)$

31. $(9k + q)(2k - q)$

32. $(.012x - .17)(.3x + .54)$

33. $(6.2m - 3.4)(.7m + 1.3)$

34. $2p - 3[4p - (8p + 1)]$

35. $5k - [k + (-3 + 5k)]$

36. $(3x - 1)(x + 2) - (2x + 5)^2$

Business *Find expressions for the revenue, cost, and profit from selling x thousand items. (See Example 11.)*

	Item Price	Fixed Costs	Variable Costs
37.	\$5.00	\$200,000	$1800x$
38.	\$8.50	\$225,000	$4200x$

39. Business Beauty Works sells its cologne wholesale for \$9.75 per bottle. The variable costs of producing x thousand bottles is $-3x^2 + 3480x - 325$ dollars, and the fixed costs of manufacturing are \$260,000. Find expressions for the revenue, cost, and profit from selling x thousand items.

40. Business A self-help guru sells her book *Be Happy in 45 Easy Steps* for \$23.50 per copy. Her fixed costs are \$145,000 and she estimates the variable cost of printing, binding, and distribution is given by $-4.2x^2 + 3220x - 425$ dollars. Find expressions for the revenue, cost, and profit from selling x thousand copies of the book.

Work these problems.

Business *The accompanying bar graph shows the net earnings (in millions of dollars) of the Starbucks Corporation. The polynomial*

$$-1.48x^4 + 50.0x^3 - 576x^2 + 2731x - 4027$$

gives a good approximation of Starbucks's net earnings in year
x, where x = 3 corresponds to 2003, x = 4 to 2004, and so on
(3 ≤ x ≤ 12). For each of the given years,

(a) use the bar graph to determine the net earnings;

(b) use the polynomial to determine the net earnings.

(Data from: www.morningstar.com.)

41. 2003   **42.** 2007

43. 2010   **44.** 2012

*Assuming that the polynomial approximation in Exercises 41–44
remains accurate in later years, use it to estimate Starbucks's net
earnings in each of the following years.*

45. 2013   **46.** 2014   **47.** 2015

48. Do the estimates in Exercises 45–47 seem plausible? Explain.

Economics *The percentage of persons living below the poverty
line in the United States in year x is approximated by the polynomial*
$-.0057x^4 + .157x^3 - 1.43x^2 + 5.14x + 6.3$, *where x = 0 corresponds to the year 2000. Determine whether each of the given
statements is true or false. (Data from: U.S. Census Bureau, Current Population Survey, Annual Social and Economic Supplements.)*

49. The percentage living in poverty was higher than 13% in 2004.

50. The percentage living in poverty was higher than 14% in 2010.

51. The percentage living in poverty was higher in 2003 than 2006.

52. The percentage living in poverty was lower in 2009 than 2008.

Health *According to data from a leading insurance company, if
a person is 65 years old, the probability that he or she will live for
another x years is approximated by the polynomial*

$$1 - .0058x - .00076x^2.$$

(Data from: Ralph DeMarr, University of New Mexico.)

Find the probability that a 65-year-old person will live to the following ages.

53. 75 (that is, 10 years past 65)   **54.** 80

55. 87   **56.** 95

57. Physical Science One of the most amazing formulas in all
of ancient mathematics is the formula discovered by the

Egyptians to find the volume of the frustum of a square pyramid, as shown in the following figure:

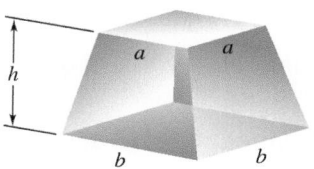

The volume of this pyramid is given by

$$(1/3)h \cdot (a^2 + ab + b^2),$$

where b is the length of the base, a is the length of the top, and
h is the height. (Data from: H. A. Freebury, *A History of Mathematics* [New York: MacMillan Company, 1968].)

(a) When the Great Pyramid in Egypt was partially completed
to a height h of 200 feet, b was 756 feet and a was 314 feet.
Calculate its volume at this stage of construction.

(b) Try to visualize the figure if a = b. What is the resulting
shape? Find its volume.

(c) Let a = b in the Egyptian formula and simplify. Are the
results the same?

58. Physical Science Refer to the formula and the discussion
in Exercise 57.

(a) Use the expression $(1/3)h(a^2 + ab + b^2)$ to determine a
formula for the volume of a pyramid with a square base b
and height h by letting a = 0.

(b) The Great Pyramid in Egypt had a square base of length 756
feet and a height of 481 feet. Find the volume of the Great
Pyramid. Compare it with the volume of the 273-foot-tall
Louisiana Superdome, which has an approximate volume
of 125 million cubic feet. (Data from: Louisiana Superdome [www.superdome.com].)

(c) The Superdome covers an area of 13 acres. How many
acres does the Great Pyramid cover? (*Hint:* 1 acre =
43,560 ft².)

59. Suppose one polynomial has degree 3 and another also has
degree 3. Find all possible values for the degree of their

(a) sum;

(b) difference;

(c) product.

Business *Use the table feature of a graphing calculator or use
a spreadsheet to make a table of values for the profit function in
Example 11, with x = 0, 5, 10, . . . , 150. Use the table to answer
the following questions.*

60. What is the profit or loss (negative profit) when 25,000 calculators are sold? when 60,000 are sold? Explain these
answers.

61. Approximately how many calculators must be sold in order for
the company to make a profit?

62. What is the profit from selling 100,000 calculators? 150,000
calculators?

1. (a) 216   (b) 244,140,625
   (c) 1   (d) 14.75789056

2. (a) 108   (b) 320   (c) −729
   (d) 729   (e) 486

3. (a) 5^9 (b) $(-3)^{14}$ (c) $(5p)^{10}$

4. (a) 6^{21} (b) $(4k)^{30}$

5. (a) 1   (b) 1   (c) 1   (d) −1

6. (a) 4   (b) 8   (c) 0   (d) Not defined

7. (a) $x^2 + 9x + 2$
   (b) $-9x + 15$
   (c) $-6x^2 + 2x + 10$

8. (a) $-12r^2 + 30r$
   (b) $8m^5 + 3m^4 - 16m^3 + 42m^2 + 18m$

9. (a) $10k^2 + 13k - 3$ (b) $14z^2 + 29z - 15$

10. (a) $C = 3x^2 + 5x + 475$ (b) $P = 4x^2 - 8x - 475$

1.3 Factoring

The number 18 can be written as a product in several ways: $9 \cdot 2, (-3)(-6), 1 \cdot 18$, etc. The numbers in each product $(9, 2, -3$, etc.) are called **factors,** and the process of writing 18 as a product of factors is called **factoring.** Thus, factoring is the reverse of multiplication.

Factoring of polynomials is a means of simplifying many expressions and of solving certain types of equations. As is the usual custom, factoring of polynomials in this text will be restricted to finding factors with *integer* coefficients (otherwise there may be an infinite number of possible factors).

Greatest Common Factor

The algebraic expression $15m + 45$ is made up of two terms: $15m$ and 45. Each of these terms has 15 as a factor. In fact, $15m = 15 \cdot m$ and $45 = 15 \cdot 3$. By the distributive property,

$$15m + 45 = 15 \cdot m + 15 \cdot 3 = 15(m + 3).$$

Both 15 and $m + 3$ are factors of $15m + 45$. Since 15 divides evenly into all terms of $15m + 45$ and is the largest number that will do so, it is called the **greatest common factor** for the polynomial $15m + 45$. The process of writing $15m + 45$ as $15(m + 3)$ is called **factoring out** the greatest common factor.

Example 1   Factor out the greatest common factor.

(a) $12p - 18q$

Solution   Both $12p$ and $18q$ are divisible by 6, and

$$12p - 18q = 6 \cdot 2p - 6 \cdot 3q$$
$$= 6(2p - 3q).$$

(b) $8x^3 - 9x^2 + 15x$

Solution   Each of these terms is divisible by x:

$$8x^3 - 9x^2 + 15x = (8x^2) \cdot x - (9x) \cdot x + 15 \cdot x$$
$$= x(8x^2 - 9x + 15).$$

(c) $5(4x - 3)^3 + 2(4x - 3)^2$

Solution   The quantity $(4x - 3)^2$ is a common factor. Factoring it out gives

$$5(4x - 3)^3 + 2(4x - 3)^2 = (4x - 3)^2[5(4x - 3) + 2]$$
$$= (4x - 3)^2(20x - 15 + 2)$$
$$= (4x - 3)^2(20x - 13). ✓$$

✓**Checkpoint 1**

Factor out the greatest common factor.

(a) $12r + 9k$

(b) $75m^2 + 100n^2$

(c) $6m^4 - 9m^3 + 12m^2$

(d) $3(2k + 1)^3 + 4(2k + 1)^4$

Factoring Quadratics

If we multiply two first-degree polynomials, the result is a quadratic. For instance, using FOIL, we see that $(x + 1)(x - 2) = x^2 - x - 2$. Since factoring is the reverse of multiplication, factoring quadratics requires using FOIL backward.

Example 2   Factor $x^2 + 9x + 18$.

Solution   We must find integers b and d such that

$$x^2 + 9x + 18 = (x + b)(x + d)$$
$$= x^2 + dx + bx + bd$$
$$x^2 + 9x + 18 = x^2 + (b + d)x + bd.$$

Since the constant coefficients on each side of the equation must be equal, we must have $bd = 18$; that is, b and d are factors of 18. Similarly, the coefficients of x must be the same, so that $b + d = 9$. The possibilities are summarized in this table:

Factors b, d of 18	Sum $b + d$
$18 \cdot 1$	$18 + 1 = 19$
$9 \cdot 2$	$9 + 2 = 11$
$6 \cdot 3$	$6 + 3 = 9$

There is no need to list negative factors, such as $(-3)(-6)$, because their sum is negative. The table suggests that 6 and 3 will work. Verify that

$$(x + 6)(x + 3) = x^2 + 9x + 18.$$

✓ **Checkpoint 2**

Factor the following.

(a) $r^2 + 7r + 10$

(b) $x^2 + 4x + 3$

(c) $y^2 + 6y + 8$

Example 3   Factor $x^2 + 3x - 10$.

Solution   As in Example 2, we must find factors b and d whose product is -10 (the constant term) and whose sum is 3 (the coefficient of x). The following table shows the possibilities.

Factors b, d of -10	Sum $b + d$
$1(-10)$	$1 + (-10) = -9$
$(-1)10$	$-1 + 10 = 9$
$2(-5)$	$2 + (-5) = -3$
$(-2)5$	$-2 + 5 = 3$

The only factors with product -10 and sum 3 are -2 and 5. So the correct factorization is

$$x^2 + 3x - 10 = (x - 2)(x + 5),$$

as you can readily verify.

It is usually not necessary to construct tables as was done in Examples 2 and 3—you can just mentally check the various possibilities. The approach used in Examples 2 and 3 (with minor modifications) also works for factoring quadratic polynomials whose leading coefficient is not 1.

Example 4   Factor $4y^2 - 11y + 6$.

Solution   We must find integers a, b, c, and d such that

$$4y^2 - 11y + 6 = (ay + b)(cy + d)$$
$$= acy^2 + ady + bcy + bd$$
$$4y^2 - 11y + 6 = acy^2 + (ad + bc)y + bd.$$

Since the coefficients of y^2 must be the same on both sides, we see that $ac = 4$. Similarly, the constant terms show that $bd = 6$. The positive factors of 4 are 4 and 1 or 2 and 2. Since the middle term is negative, we consider only negative factors of 6. The possibilities are -2 and -3 or -1 and -6. Now we try various arrangements of these factors until we find one that gives the correct coefficient of y:

$$(2y - 1)(2y - 6) = 4y^2 - 14y + 6 \qquad \text{Incorrect}$$
$$(2y - 2)(2y - 3) = 4y^2 - 10y + 6 \qquad \text{Incorrect}$$
$$(y - 2)(4y - 3) = 4y^2 - 11y + 6. \qquad \text{Correct}$$

The last trial gives the correct factorization. ✓₃

✓ Checkpoint 3

Factor the following.

(a) $x^2 - 4x + 3$

(b) $2y^2 - 5y + 2$

(c) $6z^2 - 13z + 6$

Example 5   Factor $6p^2 - 7pq - 5q^2$.

Solution   Again, we try various possibilities. The positive factors of 6 could be 2 and 3 or 1 and 6. As factors of -5, we have only -1 and 5 or -5 and 1. Try different combinations of these factors until the correct one is found:

$$(2p - 5q)(3p + q) = 6p^2 - 13pq - 5q^2 \qquad \text{Incorrect}$$
$$(3p - 5q)(2p + q) = 6p^2 - 7pq - 5q^2. \qquad \text{Correct}$$

So $6p^2 - 7pq - 5q^2$ factors as $(3p - 5q)(2p + q)$. ✓₄

✓ Checkpoint 4

Factor the following.

(a) $r^2 - 5r - 14$

(b) $3m^2 + 5m - 2$

(c) $6p^2 + 13pq - 5q^2$

NOTE In Examples 2–4, we chose positive factors of the positive first term. Of course, we could have used two negative factors, but the work is easier if positive factors are used.

Example 6   Factor $x^2 + x + 3$.

Solution   There are only two ways to factor 3, namely, $3 = 1 \cdot 3$ and $3 = (-1)(-3)$. They lead to these products:

$$(x + 1)(x + 3) = x^2 + 4x + 3 \qquad \text{Incorrect}$$
$$(x - 1)(x - 3) = x^2 - 4x + 3. \qquad \text{Incorrect}$$

Therefore, this polynomial cannot be factored.

Factoring Patterns

In some cases, you can factor a polynomial with a minimum amount of guesswork by recognizing common patterns. The easiest pattern to recognize is the *difference of squares.*

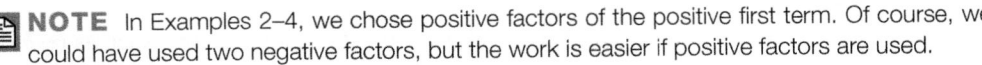

$$x^2 - y^2 = (x + y)(x - y). \qquad \text{Difference of squares}$$

To verify the accuracy of the preceding equation, multiply out the right side.

Example 7   Factor each of the following.

(a) $4m^2 - 9$

Solution   Notice that $4m^2 - 9$ is the difference of two squares, since $4m^2 = (2m)^2$ and $9 = 3^2$. Use the pattern for the difference of two squares, letting $2m$ replace x and 3 replace y. Then the pattern $x^2 - y^2 = (x + y)(x - y)$ becomes

$$4m^2 - 9 = (2m)^2 - 3^2$$
$$= (2m + 3)(2m - 3).$$

(b) $128p^2 - 98q^2$

Solution First factor out the common factor of 2:

$$128p^2 - 98q^2 = 2(64p^2 - 49q^2)$$
$$= 2[(8p)^2 - (7q)^2]$$
$$= 2(8p + 7q)(8p - 7q).$$

(c) $x^2 + 36$

Solution The *sum* of two squares cannot be factored. To convince yourself of this, check some possibilities:

$$(x + 6)(x + 6) = (x + 6)^2 = x^2 + 12x + 36;$$
$$(x + 4)(x + 9) = x^2 + 13x + 36.$$

(d) $(x - 2)^2 - 49$

Solution Since $49 = 7^2$, this is a difference of two squares. So it factors as follows:

$$(x - 2)^2 - 49 = (x - 2)^2 - 7^2$$
$$= [(x - 2) + 7][(x - 2) - 7]$$
$$= (x + 5)(x - 9). \quad \checkmark_5$$

✓**Checkpoint 5**

Factor the following.

(a) $9p^2 - 49$

(b) $y^2 + 100$

(c) $(x + 3)^2 - 64$

Another common pattern is the *perfect square*. Verify each of the following factorizations by multiplying out the right side.

$$x^2 + 2xy + y^2 = (x + y)^2$$
$$x^2 - 2xy + y^2 = (x - y)^2 \qquad \text{Perfect Squares}$$

Whenever you have a quadratic whose first and last terms are squares, it *may* factor as a perfect square. The key is to look at the middle term. To have a perfect square whose first and last terms are x^2 and y^2, the middle term must be $\pm 2xy$. To avoid errors, always check this.

Example 8 Factor each polynomial, if possible.

(a) $16p^2 - 40pq + 25q^2$

Solution The first and last terms are squares, namely, $16p^2 = (4p)^2$ and $25q^2 = (5q)^2$. So the second perfect-square pattern, with $x = 4p$ and $y = 5q$, might work. To have a perfect square, the middle term $-40pq$ must equal $-2(4p)(5q)$, which it does. So the polynomial factors as

$$16p^2 - 40pq + 25q^2 = (4p - 5q)(4p - 5q),$$

as you can easily verify.

(b) $9u^2 + 5u + 1$

Solution Again, the first and last terms are squares: $9u^2 = (3u)^2$ and $1 = 1^2$. The middle term is positive, so the first perfect-square pattern might work, with $x = 3u$ and $y = 1$. To have a perfect square, however, the middle term would have to be $2(3u) \cdot 1 = 6u$, which is *not* the middle term of the given polynomial. So it is not a perfect square—in fact, it cannot be factored.

(c) $169x^2 + 104xy^2 + 16y^4$

Solution This polynomial may be factored as $(13x + 4y^2)^2$, since $169x^2 = (13x)^2$, $16y^4 = (4y^2)^2$, and $2(13x)(4y^2) = 104xy^2$. ✓6

✓ **Checkpoint 6**

Factor.

(a) $4m^2 + 4m + 1$

(b) $25z^2 - 80zt + 64t^2$

(c) $9x^2 + 15x + 25$

Example 9   Factor each of the given polynomials.

(a) $12x^2 - 26x - 10$

Solution Look first for a greatest common factor. Here, the greatest common factor is 2: $12x^2 - 26x - 10 = 2(6x^2 - 13x - 5)$. Now try to factor $6x^2 - 13x - 5$. Possible factors of 6 are 3 and 2 or 6 and 1. The only factors of -5 are -5 and 1 or 5 and -1. Try various combinations. You should find that the quadratic factors as $(3x + 1)(2x - 5)$. Thus,

$$12x^2 - 26x - 10 = 2(3x + 1)(2x - 5).$$

(b) $4z^2 + 12z + 9 - w^2$

Solution There is no common factor here, but notice that the first three terms can be factored as a perfect square:

$$4z^2 + 12z + 9 - w^2 = (2z + 3)^2 - w^2.$$

Written in this form, the expression is the difference of squares, which can be factored as follows:

$$(2z + 3)^2 - w^2 = [(2z + 3) + w][(2z + 3) - w]$$
$$= (2z + 3 + w)(2z + 3 - w).$$

(c) $16a^2 - 100 - 48ac + 36c^2$

Solution Factor out the greatest common factor of 4 first:

$$16a^2 - 100 - 48ac + 36c^2 = 4[4a^2 - 25 - 12ac + 9c^2]$$
$$= 4[(4a^2 - 12ac + 9c^2) - 25] \quad \text{Rearrange terms and group.}$$
$$= 4[(2a - 3c)^2 - 25] \quad \text{Factor.}$$
$$= 4(2a - 3c + 5)(2a - 3c - 5) \quad \text{Factor the difference of squares. ✓7}$$

✓ **Checkpoint 7**

Factor the following.

(a) $6x^2 - 27x - 15$

(b) $9r^2 + 12r + 4 - t^2$

(c) $18 - 8xy - 2y^2 - 8x^2$

⊙ **CAUTION** Remember always to look first for a greatest common factor.

Higher Degree Polynomials

Polynomials of degree greater than 2 are often difficult to factor. However, factoring is relatively easy in two cases: *the difference and the sum of cubes*. By multiplying out the right side, you can readily verify each of the following factorizations.

$$x^3 - y^3 = (x - y)(x^2 + xy + y^2) \quad \text{Difference of cubes}$$
$$x^3 + y^3 = (x + y)(x^2 - xy + y^2) \quad \text{Sum of cubes}$$

Example 10   Factor each of the following polynomials.

(a) $k^3 - 8$

Solution Since $8 = 2^3$, use the pattern for the difference of two cubes to obtain

$$k^3 - 8 = k^3 - 2^3 = (k - 2)(k^2 + 2k + 4).$$

(b) $m^3 + 125$

Solution $m^3 + 125 = m^3 + 5^3 = (m + 5)(m^2 - 5m + 25)$

(c) $8k^3 - 27z^3$

Solution $8k^3 - 27z^3 = (2k)^3 - (3z)^3 = (2k - 3z)(4k^2 + 6kz + 9z^2)$ ✓8

✓**Checkpoint 8**

Factor the following.

(a) $a^3 + 1000$

(b) $z^3 - 64$

(c) $1000m^3 - 27z^3$

Substitution and appropriate factoring patterns can sometimes be used to factor higher degree expressions.

Example 11   Factor the following polynomials.

(a) $x^8 + 4x^4 + 3$

Solution   The idea is to make a substitution that reduces the polynomial to a quadratic or cubic that we can deal with. Note that $x^8 = (x^4)^2$. Let $u = x^4$. Then

$$
\begin{aligned}
x^8 + 4x^4 + 3 &= (x^4)^2 + 4x^4 + 3 && \text{Power of a power} \\
&= u^2 + 4u + 3 && \text{Substitute } x^4 = u. \\
&= (u + 3)(u + 1) && \text{Factor} \\
&= (x^4 + 3)(x^4 + 1). && \text{Substitute } u = x^4.
\end{aligned}
$$

(b) $x^4 - y^4$

Solution   Note that $x^4 = (x^2)^2$, and similarly for the y term. Let $u = x^2$ and $v = y^2$. Then

$$
\begin{aligned}
x^4 - y^4 &= (x^2)^2 - (y^2)^2 && \text{Power of a power} \\
&= u^2 - v^2 && \text{Substitute } x^2 = u \text{ and } y^2 = v. \\
&= (u + v)(u - v) && \text{Difference of squares} \\
&= (x^2 + y^2)(x^2 - y^2) && \text{Substitute } u = x^2 \text{ and } v = y^2. \\
&= (x^2 + y^2)(x + y)(x - y). && \text{Difference of squares} \ ✓9
\end{aligned}
$$

✓**Checkpoint 9**

Factor each of the following.

(a) $2x^4 + 5x^2 + 2$

(b) $3x^4 - x^2 - 2$

Once you understand Example 11, you can often factor without making explicit substitutions.

Example 12   Factor $256k^4 - 625m^4$.

Solution   Use the difference of squares twice, as follows:

$$
\begin{aligned}
256k^4 - 625m^4 &= (16k^2)^2 - (25m^2)^2 \\
&= (16k^2 + 25m^2)(16k^2 - 25m^2) \\
&= (16k^2 + 25m^2)(4k + 5m)(4k - 5m). \ ✓10
\end{aligned}
$$

✓**Checkpoint 10**

Factor $81x^4 - 16y^4$.

1.3 Exercises

Factor out the greatest common factor in each of the given polynomials. (See Example 1.)

1. $12x^2 - 24x$

2. $5y - 65xy$

3. $r^3 - 5r^2 + r$

4. $t^3 + 3t^2 + 8t$

5. $6z^3 - 12z^2 + 18z$

6. $5x^3 + 55x^2 + 10x$

7. $3(2y - 1)^2 + 7(2y - 1)^3$

8. $(3x + 7)^5 - 4(3x + 7)^3$

9. $3(x + 5)^4 + (x + 5)^6$

10. $3(x + 6)^2 + 6(x + 6)^4$

Factor the polynomial. (See Examples 2 and 3.)

11. $x^2 + 5x + 4$

12. $u^2 + 7u + 6$

13. $x^2 + 7x + 12$

14. $y^2 + 8y + 12$

15. $x^2 + x - 6$

16. $x^2 + 4x - 5$

17. $x^2 + 2x - 3$

18. $y^2 + y - 12$

19. $x^2 - 3x - 4$

20. $u^2 - 2u - 8$

21. $z^2 - 9z + 14$ **22.** $w^2 - 6w - 16$

23. $z^2 + 10z + 24$ **24.** $r^2 + 16r + 60$

Factor the polynomial. (See Examples 4–6.)

25. $2x^2 - 9x + 4$ **26.** $3w^2 - 8w + 4$

27. $15p^2 - 23p + 4$ **28.** $8x^2 - 14x + 3$

29. $4z^2 - 16z + 15$ **30.** $12y^2 - 29y + 15$

31. $6x^2 - 5x - 4$ **32.** $12z^2 + z - 1$

33. $10y^2 + 21y - 10$ **34.** $15u^2 + 4u - 4$

35. $6x^2 + 5x - 4$ **36.** $12y^2 + 7y - 10$

Factor each polynomial completely. Factor out the greatest common factor as necessary. (See Examples 2–9.)

37. $3a^2 + 2a - 5$ **38.** $6a^2 - 48a - 120$

39. $x^2 - 81$ **40.** $x^2 + 17xy + 72y^2$

41. $9p^2 - 12p + 4$ **42.** $3r^2 - r - 2$

43. $r^2 + 3rt - 10t^2$ **44.** $2a^2 + ab - 6b^2$

45. $m^2 - 8mn + 16n^2$ **46.** $8k^2 - 16k - 10$

47. $4u^2 + 12u + 9$ **48.** $9p^2 - 16$

49. $25p^2 - 10p + 4$ **50.** $10x^2 - 17x + 3$

51. $4r^2 - 9v^2$ **52.** $x^2 + 3xy - 28y^2$

53. $x^2 + 4xy + 4y^2$ **54.** $16u^2 + 12u - 18$

55. $3a^2 - 13a - 30$ **56.** $3k^2 + 2k - 8$

57. $21m^2 + 13mn + 2n^2$ **58.** $81y^2 - 100$

59. $y^2 - 4yz - 21z^2$ **60.** $49a^2 + 9$

61. $121x^2 - 64$ **62.** $4z^2 + 56zy + 196y^2$

Factor each of these polynomials. (See Example 10.)

63. $a^3 - 64$ **64.** $b^3 + 216$

65. $8r^3 - 27s^3$ **66.** $1000p^3 + 27q^3$

67. $64m^3 + 125$ **68.** $216y^3 - 343$

69. $1000y^3 - z^3$ **70.** $125p^3 + 8q^3$

Factor each of these polynomials. (See Examples 11 and 12.)

71. $x^4 + 5x^2 + 6$ **72.** $y^4 + 7y^2 + 10$

73. $b^4 - b^2$ **74.** $z^4 - 3z^2 - 4$

75. $x^4 - x^2 - 12$ **76.** $4x^4 + 27x^2 - 81$

77. $16a^4 - 81b^4$ **78.** $x^6 - y^6$

79. $x^8 + 8x^2$ **80.** $x^9 - 64x^3$

81. When asked to factor $6x^4 - 3x^2 - 3$ completely, a student gave the following result:
$$6x^4 - 3x^2 - 3 = (2x^2 + 1)(3x^2 - 3).$$
Is this answer correct? Explain why.

82. When can the sum of two squares be factored? Give examples.

83. Explain why $(x + 2)^3$ is not the correct factorization of $x^3 + 8$, and give the correct factorization.

84. Describe how factoring and multiplication are related. Give examples.

✓**Checkpoint Answers**

1. (a) $3(4r + 3k)$ (b) $25(3m^2 + 4n^2)$
(c) $3m^2(2m^2 - 3m + 4)$ (d) $(2k + 1)^3(7 + 8k)$

2. (a) $(r + 2)(r + 5)$ (b) $(x + 3)(x + 1)$
(c) $(y + 2)(y + 4)$

3. (a) $(x - 3)(x - 1)$ (b) $(2y - 1)(y - 2)$
(c) $(3z - 2)(2z - 3)$

4. (a) $(r - 7)(r + 2)$ (b) $(3m - 1)(m + 2)$
(c) $(2p + 5q)(3p - q)$

5. (a) $(3p + 7)(3p - 7)$ (b) Cannot be factored
(c) $(x + 11)(x - 5)$

6. (a) $(2m + 1)^2$ (b) $(5z - 8t)^2$
(c) Does not factor

7. (a) $3(2x + 1)(x - 5)$
(b) $(3r + 2 + t)(3r + 2 - t)$
(c) $2(3 - 2x - y)(3 + 2x + y)$

8. (a) $(a + 10)(a^2 - 10a + 100)$
(b) $(z - 4)(z^2 + 4z + 16)$
(c) $(10m - 3z)(100m^2 + 30mz + 9z^2)$

9. (a) $(2x^2 + 1)(x^2 + 2)$
(b) $(3x^2 + 2)(x + 1)(x - 1)$

10. $(9x^2 + 4y^2)(3x + 2y)(3x - 2y)$

1.4 Rational Expressions

A **rational expression** is an expression that can be written as the quotient of two polynomials, such as

$$\frac{8}{x - 1}, \qquad \frac{3x^2 + 4x}{5x - 6}, \qquad \text{and} \qquad \frac{2y + 1}{y^4 + 8}.$$

It is sometimes important to know the values of the variable that make the denominator 0 (in which case the quotient is not defined). For example, 1 cannot be used as a replacement for x in the first expression above and $6/5$ cannot be used in the second one, since these values make the respective denominators equal 0. *Throughout this section, we assume that all denominators are nonzero*, which means that some replacement values for the variables may have to be excluded. ✓₁

Simplifying Rational Expressions

A key tool for simplification is the following fact.

> For all expressions P, Q, R, and S, with $Q \neq 0$ and $S \neq 0$,
>
> $$\frac{PS}{QS} = \frac{P}{Q}. \qquad \text{Cancellation Property}$$

Example 1 Write each of the following rational expressions in lowest terms (so that the numerator and denominator have no common factor with integer coefficients except 1 or -1).

(a) $\dfrac{12m}{-18}$

Solution Both $12m$ and -18 are divisible by 6. By the cancellation property,

$$\frac{12m}{-18} = \frac{2m \cdot 6}{-3 \cdot 6}$$
$$= \frac{2m}{-3}$$
$$= -\frac{2m}{3}.$$

(b) $\dfrac{8x + 16}{4}$

Solution Factor the numerator and cancel:

$$\frac{8x + 16}{4} = \frac{8(x + 2)}{4} = \frac{4 \cdot 2(x + 2)}{4} = \frac{2(x + 2)}{1} = 2(x + 2).$$

The answer could also be written as $2x + 4$ if desired.

(c) $\dfrac{k^2 + 7k + 12}{k^2 + 2k - 3}$

Solution Factor the numerator and denominator and cancel:

$$\frac{k^2 + 7k + 12}{k^2 + 2k - 3} = \frac{(k + 4)(k + 3)}{(k - 1)(k + 3)} = \frac{k + 4}{k - 1}. \quad ✓_2$$

Multiplication and Division

The rules for multiplying and dividing rational expressions are the same fraction rules you learned in arithmetic.

✓ **Checkpoint 1**

What value of the variable makes each denominator equal 0?

(a) $\dfrac{5}{x - 3}$

(b) $\dfrac{2x - 3}{4x - 1}$

(c) $\dfrac{x + 2}{x}$

(d) Why do we need to determine these values?

✓ **Checkpoint 2**

Write each of the following in lowest terms.

(a) $\dfrac{12k + 36}{18}$

(b) $\dfrac{15m + 30m^2}{5m}$

(c) $\dfrac{2p^2 + 3p + 1}{p^2 + 3p + 2}$

For all expressions P, Q, R, and S, with $Q \neq 0$ and $S \neq 0$,

$$\frac{P}{Q} \cdot \frac{R}{S} = \frac{PR}{QS}$$

Multiplication Rule

and

$$\frac{P}{Q} \div \frac{R}{S} = \frac{P}{Q} \cdot \frac{S}{R} \qquad (R \neq 0).$$

Division Rule

Example 2

(a) Multiply $\dfrac{2}{3} \cdot \dfrac{y}{5}$.

Solution   Use the multiplication rule. Multiply the numerators and then the denominators:

$$\frac{2}{3} \cdot \frac{y}{5} = \frac{2 \cdot y}{3 \cdot 5} = \frac{2y}{15}.$$

The result, $2y/15$, is in lowest terms.

(b) Multiply $\dfrac{3y + 9}{6} \cdot \dfrac{18}{5y + 15}$.

Solution   Factor where possible:

$$\frac{3y + 9}{6} \cdot \frac{18}{5y + 15} = \frac{3(y + 3)}{6} \cdot \frac{18}{5(y + 3)}$$

$$= \frac{3 \cdot 18(y + 3)}{6 \cdot 5(y + 3)} \qquad \text{Multiply numerators and denominators.}$$

$$= \frac{3 \cdot 6 \cdot 3(y + 3)}{6 \cdot 5(y + 3)} \qquad 18 = 6 \cdot 3$$

$$= \frac{3 \cdot 3}{5} \qquad \text{Write in lowest terms.}$$

$$= \frac{9}{5}.$$

(c) Multiply $\dfrac{m^2 + 5m + 6}{m + 3} \cdot \dfrac{m^2 + m - 6}{m^2 + 3m + 2}$.

Solution   Factor numerators and denominators:

$$\frac{(m + 2)(m + 3)}{m + 3} \cdot \frac{(m - 2)(m + 3)}{(m + 2)(m + 1)} \qquad \text{Factor.}$$

$$= \frac{(m + 2)(m + 3)(m - 2)(m + 3)}{(m + 3)(m + 2)(m + 1)} \qquad \text{Multiply.}$$

$$= \frac{(m - 2)(m + 3)}{m + 1} \qquad \text{Lowest terms}$$

$$= \frac{m^2 + m - 6}{m + 1}. \quad \boxed{\checkmark 3}$$

✓**Checkpoint 3**

Multiply.

(a) $\dfrac{3r^2}{5} \cdot \dfrac{20}{9r}$

(b) $\dfrac{y - 4}{y^2 - 2y - 8} \cdot \dfrac{y^2 - 4}{3y}$

Example 3

(a) Divide $\dfrac{8x}{5} \div \dfrac{11x^2}{20}$.

Solution Invert the second expression and multiply (division rule):

$$\frac{8x}{5} \div \frac{11x^2}{20} = \frac{8x}{5} \cdot \frac{20}{11x^2} \qquad \text{Invert and multiply.}$$

$$= \frac{8x \cdot 20}{5 \cdot 11x^2} \qquad \text{Multiply.}$$

$$= \frac{32}{11x}. \qquad \text{Lowest terms}$$

(b) Divide $\dfrac{9p - 36}{12} \div \dfrac{5(p - 4)}{18}$.

Solution We have

$$\frac{9p - 36}{12} \cdot \frac{18}{5(p - 4)} \qquad \text{Invert and multiply.}$$

$$= \frac{9(p - 4)}{12} \cdot \frac{18}{5(p - 4)} \qquad \text{Factor.}$$

$$= \frac{27}{10}. \qquad \text{Cancel, multiply, and write in lowest terms.} \quad \checkmark_4$$

✓ **Checkpoint 4**

Divide.

(a) $\dfrac{5m}{16} \div \dfrac{m^2}{10}$

(b) $\dfrac{2y - 8}{6} \div \dfrac{5y - 20}{3}$

(c) $\dfrac{m^2 - 2m - 3}{m(m + 1)} \div \dfrac{m + 4}{5m}$

Addition and Subtraction

As you know, when two numerical fractions have the same denominator, they can be added or subtracted. The same rules apply to rational expressions.

For all expressions P, Q, R, with $Q \neq 0$,

$$\frac{P}{Q} + \frac{R}{Q} = \frac{P + R}{Q} \qquad \text{Addition Rule}$$

and

$$\frac{P}{Q} - \frac{R}{Q} = \frac{P - R}{Q}. \qquad \text{Subtraction Rule}$$

Example 4   Add or subtract as indicated.

(a) $\dfrac{4}{5k} + \dfrac{11}{5k}$

Solution Since the denominators are the same, we add the numerators:

$$\frac{4}{5k} + \frac{11}{5k} = \frac{4 + 11}{5k} = \frac{15}{5k} \qquad \text{Addition rule}$$

$$= \frac{3}{k}. \qquad \text{Lowest terms}$$

(b) $\dfrac{2x^2 + 3x + 1}{x^5 + 1} - \dfrac{x^2 - 7x}{x^5 + 1}$

Solution   The denominators are the same, so we subtract numerators, paying careful attention to parentheses:

$$\dfrac{2x^2 + 3x + 1}{x^5 + 1} - \dfrac{x^2 - 7x}{x^5 + 1} = \dfrac{(2x^2 + 3x + 1) - (x^2 - 7x)}{x^5 + 1} \qquad \text{Subtraction rule}$$

$$= \dfrac{2x^2 + 3x + 1 - x^2 - (-7x)}{x^5 + 1} \qquad \text{Subtract numerators.}$$

$$= \dfrac{2x^2 + 3x + 1 - x^2 + 7x}{x^5 + 1}$$

$$= \dfrac{x^2 + 10x + 1}{x^5 + 1}. \qquad \text{Simplify the numerator.}$$

When fractions do not have the same denominator, you must first find a common denominator before you can add or subtract. A common denominator is a denominator that has each fraction's denominator as a factor.

Example 5   Add or subtract as indicated.

(a) $\dfrac{7}{p^2} + \dfrac{9}{2p} + \dfrac{1}{3p^2}$

Solution   These three denominators are different, so we must find a common denominator that has each of p^2, $2p$, and $3p^2$ as factors. Observe that $6p^2$ satisfies these requirements. Use the cancellation property to rewrite each fraction as one that has $6p^2$ as its denominator and then add them:

$$\dfrac{7}{p^2} + \dfrac{9}{2p} + \dfrac{1}{3p^2} = \dfrac{6 \cdot 7}{6 \cdot p^2} + \dfrac{3p \cdot 9}{3p \cdot 2p} + \dfrac{2 \cdot 1}{2 \cdot 3p^2} \qquad \text{Cancellation property}$$

$$= \dfrac{42}{6p^2} + \dfrac{27p}{6p^2} + \dfrac{2}{6p^2}$$

$$= \dfrac{42 + 27p + 2}{6p^2} \qquad \text{Addition rule}$$

$$= \dfrac{27p + 44}{6p^2}. \qquad \text{Simplify.}$$

(b) $\dfrac{k^2}{k^2 - 1} - \dfrac{2k^2 - k - 3}{k^2 + 3k + 2}$

Solution   Factor the denominators to find a common denominator:

$$\dfrac{k^2}{k^2 - 1} - \dfrac{2k^2 - k - 3}{k^2 + 3k + 2} = \dfrac{k^2}{(k + 1)(k - 1)} - \dfrac{2k^2 - k - 3}{(k + 1)(k + 2)}.$$

A common denominator here is $(k + 1)(k - 1)(k + 2)$, because each of the preceding denominators is a factor of this common denominator. Write each fraction with the common denominator:

$$\frac{k^2}{(k+1)(k-1)} - \frac{2k^2-k-3}{(k+1)(k+2)}$$

$$= \frac{k^2(k+2)}{(k+1)(k-1)(k+2)} - \frac{(2k^2-k-3)(k-1)}{(k+1)(k-1)(k+2)}$$

$$= \frac{k^3+2k^2-(2k^2-k-3)(k-1)}{(k+1)(k-1)(k+2)} \qquad \text{Subtract fractions.}$$

$$= \frac{k^3+2k^2-(2k^3-3k^2-2k+3)}{(k+1)(k-1)(k+2)} \qquad \text{Multiply } (2k^2-k-3)(k-1).$$

$$= \frac{k^3+2k^2-2k^3+3k^2+2k-3}{(k+1)(k-1)(k+2)} \qquad \text{Polynomial subtraction}$$

$$= \frac{-k^3+5k^2+2k-3}{(k+1)(k-1)(k+2)}. \qquad \text{Combine terms.}$$

✓ Checkpoint 5

Add or subtract.

(a) $\dfrac{3}{4r} + \dfrac{8}{3r}$

(b) $\dfrac{1}{m-2} - \dfrac{3}{2(m-2)}$

(c) $\dfrac{p+1}{p^2-p} - \dfrac{p^2-1}{p^2+p-2}$

Complex Fractions

Any quotient of rational expressions is called a **complex fraction.** Complex fractions are simplified as demonstrated in Example 6.

Example 6   Simplify the complex fraction

$$\frac{6-\dfrac{5}{k}}{1+\dfrac{5}{k}}.$$

Solution   Multiply both numerator and denominator by the common denominator k:

$$\frac{6-\dfrac{5}{k}}{1+\dfrac{5}{k}} = \frac{k\left(6-\dfrac{5}{k}\right)}{k\left(1+\dfrac{5}{k}\right)} \qquad \text{Multiply by } \dfrac{k}{k}.$$

$$= \frac{6k-k\left(\dfrac{5}{k}\right)}{k+k\left(\dfrac{5}{k}\right)} \qquad \text{Distributive property}$$

$$= \frac{6k-5}{k+5}. \qquad \text{Simplify.}$$

1.4 Exercises

Write each of the given expressions in lowest terms. Factor as necessary. (See Example 1.)

1. $\dfrac{8x^2}{56x}$

2. $\dfrac{27m}{81m^3}$

3. $\dfrac{25p^2}{35p^3}$

4. $\dfrac{18y^4}{24y^2}$

5. $\dfrac{5m+15}{4m+12}$

6. $\dfrac{10z+5}{20z+10}$

7. $\dfrac{4(w-3)}{(w-3)(w+6)}$

8. $\dfrac{-6(x+2)}{(x+4)(x+2)}$

9. $\dfrac{3y^2-12y}{9y^3}$

10. $\dfrac{15k^2+45k}{9k^2}$

11. $\dfrac{m^2-4m+4}{m^2+m-6}$

12. $\dfrac{r^2-r-6}{r^2+r-12}$

13. $\dfrac{x^2+2x-3}{x^2-1}$

14. $\dfrac{z^2+4z+4}{z^2-4}$

Multiply or divide as indicated in each of the exercises. Write all answers in lowest terms. (See Examples 2 and 3.)

15. $\dfrac{3a^2}{64} \cdot \dfrac{8}{2a^3}$

16. $\dfrac{2u^2}{8u^4} \cdot \dfrac{10u^3}{9u}$

17. $\dfrac{7x}{11} \div \dfrac{14x^3}{66y}$

18. $\dfrac{6x^2y}{2x} \div \dfrac{21xy}{y}$

19. $\dfrac{2a + b}{3c} \cdot \dfrac{15}{4(2a + b)}$

20. $\dfrac{4(x + 2)}{w} \cdot \dfrac{3w^2}{8(x + 2)}$

21. $\dfrac{15p - 3}{6} \div \dfrac{10p - 2}{3}$

22. $\dfrac{2k + 8}{6} \div \dfrac{3k + 12}{3}$

23. $\dfrac{9y - 18}{6y + 12} \cdot \dfrac{3y + 6}{15y - 30}$

24. $\dfrac{12r + 24}{36r - 36} \div \dfrac{6r + 12}{8r - 8}$

25. $\dfrac{4a + 12}{2a - 10} \div \dfrac{a^2 - 9}{a^2 - a - 20}$

26. $\dfrac{6r - 18}{9r^2 + 6r - 24} \cdot \dfrac{12r - 16}{4r - 12}$

27. $\dfrac{k^2 - k - 6}{k^2 + k - 12} \cdot \dfrac{k^2 + 3k - 4}{k^2 + 2k - 3}$

28. $\dfrac{n^2 - n - 6}{n^2 - 2n - 8} \div \dfrac{n^2 - 9}{n^2 + 7n + 12}$

29. In your own words, explain how to find the least common denominator of two fractions.

30. Describe the steps required to add three rational expressions. You may use an example to illustrate.

Add or subtract as indicated in each of the following. Write all answers in lowest terms. (See Example 4.)

31. $\dfrac{2}{7z} - \dfrac{1}{5z}$

32. $\dfrac{4}{3z} - \dfrac{5}{4z}$

33. $\dfrac{r + 2}{3} - \dfrac{r - 2}{3}$

34. $\dfrac{3y - 1}{8} - \dfrac{3y + 1}{8}$

35. $\dfrac{4}{x} + \dfrac{1}{5}$

36. $\dfrac{6}{r} - \dfrac{3}{4}$

37. $\dfrac{1}{m - 1} + \dfrac{2}{m}$

38. $\dfrac{8}{y + 2} - \dfrac{3}{y}$

39. $\dfrac{7}{b + 2} + \dfrac{2}{5(b + 2)}$

40. $\dfrac{4}{3(k + 1)} + \dfrac{3}{k + 1}$

41. $\dfrac{2}{5(k - 2)} + \dfrac{5}{4(k - 2)}$

42. $\dfrac{11}{3(p + 4)} - \dfrac{5}{6(p + 4)}$

43. $\dfrac{2}{x^2 - 4x + 3} + \dfrac{5}{x^2 - x - 6}$

44. $\dfrac{3}{m^2 - 3m - 10} + \dfrac{7}{m^2 - m - 20}$

45. $\dfrac{2y}{y^2 + 7y + 12} - \dfrac{y}{y^2 + 5y + 6}$

46. $\dfrac{-r}{r^2 - 10r + 16} - \dfrac{3r}{r^2 + 2r - 8}$

In each of the exercises in the next set, simplify the complex fraction. (See Example 6.)

47. $\dfrac{1 + \dfrac{1}{x}}{1 - \dfrac{1}{x}}$

48. $\dfrac{2 - \dfrac{2}{y}}{2 + \dfrac{2}{y}}$

49. $\dfrac{\dfrac{1}{x + h} - \dfrac{1}{x}}{h}$

50. $\dfrac{\dfrac{1}{(x + h)^2} - \dfrac{1}{x^2}}{h}$

Work these problems.

Natural Science *Each figure in the following exercises is a dartboard. The probability that a dart which hits the board lands in the shaded area is the fraction*

$$\frac{\text{area of the shaded region}}{\text{area of the dartboard}}.$$

(a) *Express the probability as a rational expression in x. (Hint: Area formulas are given in Appendix B.)*

(b) *Then reduce the expression to lowest terms.*

51.

52.

53.

54.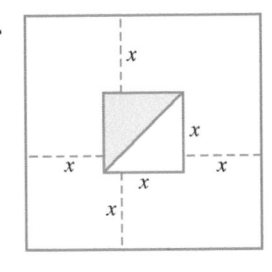

Business *In Example 11 of Section 1.2, we saw that the cost C of producing x thousand calculators is given by*

$$C = -7.2x^2 + 6995x + 230{,}000 \quad (x \le 150).$$

55. Write a rational expression that gives the average cost per calculator when x thousand are produced. (*Hint:* The average cost is the total cost C divided by the number of calculators produced.)

56. Find the average cost per calculator for each of these production levels: 20,000, 50,000, and 125,000.

Business *The cost (in millions of dollars) for a 30-second ad during the TV broadcast of the Superbowl can be approximated by*

$$\frac{.314x^2 - 1.399x + 15.0}{x + 1}$$

where x = 6 corresponds to the year 2006. (Data from: forbes.com and espn.com.)

57. How much did an ad cost in 2010?

58. How much did an ad cost in 2012?

59. If this trend continues, will the cost of an ad reach $5 million by 2018?

60. If this trend continues, when will the cost of an ad reach $6 million?

Health Economics *The average company cost per hour of an employee's health insurance in year x is approximated by*

$$\frac{.265x^2 + 1.47x + 3.63}{x + 2},$$

where x = 0 corresponds to the year 2000. (Data from: U.S. Bureau of Labor Statistics.)

61. What is the hourly health insurance cost in 2011?

62. What is the hourly health insurance cost in 2012?

63. Assuming that this model remains accurate and that an employee works 2100 hours per year, what is the annual company cost of her health care insurance in 2015?

64. Will annual costs reach $10,000 by 2020?

✓**Checkpoint Answers**

1. (a) 3   (b) 1/4   (c) 0
    (d) Because division by 0 is undefined

2. (a) $\dfrac{2(k + 3)}{3}$ or $\dfrac{2k + 6}{3}$

   (b) $3(1 + 2m)$ or $3 + 6m$ (c) $\dfrac{2p + 1}{p + 2}$

3. (a) $\dfrac{4r}{3}$ (b) $\dfrac{y - 2}{3y}$

4. (a) $\dfrac{25}{8m}$ (b) $\dfrac{1}{5}$ (c) $\dfrac{5(m - 3)}{m + 4}$

5. (a) $\dfrac{41}{12r}$ (b) $\dfrac{-1}{2(m - 2)}$ (c) $\dfrac{-p^3 + p^2 + 4p + 2}{p(p - 1)(p + 2)}$

1.5 Exponents and Radicals

Exponents were introduced in Section 1.2. In this section, the definition of exponents will be extended to include negative exponents and rational-number exponents such as 1/2 and 7/3.

Integer Exponents

Positive-integer and zero exponents were defined in Section 1.2, where we noted that

$$a^m \cdot a^n = a^{m+n}$$

for nonegative integers m and n. Now we develop an analogous property for quotients. By definition,

$$\frac{6^5}{6^2} = \frac{6 \cdot 6 \cdot 6 \cdot 6 \cdot 6}{6 \cdot 6} = 6 \cdot 6 \cdot 6 = 6^3.$$

Because there are 5 factors of 6 in the numerator and 2 factors of 6 in the denominator, the quotient has $5 - 2 = 3$ factors of 6. In general, we can make the following statement, which applies to any real number a and nonnegative integers m and n with $m > n$.

Division with Exponents

To divide a^m by a^n, *subtract* the exponents:

$$\frac{a^m}{a^n} = a^{m-n}.$$

Example 1 Compute each of the following.

(a) $\dfrac{5^7}{5^4} = 5^{7-4} = 5^3$.

(b) $\dfrac{(-8)^{10}}{(-8)^5} = (-8)^{10-5} = (-8)^5$.

(c) $\dfrac{(3c)^9}{(3c)^3} = (3c)^{9-3} = (3c)^6$. ✓1

✓ **Checkpoint 1**

Evaluate each of the following.

(a) $\dfrac{2^{14}}{2^5}$

(b) $\dfrac{(-5)^9}{(-5)^5}$

(c) $\dfrac{(xy)^{17}}{(xy)^{12}}$

When an exponent applies to the product of two numbers, such as $(7 \cdot 19)^3$, use the definitions carefully. For instance,

$$(7 \cdot 19)^3 = (7 \cdot 19)(7 \cdot 19)(7 \cdot 19) = 7 \cdot 7 \cdot 7 \cdot 19 \cdot 19 \cdot 19 = 7^3 \cdot 19^3.$$

In other words, $(7 \cdot 19)^3 = 7^3 \cdot 19^3$. This is an example of the following fact, which applies to any real numbers a and b and any nonnegative-integer exponent n.

Product to a Power

To find $(ab)^n$, apply the exponent to *every* term inside the parentheses:

$$(ab)^n = a^n b^n.$$

⊙ **CAUTION** A common mistake is to write an expression such as $(2x)^5$ as $2x^5$, rather than the correct answer $(2x)^5 = 2^5 x^5 = 32x^5$.

Analogous conclusions are valid for quotients (where a and b are any real numbers with $b \neq 0$ and n is a nonnegative-integer exponent).

Quotient to a Power

To find $\left(\dfrac{a}{b}\right)^n$, apply the exponent to both numerator and denominator:

$$\left(\frac{a}{b}\right)^n = \frac{a^n}{b^n}.$$

Example 2 Compute each of the following.

(a) $(5y)^3 = 5^3 y^3 = 125y^3$ Product to a power

(b) $(c^2 d^3)^4 = (c^2)^4 (d^3)^4$ Product to a power

       $= c^8 d^{12}$ Power of a power

(c) $\left(\dfrac{x}{2}\right)^6 = \dfrac{x^6}{2^6} = \dfrac{x^6}{64}$ Quotient to a power

(d) $\left(\dfrac{a^4}{b^3}\right)^3 = \dfrac{(a^4)^3}{(b^3)^3}$ Quotient to a power

       $= \dfrac{a^{12}}{b^9}$ Power of a power

(e) $\left(\dfrac{(rs)^3}{r^4}\right)^2$

Solution   Use several of the preceding properties in succession:

$$\left(\frac{(rs)^3}{r^4}\right)^2 = \left(\frac{r^3 s^3}{r^4}\right)^2 \qquad \text{Product to a power in numerator}$$

$$= \left(\frac{s^3}{r}\right)^2 \qquad \text{Cancel.}$$

$$= \frac{(s^3)^2}{r^2} \qquad \text{Quotient to a power}$$

$$= \frac{s^6}{r^2}. \qquad \text{Power of a power in numerator}$$

As is often the case, there is another way to reach the last expression. You should be able to supply the reasons for each of the following steps:

$$\left(\frac{(rs)^3}{r^4}\right)^2 = \frac{[(rs)^3]^2}{(r^4)^2} = \frac{(rs)^6}{r^8} = \frac{r^6 s^6}{r^8} = \frac{s^6}{r^2}.$$

Negative Exponents

The next step is to define negative-integer exponents. If they are to be defined in such a way that the quotient rule for exponents remains valid, then we must have, for example,

$$\frac{3^2}{3^4} = 3^{2-4} = 3^{-2}.$$

However,

$$\frac{3^2}{3^4} = \frac{3 \cdot 3}{3 \cdot 3 \cdot 3 \cdot 3} = \frac{1}{3^2},$$

which suggests that 3^{-2} should be defined to be $1/3^2$. Thus, we have the following definition of a negative exponent.

Negative Exponent

If n is a natural number, and if $a \neq 0$, then

$$a^{-n} = \frac{1}{a^n}.$$

Example 3   Evaluate the following.

(a) $3^{-2} = \dfrac{1}{3^2} = \dfrac{1}{9}.$

(b) $5^{-4} = \dfrac{1}{5^4} = \dfrac{1}{625}.$

(c) $x^{-1} = \dfrac{1}{x^1} = \dfrac{1}{x}.$

(d) $-4^{-2} = -\dfrac{1}{4^2} = -\dfrac{1}{16}.$

(e) $\left(\dfrac{3}{4}\right)^{-1} = \dfrac{1}{\left(\dfrac{3}{4}\right)^1} = \dfrac{1}{\dfrac{3}{4}} = \dfrac{4}{3}.$

✓ Checkpoint 2

Compute each of the following.

(a) $(3x)^4$
(b) $(r^2 s^5)^6$
(c) $\left(\dfrac{2}{z}\right)^5$
(d) $\left(\dfrac{3a^5}{(ab)^3}\right)^2$

✓ Checkpoint 3

Evaluate the following.

(a) 6^{-2}
(b) -6^{-3}
(c) -3^{-4}
(d) $\left(\dfrac{5}{8}\right)^{-1}$

There is a useful property that makes it easy to raise a fraction to a negative exponent. Consider, for example,

$$\left(\frac{2}{3}\right)^{-4} = \frac{1}{\left(\frac{2}{3}\right)^4} = \frac{1}{\left(\frac{2^4}{3^4}\right)} = 1 \cdot \frac{3^4}{2^4} = \left(\frac{3}{2}\right)^4.$$

This example is easily generalized to the following property (in which a/b is a nonzero fraction and n a positive integer).

Inversion Property

$$\left(\frac{a}{b}\right)^{-n} = \left(\frac{b}{a}\right)^{n}.$$

Example 4   Use the inversion property to compute each of the following.

(a) $\left(\frac{2}{5}\right)^{-3} = \left(\frac{5}{2}\right)^3 = \frac{5^3}{2^3} = \frac{125}{8}.$

(b) $\left(\frac{3}{x}\right)^{-5} = \left(\frac{x}{3}\right)^5 = \frac{x^5}{3^5} = \frac{x^5}{243}.$

 Checkpoint 4

Compute each of the following.

(a) $\left(\frac{5}{8}\right)^{-1}$

(b) $\left(\frac{1}{2}\right)^{-5}$

(c) $\left(\frac{a^2}{b}\right)^{-3}$

 TECHNOLOGY TIP
The FRAC key is in the MATH menu of TI graphing calculators. A FRAC program for other graphing calculators is in the Program Appendix. Fractions can be displayed on some graphing calculators by changing the number display format (in the MODES menu) to "fraction" or "exact."

When keying in negative exponents on a calculator, be sure to use the negation key (labeled $(-)$ or $+/-$), not the subtraction key. Calculators normally display answers as decimals, as shown in Figure 1.6. Some graphing calculators have a FRAC key that converts these decimals to fractions, as shown in Figure 1.7.

Figure 1.6   **Figure 1.7**

Roots and Rational Exponents

There are two numbers whose square is 16: 4 and -4. As we saw in Section 1.1, the positive one, 4, is called the *square root* (or second root) of 16. Similarly, there are two numbers whose fourth power is 16: 2 and -2. We call 2 the **fourth root** of 16. This suggests the following generalization.

If n is even, the **nth root of a** is the positive real number whose nth power is a.

All nonnegative numbers have nth roots for every natural number n, but *no negative number has a real, even nth root.* For example, there is no real number whose square is -16, so -16 has no square root.

We say that the **cube root** (or third root) of 8 is 2 because $2^3 = 8$. Similarly, since $(-2)^3 = -8$, we say that -2 is the cube root of -8. Again, we can make the following generalization.

> If n is odd, the **nth root of a** is the real number whose nth power is a.

Every real number has an nth root for every *odd* natural number n.

We can now define rational exponents. If they are to have the same properties as integer exponents, we want $a^{1/2}$ to be a number such that

$$(a^{1/2})^2 = a^{1/2} \cdot a^{1/2} = a^{1/2+1/2} = a^1 = a.$$

Thus, $a^{1/2}$ should be a number whose square is a, and it is reasonable to *define* $a^{1/2}$ to be the square root of a (if it exists). Similarly, $a^{1/3}$ is defined to be the cube root of a, and we have the following definition.

> If a is a real number and n is a positive integer, then
>
> $$a^{1/n} \text{ is defined to be the } n\text{th root of } a \text{ (if it exists).}$$

Example 5   Examine the reasoning used to evaluate the following roots.

(a) $36^{1/2} = 6$ because $6^2 = 36$.

(b) $100^{1/2} = 10$ because $10^2 = 100$.

(c) $-(225^{1/2}) = -15$ because $15^2 = 225$.

(d) $625^{1/4} = 5$ because $5^4 = 625$.

(e) $(-1296)^{1/4}$ is not a real number.

(f) $-1296^{1/4} = -6$ because $6^4 = 1296$.

(g) $(-27)^{1/3} = -3$ because $(-3)^3 = -27$.

(h) $-32^{1/5} = -2$ because $2^5 = 32$.

✓5

✓ **Checkpoint 5**

Evaluate the following.

(a) $16^{1/2}$

(b) $16^{1/4}$

(c) $-256^{1/2}$

(d) $(-256)^{1/2}$

(e) $-8^{1/3}$

(f) $243^{1/5}$

A calculator can be used to evaluate expressions with fractional exponents. Whenever it is easy to do so, enter the fractional exponents in their equivalent decimal form. For instance, to find $625^{1/4}$, enter $625^{.25}$ into the calculator. When the decimal equivalent of a fraction is an infinitely repeating decimal, however, it is best to enter the fractional exponent directly. If you use a shortened decimal approximation (such as .333 for $1/3$), you will not get the correct answers. Compare the incorrect answers in Figure 1.9 with the correct ones in Figure 1.8.

$27^{\frac{1}{3}}$
3

$27^{.333}$
2.996705973

Figure 1.8   **Figure 1.9**

For other rational exponents, the symbol $a^{m/n}$ should be defined so that the properties for exponents still hold. For example, by the product property, we want

$$(a^{1/3})^2 = a^{1/3} \cdot a^{1/3} = a^{1/3+1/3} = a^{2/3}.$$

This result suggests the following definition.

> For all integers m and all positive integers n, and for all real numbers a for which $a^{1/n}$ is a real number,
> $$a^{m/n} = (a^{1/n})^m.$$

Example 6 Verify each of the following calculations.

(a) $27^{2/3} = (27^{1/3})^2 = 3^2 = 9.$

(b) $32^{2/5} = (32^{1/5})^2 = 2^2 = 4.$

(c) $64^{4/3} = (64^{1/3})^4 = 4^4 = 256.$

(d) $25^{3/2} = (25^{1/2})^3 = 5^3 = 125.$ ✓ 6

✓ **Checkpoint 6**

Evaluate the following.

(a) $16^{3/4}$

(b) $25^{5/2}$

(c) $32^{7/5}$

(d) $100^{3/2}$

🛈 **CAUTION** When the base is negative, as in $(-8)^{2/3}$, some calculators produce an error message. On such calculators, you should first compute $(-8)^{1/3}$ and then square the result; that is, compute $[(-8)^{1/3}]^2$.

Since every terminating decimal is a rational number, decimal exponents now have a meaning. For instance, $5.24 = \frac{524}{100}$, so $3^{5.24} = 3^{524/100}$, which is easily approximated by a calculator (Figure 1.10).

Rational exponents were defined so that one of the familiar properties of exponents remains valid. In fact, it can be proved that *all* of the rules developed earlier for integer exponents are valid for rational exponents. The following box summarizes these rules, which are illustrated in Examples 7–9.

```
3^5.24
             316.3117863
 524
3^100
             316.3117863
```

Figure 1.10

Properties of Exponents

For any rational numbers m and n, and for any real numbers a and b for which the following exist,

(a) $a^m \cdot a^n = a^{m+n}$ — Product property

(b) $\dfrac{a^m}{a^n} = a^{m-n}$ — Quotient property

(c) $(a^m)^n = a^{mn}$ — Power of a power

(d) $(ab)^m = a^m \cdot b^m$ — Product to a power

(e) $\left(\dfrac{a}{b}\right)^m = \dfrac{a^m}{b^m}$ — Quotient to a power

(f) $a^0 = 1$ — Zero exponent

(g) $a^{-n} = \dfrac{1}{a^n}$ — Negative exponent

(h) $\left(\dfrac{a}{b}\right)^{-n} = \left(\dfrac{b}{a}\right)^n.$ — Inversion property

The power-of-a-power property provides another way to compute $a^{m/n}$ (when it exists):

$$a^{m/n} = a^{m(1/n)} = (a^m)^{1/n}. \tag{1}$$

For example, we can now find $4^{3/2}$ in two ways:

$$4^{3/2} = (4^{1/2})^3 = 2^3 = 8 \quad \text{or} \quad 4^{3/2} = (4^3)^{1/2} = 64^{1/2} = 8.$$

Definition of $a^{m/n}$ Statement (1)

Example 7   Simplify each of the following expressions.

(a) $7^{-4} \cdot 7^6 = 7^{-4+6} = 7^2 = 49.$ Product property

(b) $5x^{2/3} \cdot 2x^{1/4} = 10x^{2/3}x^{1/4}$
$= 10x^{2/3+1/4}$ Product property
$= 10x^{11/12}.$ $\frac{2}{3} + \frac{1}{4} = \frac{8}{12} + \frac{3}{12} = \frac{11}{12}$

(c) $\dfrac{9^{14}}{9^{-6}} = 9^{14-(-6)} = 9^{20}.$ Quotient property

(d) $\dfrac{c^5}{2c^{4/3}} = \dfrac{1}{2} \cdot \dfrac{c^5}{c^{4/3}}$
$= \dfrac{1}{2}c^{5-4/3}$ Quotient property
$= \dfrac{1}{2}c^{11/3} = \dfrac{c^{11/3}}{2}.$ $5 - \frac{4}{3} = \frac{15}{3} - \frac{4}{3} = \frac{11}{3}$

(e) $\dfrac{27^{1/3} \cdot 27^{5/3}}{27^3} = \dfrac{27^{1/3+5/3}}{27^3}$ Product property
$= \dfrac{27^2}{27^3} = 27^{2-3}$ Quotient property
$= 27^{-1} = \dfrac{1}{27}.$ Definition of negative exponent

You can use a calculator to check numerical computations, such as those in Example 7, by computing the left and right sides separately and confirming that the answers are the same in each case. Figure 1.11 shows this technique for part (e) of Example 7.

✓ **Checkpoint 7**

Simplify each of the following.
(a) $9^7 \cdot 9^{-5}$
(b) $3x^{1/4} \cdot 5x^{5/4}$
(c) $\dfrac{8^7}{8^{-3}}$
(d) $\dfrac{5^{2/3} \cdot 5^{-4/3}}{5^2}$

Figure 1.11

Example 8   Perform the indicated operations.

(a) $(2^{-3})^{-4/7} = 2^{(-3)(-4/7)} = 2^{12/7}.$ Power of a power

(b) $\left(\dfrac{3m^{5/6}}{y^{3/4}}\right)^2 = \dfrac{(3m^{5/6})^2}{(y^{3/4})^2}$ Quotient to a power
$= \dfrac{3^2(m^{5/6})^2}{(y^{3/4})^2}$ Product to a power
$= \dfrac{9m^{(5/6)2}}{y^{(3/4)2}}$ Power of a power
$= \dfrac{9m^{5/3}}{y^{3/2}}.$ $\frac{5}{6} \cdot 2 = \frac{10}{6} = \frac{5}{3}$ and $\frac{3}{4} \cdot 2 = \frac{3}{2}$

(c) $m^{2/3}(m^{7/3} + 2m^{1/3}) = m^{2/3}m^{7/3} + m^{2/3}2m^{1/3}$ Distributive property
$= m^{2/3+7/3} + 2m^{2/3+1/3} = m^3 + 2m.$ Product rule

✓ **Checkpoint 8**

Simplify each of the following.
(a) $(7^{-4})^{-2} \cdot (7^4)^{-2}$
(b) $\dfrac{c^4 c^{-1/2}}{c^{3/2}d^{1/2}}$
(c) $a^{5/8}(2a^{3/8} + a^{-1/8})$

Example 9   Simplify each expression in parts (a)–(c). Give answers with only positive exponents.

(a) $\dfrac{(m^3)^{-2}}{m^4} = \dfrac{m^{-6}}{m^4} = m^{-6-4} = m^{-10} = \dfrac{1}{m^{10}}.$

(b) $6y^{2/3} \cdot 2y^{-1/2} = 12y^{2/3-1/2} = 12y^{1/6}.$

(c) $\dfrac{x^{1/2}(x-2)^{-3}}{5(x-2)} = \dfrac{x^{1/2}}{5} \cdot \dfrac{(x-2)^{-3}}{x-2} = \dfrac{x^{1/2}}{5} \cdot (x-2)^{-3-1}$

$= \dfrac{x^{1/2}}{5} \cdot \dfrac{1}{(x-2)^4} = \dfrac{x^{1/2}}{5(x-2)^4}.$

(d) Write $a^{-1} + b^{-1}$ as a single quotient.

Solution   Be careful here. $a^{-1} + b^{-1}$ does *not* equal $(a+b)^{-1}$; the exponent properties deal only with products and quotients, not with sums. However, using the definition of negative exponents and addition of fractions, we have

$$a^{-1} + b^{-1} = \frac{1}{a} + \frac{1}{b} = \frac{b+a}{ab}. \quad \boxed{9}$$

We can use some functions of the form ax^b where both a and b are constants and b is also an exponent.

Example 10   **Social Science**   The total number of students (in millions) attending institutes of higher education can be approximated by the function

$$5.8x^{0.357} \quad (x \geq 10),$$

where $x = 10$ corresponds to the year 1990. Find the approximate number of students enrolled in higher education in 2012. (Data from: U.S. National Center for Education Statistics.)

Solution   Since 2012 is 22 years after 1990 and $x = 10$ corresponds to 1990, we have that $x = 22 + 10 = 32$ corresponds to 2012. We then obtain

$$5.8(32)^{0.357} \approx 20.0 \text{ million students.} \quad \boxed{10}$$

Radicals

Earlier, we denoted the nth root of a as $a^{1/n}$. An alternative notation for nth roots uses the radical symbol $\sqrt[n]{\ }$.

If n is an even natural number and $a \geq 0$, or if n is an odd natural number,

$$\sqrt[n]{a} = a^{1/n}.$$

In the radical expression $\sqrt[n]{a}$, a is called the *radicand* and n is called the *index*. When $n = 2$, the familiar square-root symbol $\sqrt{a}$ is used instead of $\sqrt[2]{a}$.

Example 11   Simplify the following radicals.

(a) $\sqrt[4]{16} = 16^{1/4} = 2.$

(b) $\sqrt[5]{-32} = -2.$

(c) $\sqrt[3]{1000} = 10.$

(d) $\sqrt[6]{\dfrac{64}{729}} = \left(\dfrac{64}{729}\right)^{1/6} = \dfrac{64^{1/6}}{729^{1/6}} = \dfrac{2}{3}. \quad \boxed{11}$

 Checkpoint 9

Simplify the given expressions. Give answers with only positive exponents.

(a) $(3x^{2/3})(2x^{-1})(y^{-1/3})^2$

(b) $\dfrac{(t^{-1})^2}{t^{-5}}$

(c) $\left(\dfrac{2k^{1/3}}{p^{5/4}}\right)^2 \cdot \left(\dfrac{4k^{-2}}{p^5}\right)^{3/2}$

(d) $x^{-1} - y^{-2}$

✓ Checkpoint 10

Assuming the model from Example 10 remains accurate, find the number of students for 2015.

✓ Checkpoint 11

Simplify.

(a) $\sqrt[3]{27}$

(b) $\sqrt[4]{625}$

(c) $\sqrt[6]{64}$

(d) $\sqrt[3]{\dfrac{64}{125}}$

Recall that $a^{m/n} = (a^{1/n})^m$ by definition and $a^{m/n} = (a^m)^{1/n}$ by statement (**1**) on page 36 (provided that all terms are defined). We translate these facts into radical notation as follows.

For all rational numbers m/n and all real numbers a for which $\sqrt[n]{a}$ exists,

$$a^{m/n} = (\sqrt[n]{a})^m \quad \text{or} \quad a^{m/n} = \sqrt[n]{a^m}.$$

Notice that $\sqrt[n]{x^n}$ cannot be written simply as x when n is even. For example, if $x = -5$, then

$$\sqrt{x^2} = \sqrt{(-5)^2} = \sqrt{25} = 5 \neq x.$$

However, $|-5| = 5$, so that $\sqrt{x^2} = |x|$ when x is -5. This relationship is true in general.

For any real number a and any natural number n,

$$\sqrt[n]{a^n} = |a| \quad \text{if } n \text{ is even}$$

and

$$\sqrt[n]{a^n} = a \quad \text{if } n \text{ is odd.}$$

To avoid the difficulty that $\sqrt[n]{a^n}$ is not necessarily equal to a, we shall assume that all variables in radicands represent only nonnegative numbers, as they usually do in applications.

The properties of exponents can be written with radicals as follows.

For all real numbers a and b, and for positive integers n for which all indicated roots exist,

(a) $\sqrt[n]{a} \cdot \sqrt[n]{b} = \sqrt[n]{ab}$ and

(b) $\dfrac{\sqrt[n]{a}}{\sqrt[n]{b}} = \sqrt[n]{\dfrac{a}{b}} \quad (b \neq 0).$

Example 12 Simplify the following expressions.

(a) $\sqrt{6} \cdot \sqrt{54} = \sqrt{6 \cdot 54} = \sqrt{324} = 18.$

Alternatively, simplify $\sqrt{54}$ first:

$$\sqrt{6} \cdot \sqrt{54} = \sqrt{6} \cdot \sqrt{9 \cdot 6}$$
$$= \sqrt{6} \cdot 3\sqrt{6} = 3 \cdot 6 = 18.$$

(b) $\sqrt{\dfrac{7}{64}} = \dfrac{\sqrt{7}}{\sqrt{64}} = \dfrac{\sqrt{7}}{8}.$

(c) $\sqrt{75} - \sqrt{12}.$

Solution Note that $12 = 4 \cdot 3$ and that 4 is a perfect square. Similarly, $75 = 25 \cdot 3$ and 25 is a perfect square. Consequently,

$$\sqrt{75} - \sqrt{12} = \sqrt{25 \cdot 3} - \sqrt{4 \cdot 3} \qquad \text{Factor.}$$
$$= \sqrt{25}\sqrt{3} - \sqrt{4}\sqrt{3} \qquad \text{Property (a)}$$
$$= 5\sqrt{3} - 2\sqrt{3} = 3\sqrt{3}. \qquad \text{Simplify.} \quad \checkmark_{12}$$

✓**Checkpoint 12**

Simplify.

(a) $\sqrt{3} \cdot \sqrt{27}$

(b) $\sqrt{\dfrac{3}{49}}$

(c) $\sqrt{50} + \sqrt{72}$

⚠ **CAUTION** When a and b are nonzero real numbers,

$$\sqrt[n]{a+b} \text{ is } \textbf{NOT} \text{ equal to } \sqrt[n]{a} + \sqrt[n]{b}.$$

For example,

$$\sqrt{9+16} = \sqrt{25} = 5, \text{ but } \sqrt{9} + \sqrt{16} = 3 + 4 = 7,$$

so $\sqrt{9+16} \neq \sqrt{9} + \sqrt{16}$.

Multiplying radical expressions is much like multiplying polynomials.

Example 13 Perform the following multiplications.

(a) $(\sqrt{2} + 3)(\sqrt{8} - 5) = \sqrt{2}(\sqrt{8}) - \sqrt{2}(5) + 3\sqrt{8} - 3(5)$ FOIL
$$= \sqrt{16} - 5\sqrt{2} + 3(2\sqrt{2}) - 15$$
$$= 4 - 5\sqrt{2} + 6\sqrt{2} - 15$$
$$= -11 + \sqrt{2}.$$

(b) $(\sqrt{7} - \sqrt{10})(\sqrt{7} + \sqrt{10}) = (\sqrt{7})^2 - (\sqrt{10})^2$
$$= 7 - 10 = -3. \quad ✓_{13}$$

✓**Checkpoint 13**

Multiply.

(a) $(\sqrt{5} - \sqrt{2})(3 + \sqrt{2})$

(b) $(\sqrt{3} + \sqrt{7})(\sqrt{3} - \sqrt{7})$

Rationalizing Denominators and Numerators

Before the invention of calculators, it was customary to **rationalize the denominators** of fractions (that is, write equivalent fractions with no radicals in the denominator), because this made many computations easier. Although there is no longer a computational reason to do so, rationalization of denominators (and sometimes numerators) is still used today to simplify expressions and to derive useful formulas.

Example 14 Rationalize each denominator.

(a) $\dfrac{4}{\sqrt{3}}$

Solution The key is to multiply by 1, with 1 written as a radical fraction:

$$\frac{4}{\sqrt{3}} = \frac{4}{\sqrt{3}} \cdot 1 = \frac{4}{\sqrt{3}} \cdot \frac{\sqrt{3}}{\sqrt{3}} = \frac{4\sqrt{3}}{3}.$$

(b) $\dfrac{1}{3 - \sqrt{2}}$

Solution The same technique works here, using $1 = \dfrac{3 + \sqrt{2}}{3 + \sqrt{2}}$:

$$\frac{1}{3 - \sqrt{2}} = \frac{1}{3 - \sqrt{2}} \cdot 1 = \frac{1}{3 - \sqrt{2}} \cdot \frac{3 + \sqrt{2}}{3 + \sqrt{2}} = \frac{3 + \sqrt{2}}{(3 - \sqrt{2})(3 + \sqrt{2})}$$
$$= \frac{3 + \sqrt{2}}{9 - 2} = \frac{3 + \sqrt{2}}{7}. \quad ✓_{14}$$

✓**Checkpoint 14**

Rationalize the denominator.

(a) $\dfrac{2}{\sqrt{5}}$

(b) $\dfrac{1}{2 + \sqrt{3}}$

Example 15 Rationalize the numerator of

$$\frac{2 + \sqrt{5}}{1 + \sqrt{3}}.$$

Solution As in Example 14(b), we must write 1 as a suitable fraction. Since we want to rationalize the numerator here, we multiply by the fraction $1 = \dfrac{2 - \sqrt{5}}{2 - \sqrt{5}}$:

$$\frac{2 + \sqrt{5}}{1 + \sqrt{3}} = \frac{2 + \sqrt{5}}{1 + \sqrt{3}} \cdot \frac{2 - \sqrt{5}}{2 - \sqrt{5}} = \frac{4 - 5}{2 - \sqrt{5} + 2\sqrt{3} - \sqrt{3}\sqrt{5}}$$

$$= \frac{-1}{2 - \sqrt{5} + 2\sqrt{3} - \sqrt{15}}.$$

1.5 Exercises

Perform the indicated operations and simplify your answer. (See Examples 1 and 2.)

1. $\dfrac{7^5}{7^3}$

2. $\dfrac{(-6)^{14}}{(-6)^6}$

3. $(4c)^2$

4. $(-2x)^4$

5. $\left(\dfrac{2}{x}\right)^5$

6. $\left(\dfrac{5}{xy}\right)^3$

7. $(3u^2)^3(2u^3)^2$

8. $\dfrac{(5v^2)^3}{(2v)^4}$

Perform the indicated operations and simplify your answer, which should not have any negative exponents. (See Examples 3 and 4.)

9. 7^{-1}

10. 10^{-3}

11. -6^{-5}

12. $(-x)^{-4}$

13. $(-y)^{-3}$

14. $\left(\dfrac{1}{6}\right)^{-2}$

15. $\left(\dfrac{4}{3}\right)^{-2}$

16. $\left(\dfrac{x}{y^2}\right)^{-2}$

17. $\left(\dfrac{a}{b^3}\right)^{-1}$

18. Explain why $-2^{-4} = -1/16$, but $(-2)^{-4} = 1/16$.

Evaluate each expression. Write all answers without exponents. Round decimal answers to two places. (See Examples 5 and 6.)

19. $49^{1/2}$

20. $8^{1/3}$

21. $(5.71)^{1/4}$

22. $12^{5/2}$

23. $-64^{2/3}$

24. $-64^{3/2}$

25. $(8/27)^{-4/3}$

26. $(27/64)^{-1/3}$

Simplify each expression. Write all answers using only positive exponents. (See Example 7.)

27. $\dfrac{5^{-3}}{4^{-2}}$

28. $\dfrac{7^{-4}}{7^{-3}}$

29. $4^{-3} \cdot 4^6$

30. $9^{-9} \cdot 9^{10}$

31. $\dfrac{4^{10} \cdot 4^{-6}}{4^{-4}}$

32. $\dfrac{5^{-4} \cdot 5^6}{5^{-1}}$

Simplify each expression. Assume all variables represent positive real numbers. Write answers with only positive exponents. (See Examples 8 and 9.)

33. $\dfrac{z^6 \cdot z^2}{z^5}$

34. $\dfrac{k^6 \cdot k^9}{k^{12}}$

35. $\dfrac{3^{-1}(p^{-2})^3}{3p^{-7}}$

36. $\dfrac{(5x^3)^{-2}}{x^4}$

37. $(q^{-5}r^3)^{-1}$

38. $(2y^2z^{-2})^{-3}$

39. $(2p^{-1})^3 \cdot (5p^2)^{-2}$

40. $(4^{-1}x^3)^{-2} \cdot (3x^{-3})^4$

41. $(2p)^{1/2} \cdot (2p^3)^{1/3}$

42. $(5k^2)^{3/2} \cdot (5k^{1/3})^{3/4}$

43. $p^{2/3}(2p^{1/3} + 5p)$

44. $3x^{3/2}(2x^{-3/2} + x^{3/2})$

45. $\dfrac{(x^2)^{1/3}(y^2)^{2/3}}{3x^{2/3}y^2}$

46. $\dfrac{(c^{1/2})^3(d^3)^{1/2}}{(c^3)^{1/4}(d^{1/4})^3}$

47. $\dfrac{(7a)^2(5b)^{3/2}}{(5a)^{3/2}(7b)^4}$

48. $\dfrac{(4x)^{1/2}\sqrt{xy}}{x^{3/2}y^2}$

49. $x^{1/2}(x^{2/3} - x^{4/3})$

50. $x^{1/2}(3x^{3/2} + 2x^{-1/2})$

51. $(x^{1/2} + y^{1/2})(x^{1/2} - y^{1/2})$ **52.** $(x^{1/3} + y^{1/2})(2x^{1/3} - y^{3/2})$

Match the rational-exponent expression in Column I with the equivalent radical expression in Column II. Assume that x is not zero.

I	**II**
53. $(-3x)^{1/3}$	**(a)** $\dfrac{3}{\sqrt[3]{x}}$
54. $-3x^{1/3}$	**(b)** $-3\sqrt[3]{x}$
55. $(-3x)^{-1/3}$	**(c)** $\dfrac{1}{\sqrt[3]{3x}}$
56. $-3x^{-1/3}$	**(d)** $\dfrac{-3}{\sqrt[3]{x}}$
57. $(3x)^{1/3}$	**(e)** $3\sqrt[3]{x}$
58. $3x^{-1/3}$	**(f)** $\sqrt[3]{-3x}$
59. $(3x)^{-1/3}$	**(g)** $\sqrt[3]{3x}$
60. $3x^{1/3}$	**(h)** $\dfrac{1}{\sqrt[3]{-3x}}$

Simplify each of the given radical expressions. (See Examples 11–13.)

61. $\sqrt[3]{125}$

62. $\sqrt[6]{64}$

63. $\sqrt[4]{625}$

64. $\sqrt[7]{-128}$

65. $\sqrt{63}\sqrt{7}$

66. $\sqrt[3]{81} \cdot \sqrt[3]{9}$

67. $\sqrt{81 - 4}$

68. $\sqrt{49 - 16}$

69. $\sqrt{5}\sqrt{15}$

70. $\sqrt{8}\sqrt{96}$

71. $\sqrt{50} - \sqrt{72}$

72. $\sqrt{75} + \sqrt{192}$

73. $5\sqrt{20} - \sqrt{45} + 2\sqrt{80}$ **74.** $(\sqrt{3} + 2)(\sqrt{3} - 2)$

75. $(\sqrt{5} + \sqrt{2})(\sqrt{5} - \sqrt{2})$

76. What is wrong with the statement $\sqrt[3]{4} \cdot \sqrt[3]{4} = 4$?

Rationalize the denominator of each of the given expressions. (See Example 14.)

77. $\dfrac{3}{1 - \sqrt{2}}$ **78.** $\dfrac{2}{1 + \sqrt{5}}$

79. $\dfrac{9 - \sqrt{3}}{3 - \sqrt{3}}$ **80.** $\dfrac{\sqrt{3} - 1}{\sqrt{3} - 2}$

Rationalize the numerator of each of the given expressions. (See Example 15.)

81. $\dfrac{3 - \sqrt{2}}{3 + \sqrt{2}}$ **82.** $\dfrac{1 + \sqrt{7}}{2 - \sqrt{3}}$

The following exercises are applications of exponentiation and radicals.

83. **Business** The theory of economic lot size shows that, under certain conditions, the number of units to order to minimize total cost is

$$x = \sqrt{\frac{kM}{f}},$$

where k is the cost to store one unit for one year, f is the (constant) setup cost to manufacture the product, and M is the total number of units produced annually. Find x for the following values of f, k, and M.

(a) $k = \$1, f = \$500, M = 100{,}000$

(b) $k = \$3, f = \$7, M = 16{,}700$

(c) $k = \$1, f = \$5, M = 16{,}800$

84. **Health** The threshold weight T for a person is the weight above which the risk of death increases greatly. One researcher found that the threshold weight in pounds for men aged 40–49 is related to height in inches by the equation $h = 12.3T^{1/3}$. What height corresponds to a threshold of 216 pounds for a man in this age group?

Business *The annual domestic revenue (in billions of dollars) generated by the sale of movie tickets can be approximated by the function*

$$8.19x^{0.096} \quad (x \geq 1),$$

where $x = 1$ corresponds to 2001. Assuming the model remains accurate, approximate the revenue in the following years. (Data from: www.the-numbers.com.)

85. 2010   **86.** 2013

87. 2015   **88.** 2018

Health *The age-adjusted death rates per 100,000 people for diseases of the heart can be approximated by the function*

$$262.5x^{-.156} \quad (x \geq 1),$$

where $x = 1$ corresponds to 2001. Assuming the model continues to be accurate, find the approximate age-adjusted death rate for

the following years. (Data from: U.S. National Center for Health Statistics.)

89. 2011   **90.** 2013   **91.** 2017   **92.** 2020

Social Science *The number of students receiving financial aid from the federal government in the form of Pell Grants (in millions) can be approximated by the function*

$$3.96x^{0.239} \quad (x \geq 1),$$

where $x = 1$ corresponds to the year 2001. Assuming the model remains accurate, find the number of students receiving a Pell Grant for the following years. (Data from: www.finaid.org.)

93. 2005   **94.** 2010   **95.** 2013   **96.** 2018

Health *A function that approximates the number (in millions) of CT scans performed annually in the United States is*

$$3.5x^{1.04} \quad (x \geq 5),$$

where $x = 5$ corresponds to 1995. Find the approximate number of CT scans performed in the following years. (Data from: The Wall Street Journal.)

97. 1998   **98.** 2005   **99.** 2012   **100.** 2013

✓ Checkpoint Answers

1. (a) 2^9 (b) $(-5)^4$ (c) $(xy)^5$

2. (a) $81x^4$ (b) $r^{12}s^{30}$ (c) $\dfrac{32}{z^5}$ (d) $\dfrac{9a^4}{b^6}$

3. (a) $1/36$ (b) $-1/216$ (c) $-1/81$ (d) $8/5$

4. (a) $8/5$ (b) 32 (c) b^3/a^6

5. (a) 4 (b) 2 (c) -16
    (d) Not a real number   (e) -2 (f) 3

6. (a) 8 (b) 3125 (c) 128 (d) 1000

7. (a) 81 (b) $15x^{3/2}$ (c) 8^{10}
    (d) $5^{-8/3}$ or $1/5^{8/3}$

8. (a) 1 (b) $c^2/d^{1/2}$ (c) $2a + a^{1/2}$

9. (a) $\dfrac{6}{x^{1/3}\,y^{2/3}}$ (b) t^3

    (c) $32/(p^{10}k^{7/3})$ (d) $\dfrac{y^2 - x}{xy^2}$

10. About 20.6 million

11. (a) 3 (b) 5 (c) 2 (d) $4/5$

12. (a) 9 (b) $\dfrac{\sqrt{3}}{7}$ (c) $11\sqrt{2}$

13. (a) $3\sqrt{5} + \sqrt{10} - 3\sqrt{2} - 2$ (b) -4

14. (a) $\dfrac{2\sqrt{5}}{5}$ (b) $2 - \sqrt{3}$

1.6 First-Degree Equations

An **equation** is a statement that two mathematical expressions are equal; for example,

$$5x - 3 = 13, \qquad 8y = 4, \qquad \text{and} \qquad -3p + 5 = 4p - 8$$

are equations.

The letter in each equation is called the variable. This section concentrates on **first-degree equations,** which are equations that involve only constants and the first power of the variable. All of the equations displayed above are first-degree equations, but neither of the following equations is of first degree:

$$2x^2 = 5x + 6 \qquad \text{(the variable has an exponent greater than 1);}$$
$$\sqrt{x + 2} = 4 \qquad \text{(the variable is under the radical).}$$

A **solution** of an equation is a number that can be substituted for the variable in the equation to produce a true statement. For example, substituting the number 9 for x in the equation $2x + 1 = 19$ gives

$$2x + 1 = 19$$
$$2(9) + 1 \stackrel{?}{=} 19 \qquad \text{Let } x = 9.$$
$$18 + 1 = 19. \qquad \text{True}$$

✓ Checkpoint 1

Is -4 a solution of the equations in parts (a) and (b)?

(a) $3x + 5 = -7$

(b) $2x - 3 = 5$

(c) Is there more than one solution of the equation in part (a)?

This true statement indicates that 9 is a solution of $2x + 1 = 19$. ✓₁

The following properties are used to solve equations.

Properties of Equality

1. The same number may be added to or subtracted from both sides of an equation:
$$\text{If } a = b, \text{ then } a + c = b + c \text{ and } a - c = b - c.$$

2. Both sides of an equation may be multiplied or divided by the same nonzero number:
$$\text{If } a = b \text{ and } c \neq 0, \text{ then } ac = bc \text{ and } \frac{a}{c} = \frac{b}{c}.$$

Example 1 Solve the equation $5x - 3 = 12$.

Solution Using the first property of equality, add 3 to both sides. This isolates the term containing the variable on one side of the equation:

$$5x - 3 = 12$$
$$5x - 3 + 3 = 12 + 3 \qquad \text{Add 3 to both sides.}$$
$$5x = 15.$$

Now arrange for the coefficient of x to be 1 by using the second property of equality:

$$5x = 15$$
$$\frac{5x}{5} = \frac{15}{5} \qquad \text{Divide both sides by 5.}$$
$$x = 3.$$

✓ Checkpoint 2

Solve the following.

(a) $3p - 5 = 19$

(b) $4y + 3 = -5$

(c) $-2k + 6 = 2$

The solution of the original equation, $5x - 3 = 12$, is 3. Check the solution by substituting 3 for x in the original equation. ✓₂

Example 2 Solve $2k + 3(k - 4) = 2(k - 3)$.

Solution First, simplify the equation by using the distributive property on the left-side term $3(k - 4)$ and right-side term $2(k - 3)$:

$$2k + 3(k - 4) = 2(k - 3)$$
$$2k + 3k - 12 = 2(k - 3) \quad \text{Distributive property}$$
$$2k + 3k - 12 = 2k - 6 \quad \text{Distributive property}$$
$$5k - 12 = 2k - 6. \quad \text{Collect like terms on left side.}$$

One way to proceed is to add $-2k$ to both sides:

$$5k - 12 + (-2k) = 2k - 6 + (-2k) \quad \text{Add } -2k \text{ to both sides.}$$
$$3k - 12 = -6$$
$$3k - 12 + 12 = -6 + 12 \quad \text{Add 12 to both sides.}$$
$$3k = 6$$
$$\frac{1}{3}(3k) = \frac{1}{3}(6) \quad \text{Multiply both sides by } \frac{1}{3}.$$
$$k = 2.$$

The solution is 2. Check this result by substituting 2 for k in the original equation. ✓₃

✓**Checkpoint 3**

Solve the following.

(a) $3(m - 6) + 2(m + 4)$
$= 4m - 2$

(b) $-2(y + 3) + 4y$
$= 3(y + 1) - 6$

Example 3 **Business** The percentage y of U.S. households owning Individual Retirement Accounts (IRAs) in year x is approximated by the equation

$$0.096(x - 2000) = 15y - 5.16.$$

Assuming this equation remains valid, use a calculator to determine when 44% of households will own an IRA. (Data from: ProQuest Statistical Abstract of the United States: 2013.)

Solution Since $44\% = .44$, let $y = .44$ in the equation and solve for x. To avoid any rounding errors in the intermediate steps, it is often a good idea to do all the algebra first, before using the calculator:

$$0.096(x - 2000) = 15y - 5.16$$
$$0.096(x - 2000) = 15 \cdot .44 - 5.16 \quad \text{Substitute } y = .44$$
$$.096x - .096 \cdot 2000 = 15 \cdot .44 - 5.16 \quad \text{Distributive property}$$
$$.096x = 15 \cdot .44 - 5.16 + .096 \cdot 2000 \quad \text{Add } .096 \cdot 2000 \text{ to both sides.}$$
$$x = \frac{15 \cdot .44 - 5.16 + .096 \cdot 2000}{.096} \quad \text{Divide both sides by } .096$$

```
15*.44-5.16+.096*2000
                  .096
                       2015
```

Figure 1.12

Now use a calculator to determine that $x = 2015$, as shown in Figure 1.12. So 44% of households will own an IRA in 2015. ✓₄

✓**Checkpoint 4**

In Example 3, in what year will 48% of U.S. households own an IRA?

The next three examples show how to simplify the solution of first-degree equations involving fractions. We solve these equations by multiplying both sides of the equation by a *common denominator*. This step will eliminate the fractions.

Example 4 Solve

$$\frac{r}{10} - \frac{2}{15} = \frac{3r}{20} - \frac{1}{5}.$$

Solution Here, the denominators are 10, 15, 20, and 5. Each of these numbers is a factor of 60; therefore, 60 is a common denominator. Multiply both sides of the equation by 60:

$$60\left(\frac{r}{10} - \frac{2}{15}\right) = 60\left(\frac{3r}{20} - \frac{1}{5}\right)$$

$$60\left(\frac{r}{10}\right) - 60\left(\frac{2}{15}\right) = 60\left(\frac{3r}{20}\right) - 60\left(\frac{1}{5}\right) \qquad \text{Distributive property}$$

$$6r - 8 = 9r - 12$$

$$6r - 8 + (-6r) + 12 = 9r - 12 + (-6r) + 12 \qquad \text{Add } -6r \text{ and } 12 \text{ to both sides.}$$

$$4 = 3r$$

$$r = \frac{4}{3}. \qquad \text{Multiply both sides by } 1/3.$$

✓ Checkpoint 5

Solve the following.

(a) $\dfrac{x}{2} - \dfrac{x}{4} = 6$

(b) $\dfrac{2x}{3} + \dfrac{1}{2} = \dfrac{x}{4} - \dfrac{9}{2}$

Check this solution in the original equation. ✓₅

⊘ CAUTION Multiplying *both* sides of an *equation* by a number to eliminate fractions is valid. But multiplying a single fraction by a number to simplify it is not valid. For instance, multiplying $\dfrac{3x}{8}$ by 8 *changes* it to 3x, which is *not equal* to $\dfrac{3x}{8}$.

The second property of equality (page 43) applies only to *nonzero* quantities. Multiplying or dividing both sides of an equation by a quantity involving the variable (which might be zero for some values) may lead to an **extraneous solution**—that is, a number that does not satisfy the original equation. To avoid errors in such situations, always *check your solutions in the original equation.*

Example 5 Solve

$$\frac{4}{3(k + 2)} - \frac{k}{3(k + 2)} = \frac{5}{3}.$$

Solution Multiply both sides of the equation by the common denominator $3(k + 2)$. Here, $k \neq -2$, since $k = -2$ would give a 0 denominator, making the fraction undefined. So, we have

$$3(k + 2) \cdot \frac{4}{3(k + 2)} - 3(k + 2) \cdot \frac{k}{3(k + 2)} = 3(k + 2) \cdot \frac{5}{3}.$$

Simplify each side and solve for k:

$$4 - k = 5(k + 2)$$

$$4 - k = 5k + 10 \qquad \text{Distributive property}$$

$$4 - k + k = 5k + 10 + k \qquad \text{Add } k \text{ to both sides.}$$

$$4 = 6k + 10$$

$$4 + (-10) = 6k + 10 + (-10) \qquad \text{Add } -10 \text{ to both sides.}$$

$$-6 = 6k$$

$$-1 = k. \qquad \text{Multiply both sides by } \frac{1}{6}.$$

The solution is -1. Substitute -1 for k in the original equation as a check:

$$\frac{4}{3(-1 + 2)} - \frac{-1}{3(-1 + 2)} \overset{?}{=} \frac{5}{3}$$

$$\frac{4}{3} - \frac{-1}{3} \overset{?}{=} \frac{5}{3}$$

$$\frac{5}{3} = \frac{5}{3}.$$

✓ Checkpoint 6

Solve the equation

$$\frac{5p + 1}{3(p + 1)} = \frac{3p - 3}{3(p + 1)} + \frac{9p - 3}{3(p + 1)}.$$

The check shows that -1 is the solution. ✓₆

Example 6 Solve

$$\frac{3x - 4}{x - 2} = \frac{x}{x - 2}.$$

Solution Multiplying both sides by $x - 2$ produces

$$3x - 4 = x$$
$$2x - 4 = 0 \qquad \text{Subtract } x \text{ from both sides.}$$
$$2x = 4 \qquad \text{Add 4 to both sides.}$$
$$x = 2. \qquad \text{Divide both sides by 2.}$$

Substituting 2 for x in the original equation produces fractions with 0 denominators. Since division by 0 is not defined, $x = 2$ is an extraneous solution. So the original equation has no solution. ☑7

Sometimes an equation with several variables must be solved for one of the variables. This process is called **solving for a specified variable.**

Example 7 Solve for x: $3(ax - 5a) + 4b = 4x - 2$.

Solution Use the distributive property to get

$$3ax - 15a + 4b = 4x - 2.$$

Treat x as the variable and the other letters as constants. Get all terms with x on one side of the equation and all terms without x on the other side:

$$3ax - 4x = 15a - 4b - 2 \qquad \text{Isolate terms with } x \text{ on the left.}$$
$$(3a - 4)x = 15a - 4b - 2 \qquad \text{Distributive property}$$
$$x = \frac{15a - 4b - 2}{3a - 4} \qquad \text{Multiply both sides by } \frac{1}{3a - 4}.$$

The final equation is solved for x, as required. ☑8

Absolute-Value Equations

Recall from Section 1.1 that the absolute value of a number a is either a or $-a$, whichever one is nonnegative. For instance, $|4| = 4$ and $|-7| = -(-7) = 7$.

Example 8 Solve $|x| = 3$.

Solution Since $|x|$ is either x or $-x$, the equation says that

$$x = 3 \qquad \text{or} \qquad -x = 3$$
$$x = -3.$$

The solutions of $|x| = 3$ are 3 and -3.

Example 9 Solve $|p - 4| = 2$.

Solution Since $|p - 4|$ is either $p - 4$ or $-(p - 4)$, we have

$$p - 4 = 2 \qquad \text{or} \qquad -(p - 4) = 2$$
$$p = 6 \qquad\qquad -p + 4 = 2$$
$$-p = -2$$
$$p = 2,$$

so that 6 and 2 are possible solutions. Checking them in the original equation shows that both are solutions. ☑9

✓ Checkpoint 7

Solve each equation.

(a) $\dfrac{3p}{p + 1} = 1 - \dfrac{3}{p + 1}$

(b) $\dfrac{8y}{y - 4} = \dfrac{32}{y - 4} - 3$

✓ Checkpoint 8

Solve for x.

(a) $2x - 7y = 3xk$

(b) $8(4 - x) + 6p = -5k - 11yx$

✓ Checkpoint 9

Solve each equation.

(a) $|y| = 9$

(b) $|r + 3| = 1$

(c) $|2k - 3| = 7$

Example 10   Solve $|4m - 3| = |m + 6|$.

Solution   To satisfy the equation, the quantities in absolute-value bars must either be equal or be negatives of one another. That is,

$$4m - 3 = m + 6 \qquad \text{or} \qquad 4m - 3 = -(m + 6)$$
$$3m = 9 \qquad\qquad\qquad 4m - 3 = -m - 6$$
$$m = 3 \qquad\qquad\qquad\quad 5m = -3$$
$$m = -\frac{3}{5}.$$

✓ **Checkpoint 10**

Solve each equation.

(a) $|r + 6| = |2r + 1|$

(b) $|5k - 7| = |10k - 2|$

Check that the solutions for the original equation are 3 and $-3/5$. ✓₁₀

Applications

One of the main reasons for learning mathematics is to be able to use it to solve practical problems. There are no hard-and-fast rules for dealing with real-world applications, except perhaps to use common sense. However, you will find it much easier to deal with such problems if you do not try to do everything at once. After reading the problem carefully, attack it in stages, as suggested in the following guidelines.

Solving Applied Problems

Step 1   Read the problem carefully, focusing on the facts you are given and the unknown values you are asked to find. Look up any words you do not understand. You may have to read the problem more than once, until you understand exactly what you are being asked to do.

Step 2   Identify the unknown. (If there is more than one, choose one of them, and see Step 3 for what to do with the others.) Name the unknown with some variable that you *write down*. Many students try to skip this step. They are eager to get on with the writing of the equation. But this is an important step. If you do not know what the variable represents, how can you write a meaningful equation or interpret a result?

Step 3   Decide on a variable expression to represent any other unknowns in the problem. For example, if x represents the width of a rectangle, and you know that the length is one more than twice the width, then *write down* the fact that the length is $1 + 2x$.

Step 4   Draw a sketch or make a chart, if appropriate, showing the information given in the problem.

Step 5   Using the results of Steps 1–4, write an equation that expresses a condition that must be satisfied.

Step 6   Solve the equation.

Step 7   Check the solution in the words of the *original problem*, not just in the equation you have written.

Example 11   **Finance**   A financial manager has \$15,000 to invest for her company. She plans to invest part of the money in tax-free bonds at 5% interest and the remainder in taxable bonds at 8%. She wants to earn \$1020 per year in interest from the investments. Find the amount she should invest at each rate.

Solution

Step 1   We are asked to find how much of the $15,000 should be invested at 5% and how much at 8%, in order to earn the required interest.

Step 2   Let x represent the amount to be invested at 5%.

Step 3   After x dollars are invested, the remaining amount is $15,000 - x$ dollars, which is to be invested at 8%.

Step 4   Interest for one year is given by rate $\times$ amount invested. For instance, 5% of x dollars is $.05x$. The given information is summarized in the following chart.

Investment	Amount Invested	Interest Rate	Interest Earned in One Year
Tax-free bonds	x	5% = .05	$.05x$
Taxable bonds	$15,000 - x$	8% = .08	$.08(15,000 - x)$
Totals	15,000		1020

Step 5   Because the total interest is to be $1020, the last column of the table shows that

$$.05x + .08(15,000 - x) = 1020.$$

Step 6   Solve the preceding equation as follows:

$$.05x + .08(15,000 - x) = 1020$$
$$.05x + .08(15,000) - .08x = 1020$$
$$.05x + 1200 - .08x = 1020$$
$$-.03x = -180$$
$$x = 6000.$$

The manager should invest $6000 at 5% and $15,000 - \$6000 = \$9000$ at 8%.

Step 7   Check these results in the original problem. If $6000 is invested at 5%, the interest is $.05(6000) = \$300$. If $9000 is invested at 8%, the interest is $.08(9000) = \$720$. So the total interest is $\$300 + \$720 = \$1020$ as required ✓11

✓ **Checkpoint 11**

An investor owns two pieces of property. One, worth twice as much as the other, returns 6% in annual interest, while the other returns 4%. Find the value of each piece of property if the total annual interest earned is $8000.

Example 12   **Business**   Spotify and Rhapsody are digital music streaming services. In 2012, *Time* magazine reported that Spotify acquired in 7 business quarters (a quarter is a 3-month period) the same number of users as Rhapsody acquired in 11 years (44 quarters). Spotify's average rate of user acquisition per quarter was 120,000 more than Rhapsody's average rate per quarter. Find the average rate of user acquisition per quarter for each company.

Solution

Step 1   We must find Spotify's user acquisition rate and Rhapsody's user acquisition rate.

Step 2   Let x represent Rhapsody's rate.

Step 3   Since Spotify's rate is 120,000 users per quarter faster than Rhapsody's, its rate is $x + 120,000$.

Step 4   In general, the number of users can be found by the formula:

Number of users = number of quarters $\times$ rate of users per quarter

So, for Rhapsody, number of users = $44x$ and for

Spotify, the number of users = $7(x + 120,000)$

We can collect these facts to make a chart, which organizes the information given in the problem.

	Quarters	Rate	Number of Users
Rhapsody	44	x	$44x$
Spotify	7	$x + 120,000$	$7(x + 120,000)$

Step 5   Because both companies obtained the *same number of users*, the equation is

$$44x = 7(x + 120,000).$$

Step 6   If we distribute the 7 through the quantity on the right side of the equation, we obtain

$$44x = 7x + 840,000$$
$$37x = 840,000 \qquad \text{Add } -7x \text{ to each side.}$$
$$x \approx 22,703 \qquad \text{Divide each side by 37.}$$

Step 7   Since x represents Rhapsody's rate, Rhapsody acquired, on average, 22,702 users per quarter. Spotify's rate is $x + 120,000$, or $22,702 + 120,000 = 142,702$ users per quarter. ✓12

✓**Checkpoint 12**

In Example 12, suppose Spotify had taken 12 quarters and Rhapsody had taken 40 quarters to reach the same number of users. Assuming that Spotify acquired users at a rate 100,000 per quarter more than Rhapsody, find the average rate at which

(a) Rhapsody had acquired users.

(b) Spotify had acquired users.

Example 13   **Business**   An oil company needs to fill orders for 89-octane gas, but has only 87- and 93-octane gas on hand. The octane rating is the percentage of isooctane in the standard fuel. How much of each type should be mixed together to produce 100,000 gallons of 89-octane gas?

Solution

Step 1   We must find how much 87-octane gas and how much 93-octane gas are needed for the 100,000 gallon mixture.

Step 2   Let x be the amount of 87-octane gas.

Step 3   Then $100,000 - x$ is the amount of 93-octane gas.

Step 4   We can summarize the relevant information in a chart.

Type of Gas	Quantity	% Isooctane	Amount of Isooctane
87-octane	x	87%	$.87x$
93-octane	$100,000 - x$	93%	$.93(100,000 - x)$
Mixture	$100,000$	89%	$.89(100,000)$

Step 5   The amount of isooctane satisfies this equation:

$$.87x + .93(100,000 - x) = .89(100,000).$$

Step 6   Solving this equation yields

$$.87x + 93,000 - .93x = .89(100,000) \qquad \text{Distribute the left side.}$$
$$.87x + 93,000 - .93x = 89,000 \qquad \text{Multiply on the right side.}$$
$$-.06x = -4000 \qquad \text{Combine terms and add } -93,000 \text{ to each side.}$$
$$x = \frac{-4000}{-.06} \approx 66,667.$$

Step 7   So the distributor should mix 66,667 gallons of 87-octane gas with $100,000 - 66,667 = 33,333$ gallons of 93-octane gas. Then the amount of isooctane in the mixture is

$$.87(66,667) + .93(33,333)$$
$$\approx 58,000 + 31,000$$
$$= 89,000.$$

✓**Checkpoint 13**

How much 89-octane gas and how much 94-octane gas are needed to produce 1500 gallons of 91-octane gas?

Hence, the octane rating of the mixture is $\dfrac{89,000}{100,000} = .89$ as required. ✓13

1.6 Exercises

Solve each equation. (See Examples 1–6.)

1. $3x + 8 = 20$

2. $4 - 5y = 19$

3. $.6k - .3 = .5k + .4$

4. $2.5 + 5.04m = 8.5 - .06m$

5. $2a - 1 = 4(a + 1) + 7a + 5$

6. $3(k - 2) - 6 = 4k - (3k - 1)$

7. $2[x - (3 + 2x) + 9] = 3x - 8$

8. $-2[4(k + 2) - 3(k + 1)] = 14 + 2k$

9. $\dfrac{3x}{5} - \dfrac{4}{5}(x + 1) = 2 - \dfrac{3}{10}(3x - 4)$

10. $\dfrac{4}{3}(x - 2) - \dfrac{1}{2} = 2\left(\dfrac{3}{4}x - 1\right)$

11. $\dfrac{5y}{6} - 8 = 5 - \dfrac{2y}{3}$

12. $\dfrac{x}{2} - 3 = \dfrac{3x}{5} + 1$

13. $\dfrac{m}{2} - \dfrac{1}{m} = \dfrac{6m + 5}{12}$

14. $-\dfrac{3k}{2} + \dfrac{9k - 5}{6} = \dfrac{11k + 8}{k}$

15. $\dfrac{4}{x - 3} - \dfrac{8}{2x + 5} + \dfrac{3}{x - 3} = 0$

16. $\dfrac{5}{2p + 3} - \dfrac{3}{p - 2} = \dfrac{4}{2p + 3}$

17. $\dfrac{3}{2m + 4} = \dfrac{1}{m + 2} - 2$

18. $\dfrac{8}{3k - 9} - \dfrac{5}{k - 3} = 4$

Use a calculator to solve each equation. Round your answer to the nearest hundredth. (See Example 3.)

19. $9.06x + 3.59(8x - 5) = 12.07x + .5612$

20. $-5.74(3.1 - 2.7p) = 1.09p + 5.2588$

21. $\dfrac{2.63r - 8.99}{1.25} - \dfrac{3.90r - 1.77}{2.45} = r$

22. $\dfrac{8.19m + 2.55}{4.34} - \dfrac{8.17m - 9.94}{1.04} = 4m$

Solve each equation for x. (See Example 7.)

23. $4(a + x) = b - a + 2x$

24. $(3a - b) - bx = a(x - 2)$ $(a \neq -b)$

25. $5(b - x) = 2b + ax$ $(a \neq -5)$

26. $bx - 2b = 2a - ax$

Solve each equation for the specified variable. Assume that all denominators are nonzero. (See Example 7.)

27. $PV = k$ for V

28. $i = prt$ for p

29. $V = V_0 + gt$ for g

30. $S = S_0 + gt^2 + k$ for g

31. $A = \dfrac{1}{2}(B + b)h$ for B

32. $C = \dfrac{5}{9}(F - 32)$ for F

Solve each equation. (See Examples 8–10.)

33. $|2h - 1| = 5$

34. $|4m - 3| = 12$

35. $|6 + 2p| = 10$

36. $|-5x + 7| = 15$

37. $\left|\dfrac{5}{r - 3}\right| = 10$

38. $\left|\dfrac{3}{2h - 1}\right| = 4$

Solve the following applied problems.

Health *According to the American Heart Association, the number y of brain neurons (in billions) that are lost in a stroke lasting x hours is given by $y = \dfrac{x}{8}$. Find the length of the stroke for the given number of neurons lost.*

39. $1{,}250{,}000{,}000$

40. $2{,}400{,}000{,}000$

Natural Science *The equation that relates Fahrenheit temperature F to Celsius temperature C is*

$$C = \dfrac{5}{9}(F - 32).$$

Find the Fahrenheit temperature corresponding to these Celsius temperatures.

41. -5

42. -15

43. 22

44. 36

Finance *The gross federal debt y (in trillions of dollars) in year x is approximated by*

$$y = 1.16x + 1.76,$$

where x is the number of years after 2000. Assuming the trend continues, in what year will the federal debt be the given amount? (Data from: U.S. Office of Management and Budget.)

45. $13.36 trillion

46. $16.84 trillion

47. $19.16 trillion

48. $24.96 trillion

Health Economics *The total health care expenditures E in the United States (in trillions of dollars) can be approximated by*

$$E = .118x + 1.45,$$

where x is the number of years after 2000. Assuming the trend continues, determine the year in which health care expenditures are at the given level. (*Data from: U.S. Centers for Medicare and Medicaid Services.*)

49. $2.63 trillion   **50.** $2.866 trillion

51. $3.338 trillion   **52.** $3.574 trillion

Finance *The percentage y (written as a decimal) of U.S. house-holds who owned Roth Individual Retirement Accounts (IRAs) in year x is given by the equation*

$$.09(x - 2004) = 12y - 1.44.$$

Find the year in which the given percentage of U.S. households own a Roth IRA. (Data from: Proquest Statistical Abstract of the United States: 2013.)

53. 18.0%   **54.** 19.5%

55. 21%   **56.** 23.25%

Finance *The total amount A (in millions of dollars) donated within a state for charitable contributions claimed on individual federal tax returns can be modeled by the function*

$$A = 4.35x - 12$$

where x is the total number of returns filed (in thousands) for the state. For the given amounts A donated, determine the number of returns that were filed within the following states. (Data from: Proquest Statistical Abstract of the United States: 2013.)

57. California: $A = $20,777 million

58. New York: $A = $13,732 million

59. Texas: $A = $13,360 million

60. Florida: $A = $9596 million

Business *When a loan is paid off early, a portion of the finance charge must be returned to the borrower. By one method of calculating the finance charge (called the rule of 78), the amount of unearned interest (finance charge to be returned) is given by*

$$u = f \cdot \frac{n(n + 1)}{q(q + 1)},$$

where u represents unearned interest, f is the original finance charge, n is the number of payments remaining when the loan is paid off, and q is the original number of payments. Find the amount of the unearned interest in each of the given cases.

61. Original finance charge = $800, loan scheduled to run 36 months, paid off with 18 payments remaining

62. Original finance charge = $1400, loan scheduled to run 48 months, paid off with 12 payments remaining

Business *Solve the following investment problems. (See Example 11.)*

63. Joe Gonzalez received $52,000 profit from the sale of some land. He invested part at 5% interest and the rest at 4% interest. He earned a total of $2290 interest per year. How much did he invest at 5%?

64. Weijen Luan invests $20,000 received from an insurance settlement in two ways: some at 6% and some at 4%. Altogether, she makes $1040 per year in interest. How much is invested at 4%?

65. Maria Martinelli bought two plots of land for a total of $120,000. On the first plot, she made a profit of 15%. On the second, she lost 10%. Her total profit was $5500. How much did she pay for each piece of land?

66. Suppose $20,000 is invested at 5%. How much additional money must be invested at 4% to produce a yield of 4.8% on the entire amount invested?

Solve the given applied problems. (See Example 12.)

According to data from comScore.com, two social media sites, Tumblr.com and Pinterest.com, acquired the same number of unique visitors in 2012. Tumblr.com took 63 months to acquire these visitors while Pinterest.com took 30 months. Pinterest's rate of visitor growth was 450,000 more a month, on average, than Tumblr's average growth per month.

67. Find the average rate of growth of Tumblr.com.

68. Find the average rate of growth of Pinterest.com.

69. Approximately how many unique visitors did Tumblr.com acquire in 63 months?

70. Approximately how many unique visitors did Pinterest.com acquire in 30 months?

Natural Science *Using the same assumptions about octane ratings as in Example 13, solve the following problems.*

71. How many liters of 94-octane gasoline should be mixed with 200 liters of 99-octane gasoline to get a mixture that is 97-octane gasoline?

72. A service station has 92-octane and 98-octane gasoline. How many liters of each gasoline should be mixed to provide 12 liters of 96-octane gasoline for a chemistry experiment?

Solve the following applied problems.

73. **Business** A major car rental firm charges $78 a day for a full-size car in Tampa, Florida, with unlimited mileage. Another firm offers a similar car for $55 a day plus 22 cents per mile. How far must you drive in a day in order for the cost to be the same for both vehicles?

74. **Business** A car radiator contains 8.5 quarts of fluid, 35% of which is antifreeze. How much fluid should be drained and replaced with pure (100%) antifreeze in order that the new mixture be 65% antifreeze?

Business *Massachusetts has a graduated fine system for speeding, meaning you can pay a base fine and then have more charges added on top. For example, the base fine for speeding is $100. But that is just the start. If you are convicted of going more than 10 mph over the speed limit, add $10 for each additional mph you were traveling over the speed limit plus 10 mph. Thus, the amount of the fine y (in dollars) for driving x miles over the speed limit (when the speed limit is 65 miles per hour) can be represented as*

$$y = 10(x - 75) + 100, \quad x \geq 75.$$

(Data from: www.dmv.org.)

75. If Paul was fined $180 for speeding, how fast was he going?

76. If Sarah was fined $120 for speeding, how fast was she going?

Jack borrowed his father's luxury car and promised to return it with a full tank of premium gas, which costs $3.80 per gallon. From experience, he knows that he needs 15.5 gallons. He has, however, only $50 (and no credit card). He decides to get as much premium as possible and fill the remainder of the tank with regular gas, which costs $3.10 per gallon.

77. How much of each type of gas should he get?

78. If he has $53, how much of each type of gas should he get?

✓ **Checkpoint Answers**

1. (a) Yes   **(b)** No   **(c)** No

2. (a) 8   **(b)** −2   **(c)** 2

3. (a) 8   **(b)** −3

4. Early 2021 ($x = 2021.25$)

5. (a) 24   **(b)** −12

6. 1

7. Neither equation has a solution.

8. (a) $x = \dfrac{7y}{2 - 3k}$ **(b)** $x = \dfrac{5k + 32 + 6p}{8 - 11y}$

9. (a) 9, −9   **(b)** −2, −4   **(c)** 5, −2

10. (a) 5, −7/3   **(b)** −1, 3/5

11. 6% return: $100,000; 4% return: $50,000

12. (a) 42,857 per quarter
    (b) 142,857 per quarter

13. 900 gallons of 89-octane gas; 600 gallons of 94-octane gas

1.7 Quadratic Equations

An equation that can be written in the form

$$ax^2 + bx + c = 0,$$

where a, b, and c are real numbers with $a \neq 0$, is called a **quadratic equation.** For example, each of

$$2x^2 + 3x + 4 = 0, \qquad x^2 = 6x - 9, \qquad 3x^2 + x = 6, \qquad \text{and} \qquad x^2 = 5$$

is a quadratic equation. A solution of an equation that is a real number is said to be a **real solution** of the equation.

One method of solving quadratic equations is based on the following property of real numbers.

Zero-Factor Property

If a and b are real numbers, with $ab = 0$, then $a = 0$ or $b = 0$ or both.

Example 1   Solve the equation $(x - 4)(3x + 7) = 0$.

Solution   By the zero-factor property, the product $(x - 4)(3x + 7)$ can equal 0 only if at least one of the factors equals 0. That is, the product equals zero only if $x - 4 = 0$ or $3x + 7 = 0$. Solving each of these equations separately will give the solutions of the original equation:

$$x - 4 = 0 \qquad \text{or} \qquad 3x + 7 = 0$$
$$x = 4 \qquad \text{or} \qquad 3x = -7$$
$$x = -\frac{7}{3}.$$

The solutions of the equation $(x - 4)(3x + 7) = 0$ are 4 and −7/3. Check these solutions by substituting them into the original equation. ✓₁

✓ **Checkpoint 1**

Solve the following equations.

(a) $(y - 6)(y + 2) = 0$

(b) $(5k - 3)(k + 5) = 0$

(c) $(2r - 9)(3r + 5) \cdot (r + 3) = 0$

Example 2 Solve $6r^2 + 7r = 3$.

Solution Rewrite the equation as

$$6r^2 + 7r - 3 = 0.$$

Now factor $6r^2 + 7r - 3$ to get

$$(3r - 1)(2r + 3) = 0.$$

By the zero-factor property, the product $(3r - 1)(2r + 3)$ can equal 0 only if

$$3r - 1 = 0 \quad \text{or} \quad 2r + 3 = 0.$$

Solving each of these equations separately gives the solutions of the original equation:

$$3r = 1 \quad \text{or} \quad 2r = -3$$
$$r = \frac{1}{3} \qquad r = -\frac{3}{2}.$$

Verify that both $1/3$ and $-3/2$ are solutions by substituting them into the original equation. ✓2

An equation such as $x^2 = 5$ has two solutions: $\sqrt{5}$ and $-\sqrt{5}$. This fact is true in general.

✓**Checkpoint 2**

Solve each equation by factoring.
(a) $y^2 + 3y = 10$
(b) $2r^2 + 9r = 5$
(c) $4k^2 = 9k$

Square-Root Property

If $b > 0$, then the solutions of $x^2 = b$ are $\sqrt{b}$ and $-\sqrt{b}$.

The two solutions are sometimes abbreviated $\pm \sqrt{b}$.

Example 3 Solve each equation.

(a) $m^2 = 17$

Solution By the square-root property, the solutions are $\sqrt{17}$ and $-\sqrt{17}$, abbreviated $\pm\sqrt{17}$.

(b) $(y - 4)^2 = 11$

Solution Use a generalization of the square-root property, we work as follows.

$$(y - 4)^2 = 11$$
$$y - 4 = \sqrt{11} \quad \text{or} \quad y - 4 = -\sqrt{11}$$
$$y = 4 + \sqrt{11} \qquad y = 4 - \sqrt{11}.$$

Abbreviate the solutions as $4 \pm \sqrt{11}$. ✓3

✓**Checkpoint 3**

Solve each equation by using the square-root property.
(a) $p^2 = 21$
(b) $(m + 7)^2 = 15$
(c) $(2k - 3)^2 = 5$

When a quadratic equation cannot be easily factored, it can be solved by using the following formula, which you should memorize.[*]

Quadratic Formula

The solutions of the quadratic equation $ax^2 + bx + c = 0$, where $a \neq 0$, are given by

$$x = \frac{-b \pm \sqrt{b^2 - 4ac}}{2a}.$$

[*]A proof of the quadratic formula can be found in many College Algebra books.

CAUTION When using the quadratic formula, remember that the equation must be in the form $ax^2 + bx + c = 0$. Also, notice that the fraction bar in the quadratic formula extends under *both* terms in the numerator. Be sure to add $-b$ to $\pm \sqrt{b^2 - 4ac}$ *before* dividing by $2a$.

Example 4   Solve $x^2 + 1 = 4x$.

Solution   First add $-4x$ to both sides to get 0 alone on the right side:

$$x^2 - 4x + 1 = 0.$$

Now identify the values of a, b, and c. Here, $a = 1$, $b = -4$, and $c = 1$. Substitute these numbers into the quadratic formula to obtain

$$x = \frac{-(-4) \pm \sqrt{(-4)^2 - 4(1)(1)}}{2(1)}$$

$$= \frac{4 \pm \sqrt{16 - 4}}{2}$$

$$= \frac{4 \pm \sqrt{12}}{2}$$

$$= \frac{4 \pm 2\sqrt{3}}{2} \qquad \sqrt{12} = \sqrt{4 \cdot 3} = \sqrt{4} \cdot \sqrt{3} = 2\sqrt{3}$$

$$= \frac{2(2 \pm \sqrt{3})}{2} \qquad \text{Factor } 4 \pm 2\sqrt{3}.$$

$$x = 2 \pm \sqrt{3}. \qquad \text{Cancel 2.}$$

The $\pm$ sign represents the two solutions of the equation. First use $+$ and then use $-$ to find each of the solutions: $2 + \sqrt{3}$ and $2 - \sqrt{3}$. ✔️ 4

Example 4 shows that the quadratic formula produces exact solutions. In many real-world applications, however, you must use a calculator to find decimal approximations of the solutions. The approximate solutions in Example 4 are

$$x = 2 + \sqrt{3} \approx 3.732050808 \qquad \text{and} \qquad x = 2 - \sqrt{3} \approx .2679491924,$$

as shown in Figure 1.13.

✓ Checkpoint 4

Use the quadratic formula to solve each equation.

(a) $x^2 - 2x = 2$

(b) $u^2 - 6u + 4 = 0$

$2+\sqrt{3}$
$\qquad$ 3.732050808
$2-\sqrt{3}$
$\qquad$ .2679491924

Figure 1.13

Example 5   **Business**   Many companies in recent years saw their net earnings follow a parabolic pattern because of the recession that began in 2008. One such example is Motorola Corporation. The net earnings for Motorola Corporation E (in millions of dollars) can be approximated by the function

$$E = 545.9x^2 - 10{,}408x + 48{,}085 \quad (6 \le x \le 12),$$

where $x = 6$ corresponds to the year 2006. Use the quadratic formula and a calculator to find the year in which net earnings recovered to \$1799 million. (Data from: www.morningstar.com.)

Solution   To find the year x, solve the equation above when $E = 1799$:

$$545.9x^2 - 10{,}408x + 48{,}085 = E$$

$$545.9x^2 - 10{,}408x + 48{,}085 = 1799 \qquad \text{Substitute } E = 1799.$$

$$545.9x^2 - 10{,}408x + 46{,}286 = 0 \qquad \text{Subtract 1799 from both sides.}$$

To apply the quadratic formula, first compute the radical part:

$$\sqrt{b^2 - 4ac} = \sqrt{(10{,}408)^2 - 4(545.9)(46{,}286)} = \sqrt{7{,}256{,}354.4}.$$

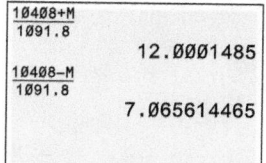

Figure 1.14

Then store $\sqrt{7{,}256{,}354.4}$ (which we denote by M) in the calculator memory. (Check your instruction manual for how to store and recall numbers.) By the quadratic formula, the exact solutions of the equation are

$$x = \frac{-b \pm \sqrt{b^2 - 4ac}}{2a} = \frac{-b \pm M}{2a} = \frac{-(-10{,}408) \pm M}{2(545.9)} = \frac{10{,}408 \pm M}{1091.8}.$$

Figure 1.14 shows that the approximate solutions are

$$\frac{10{,}408 + M}{1091.8} \approx 12.0 \qquad \frac{10{,}408 - M}{1091.8} \approx 7.1.$$

Since we were told that net earnings had recovered, we use the solution later in time and $x = 12$ corresponds to 2012. ✓₅

✓ **Checkpoint 5**

Use the equation of Example 5 to find the year in which net earnings were first −$140 million dollars.

Example 6   Solve $9x^2 - 30x + 25 = 0$.

Solution   Applying the quadratic formula with $a = 9$, $b = -30$, and $c = 25$, we have

$$x = \frac{-(-30) \pm \sqrt{(-30)^2 - 4(9)(25)}}{2(9)}$$

$$= \frac{30 \pm \sqrt{900 - 900}}{18} = \frac{30 \pm 0}{18} = \frac{30}{18} = \frac{5}{3}.$$

Therefore, the given equation has only one real solution. The fact that the solution is a rational number indicates that this equation could have been solved by factoring.

⬈ **TECHNOLOGY TIP**

You can approximate the solutions of quadratic equations on a graphing calculator by using a quadratic formula program (see the Program Appendix) or using a built-in quadratic equation solver if your calculator has one. Then you need only enter the values of the coefficients a, b, and c to obtain the approximate solutions.

Example 7   Solve $x^2 - 6x + 10 = 0$.

Solution   Apply the quadratic formula with $a = 1$, $b = -6$, and $c = 10$:

$$x = \frac{-(-6) \pm \sqrt{(-6)^2 - 4(1)(10)}}{2(1)}$$

$$= \frac{6 \pm \sqrt{36 - 40}}{2}$$

$$= \frac{6 \pm \sqrt{-4}}{2}.$$

Since no negative number has a square root in the real-number system, $\sqrt{-4}$ is not a real number. Hence, the equation has no real solutions. ✓₆

Examples 4–7 show that the number of solutions of the quadratic equation $ax^2 + bx + c = 0$ is determined by $b^2 - 4ac$, the quantity under the radical, which is called the **discriminant** of the equation. ✓₇

✓ **Checkpoint 6**

Solve each equation.
(a) $9k^2 - 6k + 1 = 0$
(b) $4m^2 + 28m + 49 = 0$
(c) $2x^2 - 5x + 5 = 0$

✓ **Checkpoint 7**

Use the discriminant to determine the number of real solutions of each equation.
(a) $x^2 + 8x + 3 = 0$
(b) $2x^2 + x + 3 = 0$
(c) $x^2 - 194x + 9409 = 0$

The Discriminant

The equation $ax^2 + bx + c = 0$ has either two, or one, or no real solutions.

If $b^2 - 4ac > 0$, there are two real solutions. (*Examples 4 and 5*)
If $b^2 - 4ac = 0$, there is one real solution. (*Example 6*)
If $b^2 - 4ac < 0$, there are no real solutions. (*Example 7*)

Applications

Quadratic equations arise in a variety of settings, as illustrated in the next set of examples. Example 8 depends on the following useful fact from geometry.

> ### The Pythagorean Theorem
>
> In a right triangle with legs of lengths a and b and hypotenuse of length c,
>
> $$a^2 + b^2 = c^2.$$

Example 8   **Business**   The size of a flat screen television is the diagonal measurement of its screen. The height of the screen is approximately 63% of its width. Kathy claims that John's 39-inch flat screen has only half of the viewing area that her 46-inch flat screen television has. Is Kathy right?

Solution   First, find the area of Kathy's screen. Let x be its width. Then its height is 63% of x (that is, $.63x$, as shown in Figure 1.15). By the Pythagorean theorem,

$$x^2 + (.63x)^2 = 46^2$$
$$x^2 + .3969x^2 = 2116 \qquad \text{Expand } (.63x)^2 \text{ and } 46^2.$$
$$(1 + .3969)x^2 = 2116 \qquad \text{Distributive property}$$
$$1.3969x^2 = 2116$$
$$x^2 = 1514.78 \qquad \text{Divide both sides by 1.3969.}$$
$$x = \pm\sqrt{1514.78} \qquad \text{Square-root property}$$
$$x \approx \pm 38.9.$$

Figure 1.15

We can ignore the negative solution, since x is a width. Thus, the width is 38.9 inches and the height is $.63x = .63(38.9) \approx 24.5$ inches, so the area is

$$\text{Area} = \text{width} \times \text{height} = 38.9 \times 24.5 = 953.1 \text{ square inches.}$$

Next we find the area of John's television in a similar manner. Let y be the width of John's television. Then its height is 63% of y. By the Pythagorean theorem,

$$y^2 + (.63y)^2 = 39^2$$
$$y^2 + .3969y^2 = 1521 \qquad \text{Expand } (.63y)^2 \text{ and } 39^2.$$
$$(1 + .3969)y^2 = 1521 \qquad \text{Distributive property}$$
$$1.3969y^2 = 1521$$
$$y^2 = 1088.84 \qquad \text{Divide both sides by 1.3969.}$$
$$y = \pm\sqrt{1088.84} \qquad \text{Square-root property}$$
$$y \approx \pm 33.0.$$

Again, we can ignore the negative solution, since y is a width. Thus, the width is 33.0 inches and the height is $.63y = .63(33.0) \approx 20.8$ inches, so the area is

$$\text{Area} = \text{width} \times \text{height} = 33.0 \times 20.8 = 686.4 \text{ square inches.}$$

Since half of 953.1 square inches (the area of Kathy's television) is 476.55 square inches, Kathy is wrong because John's viewing area is 686.4 square inches.

✓**Checkpoint 8**

If John's television was only a 26-inch flat screen television, would Kathy have been right?

Example 9   **Business**   A landscape architect wants to make an exposed gravel border of uniform width around a small shed behind a company plant. The shed is 10 feet by 6 feet. He has enough gravel to cover 36 square feet. How wide should the border be?

Solution   A sketch of the shed with border is given in Figure 1.16. Let x represent the width of the border. Then the width of the large rectangle is $6 + 2x$, and its length is $10 + 2x$.

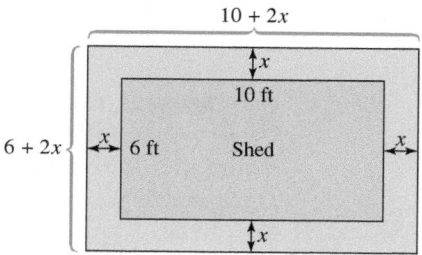

Figure 1.16

We must write an equation relating the given areas and dimensions. The area of the large rectangle is $(6 + 2x)(10 + 2x)$. The area occupied by the shed is $6 \cdot 10 = 60$. The area of the border is found by subtracting the area of the shed from the area of the large rectangle. This difference should be 36 square feet, giving the equation

$$(6 + 2x)(10 + 2x) - 60 = 36.$$

Solve this equation with the following sequence of steps:

$60 + 32x + 4x^2 - 60 = 36$	Multiply out left side.
$4x^2 + 32x - 36 = 0$	Simplify.
$x^2 + 8x - 9 = 0$	Divide both sides by 4.
$(x + 9)(x - 1) = 0$	Factor.
$x + 9 = 0 \quad$ or $\quad x - 1 = 0$	Zero-factor property.
$x = -9 \quad$ or $\quad x = 1.$	

The number -9 cannot be the width of the border, so the solution is to make the border 1 foot wide.

✓ **Checkpoint 9**

The length of a picture is 2 inches more than the width. It is mounted on a mat that extends 2 inches beyond the picture on all sides. What are the dimensions of the picture if the area of the mat is 99 square inches?

Example 10 **Physical Science** If an object is thrown upward, dropped, or thrown downward and travels in a straight line subject only to gravity (with wind resistance ignored), the height h of the object above the ground (in feet) after t seconds is given by

$$h = -16t^2 + v_0t + h_0,$$

where h_0 is the height of the object when $t = 0$ and v_0 is the initial velocity at time $t = 0$. The value of v_0 is taken to be positive if the object moves upward and negative if it moves downward. Suppose that a golf ball is thrown downward from the top of a 625-foot-high building with an initial velocity of 65 feet per second. How long does it take to reach the ground?

Solution In this case, $h_0 = 625$ (the height of the building) and $v_0 = -65$ (negative because the ball is thrown downward). The object is on the ground when $h = 0$, so we must solve the equation

$$h = -16t^2 + v_0t + h_0$$
$$0 = -16t^2 - 65t + 625. \quad \text{Let } h = 0, v_0 = -65, \text{ and } h_0 = 625.$$

Using the quadratic formula and a calculator, we see that

$$t = \frac{-(-65) \pm \sqrt{(-65)^2 - 4(-16)(625)}}{2(-16)} = \frac{65 \pm \sqrt{44{,}225}}{-32} \approx \begin{cases} -8.60 \\ \text{or} \\ 4.54 \end{cases}$$

Only the positive answer makes sense in this case. So it takes about 4.54 seconds for the ball to reach the ground.

In some applications, it may be necessary to solve an equation in several variables for a specific variable.

> **Example 11** Solve $v = mx^2 + x$ for x. (Assume that m and v are positive.)
>
> **Solution** The equation is quadratic in x because of the x^2 term. Before we use the quadratic formula, we write the equation in standard form:
>
> $$v = mx^2 + x$$
> $$0 = mx^2 + x - v.$$
>
> Let $a = m$, $b = 1$, and $c = -v$. Then the quadratic formula gives
>
> $$x = \frac{-1 \pm \sqrt{1^2 - 4(m)(-v)}}{2m}$$
>
> $$x = \frac{-1 \pm \sqrt{1 + 4mv}}{2m}. \quad \checkmark 10$$

✓ **Checkpoint 10**

Solve each of the given equations for the indicated variable. Assume that all variables are positive.

(a) $k = mp^2 - bp$ for p

(b) $r = \dfrac{APk^2}{3}$ for k

1.7 Exercises

Use factoring to solve each equation. (See Examples 1 and 2.)

1. $(x + 4)(x - 14) = 0$
2. $(p - 16)(p - 5) = 0$
3. $x(x + 6) = 0$
4. $x^2 - 2x = 0$
5. $2z^2 = 4z$
6. $x^2 - 64 = 0$
7. $y^2 + 15y + 56 = 0$
8. $k^2 - 4k - 5 = 0$
9. $2x^2 = 7x - 3$
10. $2 = 15z^2 + z$
11. $6r^2 + r = 1$
12. $3y^2 = 16y - 5$
13. $2m^2 + 20 = 13m$
14. $6a^2 + 17a + 12 = 0$
15. $m(m + 7) = -10$
16. $z(2z + 7) = 4$
17. $9x^2 - 16 = 0$
18. $36y^2 - 49 = 0$
19. $16x^2 - 16x = 0$
20. $12y^2 - 48y = 0$

Solve each equation by using the square-root property. (See Example 3.)

21. $(r - 2)^2 = 7$
22. $(b + 4)^2 = 27$
23. $(4x - 1)^2 = 20$
24. $(3t + 5)^2 = 11$

Use the quadratic formula to solve each equation. If the solutions involve square roots, give both the exact and approximate solutions. (See Examples 4–7.)

25. $2x^2 + 7x + 1 = 0$
26. $3x^2 - x - 7 = 0$
27. $4k^2 + 2k = 1$
28. $r^2 = 3r + 5$
29. $5y^2 + 5y = 2$
30. $2z^2 + 3 = 8z$
31. $6x^2 + 6x + 4 = 0$
32. $3a^2 - 2a + 2 = 0$
33. $2r^2 + 3r - 5 = 0$
34. $8x^2 = 8x - 3$
35. $2x^2 - 7x + 30 = 0$
36. $3k^2 + k = 6$
37. $1 + \dfrac{7}{2a} = \dfrac{15}{2a^2}$
38. $5 - \dfrac{4}{k} - \dfrac{1}{k^2} = 0$

Use the discriminant to determine the number of real solutions of each equation. You need not solve the equations.

39. $25t^2 + 49 = 70t$
40. $9z^2 - 12z = 1$
41. $13x^2 + 24x - 5 = 0$
42. $20x^2 + 19x + 5 = 0$

Use a calculator and the quadratic formula to find approximate solutions of each equation. (See Example 5.)

43. $4.42x^2 - 10.14x + 3.79 = 0$
44. $3x^2 - 82.74x + 570.4923 = 0$
45. $7.63x^2 + 2.79x = 5.32$
46. $8.06x^2 + 25.8726x = 25.047256$

Solve the following problems. (See Example 3.)

47. **Physical Science** According to the Federal Aviation Administration, the maximum recommended taxiing speed x (in miles per hour) for a plane on a curved runway exit is given by $R = .5x^2$, where R is the radius of the curve (in feet). Find the maximum taxiing speed for planes on such exits when the radius of the exit is
    (a) 450 ft   (b) 615 ft   (c) 970 ft

48. **Social Science** The enrollment E in public colleges and universities (in millions) is approximated by $E = .011x^2 + 10.7$ where x is the number of years since 1990. Find the year when enrollment is the following. (Data from: ProQuest Statistical Abstract of the United States: 2013.)
    (a) 14.7 million   (b) 17.6 million

49. **Social Science** The number of traffic fatalities F (in thousands) where a driver involved in the crash had a blood alcohol level of .08 or higher can be approximated by the function

    $$F = -.079x^2 + .46x + 13.3 \quad (0 \le x \le 10),$$

    where $x = 0$ corresponds to the year 2000. Determine in what year the number of fatalities is approximately the given number. (Data from: National Highway Traffic Safety Administration.)
    (a) 12,600   (b) 11,000

50. Finance The total assets A of private and public pension funds (in trillions of dollars) can be approximated by the function

$$A = .237x^2 - 3.96x + 28.2 \quad (6 \le x \le 11),$$

where $x = 6$ corresponds to the year 2006. (Data from: Board of Governors of the Federal Reserve System.)

(a) What were the assets in 2008?

(b) What year after 2008 produced $12.3 trillion in assets?

51. Finance The assets A of public pension funds (in trillions of dollars) can be approximated by the function

$$A = .169x^2 - 2.85x + 19.6 \quad (6 \le x \le 11),$$

where $x = 6$ corresponds to the year 2006. (Data from: Board of Governors of the Federal Reserve System.)

(a) What were the assets in 2009?

(b) What year before 2008 produced $7.9 trillion in assets?

52. Business The net income for Apple A (in billions) can be approximated by the function

$$A = .877x^2 - 9.33x + 23.4 \quad (6 \le x \le 12),$$

where $x = 6$ corresponds to 2006. Find the year in which net income was the following. (Data from: www.morningstar.com.)

(a) $17.8 billion   (b) $37.7 billion

Solve the following problems. (See Examples 8 and 9).

53. Physical Science A 13-foot-long ladder leans on a wall, as shown in the accompanying figure. The bottom of the ladder is 5 feet from the wall. If the bottom is pulled out 2 feet farther from the wall, how far does the top of the ladder move down the wall? [*Hint:* Draw pictures of the right triangle formed by the ladder, the ground, and the wall before and after the ladder is moved. In each case, use the Pythagorean theorem to find the distance from the top of the ladder to the ground.]

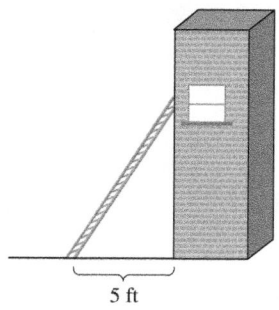

5 ft

54. Physical Science A 15-foot-long pole leans against a wall. The bottom is 9 feet from the wall. How much farther should the bottom be pulled away from the wall so that the top moves the same amount down the wall?

55. Physical Science Two trains leave the same city at the same time, one going north and the other east. The eastbound train travels 20 mph faster than the northbound one. After 5 hours, the trains are 300 miles apart. Determine the speed of each train, using the following steps.

(a) Let x denote the speed of the northbound train. Express the speed of the eastbound train in terms of x.

(b) Write expressions that give the distance traveled by each train after 5 hours.

(c) Use part (b) and the fact that the trains are 300 miles apart after 5 hours to write an equation. (A diagram of the situation may help.)

(d) Solve the equation and determine the speeds of the trains.

56. Physical Science Chris and Josh have received walkie-talkies for Christmas. If they leave from the same point at the same time, Chris walking north at 2.5 mph and Josh walking east at 3 mph, how long will they be able to talk to each other if the range of the walkie-talkies is 4 miles? Round your answer to the nearest minute.

57. Physical Science An ecology center wants to set up an experimental garden. It has 300 meters of fencing to enclose a rectangular area of 5000 square meters. Find the length and width of the rectangle as follows.

(a) Let $x =$ the length and write an expression for the width.

(b) Write an equation relating the length, width, and area, using the result of part (a).

(c) Solve the problem.

58. Business A landscape architect has included a rectangular flower bed measuring 9 feet by 5 feet in her plans for a new building. She wants to use two colors of flowers in the bed, one in the center and the other for a border of the same width on all four sides. If she can get just enough plants to cover 24 square feet for the border, how wide can the border be?

59. Physical Science Joan wants to buy a rug for a room that is 12 feet by 15 feet. She wants to leave a uniform strip of floor around the rug. She can afford 108 square feet of carpeting. What dimensions should the rug have?

60. Physical Science In 2012, Dario Franchitti won the 500-mile Indianapolis 500 race. His speed (rate) was, on average, 92 miles per hour faster than that of the 1911 winner, Ray Haroun. Franchitti completed the race in 3.72 hours less time than Harroun. Find Harroun's and Franchitti's rates to the nearest tenth.

Physical Science *Use the height formula in Example 10 to work the given problems. Note that an object that is dropped (rather than thrown downward) has initial velocity $v_0 = 0$.*

61. How long does it take a baseball to reach the ground if it is dropped from the top of a 625-foot-high building? Compare the answer with that in Example 10.

62. After the baseball in Exercise 61 is dropped, how long does it take for the ball to fall 196 feet? (*Hint:* How high is the ball at that time?)

63. You are standing on a cliff that is 200 feet high. How long will it take a rock to reach the ground if

(a) you drop it?

(b) you throw it downward at an initial velocity of 40 feet per second?

(c) How far does the rock fall in 2 seconds if you throw it downward with an initial velocity of 40 feet per second?

64. A rocket is fired straight up from ground level with an initial velocity of 800 feet per second.

(a) How long does it take the rocket to rise 3200 feet?

(b) When will the rocket hit the ground?

65. A ball is thrown upward from ground level with an initial velocity of 64 ft per second. In how many seconds will the ball reach the given height?

(a) 64 ft
(b) 39 ft

(c) Why are two answers possible in part (b)?

66. Physical Science A ball is thrown upward from ground level with an initial velocity of 100 feet per second. In how many seconds will the ball reach the given height?

(a) 50 ft
(b) 35 ft

Solve each of the given equations for the indicated variable. Assume that all denominators are nonzero and that all variables represent positive real numbers. (See Example 11.)

67. $S = \frac{1}{2}gt^2$ for t

68. $a = \pi r^2$ for r

69. $L = \frac{d^4 k}{h^2}$ for h

70. $F = \frac{kMv^2}{r}$ for v

71. $P = \frac{E^2 R}{(r + R)^2}$ for R

72. $S = 2\pi rh + 2\pi r^2$ for r

73. Solve the equation $z^4 - 2z^2 = 15$ as follows.

(a) Let $x = z^2$ and write the equation in terms of x.

(b) Solve the new equation for x.

(c) Set z^2 equal to each positive answer in part (b) and solve the resulting equation.

Solve each of the given equations. (See Exercise 73.)

74. $6p^4 = p^2 + 2$

75. $2q^4 + 3q^2 - 9 = 0$

76. $4a^4 = 2 - 7a^2$

77. $z^4 - 3z^2 - 1 = 0$

78. $2r^4 - r^2 - 5 = 0$

✓ Checkpoint Answers

1. (a) $6, -2$ (b) $3/5, -5$ (c) $9/2, -5/3, -3$

2. (a) $2, -5$ (b) $1/2, -5$ (c) $9/4, 0$

3. (a) $\pm\sqrt{21}$ (b) $-7 \pm \sqrt{15}$ (c) $(3 \pm \sqrt{5})/2$

4. (a) $x = 1 + \sqrt{3}$ or $1 - \sqrt{3}$
   (b) $u = 3 + \sqrt{5}$ or $3 - \sqrt{5}$

5. Late 2007

6. (a) $1/3$ (b) $-7/2$ (c) No real solutions

7. (a) 2 (b) 0 (c) 1

8. Yes, area $= 304.92$ sq. in.

9. 5 inches by 7 inches

10. (a) $p = \dfrac{b \pm \sqrt{b^2 + 4mk}}{2m}$

   (b) $k = \pm\sqrt{\dfrac{3r}{AP}}$ or $\dfrac{\pm\sqrt{3rAP}}{AP}$

CHAPTER 1 Summary and Review

Key Terms and Symbols

1.1 $\approx$ is approximately equal to
π pi
$|a|$ absolute value of a
real number
natural (counting) number
whole number
integer
rational number
irrational number
properties of real numbers
order of operations
square roots
number line
interval
interval notation
absolute value

1.2 a^n a to the power n
exponent or power

multiplication with exponents
power of a power rule
zero exponent
base
polynomial
variable
coefficient
term
constant term
degree of a polynomial
zero polynomial
leading coefficient
quadratics
cubics
like terms
FOIL
revenue
fixed cost

variable cost
profit

1.3 factor
factoring
greatest common factor
difference of squares
perfect squares
sum and difference of cubes

1.4 rational expression
cancellation property
operations with rational expressions
complex fraction

1.5 $a^{1/n}$ nth root of a
$\sqrt{a}$ square root of a
$\sqrt[n]{a}$ nth root of a
properties of exponents
radical
radicand

index
rationalizing the denominator
rationalizing the numerator

1.6 first-degree equation
solution of an equation
properties of equality
extraneous solution
solving for a specified variable
absolute-value equations
solving applied problems

1.7 quadratic equation
real solution
zero-factor property
square-root property
quadratic formula
discriminant
Pythagorean theorem

Chapter 1 Key Concepts

Factoring

$$x^2 + 2xy + y^2 = (x + y)^2 \qquad\qquad x^3 - y^3 = (x - y)(x^2 + xy + y^2)$$
$$x^2 - 2xy + y^2 = (x - y)^2 \qquad\qquad x^3 + y^3 = (x + y)(x^2 - xy + y^2)$$
$$x^2 - y^2 = (x + y)(x - y)$$

Properties of Radicals

Let a and b be real numbers, n be a positive integer, and m be any integer for which the given relationships exist. Then

$$a^{m/n} = \sqrt[n]{a^m} = (\sqrt[n]{a})^m; \qquad \sqrt[n]{a^n} = |a| \text{ if } n \text{ is even}; \qquad \sqrt[n]{a^n} = a \text{ if } n \text{ is odd};$$

$$\sqrt[n]{a} \cdot \sqrt[n]{b} = \sqrt[n]{ab}; \qquad \frac{\sqrt[n]{a}}{\sqrt[n]{b}} = \sqrt[n]{\frac{a}{b}} \;\; (b \neq 0).$$

Properties of Exponents

Let a, b, r, and s be any real numbers for which the following exist. Then

$$a^{-r} = \frac{1}{a^r} \qquad\qquad a^0 = 1 \qquad\qquad \left(\frac{a}{b}\right)^r = \frac{a^r}{b^r}$$

$$a^r \cdot a^s = a^{r+s} \qquad\qquad (a^r)^s = a^{rs} \qquad\qquad a^{1/r} = \sqrt[r]{a}$$

$$\frac{a^r}{a^s} = a^{r-s} \qquad\qquad (ab)^r = a^r b^r \qquad\qquad \left(\frac{a}{b}\right)^{-r} = \left(\frac{b}{a}\right)^r$$

Absolute Value

Assume that a and b are real numbers with $b > 0$.

The solutions of $|a| = b$ or $|a| = |b|$ are $a = b$ or $a = -b$.

Quadratic Equations

Facts needed to solve quadratic equations (in which a, b, and c are real numbers):

Factoring If $ab = 0$, then $a = 0$ or $b = 0$ or both.

Square-Root Property If $b > 0$, then the solutions of $x^2 = b$ are $\sqrt{b}$ and $-\sqrt{b}$.

Quadratic Formula The solutions of $ax^2 + bx + c = 0$ (with $a \neq 0$) are

$$x = \frac{-b \pm \sqrt{b^2 - 4ac}}{2a}.$$

Discriminant There are two real solutions of $ax^2 + bx + c = 0$ if $b^2 - 4ac > 0$, one real solution if $b^2 - 4ac = 0$, and no real solutions if $b^2 - 4ac < 0$.

Chapter 1 Review Exercises

Name the numbers from the list $-12, -6, -9/10, -\sqrt{7}, -\sqrt{4},$ $0, 1/8, \pi/4, 6,$ *and* $\sqrt{11}$ *that are*

1. whole numbers
2. integers
3. rational numbers
4. irrational numbers

Identify the properties of real numbers that are illustrated in each of the following expressions.

5. $9[(-3)4] = 9[4(-3)]$

6. $7(4 + 5) = (4 + 5)7$

7. $6(x + y - 3) = 6x + 6y + 6(-3)$

8. $11 + (5 + 3) = (11 + 5) + 3$

Express each statement in symbols.

9. x is at least 9.
10. x is negative.

Write the following numbers in numerical order from smallest to largest.

11. $|6 - 4|, -|-2|, |8 + 1|, -|3 - (-2)|$

12. $\sqrt{7}, -\sqrt{8}, -|\sqrt{16}|, |-\sqrt{12}|$

Write the following without absolute-value bars.

13. $7 - |-8|$
14. $|-3| - |-9 + 6|$

Graph each of the following on a number line.

15. $x \geq -3$
16. $-4 < x \leq 6$

Use the order of operations to simplify each of the following.

17. $\dfrac{-9 + (-6)(-3) \div 9}{6 - (-3)}$
18. $\dfrac{20 \div 4 \cdot 2 \div 5 - 1}{-9 - (-3) - 12 \div 3}$

Perform each of the indicated operations.

19. $(3x^4 - x^2 + 5x) - (-x^4 + 3x^2 - 6x)$

20. $(-8y^3 + 8y^2 - 5y) - (2y^3 + 4y^2 - 10)$

21. $(5k - 2h)(5k + 2h)$
22. $(2r - 5y)(2r + 5y)$

23. $(3x + 4y)^2$
24. $(2a - 5b)^2$

Factor each of the following as completely as possible.

25. $2kh^2 - 4kh + 5k$
26. $2m^2n^2 + 6mn^2 + 16n^2$

27. $5a^4 + 12a^3 + 4a^2$
28. $24x^3 + 4x^2 - 4x$

29. $144p^2 - 169q^2$
30. $81z^2 - 25x^2$

31. $27y^3 - 1$
32. $125a^3 + 216$

Perform each operation.

33. $\dfrac{3x}{5} \cdot \dfrac{45x}{12}$

34. $\dfrac{5k^2}{24} - \dfrac{70k}{36}$

35. $\dfrac{c^2 - 3c + 2}{2c(c - 1)} \div \dfrac{c - 2}{8c}$

36. $\dfrac{p^3 - 2p^2 - 8p}{3p(p^2 - 16)} \div \dfrac{p^2 + 4p + 4}{9p^2}$

37. $\dfrac{2m^2 - 4m + 2}{m^2 - 1} \div \dfrac{6m + 18}{m^2 + 2m - 3}$

38. $\dfrac{x^2 + 6x + 5}{4(x^2 + 1)} \cdot \dfrac{2x(x + 1)}{x^2 - 25}$

Simplify each of the given expressions. Write all answers without negative exponents. Assume that all variables represent positive real numbers.

39. 5^{-3}

40. 10^{-2}

41. -8^0

42. $\left(-\dfrac{5}{6}\right)^{-2}$

43. $4^6 \cdot 4^{-3}$

44. $7^{-5} \cdot 7^{-2}$

45. $\dfrac{8^{-5}}{8^{-4}}$

46. $\dfrac{6^{-3}}{6^4}$

47. $5^{-1} + 2^{-1}$

48. $5^{-2} + 5^{-1}$

49. $\dfrac{5^{1/3} \cdot 5^{1/2}}{5^{3/2}}$

50. $\dfrac{2^{3/4} \cdot 2^{-1/2}}{2^{1/4}}$

51. $(3a^2)^{1/2} \cdot (3^2a)^{3/2}$

52. $(4p)^{2/3} \cdot (2p^3)^{3/2}$

Simplify each of the following expressions.

53. $\sqrt[3]{27}$

54. $\sqrt[6]{-64}$

55. $\sqrt[3]{54p^3q^5}$

56. $\sqrt[4]{64a^5b^3}$

57. $3\sqrt{3} - 12\sqrt{12}$

58. $8\sqrt{7} + 2\sqrt{63}$

Rationalize each denominator.

59. $\dfrac{\sqrt{3}}{1 + \sqrt{2}}$

60. $\dfrac{4 + \sqrt{2}}{4 - \sqrt{5}}$

Solve each equation.

61. $3x - 4(x - 2) = 2x + 9$

62. $4y + 9 = -3(1 - 2y) + 5$

63. $\dfrac{2m}{m - 3} = \dfrac{6}{m - 3} + 4$

64. $\dfrac{15}{k + 5} = 4 - \dfrac{3k}{k + 5}$

Solve for x.

65. $8ax - 3 = 2x$

66. $b^2x - 2x = 4b^2$

Solve each equation.

67. $\left|\dfrac{2 - y}{5}\right| = 8$

68. $|4k + 1| = |6k - 3|$

Find all real solutions of each equation.

69. $(b + 7)^2 = 5$

70. $(2p + 1)^2 = 7$

71. $2p^2 + 3p = 2$

72. $2y^2 = 15 + y$

73. $2q^2 - 11q = 21$

74. $3x^2 + 2x = 16$

75. $6k^4 + k^2 = 1$

76. $21p^4 = 2 + p^2$

Solve each equation for the specified variable.

77. $p = \dfrac{E^2R}{(r + R)^2}$ for r

78. $p = \dfrac{E^2R}{(r + R)^2}$ for E

79. $K = s(s - a)$ for s

80. $kz^2 - hz - t = 0$ for z

Work these problems.

81. **Finance** The percent change in stock price in 2012 for retailers The Gap and J. C. Penny was +67% and −44% respectively. Find the difference in the percent change for these two companies in 2012. (Data from: money.cnn.com.)

82. **Finance** The percent change in stock price in 2012 for tech companies Dell and Hewlett-Packard was −31% and −45% respectively. Find the difference in the percent change for these two companies in 2012. (Data from: money.cnn.com.)

83. **Business** A new PC is on sale for 20% off. The sale price is $895. What was the original price?

84. **Business** The stock price of eBay increased 68% in 2012. If the price was $51 a share at the end of 2012, at what price did it begin the year?

85. **Finance** The amount of outlays O of the U.S. government per year (in trillions of dollars) can be approximated by the function

$$O = .2x + 1.5,$$

where $x = 6$ corresponds to the year 2006. Find the year in which the outlays are the following. (Data from: U.S. Office of Management and Budget.)

(a) $3.3 trillion

(b) $3.9 trillion

86. **Business** Estimated revenue R (in billions of dollars) from the general newspaper industry can be approximated by the function

$$R = -3.6x + 64.4,$$

where $x = 6$ corresponds to the year 2006. In what year was revenue $28.4 billion? (Data from: U.S. Census Bureau.)

87. **Business** The number (in millions) of new vehicles V sold or leased in the United States can be approximated by the function $V = .89x^2 - 17.9x + 139.3$ where $x = 6$ corresponds to 2006. Find the total sales for 2012. (Data from: U.S. Bureau of Transportation Statistics.)

88. **Business** The total sales (in billions of dollars) of alcoholic beverages A in the United States can be approximated by the function $A = -.023x^3 + .38x^2 + 3.29x + 107$ where $x = 0$ corresponds to the year 2000. (Data from: U.S. Department of Agriculture.)

(a) Find the total sales in 2010.

(b) In what year did sales become greater than $140 billion.

89. Business   The number (in millions) of flight departures F within the United States per year can be approximated by the function

$$F = \frac{0.004x^2 + 10.3x + 5.8}{x + 1},$$

where $x = 1$ corresponds to the year 2001. (Data from: U.S. Bureau of Transportation Statistics.)

(a) How many flights departed in 2009?

(b) If the trend continues, when will the number of flights exceed 10 million?

90. Business   The total amount of sales from manufacturing (in trillions of dollars) within the United States M can be approximated by

$$M = \frac{.122x^2 + 5.48x + 6.5}{x + 2},$$

where $x = 1$ corresponds to the year 2001. (Data from U.S. Census Bureau.)

(a) What were the sales in 2009?

(b) In what year did sales exceed $6.0 trillion?

91. Economics   The total amount (in billions of dollars) of research and development spending by the U.S. government R can be approximated by

$$R = 4.33x^{0.66},$$

where $x = 8$ corresponds to 1998. (Data from: www.nsf.gov/statistics/)

(a) Find the spending in 2000.

(b) Find the spending in 2010.

92. Economics   The total number (in millions) of employees within the United States in the service-providing industry E can be approximated by

$$E = 91.5x^{0.07},$$

where $x = 10$ corresponds to the year 2000. Assume the trend continues indefinitely. (Data from: ProQuest Statistical Abstract of the United States: 2013.)

(a) How many employees will there be in the year 2015?

(b) In what year will there be more than 115 million employees?

93. Finance   Kinisha borrowed $2000 from a credit union at 12% annual interest and borrowed $500 from her aunt at 7% annual interest. What single rate of interest on $2500 results in the same total amount of interest?

94. Business   A butcher makes a blend of stew meat from beef that sells for $2.80 a pound and pork that sells for $3.25 a pound. How many pounds of each meat should be used to get 30 pounds of a mix that can be sold for $3.10 a pound?

95. Business   The number of patents P granted for new inventions within each U.S. state in the year 2011 is approximated by

$$P = 18.2x^2 - 26.0x + 789,$$

where x is the population of the state in millions. (Data from: U.S. Patent and Trademark Office).

(a) What is the number of patents granted for the state of New York with a population of 19.47 million?

(b) Approximate the population of Illinois with its number of patents at 3806.

96. Business   Within the state of California, the number (in thousands) of patents C granted for new inventions can be approximated by

$$C = .22x^2 - 1.9x + 23.0,$$

where $x = 2$ corresponds to the year 2002. (Data from: U.S. Patent and Trademark Office.)

(a) What was the number of patents issued in California for 2011?

(b) What most recent year saw California hit 24 thousand patents?

97. Business   A concrete mixer needs to know how wide to make a walk around a rectangular fountain that is 10 by 15 feet. She has enough concrete to cover 200 square feet. To the nearest tenth of a foot, how wide should the walk be in order to use up all the concrete?

98. Physical Science   A new homeowner needs to put up a fence to make his yard secure. The house itself forms the south boundary and the garage forms the west boundary of the property, so he needs to fence only 2 sides. The area of the yard is 4000 square feet. He has enough material for 160 feet of fence. Find the length and width of the yard (to the nearest foot).

99. Physical Science   A projectile is launched from the ground vertically upward at a rate of 150 feet per second. How many seconds will it take for the projectile to be 200 feet from the ground on its downward trip?

100. Physical Science   Suppose a tennis ball is thrown downward from the top of a 700-foot-high building with an initial velocity of 55 feet per second. How long does it take to reach the ground?

Case Study 1   Consumers Often Need to Just Do the Math

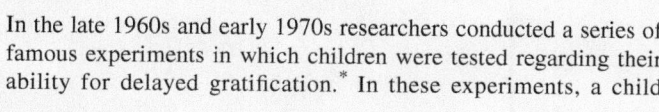

In the late 1960s and early 1970s researchers conducted a series of famous experiments in which children were tested regarding their ability for delayed gratification.[*] In these experiments, a child would be offered a marshmallow, cookie, or pretzel and told that if they did not eat the treat, they could have two of the treats when the researcher returned (after about 15 minutes). Of course, some children would eat the treat immediately, and others would wait and receive two of the treats.

---

[*]Mischel, Walter, Ebbe B. Ebbesen, and Antonette Raskoff Zeiss. (1972). "Cognitive and attentional mechanisms in delay of gratification." *Journal of Personality and Social Psychology*, pp. 204–218.

Similar studies occur in studying consumer behavior among adults. Often when making purchases, consumers will purchase an appliance that initially costs less, but in the long run costs more money when one accounts for the operating expense. Imagine trying to decide whether to buy a new furnace for $4500 that is 80% efficient versus a new furnace that is 90% efficient that costs $5700. Each furnace is expected to last at least 20 years. The furnace with the 90% efficiency is estimated to cost $1800 a year to operate, while the 80% efficiency furnace is estimated to cost $2100 a year to operate—a difference of $300 a year. Thus, the original price differential of $1200 would be made up in four years. Over the course of 16 additional years, the 90% efficiency furnace would end up saving the buyer $4800.

For other appliances, the difference in total expenditures may not be as dramatic, but can still be substantial. The energy guide tags that often accompany new appliances help make it easier for consumers "to do the math" by communicating the yearly operating costs of an appliance. For example, a Kenmore new side-by-side 25.4 cubic foot refrigerator retails for $1128. The energy guide estimates the cost of operation for a year to be $72. A similarly sized new Frigidaire refrigerator retails for $1305, and the energy guide information estimates the annual cost to be $43. Over 10 years, which refrigerator costs the consumer more money?

We can write mathematical expressions to answer this question. With an initial cost of $1128, and an annual operating cost of $72, for x years of operation the cost C for the Kenmore refrigerator is

$$C = 1128 + 72x$$

For 10 years, the Kenmore would cost $C = 1128 + 72(10) = $1848. For the Frigidaire model, the cost is

$$C = 1305 + 43x.$$

For 10 years, the Frigidaire would cost $C = 1305 + 43(10) = $1735.

Thus, the Frigidaire refrigerator costs $113 less in total costs over 10 years.

Behavior when a consumer seeks the up-front savings sounds very similar to the delayed gratification studies among children. These kinds of behavior are of interest to both psychologists and economists. The implications are also very important in the marketing of energy-efficient appliances that often do have a higher initial cost, but save consumers money over the lifetime of the product.

One tool to help consumers make the best choice in the long run is simply to take the time to "just do the math," as the common expression goes. The techniques of this chapter can be applied to do just that!

Exercises

1. On the homedepot.com website, a General Electric 40-gallon electric hot water tank retails for $218 and the estimated annual cost of operation is $508. Write an expression for the cost to buy and run the hot water tank for x years.

2. On the homedepot.com website, a General Electric 40-gallon gas hot water tank retails for $328 and the estimated annual cost of operation is $309. Write an expression for the cost to buy and run the hot water tank for x years.

3. Over ten years, does the electric or gas hot water tank cost more? By how much?

4. In how many years will the total for the two hot water tanks be equal?

5. On the Lowes website, a Maytag 25-cubic-foot refrigerator was advertised for $1529.10 with an estimated cost per month in electricity of $50 a year. Write an expression for the cost to buy and run the refrigerator for x years.

6. On the HomeDepot website, an LG Electronics 25-cubic-foot refrigerator was advertised for $1618.20 with an estimated cost per month in electricity of $44 a year. Write an expression for the cost to buy and run the refrigerator for x years.

7. Over ten years, which refrigerator (the Maytag or the LG) costs the most? By how much?

8. In how many years will the total for the two refrigerators be equal?

Extended Project

A high-end real estate developer needs to install 50 new washing machines in a building she leases to tenants (with utilities included in the monthly rent). She knows that energy-efficient front loaders cost less per year to run, but they can be much more expensive than traditional top loaders. Investigate by visiting an appliance store or using the Internet, the prices and energy efficiency of two comparable front-loading and top-loading washing machines.

1. Estimate how many years it will take for the total expenditure (including purchase and cost of use) for the 50 front-loading machines to equal the total expenditure for the 50 top-loading machines.

2. The energy guide ratings use data that is often several years old. If the owner believes that current energy costs are 20% higher than what is indicated with the energy guide, redo the calculations for (1) above and determine if it will take less time for the two total expenditures to be equal.

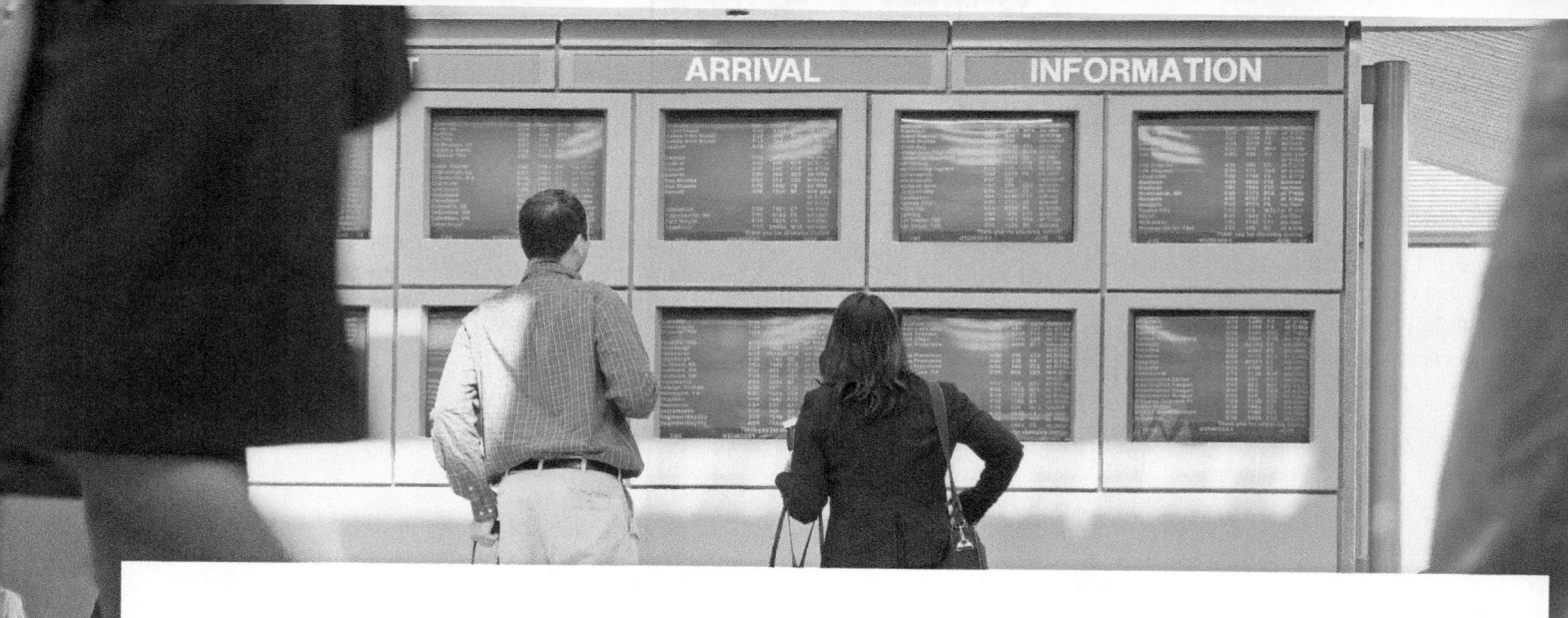

Graphs, Lines, and Inequalities

2

CHAPTER

Data from current and past events is often a useful tool in business and in the social and health sciences. Gathering data is the first step in developing mathematical models that can be used to analyze a situation and predict future performance. For examples of linear models in transportation, business, and health see Exercises 15, 16, and 21 on page 94.

Graphical representations of data are commonly used in business and in the health and social sciences. Lines, equations, and inequalities play an important role in developing mathematical models from such data. This chapter presents both algebraic and graphical methods for dealing with these topics.

2.1   Graphs

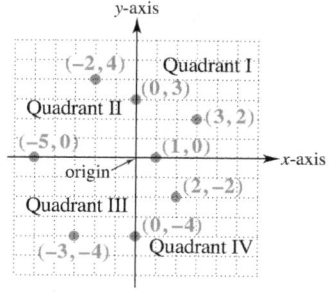

Figure 2.1

Just as the number line associates the points on a line with real numbers, a similar construction in two dimensions associates points in a plane with *ordered pairs* of real numbers. A **Cartesian coordinate system,** as shown in Figure 2.1, consists of a horizontal number line (usually called the *x*-**axis**) and a vertical number line (usually called the *y*-**axis**). The point where the number lines meet is called the **origin.** Each point in a Cartesian coordinate system is labeled with an **ordered pair** of real numbers, such as $(-2, 4)$ or $(3, 2)$. Several points and their corresponding ordered pairs are shown in Figure 2.1.

For the point labeled $(-2, 4)$, for example, -2 is the *x*-**coordinate** and 4 is the *y*-**coordinate.** You can think of these coordinates as directions telling you how to move to this point from the origin: You go 2 horizontal units to the left (*x*-coordinate) and 4 vertical

65

✓**Checkpoint 1**

Locate $(-1, 6)$, $(-3, -5)$, $(4, -3)$, $(0, 2)$, and $(-5, 0)$ on a coordinate system.

Answers to Checkpoint exercises are found at the end of the section.

units upward (y-coordinate). From now on, instead of referring to "the point labeled by the ordered pair $(-2, 4)$," we will say "the point $(-2, 4)$." ✓₁

The x-axis and the y-axis divide the plane into four parts, or **quadrants,** which are numbered as shown in Figure 2.1. The points on the coordinate axes belong to no quadrant.

Equations and Graphs

A **solution of an equation** in two variables, such as

$$y = -2x + 3$$

or

$$y = x^2 + 7x - 2,$$

is an ordered pair of numbers such that the substitution of the first number for x and the second number for y produces a true statement.

Example 1   Which of the following are solutions of $y = -2x + 3$?

(a) $(2, -1)$

Solution   This is a solution of $y = -2x + 3$ because "$-1 = -2 \cdot 2 + 3$" is a true statement.

(b) $(4, 7)$

✓**Checkpoint 2**

Which of the following are solutions of
$$y = x^2 + 5x - 3?$$

(a) $(1, 3)$

(b) $(-2, -3)$

(c) $(-1, -7)$

Solution   Since $-2 \cdot 4 + 3 = -5$, and not 7, the ordered pair $(4, 7)$ is not a solution of $y = -2x + 3$. ✓₂

Equations in two variables, such as $y = -2x + 3$, typically have an infinite number of solutions. To find one, choose a number for x and then compute the value of y that produces a solution. For instance, if $x = 5$, then $y = -2 \cdot 5 + 3 = -7$, so that the pair $(5, -7)$ is a solution of $y = -2x + 3$. Similarly, if $x = 0$, then $y = -2 \cdot 0 + 3 = 3$, so that $(0, 3)$ is also a solution.

The **graph** of an equation in two variables is the set of points in the plane whose coordinates (ordered pairs) are solutions of the equation. Thus, the graph of an equation is a picture of its solutions. Since a typical equation has infinitely many solutions, its graph has infinitely many points.

✓**Checkpoint 3**

Graph $x = 5y$.

Example 2   Sketch the graph of $y = -2x + 5$.

Solution   Since we cannot plot infinitely many points, we construct a table of y-values for a reasonable number of x-values, plot the corresponding points, and make an "educated guess" about the rest. The table of values and points in Figure 2.2 suggests that the graph is a straight line, as shown in Figure 2.3. ✓₃

x	$-2x + 5$
-1	7
0	5
2	1
4	-3
5	-5

Figure 2.2

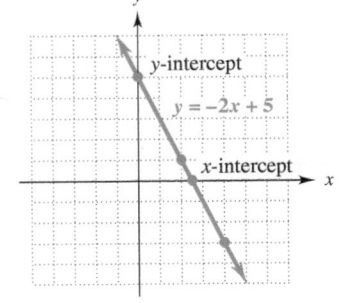

Figure 2.3

An **x-intercept** of a graph is the x-coordinate of a point where the graph intersects the x-axis. The y-coordinate of this point is 0, since it is on the axis. Consequently, to find the x-intercepts of the graph of an equation, set $y = 0$ and solve for x. For instance, in Example 2, the x-intercept of the graph of $y = -2x + 5$ (see Figure 2.3) is found by setting $y = 0$ and solving for x:

$$0 = -2x + 5$$
$$2x = 5$$
$$x = \frac{5}{2}.$$

Similarly, a **y-intercept** of a graph is the y-coordinate of a point where the graph intersects the y-axis. The x-coordinate of this point is 0. The y-intercepts are found by setting $x = 0$ and solving for y. For example, the graph of $y = -2x + 5$ in Figure 2.3 has y-intercept 5. ✔4

✓ **Checkpoint 4**

Find the x- and y-intercepts of the graphs of these equations.

(a) $3x + 4y = 12$

(b) $5x - 2y = 8$

Example 3   Find the x- and y-intercepts of the graph of $y = x^2 - 2x - 8$, and sketch the graph.

Solution   To find the y-intercept, set $x = 0$ and solve for y:

$$y = x^2 - 2x - 8 = 0^2 - 2 \cdot 0 - 8 = -8.$$

The y-intercept is -8. To find the x-intercept, set $y = 0$ and solve for x.

$$x^2 - 2x - 8 = y$$
$$x^2 - 2x - 8 = 0 \qquad \text{Set } y = 0.$$
$$(x + 2)(x - 4) = 0 \qquad \text{Factor.}$$
$$x + 2 = 0 \quad \text{or} \quad x - 4 = 0 \qquad \text{Zero-factor property}$$
$$x = -2 \quad \text{or} \quad x = 4$$

The x-intercepts are -2 and 4. Now make a table, using both positive and negative values for x, and plot the corresponding points, as in Figure 2.4. These points suggest that the entire graph looks like Figure 2.5.

x	$x^2 - 2x - 8$
-3	7
-2	0
-1	-5
0	-8
1	-9
3	-5
4	0
5	7

Figure 2.4

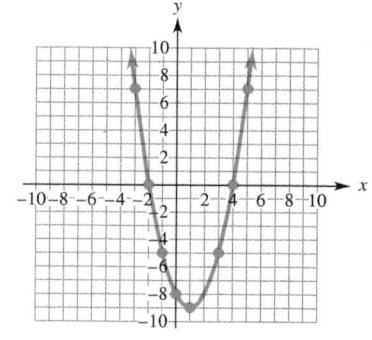

Figure 2.5

Example 4   Sketch the graph of $y = \sqrt{x + 2}$.

Solution   Notice that $\sqrt{x + 2}$ is a real number only when $x + 2 \geq 0$—that is, when $x \geq -2$. Furthermore, $y = \sqrt{x + 2}$ is always nonnegative. Hence, all points on the graph lie on or above the x-axis and on or to the right of $x = -2$. Computing some typical values, we obtain the graph in Figure 2.6.

x	$\sqrt{x+2}$
-2	0
0	$\sqrt{2} \approx 1.414$
2	2
5	$\sqrt{7} \approx 2.646$
7	3
9	$\sqrt{11} \approx 3.317$

Figure 2.6

Example 2 shows that the solution of the equation $-2x + 5 = 0$ is the x-intercept of the graph of $y = -2x + 5$. Example 3 shows that the solutions of the equation $x^2 - 2x - 8 = 0$ are the x-intercepts of the graph $y = x^2 - 2x - 8$. Similar facts hold in the general case.

Intercepts and Equations

The real solutions of a one-variable equation of the form

$$\textbf{expression in } x = 0$$

are the x-intercepts of the graph of

$$y = \textbf{ same expression in } x.$$

Graph Reading

Information is often given in graphical form, so you must be able to read and interpret graphs—that is, translate graphical information into statements in English.

Example 5   **Finance**   Newspapers and websites summarize activity of the S&P 500 Index in graphical form. The results for the 20 trading days for the month of December, 2012 are displayed in Figure 2.7. The first coordinate of each point on the graph is the trading day in December, and the second coordinate represents the closing price of the S&P 500 on that day. (Data from: www.morningstar.com.)

Figure 2.7

(a) What was the value of the S&P 500 Index on day 11 and day 17?

Solution   The point $(11, 1430)$ is on the graph, which means that the value of the index was 1430. The point $(17, 1420)$ is on the graph, which means that the value of the index was 1420 on that day.

(b) On what days was the value of the index above 1425?

Solution   Look for points whose second coordinates are greater than 1425—that is, points that lie above the horizontal line through 1425 (shown in red in Figure 2.7). The first coordinates of these points are the days when the index value was above 1425. We see these days occurred on days 7, 8, 11, 12, 13, 14, 15, 16, and 20. ✔5

The next example deals with the basic business relationship that was introduced in Section 1.2:

$$\text{Profit} = \text{Revenue} - \text{Cost}.$$

✓**Checkpoint 5**

From Figure 2.7 determine when the S&P 500 had its highest point and its lowest point. What where the index values on those days?

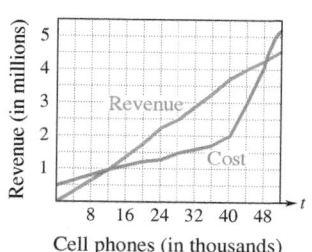

Figure 2.8

Example 6   **Business**   Monthly revenue and costs for the Webster Cell Phone Company are determined by the number t of phones produced and sold, as shown in Figure 2.8.

(a) How many phones should be produced each month if the company is to make a profit (assuming that all phones produced are sold)?

Solution   Profit is revenue minus cost, so the company makes a profit whenever revenue is greater than cost—that is, when the revenue graph is above the cost graph. Figure 2.8 shows that this occurs between $t = 12$ and $t = 48$—that is, when 12,000 to 48,000 phones are produced. If the company makes fewer than 12,000 phones, it will lose money (because costs will be greater than revenue.) It also loses money by making more than 48,000 phones. (One reason might be that high production levels require large amounts of over-time pay, which drives costs up too much.)

(b) Is it more profitable to make 40,000 or 44,000 phones?

Solution   On the revenue graph, the point with first coordinate 40 has second coordinate of approximately 3.7, meaning that the revenue from 40,000 phones is about 3.7 million dollars. The point with first coordinate 40 on the cost graph is (40, 2), meaning that the cost of producing 40,000 phones is 2 million dollars. Therefore, the profit on 40,000 phones is about $3.7 - 2 = 1.7$ million dollars. For 44,000 phones, we have the approximate points (44, 4) on the revenue graph and (44, 3) on the cost graph. So the profit on 44,000 phones is $4 - 3 = 1$ million dollars. Consequently, it is more profitable to make 40,000 phones. ✔6

✓**Checkpoint 6**

In Example 6, find the profit from making

(a) 32,000 phones;

(b) 4000 phones.

⬈ Technology and Graphs

A graphing calculator or computer graphing program follows essentially the same procedure used when graphing by hand: The calculator selects a large number of x-values (95 or more), equally spaced along the x-axis, and plots the corresponding points, simultaneously connecting them with line segments. Calculator-generated graphs are generally quite accurate, although they may not appear as smooth as hand-drawn ones. The next example illustrates the basics of graphing on a graphing calculator. (Computer graphing software operates similarly.)

Example 7   Use a graphing calculator to sketch the graph of the equation

$$2x^3 - 2y - 10x + 2 = 0.$$

Solution   *First, set the **viewing window**—*the portion of the coordinate plane that will appear on the screen. Press the WINDOW key (labeled RANGE or PLOT-SETUP on some calculators) and enter the appropriate numbers, as in Figure 2.9 (which shows the screen from a TI-84+; other calculators are similar). Then the calculator will display the portion of the plane inside the dashed lines shown in Figure 2.10—that is, the points (x, y) with $-9 \leq x \leq 9$ and $-6 \leq y \leq 6$.

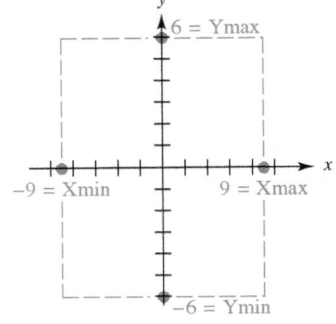

Figure 2.9   **Figure 2.10**

In Figure 2.9, we have set Xscl $= 2$ and Yscl $= 1$, which means the **tick marks** on the x-axis are two units apart and the tick marks on the y-axis are one unit apart (as shown in Figure 2.10).

Second, enter the equation to be graphed in the equation memory. To do this, you must first solve the equation for y (because a calculator accepts only equations of the form $y =$ expression in x):

$$2y = 2x^3 - 10x + 2$$
$$y = x^3 - 5x + 1.$$

Now press the Y $=$ key (labeled SYMB on some calculators) and enter the equation, using the "variable key" for x. (This key is labeled X, T, θ, n or X, θ, T or x-VAR, depending on the calculator.) Figure 2.11 shows the equation entered on a TI-84+; other calculators are similar. Now press GRAPH (or PLOT or DRW on some calculators), and obtain Figure 2.12.

Figure 2.11   **Figure 2.12**

Finally, if necessary, change the viewing window to obtain a more readable graph. It is difficult to see the y-intercept in Figure 2.12, so press WINDOW and change the viewing window (Figure 2.13); then press GRAPH to obtain Figure 2.14, in which the y-intercept at $y = 1$ is clearly shown. (It isn't necessary to reenter the equation.) ✓₇

✓ **Checkpoint 7**

Use a graphing calculator to graph $y = 18x - 3x^3$ in the following viewing windows:

(a) $-10 \leq x \leq 10$ and $-10 \leq y \leq 10$ with Xscl $= 1$, Yscl $= 1$;

(b) $-5 \leq x \leq 5$ and $-20 \leq y \leq 20$ with Xscl $= 1$, Yscl $= 5$.

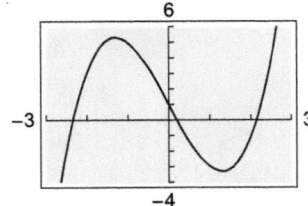

Figure 2.13   **Figure 2.14**

◢ **Technology Tools**

In addition to graphing equations, graphing calculators (and graphing software) provide convenient tools for solving equations and reading graphs. For example, when you have graphed an equation, you can readily determine the points the calculator plotted. Press **trace** (a cursor will appear on the graph), and use the left and right arrow keys to move the cursor along the graph. The coordinates of the point the cursor is on appear at the bottom of the screen.

Recall that the solutions of an equation, such as $x^3 - 5x + 1 = 0$, are the x-intercepts of the graph of $y = x^3 - 5x + 1$. (See the box on page 68.) A **graphical root finder** enables you to find these x-intercepts and thus to solve the equation.

Example 8 Use a graphical root finder to solve $x^3 - 5x + 1 = 0$.

Solution First, graph $y = x^3 - 5x + 1$. The x-intercepts of this graph are the solutions of the equation. To find these intercepts, look for "root" or "zero" in the appropriate menu.* Check your instruction manual for the proper syntax. A typical root finder (see Figure 2.15) shows that two of the solutions (x-intercepts) are $x \approx .2016$ and $x \approx 2.1284$. For the third solution, see Checkpoint 8. ✔8

(a)

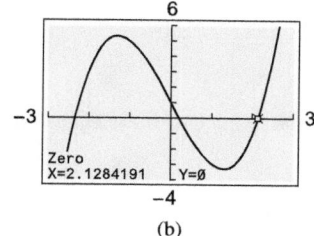
(b)

Figure 2.15

Many graphs have peaks and valleys (for instance, the graphs in Figure 2.15). A **maximum/minimum finder** provides accurate approximations of the locations of the "tops" of the peaks and the "bottoms" of the valleys.

Example 9 **Business** The net income (in millions of dollars) for Marriott International, Inc. can be approximated by

$$6.159x^3 - 130.9x^2 + 783.4x - 749,$$

where $x = 2$ corresponds to the year 2002. In what year was the net income the highest? What was the net income that year? (Data from: www.morningstar.com.)

Solution The graph of $y = 6.159x^3 - 130.9x^2 + 783.4x - 749$ is shown in Figure 2.16. The highest net income corresponds to the highest point on this graph. To find this point, look for "maximum" or "max" or "extremum" in the same menu as the graphical root finder. Check your instruction manual for the proper syntax. A typical maximum finder (Figure 2.17) shows that the highest point has approximate coordinates (4.29, 688.96). The first coordinate is the year and the second is the net income (in millions). So the largest net income occurred in 2004 and the net income was approximately $689 million. ✔9

Figure 2.16

Figure 2.17

✓ **Checkpoint 8**

Use a graphical root finder to approximate the third solution of the equation in Example 8.

✓ **Checkpoint 9**

Use a minimum finder to locate the approximate coordinates of the lowest point on the graph in Figure 2.16.

---

*CALC on TI-84+, GRAPH MATH on TI-86, G-SOLV on Casio.

2.1 Exercises

State the quadrant in which each point lies.

1. $(1, -2), (-2, 1), (3, 4), (-5, -6)$

2. $(\pi, 2), (3, -\sqrt{2}), (4, 0), (-\sqrt{3}, \sqrt{3})$

Determine whether the given ordered pair is a solution of the given equation. (See Example 1.)

3. $(1, -3); 3x - y - 6 = 0$

4. $(2, -1); x^2 + y^2 - 6x + 8y = -15$

5. $(3, 4); (x - 2)^2 + (y + 2)^2 = 6$

6. $(1, -1); \dfrac{x^2}{2} + \dfrac{y^2}{3} = -4$

Sketch the graph of each of these equations. (See Example 2.)

7. $4y + 3x = 12$ 8. $2x + 7y = 14$

9. $8x + 3y = 12$ 10. $9y - 4x = 12$

11. $x = 2y + 3$ 12. $x - 3y = 0$

List the x-intercepts and y-intercepts of each graph.

13.

14.

15.

16.

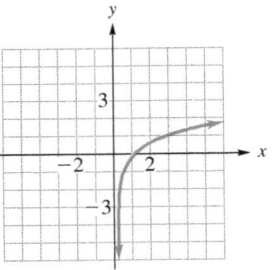

Find the x-intercepts and y-intercepts of the graph of each equation. You need not sketch the graph. (See Example 3.)

17. $3x + 4y = 12$ 18. $x - 2y = 5$

19. $2x - 3y = 24$ 20. $3x + y = 4$

21. $y = x^2 - 9$ 22. $y = x^2 + 4$

23. $y = x^2 + x - 20$ 24. $y = 5x^2 + 6x + 1$

25. $y = 2x^2 - 5x + 7$ 26. $y = 3x^2 + 4x - 4$

Sketch the graph of the equation. (See Examples 2–4.)

27. $y = x^2$ 28. $y = x^2 + 2$

29. $y = x^2 - 3$ 30. $y = 2x^2$

31. $y = x^2 - 6x + 5$ 32. $y = x^2 + 2x - 3$

33. $y = x^3$ 34. $y = x^3 - 3$

35. $y = x^3 + 1$ 36. $y = x^3/2$

37. $y = \sqrt{x + 4}$ 38. $y = \sqrt{x - 2}$

39. $y = \sqrt{4 - x^2}$ 40. $y = \sqrt{9 - x^2}$

Business   *An article in the Wall Street Journal on March 17, 2012 spoke of the increase in production of pipe tobacco as stores and consumers found that pipe tobacco is often not subject to the same taxes as cigarette tobacco. The graph below shows the production of pipe tobacco (in millions of pounds) and of roll-your-own tobacco (in millions of pounds). (Data from: Alcohol and Tobacco Tax and Trade Bureau.) (See Examples 5 and 6.)*

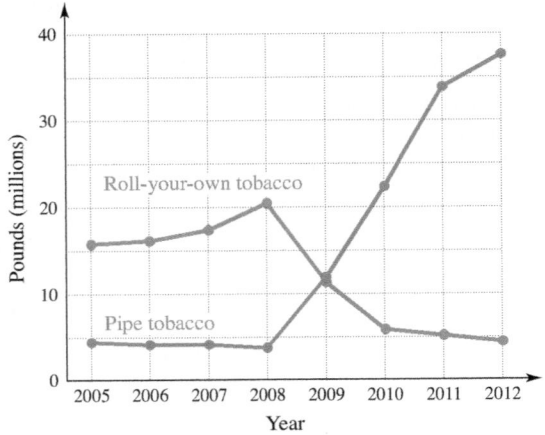

41. In what year did roll-your-own tobacco hit its peak of production? What was that peak production?

42. In what year did both roll-your-own tobacco and pipe tobacco have approximately the same level of production? How much was produced for each?

43. In what year did pipe tobacco production exceed roll-your-own tobacco by at least 25 million pounds?

44. In what years did roll-your-own tobacco production exceed pipe tobacco production by less than 10 million pounds?

Business *Use the revenue and cost graphs for the Webster Cell Phone Company in Example 6 to do Exercises 45–48.*

45. Find the approximate cost of manufacturing the given number of phones.

(a) 20,000   (b) 36,000   (c) 48,000

46. Find the approximate revenue from selling the given number of phones.

(a) 12,000   (b) 24,000   (c) 36,000

47. Find the approximate profit from manufacturing the given number of phones.

(a) 20,000   (b) 28,000   (c) 36,000

48. The company must replace its aging machinery with better, but much more expensive, machines. In addition, raw material prices increase, so that monthly costs go up by $250,000. Owing to competitive pressure, phone prices cannot be increased, so revenue remains the same. Under these new circumstances, find the approximate profit from manufacturing the given number of phones.

(a) 20,000   (b) 36,000   (c) 40,000

Business *The graph below gives the annual per-person retail availability of beef, chicken, and pork (in pounds) from 2001 to 2010. Use the graph to answer the following questions. (Data from: U.S. Department of Agriculture.)*

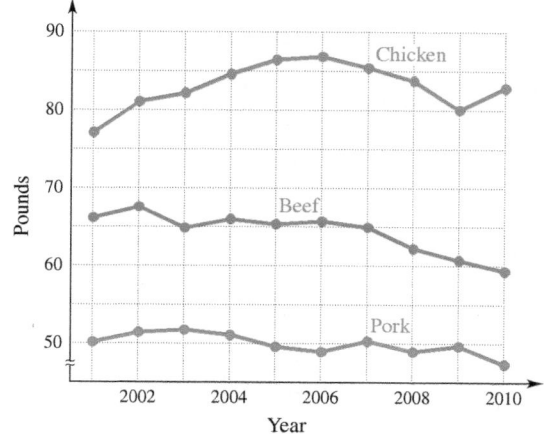

49. What is the approximate annual per-person retail availability of beef, chicken, and pork in 2010?

50. In what year was annual availability of beef the highest?

51. In what year was annual availability of chicken the lowest?

52. How much did the annual availability of beef decrease from 2001 to 2010?

Business *The graph below gives the total sales (in billions of dollars) at grocery stores within the United States from 2005 to 2015. (Years 2011–2015 are projections.) Use the graph to answer the following questions. (Data from: U.S. Census Bureau.)*

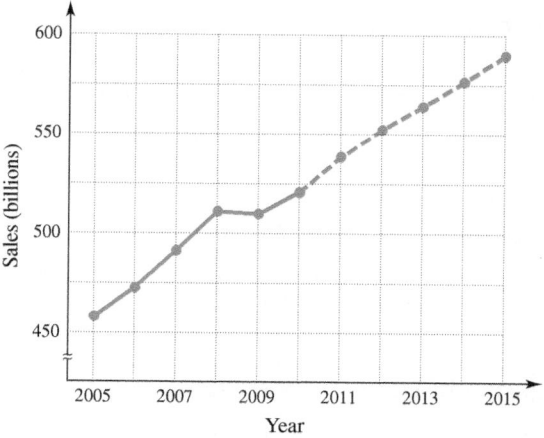

53. What were the total sales at grocery stores in 2008?

54. In what years are total sales below $525 billion (including projections)?

55. In what years are total sales above $500 billion (including projections)?

56. How much are grocery sales projected to increase from 2010 to 2015?

Business *The graph below shows the closing share prices (in dollars) for Hewlett-Packard Corporation and Intel Corporation on the 21 trading days of the month of January, 2013. Use this graph to answer the following questions.*

57. What was the approximate closing share price for Hewlett-Packard on day 21? for Intel?

58. What was the approximate closing share price for Hewlett-Packard on day 9? for Intel?

59. What was the highest closing share price for Hewlett-Packard and on what day did this occur?

60. What was the highest closing share price for Intel and on what day did this occur?

61. Was the difference in share price between the two companies ever more than $7.00?

62. Over the course of the month, what was the gain in share price for Hewlett-Packard?

☑ *Use a graphing calculator to find the graph of the equation. (See Example 7.)*

63. $y = x^2 + x + 1$ **64.** $y = 2 - x - x^2$

65. $y = (x - 3)^3$ **66.** $y = x^3 + 2x^2 + 2$

67. $y = x^3 - 3x^2 + x - 1$ **68.** $y = x^4 - 5x^2 - 2$

☑ *Use a graphing calculator for Exercises 69–70.*

69. Graph $y = x^4 - 2x^3 + 2x$ in a window with $-3 \le x \le 3$. Is the "flat" part of the graph near $x = 1$ really a horizontal line segment? (*Hint:* Use the trace feature to move along the "flat" part and watch the y-coordinates. Do they remain the same [as they should on a horizontal segment]?)

70. **(a)** Graph $y = x^4 - 2x^3 + 2x$ in the **standard window** (the one with $-10 \le x \le 10$ and $-10 \le y \le 10$). Use the trace feature to approximate the coordinates of the lowest point on the graph.

(b) Use a minimum finder to obtain an accurate approximation of the lowest point. How does this compare with your answer in part (a)?

☑ *Use a graphing calculator to approximate all real solutions of the equation. (See Example 8.)*

71. $x^3 - 3x^2 + 5 = 0$

72. $x^3 + x - 1 = 0$

73. $2x^3 - 4x^2 + x - 3 = 0$

74. $6x^3 - 5x^2 + 3x - 2 = 0$

75. $x^5 - 6x + 6 = 0$

76. $x^3 - 3x^2 + x - 1 = 0$

☑ *Use a graphing calculator to work Exercises 77–80. (See Examples 8 and 9.)*

Finance   *The financial assets of the mutual fund industry (in trillions of dollars) can be approximated by*

$$y = .0556x^3 - 1.286x^2 + 9.76x - 17.4,$$

where $x = 5$ corresponds to 2005. (Data from: Board of Governors of the Federal Reserve System.)

77. Find the maximum value of the total assets between 2005 and 2008.

78. Find the minimum value of the total assets between 2008 and 2011.

Finance   *The financial assets of households (in trillions of dollars) can be approximated by*

$$y = .328x^3 - 7.75x^2 + 59.03x - 97.1,$$

where $x = 5$ corresponds to 2005. (Data from: Board of Governors of the Federal Reserve System.)

79. Find the minimum value of the household assets between 2007 and 2011.

80. Find the maximum value of the household assets between 2005 and 2008.

✓ Checkpoint Answers

1.

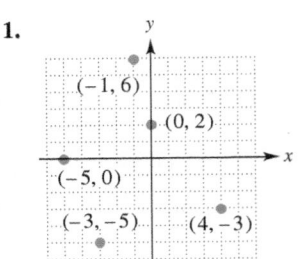

2. (a) and (c)

3.

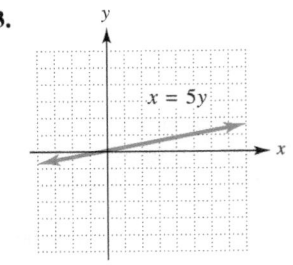

4. **(a)** x-intercept 4, y-intercept 3

   (b) x-intercept $8/5$, y-intercept -4

5. The highest was 1446 on day 12

   The lowest was 1407 on day 11

6. **(a)** About $1,200,000 (rounded)

   (b) About $-$500,000
   (that is, a loss of $500,000)

7. **(a)**

   (b)

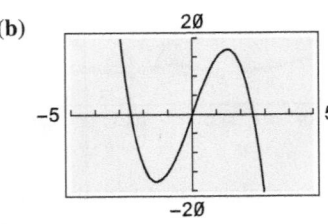

8. $x \approx -2.330059$

9. $(9.88, 153.19)$

2.2   Equations of Lines

Straight lines, which are the simplest graphs, play an important role in a wide variety of applications. They are considered here from both a geometric and an algebraic point of view.

The key geometric feature of a nonvertical straight line is how steeply it rises or falls as you move from left to right. The "steepness" of a line can be represented numerically by a number called the *slope* of the line.

To see how the slope is defined, start with Figure 2.18, which shows a line passing through the two different points $(x_1, y_1) = (-5, 6)$ and $(x_2, y_2) = (4, -7)$. The difference in the two x-values,

$$x_2 - x_1 = 4 - (-5) = 9,$$

is called the **change in x.** Similarly, the **change in y** is the difference in the two y-values:

$$y_2 - y_1 = -7 - 6 = -13.$$

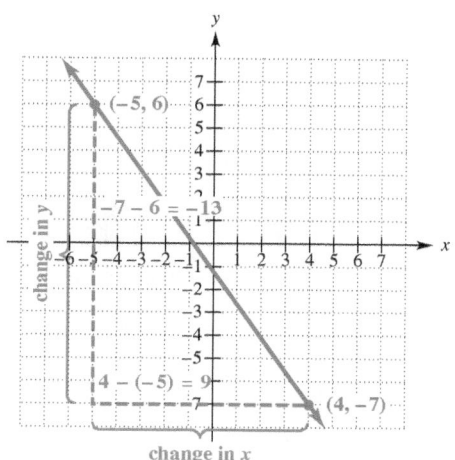

Figure 2.18

The **slope** of the line through the two points (x_1, y_1) and (x_2, y_2), where $x_1 \neq x_2$, is defined as the quotient of the change in y and the change in x:

$$\textbf{slope} = \frac{\textbf{change in } y}{\textbf{change in } x} = \frac{y_2 - y_1}{x_2 - x_1}.$$

The slope of the line in Figure 2.18 is

$$\text{slope} = \frac{-7 - 6}{4 - (-5)} = -\frac{13}{9}.$$

Using similar triangles from geometry, we can show that the slope is independent of the choice of points on the line. That is, the same value of the slope will be obtained for *any* choice of two different points on the line.

Example 1   Find the slope of the line through the points $(-6, 8)$ and $(5, 4)$.

Solution   Let $(x_1, y_1) = (-6, 8)$ and $(x_2, y_2) = (5, 4)$. Use the definition of slope as follows:

$$\text{slope} = \frac{y_2 - y_1}{x_2 - x_1} = \frac{4 - 8}{5 - (-6)} = \frac{-4}{11} = -\frac{4}{11}.$$

The slope can also by found by letting $(x_1, y_1) = (5, 4)$ and $(x_2, y_2) = (-6, 8)$. In that case,

$$\text{slope} = \frac{y_2 - y_1}{x_2 - x_1} = \frac{8 - 4}{-6 - 5} = \frac{4}{-11} = -\frac{4}{11},$$

which is the same answer.

✔ **Checkpoint 1**

Find the slope of the line through the following pairs of points.

(a) $(5, 9), (-5, -3)$

(b) $(-4, 2), (-2, -7)$

Figure 2.19

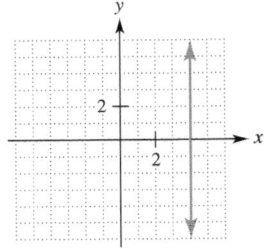

Figure 2.20

🛇 **CAUTION** When finding the slope of a line, be careful to subtract the *x*-values and the *y*-values in the same order. For example, with the points (4, 3) and (2, 9), if you use 9 − 3 for the numerator, you must use 2 − 4 (*not* 4 − 2) for the denominator.

Example 2   Find the slope of the horizontal line in Figure 2.19.

Solution   Every point on the line has the same *y*-coordinate, −5. Choose any two of them to compute the slope, say, $(x_1, y_1) = (-3, -5)$ and $(x_2, y_2) = (2, -5)$:

$$\text{slope} = \frac{-5 - (-5)}{2 - (-3)}$$

$$= \frac{0}{5}$$

$$= 0.$$

Example 3   What is the slope of the vertical line in Figure 2.20?

Solution   Every point on the line has the same *x*-coordinate, 4. If we attempt to compute the slope with two of these points, say, $(x_1, y_1) = (4, -2)$ and $(x_2, y_2) = (4, 1)$, we obtain

$$\text{slope} = \frac{1 - (-2)}{4 - 4}$$

$$= \frac{3}{0}.$$

Division by 0 is not defined, so the slope of this line is undefined.

The arguments used in Examples 2 and 3 work in the general case and lead to the following conclusion.

The slope of every horizontal line is 0.

The slope of every vertical line is undefined.

Slope–Intercept Form

The slope can be used to develop an algebraic description of nonvertical straight lines. Assume that a line with slope m has y-intercept b, so that it goes through the point $(0, b)$. (See Figure 2.21.) Let (x, y) be any point on the line other than $(0, b)$. Using the definition of slope with the points $(0, b)$ and (x, y) gives

$$m = \frac{y - b}{x - 0}$$

$$m = \frac{y - b}{x}$$

$$mx = y - b \qquad \text{Multiply both sides by } x.$$

$$y = mx + b. \qquad \text{Add } b \text{ to both sides. Reverse the equation.}$$

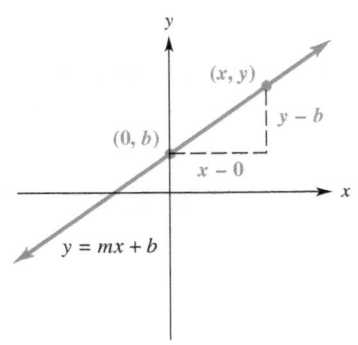

Figure 2.21

In other words, the coordinates of any point on the line satisfy the equation $y = mx + b$.

Slope–Intercept Form

If a line has slope m and y-intercept b, then it is the graph of the equation

$$y = mx + b.$$

This equation is called the **slope–intercept form** of the equation of the line.

Example 4   Find an equation for the line with y-intercept $7/2$ and slope $-5/2$.

Solution   Use the slope–intercept form with $b = 7/2$ and $m = -5/2$:

$$y = mx + b$$

$$y = -\frac{5}{2}x + \frac{7}{2}. \quad ✓2$$

✓ **Checkpoint 2**

Find an equation for the line with

(a) y-intercept -3 and slope $2/3$;

(b) y-intercept $1/4$ and slope $-3/2$.

Example 5   Find the equation of the horizontal line with y-intercept 3.

Solution   The slope of the line is 0 (why?) and its y-intercept is 3, so its equation is

$$y = mx + b$$
$$y = 0x + 3$$
$$y = 3.$$

The argument in Example 5 also works in the general case.

If k is a constant, then the graph of the equation $y = k$ is the horizontal line with y-intercept k.

Example 6   Find the slope and y-intercept for each of the following lines.

(a) $5x - 3y = 1$

Solution   Solve for y:

$$5x - 3y = 1$$
$$-3y = -5x + 1 \quad \text{Subtract } 5x \text{ from both sides.}$$
$$y = \frac{5}{3}x - \frac{1}{3}. \quad \text{Divide both sides by } -3.$$

This equation is in the form $y = mx + b$, with $m = 5/3$ and $b = -1/3$. So the slope is $5/3$ and the y-intercept is $-1/3$.

(b) $-9x + 6y = 2$

Solution   Solve for y:

$$-9x + 6y = 2$$
$$6y = 9x + 2 \quad \text{Add } 9x \text{ to both sides.}$$
$$y = \frac{3}{2}x + \frac{1}{3}. \quad \text{Divide both sides by } 6.$$

✓ **Checkpoint 3**

Find the slope and y-intercept of

(a) $x + 4y = 6$;

(b) $3x - 2y = 1$.

The slope is $3/2$ (the coefficient of x), and the y-intercept is $1/3$.   ✓3

The slope–intercept form can be used to show how the slope measures the steepness of a line. Consider the straight lines A, B, C, and D given by the following equations, where each has y-intercept 0 and slope as indicated:

$$A: y = .5x; \qquad B: y = x; \qquad C: y = 3x; \qquad D: y = 7x.$$
$$\text{Slope }.5 \qquad \text{Slope }1 \qquad \text{Slope }3 \qquad \text{Slope }7$$

For these lines, Figure 2.22 shows that the bigger the slope, the more steeply the line rises from left to right. ✓₄

✓**Checkpoint 4**

(a) List the slopes of the following lines:
$E: y = -.3x; \quad F: y = -x;$
$G: y = -2x; \quad H: y = -5x.$

(b) Graph all four lines on the same set of axes.

(c) How are the slopes of the lines related to their steepness?

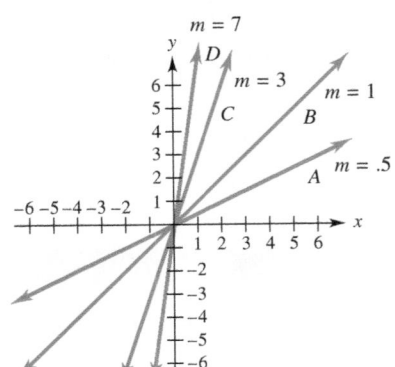

Figure 2.22

The preceding discussion and Checkpoint 4 may be summarized as follows.

Direction of Line (moving from left to right)	Slope
Upward	**Positive** (larger for steeper lines)
Horizontal	**0**
Downward	**Negative** (larger in absolute value for steeper lines)
Vertical	**Undefined**

Example 7 Sketch the graph of $x + 2y = 5$, and label the intercepts.

Solution Find the x-intercept by setting $y = 0$ and solving for x:

$$x + 2 \cdot 0 = 5$$
$$x = 5.$$

The x-intercept is 5, and $(5, 0)$ is on the graph. The y-intercept is found similarly, by setting $x = 0$ and solving for y:

$$0 + 2y = 5$$
$$y = 5/2.$$

✓**Checkpoint 5**

Graph the given lines and label the intercepts.

(a) $3x + 4y = 12$

(b) $5x - 2y = 8$

The y-intercept is $5/2$, and $(0, 5/2)$ is on the graph. The points $(5, 0)$ and $(0, 5/2)$ can be used to sketch the graph, as shown on the following page (Figure 2.23). ✓₅

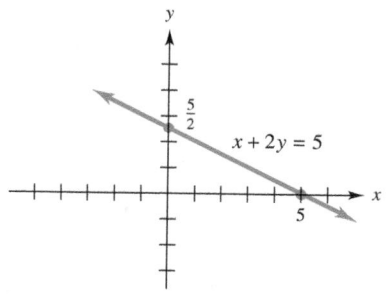

Figure 2.23

⬈ **TECHNOLOGY TIP** To graph a linear equation on a graphing calculator, you must first put the equation in slope–intercept form $y = mx + b$ so that it can be entered in the equation memory (called the $Y =$ list on some calculators). Vertical lines cannot be graphed on most calculators.

Slopes of Parallel and Perpendicular Lines

We shall assume the following facts without proof. The first one is a consequence of the fact that the slope measures steepness and that parallel lines have the same steepness.

Two nonvertical lines are **parallel** whenever they have the same slope.

Two nonvertical lines are **perpendicular** whenever the product of their slopes is -1.

Example 8   Determine whether each of the given pairs of lines are *parallel*, *perpendicular*, or *neither*.

(a) $2x + 3y = 5$ and $4x + 5 = -6y$.

Solution   Put each equation in slope–intercept form by solving for y:

$$3y = -2x + 5 \qquad\qquad -6y = 4x + 5$$
$$y = -\frac{2}{3}x + \frac{5}{3} \qquad\qquad y = -\frac{2}{3}x - \frac{5}{6}.$$

In each case, the slope (the coefficient of x) is $-2/3$, so the lines are parallel. See Figure 2.24(a).

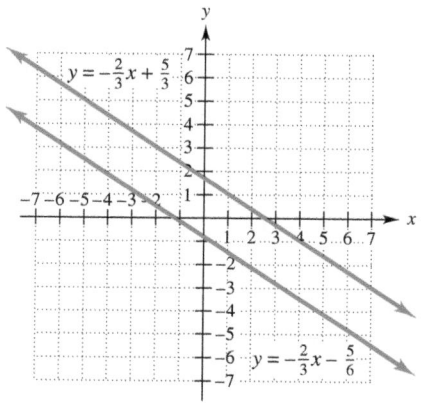

Figure 2.24(a)

(b) $3x = y + 7$ and $x + 3y = 4$.

Solution   Put each equation in slope–intercept form to determine the slope of the associated line:

$$3x = y + 7 \qquad\qquad 3y = -x + 4$$

$$y = 3x - 7 \qquad\qquad y = -\frac{1}{3}x + \frac{4}{3}$$

$$\text{slope } 3 \qquad\qquad \text{slope } -1/3.$$

Since $3(-1/3) = -1$, these lines are perpendicular. See Figure 2.24(b).

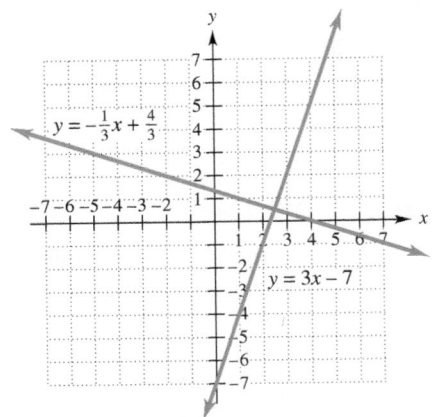

Figure 2.24(b)

(c) $x + y = 4$ and $x - 2y = 3$.

Solution   Verify that the slope of the first line is -1 and the slope of the second is $1/2$. The slopes are not equal and their product is not -1, so the lines are neither parallel nor perpendicular. See Figure 2.24(c). ✓ 6

Checkpoint 6

Tell whether the lines in each of the following pairs are *parallel*, *perpendicular*, or *neither*.

(a) $x - 2y = 6$ and $2x + y = 5$

(b) $3x + 4y = 8$ and $x + 3y = 2$

(c) $2x - y = 7$ and $2y = 4x - 5$

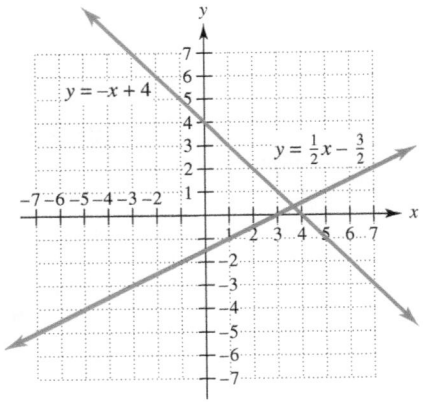

Figure 2.24(c)

✈ **TECHNOLOGY TIP** Perpendicular lines may not appear perpendicular on a graphing calculator unless you use a *square window*—a window in which a one-unit segment on the y-axis is the same length as a one-unit segment on the x-axis. To obtain such a window on most calculators, use a viewing window in which the y-axis is about two-thirds as long as the x-axis. The SQUARE (or ZSQUARE) key in the ZOOM menu will change the current window to a square window by automatically adjusting the length of one of the axes.

Point–Slope Form

The slope–intercept form of the equation of a line is usually the most convenient for graphing and for understanding how slopes and lines are related. However, it is not always the best way to *find* the equation of a line. In many situations (particularly in calculus), the slope and a point on the line are known and you must find the equation of the line. In such cases, the best method is to use the *point–slope form*, which we now explain.

Suppose that a line has slope m and that (x_1, y_1) is a point on the line. Let (x, y) represent any other point on the line. Since m is the slope, then, by the definition of slope,

$$\frac{y - y_1}{x - x_1} = m.$$

Multiplying both sides by $x - x_1$ yields

$$y - y_1 = m(x - x_1).$$

> ### Point–Slope Form
>
> If a line has slope m and passes through the point (x_1, y_1), then
>
> $$\boldsymbol{y - y_1 = m(x - x_1)}$$
>
> is the **point–slope form** of the equation of the line.

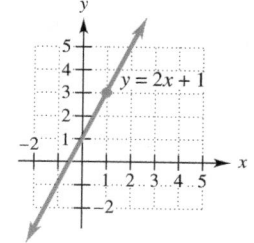

Figure 2.25

Example 9   Find the equation of the line satisfying the given conditions.

(a) Slope 2; the point $(1, 3)$ is on the line.

Solution   Use the point–slope form with $m = 2$ and $(x_1, y_1) = (1, 3)$. Substitute $x_1 = 1$, $y_1 = 3$, and $m = 2$ into the point–slope form of the equation.

$$y - y_1 = m(x - x_1)$$
$$y - 3 = 2(x - 1). \qquad \text{Point–slope form}$$

For some purposes, this form of the equation is fine; in other cases, you may want to rewrite it in the slope–intercept form.

Using algebra, we obtain the slope–intercept form of this equation:

$$y - 3 = 2(x - 1)$$
$$y - 3 = 2x - 2 \qquad \text{Distributive property}$$
$$y = 2x + 1 \qquad \text{Add 3 to each side to obtain slope-intercept form.}$$

See Figure 2.25 for the graph.

(b) Slope -3; the point $(-4, 1)$ is on the line.

Solution   Use the point–slope form with $m = -3$ and $(x_1, y_1) = (-4, 1)$:

$$y - y_1 = m(x - x_1)$$
$$y - 1 = -3[x - (-4)]. \qquad \text{Point–slope form}$$

Using algebra, we obtain the slope–intercept form of this equation:

$$y - 1 = -3(x + 4)$$
$$y - 1 = -3x - 12 \qquad \text{Distributive property}$$
$$y = -3x - 11. \qquad \text{Slope–intercept form}$$

See Figure 2.26. ✓₇

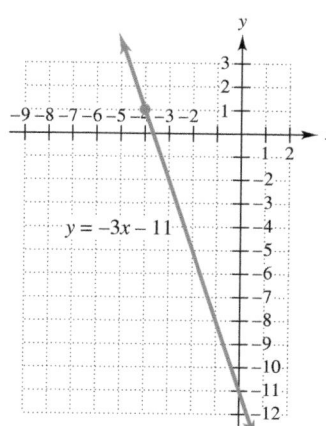

Figure 2.26

✓ Checkpoint 7

Find both the point–slope and the slope–intercept form of the equation of the line having the given slope and passing through the given point.

(a) $m = -3/5, (5, -2)$

(b) $m = 1/3, (6, 8)$

The point–slope form can also be used to find an equation of a line, given two different points on the line. The procedure is shown in the next example.

Example 10   Find an equation of the line through $(5, 4)$ and $(-10, -2)$.

Solution   Begin by using the definition of the slope to find the slope of the line that passes through the two points:

$$\text{slope} = m = \frac{-2 - 4}{-10 - 5} = \frac{-6}{-15} = \frac{2}{5}.$$

Use $m = 2/5$ and either of the given points in the point–slope form. If $(x_1, y_1) = (5, 4)$, then

$$y - y_1 = m(x - x_1)$$

$$y - 4 = \frac{2}{5}(x - 5) \qquad \text{Let } y_1 = 4, m = \frac{2}{5}, \text{ and } x_1 = 5.$$

$$y - 4 = \frac{2}{5}x - \frac{10}{5} \qquad \text{Distributive property}$$

$$y = \frac{2}{5}x + 2 \qquad \text{Add 4 to both sides and simplify.}$$

See Figure 2.27. Check that the results are the same when $(x_1, y_1) = (-10, -2)$.

Figure 2.27

Checkpoint 8

Find an equation of the line through

(a) $(2, 3)$ and $(-4, 6)$;

(b) $(-8, 2)$ and $(3, -6)$.

Vertical Lines

The equation forms we just developed do not apply to vertical lines, because the slope is not defined for such lines. However, vertical lines can easily be described as graphs of equations.

Example 11   Find the equation whose graph is the vertical line in Figure 2.28.

Solution   Every point on the line has x-coordinate -1 and hence has the form $(-1, y)$. Thus, every point is a solution of the equation $x + 0y = -1$, which is usually written simply as $x = -1$. Note that -1 is the x-intercept of the line.

The argument in Example 11 also works in the general case.

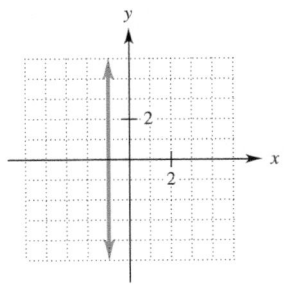

Figure 2.28

If k is a constant, then the graph of the equation $x = k$ is the vertical line with x-intercept k.

Linear Equations

An equation in two variables whose graph is a straight line is called a **linear equation.** Linear equations have a variety of forms, as summarized in the following table.

Equation	Description
$x = k$	**Vertical line,** x-intercept k, no y-intercept, undefined slope
$y = k$	**Horizontal line,** y-intercept k, no x-intercept, slope 0
$y = mx + b$	**Slope–intercept form,** slope m, y-intercept b
$y - y_1 = m(x - x_1)$	**Point–slope form,** slope m, the line passes through (x_1, y_1)
$ax + by = c$	**General form.** If $a \neq 0$ and $b \neq 0$, the line has x-intercept c/a, y-intercept c/b, and slope $-a/b$.

Note that every linear equation can be written in general form. For example, $y = 4x - 5$ can be written in general form as $4x - y = 5$, and $x = 6$ can be written in general form as $x + 0y = 6$.

Applications

Many relationships are linear or almost linear, so that they can be approximated by linear equations.

Example 12 **Business** The world-wide sales (in billions of dollars) of men's razor blades can be approximated by the linear equation

$$y = .76x + 4.44,$$

where $x = 6$ corresponds to the year 2006. The graph appears in Figure 2.29. (Data from: *Wall Street Journal,* April 12, 2012.)

(a) What were the approximate razor sales in 2011?

Solution Substitute $x = 11$ in the equation and use a calculator to compute y:

$$y = .76x + 4.44$$
$$y = .76(11) + 4.44 = 12.80.$$

The approximate sales in 2011 were $12.8 billion.

(b) In what year did sales reach $10.5 billion?

Solution Substitute $y = 10.5$ into the equation and solve for x:

$$10.5 = .76x + 4.44$$
$$10.5 - 4.44 = .76x \qquad \text{Subtract 4.44 from each side.}$$
$$x = \frac{10.5 - 4.44}{.76} \qquad \text{Divide each side by .76 and reverse the equation.}$$
$$x = 8.0.$$

The year was 2008.

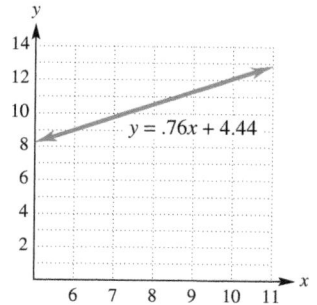

Figure 2.29

Example 13   **Education** According to the National Center for Education Statistics, the average cost of tuition and fees at public four-year universities was $3768 in the year 2000 and grew in an approximately linear fashion to $8751 in the year 2011.

(a) Find a linear equation for these data.

Solution Measure time along the x-axis and cost along the y-axis. Then the x-coordinate of each point is a year and the y-coordinate is the average cost of tuition and fees in that year. For convenience, let $x = 0$ correspond to 2000, and so $x = 11$ is 2011. Then the given data points are (0, 3768) and (11, 8751). The slope of the line joining these two points is

$$\frac{8751 - 3768}{11 - 0} = \frac{4983}{11} = 453.$$

Since we already know the y-intercept $b = 3768$ and the slope $m = 453$, we can write the equation as

$$y = mx + b = 453x + 3768.$$

We could also use the point-slope form with the point (11, 8751), to obtain the equation of the line:

$$y - 8751 = 453(x - 11) \qquad \text{Point–slope form}$$
$$y - 8751 = 453x - 4983 \qquad \text{Distributive property}$$
$$y = 453x + 3768. \qquad \text{Add 8751 to both sides.}$$

Figure 2.30 shows the derived equation.

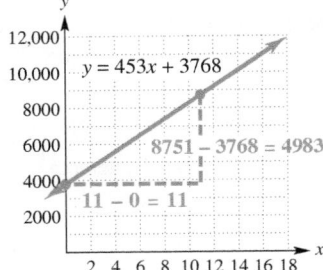

Figure 2.30

✓ Checkpoint 9

The average cost of tuition and fees at private four-year universities was $19,307 in 2000 and $34,805 in 2011.

(a) Let $x = 0$ correspond to 2000, and find a linear equation for the given data. (*Hint: Round the slope to the nearest integer.*)

(b) Assuming that your equation remains accurate, estimate the average cost in 2017.

(b) Use this equation to estimate the average cost of tuition and fees in the fall of 2009.

Solution Since 2009 corresponds to $x = 9$, let $x = 9$ in the equation part of (a). Then

$$y = 453(9) + 3768 = \$7845.$$

(c) Assuming the equation remains valid beyond the fall of 2011, estimate the average cost of tuition and fees in the fall of 2018.

Solution The year 2018 corresponds to $x = 18$, so the average cost is

$$y = 453(18) + 3768 = \$11{,}922. \; \blacksquare_9$$

2.2 Exercises

Find the slope of the given line, if it is defined. (See Examples 1–3.)

1. The line through (2, 5) and (0, 8)

2. The line through (9, 0) and (12, 12)

3. The line through (−4, 14) and (3, 0)

4. The line through (−5, −2) and (−4, 11)

5. The line through the origin and (−4, 10)

6. The line through the origin and (8, −2)

7. The line through (−1, 4) and (−1, 6)

8. The line through (−3, 5) and (2, 5)

Find an equation of the line with the given y-intercept and slope m. (See Examples 4 and 5.)

9. $5, m = 4$

10. $-3, m = -7$

11. $1.5, m = -2.3$

12. $-4.5, m = 2.5$

13. $4, m = -3/4$

14. $-3, m = 4/3$

Find the slope m and the y-intercept b of the line whose equation is given. (See Example 6.)

15. $2x - y = 9$

16. $x + 2y = 7$

17. $6x = 2y + 4$

18. $4x + 3y = 24$

19. $6x - 9y = 16$

20. $4x + 2y = 0$

21. $2x - 3y = 0$

22. $y = 7$

23. $x = y - 5$

24. On one graph, sketch six straight lines that meet at a single point and satisfy this condition: one line has slope 0, two lines have positive slope, two lines have negative slope, and one line has undefined slope.

25. For which of the line segments in the figure is the slope

(a) largest?

(b) smallest?

(c) largest in absolute value?

(d) closest to 0?

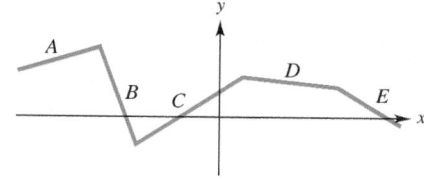

26. Match each equation with the line that most closely resembles its graph. (*Hint:* Consider the signs of m and b in the slope–intercept form.)

(a) $y = 3x + 2$

(b) $y = -3x + 2$

(c) $y = 3x - 2$

(d) $y = -3x - 2$

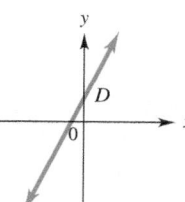

Sketch the graph of the given equation and label its intercepts. (See Example 7.)

27. $2x - y = -2$

28. $2y + x = 4$

29. $2x + 3y = 4$

30. $-5x + 4y = 3$

31. $4x - 5y = 2$

32. $3x + 2y = 8$

Determine whether each pair of lines is parallel, perpendicular, or neither. (See Example 8.)

33. $4x - 3y = 6$ and $3x + 4y = 8$

34. $2x - 5y = 7$ and $15y - 5 = 6x$

35. $3x + 2y = 8$ and $6y = 5 - 9x$

36. $x - 3y = 4$ and $y = 1 - 3x$

37. $4x = 2y + 3$ and $2y = 2x + 3$

38. $2x - y = 6$ and $x - 2y = 4$

39. **(a)** Find the slope of each side of the triangle with vertices $(9, 6), (-1, 2)$, and $(1, -3)$.

(b) Is this triangle a right triangle? (*Hint:* Are two sides perpendicular?)

40. **(a)** Find the slope of each side of the quadrilateral with vertices $(-5, -2), (-3, 1), (3, 0)$, and $(1, -3)$.

(b) Is this quadrilateral a parallelogram? (*Hint:* Are opposite sides parallel?)

Find an equation of the line with slope m that passes through the given point. Put the answer in slope–intercept form. (See Example 10.)

41. $(-3, 2), m = -2/3$

42. $(-5, -2), m = 4/5$

43. $(2, 3), m = 3$

44. $(3, -4), m = -1/4$

45. $(10, 1), m = 0$

46. $(-3, -9), m = 0$

47. $(-2, 12)$, undefined slope

48. $(1, 1)$, undefined slope

Find an equation of the line that passes through the given points. (See Example 10.)

49. $(-1, 1)$ and $(2, 7)$

50. $(2, 5)$ and $(0, 6)$

51. $(1, 2)$ and $(3, 9)$

52. $(-1, -2)$ and $(2, -1)$

Find an equation of the line satisfying the given conditions.

53. Through the origin with slope 5

54. Through the origin and horizontal

55. Through $(6, 8)$ and vertical

56. Through $(7, 9)$ and parallel to $y = 6$

57. Through $(3, 4)$ and parallel to $4x - 2y = 5$

58. Through $(6, 8)$ and perpendicular to $y = 2x - 3$

59. x-intercept 6; y-intercept -6

60. Through $(-5, 2)$ and parallel to the line through $(1, 2)$ and $(4, 3)$

61. Through $(-1, 3)$ and perpendicular to the line through $(0, 1)$ and $(2, 3)$

62. y-intercept 3 and perpendicular to $2x - y + 6 = 0$

Business   *The lost value of equipment over a period of time is called depreciation. The simplest method for calculating depreciation is straight-line depreciation. The annual straight-line depreciation D of an item that cost x dollars with a useful life of n years is $D = (1/n)x$. Find the depreciation for items with the given characteristics.*

63. Cost: $15,965; life 12 yr

64. Cost: $41,762; life 15 yr

65. Cost: $201,457; life 30 yr

66. Business   Ral Corp. has an incentive compensation plan under which a branch manager receives 10% of the branch's income after deduction of the bonus, but before deduction of income tax. The income of a particular branch before the bonus and income tax was $165,000. The tax rate was 30%. The bonus amounted to

(a) $12,600   (b) $15,000

(c) $16,500   (d) $18,000

67. Business   According to data from the U.S. Centers for Medicare and Medicaid Services, the sales (in billions of dollars) from drug prescriptions can be approximated by

$$y = 13.69x + 133.6,$$

where $x = 1$ corresponds to the year 2001. Find the approximate sales from prescription drugs in the following years.

(a) 2005

(b) 2010

(c) Assuming this model remains accurate, in what year will the prescriptions be $340 billion?

68. Business   The total revenue generated from hospital care (in billions of dollars) can be approximated by

$$y = 40.89x + 405.3,$$

where $x = 1$ corresponds to the year 2001. (Data from: U.S. Centers for Medicare and Medicaid Services.)

(a) What was the approximate revenue generated from hospital stays in 2010?

(b) Assuming the model remains accurate, in what year will revenue be approximately $1 trillion?

69. Business   The number of employees (in thousands) working in the motion picture and sound recording industries can be approximated by

$$y = -1.8x + 384.6,$$

where $x = 0$ corresponds to the year 2000. (Data from: U.S. Bureau of Labor Statistics.)

(a) What was the number of employees in the year 2000?

(b) What was the number of employees in the year 2010?

(c) Assuming the model remains accurate, in what year will the number of employees be 350,000?

70. Business   The number of golf facilities in the United States has been declining and can be approximated with the equation

$$y = -42.1x + 16,288,$$

where $x = 5$ corresponds to the year 2005. (Data from: National Golf Association.)

(a) How many golf facilities were there in 2010?

(b) If the trend continues to hold, in what year will there be 15,500 golf facilities?

71. Business   In the United States, total sales related to lawn care were approximately $35.1 billion in 2005 and $29.7 billion in 2011. (Data from: The National Gardening Association.)

(a) Let the x-axis denote time and the y-axis denote the sales related to lawn care (in billions of dollars). Let $x = 5$ correspond to 2005. Fill in the blanks. The given data is represented by the points (_____, $35.1) and (11, _____).

(b) Find the linear equation determined by the two points in part (a).

(c) Use the equation in part (b) to estimate the sales produced in 2009.

(d) If the model remains accurate, when will lawn care sales reach $25 billion?

72. Business   According the Bureau of Labor Statistics, there were approximately 16.3 million union workers in the year 2000 and 14.9 million union workers in the year 2010.

(a) Consider the change in union workers to be linear and write an equation expressing the number y of union workers in terms of the number x of years since 2000.

(b) Assuming that the equation in part (a) remains accurate, use it to predict the number of union workers in 2015.

73. Business   The demand for chicken legs in the chicken industry has increased. According to the U.S. Department of Agriculture, in the year 2002, the average price per pound of chicken legs was $.40 a pound, while in 2012, the price had risen to $.75 a pound.

(a) Write an equation assuming a linear trend expressing the price per pound of leg meat y in terms of the number x of years since 2002.

(b) Assuming the future accuracy of the equation you found in part (a), predict the price per pound of chicken legs in 2014.

74. Business   Similar to Exercise 73, the price per pound of chicken thighs was $.60 a pound in the year 2002 and $1.25 in 2012.

(a) If the price of thigh meat is linear, express the price per pound of thigh meat y in terms of the number x of years since the year 2002.

(b) Use your expression from (a) to find the price of thigh meat in the year 2010.

75. Social Science   According to data from the U.S. Drug Enforcement Administration, there were 36,845 federal drug arrests in the year 2000 and 27,200 in the year 2010.

(a) Write a linear equation expressing the number of federal drug arrests y in terms of the number x of years since 2000.

(b) Using the equation you found in (a), find the number of federal drug arrests in 2006.

76. Social Science   According to data from the U.S. Drug Enforcement Administration, the total seizure of drugs (in millions of pounds) was 1.5 in the year 2000 and 4.5 in the year 2010.

(a) Write a linear equation expressing the weight in pounds from the seizure of drugs y in terms of the number x of years since 2000.

(b) How much was seized in 2007?

(c) If the trend continues, in what year will the total of seized drugs be 5.7 million pounds?

77. Physical Science   The accompanying graph shows the winning time (in minutes) at the Olympic Games from 1952 to 2008 for the men's 5000-meter run, together with a linear approximation of the data. (Data from: *The World Almanac and Book of Facts*: 2009.)

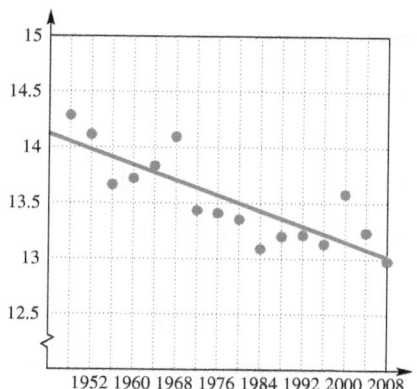

1952 1960 1968 1976 1984 1992 2000 2008

(a) The equation for the linear approximation is

$$y = -.01723x + 47.61.$$

What does the slope of this line represent? Why is the slope negative?

(b) Use the approximation to estimate the winning time in the 2012 Olympics. If possible, check this estimate against the actual time.

78. Business The accompanying graph shows the number of civilians in the U.S. labor force (in millions) in selected years (with the year 2020 projected). (Data from: U.S. Bureau of Labor Statistics.)

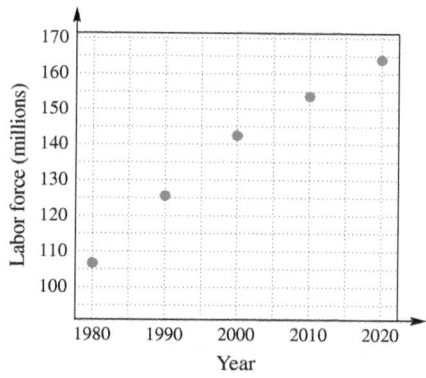

(a) Use the data points (1980, 106.9) and (2010, 153.9) to estimate the slope of the line shown. Interpret this number.

(b) Use part (a) and the point (2010, 153.9) to approximate the civilian labor force in 2015.

✓Checkpoint Answers

1. (a) 6/5   **(b)** −9/2

2. (a) $y = \dfrac{2}{3}x - 3$ **(b)** $y = -\dfrac{3}{2}x + \dfrac{1}{4}$

3. (a) Slope −1/4; y-intercept 3/2
   (b) Slope 3/2; y-intercept −1/2

4. (a) Slope of $E = -.3$; slope of $F = -1$; slope of $G = -2$; slope of $H = -5$.

   (b)
   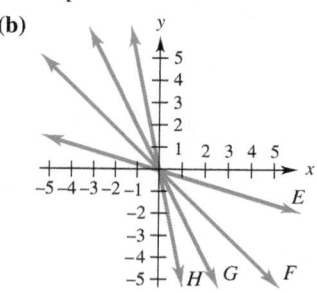

   (c) The larger the slope in absolute value, the more steeply the line falls from left to right.

5. (a)

(b)
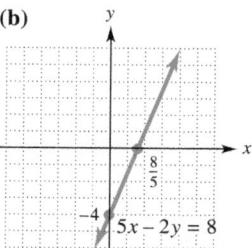

6. (a) Perpendicular   **(b)** Neither   **(c)** Parallel

7. (a) $y + 2 = -\dfrac{3}{5}(x - 5)$; $y = -\dfrac{3}{5}x + 1$.

   (b) $y - 8 = \dfrac{1}{3}(x - 6)$; $y = \dfrac{1}{3}x + 6$.

8. (a) $2y = -x + 8$ **(b)** $11y = -8x - 42$

9. (a) $y = 1409x + 19{,}307$ **(b)** $43{,}260

2.3 Linear Models

In business and science, it is often necessary to make judgments on the basis of data from the past. For instance, a stock analyst might use a company's profits in previous years to estimate the next year's profits. Or a life insurance company might look at life expectancies of people born in various years to predict how much money it should expect to pay out in the next year.

In such situations, the available data is used to construct a mathematical model, such as an equation or a graph, which is used to approximate the likely outcome in cases where complete data is not available. In this section, we consider applications in which the data can be modeled by a linear equation.

Figure 2.31

Figure 2.32

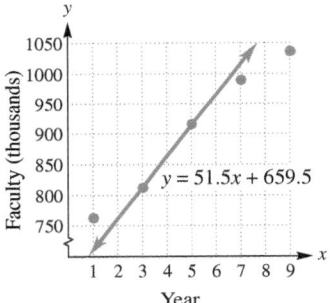

Figure 2.33

✓**Checkpoint 1**

Use the points (5, 917) and
(9, 1038) to find another model for
the data in Example 1.

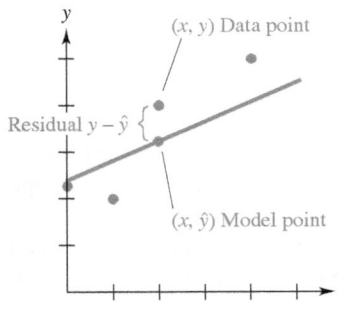

Figure 2.34

The simplest way to construct a linear model is to use the line determined by two of the data points, as illustrated in the following example.

Example 1   **Social Science**   The number of full-time faculty at four-year colleges and universities (in thousands) in selected years is shown in the following table. (Data from: U.S. National Center for Education Statistics.)

Year	2001	2003	2005	2007	2009
Number of Faculty	764	814	917	991	1038

(a) Let $x = 1$ correspond to 2001, and plot the points (x, y), where x is the year and y is the number of full-time faculty at four-year colleges and universities.

Solution The data points are $(1, 764)$, $(3, 814)$, $(5, 917)$, $(7, 991)$, and $(9, 1038)$, as shown in Figure 2.31.

(b) Use the data points $(5, 917)$ and $(9, 991)$ to find a line that models the data.

Solution The slope of the line through $(5, 917)$ and $(7, 991)$ is $\dfrac{991 - 917}{7 - 5} = \dfrac{74}{2} = 37$.

Using the point $(5, 917)$ and the slope 37, we find that the equation of this line is

$$y - 917 = 37(x - 5) \qquad \text{Point–slope form for the equation of a line}$$
$$y - 917 = 37x - 185 \qquad \text{Distributive property}$$
$$y = 37x + 732 \qquad \text{Slope–intercept form}$$

The line and the data points are shown in Figure 2.32. Although the line fits the two points we used to calculate the slope perfectly, it overestimates the remaining three data points.

(c) Use the points $(3, 814)$ and $(5, 917)$ to find another line that models the data.

The slope of the line is $\dfrac{917 - 814}{5 - 3} = \dfrac{103}{2} = 51.5$. Using the point $(3, 814)$ and the slope 51.5, we find that the equation of this line is

$$y - 814 = 51.5(x - 3) \qquad \text{Point–slope form for the equation of a line}$$
$$y - 814 = 51.5x - 154.5 \qquad \text{Distributive property}$$
$$y = 51.5x + 659.5 \qquad \text{Slope–intercept form}$$

The line and the data points are shown in Figure 2.33. This line passes through two data points, but significantly underestimates the number of faculty in 2001 and over-estimates the number of faculty in 2009. ✓₁

Opinions may vary as to which of the lines in Example 1 best fits the data. To make a decision, we might try to measure the amount of error in each model. One way to do this is to compute the difference between the number of faculty y and the amount $\hat{y}$ given by the model. If the data point is (x, y) and the corresponding point on the line is $(x, \hat{y})$, then the difference $y - \hat{y}$ measures the error in the model for that particular value of x. The number $y - \hat{y}$ is called a **residual**. As shown in Figure 2.34, the residual $y - \hat{y}$ is the vertical distance from the data point to the line (positive when the data point is above the line, negative when it is below the line, and 0 when it is on the line).

One way to determine how well a line fits the data points is to compute the sum of its residuals—that is, the sum of the individual errors. Unfortunately, however, the sum of the residuals of two different lines might be equal, thwarting our effort to decide which is the better fit. Furthermore, the residuals may sum to 0, which doesn't mean that there is no error, but only that the positive and negative errors (which might be quite large) cancel each other out. (See Exercise 11 at the end of this section for an example.)

To avoid this difficulty, mathematicians use the sum of the *squares* of the residuals to measure how well a line fits the data points. When the sum of the squares is used, a smaller sum means a smaller overall error and hence a better fit. The error is 0 only when all the data points lie on the line (a perfect fit).

Example 2   **Social Science**   Two linear models for the number of full-time faculty at four-year colleges and universities were constructed in Example 1:

$$y = 37x + 732 \quad \text{and} \quad y = 51.5x + 659.5.$$

For each model, determine the five residuals, square of each residual, and the sum of the squares of the residuals.

Solution The information for each model is summarized in the following tables:

$$y = 37x + 732$$

Data Point (x, y)	Model Point $(x, \hat{y})$	Residual $y - \hat{y}$	Squared Residual $(y - \hat{y})^2$
(1, 764)	(1, 769)	−5	25
(3, 814)	(3,843)	−29	841
(5, 917)	(5, 917)	0	0
(7, 991)	(7, 991)	0	0
(9, 1038)	(9, 1065)	−27	729
			Sum = 1595

$$y = 51.5x + 659.5$$

Data Point (x, y)	Model Point $(x, \hat{y})$	Residual $y - \hat{y}$	Squared Residual $(y - \hat{y})^2$
(1, 764)	(1, 711)	53	2809
(3, 814)	(3, 814)	0	0
(5, 917)	(5, 917)	0	0
(7, 991)	(7, 1020)	−29	841
(9, 1038)	(9, 1123)	−85	7225
			Sum = 10,875

✓**Checkpoint 2**

Another model for the data in Examples 1 and 2 is $y = 34.25x + 729.75$. Use this line to find

(a) the residuals and

(b) the sum of the squares of the residuals.

(c) Does this line fit the data better than the two lines in Example 2?

According to this measure of the error, the line $y = 37x + 732$ is a better fit for the data because the sum of the squares of its residuals is smaller than the sum of the squares of the residuals for $y = 51.5x + 659.5$. ✓2

⬈ **Linear Regression (Optional)***

Mathematical techniques from multivariable calculus can be used to prove the following result.

> For any set of data points, there is one, and only one, line for which the sum of the squares of the residuals is as small as possible.

---
*Examples 3–6 require either a graphing calculator or a spreadsheet program.

This *line of best fit* is called the **least-squares regression line,** and the computational process for finding its equation is called **linear regression.** Linear-regression formulas are quite complicated and require a large amount of computation. Fortunately, most graphing calculators and spreadsheet programs can do linear regression quickly and easily.

 NOTE The process outlined here works for most TI graphing calculators. Other graphing calculators and spreadsheet programs operate similarly, but check your instruction manual or see the Graphing Calculator Appendix.

 Example 3 **Social Science** Recall the number of full-time faculty at four-year colleges and universities (in thousands) in selected years was as follows.

Year	2001	2003	2005	2007	2009
Number of Faculty	764	814	917	991	1038

Use a graphing calculator to do the following:

(a) Plot the data points with $x = 1$ corresponding to 2001.

Solution The data points are (1, 764), (3, 814), (5, 917), (7, 991), and (9, 1038). Press STAT EDIT to bring up the statistics editor. Enter the x-coordinates as list L_1 and the corresponding y-coordinates as L_2, as shown in Figure 2.35. To plot the data points, go to the STAT PLOT menu, choose a plot (here it is Plot 1), choose ON, and enter the lists L_1 and L_2 as shown in Figure 2.36. Then set the viewing window as usual and press GRAPH to produce the plot in Figure 2.37.

Figure 2.35

Figure 2.36

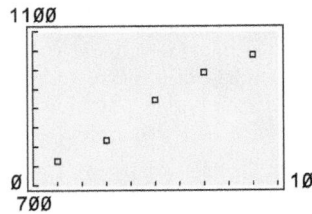

Figure 2.37

(b) Find the least squares regression line for these data.

Solution Go to the STAT CALC menu and choose LINREG, which returns you to the home screen. As shown in Figure 2.38, enter the list names and the place where the equation of the regression line should be stored (here, Y_1 is chosen; it is on the VARS Y-VARS FUNCTION menu); then press ENTER. Figure 2.39 shows that the equation of the regression line is

$$y = 36.25x + 723.55.$$

✓ Checkpoint 3

Use the least-squares regression line $y = 36.25x + 723.55$ and the data points of Example 3 to find

(a) the residuals and

(b) the sum of the squares of the residuals.

(c) How does this line compare with those in Example 1 and Checkpoint 2?

Figure 2.38

Figure 2.39

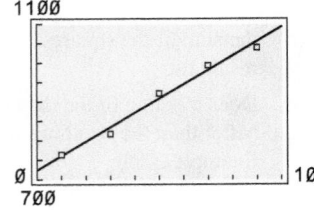

Figure 2.40

(c) Graph the data points and the regression line on the same screen.

Solution Press GRAPH to see the line plotted with the data points (Figure 2.40).

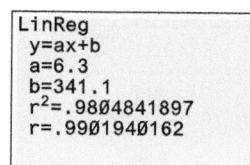

```
LinReg
 y=ax+b
 a=6.3
 b=341.1
 r²=.9804841897
 r=.9901940162
```

Figure 2.41

Figure 2.42

✓**Checkpoint 4**

Using only the data from 2005 and later in Example 4, find the equation of the least-squares regression line. Round the coefficients to two decimal places.

📈 **Example 4**   **Social Science**   The following table gives the number (in thousands) of full-time faculty at two-year colleges. (Data from: U.S. National Center for Education Statistics.)

Year	2001	2003	2005	2007	2009
Number of Faculty	349	359	373	381	401

(a) Let $x = 1$ correspond to the year 2001. Use a graphing calculator or spreadsheet program to find the least-squares regression line that models the data in the table.

Solution   The data points are $(1, 349)$, $(3, 359)$, $(5, 373)$, $(7, 381)$, and $(9, 401)$. Enter the x-coordinates as list L_1 and the corresponding y-coordinates as list L_2 in a graphing calculator and then find the regression line as in Figure 2.41.

(b) Plot the data points and the regression line on the same screen.

Solution   See Figure 2.42, which shows that the line is a reasonable model for the data.

(c) Assuming the trend continues, estimate the number of faculty in the year 2015.

Solution   The year 2015 corresponds to $x = 15$. Substitute $x = 15$ into the regression-line equation:

$$y = 6.3(15) + 341.1 = 435.6.$$

This model estimates that the number of full-time faculty at two-year colleges will be approximately 435,600 in the year 2015. ✓₄

📈 **Correlation**

Although the "best fit" line can always be found by linear regression, it may not be a good model. For instance, if the data points are widely scattered, no straight line will model the data accurately. We calculate a value called the **correlation coefficient** to assess the fit of the regression line to the scatterplot. It measures how closely the data points fit the regression line and thus indicates how good the regression line is for predictive purposes.

The correlation coefficient r is always between -1 and 1. When $r = \pm 1$, the data points all lie on the regression line (a perfect fit). When the absolute value of r is close to 1, the line fits the data quite well, and when r is close to 0, the line is a poor fit for the data (but some other curve might be a good fit). Figure 2.43 shows how the value of r varies, depending on the pattern of the data points.

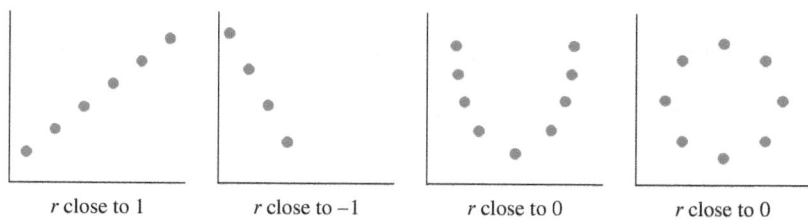

r close to 1 r close to -1 r close to 0 r close to 0

Figure 2.43

📈 **Example 5**   **Business**   The number of unemployed people in the U.S. labor force (in millions) in recent years is shown in the table. (Data from: U.S. Department of Labor, Bureau of Labor Statistics.)

Figure 2.44

```
LinReg
  y=ax+b
  a=.3654158927
  b=3.915079119
  r²=.4781968171
  r=.6915177634
```

Figure 2.45

✓**Checkpoint 5**

Using only the data from 2002 and later in Example 5, find

(a) the equation of the least-squares regression line and

(b) the correlation coefficient.

(c) How well does this line fit the data?

Year	Unemployed	Year	Unemployed	Year	Unemployed
1994	7.996	2000	5.692	2006	7.001
1995	7.404	2001	6.801	2007	7.078
1996	7.236	2002	8.378	2008	8.924
1997	6.739	2003	8.774	2009	14.265
1998	6.210	2004	8.149	2010	14.825
1999	5.880	2005	7.591	2011	13.747

Determine whether a linear equation is a good model for these data or not.

Solution   Let $x = 4$ correspond to 1994, and plot the data points (4, 7.996), etc., either by hand or with a graphing calculator, as in Figure 2.44. They do not form a linear pattern (because unemployment tends to rise and fall). Alternatively, you could compute the regression equation for the data, as in Figure 2.45. Figure 2.45 shows that the correlation coefficient is $r \approx .69$, which is a relatively high value. However, we can see that, even though the correlation is somewhat high, a straight line is not a good fit because of the peaks and valleys in Figure 2.44. ✓5

Example 6   **Education**   Enrollment projections (in millions) for all U.S. colleges and universities in selected years are shown in the following table: (Data from: U.S. Center for Educational Statistics.)

Year	2005	2007	2008	2009	2010
Enrollment	17.5	18.2	19.1	20.4	21.0

(a) Let $x = 5$ correspond to the year 2005. Use a graphing calculator or spreadsheet program to find a linear model for the data and determine how well it fits the data points.

Solution   The least-squares regression line (with coefficients rounded) is

$$y = .74x + 13.5,$$

as shown in Figure 2.46. The correlation coefficient is $r \approx .97$, which is very close to 1, and Figure 2.47 shows a linear trend. Thus, the line fits the data well.

(b) Assuming the trend continues, predict the enrollment in 2015.

Solution   Let $x = 15$ (corresponding to 2015) in the regression equation:

$$y = .74(15) + 13.5 = 24.6.$$

Therefore, the enrollment in 2015 will be approximately 24.6 million students.

```
LinReg
  y=ax+b
  a=.7391891892
  b=13.47432432
  r²=.9433889092
  r=.9712820956
```

Figure 2.46

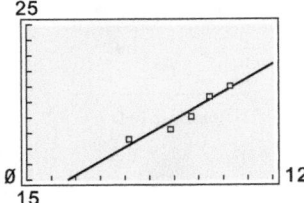

Figure 2.47

(c) According to this model, in what year will enrollment reach 30 million?

Solution   Let $y = 30$ and solve the regression equation for x:

$$y = .74x + 13.5$$
$$30 = .74x + 13.5 \qquad \text{Let } y = 30.$$
$$16.5 = .74x \qquad \text{Subtract 13.5 from both sides.}$$
$$x \approx 22.3. \qquad \text{Divide both sides by 0.74.}$$

Since these enrollment figures change once a year, use the nearest integer value for x, namely, 22. So enrollment will reach 30 million in 2022.

2.3 Exercises

1. **Physical Science**   The following table shows equivalent Fahrenheit and Celsius temperatures:

Degrees Fahrenheit	32	68	104	140	176	212
Degrees Celsius	0	20	40	60	80	100

   (a)   Choose any two data points and use them to construct a linear equation that models the data, with x being Fahrenheit and y being Celsius.

   (b)   Use the model in part (a) to find the Celsius temperature corresponding to

$$50° \text{ Fahrenheit and } 75° \text{ Fahrenheit.}$$

Physical Science   *Use the linear equation derived in Exercise 1 to work the following problems.*

2. Convert each temperature.

   (a)   58°F to Celsius   (b)   50°C to Fahrenheit

   (c)   −10°C to Fahrenheit   (d)   −20°F to Celsius

3. According to the *World Almanac and Book of Facts*, 2008, Venus is the hottest planet, with a surface temperature of 867° Fahrenheit. What is this temperature in degrees Celsius?

4. Find the temperature at which Celsius and Fahrenheit temperatures are numerically equal.

In each of the next set of problems, assume that the data can be modeled by a straight line and that the trend continues indefinitely. Use two data points to find such a line and then answer the question. (See Example 1.)

5. **Business**   The Consumer Price Index (CPI), which measures the cost of a typical package of consumer goods, was 201.6 in the year 2006 and 224.9 in the year 2011. Let $x = 6$ correspond to 2006, and estimate the CPI in 2008 and 2015. (Data from: U.S. Bureau of Labor Statistics.)

6. **Finance**   The approximate number (in millions) of individual tax returns filed with the Internal Revenue Service in the year 2001 was 127.1 and in the year 2011 it was 140.8. Let $x = 1$ correspond to 2001, and estimate the number of returns filed in 2005 and 2012. (Data from: U.S. Internal Revenue Service.)

7. **Business**   The number (in millions) of employees working in the finance and insurance industries was 6.0 in the year 2000 and 6.5 in the year 2008. Let $x = 0$ correspond to 2000, and estimate the number of employees in 2010. (Data from: U.S. Census Bureau.)

8. **Business**   The number (in millions) of employees working in the health care and social assistance industries was 14.1 in the year 2000 and 17.2 in the year 2008. Let $x = 0$ correspond to 2000, and estimate the number of employees in 2014. (Data from: U.S. Census Bureau.)

9. **Physical Science**   Suppose a baseball is thrown at 85 miles per hour. The ball will travel 320 feet when hit by a bat swung at 50 miles per hour and will travel 440 feet when hit by a bat swung at 80 miles per hour. Let y be the number of feet traveled by the ball when hit by a bat swung at x miles per hour. (*Note*: The preceding data are valid for $50 \leq x \leq 90$, where the bat is 35 inches long, weighs 32 ounces, and strikes a waist-high pitch so that the place of the swing lies at 10° from the diagonal). [Data from: Robert K. Adair, *The Physics of Baseball* (HarperCollins, 1990)]. How much farther will a ball travel for each mile-per-hour increase in the speed of the bat?

10. **Physical Science**   Ski resorts require large amounts of water in order to make snow. Snowmass Ski Area in Colorado plans to pump at least 1120 gallons of water per minute for at least 12 hours a day from Snowmass Creek between mid-October and late December. Environmentalists are concerned about the effects on the ecosystem. Find the minimum amount of water pumped in 30 days. [*Hint*: Let y be the total number of gallons pumped x days after pumping begins. Note that (0, 0) is on the graph of the equation.] (Data from: York Snow, Inc.)

In each of the next two problems, two linear models are given for the data. For each model,

(a) *find the residuals and their sum;*

(b) *find the sum of the squares of the residuals;*

(c) *decide which model is the better fit. (See Example 2.)*

11. **Finance**   The following table shows the number of operating federal credit unions in the United States for several years.

Year	2007	2008	2009	2010	2011
Number of federal credit unions	5036	4847	4714	4589	4447

   Let $x = 7$ correspond to the year 2007. Two equations that model the data are $y = -143.6x + 6019$ and $y = -170.2x + 6250$. (Data from: National Credit Union Association.)

12. **Business**   The percentage of households using direct deposit for selected years is shown in the following table. (Data from: Board of Governors of the Federal Reserve System.)

Year	1995	1998	2001	2004	2007
Percent of households	53	67	71	75	80

   Let $x = 5$ correspond to the year 1995. Two equations that model the data are $y = 2.1x + 47$ and $y = 2.8x + 44$.

✐ *In each of the following problems, determine whether a straight line is a good model for the data. Do this visually by plotting the data points and by finding the correlation coefficient for the least-squares regression line. (See Examples 5 and 6.)*

13. **Business**   The accompanying table gives the total sales (in billions of dollars) for the aerospace industry. Let $x = 6$

correspond to the year 2006. (Data from: ProQuest Statistical Abstract of the United States 2013.)

Year	2006	2007	2008	2009	2010	2011
Total Sales	177.3	192.0	194.7	203.0	203.6	210.0

14. Business The accompanying table gives the number (in thousands) of new houses built for each of the years. Let $x = 6$ correspond to the year 2006. (Data from: U.S. Census Bureau.)

Year	2006	2007	2008	2009	2010	2011
Total Sales	1801	1355	906	554	587	609

In Exercises 15–18 find the required linear model using least-squares regression. (See Examples 3–6.)

15. Business Use the data on sales of the aerospace industry in Exercise 13.

   (a) Find a linear model for the data with $x = 6$ corresponding to the year 2006.

   (b) Assuming the trend continues, estimate the total sales for the year 2015.

16. Health The accompanying table shows the number of deaths per 100,000 people from heart disease in selected years. (Data from: U.S. National Center for Health Statistics.)

Year	1985	1990	1995	2000	2005	2010
Deaths	375.0	321.8	293.4	257.6	211.1	178.5

   (a) Find a linear model for the data with $x = 5$ corresponding to the year 1985.

   (b) Assuming the trend continues, estimate the number of deaths per 100,000 people for the year 2015.

17. Business The accompanying table shows the revenue (in billions of dollars) from newspaper publishers. (Data from: U.S. Census Bureau.)

Year	2006	2007	2008	2009	2010
Revenue	48.9	47.6	43.9	36.4	34.7

   (a) Find a linear model for the data with $x = 6$ corresponding to the year 2006.

   (b) Assuming the trend continues, estimate the revenue in 2016.

18. Health Researchers wish to determine if a relationship exists between age and systolic blood pressure (SBP). The accompanying table gives the age and systolic blood pressure for 10 adults.

Age (x)	35	37	42	46	53	57	61	65	69	74
SBP (y)	102	127	120	131	126	137	140	130	148	147

   (a) Find a linear model for these data using age (x) to predict systolic blood pressure (y).

   (b) Use the results from part (a) to predict the systolic blood pressure for a person who is 42-years-old, 53-years-old, and 69-years-old. How well do the actual data agree with the predicted values?

   (c) Use the results from part (a) to predict the systolic blood pressure for a person who is 45-years-old and 70-years-old.

Work these problems.

19. Business The estimated operating revenue (in billions of dollars) from Internet publishing and broadcasting is given in the accompanying table. (Data from: U.S. Census Bureau.)

Year	2006	2007	2008	2009	2010
Revenue	11.5	15.0	17.8	19.1	21.3

   (a) Find the least squares regression line that models these data with $x = 6$ corresponding to the year 2006.

   (b) Assuming the trend continues, estimate the operating revenue in the years 2012 and 2014.

20. Business The number of basic cable television subscribers (in millions) is shown in the following table for various years. (Data from: ProQuest Statistical Abstract of the United States 2013.)

Year	2002	2004	2006	2008	2010
Subscribers	66.5	65.7	65.3	64.3	61.0

   (a) Find the least-squares regression line that models these data with $x = 2$ corresponding to the year 2002.

   (b) Find the number of subscribers for the year 2009.

   (c) If the trend continues indefinitely, determine in what year there will be 55 million subscribers.

   (d) Find the correlation coefficient.

21. Social Science The number (in thousands) of traffic fatalities by year is displayed in the accompanying table. (Data from: U.S. National Highway Traffic Administration.)

Year	2005	2007	2008	2009	2010
Traffic Fatalities	43.5	41.3	37.4	33.9	32.9

   (a) Find the least-squares regression line that models these data with $x = 5$ corresponding to the year 2005.

   (b) Find the number of deaths for the year 2006.

   (c) If the trend continues indefinitely, determine in what year there will be 28 thousand deaths.

   (d) Find the correlation coefficient.

22. Health The following table shows men's and women's life expectancy at birth (in years) for selected birth years in the United States: (Data from: U.S. Center for National Health Statistics.)

	Life Expectancy	
Birth Year	**Men**	**Women**
1970	67.1	74.7
1975	68.8	76.6
1980	70.0	77.4
1985	71.1	78.2
1990	71.8	78.8
1995	72.5	78.9
1998	73.8	79.5
2000	74.3	79.7
2001	74.4	79.8
2004	75.2	80.4
2010	75.6	81.4

(a) Find the least-squares regression line for the men's data, with $x = 70$ corresponding to 1970.

(b) Find the least-squares regression line for the women's data, with $x = 70$ corresponding to 1970.

(c) Suppose life expectancy continues to increase as predicted by the equations in parts (a) and (b). Will men's life expectancy ever be the same as women's? If so, in what birth year will this occur?

✓**Checkpoint Answers**

1. $y = 30.25x + 765.75$

2. **(a)** 0, –18.5, 16, 21.5, 0
   (b) 1060.5
   (c) Yes, because the sum of the squares of the residuals is lower.

3. **(a)** 4.2, –18.3, 12.2, 13.7, –11.8
   (b) 828.30
   (c) It fits the data best because the sum of the squares of its residuals is smallest.

4. $y = 7x + 336$

5. **(a)** $y = .76x - 2.66$
   (b) $r \approx .74$
   (c) It fits reasonably well because $|r|$ is close to 1 and the pattern is linear.

2.4 Linear Inequalities

An **inequality** is a statement that one mathematical expression is greater than (or less than) another. Inequalities are very important in applications. For example, a company wants revenue to be *greater than* costs and must use *no more than* the total amount of capital or labor available.

Inequalities may be solved by algebraic or geometric methods. In this section, we shall concentrate on algebraic methods for solving **linear inequalities**, such as

$$4 - 3x \leq 7 + 2x \quad \text{and} \quad -2 < 5 + 3m < 20,$$

and absolute-value inequalities, such as $|x - 2| < 5$. The following properties are the basic algebraic tools for working with inequalities.

> **Properties of Inequality**
>
> For real numbers a, b, and c,
>
> **(a)** if $a < b$, then $a + c < b + c$;
>
> **(b)** if $a < b$, and if $c > 0$, then $ac < bc$;
>
> **(c)** if $a < b$, and if $c < 0$, then $ac > bc$.

Throughout this section, definitions are given only for $<$, but they are equally valid for $>$, $\leq$, and $\geq$.

CAUTION Pay careful attention to part (c) in the previous box; if both sides of an inequality are multiplied by a negative number, the direction of the inequality symbol must be reversed. For example, starting with the true statement $-3 < 5$ and multiplying both sides by the positive number 2 gives

$$-3 \cdot 2 < 5 \cdot 2,$$

or

$$-6 < 10,$$

still a true statement. However, starting with $-3 < 5$ and multiplying both sides by the negative number -2 gives a true result only if the direction of the inequality symbol is reversed:

$$-3(-2) > 5(-2)$$
$$6 > -10.$$

✓ **Checkpoint 1**

(a) First multiply both sides of $-6 < -1$ by 4, and then multiply both sides of $-6 < -1$ by -7.

(b) First multiply both sides of $9 \geq -4$ by 2, and then multiply both sides of $9 \geq -4$ by -5.

(c) First add 4 to both sides of $-3 < -1$, and then add -6 to both sides of $-3 < -1$.

Example 1   Solve $3x + 5 > 11$. Graph the solution.

Solution   First add -5 to both sides:

$$3x + 5 + (-5) > 11 + (-5)$$
$$3x > 6.$$

Now multiply both sides by $1/3$:

$$\frac{1}{3}(3x) > \frac{1}{3}(6)$$
$$x > 2.$$

(Why was the direction of the inequality symbol not changed?) In interval notation (introduced in Section 1.1), the solution is the interval $(2, \infty)$, which is graphed on the number line in Figure 2.48. The parenthesis at 2 shows that 2 is not included in the solution.

Figure 2.48

As a partial check, note that 0, which is not part of the solution, makes the inequality false, while 3, which is part of the solution, makes it true:

$$\overset{?}{3(0) + 5 > 11} \qquad\qquad \overset{?}{3(3) + 5 > 11}$$
$$5 > 11 \quad \text{False} \qquad\qquad 14 > 11. \quad \text{True}$$

✓ **Checkpoint 2**

Solve these inequalities. Graph each solution.

(a) $5z - 11 < 14$

(b) $-3k \leq -12$

(c) $-8y \geq 32$

Example 2   Solve $4 - 3x \leq 7 + 2x$.

Solution   Add -4 to both sides:

$$4 - 3x + (-4) \leq 7 + 2x + (-4)$$
$$-3x \leq 3 + 2x.$$

Add $-2x$ to both sides (remember that *adding* to both sides never changes the direction of the inequality symbol):

$$-3x + (-2x) \leq 3 + 2x + (-2x)$$
$$-5x \leq 3.$$

Multiply both sides by $-1/5$. Since $-1/5$ is negative, change the direction of the inequality symbol:

$$-\frac{1}{5}(-5x) \geq -\frac{1}{5}(3)$$

$$x \geq -\frac{3}{5}.$$

Figure 2.49 shows a graph of the solution, $[-3/5, \infty)$. The bracket in Figure 2.49 shows that $-3/5$ is included in the solution.

✓ Checkpoint 3

Solve these inequalities. Graph each solution.

(a) $8 - 6t \geq 2t + 24$

(b) $-4r + 3(r + 1) < 2r$

Figure 2.49

Example 3 Solve $-2 < 5 + 3m < 20$. Graph the solution.

Solution The inequality $-2 < 5 + 3m < 20$ says that $5 + 3m$ is between -2 and 20. We can solve this inequality with an extension of the properties given at the beginning of this section. Work as follows, first adding -5 to each part:

$$-2 + (-5) < 5 + 3m + (-5) < 20 + (-5)$$
$$-7 < 3m < 15.$$

Now multiply each part by $1/3$:

$$-\frac{7}{3} < m < 5.$$

✓ Checkpoint 4

Solve each of the given inequalities. Graph each solution.

(a) $9 < k + 5 < 13$

(b) $-6 \leq 2z + 4 \leq 12$

A graph of the solution, $(-7/3, 5)$, is given in Figure 2.50.

Figure 2.50

Example 4 The formula for converting from Celsius to Fahrenheit temperature is

$$F = \frac{9}{5}C + 32.$$

What Celsius temperature range corresponds to the range from 32°F to 77°F?

Solution The Fahrenheit temperature range is $32 < F < 77$. Since $F = (9/5)C + 32$, we have

$$32 < \frac{9}{5}C + 32 < 77.$$

Solve the inequality for C:

$$32 < \frac{9}{5}C + 32 < 77$$

$$0 < \frac{9}{5}C < 45 \qquad \text{Subtract 32 from each part.}$$

$$\frac{5}{9} \cdot 0 < \frac{5}{9} \cdot \frac{9}{5}C < \frac{5}{9} \cdot 45 \qquad \text{Multiply each part by } \frac{5}{9}.$$

$$0 < C < 25.$$

✓ Checkpoint 5

In Example 4, what Celsius temperatures correspond to the range from 5°F to 95°F?

The corresponding Celsius temperature range is 0°C to 25°C.

A product will break even or produce a profit only if the revenue R from selling the product at least equals the cost C of producing it—that is, if $R \geq C$.

Example 5   **Business** A company analyst has determined that the cost to produce and sell x units of a certain product is $C = 20x + 1000$. The revenue for that product is $R = 70x$. Find the values of x for which the company will break even or make a profit on the product.

Solution   Solve the inequality $R \geq C$:

$$R \geq C$$
$$70x \geq 20x + 1000 \qquad \text{Let } R = 70x \text{ and } C = 20x + 1000.$$
$$50x \geq 1000 \qquad \text{Subtract } 20x \text{ from both sides.}$$
$$x \geq 20. \qquad \text{Divide both sides by 50.}$$

The company must produce and sell 20 items to break even and more than 20 to make a profit.

Example 6   **Business** A pretzel manufacturer can sell a 6-ounce bag of pretzels to a wholesaler for \$.35 a bag. The variable cost of producing each bag is \$.25 per bag, and the fixed cost for the manufacturing operation is \$110,000.[*] How many bags of pretzels need to be sold in order to break even or earn a profit?

Solution   Let x be the number of bags produced. Then the revenue equation is

$$R = .35x,$$

and the cost is given by

$$\text{Cost} = \text{Fixed Costs} + \text{Variable Costs}$$
$$C = 110,000 + .25x.$$

We now solve the inequality $R \geq C$:

$$R \geq C$$
$$.35x \geq 110,000 + .25x$$
$$.1x \geq 110,000$$
$$x \geq 1,110,000.$$

The manufacturer must produce and sell 1,110,000 bags of pretzels to break even and more than that to make a profit.

Absolute-Value Inequalities

You may wish to review the definition of absolute value in Section 1.1 before reading the following examples, which show how to solve inequalities involving absolute values.

Example 7   Solve each inequality.

(a) $|x| < 5$

Solution   Because absolute value gives the distance from a number to 0, the inequality $|x| < 5$ is true for all real numbers whose distance from 0 is less than 5. This includes all numbers between -5 and 5, or numbers in the interval $(-5, 5)$. A graph of the solution is shown in Figure 2.51 on the following page.

---

[*]Variable costs, fixed costs, and revenue were discussed on page 15.

Figure 2.51

(b) $|x| > 5$

Solution The solution of $|x| > 5$ is given by all those numbers whose distance from 0 is *greater* than 5. This includes the numbers satisfying $x < -5$ or $x > 5$. A graph of the solution, all numbers in

$$(-\infty, -5) \qquad \text{or} \qquad (5, \infty),$$

is shown in Figure 2.52.

✓**Checkpoint 6**

Solve each inequality. Graph each solution.

(a) $|x| \le 1$

(b) $|y| \ge 3$

Figure 2.52

The preceding examples suggest the following generalizations.

Assume that a and b are real numbers and that b is positive.

1. Solve $|a| < b$ by solving $-b < a < b$.

2. Solve $|a| > b$ by solving $a < -b$ or $a > b$.

Example 8   Solve $|x - 2| < 5$.

Solution   Replace a with $x - 2$ and b with 5 in property (1) in the box above. Now solve $|x - 2| < 5$ by solving the inequality

$$-5 < x - 2 < 5.$$

Add 2 to each part, getting the solution

$$-3 < x < 7,$$

Figure 2.53

✓**Checkpoint 7**

Solve each inequality. Graph each solution.

(a) $|p + 3| < 4$

(b) $|2k - 1| \le 7$

which is graphed in Figure 2.53. ✓7

Example 9   Solve $|2 - 7m| - 1 > 4$.

Solution   First add 1 to both sides:

$$|2 - 7m| > 5$$

Now use property (2) from the preceding box to solve $|2 - 7m| > 5$ by solving the inequality

$$2 - 7m < -5 \qquad \text{or} \qquad 2 - 7m > 5.$$

Solve each part separately:

$$-7m < -7 \qquad \text{or} \qquad -7m > 3$$

$$m > 1 \qquad \text{or} \qquad m < -\frac{3}{7}.$$

✓**Checkpoint 8**

Solve each inequality. Graph each solution.

(a) $|y - 2| > 5$

(b) $|3k - 1| \ge 2$

(c) $|2 + 5r| - 4 \ge 1$

The solution, all numbers in $\left(-\infty, -\frac{3}{7}\right)$ or $(1, \infty)$, is graphed in Figure 2.54.

Figure 2.54

✓ **Checkpoint 9**

Solve each inequality.

(a) $|5m - 3| > -10$

(b) $|6 + 5a| < -9$

(c) $|8 + 2r| > 0$

Example 10 Solve $|3 - 7x| \geq -8$.

Solution The absolute value of a number is always nonnegative. Therefore, $|3 - 7x| \geq -8$ is always true, so the solution is the set of all real numbers. Note that the inequality $|3 - 7x| \leq -8$ has no solution, because the absolute value of a quantity can never be less than a negative number. ✓ 9

2.4 Exercises

1. Explain how to determine whether a parenthesis or a bracket is used when graphing the solution of a linear inequality.

2. The three-part inequality $p < x < q$ means "p is less than x and x is less than q." Which one of the given inequalities is not satisfied by any real number x? Explain why.

   (a) $-3 < x < 5$ (b) $0 < x < 4$

   (c) $-7 < x < -10$ (d) $-3 < x < -2$

Solve each inequality and graph each solution. (See Examples 1–3.)

3. $-8k \leq 32$ 4. $-4a \leq 36$

5. $-2b > 0$ 6. $6 - 6z < 0$

7. $3x + 4 \leq 14$ 8. $2y - 7 < 9$

9. $-5 - p \geq 3$ 10. $5 - 3r \leq -4$

11. $7m - 5 < 2m + 10$ 12. $6x - 2 > 4x - 10$

13. $m - (4 + 2m) + 3 < 2m + 2$

14. $2p - (3 - p) \leq -7p - 2$

15. $-2(3y - 8) \geq 5(4y - 2)$

16. $5r - (r + 2) \geq 3(r - 1) + 6$

17. $3p - 1 < 6p + 2(p - 1)$

18. $x + 5(x + 1) > 4(2 - x) + x$

19. $-7 < y - 2 < 5$ 20. $-3 < m + 6 < 2$

21. $8 \leq 3r + 1 \leq 16$ 22. $-6 < 2p - 3 \leq 5$

23. $-4 \leq \dfrac{2k - 1}{3} \leq 2$ 24. $-1 \leq \dfrac{5y + 2}{3} \leq 4$

25. $\dfrac{3}{5}(2p + 3) \geq \dfrac{1}{10}(5p + 1)$

26. $\dfrac{8}{3}(z - 4) \leq \dfrac{2}{9}(3z + 2)$

In the following exercises, write a linear inequality that describes the given graph.

27.
   $-6\ -4\ -2\ \ 0\ \ 2\ \ 4\ \ 6$

28.
   $-6\ -4\ -2\ \ 0\ \ 2\ \ 4\ \ 6$

29.
   $-6\ -4\ -2\ \ 0\ \ 2\ \ 4\ \ 6$

30.
   $-6\ -4\ -2\ \ 0\ \ 2\ \ 4\ \ 6$

Business *In Exercises 31–36, find all values of x for which the given products will at least break even. (See Examples 5 and 6.)*

31. The cost to produce x units of wire is $C = 50x + 6000$, while the revenue is $R = 65x$.

32. The cost to produce x units of squash is $C = 100x + 6000$, while the revenue is $R = 500x$.

33. $C = 85x + 1000$; $R = 105x$

34. $C = 70x + 500$; $R = 60x$

35. $C = 1000x + 5000$; $R = 900x$

36. $C = 25{,}000x + 21{,}700{,}000$; $R = 102{,}500x$

Solve each inequality. Graph each solution. (See Examples 7–10.)

37. $|p| > 7$ 38. $|m| < 2$

39. $|r| \leq 5$ 40. $|a| < -2$

41. $|b| > -5$ 42. $|2x + 5| < 1$

43. $\left| x - \dfrac{1}{2} \right| < 2$ 44. $|3z + 1| \geq 4$

45. $|8b + 5| \geq 7$ 46. $\left| 5x + \dfrac{1}{2} \right| - 2 < 5$

Work these problems.

Physical Science *The given inequality describes the monthly average high daily temperature T in degrees Fahrenheit in the given location. (Data from: Weatherbase.com.) What range of temperatures corresponds to the inequality?*

47. $|T - 83| \leq 7$; Miami, Florida

48. $|T - 63| \leq 27$; Boise, Idaho

49. $|T - 61| \leq 21$; Flagstaff, Arizona

50. $|T - 43| \leq 22$; Anchorage, Alaska

51. **Natural Science** Human beings emit carbon dioxide when they breathe. In one study, the emission rates of carbon dioxide by college students were measured both during lectures and during exams. The average individual rate R_L (in grams per hour) during a lecture class satisfied the inequality $|R_L - 26.75| \leq 1.42$, whereas during an exam, the rate R_E satisfied the inequality $|R_E - 38.75| \leq 2.17$. (Data from: T.C. Wang, *ASHRAE Transactions* 81 [Part 1], 32 [1975].)

   (a) Find the range of values for R_L and R_E.

   (b) A class had 225 students. If T_L and T_E represent the total amounts of carbon dioxide (in grams) emitted during a one-hour lecture and one-hour exam, respectively, write inequalities that describe the ranges for T_L and T_E.

52. **Social Science** When administering a standard intelligence quotient (IQ) test, we expect about one-third of the scores to be more than 12 units above 100 or more than 12 units below 100. Describe this situation by writing an absolute value inequality.

53. **Social Science** A Gallup poll found that among Americans aged 18–34 years who consume alcohol, between 35% and 43% prefer beer. Let B represent the percentage of American alcohol consumers who prefer beer. Write the preceding information as an inequality. (Data from: Gallup.com.)

54. **Social Science** A Gallup poll in February 2013 found that between 17% and 19% of Americans considered themselves underemployed (working part-time or not working at all, but wanting to work full-time). Let U represent the percentage of underemployed workers. Write the preceding information as an inequality. (Data from: Gallup.com.)

55. **Finance** The following table shows the 2012 federal income tax for a single person. (Data from: Internal Revenue Service.)

If Taxable Income Is Over	But Not Over	Tax Rate
$0	$8700	10%
$8700	$35,350	15%
$35,350	$85,650	25%
$85,650	$178,650	28%
$178,650	$388,350	33%
$388,350	No limits	35%

Let x denote the taxable income. Write each of the six income ranges in the table as an inequality.

56. **Health** Federal guidelines require drinking water to have less than .050 milligrams per liter of lead. A test using 21 samples of water in a Midwestern city found that the average amount of lead in the samples was 0.040 milligrams per liter. All samples had lead content within 5% of the average.
   (a) Select a variable and write down what it represents.
   (b) Write an inequality to express the results obtained from the sample.
   (c) Did all the samples meet the federal requirement?

✓**Checkpoint Answers**

1. (a) $-24 < -4; 42 > 7$ (b) $18 \geq -8; -45 \leq 20$
   (c) $1 < 3; -9 < -7$

2. (a) $z < 5$ (b) $k \geq 4$
   (c) $y \leq -4$

3. (a) $t \leq -2$ (b) $r > 1$

4. (a) $4 < k < 8$ (b) $-5 \leq z \leq 4$

5. $-15°C$ to $35°C$

6. (a) $[-1, 1]$
   (b) All numbers in $(-\infty, -3]$ or $[3, \infty)$

7. (a) $(-7, 1)$ (b) $[-3, 4]$

8. (a) All numbers in $(-\infty, -3)$ or $(7, \infty)$
   (b) All numbers in $\left(-\infty, -\frac{1}{3}\right]$ or $[1, \infty)$
   (c) All numbers in $\left(-\infty, -\frac{7}{5}\right]$ or $\left[\frac{3}{5}, \infty\right)$

9. (a) All real numbers
   (b) No solution
   (c) All real numbers except -4

2.5 Polynomial and Rational Inequalities

This section deals with the solution of polynomial and rational inequalities, such as

$$r^2 + 3r - 4 \geq 0, \quad x^3 - x \leq 0, \quad \text{and} \quad \frac{2x-1}{3x+4} < 5.$$

We shall concentrate on algebraic solution methods, but to understand why these methods work, we must first look at such inequalities from a graphical point of view.

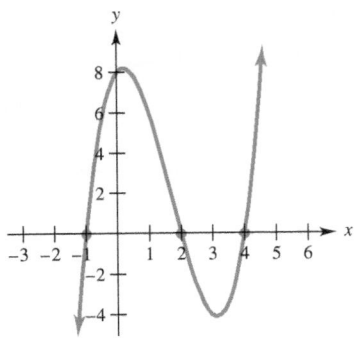

Figure 2.55

Example 1　Use the graph of $y = x^3 - 5x^2 + 2x + 8$ in Figure 2.55 to solve each of the given inequalities.

(a) $x^3 - 5x^2 + 2x + 8 > 0$

Solution　Each point on the graph has coordinates of the form $(x, x^3 - 5x^2 + 2x + 8)$. The number x is a solution of the inequality exactly when the second coordinate of this point is positive—that is, when the point lies *above* the x-axis. So to solve the inequality, we need only find the first coordinates of points on the graph that are above the x-axis. This information can be read from Figure 2.55. The graph is above the x-axis when $-1 < x < 2$ and when $x > 4$. Therefore, the solutions of the inequality are all numbers x in the interval $(-1, 2)$ or the interval $(4, \infty)$.

(b) $x^3 - 5x^2 + 2x + 8 < 0$

Solution　The number x is a solution of the inequality exactly when the second coordinate of the point $(x, x^3 - 5x^2 + 2x + 8)$ on the graph is negative—that is, when the point lies *below* the x-axis. Figure 2.55 shows that the graph is below the x-axis when $x < -1$ and when $2 < x < 4$. Hence, the solutions are all numbers x in the interval $(-\infty, -1)$ or the interval $(2, 4)$.

The solution process in Example 1 depends only on knowing the graph and its x-intercepts (that is, the points where the graph intersects the x-axis). This information can often be obtained algebraically, without doing any graphing.

Steps for Solving an Inequality Involving a Polynomial

1. Rewrite the inequality so that all the terms are on the left side and 0 is on the right side.
2. Find the x-intercepts by setting $y = 0$ and solving for x.
3. Divide the x-axis (number line) into regions using the solutions found in Step 2.
4. Test a point in each region by choosing a value for x and substituting it into the equation for y.
5. Determine which regions satisfy the original inequality and graph the solution.

Example 2　Solve each of the given quadratic inequalities.

(a) $x^2 - x < 12$

Solution

Step 1　Rewrite the inequality so that all the terms are on the left side and 0 is on the right side.
　　　　　Hence we add –12 to each side and obtain $x^2 - x - 12 < 0$.

Step 2　Find the x-intercepts by setting $y = 0$ and solving for x.
　　　　　We find the x-intercepts of $y = x^2 - x - 12$ by setting $y = 0$ and solving for x:

$$x^2 - x - 12 = 0$$
$$(x + 3)(x - 4) = 0$$
$$x + 3 = 0 \quad \text{or} \quad x - 4 = 0$$
$$x = -3 \qquad\qquad x = 4.$$

Step 3　Divide the x-axis (number line) into regions using the solutions found in Step 2.
　　　　　These numbers divide the x-axis into three regions, as indicated in Figure 2.56.

Figure 2.56

Step 4 Test a point in each region by choosing a value for x and substituting it in to the equation for y.

In each region, the graph of $y = x^2 - x - 12$ is an unbroken curve, so it will be entirely above or entirely below the axis. It can pass from above to below the x-axis only at the x-intercepts. To see whether the graph is above or below the x-axis when x is in region A, choose a value of x in region A, say, $x = -5$, and substitute it into the equation:

$$y = x^2 - x - 12 = (-5)^2 - (-5) - 12 = 18.$$

Therefore, the point $(-5, 18)$ is on the graph. Since its y-coordinate 18 is positive, this point lies above the x-axis; hence, the entire graph lies above the x-axis in region A.

Similarly, we can choose a value of x in region B, say, $x = 0$. Then

$$y = x^2 - x - 12 = 0^2 - 0 - 12 = -12,$$

so that $(0, -12)$ is on the graph. Since this point lies below the x-axis (why?), the entire graph in region B must be below the x-axis. Finally, in region C, let $x = 5$. Then $y = 5^2 - 5 - 12 = 8$, so that $(5, 8)$ is on the graph, and the entire graph in region C lies above the x-axis. We can summarize the results as follows:

Interval	$x < -3$	$-3 < x < 4$	$x > 4$
Test value in interval	-5	0	5
Value of $x^2 - x - 12$	18	-12	8
Graph	above x-axis	below x-axis	above x-axis
Conclusion	$x^2 - x - 12 > 0$	$x^2 - x - 12 < 0$	$x^2 - x - 12 > 0$

Step 5 Determine which regions satisfy the original inequality and graph the solution.

The last row shows that the only region where $x^2 - x - 12 < 0$ is region B, so the solutions of the inequality are all numbers x with $-3 < x < 4$—that is, the interval $(-3, 4)$, as shown in the number line graph in Figure 2.57.

Figure 2.57

(b) $x^2 - x - 12 > 0$

Solution Use the chart in part (a). The last row shows that $x^2 - x - 12 > 0$ only when x is in region A or region C. Hence, the solutions of the inequality are all numbers x with $x < -3$ or $x > 4$—that is, all numbers in the interval $(-\infty, -3)$ or the interval $(4, \infty)$. ✓₁

✓ **Checkpoint 1**

Solve each inequality. Graph the solution on the number line.

(a) $x^2 - 2x < 15$

(b) $2x^2 - 3x - 20 < 0$

Example 3   Solve the quadratic inequality $r^2 + 3r \geq 4$.

Solution

Step 1 First rewrite the inequality so that one side is 0:

$$r^2 + 3r \geq 4$$
$$r^2 + 3r - 4 \geq 0. \quad \text{Add } -4 \text{ to both sides.}$$

Step 2 Now solve the corresponding equation (which amounts to finding the x-intercepts of $y = r^3 + 3r - 4$):

$$r^2 + 3r - 4 = 0$$
$$(r - 1)(r + 4) = 0$$
$$r = 1 \quad \text{or} \quad r = -4.$$

Step 3 These numbers separate the number line into three regions, as shown in Figure 2.58. Test a number from each region:

Step 4 Let $r = -5$ from region A: $(-5)^2 + 3(-5) - 4 = 6 > 0$.

Let $r = 0$ from region B: $(0)^2 + 3(0) - 4 = -4 < 0$.

Let $r = 2$ from region C: $(2)^2 + 3(2) - 4 = 6 > 0$.

Step 5 We want the inequality to be positive or 0. The solution includes numbers in region A and in region C, as well as -4 and 1, the endpoints. The solution, which includes all numbers in the interval $(-\infty, -4]$ or the interval $[1, \infty)$, is graphed in Figure 2.58. ✓ 2

✓ **Checkpoint 2**

Solve each inequality. Graph each solution.

(a) $k^2 + 2k - 15 \geq 0$

(b) $3m^2 + 7m \geq 6$

Figure 2.58

Example 4 Solve $q^3 - 4q > 0$.

Solution

Step 1 Step 1 is already complete in the statement of the problem.

Step 2 Solve the corresponding equation by factoring:

$$q^3 - 4q = 0$$
$$q(q^2 - 4) = 0$$
$$q(q + 2)(q - 2) = 0$$
$$q = 0 \quad \text{or} \quad q + 2 = 0 \quad \text{or} \quad q - 2 = 0$$
$$q = 0 \qquad\qquad q = -2 \qquad\qquad q = 2.$$

Step 3 These three numbers separate the number line into the four regions shown in Figure 2.59.

Step 4 Test a number from each region:

A: If $q = -3, (-3)^3 - 4(-3) = -15 < 0$.

B: If $q = -1, (-1)^3 - 4(-1) = 3 > 0$.

C: If $q = 1, (1)^3 - 4(1) = -3 < 0$.

D: If $q = 3, (3)^3 - 4(3) = 15 > 0$.

Step 5 The numbers that make the polynomial positive are in the interval $(-2, 0)$ or the interval $(2, \infty)$, as graphed in Figure 2.59. ✓ 3

✓ **Checkpoint 3**

Solve each inequality. Graph each solution.

(a) $m^3 - 9m > 0$

(b) $2k^3 - 50k \leq 0$

Figure 2.59

Figure 2.60

✓**Checkpoint 4**

Use graphical methods to find approximate solutions of these inequalities.

(a) $x^2 - 6x + 2 > 0$

(b) $x^2 - 6x + 2 < 0$

A graphing calculator can be used to solve inequalities without the need to evaluate at a test number in each interval. It is also useful for finding approximate solutions when the x-intercepts of the graph cannot be found algebraically.

Example 5 Use a graphing calculator to solve $x^3 - 5x^2 + x + 6 > 0$.

Solution Begin by graphing $y = x^3 - 5x^2 + x + 6$ (Figure 2.60). Find the x-intercepts by solving $x^3 - 5x^2 + x + 6 = 0$. Since this cannot readily be done algebraically, use the graphical root finder to determine that the solutions (x-intercepts) are approximately $-.9254$, 1.4481, and 4.4774.

The graph is above the x-axis when $-.9254 < x < 1.4481$ and when $x > 4.4774$. Therefore, the approximate solutions of the inequality are all numbers in the interval $(-.9254, 1.4481)$ or the interval $(4.4774, \infty)$. ✓ 4

Example 6 **Business** A company sells wholesale portable DVD players for $39 each. The variable cost of producing x thousand players is $5.5x - 4.9x^2$ (in thousands of dollars), and the fixed cost is $550 (in thousands). Find the values of x for which the company will break even or make a profit on the product.

Solution If x thousand DVD players are sold at $39 each, then

$$R = 39 \times x = 39x.$$

The cost function (in thousands of dollars) is

$$\text{Cost} = \text{Fixed Costs} + \text{Variable Costs}$$
$$C = 550 + (5.5x - 4.9x^2).$$

Therefore, to break even or earn a profit, we need Revenue (R) greater than or equal to Cost (C).

$$R \geq C$$
$$39x \geq 550 + 5.5x - 4.9x^2$$
$$4.9x^2 + 33.5x - 550 \geq 0.$$

Now graph $4.9x^2 + 33.5x - 550$. Since x has to be positive in this situation (why?), we need only look at the graph in the right half of the plane. Here, and in other cases, you may have to try several viewing windows before you find one that shows what you need. Once you find a suitable window, such as in Figure 2.61, use the graphical root finder to determine the relevant x-intercept. Figure 2.61 shows the intercept is approximately $x \approx 7.71$. Hence, the company must manufacture at least $7.71 \times 1000 = 7710$ portable DVD players to make a profit.

Figure 2.61

Rational Inequalities

Inequalities with quotients of algebraic expressions are called **rational inequalities**. These inequalities can be solved in much the same way as polynomial inequalities can.

> ### Steps for Solving Inequalities Involving Rational Expressions
>
> 1. Rewrite the inequality so that all the terms are on the left side and the 0 is on the right side.
> 2. Write the left side as a single fraction.
> 3. Set the numerator and the denominator equal to 0 and solve for x.
> 4. Divide the x-axis (number line) into regions using the solutions found in Step 3.
> 5. Test a point in each region by choosing a value for x and substituting it into the equation for y.
> 6. Determine which regions satisfy the original inequality and graph the solution.

Example 7   Solve the rational inequality

$$\frac{5}{x+4} \geq 1.$$

Solution

Step 1   Write an equivalent inequality with one side equal to 0:

$$\frac{5}{x+4} \geq 1$$

$$\frac{5}{x+4} - 1 \geq 0.$$

Step 2   Write the left side as a single fraction:

$$\frac{5}{x+4} - \frac{x+4}{x+4} \geq 0 \qquad \text{Obtain a common denominator.}$$

$$\frac{5-(x+4)}{x+4} \geq 0 \qquad \text{Subtract fractions.}$$

$$\frac{5-x-4}{x+4} \geq 0 \qquad \text{Distributive property}$$

$$\frac{1-x}{x+4} \geq 0.$$

Step 3   The quotient can change sign only at places where the denominator is 0 or the numerator is 0. (In graphical terms, these are the only places where the graph of $y = \dfrac{1-x}{x+4}$ can change from above the x-axis to below.) This happens when

$$1 - x = 0 \qquad \text{or} \qquad x + 4 = 0$$
$$x = 1 \qquad \text{or} \qquad x = -4.$$

Step 4   As in the earlier examples, the numbers -4 and 1 divide the x-axis into three regions:

$$x < -4, \quad -4 < x < 1, \quad x > 1.$$

Step 5   Test a number from each of these regions:

$$\text{Let } x = -5: \quad \frac{1-(-5)}{-5+4} = -6 < 0.$$

$$\text{Let } x = 0: \quad \frac{1-0}{0+4} = \frac{1}{4} > 0.$$

$$\text{Let } x = 2: \quad \frac{1-2}{2+4} = -\frac{1}{6} < 0.$$

Step 6   The test shows that numbers in $(-4, 1)$ satisfy the inequality. With a quotient, the endpoints must be considered individually to make sure that no denominator is 0. In this inequality, -4 makes the denominator 0, while 1 satisfies the given inequality. Write the solution in interval notation as $(-4, 1]$ and graphically as in Figure 2.62.

Checkpoint 5

Solve each inequality.

(a) $\dfrac{3}{x-2} \geq 4$

(b) $\dfrac{p}{1-p} < 3$

(c) Why is 2 excluded from the solution in part (a)?

Figure 2.62

CAUTION As suggested by Example 7, be very careful with the endpoints of the intervals in the solution of rational inequalities. ✓₅

Example 8 Solve

$$\frac{2x - 1}{3x + 4} < 5.$$

Solution

Step 1 Write an equivalent inequality with 0 on one side by adding −5 to each side.

$$\frac{2x - 1}{3x + 4} - 5 < 0 \qquad \text{Get 0 on the right side.}$$

Step 2 Write the left side as a single fraction by using $3x + 4$ as a common denominator.

$$\frac{2x - 1 - 5(3x + 4)}{3x + 4} < 0 \qquad \text{Obtain a common denominator.}$$

$$\frac{-13x - 21}{3x + 4} < 0 \qquad \text{Distribute in the numerator and combine terms.}$$

Step 3 Set the numerator and denominator each equal to 0 and solve the two equations:

$$-13x - 21 = 0 \qquad \text{or} \qquad 3x + 4 = 0$$

$$x = -\frac{21}{13} \qquad \text{or} \qquad x = -\frac{4}{3}$$

Step 4 The values $-21/13$ and $-4/3$ divide the x-axis into three regions:

$$x < -\frac{21}{13}, \; -\frac{21}{13} < x < -\frac{4}{3}, x > -\frac{4}{3}.$$

Steps 5 and 6 Testing points from each interval yields that the quotient is negative for numbers in the interval $(-\infty, -21/13)$ or $(-4/3, \infty)$. Neither endpoint satisfies the given inequality. ✓6

Figure 2.63

✓**Checkpoint 6**

Solve each rational inequality.

(a) $\dfrac{3y - 2}{2y + 5} < 1$

(b) $\dfrac{3c - 4}{2 - c} \geq -5$

✓**Checkpoint 7**

(a) Solve the inequality

$$\frac{10}{x + 2} \geq 3$$

by first multiplying both sides by $x + 2$.

(b) Show that this method produces a wrong answer by testing $x = -3$.

⊘ **CAUTION** In problems like those in Examples 7 and 8, you should *not* begin by multiplying both sides by the denominator to simplify the inequality. Doing so will usually produce a wrong answer. For the reason, see Exercise 38. For an example, see Checkpoint 7. ✓7

◄ **TECHNOLOGY TIP** Rational inequalities can also be solved graphically. In Example 7, for instance, after rewriting the original inequality in the form $\dfrac{1 - x}{x + 4} \geq 0$, determine the values of x that make the numerator and denominator 0 (namely, $x = 1$ and $x = -4$). Then graph $\dfrac{1 - x}{x + 4}$. Figure 2.64 shows that the graph is above the x-axis when it is between the vertical asymptote at $x = -4$ and the x-intercept at $x = 1$. So the solution of the inequality is the interval $(-4, 1]$. (When the values that make the numerator and denominator 0 cannot be found algebraically, as they were here, you can use the root finder to approximate them.)

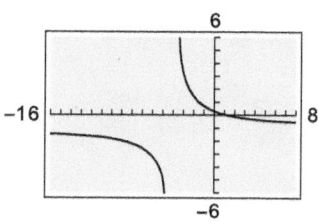

Figure 2.64

2.5 Exercises

Solve each of these quadratic inequalities. Graph the solutions on the number line. (See Examples 2 and 3.)

1. $(x + 4)(2x - 3) \leq 0$ **2.** $(5y - 1)(y + 3) > 0$

3. $r^2 + 4r > -3$ **4.** $z^2 + 6z > -8$

5. $4m^2 + 7m - 2 \leq 0$ **6.** $6p^2 - 11p + 3 \leq 0$

7. $4x^2 + 3x - 1 > 0$ **8.** $3x^2 - 5x > 2$

9. $x^2 \leq 36$ **10.** $y^2 \geq 9$

11. $p^2 - 16p > 0$ **12.** $r^2 - 9r < 0$

Solve these inequalities. (See Example 4.)

13. $x^3 - 9x \geq 0$ **14.** $p^3 - 25p \leq 0$

15. $(x + 7)(x + 2)(x - 2) \geq 0$

16. $(2x + 4)(x^2 - 9) \leq 0$

17. $(x + 5)(x^2 - 2x - 3) < 0$

18. $x^3 - 2x^2 - 3x \leq 0$ **19.** $6k^3 - 5k^2 < 4k$

20. $2m^3 + 7m^2 > 4m$

21. A student solved the inequality $p^2 < 16$ by taking the square root of both sides to get $p < 4$. She wrote the solution as $(-\infty, 4)$. Is her solution correct?

Use a graphing calculator to solve these inequalities. (See Example 5.)

22. $6x + 7 < 2x^2$ **23.** $.5x^2 - 1.2x < .2$

24. $3.1x^2 - 7.4x + 3.2 > 0$

25. $x^3 - 2x^2 - 5x + 7 \geq 2x + 1$

26. $x^4 - 6x^3 + 2x^2 < 5x - 2$

27. $2x^4 + 3x^3 < 2x^2 + 4x - 2$

28. $x^5 + 5x^4 > 4x^3 - 3x^2 - 2$

Solve these rational inequalities. (See Examples 7 and 8.)

29. $\dfrac{r - 4}{r - 1} \geq 0$ **30.** $\dfrac{z + 6}{z + 4} > 1$

31. $\dfrac{a - 2}{a - 5} < -1$ **32.** $\dfrac{1}{3k - 5} < \dfrac{1}{3}$

33. $\dfrac{1}{p - 2} < \dfrac{1}{3}$ **34.** $\dfrac{7}{k + 2} \geq \dfrac{1}{k + 2}$

35. $\dfrac{5}{p + 1} > \dfrac{12}{p + 1}$ **36.** $\dfrac{x^2 - 4}{x} > 0$

37. $\dfrac{x^2 - x - 6}{x} < 0$

38. Determine whether $x + 4$ is positive or negative when

(a) $x > -4$;   (b) $x < -4$.

(c) If you multiply both sides of the inequality $\dfrac{1 - x}{x + 4} \geq 0$ by $x + 4$, should you change the direction of the inequality sign? If so, when?

(d) Explain how you can use parts (a)–(c) to solve $\dfrac{1 - x}{x + 4} \geq 0$ correctly.

Use a graphing calculator to solve these inequalities. You may have to approximate the roots of the numerators or denominators.

39. $\dfrac{2x^2 + x - 1}{x^2 - 4x + 4} \leq 0$

40. $\dfrac{x^3 - 3x^2 + 5x - 29}{x^2 - 7} > 3$

41. Business An analyst has found that her company's profits, in hundreds of thousands of dollars, are given by $P = 2x^2 - 12x - 32$, where x is the amount, in hundreds of dollars, spent on advertising. For what values of x does the company make a profit?

42. Business The commodities market is highly unstable; money can be made or lost quickly on investments in soybeans, wheat, and so on. Suppose that an investor kept track of his total profit P at time t, in months, after he began investing, and he found that $P = 4t^2 - 30t + 14$. Find the time intervals during which he has been ahead.

43. Business The manager of a 200-unit apartment complex has found that the profit is given by

$$P = x^2 + 300x - 18,000,$$

where x is the number of apartments rented. For what values of x does the complex produce a profit?

Use a graphing calculator or other technology to complete Exercises 44–48. You may need to find a larger viewing window for some of these problems.

44. Business A door-to-door knife salesman finds that his weekly profit can be modeled by the equation

$$P = x^2 + 5x - 530$$

where x is the number of pitches he makes in a week. For what values of x does the salesman need to make in order to earn a profit?

45. Business The number of subscribers for cellular telecommunications (in millions) can be approximated by $.79x^2 + 5.4x + 178$ where $x = 7$ corresponds to the year 2007. Assuming the model to be valid indefinitely, in what years was the number of subscribers higher than 300 million? (Data from: ProQuest Statistical Abstract of the United States 2013.)

46. Business The percentage of delinquent real estate loans can be approximated by $-.65x^2 + 13.6x - 61.1$ where $x = 7$ corresponds to the year 2007. Assuming the model holds up to and including 2014, find the years in which the percentage of delinquent real estate loans was greater than 8%. (Data from: U.S. Federal Reserve.)

47. Finance The amount of outstanding mortgage debt (in trillions of dollars) can be approximated by $-.2x^2 + 3.44x + .16$ where $x = 4$ corresponds to the year 2004. Assuming the model holds up to and including 2014, find the years in which the amount of outstanding mortgage debt was higher than $13 trillion. (Data from: Board of Governors of the Federal Reserve.)

48. Finance Similar to Exercise 47, the amount of outstanding debt for home mortgages (in trillions of dollars) can be approximated by $-.15x^2 + 2.53x + .66$ where $x = 4$ corresponds to the year 2004. Assuming the model holds up to and including 2014, find the years in which the amount of outstanding home mortgage debt was higher than $9 trillion. (Data from: Board of Governors of the Federal Reserve.)

✓ Checkpoint Answers

1. (a) $(-3, 5)$

(b) $(-5/2, 4)$

2. (a) All numbers in $(-\infty, -5]$ or $[3, \infty)$

(b) All numbers in $(-\infty, -3]$ or $[2/3, \infty)$

3. (a) All numbers in $(-3, 0)$ or $(3, \infty)$

(b) All numbers in $(-\infty, -5]$ or $[0, 5]$

4. (a) All numbers in $(-\infty, .3542)$ or $(5.6458, \infty)$

(b) All numbers in $(.3542, 5.6458)$

5. (a) $(2, 11/4]$

(b) All numbers in $(-\infty, 3/4)$ or $(1, \infty)$

(c) When $x = 2$, the fraction is undefined.

6. (a) $(-5/2, 7)$

(b) All numbers in $(-\infty, 2)$ or $[3, \infty)$

7. (a) $x \le \dfrac{4}{3}$

(b) $x = -3$ is a solution of $x \le \dfrac{4}{3}$, but not of the original inequality $\dfrac{10}{x + 2} \ge 3$.

CHAPTER 2 Summary and Review

Key Terms and Symbols[*]

2.1 Cartesian coordinate system
x-axis
y-axis
origin
ordered pair
x-coordinate
y-coordinate
quadrant
solution of an equation
graph

x-intercept
y-intercept
[viewing window]
[trace]
[graphical root finder]
[maximum and minimum finder]
graph reading
2.2 change in x
change in y

slope
slope–intercept form
parallel and perpendicular lines
point–slope form
linear equations
general form
2.3 linear models
residual
[least-squares regression line]

[linear regression]
[correlation coefficient]
2.4 linear inequality
properties of inequality
absolute-value inequality
2.5 polynomial inequality
algebraic solution methods
[graphical solution methods]
rational inequality

Chapter 2 Key Concepts

Slope of a Line

The **slope** of the line through the points (x_1, y_1) and (x_2, y_2), where $x_1 \ne x_2$, is $m = \dfrac{y_2 - y_1}{x_2 - x_1}$.

Equation of a Line

The line with equation $y = mx + b$ has slope m and y-intercept b.

The line with equation $y - y_1 = m(x - x_1)$ has slope m and goes through (x_1, y_1).

The line with equation $ax + by = c$ (with $a \ne 0, b \ne 0$) has x-intercept c/a and y-intercept c/b.

*Terms in brackets deal with material in which a graphing calculator or other technology is used.

The line with equation $x = k$ is vertical, with x-intercept k, no y-intercept, and undefined slope.

The line with equation $y = k$ is horizontal, with y-intercept k, no x-intercept, and slope 0.

Parellel and Perpendicular Lines   Nonvertical **parallel lines** have the same slope, and **perpendicular lines,** if neither is vertical, have slopes with a product of -1.

Chapter 2 Review Exercises

Which of the ordered pairs $(-2, 3), (0, -5), (2, -3), (3, -2),$ *(4, 3), and (7, 2) are solutions of the given equation?*

1. $y = x^2 - 2x - 5$ 2. $x - y = 5$

Sketch the graph of each equation.

3. $5x - 3y = 15$ 4. $2x + 7y - 21 = 0$

5. $y + 3 = 0$ 6. $y - 2x = 0$

7. $y = .25x^2 + 1$ 8. $y = \sqrt{x + 4}$

9. The following temperature graph was recorded in Bratenahl, Ohio:

(a) At what times during the day was the temperature over 55°?

(b) When was the temperature below 40°?

10. Greenville, South Carolina, is 500 miles south of Bratenahl, Ohio, and its temperature is 7° higher all day long. (See the graph in Exercise 9.) At what time was the temperature in Greenville the same as the temperature at noon in Bratenahl?

11. In your own words, define the slope of a line.

In Exercises 12–21, find the slope of the line defined by the given conditions.

12. Through $(-1, 3)$ and $(2, 6)$

13. Through $(4, -5)$ and $(1, 4)$

14. Through $(8, -3)$ and the origin

15. Through $(8, 2)$ and $(0, 4)$

16. $3x + 5y = 25$ 17. $6x - 2y = 7$

18. $x - 2 = 0$ 19. $y = -4$

20. Parallel to $3x + 8y = 0$

21. Perpendicular to $x = 3y$

22. Graph the line through $(0, 5)$ with slope $m = -2/3$.

23. Graph the line through $(-4, 1)$ with $m = 3$.

24. What information is needed to determine the equation of a line?

Find an equation for each of the following lines.

25. Through $(5, -1)$, slope $2/3$

26. Through $(8, 0)$, slope $-1/4$

27. Through $(5, -2)$ and $(1, 3)$

28. Through $(2, -3)$ and $(-3, 4)$

29. Undefined slope, through $(-1, 4)$

30. Slope 0, through $(-2, 5)$

31. x-intercept -3, y-intercept 5

32. Here is a sample SAT question: Which of the following is an equation of the line that has a y-intercept of 2 and an x-intercept of 3?

   (a) $-2x + 3y = 4$ (b) $-2x + 3y = 6$

   (c) $2x + 3y = 4$ (d) $2x + 3y = 6$

   (e) $3x + 2y = 6$

33. **Business**   According to the U.S. Department of Agriculture, in 2005, the United States exported 14.0 million hectoliters of fruit juices and wine. In 2011, that number was 17.3 million hectoliters.

   (a) Assuming the increase in exports of fruit juice and wine is linear, write an equation that gives the amount exported in year x, with $x = 5$ corresponding to the year 2005.

   (b) Is the slope of the line positive or negative? Why?

   (c) Assuming the linear trend continues, estimate the amount exported in the year 2014.

34. **Business**   In the year 2005, the total domestic fish and shellfish catch was 9.7 billion pounds. In 2010, the total was 8.2 billion pounds. (Data from: U.S. National Oceanic and Atmospheric Administration.)

   (a) Assuming the decline in fish and shellfish catch is linear, write an equation that gives the amount of the catch produced in year x, where $x = 5$ corresponds to the year 2005.

   (b) Graph the equation for the years 2005 through 2010.

   (c) Assuming the trend continues, estimate the total fish and shellfish catch in the year 2013.

35. **Business**   The following table gives the total compensation (in dollars) per full-time employee for various years. (Data from: U.S. Bureau of Economic Analysis.)

Year	2000	2005	2010	2011
Compensation	47,059	56,620	66,249	68,129

(a) Use the data from the years 2000 and 2010 to find a linear model for the data, with $x = 0$ corresponding to the year 2000.

(b) Find the least-squares regression line for the data.

(c) Use the models from part (a) and (b) to estimate the compensation for the year 2011. Compare the estimates to the actual compensation of $68,129 for the year 2011.

(d) Assume the trend continues and use the model for (b) to estimate the compensation per full-time employee in the year 2015.

36. Business If current trends continue, the median weekly earnings (in dollars) that a male can expect to earn is approximated by the equation $y = 17.4x + 639$, where $x = 0$ corresponds to the year 2000. The equation $y = 17.3x + 495$ approximates median weekly earnings for females. (Data from: U.S. Bureau of Labor Statistics.)

(a) In what year will males achieve median weekly earnings of $900?

(b) In what year will females achieve median weekly earnings of $900?

⚡ 37. Business The following table shows the total private philanthropy donations (in billions of dollars) for various years. (Data from: Center on Philanthropy at Indiana University.)

Year	1990	1995	2000	2005	2010
Philanthropy	101	124	230	288	287

(a) Let $x = 0$ correspond to the year 1990, and find the least-squares regression line for the data.

(b) Graph the data from the years 1990 to 2010 with the least-squares regression line.

(c) Does the least-squares regression line form a good fit?

(d) What is the correlation coefficient?

⚡ 38. Economics According to the U.S. Department of Education, the average financial aid award (in dollars) for a full-time student is given in the following table for various years:

Year	2000	2005	2008	2009	2010	2011
Amount	2925	3407	3791	4056	4232	4341

(a) Let $x = 0$ correspond to the year 2000, and find the least-squares regression line for the data.

(b) Graph the data from the years 2000 to 2011 with the least-squares regression line.

(c) Does the least-squares regression line form a good fit?

(d) What is the correlation coefficient?

Solve each inequality.

39. $-6x + 3 < 2x$

40. $12z \geq 5z - 7$

41. $2(3 - 2m) \geq 8m + 3$

42. $6p - 5 > -(2p + 3)$

43. $-3 \leq 4x - 1 \leq 7$

44. $0 \leq 3 - 2a \leq 15$

45. $|b| \leq 8$

46. $|a| > 7$

47. $|2x - 7| \geq 3$

48. $|4m + 9| \leq 16$

49. $|5k + 2| - 3 \leq 4$

50. $|3z - 5| + 2 \geq 10$

51. Natural Science Here is a sample SAT question: For pumpkin carving, Mr. Sephera will not use pumpkins that weigh less than 2 pounds or more than 10 pounds. If x represents the weight of a pumpkin (in pounds) that he will *not* use, which of the following inequalities represents all possible values of x?

(a) $|x - 2| > 10$ (b) $|x - 4| > 6$

(c) $|x - 5| > 5$ (d) $|x - 6| > 4$

(e) $|x - 10| > 4$

52. Business Prices at several retail outlets for a new 24-inch, 2-cycle snow thrower were all within $55 of $600. Write this information as an inequality, using absolute-value notation.

53. Business The amount of renewable energy consumed by the industrial sector of the U.S. economy (in trillion BTUs) was 1873 in the year 2005 and 2250 in the year 2010. Assume the amount of energy consumed is increasing linearly. (Data from: U.S. Energy Information Administration.)

(a) Find the linear equation that gives the number of BTUs consumed with $x = 5$ corresponding to the year 2005.

(b) Assume the linear equation that gives the amount of energy consumed continues indefinitely. Determine when the consumption will exceed 2500.

54. Business One car rental firm charges $125 for a weekend rental (Friday afternoon through Monday morning) and gives unlimited mileage. A second firm charges $95 plus $.20 a mile. For what range of miles driven is the second firm cheaper?

Solve each inequality.

55. $r^2 + r - 6 < 0$

56. $y^2 + 4y - 5 \geq 0$

57. $2z^2 + 7z \geq 15$

58. $3k^2 \leq k + 14$

59. $(x - 3)(x^2 + 7x + 10) \leq 0$

60. $(x + 4)(x^2 - 1) \geq 0$

61. $\dfrac{m + 2}{m} \leq 0$

62. $\dfrac{q - 4}{q + 3} > 0$

63. $\dfrac{5}{p + 1} > 2$

64. $\dfrac{6}{a - 2} \leq -3$

65. $\dfrac{2}{r + 5} \leq \dfrac{3}{r - 2}$

66. $\dfrac{1}{z - 1} > \dfrac{2}{z + 1}$

⚡ 67. Business The net income (in millions of dollars) generated by the satellite radio company SiriusXM can be approximated by the equation $y = 340.1x^2 - 5360x + 18{,}834$, where $x = 6$ corresponds to the year 2006. In what years between 2006 and 2012 did SiriusXM have positive net income? (Data from: www.morningstar.com.)

⚡ 68. Business The net income (in millions of dollars) generated by Xerox corporation can be approximated by the equation $y = 89.29x^2 - 1577x + 7505$, where $x = 6$ corresponds to the year 2006. In what years between 2006 and 2012 did Xerox have net income higher than $1000 million? (Data from: www.morningstar.com.)

Case Study 2 Using Extrapolation and Interpolation for Prediction

One reason for developing a mathematical model is to make predictions. If your model is a least-squares line, you can predict the y-value corresponding to some new x-value by substituting that x-value into an equation of the form $\hat{y} = mx + b$. (We use $\hat{y}$ to remind us that we're getting a predicted value rather than an actual data value.) Data analysts distinguish between two very different kinds of prediction: *interpolation* and *extrapolation*. An interpolation uses a new x inside the x-range of your original data. For example, if you have inflation data at five-year intervals from 1950 to 2010, estimating the rate of inflation in 1957 is an interpolation problem. But if you use the same data to estimate what the inflation rate was in 1920, or what it will be in 2020, you are extrapolating.

In general, interpolation is much safer than extrapolation, because data that are approximately linear over a short interval may be nonlinear over a larger interval. Let us examine a case of the dangers of extrapolation. Figure 1 shows the net income (in millions of dollars) for the Starbucks Corporation from the years 2001–2007. Also on Figure 1, we see the least-squares regression line. (Data from: www.morningstar.com.)

As we know, however, the year 2008 saw the start of a deep recession in the United States, and the net earnings for Starbucks were actually $316 million in the year 2008 and $391 million in the year 2009—substantially lower than the predictions.

Using the past to predict the future is generally a dangerous business because we often cannot foresee events with major impact such as recessions, natural disasters, etc. Predictions into the future are often made, however, because planning has to occur and we use the best data we have available. One merely needs to realize that predictions into the future are highly likely to be inaccurate.

One way to determine if a model is likely to be inaccurate in the future is to examine the residuals. In Section 2.3, we defined a residual to be the difference between the actual value y and its predicted value $\hat{y}$.

$$\text{Residual} = y - \hat{y}.$$

Graphing these residuals on the y-axis and the predictor variable on the x-axis can be illuminating. Let's look at another historical example. Figure 2 shows the total household debt (in trillions of dollars) from the years 2004 through 2010. (Data from: Federal Reserve Bank of New York.)

Figure 1

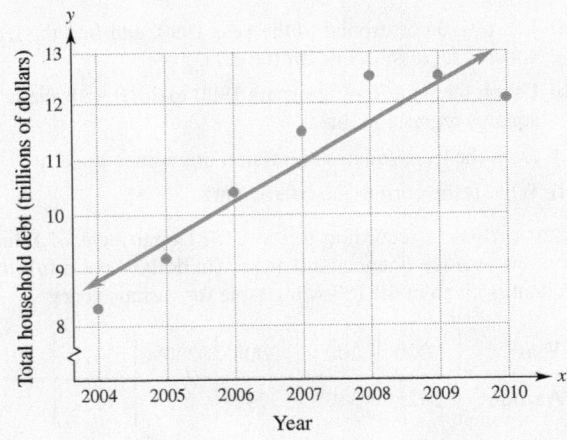

Figure 2

As we can see from graph, the fit is quite good and the linear trend seems quite clear. Additionally, the correlation coefficient is $r \approx .99$, which is quite high. The least-squares regression equation is

$$y = 85.7x + 55.3,$$

where $x = 1$ corresponds to 2001. If we extrapolate to the next two years, we predict the net earnings for Starbucks to be

2008: $85.7(8) + 55.3 = \$740.9$ million

2009: $85.7(9) + 55.3 = \$826.6$ million

The regression equation for the least-squares line in Figure 2 is

$$y = .7x + 5.9,$$

where $x = 4$ corresponds to the year 2004. Since the correlation coefficient r is approximately .93, our linear model appears to fit the data well. We notice, however, that the predictions overpredict, then underpredict, and then overpredict. We can get a better look at this pattern by plotting the residuals. To find them, we put each value of the independent variable into the regression equation, calculate the predicted value $\hat{y}$, and subtract it from the actual value of y as in the table.

Year	2004	2005	2006	2007	2008	2009	2010
x	4	5	6	7	8	9	10
y	8.3	9.2	10.4	11.5	12.5	12.5	12.1
$\hat{y}$	8.7	9.4	10.1	10.8	11.5	12.2	12.9
Residual $y - \hat{y}$	–.4	–.2	.3	.7	1.0	.3	–.8

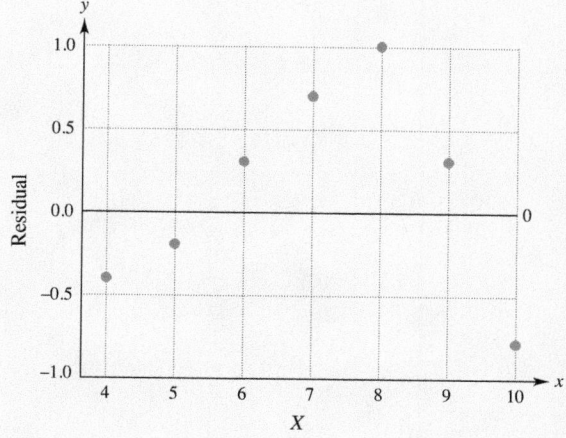

Figure 3

The residuals in Figure 3 indicate that our data have a nonlinear U-shaped component that is not captured by a linear model. When a residual plot shows a pattern such as this (or a similar pattern with an upside down U), extrapolating from the data is probably not a good idea. Our prediction for the year 2011, for example, would be

$$\hat{y} = .7(11) + 5.9 = \$13.6 \text{ trillion},$$

which is far higher than the actual value of $11.8 trillion.

Exercises

Business The following table gives the number of completed new single family homes (in thousands) from the years 2002 to 2012. (Data from: U.S. Census Bureau.)

Year	Housing Units	Year	Housing Units
2002	1648	2008	1120
2003	1679	2009	794
2004	1842	2010	652
2005	1931	2011	585
2006	1979	2012	650
2007	1503		

1. If you have access to the appropriate technology, verify that the least-squares regression line that models these data (with rounded coefficients) is $y = -146.1x + 2330$, where $x = 2$ corresponds to the year 2002.

2. Use the model from Exercise 1 to calculate the predicted values $\hat{y}$ for each year in the table.

3. Use your answers from Exercise 2 to calculate the residuals for each year in the table. Make a graph of the residuals similar to Figure 3.

4. Do you think the linear model of Exercise 1 is a good fit for these data? Why or why not?

Business The following table gives the average hourly earnings (in dollars) of U.S. production workers from 1970 to 2010. (Data from: U.S. Bureau of Labor Statistics.)

Year	Average Hourly Wage (Dollars)
1970	3.40
1975	4.73
1980	6.85
1985	8.74
1990	10.20
1995	11.65
2000	14.02
2005	16.13
2010	16.26

5. If you have appropriate technology, verify that the least-squares regression line that models these data (with coefficients rounded) is $y = .343x - 20.65$, where y is the average hourly wage in year x and $x = 0$ corresponds to 1900.

6. Use the model from Exercise 5 to interpolate a prediction of the hourly wage in 2002. The actual value was $14.97. How close was your prediction?

7. Use the model from Exercise 5 to extrapolate to 1960 and predict the hourly average wage. Why is this prediction nonsensical?

8. Using the model from Exercise 5, find the average hourly wage for each year in the table, and subtract it from the actual value in the second column. This gives you a table of the residuals. Plot your residuals as points on a graph.

9. What will happen if you try linear regression on the *residuals*? If you're not sure, use technology such as a graphing calculator to find the regression equation for the residuals. Why does this result make sense?

Extended Project

Go the library or use the Internet to obtain the average amount of student loan debt for the most recent years available.

1. Create a scatterplot of the data with the amount on the y-axis and the year on the x-axis and assess the trend.
2. Fit a linear model to the data and predict the loan debt amount for each year.

3. Calculate the residuals from each year in the data set. Graph the residuals.
4. Do the residuals show a U-shape?
5. Find the correlation coefficient for your data.

Functions and Graphs

3

The modern world is overwhelmed with data—from the cost of college to mortgage rates, health care expenditures, and hundreds of other pieces of information. Functions enable us to construct mathematical models that can sometimes be used to estimate outcomes. Graphs of functions allow us to visualize a situation and to detect trends more easily. See Example 11 on page 129 and Exercises 57 and 58 on page 179.

Functions are an extremely useful way of describing many real-world situations in which the value of one quantity varies with, depends on, or determines the value of another. In this chapter, you will be introduced to functions, learn how to use functional notation, develop skills in constructing and interpreting the graphs of functions, and, finally, learn to apply this knowledge in a variety of situations.

3.1   Functions

To understand the origin of the concept of a function, we consider some real-life situations in which one numerical quantity depends on, corresponds to, or determines another.

Example 1   The amount of the electric bill you pay depends on the amount of kilowatt hours (kWh) consumed. The way in which the usage determines the bill is given by the rate per kWh.

Example 2   **Economics**   The graph in Figure 3.1 shows the poverty rate from the years 1959 to 2011. The blue vertical bands indicate times of economic recession. The graph displays the percentage living in poverty that corresponds to each year. (Source: DeNavas-Walt, Carmen, Bernadette D. Proctor, and Jessica C. Smith, U.S. Census Bureau, Current Population Reports, P60-243, Income, Poverty, and Health Insurance Coverage in the United States: 2011, U.S. Government Printing Office, Washington, DC, 2012.)

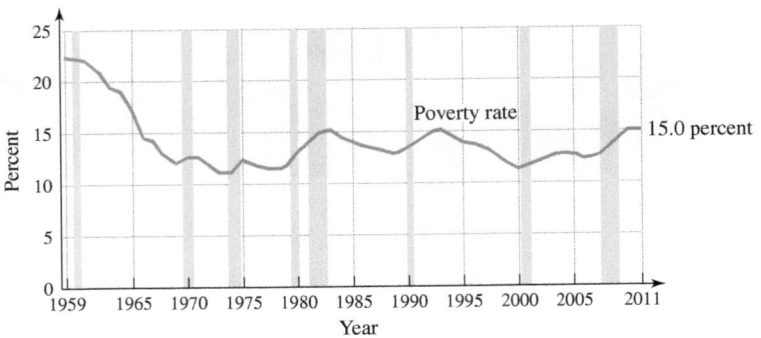

Figure 3.1

Example 3   **Physical Science**   Suppose a rock is dropped straight down from a high point. From physics, we know that the distance traveled by the rock in t seconds is $16t^2$ feet. So the distance depends on the time.

These examples share a couple of features. First, each involves two sets of numbers, which we can think of as inputs and outputs. Second, in each case, there is a rule by which each input determines an output, as summarized here:

	Set of Inputs	Set of Outputs	Rule
Example 1	All usages	All bill amounts	The rate per kWh
Example 2	Year	Poverty rate	Time-rate graph
Example 3	Seconds elapsed after dropping the rock	Distances the rock travels	Distance $= 16t^2$

Each of these examples may be mentally represented by an idealized calculator that has a single operation key: A number is entered [*input*], the rule key is pushed [*rule*], and an answer is displayed [*output*]. The formal definition of a function incorporates these same common features (input–rule–output), with a slight change in terminology.

A **function** consists of a set of inputs called the **domain,** a set of outputs called the **range,** and a rule by which each input determines *exactly one* output.

✓**Checkpoint 1**

Find the domain and range of the function in Example 3, assuming (unrealistically) that the rock can fall forever.

Answers to Checkpoint exercises are found at the end of the section.

Example 4   Find the domains and ranges for the functions in Examples 1 and 2.

Solution   In Example 1, the domain consists of all possible usage amounts and the range consists of all possible bill amounts.

In Example 2, the domain is the set of years from 1959 to 2011, all real numbers in the interval [1959, 2011]. The range consists of the poverty rates that actually occur during those years. Figure 3.1 suggests that these are all numbers in the interval [11, 22]. ✓₁

Be sure that you understand the phrase "exactly one output" in the definition of the rule of a function. In Example 2, for instance, each year (input) determines exactly one poverty rate (output)—you can't have two different rates at the same time. However, it is quite possible to have the same rate (output) at two different times (inputs). In other words, we can say the following:

> **In a function, each input produces a single output,**
> **but different inputs may produce the same output.**

Example 5   Which of the following rules describe functions?

(a) Use the optical reader at the checkout counter of the supermarket to convert codes to prices.

Solution   For each code, the reader produces exactly one price, so this is a function.

(b) Enter a number in a calculator and press the x^2 key.

Solution   This is a function, because the calculator produces just one number x^2 for each number x that is entered.

(c) Assign to each number x the number y given by this table:

x	1	1	2	2	3	3
y	3	−3	−5	−5	8	−8

Solution   Since $x = 1$ corresponds to more than one y-value (as does $x = 3$), this table does not define a function.

(d) Assign to each number x the number y given by the equation $y = 3x - 5$.

Solution   Because the equation determines a unique value of y for each value of x, it defines a function. ✓ 2

The equation $y = 3x - 5$ in part (d) of Example 5 defines a function, with x as input and y as output, because each value of x determines a *unique* value of y. In such a case, the equation is said to **define y as a function of x.**

Example 6   Decide whether each of the following equations defines y as a function of x.

(a) $y = -4x + 11$

Solution   For a given value of x, calculating $-4x + 11$ produces exactly one value of y. (For example, if $x = -7$, then $y = -4(-7) + 11 = 39$). Because one value of the input variable leads to exactly one value of the output variable, $y = -4x + 11$ defines y as a function of x.

(b) $y^2 = x$

Solution   Suppose $x = 36$. Then $y^2 = x$ becomes $y^2 = 36$, from which $y = 6$ or $y = -6$. Since one value of x can lead to two values of y, $y^2 = x$ does *not* define y as a function of x. ✓ 3

Almost all the functions in this text are defined by formulas or equations, as in part (a) of Example 6. The domain of such a function is determined by the following **agreement on domains.**

✓ **Checkpoint 2**

Do the following define functions?

(a) The correspondence defined by the rule $y = x^2 + 5$, where x is the input and y is the output.

(b) The correspondence defined by entering a nonzero number in a calculator and pressing the $1/x$ key.

(c) The correspondence between a computer, x, and several users of the computer, y.

✓ **Checkpoint 3**

Do the following define y as a function of x?

(a) $y = -6x + 1$

(b) $y = x^2$

(c) $x = y^2 - 1$

(d) $y < x + 2$

Unless otherwise stated, assume that the domain of any function defined by a formula or an equation is the largest set of real numbers (inputs) that each produces a real number as output.

Example 7   Each of the given equations defines y as a function of x. Find the domain of each function.

(a) $y = x^4$

Solution Any number can be raised to the fourth power, so the domain is the set of all real numbers, which is sometimes written as $(-\infty, \infty)$.

(b) $y = \sqrt{x - 6}$

Solution For y to be a real number, $x - 6$ must be nonnegative. This happens only when $x - 6 \geq 0$—that is, when $x \geq 6$. So the domain is the interval $[6, \infty)$.

(c) $y = \sqrt{4 - x}$

Solution For y to be a real number here, we must have $4 - x \geq 0$, which is equivalent to $x \leq 4$. So the domain is the interval $(-\infty, 4]$.

(d) $y = \dfrac{1}{x + 3}$

Solution Because the denominator cannot be 0, $x \neq -3$ and the domain consists of all numbers in the intervals,

$$(-\infty, -3) \quad \text{or} \quad (-3, \infty).$$

(e) $y = \dfrac{\sqrt{x}}{x^2 - 3x + 2}$

Solution The numerator is defined only when $x \geq 0$. The domain cannot contain any numbers that make the denominator 0—that is, the numbers that are solutions of

$$x^2 - 3x + 2 = 0.$$
$$(x - 1)(x - 2) = 0 \qquad \text{Factor.}$$
$$x - 1 = 0 \quad \text{or} \quad x - 2 = 0 \qquad \text{Zero-factor property}$$
$$x = 1 \quad \text{or} \qquad x = 2.$$

Therefore, the domain consists of all nonnegative real numbers except 1 and 2. ✓₄

✓ **Checkpoint 4**

Give the domain of each function.

(a) $y = 3x + 1$

(b) $y = x^2$

(c) $y = \sqrt{-x}$

(d) $y = \dfrac{3}{x^2 - 1}$

Functional Notation

In actual practice, functions are seldom presented in the style of domain–rule–range, as they have been here. Functions are usually denoted by a letter such as f. If x is an input, then $f(x)$ denotes the output number that the function f produces from the input x. The symbol $f(x)$ is read "f of x." The rule is usually given by a formula, such as $f(x) = \sqrt{x^2 + 1}$. This formula can be thought of as a set of directions:

Name of function   Input number

$$\underbrace{f(x)} = \sqrt{x^2 + 1}$$

Output number   Directions that tell you what to do with input x in order to produce the corresponding output $f(x)$—namely, "square it, add 1, and take the square root of the result."

For example, to find $f(3)$ (the output number produced by the input 3), simply replace x by 3 in the formula:

$$f(3) = \sqrt{3^2 + 1}$$
$$= \sqrt{10}.$$

Similarly, replacing x respectively by -5 and 0 shows that

$$f(-5) = \sqrt{(-5)^2 + 1} \quad \text{and} \quad f(0) = \sqrt{0^2 + 1}$$
$$= \sqrt{26} \qquad\qquad\qquad = 1.$$

These directions can be applied to any quantities, such as $a + b$ or c^4 (where a, b, and c are real numbers). Thus, to compute $f(a + b)$, the output corresponding to input $a + b$, we square the input [obtaining $(a + b)^2$], add 1 [obtaining $(a + b)^2 + 1$], and take the square root of the result:

$$f(a + b) = \sqrt{(a + b)^2 + 1}$$
$$= \sqrt{a^2 + 2ab + b^2 + 1}.$$

Similarly, the output $f(c^4)$, corresponding to the input c^4, is computed by squaring the input $[(c^4)^2]$, adding 1 $[(c^4)^2 + 1]$, and taking the square root of the result:

$$f(c^4) = \sqrt{(c^4)^2 + 1}$$
$$= \sqrt{c^8 + 1}.$$

Example 8   Let $g(x) = -x^2 + 4x - 5$. Find each of the given outputs.

(a) $g(-2)$

Solution   Replace x with -2:

$$g(-2) = -(-2)^2 + 4(-2) - 5$$
$$= -4 - 8 - 5$$
$$= -17.$$

(b) $g(x + h)$

Solution   Replace x by the quantity $x + h$ in the rule of g:

$$g(x + h) = -(x + h)^2 + 4(x + h) - 5$$
$$= -(x^2 + 2xh + h^2) + (4x + 4h) - 5$$
$$= -x^2 - 2xh - h^2 + 4x + 4h - 5.$$

(c) $g(x + h) - g(x)$

Solution   Use the result from part (b) and the rule for $g(x)$:

$$g(x + h) - g(x) = \overbrace{(-x^2 - 2xh - h^2 + 4x + 4h - 5)}^{g(x+h)} - \overbrace{(-x^2 + 4x - 5)}^{g(x)}$$
$$= -2xh - h^2 + 4h.$$

(d) $\dfrac{g(x + h) - g(x)}{h}$ (assuming that $h \neq 0$)

Solution   The numerator was found in part (c). Divide it by h as follows:

$$\frac{g(x + h) - g(x)}{h} = \frac{-2xh - h^2 + 4h}{h}$$
$$= \frac{h(-2x - h + 4)}{h}$$
$$= -2x - h + 4.$$

The quotient found in Example 8(d),

$$\frac{g(x + h) - g(x)}{h},$$

is called the **difference quotient** of the function g. Difference quotients are important in calculus. ☑5

☑ **Checkpoint 5**

Let $f(x) = 5x^2 - 2x + 1$. Find the following.

(a) $f(1)$

(b) $f(3)$

(c) $f(1 + 3)$

(d) $f(1) + f(3)$

(e) $f(m)$

(f) $f(x + h) - f(x)$

(g) $\dfrac{f(x + h) - f(x)}{h}$ $(h \neq 0)$

CAUTION Functional notation is *not* the same as ordinary algebraic notation. You cannot simplify an expression such as $f(x + h)$ by writing $f(x) + f(h)$. To see why, consider the answers to Checkpoints 5(c) and (d), which show that

$$f(1 + 3) \neq f(1) + f(3).$$

Applications

Example 9   **Finance**   If you were a single person in Connecticut in 2013 with a taxable income of x dollars and $x \leq \$500,000$ then your state income tax T was determined by the rule

$$T(x) = \begin{cases} .03x & \text{if } 0 \leq x \leq 10,000 \\ 300 + .05(x - 10,000) & \text{if } 10,000 \leq x \leq 500,00 \end{cases}$$

Find the income tax paid by a single person with the given taxable income. (Data from: www.taxbrackets.org.)

(a) $9200

Solution   We must find $T(9200)$. Since 9200 is less than 10,000, the first part of the rule applies:

$$T(x) = .03x$$
$$T(9200) = .03(9200) = \$276. \quad \text{Let } x = 9200.$$

(b) $30,000

Solution   Now we must find $T(30,000)$. Since 30,000 is greater than $10,000, the second part of the rule applies:

$$T(x) = 300 + .05(x - 10,000)$$
$$T(30,000) = 300 + .05(30,000 - 10,000) \quad \text{Let } x = 30,000.$$
$$= 300 + .05(20,000) \quad \text{Simplify.}$$
$$= 300 + 1000 = \$1300. \text{ ☑6}$$

A function with a multipart rule, as in Example 9, is called a **piecewise-defined function.**

☑ **Checkpoint 6**

Use Example 9 to find the tax on each of these incomes.

(a) $48,750

(b) $7345

Example 10   **Business**   Suppose the projected sales (in thousands of dollars) of a small company over the next 10 years are approximated by the function

$$S(x) = .07x^4 - .05x^3 + 2x^2 + 7x + 62.$$

(a) What are the projected sales for the current year?

Solution   The current year corresponds to $x = 0$, and the sales for this year are given by $S(0)$. Substituting 0 for x in the rule for S, we see that $S(0) = 62$. So the current projected sales are $62,000.

Checkpoint 7

A developer estimates that the total cost of building x large apartment complexes in a year is approximated by

$$A(x) = x^2 + 80x + 60,$$

where $A(x)$ represents the cost in hundred thousands of dollars. Find the cost of building

(a) 4 complexes;

(b) 10 complexes.

(b) What will sales be in four years?

Solution The sales in four years from now are given by $S(4)$, which can be computed by hand or with a calculator:

$$S(x) = .07x^4 - .05x^3 + 2x^2 + 7x + 62$$
$$S(4) = .07(4)^4 - .05(4)^3 + 2(4)^2 + 7(4) + 62 \qquad \text{Let } x = 4.$$
$$= 136.72.$$

Thus, sales are projected to be $136,720. ✓7

X	Y1
5	184.5
6	255.92
7	359.92
8	507.12
9	709.82
10	982
11	1339.3

X=5

Figure 3.2

Example 11 Business Use the table feature of the graphing calculator to find the projected sales of the company in Example 10 for years 5 through 10.

Solution Enter the sales equation $y = .07x^4 - .05x^3 + 2x^2 + 7x + 62$ into the equation memory of the calculator (often called the $Y =$ list). Check your instruction manual for how to set the table to start at $x = 5$ and go at least through $x = 10$. Then display the table, as in Figure 3.2. The figure shows that sales are projected to rise from $184,500 in year 5 to $982,000 in year 10.

3.1 Exercises

For each of the following rules, state whether it defines y as a function of x or not. (See Examples 5 and 6.)

1.

x	3	2	1	0	-1	-2	-3
y	9	4	1	0	1	4	9

2.

x	9	4	1	0	1	4	9
y	3	2	1	0	-1	-2	-3

3. $y = x^3$

4. $y = \sqrt{x - 1}$

5. $x = |y + 2|$

6. $x = y^2 + 3$

7. $y = \dfrac{-1}{x - 1}$

8. $y = \dfrac{4}{2x + 3}$

State the domain of each function. (See Example 7.)

9. $f(x) = 4x - 1$

10. $f(x) = 2x + 7$

11. $f(x) = x^4 - 1$

12. $f(x) = (2x + 5)^2$

13. $f(x) = \sqrt{-x} + 3$

14. $f(x) = \sqrt{5 - x}$

15. $g(x) = \dfrac{1}{x - 2}$

16. $g(x) = \dfrac{x}{x^2 + x - 2}$

17. $g(x) = \dfrac{x^2 + 4}{x^2 - 4}$

18. $g(x) = \dfrac{x^2 - 1}{x^2 + 1}$

19. $h(x) = \dfrac{\sqrt{x + 4}}{x^2 + x - 12}$

20. $h(x) = |5 - 4x|$

21. $g(x) = \begin{cases} 1/x & \text{if } x < 0 \\ \sqrt{x^2 + 1} & \text{if } x \geq 0 \end{cases}$

22. $f(x) = \begin{cases} 2x + 3 & \text{if } x < 4 \\ x^2 - 1 & \text{if } 4 \leq x \leq 10 \end{cases}$

For each of the following functions, find

(a) $f(4)$; (b) $f(-3)$; (c) $f(2.7)$; (d) $f(-4.9)$.

(See Examples 8 and 9.)

23. $f(x) = 8$

24. $f(x) = 0$

25. $f(x) = 2x^2 + 4x$

26. $f(x) = x^2 - 2x$

27. $f(x) = \sqrt{x + 3}$

28. $f(x) = \sqrt{5 - x}$

29. $f(x) = |x^2 - 6x - 4|$

30. $f(x) = |x^3 - x^2 + x - 1|$

31. $f(x) = \dfrac{\sqrt{x - 1}}{x^2 - 1}$

32. $f(x) = \sqrt{-x} + \dfrac{2}{x + 1}$

33. $f(x) = \begin{cases} x^2 & \text{if } x < 2 \\ 5x - 7 & \text{if } x \geq 2 \end{cases}$

34. $f(x) = \begin{cases} -2x + 4 & \text{if } x \leq 1 \\ 3 & \text{if } 1 < x < 4 \\ x + 1 & \text{if } x \geq 4 \end{cases}$

For each of the following functions, find

(a) $f(p)$; (b) $f(-r)$; (c) $f(m + 3)$.

(See Example 8.)

35. $f(x) = 6 - x$

36. $f(x) = 3x + 5$

37. $f(x) = \sqrt{4 - x}$

38. $f(x) = \sqrt{-2x}$

39. $f(x) = x^3 + 1$

40. $f(x) = 3 - x^3$

41. $f(x) = \dfrac{3}{x - 1}$

42. $f(x) = \dfrac{-1}{5 + x}$

For each of the following functions, find the difference quotient

$$\frac{f(x + h) - f(x)}{h} \quad (h \neq 0).$$

(See Example 8.)

43. $f(x) = 2x - 4$

44. $f(x) = 2 + 4x$

45. $f(x) = x^2 + 1$

46. $f(x) = x^2 - x$

✒ *If you have a graphing calculator with table-making ability, display a table showing the (approximate) values of the given function at $x = 3.5, 3.9, 4.3, 4.7, 5.1,$ and 5.5. (See Example 11.)*

47. $g(x) = 3x^4 - x^3 + 2x$

48. $f(x) = \sqrt{x^2 - 2.4x + 8}$

✒ *Use a calculator to work these exercises. (See Examples 9 and 10.)*

49. Finance The Minnesota state income tax for a single person in 2013 was determined by the rule

$$T(x) = \begin{cases} .0535x & \text{if } 0 \leq x \leq 23{,}100 \\ 1235.85 + .0705(x - 23{,}100) & \text{if } 23{,}100 < x \leq 75{,}891 \\ 4957.62 + .0785(x - 75{,}891) & \text{if } x > 75{,}891, \end{cases}$$

where x is the person's taxable income. Find the tax on each of these incomes. (Data from: www.taxbrackets.org.)

(a) $20,000

(b) $70,000

(c) $120,000

50. Economics The gross domestic product (GDP) of the United States, which measures the overall size of the U.S. economy in trillions of dollars, is approximated by the function

$$f(x) = -.017x^2 + .68x + 9.6,$$

where $x = 0$ corresponds to the year 2000. Estimate the GDP in the given years. (Data from: U.S. Bureau of Economic Analysis.)

(a) 2005

(b) 2009

(c) 2011

51. Business The net revenue for Ford Motor Company (in billions of dollars) between the years 2006 and 2012 is approximated by

$$R(x) = -.722x^3 + 19.23x^2 - 161.2x + 421.8,$$

where $x = 6$ corresponds to the year 2006. (Data from: www.morningstar.com.)

(a) What was the net revenue in 2008?

(b) What was the net revenue in 2011?

52. Business The number of passengers enplaned (in millions) for the years 2000–2011 can be approximated by the function

$$f(x) = .377x^4 - 9.23x^3 + 71.4x^2 - 163x + 666,$$

where $x = 0$ corresponds to the year 2000. Find the number of enplaned passengers in the following years. (Data from: Airlines for America.)

(a) 2004

(b) 2009

(c) 2010

53. Business The value (in millions of dollars) of electric household ranges and ovens shipped in the United States can be approximated by the function

$$g(x) = -21.1x^2 + 205x + 2164,$$

where $x = 0$ corresponds to the year 2000. (Data from: U.S. Census Bureau.)

(a) What is the value of the ranges and ovens shipped in 2001?

(b) What is the value of the ranges and ovens shipped in 2009?

54. Natural Science High concentrations of zinc ions in water are lethal to rainbow trout. The function

$$f(x) = \left(\frac{x}{1960}\right)^{-.833}$$

gives the approximate average survival time (in minutes) for trout exposed to x milligrams per liter (mg/L) of zinc ions. Find the survival time (to the nearest minute) for the given concentrations of zinc ions.

(a) 110

(b) 525

(c) 1960

(d) 4500

55. Physical Science The distance from Chicago to Sacramento, California, is approximately 2050 miles. A plane flying directly to Sacramento passes over Chicago at noon. If the plane travels at 500 mph, find the rule of the function $f(t)$ that gives the distance of the plane from Sacramento at time t hours (with $t = 0$ corresponding to noon).

56. Physical Science The distance from Toronto, Ontario to Dallas, Texas is approximately 1200 miles. A plane flying directly to Dallas passes over Toronto at 2 p.m. If the plane travels at 550 mph, find the rule of the function $f(t)$ that gives the distance of the plane from Dallas at time t hours (with $t = 0$ corresponding to 2 pm).

57. Business A pretzel factory has daily fixed costs of $1800. In addition, it costs 50 cents to produce each bag of pretzels. A bag of pretzels sells for $1.20.

(a) Find the rule of the cost function $c(x)$ that gives the total daily cost of producing x bags of pretzels.

(b) Find the rule of the revenue function $r(x)$ that gives the daily revenue from selling x bags of pretzels.

(c) Find the rule of the profit function $p(x)$ that gives the daily profit from x bags of pretzels.

58. Business An aluminum can factory has daily fixed costs of $120,000 per day. In addition, it costs $.03 to produce each can. They can sell a can to a soda manufacturer for $.05 a can.

(a) Find the rule of the cost function $c(x)$ that gives the total daily cost of producing x aluminum cans.

(b) Find the rule of the revenue function $r(x)$ that gives the daily revenue from selling x aluminum cans.

(c) Find the rule of the profit function $p(x)$ that gives the daily profit from x aluminum cans.

📈 *Use the table feature of a graphing calculator to do these exercises.*
(See Example 11.)

59. Business   The value (in millions of dollars) of new orders for all manufacturing industries can be approximated by the function

$$h(x) = -4.83x^3 + 50.3x^2 + 25.5x + 4149,$$

where $x = 0$ corresponds to the year 2000. Create a table that gives the value of the sales for the years 2005–2010. (Data from: U.S. Census Bureau.)

60. Business   The value added to the economy (in billions of dollars) for agricultural production can be approximated by the function

$$g(x) = -.35x^3 + 5.34x^2 - 5.17x + 217.3,$$

where $x = 0$ corresponds to 2000. Create a table that gives the value added to the economy for the years 2007–2010. (Data from: U.S. Department of Agriculture.)

✓ **Checkpoint Answers**

1. The domain consists of all possible times—that is, all nonnegative real numbers. The range consists of all possible distances; thus, the range is also the set of all nonnegative real numbers.

2. (a) Yes   (b) Yes   (c) No

3. (a) Yes   (b) Yes   (c) No   (d) No

4. (a) $(-\infty, \infty)$ (b) $(-\infty, \infty)$ (c) $(-\infty, 0]$
   (d) All real numbers except 1 and -1

5. (a) 4   (b) 40   (c) 73   (d) 44
   (e) $5m^2 - 2m + 1$ (f) $10xh + 5h^2 - 2h$
   (g) $10x + 5h - 2$

6. (a) \$2237.50   (b) \$220.35

7. (a) \$39,600,000   (b) \$96,000,000

3.2   Graphs of Functions

The **graph** of a function $f(x)$ is defined to be the graph of the *equation* $y = f(x)$. It consists of all points $(x, f(x))$—that is, every point whose first coordinate is an input number from the domain of f and whose second coordinate is the corresponding output number.

> **Example 1**   The graph of the function $g(x) = .5x - 3$ is the graph of the equation $y = .5x - 3$. So the graph is a straight line with slope .5 and y-intercept -3, as shown in Figure 3.3.
>
>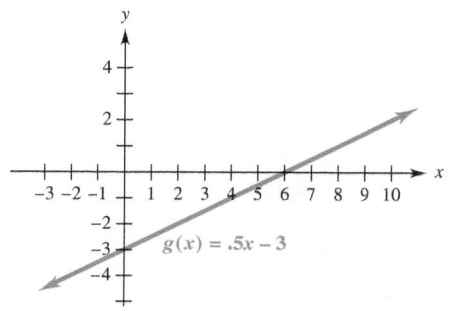
>
> **Figure 3.3**

A function whose graph is a straight line, as in Example 1, is called a **linear function.** The rule of a linear function can always be put into the form

$$f(x) = ax + b$$

for some constants a and b.

Piecewise Linear Functions

We now consider functions whose graphs consist of straight-line segments. Such functions are called **piecewise linear functions** and are typically defined with different equations for different parts of the domain.

Example 2   Graph the following function:

$$f(x) = \begin{cases} x + 1 & \text{if } x \le 2 \\ -2x + 7 & \text{if } x > 2. \end{cases}$$

Solution   Consider the two parts of the rule of f. The graphs of $y = x + 1$ and $y = -2x + 7$ are straight lines. The graph of f consists of

the part of the line $y = x + 1$ with $x \le 2$ and

the part of the line $y = -2x + 7$ with $x > 2$.

Each of these line segments can be graphed by plotting two points in the appropriate interval, as shown in Figure 3.4.

$x \le 2$		
x	0	2
$y = x + 1$	1	3

$x > 2$		
x	3	4
$y = -2x + 7$	1	-1

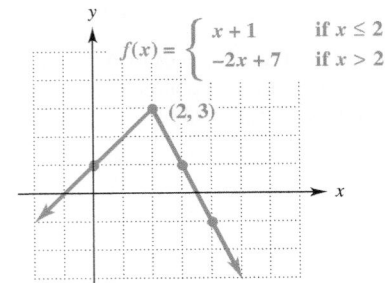

Figure 3.4

Note that the left and right parts of the graph each extend to the vertical line through $x = 2$, where the two halves of the graph meet at the point (2, 3). ✓ 1

✓ Checkpoint 1

Graph

$$f(x) = \begin{cases} x + 2 & \text{if } x < 0 \\ 2 - x & \text{if } x \ge 0. \end{cases}$$

Example 3   Graph the function

$$f(x) = \begin{cases} x - 2 & \text{if } x \le 3 \\ -x + 8 & \text{if } x > 3. \end{cases}$$

Solution   The graph consists of parts of two lines. To find the left side of the graph, choose two values of x with $x \le 3$, say, $x = 0$ and $x = 3$. Then find the corresponding points on $y = x - 2$, namely, $(0, -2)$ and $(3, 1)$. Use these points to draw the line segment to the left of $x = 3$, as in Figure 3.5. Next, choose two values of x with $x > 3$, say, $x = 4$ and $x = 6$, and find the corresponding points on $y = -x + 8$, namely, $(4, 4)$ and $(6, 2)$. Use these points to draw the line segment to the right of $x = 3$, as in Figure 3.5.

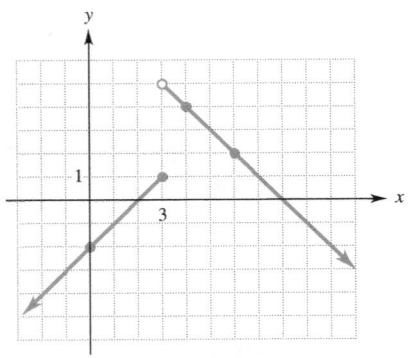

$$f(x) = \begin{cases} x - 2 & \text{if } x \le 3 \\ -x + 8 & \text{if } x > 3 \end{cases}$$

Figure 3.5

✓ **Checkpoint 2**

Graph

$$f(x) = \begin{cases} -2x - 3 & \text{if } x < 1 \\ x - 2 & \text{if } x \geq 1. \end{cases}$$

✓ **Checkpoint 3**

Graph $f(x) = |3x - 4|$.

Note that both line segments of the graph of f extend to the vertical line through $x = 3$. The closed circle at $(3, 1)$ indicates that this point is on the graph of f, whereas the open circle at $(3, 5)$ indicates that this point is *not* on the graph of f (although it is on the graph of the line $y = -x + 8$). ✓2

Example 4   Graph the **absolute-value function,** whose rule is $f(x) = |x|$.

Solution   The definition of absolute value on page 8 shows that the rule of f can be written as

$$f(x) = \begin{cases} x & \text{if } x \geq 0 \\ -x & \text{if } x < 0. \end{cases}$$

So the right half of the graph (that is, where $x \geq 0$) will consist of a portion of the line $y = x$. It can be graphed by plotting two points, say, $(0, 0)$ and $(1, 1)$. The left half of the graph (where $x < 0$) will consist of a portion of the line $y = -x$, which can be graphed by plotting $(-2, 2)$ and $(-1, 1)$, as shown in Figure 3.6. ✓3

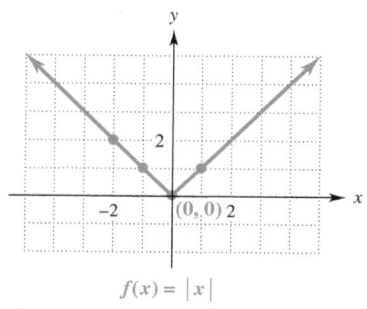

$$f(x) = |x|$$

Figure 3.6

✎ **TECHNOLOGY TIP** To graph most piecewise linear functions on a graphing calculator, you must use a special syntax. For example, on TI calculators, the best way to obtain the graph in Example 3 is to graph two separate equations on the same screen:

$$y_1 = (x - 2)/(x \leq 3) \quad \text{and} \quad y_2 = (-x + 8)/(x > 3).$$

The inequality symbols are in the TEST (or CHAR) menu. However, most calculators will graph absolute-value functions directly. To graph $f(x) = |x + 2|$, for instance, graph the equation $y = abs(x + 2)$. "Abs" (for absolute value) is on the keyboard or in the MATH menu.

Step Functions

The **greatest-integer function,** usually written $f(x) = [x]$, is defined by saying that $[x]$ denotes the largest integer that is less than or equal to x. For example, $[8] = 8, [7.45] = 7, [\pi] = 3, [-1] = -1, [-2.6] = -3$, and so on.

Example 5   Graph the greatest-integer function $f(x) = [x]$.

Solution   Consider the values of the function between each two consecutive integers—for instance,

x	$-2 \leq x < -1$	$-1 \leq x < 0$	$0 \leq x < 1$	$1 \leq x < 2$	$2 \leq x < 3$
$[x]$	-2	-1	0	1	2

Thus, between $x = -2$ and $x = -1$, the value of $f(x) = [x]$ is always -2, so the graph there is a horizontal line segment, all of whose points have second coordinate -2. The rest of the graph is obtained similarly (Figure 3.7). An open circle in that figure indicates that the endpoint of the segment is *not* on the graph, whereas a closed circle indicates that the endpoint *is* on the graph. ✓4

✓**Checkpoint 4**

Graph $y = [\frac{1}{2}x + 1]$.

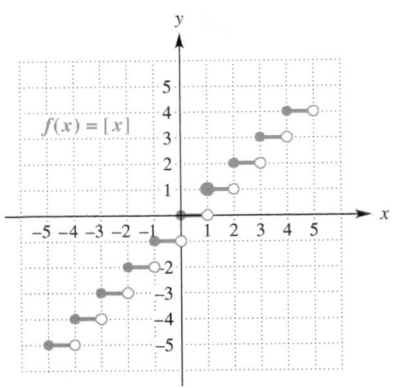

Figure 3.7

Functions whose graphs resemble the graph of the greatest-integer function are sometimes called **step functions.**

Example 6   **Business**   In 2013, the U.S. Post Office charged to ship a flat envelope first class to Eastern Europe, Europe, or Australia a fee of $2.05 for up to and including the first ounce, $.85 for each additional ounce or fraction of an ounce up to and including 8 ounces, and then $1.70 for each additional four ounces or less, up to a peak of 64 ounces. Let $D(x)$ represent the cost to send a flat envelope weighing x ounces. Graph $D(x)$ for x in the interval $(0, 20]$.

Solution   For x in the interval $(0, 1]$, $y = 2.05$. For x in $(1, 2]$, $y = 2.05 + .85 = 2.90$. For x in $(2, 3]$, $y = 2.90 + .85 = 3.75$, and so on up to x in $(7, 8]$, $y = 7.15 + .85 = 8.00$. Then for x in $(8, 12]$, $y = 8.00 + 1.70 = 9.70$. For x in $(12, 16]$, $y = 9.70 + 1.70 = 11.40$, and x in $(16, 20]$, $y = 11.40 + 1.70 = 13.10$. The graph, which is that of a step function, is shown in Figure 3.8. ✓5

✓**Checkpoint 5**

To mail a letter to the regions described in Example 6, the U.S. Post Office charges $1.10 for up to and including the first ounce, an additional $.95 for up to and including 2 ounces, an additional $.95 for up to and including 3 ounces, and then an additional $.95 to a maximum weight of 3.5 ounces. Let $L(x)$ represent the cost of sending a letter to those regions where x represents the weight of the letter in ounces. Graph $L(x)$ for x in the interval $(0, 3.5]$.

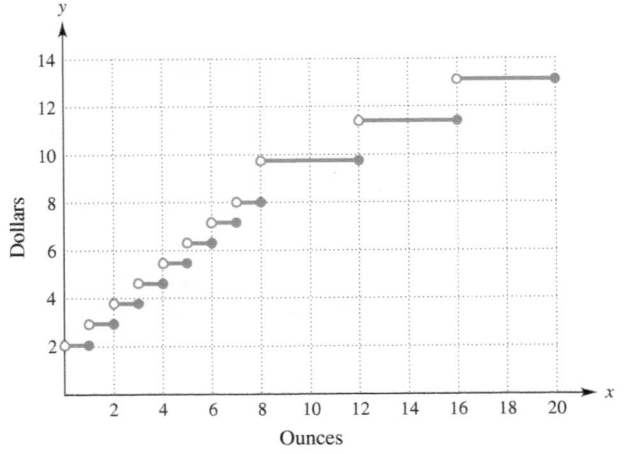

Figure 3.8

📐 **TECHNOLOGY TIP** On most graphing calculators, the greatest-integer function is denoted INT or FLOOR. (Look on the MATH menu or its NUM submenu.) Casio calculators use INTG for the greatest-integer function and INT for a different function. When graphing these functions, put your calculator in "dot" graphing mode rather than the usual "connected" mode to avoid erroneous vertical line segments in the graph.

Other Functions

The graphs of many functions do not consist only of straight-line segments. As a general rule when graphing functions by hand, you should follow the procedure introduced in Section 2.1 and summarized here.

Graphing a Function by Plotting Points

1. Determine the domain of the function.

2. Select a few numbers in the domain of f (include both negative and positive ones when possible), and compute the corresponding values of $f(x)$.

3. Plot the points $(x, f(x))$ computed in Step 2. Use these points and any other information you may have about the function to make an educated guess about the shape of the entire graph.

4. Unless you have information to the contrary, assume that the graph is continuous (unbroken) wherever it is defined.

This method was used to find the graphs of the functions $f(x) = x^2 - 2x - 8$ and $g(x) = \sqrt{x + 2}$ in Examples 3 and 4 of Section 2.1. Here are some more examples.

Example 7   Graph $g(x) = \sqrt{x - 1}$.

Solution   Because the rule of the function is defined only when $x - 1 \geq 0$ (that is, when $x \geq 1$), the domain of g is the interval $[1, \infty)$. Use a calculator to make a table of values such as the one in Figure 3.9. Plot the corresponding points and connect them to get the graph in Figure 3.9. ☑6

✓ Checkpoint 6

Graph $f(x) = \sqrt{5 - 2x}$.

x	$g(x) = \sqrt{x-1}$
1	0
2	1
3	$\sqrt{2} \approx 1.414$
5	2
7	$\sqrt{6} \approx 2.449$
10	3

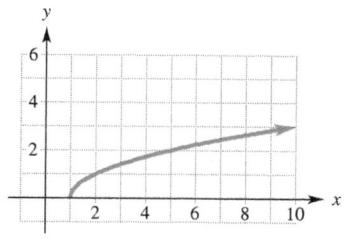

Figure 3.9

Example 8   Graph the function whose rule is

$$f(x) = 3 - \frac{x^3}{4}.$$

Solution   Make a table of values and plot the corresponding points. They suggest the graph in Figure 3.10.

x	$f(x) = 3 - \dfrac{x^3}{4}$
-4	19.0
-3	9.8
-2	5.0
-1	3.3
0	3.0
1	2.8
2	1.0
3	-3.8
4	-13.0

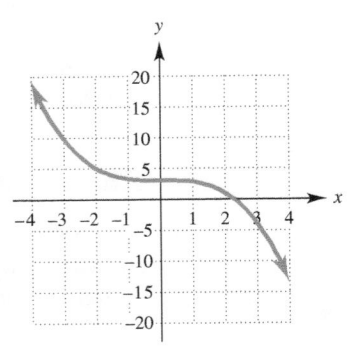

Figure 3.10

Example 9 Graph the piecewise defined function

$$f(x) = \begin{cases} x^2 & \text{if } x \le 2 \\ \sqrt{x - 1} & \text{if } x > 2. \end{cases}$$

Solution When $x \le 2$, the rule of the function is $f(x) = x^2$. Make a table of values such as the one in Figure 3.11. Plot the corresponding points and connect them to get the left half of the graph in Figure 3.11. When $x > 2$, the rule of the function is $f(x) = \sqrt{x - 1}$, whose graph is shown in Figure 3.9. In Example 7, the entire graph was given, beginning at $x = 1$. Here we use only the part of the graph to the right of $x = 2$, as shown in Figure 3.11. The open circle at $(2, 1)$ indicates that this point is not part of the graph of f (why?).

x	x^2
-2	4
-1	1
0	0
1	1
2	4

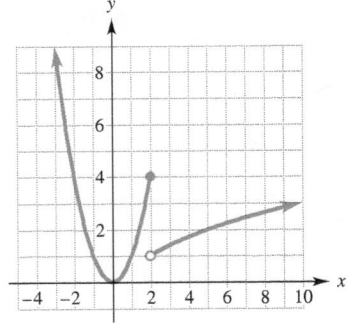

Figure 3.11

Graph Reading

Graphs are often used in business and the social sciences to present data. It is just as important to know how to *read* such graphs as it is to construct them.

Example 10 **Business** Figure 3.12, on the following page, shows the median sales prices (in thousands of dollars) of new privately owned one-family houses by region of the United States (northeast, midwest, south, and west) from the years 2005 to 2011. (Data from: U.S. Census Bureau and U.S. Department of Housing and Urban Development.)

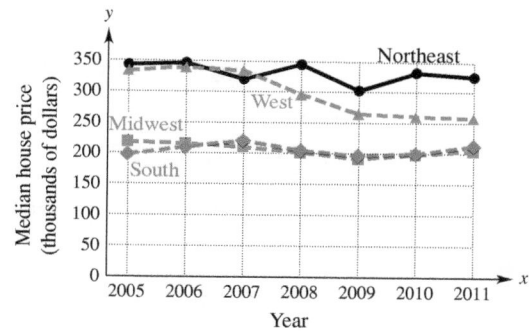

Figure 3.12

(a) How do prices in the west compare with those in the midwest over the period shown in the graph?

Solution   The prices of the houses in the west started out approximately $100,000 higher than those in the midwest. In both regions prices declined until 2009 when prices in the midwest inched higher while those in the west continued to decline. In 2011, the gap between the two regions had shrunk to just over $50,000.

(b) Which region typically had the highest price?

Solution   The northeast had the highest median price for all years except for 2007 when the west had the highest price.

Example 11   Figure 3.13 is the graph of the function f whose rule is $f(x)$ = average interest rate on a 30-year fixed-rate mortgage for a new home in year x. (Data from: www.fhfa.gov.)

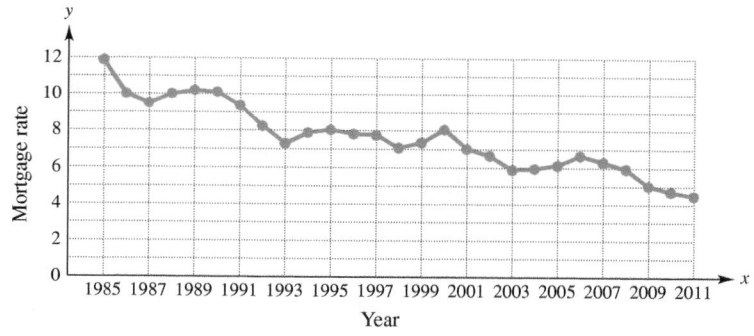

Figure 3.13

(a) Find the function values of $f(1988)$ and $f(2009)$.

Solution   The point (1988, 10) is on the graph, which means that $f(1988) = 10$. Similarly, $f(2009) = 5$, because the point (2009, 5) is on the graph. These values tell us the average mortgage rates were 10% in the year 1988 and 5% in the year 2009.

(b) During what period were mortgage rates at or above 7%?

Solution   Look for points on the graph whose second coordinates are 7 or more—that is, points on or above the horizontal line through 7. These points represent the period from 1985 to 2001.

(c) During what period were mortgage rates at or below 5%?

Solution   Look for points that are at or below the horizontal line through 5—that is, points with second coordinates less than or equal to 5. They occur from 2009 to 2011.

The Vertical-Line Test

The following fact distinguishes function graphs from other graphs.

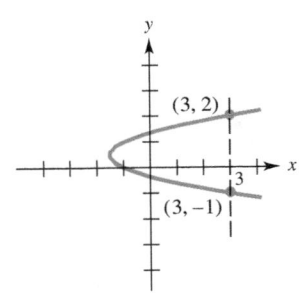

Figure 3.14

> ### Vertical-Line Test
>
> No vertical line intersects the graph of a function $y = f(x)$ at more than one point.

In other words, if a vertical line intersects a graph at more than one point, the graph is not the graph of a function. To see why this is true, consider the graph in Figure 3.14. The vertical line $x = 3$ intersects the graph at two points. If this were the graph of a function f, it would mean that $f(3) = 2$ (because $(3, 2)$ is on the graph) and that $f(3) = -1$ (because $(3, -1)$ is on the graph). This is impossible, because a *function* can have only one value when $x = 3$ (because each input determines exactly one output). Therefore, the graph in Figure 3.14 cannot be the graph of a function. A similar argument works in the general case.

Example 12 Use the vertical-line test to determine which of the graphs in Figure 3.15 are the graphs of functions.

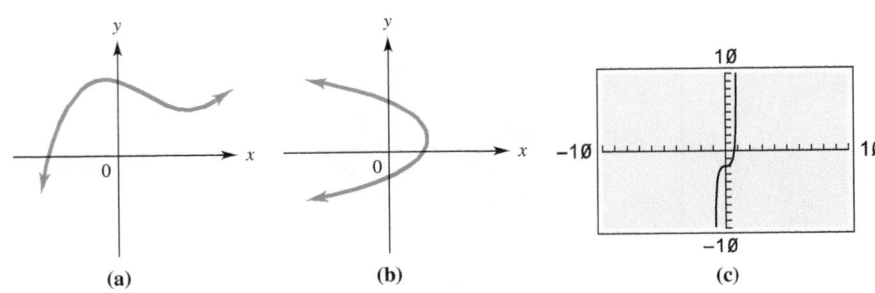

Figure 3.15

Solution To use the vertical-line test, imagine dragging a ruler held vertically across the graph from left to right. If the graph is that of a function, the edge of the ruler would hit the graph only once for every x-value. If you do this for graph (a), every vertical line intersects the graph in at most one point, so this graph is the graph of a function. Many vertical lines (including the y-axis) intersect graph (b) twice, so it is not the graph of a function.

Graph (c) appears to fail the vertical-line test near $x = 1$ and $x = -1$, indicating that it is not the graph of a function. But this appearance is misleading because of the low resolution of the calculator screen. The table in Figure 3.16 and the very narrow segment of the graph in Figure 3.17 show that the graph actually rises as it moves to the right. The same thing happens near $x = -1$. So this graph *does* pass the vertical-line test and *is* the graph of a function. (Its rule is $f(x) = 15x^{11} - 2$). The moral of this story is that you can't always trust images produced by a graphing calculator. When in doubt, try other viewing windows or a table to see what is really going on. ✓7

✓ **Checkpoint 7**

Find a viewing window that indicates the actual shape of the graph of the function $f(x) = 15x^{11} - 2$ of Example 12 near the point $(-1, -17)$.

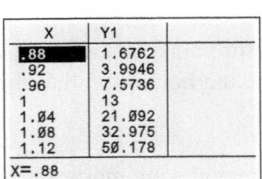

X	Y1
.88	1.6762
.92	3.9946
.96	7.5736
1	13
1.04	21.092
1.08	32.975
1.12	50.178
X=.88	

Figure 3.16

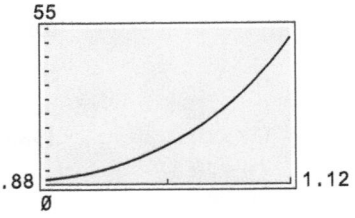

Figure 3.17

3.2 Exercises

Graph each function. (See Examples 1–4.)

1. $f(x) = -.5x + 2$ **2.** $g(x) = 3 - x$

3. $f(x) = \begin{cases} x + 3 & \text{if } x \le 1 \\ 4 & \text{if } x > 1 \end{cases}$

4. $g(x) = \begin{cases} 2x - 1 & \text{if } x < 0 \\ -1 & \text{if } x \ge 0 \end{cases}$

5. $y = \begin{cases} 4 - x & \text{if } x \le 0 \\ 3x + 4 & \text{if } x > 0 \end{cases}$

6. $y = \begin{cases} x + 5 & \text{if } x \le 1 \\ 2 - 3x & \text{if } x > 1 \end{cases}$

7. $f(x) = \begin{cases} |x| & \text{if } x < 2 \\ -2x & \text{if } x \ge 2 \end{cases}$

8. $g(x) = \begin{cases} -|x| & \text{if } x \le 1 \\ 2x & \text{if } x > 1 \end{cases}$

9. $f(x) = |x - 4|$ **10.** $g(x) = |4 - x|$

11. $f(x) = |3 - 3x|$ **12.** $g(x) = -|x|$

13. $y = -|x - 1|$ **14.** $f(x) = |x| - 2$

15. $y = |x - 2| + 3$

16. $|x| + |y| = 1$ (*Hint:* This is not the graph of a function, but is made up of four straight-line segments. Find them by using the definition of absolute value in these four cases: $x \ge 0$ and $y \ge 0$; $x \ge 0$ and $y < 0$; $x < 0$ and $y \ge 0$; $x < 0$ and $y < 0$).

Graph each function. (See Examples 5 and 6.)

17. $f(x) = [x - 3]$ **18.** $g(x) = [x + 3]$

19. $g(x) = [-x]$

20. $f(x) = [x] + [-x]$ (The graph contains horizontal segments, but is *not* a horizontal line.)

21. Business The accompanying table gives rates charged by the U.S. Postal Service for first-class letters in March 2013. Graph the function $f(x)$ that gives the price of mailing a first-class letter, where x represents the weight of the letter in ounces and $0 \le x \le 3.5$.

Weight Not Over	Price
1 ounce	$0.46
2 ounces	$0.66
3 ounces	$0.86
3.5 ounces	$1.06

22. Business The accompanying table gives rates charged by the U.S. Postal Service for first-class large flat envelopes in March, 2013. Graph the function $f(x)$ that gives the price of mailing a first-class large flat envelope, where x represents the weight of the envelope in ounces and $0 \le x \le 6$.

Weight Not Over	Price
1 ounce	$0.92
2 ounces	$1.12
3 ounces	$1.32
4 ounces	$1.53
5 ounces	$1.72
6 ounces	$1.92

Graph each function. (See Examples 7–9.)

23. $f(x) = 3 - 2x^2$

24. $g(x) = 2 - x^2$

25. $h(x) = x^3/10 + 2$

26. $f(x) = x^3/20 - 3$

27. $g(x) = \sqrt{-x}$

28. $h(x) = \sqrt{x} - 1$

29. $f(x) = \sqrt[3]{x}$

30. $g(x) = \sqrt[3]{x - 4}$

31. $f(x) = \begin{cases} x^2 & \text{if } x < 2 \\ -2x + 2 & \text{if } x \ge 2 \end{cases}$

32. $g(x) = \begin{cases} \sqrt{-x} & \text{if } x \le -4 \\ \dfrac{x^2}{4} & \text{if } x > -4 \end{cases}$

Determine whether each graph is a graph of a function or not. (See Example 12.)

33.

34.

35.

36.

37.

38.

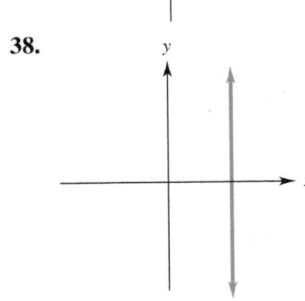

Use a graphing calculator or other technology to graph each of the given functions. If the graph has any endpoints, indicate whether they are part of the graph or not.

39. $f(x) = .2x^3 - .8x^2 - 4x + 9.6$

40. $g(x) = .1x^4 - .3x^3 - 1.3x^2 + 1.5x$

41. $g(x) = \begin{cases} 2x^2 + x & \text{if } x < 1 \\ x^3 - x - 1 & \text{if } x \geq 1 \end{cases}$ *(Hint:* See the Technology Tip on page 125)

42. $f(x) = \begin{cases} x|x| & \text{if } x \leq 0 \\ -x^2|x| + 2 & \text{if } x > 0 \end{cases}$

Use a graphical root finder to determine the x-intercepts of the graph of

43. f in Exercise 39;   **44.** g in Exercise 40.

Use a maximum–minimum finder to determine the location of the peaks and valleys in the graph of

45. g in Exercise 40;   **46.** f in Exercise 39.

See Examples 2, 3, 10, and 11 as you do Exercises 47–52.

47. Finance   The Maine state income tax for a single person in 2013 was determined by the rule

$$T(x) = \begin{cases} .02x & \text{if } 0 \leq x \leq 5099 \\ 101.98 + .045(x - 5099) & \text{if } 5099 < x \leq 10{,}149 \\ 329.23 + .07(x - 10{,}149) & \text{if } 10{,}149 < x \leq 20{,}349 \\ 1043.23 + .085(x - 20{,}349) & \text{if } x > 20{,}349, \end{cases}$$

where x is the person's taxable income in dollars. Graph the function $T(x)$ for taxable incomes between 0 and $24,000.

48. Finance   The Alabama state income tax for a single person in 2013 was determined by the rule

$$T(x) = \begin{cases} .02x & \text{if } 0 \leq x \leq 500 \\ 10 + .04(x - 500) & \text{if } 500 < x \leq 3000 \\ 110 + .05(x - 3000) & \text{if } x > 3000 \end{cases}$$

where x is the person's taxable income in dollars. Graph the function $T(x)$ for taxable incomes between 0 and $5000.

49. Finance   The price of KeyCorp stock can be approximated by the function

$$f(x) = \begin{cases} 9.04 - .027x & \text{if } 0 < x \leq 43 \\ 7.879 + .032(x - 43) & \text{if } 43 < x \leq 113 \end{cases}$$

where x represents the number of trading days past September 14, 2012. (Data from: www.morningstar.com.)

(a) Graph $f(x)$.

(b) What is the lowest stock price during the period defined by $f(x)$?

50. Natural Science   The number of minutes of daylight in Washington, DC, can be modeled by the function

$$g(x) = \begin{cases} .0106x^2 + 1.24x + 565 & \text{if } 1 \leq x < 84 \\ -.0202x^2 + 6.97x + 295 & \text{if } 84 \leq x < 263 \\ .0148x^2 - 11.1x + 2632 & \text{if } 263 \leq x \leq 365, \end{cases}$$

where x represents the number of days of the year, starting on January 1. Find the number of minutes of daylight on

(a) day 32.   **(b)** day 90.

(c) day 200.   **(d)** day 270.

(e) Graph $g(x)$.

(f) On what day is the number of minutes of daylight the greatest?

51. Health   The following table shows the consumer price index (CPI) for medical care in selected years: (Data from: U.S. Bureau of Labor Statistics.)

Year	Medical-Care CPI
1950	15.1
1980	74.9
2010	388.4

(a) Let $x = 0$ correspond to 1950. Find the rule of a piecewise linear function that models these data—that is, a piecewise linear function f with $f(0) = 15.1$, $f(30) = 74.9$, and $f(60) = 388.4$. Round all coefficients in your final answer to one decimal place.

(b) Graph the function f for $0 \leq x \leq 65$.

(c) Use the function to estimate the medical-care CPI in 2004.

(d) Assuming that this model remains accurate after 2010, estimate the medical-care CPI for 2015.

52. Business   The graph on the following page from the U.S. Office of Management and Budget shows the federal debt from the year 2007 to the year 2012 (in billions of dollars), with $x = 7$ corresponding to the year 2007. Find the rule of a linear function g that passes through the two points corresponding to 2007 and 2012. Draw the graph of g.

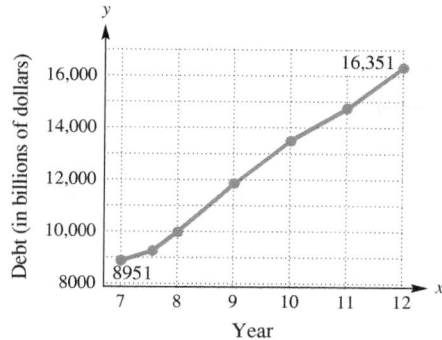

Year

Finance *Use the accompanying graph to answer Exercises 53 and 54. The graph shows the annual percent change in various consumer price indexes (CPIs). (See Examples 10 and 11.) (Data from: U.S. Census Bureau.)*

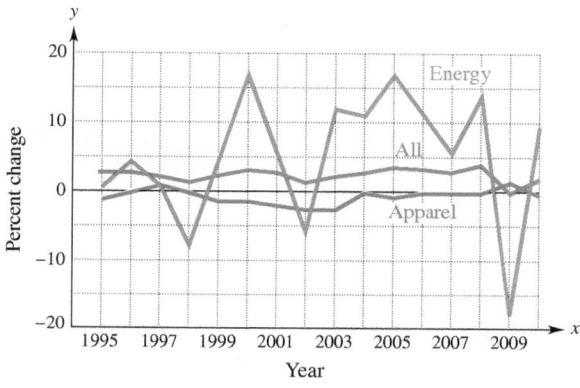

Year

53. (a) Was there any period between 1995 and 2010 when all three indexes showed a decrease?

(b) During what years did the CPI for energy show a decrease?

(c) When was the CPI for energy decreasing at the fastest rate?

54. (a) During what years did the CPI for apparel show an increase?

(b) When was the CPI for apparel increasing at the greatest rate?

55. Finance The following graph shows the number of FDIC-insured financial institutions in the United States for the year 1990 through the year 2010. (Data from: U.S. Federal Deposit Insurance Corporation.)

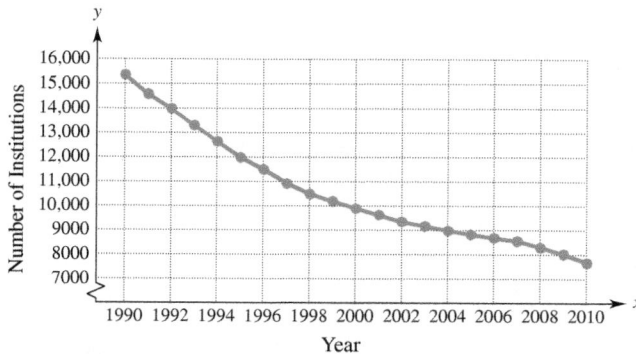

Year

(a) Is this the graph of a function?

(b) What does the domain represent?

(c) Estimate the range.

56. Finance The following graph shows the percent-per-year yield of the 10-year U.S. Treasury Bond from the year 2000 to the year 2010. (Data from: Board of Governors of the Federal Reserve System.)

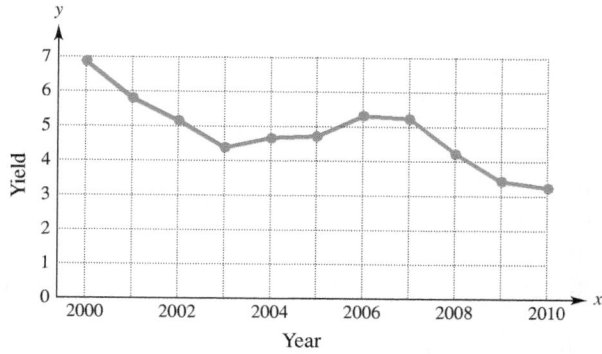

Year

(a) Is this the graph of a function?

(b) What does the domain represent?

(c) Estimate the range.

57. Business Whenever postage rates change, some newspaper publishes a graph like this one, which shows the price of a first-class stamp from 1982 to 2008:

Year

(a) Let f be the function whose rule is

$$f(x) = \text{cost of a first-class stamp in year } x.$$

Find $f(2000)$ and $f(2011)$.

(b) Explain why the graph in the figure is not the graph of the *function f*. What must be done to the figure to make it an accurate graph of the function f?

58. Business A chain-saw rental firm charges $20 per day or fraction of a day to rent a saw, plus a fixed fee of $7 for resharpening the blade. Let $S(x)$ represent the cost of renting a saw for x days. Find each of the following.

(a) $S\left(\dfrac{1}{2}\right)$ **(b)** $S(1)$ **(c)** $S\left(1\dfrac{2}{3}\right)$ **(d)** $S\left(4\dfrac{3}{4}\right)$

(e) What does it cost to rent for $5\dfrac{7}{8}$ days?

(f) A portion of the graph of $y = S(x)$ is shown on the following page. Explain how the graph could be continued.

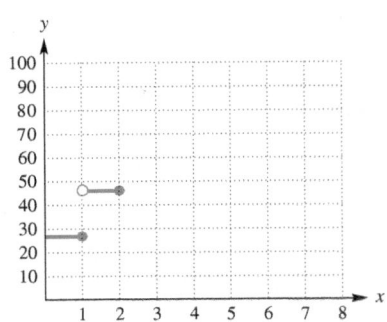

(g) What is the domain variable?

(h) What is the range variable?

(i) Write a sentence or two explaining what (c) and its answer represent.

(j) We have left $x = 0$ out of the graph. Discuss why it should or should not be included. If it were included, how would you define $S(0)$?

59. Business Sarah Hendrickson needs to rent a van to pick up a new couch she has purchased. The cost of the van is $19.99 for the first 75 minutes and then an additional $5 for each block of 15 minutes beyond 75. Find the cost to rent a van for

(a) 2 hours;   **(b)** 1.5 hours;

(c) 3.5 hours;   **(d)** 4 hours.

(e) Graph the ordered pairs (hours, cost).

60. Business A delivery company charges $25 plus 60¢ per mile or part of a mile. Find the cost for a trip of

(a) 3 miles;   **(b)** 4.2 miles;

(c) 5.9 miles;   **(d)** 8 miles.

(e) Graph the ordered pairs (miles, cost).

(f) Is this a function?

Work these problems.

61. Natural Science A laboratory culture contains about 1 million bacteria at midnight. The culture grows very rapidly until noon, when a bactericide is introduced and the bacteria population plunges. By 4 p.m., the bacteria have adapted to the bactericide and the culture slowly increases in population until 9 p.m., when the culture is accidentally destroyed by the cleanup crew. Let $g(t)$ denote the bacteria population at time t (with $t = 0$ corresponding to midnight). Draw a plausible graph of the function g. (Many correct answers are possible.)

62. Physical Science A plane flies from Austin, Texas, to Cleveland, Ohio, a distance of 1200 miles. Let f be the function whose rule is

$f(t) = $ distance (in miles) from Austin at time t hours,

with $t = 0$ corresponding to the 4 p.m. takeoff. In each part of this exercise, draw a plausible graph of f under the given circumstances. (There are many correct answers for each part.)

(a) The flight is nonstop and takes between 3.5 and 4 hours.

(b) Bad weather forces the plane to land in Dallas (about 200 miles from Austin) at 5 p.m., remain overnight, and leave at 8 a.m. the next day, flying nonstop to Cleveland.

(c) The plane flies nonstop, but due to heavy traffic it must fly in a holding pattern for an hour over Cincinnati (about 200 miles from Cleveland) and then go on to Cleveland.

✓**Checkpoint Answers**

1.   **2.**

3.   **4.**

5.   **6.**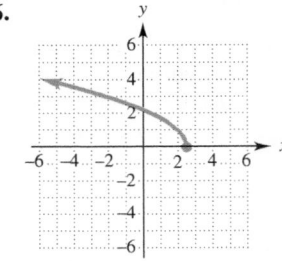

7. There are many correct answers, including, $-1.4 \le x \le -.6$ and $-30 \le y \le 0$.

3.3 Applications of Linear Functions

Most of this section deals with the basic business relationships that were introduced in Section 1.2:

$$\text{Revenue} = (\text{Price per item}) \times (\text{Number of items});$$
$$\text{Cost} = \text{Fixed Costs} + \text{Variable Costs};$$
$$\text{Profit} = \text{Revenue} - \text{Cost}.$$

The examples will use only linear functions, but the methods presented here also apply to more complicated functions.

Cost Analysis

Recall that fixed costs are for such things as buildings, machinery, real-estate taxes, and product design. Within broad limits, the fixed cost is constant for a particular product and does not change as more items are made. Variable costs are for labor, materials, shipping, and so on, and depend on the number of items made.

If $C(x)$ is the cost of making x items, then the fixed cost (the cost that occurs even when no items are produced) can be found by letting $x = 0$. For example, for the cost function $C(x) = 45x + 250{,}000$, the fixed cost is

$$C(0) = 45(0) + 250{,}000 = \$250{,}000.$$

In this case, the variable cost of making x items is $45x$—that is, \$45 per item manufactured.

Example 1   **Business**   An anticlot drug can be made for \$10 per unit. The total cost to produce 100 units is \$1500.

(a) Assuming that the cost function is linear, find its rule.

Solution   Since the cost function $C(x)$ is linear, its rule is of the form $C(x) = mx + b$. We are given that m (the cost per item) is 10, so the rule is $C(x) = 10x + b$. To find b, use the fact that it costs \$1500 to produce 100 units, which means that

$$C(100) = 1500$$
$$10(100) + b = 1500 \qquad {\scriptstyle C(x)\ =\ 10x\ +\ b.}$$
$$1000 + b = 1500$$
$$b = 500.$$

So the rule of the cost function is $C(x) = 10x + 500$.

(b) What are the fixed costs?

✓**Checkpoint 1**

The total cost of producing 10 calculators is \$100. The variable costs per calculator are \$4. Find the rule of the linear cost function.

Solution   The fixed costs are $C(0) = 10(0) + 500 = \$500$. ✓₁

If $C(x)$ is the total cost to produce x items, then the **average cost** per item is given by

$$\overline{C}(x) = \frac{C(x)}{x}.$$

As more and more items are produced, the average cost per item typically decreases.

Example 2   **Business**   Find the average cost of producing 100 and 1000 units of the anticlot drug in Example 1.

Solution   The cost function is $C(x) = 10x + 500$, so the average cost of producing 100 units is

$$\overline{C}(100) = \frac{C(100)}{100} = \frac{10(100) + 500}{100} = \frac{1500}{100} = \$15.00 \text{ per unit.}$$

✓**Checkpoint 2**

In Checkpoint 1, find the average cost per calculator when 100 are produced.

The average cost of producing 1000 units is

$$\overline{C}(1000) = \frac{C(1000)}{1000} = \frac{10(1000) + 500}{1000} = \frac{10{,}500}{1000} = \$10.50 \text{ per unit.} \text{ ✓}_2$$

Rates of Change

The rate at which a quantity (such as revenue or profit) is changing can be quite important. For instance, if a company determines that the rate of change of its revenue is decreasing, then sales growth is slowing down, a trend that may require a response.

x	$f(x) = 3x + 5$
1	8
2	11
3	14
4	17
5	20

The rate of change of a linear function is easily determined. For example, suppose $f(x) = 3x + 5$ and consider the table of values in the margin. The table shows that each time x changes by 1, the corresponding value of $f(x)$ changes by 3. Thus, the rate of change of $f(x) = 3x + 5$ with respect to x is 3, which is the slope of the line $y = 3x + 5$. The same thing happens for any linear function:

> **The rate of change of a linear function $f(x) = mx + b$ is the slope m.**

In particular, the rate of change of a linear function is constant.

The value of a computer, or an automobile, or a machine *depreciates* (decreases) over time. **Linear depreciation** means that the value of the item at time x is given by a linear function $f(x) = mx + b$. The slope m of this line gives the rate of depreciation.

Example 3   Business   According to the *Kelley Blue Book*, a Ford Mustang two-door convertible that is worth $14,776 today will be worth $10,600 in two years (if it is in excellent condition with average mileage).

(a) Assuming linear depreciation, find the depreciation function for this car.

Solution   We know the car is worth $14,776 now ($x = 0$) and will be worth $10,600 in two years ($x = 2$). So the points $(0, 14,776)$ and $(2, 10,600)$ are on the graph of the linear-depreciation function and can be used to determine its slope:

$$m = \frac{10,600 - 14,776}{2} = \frac{-4176}{2} = -2088.$$

Using the point $(0, 14,776)$, we find that the equation of the line is

$$y - 14,776 = -2088(x - 0) \qquad \text{Point–slope form}$$
$$y = -2088x + 14,776. \qquad \text{Slope–intercept form}$$

Therefore, the rule of the depreciation function is $f(x) = -2088x + 14,776$.

(b) What will the car be worth in 4 years?

Solution   Evaluate f when $x = 4$:

$$f(x) = -2088x + 14,776$$
$$f(4) = -2088(4) + 14,776 = \$6424.$$

(c) At what rate is the car depreciating?

Solution   The depreciation rate is given by the slope of $f(x) = -2088x + 14,776$, namely, -2088. This negative slope means that the car is decreasing in value an average of $2088 a year. ✓₃

✓Checkpoint 3

Using the information from Example 3, determine what the car will be worth in 6 years.

In economics, the rate of change of the cost function is called the **marginal cost.** Marginal cost is important to management in making decisions in such areas as cost control, pricing, and production planning. When the cost function is linear, say, $C(x) = mx + b$, the marginal cost is the number m (the slope of the graph of C). Marginal cost can also be thought of as the cost of producing one more item, as the next example demonstrates.

Example 4   **Business**   An electronics company manufactures handheld PCs. The cost function for one of its models is $C(x) = 160x + 750{,}000$.

(a) What are the fixed costs for this product?

Solution   The fixed costs are $C(0) = 160(0) + 750{,}000 = \$750{,}000$.

(b) What is the marginal cost?

Solution   The slope of $C(x) = 160x + 750{,}000$ is 160, so the marginal cost is \$160 per item.

(c) After 50,000 units have been produced, what is the cost of producing one more?

Solution   The cost of producing 50,000 is

$$C(50{,}000) = 160(50{,}000) + 750{,}000 = \$8{,}750{,}000.$$

The cost of 50,001 units is

$$C(50{,}001) = 160(50{,}001) + 750{,}000 = \$8{,}750{,}160.$$

The cost of the additional unit is the difference

$$C(50{,}001) - C(50{,}000) = 8{,}750{,}160 - 8{,}750{,}000 = \$160.$$

Thus, the cost of one more item is the marginal cost. ✔4

> ✓**Checkpoint 4**
>
> The cost in dollars to produce x kilograms of chocolate candy is given by $C(x) = 3.5x + 800$. Find each of the following.
>
> **(a)** The fixed cost
>
> **(b)** The total cost for 12 kilograms
>
> **(c)** The marginal cost of the 40th kilogram
>
> **(d)** The marginal cost per kilogram

Similarly, the rate of change of a revenue function is called the **marginal revenue**. When the revenue function is linear, the marginal revenue is the slope of the line, as well as the revenue from producing one more item.

Example 5   **Business**   The energy company New York State Electric and Gas charges each residential customer a basic fee for electricity of \$15.11, plus \$.0333 per kilowatt hour (kWh).

(a) Assuming there are 700,000 residential customers, find the company's revenue function.

Solution   The monthly revenue from the basic fee is

$$15.11(700{,}000) = \$10{,}577{,}000.$$

If x is the total number of kilowatt hours used by all customers, then the revenue from electricity use is $.0333x$. So the monthly revenue function is given by

$$R(x) = .0333x + 10{,}577{,}000.$$

(b) What is the marginal revenue?

Solution   The marginal revenue (the rate at which revenue is changing) is given by the slope of the rate function: \$0.0333 per kWh. ✔5

> ✓**Checkpoint 5**
>
> Assume that the average customer in Example 5 uses 1600 kWh in a month.
>
> **(a)** What is the total number of kWh used by all customers?
>
> **(b)** What is the company's monthly revenue?

Examples 4 and 5 are typical of the general case, as summarized here.

> In a **linear cost function** $C(x) = mx + b$, the marginal cost is m (the slope of the cost line) and the fixed cost is b (the y-intercept of the cost line). The marginal cost is the cost of producing one more item.
>
> Similarly, in a **linear revenue function** $R(x) = kx + d$, the marginal revenue is k (the slope of the revenue line), which is the revenue from selling one more item.

Break-Even Analysis

A typical company must analyze its costs and the potential market for its product to determine when (or even whether) it will make a profit.

Example 6   **Business**   A company manufactures a 42-inch plasma HDTV that sells to retailers for $550. The cost of making x of these TVs for a month is given by the cost function $C(x) = 250x + 213,000$.

(a) Find the function R that gives the revenue from selling x TVs.

Solution   Since revenue is the product of the price per item and the number of items, $R(x) = 550x$.

(b) What is the revenue from selling 600 TVs?

Solution   Evaluate the revenue function R at 600:

$$R(600) = 550(600) = \$330,000.$$

(c) Find the profit function P.

Solution   Since Profit = Revenue − Cost,

$$P(x) = R(x) - C(x) = 550x - (250x + 213,000) = 300x - 213,000.$$

(d) What is the profit from selling 500 TVs?

Solution   Evaluate the profit function at 500 to obtain

$$P(500) = 300(500) - 213,000 = -63,000,$$

that is, a loss of $63,000.

A company can make a profit only if the revenue on a product exceeds the cost of manufacturing it. The number of units at which revenue equals cost (that is, profit is 0) is the **break-even point.**

Example 7   **Business**   Find the break-even point for the company in Example 6.

Solution   The company will break even when revenue equals cost—that is, when

$$R(x) = C(x)$$
$$550x = 250x + 213,000$$
$$300x = 213,000$$
$$x = 710.$$

The company breaks even by selling 710 TVs. The graphs of the revenue and cost functions and the break-even point (where $x = 710$) are shown in the Figure 3.18. The company must sell more than 710 TVs ($x > 710$) in order to make a profit. ✓6

✓**Checkpoint 6**

For a certain newsletter, the cost equation is $C(x) = 0.90x + 1500$, where x is the number of newsletters sold. The newsletter sells for $1.25 per copy. Find the break-even point.

Figure 3.18

Intersection
X=710　　　　Y=390500

Figure 3.19

 TECHNOLOGY TIP The break-even point in Example 7 can be found on a graphing calculator by graphing the cost and revenue functions on the same screen and using the calculator's intersection finder, as shown in Figure 3.19. Depending on the calculator, the intersection finder is in the CALC or G-SOLVE menu or in the MATH or FCN submenu of the GRAPH menu.

Supply and Demand

The supply of and demand for an item are usually related to its price. Producers will supply large numbers of the item at a high price, but consumer demand will be low. As the price of the item decreases, consumer demand increases, but producers are less willing to supply large numbers of the item. The curves showing the quantity that will be supplied at a given price and the quantity that will be demanded at a given price are called **supply and demand curves,** respectively. In supply-and-demand problems, we use p for price and q for quantity. We will discuss the economic concepts of supply and demand in more detail in later chapters.

Example 8 　**Economics** 　Joseph Nolan has studied the supply and demand for aluminum siding and has determined that the price per unit,[*] p, and the quantity demanded, q, are related by the linear equation

$$p = 60 - \frac{3}{4}q.$$

(a) Find the demand at a price of \$40 per unit.

Solution 　Let $p = 40$. Then we have

$$p = 60 - \frac{3}{4}q$$

$$40 = 60 - \frac{3}{4}q \qquad \textit{Let p = 40.}$$

$$-20 = -\frac{3}{4}q \qquad \textit{Add −60 to both sides.}$$

$$\frac{80}{3} = q. \qquad \textit{Multiply both sides by } -\frac{4}{3}.$$

At a price of \$40 per unit, $80/3$ (or $26\frac{2}{3}$) units will be demanded.

(b) Find the price if the demand is 32 units.

Solution 　Let $q = 32$. Then we have

$$p = 60 - \frac{3}{4}q$$

$$p = 60 - \frac{3}{4}(32) \qquad \textit{Let q = 32.}$$

$$p = 60 - 24$$

$$p = 36.$$

With a demand of 32 units, the price is \$36.

(c) 　Graph $p = 60 - \frac{3}{4}q$.

Solution 　It is customary to use the horizontal axis for the quantity q and the vertical axis for the price p. In part (a), we saw that $80/3$ units would be demanded at a price of

---

[*]An appropriate unit here might be, for example, one thousand square feet of siding.

$40 per unit; this gives the ordered pair (80/3, 40). Part (b) shows that with a demand of 32 units, the price is $36, which gives the ordered pair (32, 36). Using the points (80/3, 40) and (32, 36) yields the demand graph depicted in Figure 3.20. Only the portion of the graph in Quadrant I is shown, because supply and demand are meaningful only for positive values of p and q. ✔ 7

✓**Checkpoint 7**

Suppose price and quantity demanded are related by
$p = 100 - 4q$.

(a) Find the price if the quantity demanded is 10 units.

(b) Find the quantity demanded if the price is $80.

(c) Write the corresponding ordered pairs.

Figure 3.20

(d) From Figure 3.20, at a price of $30, what quantity is demanded?

Solution Price is located on the vertical axis. Look for 30 on the p-axis, and read across to where the line $p = 30$ crosses the demand graph. As the graph shows, this occurs where the quantity demanded is 40.

(e) At what price will 60 units be demanded?

Solution Quantity is located on the horizontal axis. Find 60 on the q-axis, and read up to where the vertical line $q = 60$ crosses the demand graph. This occurs where the price is about $15 per unit.

(f) What quantity is demanded at a price of $60 per unit?

Solution The point (0, 60) on the demand graph shows that the demand is 0 at a price of $60 (that is, there is no demand at such a high price).

Example 9 **Economics** Suppose the economist in Example 8 concludes that the supply q of siding is related to its price p by the equation

$$p = .85q.$$

(a) Find the supply if the price is $51 per unit.

Solution $51 = .85q$ Let $p = 51$.

                               $60 = q$.   Divide both sides by .85

If the price is $51 per unit, then 60 units will be supplied to the marketplace.

(b) Find the price per unit if the supply is 20 units.

Solution $p = .85(20) = 17$.   Let $q = 20$.

If the supply is 20 units, then the price is $17 per unit.

(c) Graph the supply equation $p = .85q$.

Solution As with demand, each point on the graph has quantity q as its first coordinate and the corresponding price p as its second coordinate. Part (a) shows that the ordered pair (60, 51) is on the graph of the supply equation, and part (b) shows that (20, 17) is on the graph. Using these points, we obtain the supply graph in Figure 3.21.

Figure 3.21

(d) Use the graph in Figure 3.21 to find the approximate price at which 35 units will be supplied. Then use algebra to find the exact price.

Solution The point on the graph with first coordinate $q = 35$ is approximately $(35, 30)$. Therefore, 35 units will be supplied when the price is approximately \$30. To determine the exact price algebraically, substitute $q = 35$ into the supply equation:

$$p = .85q = .85(35) = \$29.75.$$

Figure 3.22

Example 10 **Economics** The supply and demand curves of Examples 8 and 9 are shown in Figure 3.22. Determine graphically whether there is a surplus or a shortage of supply at a price of \$40 per unit.

Solution Find 40 on the vertical axis in Figure 3.22 and read across to the point where the horizontal line $p = 40$ crosses the supply graph (that is, the point corresponding to a price of \$40). This point lies above the demand graph, so supply is greater than demand at a price of \$40, and there is a surplus of supply.

Supply and demand are equal at the point where the supply curve intersects the demand curve. This is the **equilibrium point.** Its second coordinate is the **equilibrium price,** the price at which the same quantity will be supplied as is demanded. Its first coordinate is the quantity that will be demanded and supplied at the equilibrium price; this number is called the **equilibrium quantity.**

Example 11 **Economics** In the situation described in Examples 8–10, what is the equilibrium quantity? What is the equilibrium price?

Solution The equilibrium point is where the supply and demand curves in Figure 3.22 intersect. To find the quantity q at which the price given by the demand equation $p = 60 - .75q$ (Example 8) is the same as that given by the supply equation $p = .85q$ (Example 9), set these two expressions for p equal to each other and solve the resulting equation:

$$60 - .75q = .85q$$
$$60 = 1.6q$$
$$37.5 = q.$$

Therefore, the equilibrium quantity is 37.5 units, the number of units for which supply will equal demand. Substituting $q = 37.5$ into either the demand or supply equation shows that

$$p = 60 - .75(37.5) = 31.875 \quad \text{or} \quad p = .85(37.5) = 31.875.$$

Checkpoint 8

The demand for a certain commodity is related to the price by $p = 80 - (2/3)q$. The supply is related to the price by $p = (4/3)q$. Find

(a) the equilibrium quantity;

(b) the equilibrium price.

So the equilibrium price is \$31.875 (or \$31.88, rounded). (To avoid error, it is a good idea to substitute into both equations, as we did here, to be sure that the same value of p results; if it does not, a mistake has been made.) In this case, the equilibrium point—the point whose coordinates are the equilibrium quantity and price—is (37.5, 31.875). ✓₈

⬆ **TECHNOLOGY TIP** The equilibrium point (37.5, 31.875) can be found on a graphing calculator by graphing the supply and demand curves on the same screen and using the calculator's intersection finder to locate their point of intersection.

3.3 Exercises

Business *Write a cost function for each of the given scenarios. Identify all variables used. (See Example 1.)*

1. A chain-saw rental firm charges \$25, plus \$5 per hour.

2. A trailer-hauling service charges \$95, plus \$8 per mile.

3. A parking garage charges \$8.00, plus \$2.50 per half hour.

4. For a 1-day rental, a car rental firm charges \$65, plus 45¢ per mile.

Business *Assume that each of the given situations can be expressed as a linear cost function. Find the appropriate cost function in each case. (See Examples 1 and 4.)*

5. Fixed cost, \$200; 50 items cost \$2000 to produce.

6. Fixed cost, \$2000; 40 items cost \$5000 to produce.

7. Marginal cost, \$120; 100 items cost \$15,800 to produce.

8. Marginal cost, \$90; 150 items cost \$16,000 to produce.

Business *In Exercises 9–12, a cost function is given. Find the average cost per item when the required numbers of items are produced. (See Example 2.)*

9. $C(x) = 12x + 1800$; 50 items, 500 items, 1000 items

10. $C(x) = 80x + 12,000$; 100 items, 1000 items, 10,000 items

11. $C(x) = 6.5x + 9800$; 200 items, 2000 items, 5000 items

12. $C(x) = 8.75x + 16,500$; 1000 items, 10,000 items, 75,000 items

Business *Work these exercises. (See Example 3.)*

13. A Volkswagen Beetle convertible sedan is worth \$16,615 now and is expected to be worth \$8950 in 4 years.

(a) Find a linear depreciation function for this car.

(b) Estimate the value of the car 5 years from now.

(c) At what rate is the car depreciating?

14. A computer that cost \$1250 new is expected to depreciate linearly at a rate of \$250 per year.

(a) Find the depreciation function f.

(b) Explain why the domain of f is [0, 5].

15. A machine is now worth \$120,000 and will be depreciated linearly over an 8-year period, at which time it will be worth \$25,000 as scrap.

(a) Find the rule of the depreciation function f.

(b) What is the domain of f?

(c) What will the machine be worth in 6 years?

16. A house increases in value in an approximately linear fashion from \$222,000 to \$300,000 in 6 years.

(a) Find the *appreciation function* that gives the value of the house in year x.

(b) If the house continues to appreciate at this rate, what will it be worth 12 years from now?

Business *Work these problems. (See Example 4.)*

17. The total cost (in dollars) of producing x college algebra books is $C(x) = 42.5x + 80,000$.

(a) What are the fixed costs?

(b) What is the marginal cost per book?

(c) What is the total cost of producing 1000 books? 32,000 books?

(d) What is the average cost when 1000 are produced? when 32,000 are produced?

18. The total cost (in dollars) of producing x DVDs is $C(x) = 6.80x + 450,000$.

(a) What are the fixed costs?

(b) What is the marginal cost per DVD?

(c) What is the total cost of producing 50,000 DVDs? 600,000 DVDs?

(d) What is the average cost per DVD when 50,000 are produced? when 500,000 are produced?

19. The manager of a restaurant found that the cost of producing 100 cups of coffee is \$11.02, while the cost of producing 400 cups is \$40.12. Assume that the cost $C(x)$ is a linear function of x, the number of cups produced.

(a) Find a formula for $C(x)$.

(b) Find the total cost of producing 1000 cups.

(c) Find the total cost of producing 1001 cups.

(d) Find the marginal cost of producing the 1000th cup.

(e) What is the marginal cost of producing *any* cup?

20. In deciding whether to set up a new manufacturing plant, company analysts have determined that a linear function is a reasonable estimation for the total cost $C(x)$ in dollars of producing x items. They estimate the cost of producing 10,000 items as $547,500 and the cost of producing 50,000 items as $737,500.

(a) Find a formula for $C(x)$.

(b) Find the total cost of producing 100,000 items.

(c) Find the marginal cost of the items to be produced in this plant.

Business *Work these problems. (See Example 5.)*

21. For the year 2013, a resident of the city of Dallas, Texas with a 5/8 inch water meter pays $4.20 per month plus $1.77 per 1000 gallons of water used (up to 4000 gallons). If the city of Dallas has 550,000 customers that use less than 4000 gallons a month, find its monthly revenue function $R(x)$, where the total number of gallons x is measured in thousands.

22. The Lacledge Gas Company in St. Louis, Missouri in the winter of 2012–2013 charged customers $21.32 per month plus $1.19071 per therm for the first 30 therms of gas used and $.57903 for each therm above 30.

(a) How much revenue does the company get from a customer who uses exactly 30 therms of gas in a month?

(b) Find the rule of the function $R(x)$ that gives the company's monthly revenue from one customer, where x is the number of therms of gas used. (*Hint*: $R(x)$ is a piecewise-defined function that has a two-part rule, one part for $x \leq 30$ and the other for $x > 30$.)

Business *Assume that each row of the accompanying table has a linear cost function. Find (a) the cost function; (b) the revenue function; (c) the profit function; (d) the profit on 100 items. (See Example 6.)*

	Fixed Cost	Marginal Cost per Item	Item Sells For
23.	$750	$10	$35
24.	$150	$11	$20
25.	$300	$18	$28
26.	$17,000	$30	$80
27.	$20,000	$12.50	$30

28. Business In the following profit–volume chart, *EF* and *GH* represent the profit–volume graphs of a single-product company for, 2012 and 2013, respectively. (Adapted from: Uniform CPA Examination, American Institute of Certified Public Accountants.)

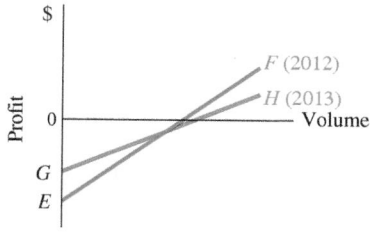

If the 2012 and 2013 unit sales prices are identical, how did the total fixed costs and unit variable costs of 2013 change compared with their values in 2012? Choose one:

	2012 Total Fixed Costs	2013 Unit Variable Costs
(a)	Decreased	Increased
(b)	Decreased	Decreased
(c)	Increased	Increased
(d)	Increased	Decreased

Use algebra to find the intersection points of the graphs of the given equations. (See Examples 7 and 11.)

29. $2x - y = 7$ and $y = 8 - 3x$

30. $6x - y = 2$ and $y = 4x + 7$

31. $y = 3x - 7$ and $y = 7x + 4$

32. $y = 3x + 5$ and $y = 12 - 2x$

Business *Work the following problems. (See Example 7.)*

33. An insurance company claims that for x thousand policies, its monthly revenue in dollars is given by $R(x) = 125x$ and its monthly cost in dollars is given by $C(x) = 100x + 5000$.

(a) Find the break-even point.

(b) Graph the revenue and cost equations on the same axes.

(c) From the graph, estimate the revenue and cost when $x = 100$ (100,000 policies).

34. The owners of a parking lot have determined that their weekly revenue and cost in dollars are given by $R(x) = 80x$ and $C(x) = 50x + 2400$, where x is the number of long-term parkers.

(a) Find the break-even point.

(b) Graph $R(x)$ and $C(x)$ on the same axes.

(c) From the graph, estimate the revenue and cost when there are 60 long-term parkers.

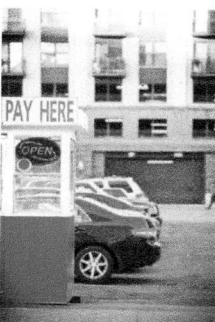

35. The revenue (in millions of dollars) from the sale of x units at a home supply outlet is given by $R(x) = .21x$. The profit (in millions of dollars) from the sale of x units is given by $P(x) = .084x - 1.5$.

(a) Find the cost equation.

(b) What is the cost of producing 7 units?

(c) What is the break-even point?

36. The profit (in millions of dollars) from the sale of x million units of Blue Glue is given by $P(x) = .7x - 25.5$. The cost is given by $C(x) = .9x + 25.5$.

   (a) Find the revenue equation.

   (b) What is the revenue from selling 10 million units?

   (c) What is the break-even point?

Business *Suppose you are the manager of a firm. The accounting department has provided cost estimates, and the sales department sales estimates, on a new product. You must analyze the data they give you, determine what it will take to break even, and decide whether to go ahead with production of the new product. (See Example 7.)*

37. Cost is estimated by $C(x) = 80x + 7000$ and revenue is estimated by $R(x) = 95x$; no more than 400 units can be sold.

38. Cost is $C(x) = 140x + 3000$ and revenue is $R(x) = 125x$.

39. Cost is $C(x) = 125x + 42{,}000$ and revenue is $R(x) = 165.5x$; no more than 2000 units can be sold.

40. Cost is $C(x) = 1750x + 95{,}000$ and revenue is $R(x) = 1975x$; no more than 600 units can be sold.

41. Business The accompanying graph shows the percentage of females in the workforce for Ireland and South Korea for the years 1980 through 2010. Estimate the break-even point (the point at which the two countries had the same percentage of females in the workforce.) (Data from: Organisation for Economic Co-operation and Development.)

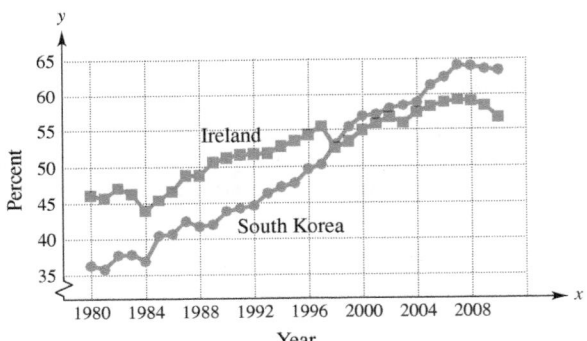

42. Social Science Gallup conducts an annual poll of residents of 130 countries around the world to ask about approval of world leadership. The graph below shows the percentage of respondents who approve of the job performance of the leadership of the United States and Great Britain from the years 2007 to 2012. Estimate the year in which the break-even point (the year in which the opinion on leadership was the same) occurred.

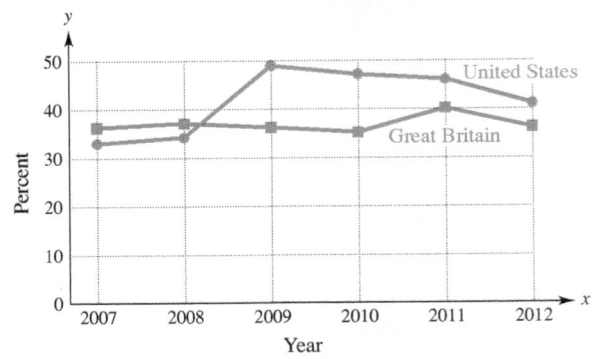

43. Social Science The population (in millions of people) of Florida from the year 2000 to the year 2010 can be approximated by the function $f(x) = .292x + 16.17$. Similarly, the population of (in millions of people) of New York can be approximated by the function $g(x) = .026x + 19.04$. For both of these models, let $x = 0$ correspond to the year 2000. (Data from: U.S. Census Bureau.)

   (a) Graph both functions on the same coordinate axes for $x = 0$ to $x = 10$.

   (b) Do the graphs intersect in this window?

   (c) If trends continue at the same rate, will Florida overtake New York in population? If so, estimate what year that will occur.

44. Social Science The population (in millions of people) of Massachusetts from the year 2000 to the year 2010 can be approximated by the function $f(x) = .019x + 6.36$. Similarly, the population (in millions of people) of Arizona can be approximated by the function $g(x) = .130x + 5.15$. For both of these models, let $x = 0$ correspond to the year 2000. (Data from: U.S. Census Bureau.)

   (a) Graph both functions on the same coordinate axes for $x = 0$ to $x = 10$.

   (b) Do the graphs intersect in this window?

   (c) If trends continue at the same rate, will Arizona overtake Massachusetts in population? If so, estimate what year that will occur.

Business *Use the supply and demand curves in the accompanying graph to answer Exercises 45–48. (See Examples 8–11.)*

45. At what price are 20 items supplied?

46. At what price are 20 items demanded?

47. Find the equilibrium quantity.

48. Find the equilibrium price.

Economics *Work the following exercises. (See Examples 8–11.)*

49. Suppose that the demand and price for a certain brand of shampoo are related by

$$p = 16 - \frac{5}{4}q,$$

where p is price in dollars and q is demand. Find the price for a demand of

   (a) 0 units;   **(b)** 4 units;   **(c)** 8 units.

Find the demand for the shampoo at a price of

(d) $6; **(e)** $11; **(f)** $16.

(g) Graph $p = 16 - (5/4)q$.

Suppose the price and supply of the shampoo are related by

$$p = \frac{3}{4}q,$$

where q represents the supply and p the price. Find the supply when the price is

(h) $0; **(i)** $10; **(j)** $20.

(k) Graph $p = (3/4)q$ on the same axes used for part (g).

(l) Find the equilibrium quantity.

(m) Find the equilibrium price.

50. Let the supply and demand for radial tires in dollars be given by

$$\text{supply:} \, p = \frac{3}{2}q; \quad \text{demand:} \, p = 81 - \frac{3}{4}q.$$

(a) Graph these equations on the same axes.

(b) Find the equilibrium quantity.

(c) Find the equilibrium price.

51. Let the supply and demand for bananas in cents per pound be given by

$$\text{supply:} \, p = \frac{2}{5}q; \quad \text{demand:} \, p = 100 - \frac{2}{5}q.$$

(a) Graph these equations on the same axes.

(b) Find the equilibrium quantity.

(c) Find the equilibrium price.

(d) On what interval does demand exceed supply?

52. Let the supply and demand for sugar be given by

$$\text{supply:} \, p = 1.4q - .6$$

and

$$\text{demand:} \, p = -2q + 3.2,$$

where p is in dollars.

(a) Graph these on the same axes.

(b) Find the equilibrium quantity.

(c) Find the equilibrium price.

(d) On what interval does supply exceed demand?

53. Explain why the graph of the (total) cost function is always above the x-axis and can never move downward as you go from left to right. Is the same thing true of the graph of the average cost function?

54. Explain why the graph of the profit function can rise or fall (as you go from left to right) and can be below the x-axis.

✓**Checkpoint Answers**

1. $C(x) = 4x + 60$. **2.** $4.60 **3.** $2248

4. **(a)** $800 **(b)** $842 **(c)** $3.50 **(d)** $3.50

5. **(a)** 1,120,000,000 **(b)** $47,873,000

6. 4286 newsletters

7. **(a)** $60 **(b)** 5 units **(c)** (10, 60); (5, 80)

8. **(a)** 40 **(b)** $160/3 \approx$ $53.33

3.4 Quadratic Functions and Applications

A **quadratic function** is a function whose rule is given by a quadratic polynomial, such as

$$f(x) = x^2, \quad g(x) = 3x^2 + 30x + 67, \quad \text{and} \quad h(x) = -x^2 + 4x.$$

Thus, a quadratic function is a function whose rule can be written in the form

$$f(x) = ax^2 + bx + c$$

for some constants a, b, and c, with $a \neq 0$.

Example 1 Graph each of these quadratic functions:

$$f(x) = x^2; \quad g(x) = 4x^2; \quad h(x) = -.2x^2.$$

Solution In each case, choose several numbers (negative, positive, and 0) for x, find the values of the function at these numbers, and plot the corresponding points. Then connect the points with a smooth curve to obtain Figure 3.23, on the next page.

$f(x) = x^2$					
x	-2	-1	0	1	2
x^2	4	1	0	1	4

$g(x) = 4x^2$					
x	-2	-1	0	1	2
$4x^2$	16	4	0	4	16

$h(x) = -.2x^2$						
x	-5	-3	-1	0	2	4
$-.2x^2$	-5	-1.8	$-.2$	0	$-.8$	-3.2

(a)

(b)

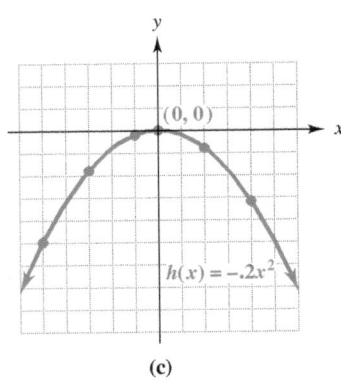

(c)

Figure 3.23

Each of the curves in Figure 3.23 is a **parabola.** It can be shown that the graph of every quadratic function is a parabola. Parabolas have many useful properties. Cross sections of radar dishes and spotlights form parabolas. Disks often visible on the sidelines of televised football games are microphones having reflectors with parabolic cross sections. These microphones are used by the television networks to pick up the signals shouted by the quarterbacks.

All parabolas have the same basic "cup" shape, although the cup may be broad or narrow and open upward or downward. The general shape of a parabola is determined by the coefficient of x^2 in its rule, as summarized here and illustrated in Example 1. ✓₁

✓ **Checkpoint 1**

Graph each quadratic function.

(a) $f(x) = x^2 - 4$

(b) $g(x) = -x^2 + 4$

The graph of a quadratic function $f(x) = ax^2 + bx + c$ is a parabola.

If $a > 0$, the parabola opens upward. [*Figure 3.23(a) and 3.23(b)*]

If $a < 0$, the parabola opens downward. [*Figure 3.23(c)*]

If $|a| < 1$, the parabola appears wider than the graph of $y = x^2$. [*Figure 3.23(c)*]

If $|a| > 1$, the parabola appears narrower than the graph of $y = x^2$.
  [*Figure 3.23(b)*]

When a parabola opens upward [as in Figure 3.23(a), (b)], its lowest point is called the **vertex.** When a parabola opens downward [as in Figure 3.23(c)], its highest point is called the **vertex.** The vertical line through the vertex of a parabola is called the **axis of the parabola.** For example, (0, 0) is the vertex of each of the parabolas in Figure 3.23, and the axis of each parabola is the y-axis. If you were to fold the graph of a parabola along its axis, the two halves of the parabola would match exactly. This means that a parabola is *symmetric* about its axis.

Although the vertex of a parabola can be approximated by a graphing calculator's maximum or minimum finder, its exact coordinates can be found algebraically, as in the following examples.

Example 2   Consider the function $g(x) = 2(x - 3)^2 + 1$.

(a) Show that g is a quadratic function.

Solution   Multiply out the rule of g to show that it has the required form:

$$g(x) = 2(x - 3)^2 + 1$$
$$= 2(x^2 - 6x + 9) + 1$$
$$= 2x^2 - 12x + 18 + 1$$
$$g(x) = 2x^2 - 12x + 19.$$

According to the preceding box, the graph of g is a somewhat narrow, upward-opening parabola.

(b) Show that the vertex of the graph of $g(x) = 2(x - 3)^2 + 1$ is (3, 1).

Solution   Since $g(3) = 2(3 - 3)^2 + 1 = 0 + 1 = 1$, the point (3, 1) is on the graph. The vertex of an upward-opening parabola is the lowest point on the graph, so we must show that (3, 1) is the lowest point. Let x be any number except 3 (so that $x - 3 \neq 0$). Then the quantity $2(x - 3)^2$ is positive, and hence

$$g(x) = 2(x - 3)^2 + 1 = \text{(a positive number)} + 1,$$

which means that $g(x) > 1$. Therefore, every point $(x, g(x))$ on the graph, where $x \neq 3$, has second coordinate $g(x)$ greater than 1. Hence $(x, g(x))$ lies *above* (3, 1). In other words, (3, 1) is the lowest point on the graph—the vertex of the parabola.

(c) Graph $g(x) = 2(x - 3)^2 + 1$.

Solution   Plot some points on both sides of the vertex (3, 1) to obtain the graph in Figure 3.24. The vertical line $x = 3$ through the vertex is the axis of the parabola.

x	y
1	9
2	3
3	1
4	3
5	9

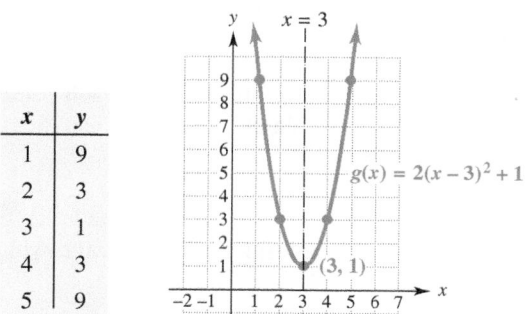

Figure 3.24

In Example 2, notice how the rule of the function g is related to the coordinates of the vertex:

$$g(x) = 2(x - 3)^2 + 1. \qquad (3, 1).$$

Arguments similar to those in Example 2 lead to the following fact.

The graph of the quadratic function $f(x) = a(x - h)^2 + k$ is a parabola with vertex (h, k). It opens upward when $a > 0$ and downward when $a < 0$.

Example 3   Determine algebraically whether the given parabola opens upward or downward, and find its vertex.

(a) $f(x) = -3(x - 4)^2 - 7$

Solution The rule of the function is in the form $f(x) = a(x - h)^2 + k$ (with $a = -3, h = 4$, and $k = -7$). The parabola opens downward ($a < 0$), and its vertex is $(h, k) = (4, -7)$.

(b) $g(x) = 2(x + 3)^2 + 5$

Solution Be careful here: The vertex is *not* (3, 5). To put the rule of $g(x)$ in the form $a(x - h)^2 + k$, we must rewrite it so that there is a minus sign inside the parentheses:

$$g(x) = 2(x + 3)^2 + 5$$
$$= 2(x - (-3))^2 + 5.$$

This is the required form, with $a = 2, h = -3$, and $k = 5$. The parabola opens upward, and its vertex is $(-3, 5)$. ✓ 2

✓ **Checkpoint 2**

Determine the vertex of each parabola, and graph the parabola.

(a) $f(x) = (x + 4)^2 - 3$

(b) $f(x) = -2(x - 3)^2 + 1$

Example 4 Find the rule of a quadratic function whose graph has vertex (3, 4) and passes through the point (6, 22).

Solution The graph of $f(x) = a(x - h)^2 + k$ has vertex (h, k). We want $h = 3$ and $k = 4$, so that $f(x) = a(x - 3)^2 + 4$. Since (6, 22) is on the graph, we must have $f(6) = 22$. Therefore,

$$f(x) = a(x - 3)^2 + 4$$
$$f(6) = a(6 - 3)^2 + 4$$
$$22 = a(3)^2 + 4$$
$$9a = 18$$
$$a = 2.$$

Thus, the graph of $f(x) = 2(x - 3)^2 + 4$ is a parabola with vertex (3, 4) that passes through (6, 22).

The vertex of each parabola in Examples 2 and 3 was easily determined because the rule of the function had the form

$$f(x) = a(x - h)^2 + k.$$

The rule of *any* quadratic function can be put in this form by using the technique of **completing the square**, which is illustrated in the next example.

Example 5 Determine the vertex of the graph of $f(x) = x^2 - 4x + 2$. Then graph the parabola.

Solution In order to get $f(x)$ in the form $a(x - h)^2 + k$, take half the coefficient of x, namely $\frac{1}{2}(-4) = -2$, and *square it*: $(-2)^2 = 4$. Then proceed as follows.

✓ **Checkpoint 3**

Rewrite the rule of each function by completing the square, and use this form to find the vertex of the graph.

(a) $f(x) = x^2 + 6x + 5$

(*Hint:* add and subtract the square of half the coefficient of *x*.)

(b) $g(x) = x^2 - 12x + 33$

$f(x) = x^2 - 4x + 2$	
$= x^2 - 4x + \underline{\quad} + 2$	Leave space for the squared term and its negative.
$= x^2 - 4x + 4 - 4 + 2$	Add and subtract 4.
$= (x^2 - 4x + 4) - 4 + 2$	Insert parentheses.
$= (x - 2)^2 - 2$	Factor expression in parentheses and add.

Adding and subtracting 4 did not change the rule of $f(x)$, but did make it possible to have a perfect square as part of its rule: $f(x) = (x - 2)^2 - 2$. Now we can see that the graph is an upward-opening parabola, as shown in Figure 3.25, on the following page. ✓ 3

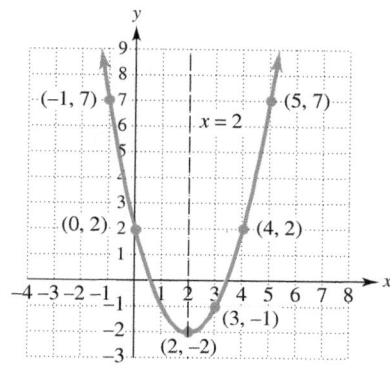

Figure 3.25

⚠ **CAUTION** The technique of completing the square only works when the coefficient of x^2 is 1. To find the vertex of a quadratic function such as

$$f(x) = 2x^2 + 12x - 19,$$

you must first factor out the coefficient of x^2 and write the rule as

$$f(x) = 2(x^2 + 6x - \tfrac{19}{2}).$$

Now complete the square on the expression in parentheses by adding and subtracting 9 (the square of half the coefficient of x), and proceed as in Example 5.

The technique of completing the square can be used to rewrite the general equation $f(x) = ax^2 + bx + c$ in the form $f(x) = a(x - h)^2 + k$. When this is done, we obtain a formula for the coordinates of the vertex.

> The graph of $f(x) = ax^2 + bx + c$ is a parabola with vertex (h, k), where
>
> $$h = \frac{-b}{2a} \quad \text{and} \quad k = f(h).$$

Additionally, the fact that the vertex of a parabola is the highest or lowest point on the graph can be used in applications to find a maximum or minimum value.

Example 6 **Business** Lynn Wolf owns and operates Wolf's microbrewery. She has hired a consultant to analyze her business operations. The consultant tells her that her daily profits from the sale of x cases of beer are given by

$$P(x) = -x^2 + 120x.$$

Find the vertex, determine if it is a maximum or minimum, write the equation of the axis of the parabola, and compute the x- and y-intercepts of the profit function $P(x)$.

Solution Since $a = -1$ and $b = 120$, the x-value of the vertex is

$$\frac{-b}{2a} = \frac{-120}{2(-1)} = 60.$$

The y-value of the vertex is

$$P(60) = -(60)^2 + 120(60) = 3600.$$

The vertex is (60, 3600) and since a is negative, it is a maximum because the parabola opens downward. The axis of the parabola is $x = 60$. The intercepts are found by setting x and y equal to 0.

x-intercepts	**y-intercept**

x-intercepts

Set $P(x) = y = 0$, so that

$$0 = -x^2 + 120x$$
$$0 = x(-x + 120)$$
$$x = 0 \quad \text{or} \quad -x + 120 = 0$$
$$-x = -120$$
$$x = 120$$

The x–intercepts are 0 and 120.

y-intercept

Set $x = 0$ to obtain

$$P(0) = 0^2 + 120(0) = 0$$

The y-intercept is 0.

✓ **Checkpoint 4**

When a company sells x units of a product, its profit is $P(x) = -2x^2 + 40x + 280$. Find

(a) the number of units which should be sold so that maximum profit is received;

(b) the maximum profit.

Figure 3.26 shows the profit function $P(x)$. ✓4

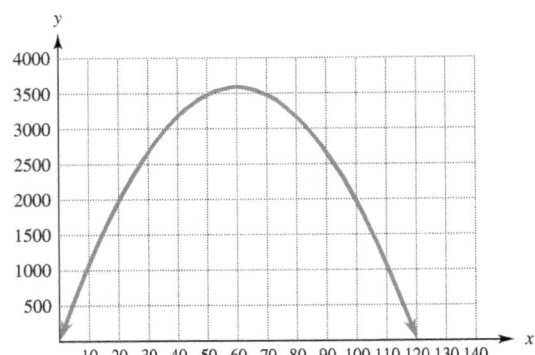

Figure 3.26

🖅 **TECHNOLOGY TIP** The maximum or minimum finder on a graphing calculator can approximate the vertex of a parabola with a high degree of accuracy. The max–min finder is in the CALC menu or in the MATH or FCN submenu of the GRAPH menu. Similarly, the calculator's graphical root finder can approximate the x-intercepts of a parabola.

🗘 Supply and demand curves were introduced in Section 3.3. Here is a quadratic example.

Example 7 **Economics** Suppose that the price of and demand for an item are related by

$$p = 150 - 6q^2, \qquad \text{Demand function}$$

where p is the price (in dollars) and q is the number of items demanded (in hundreds). Suppose also that the price and supply are related by

$$p = 10q^2 + 2q, \qquad \text{Supply function}$$

where q is the number of items supplied (in hundreds). Find the equilibrium quantity and the equilibrium price.

Solution The graphs of both of these equations are parabolas (Figure 3.27), as seen on the following page. Only those portions of the graphs which lie in the first quadrant are included, because none of supply, demand, or price can be negative.

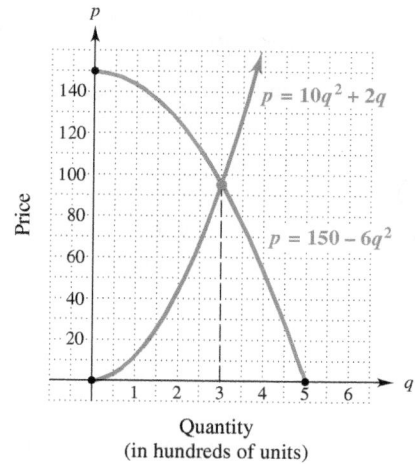

Figure 3.27

The point where the demand and supply curves intersect is the equilibrium point. Its first coordinate is the equilibrium quantity, and its second coordinate is the equilibrium price. These coordinates may be found in two ways.

Algebraic Method   At the equilibrium point, the second coordinate of the demand curve must be the same as the second coordinate of the supply curve, so that

$$150 - 6q^2 = 10q^2 + 2q.$$

Write this quadratic equation in standard form as follows:

$$0 = 16q^2 + 2q - 150 \qquad \text{Add } -150 \text{ and } 6q^2 \text{ to both sides.}$$
$$0 = 8q^2 + q - 75. \qquad \text{Multiply both sides by } \frac{1}{2}.$$

This equation can be solved by the quadratic formula, given in Section 1.7. Here, $a = 8$, $b = 1$, and $c = -75$:

$$q = \frac{-1 \pm \sqrt{1 - 4(8)(-75)}}{2(8)}$$

$$= \frac{-1 \pm \sqrt{1 + 2400}}{16} \qquad -4(8)(-75) = 2400$$

$$= \frac{-1 \pm 49}{16} \qquad \sqrt{1 + 2400} = \sqrt{2401} = 49$$

$$q = \frac{-1 + 49}{16} = \frac{48}{16} = 3 \quad \text{or} \quad q = \frac{-1 - 49}{16} = -\frac{50}{16} = -\frac{25}{8}.$$

It is not possible to make $-25/8$ units, so discard that answer and use only $q = 3$. Hence, the equilibrium quantity is 300. Find the equilibrium price by substituting 3 for q in either the supply or the demand function (and check your answer by using the other one). Using the supply function gives

$$p = 10q^2 + 2q$$
$$p = 10 \cdot 3^2 + 2 \cdot 3 \qquad \text{Let } q = 3.$$
$$= 10 \cdot 9 + 6$$
$$p = \$96.$$

Figure 3.28

✓**Checkpoint 5**

The price and demand for an item are related by $p = 32 - x^2$, while price and supply are related by $p = x^2$. Find

(a) the equilibrium quantity;

(b) the equilibrium price.

Graphical Method   Graph the two functions on a graphing calculator, and use the intersection finder to determine that the equilibrium point is $(3, 96)$, as in Figure 3.28. ✓5

Example 8   **Business**   The rental manager of a small apartment complex with 16 units has found from experience that each $40 increase in the monthly rent results in an empty apartment. All 16 apartments will be rented at a monthly rent of $500. How many $40 increases will produce maximum monthly income for the complex?

Solution   Let x represent the number of $40 increases. Then the number of apartments rented will be $16 - x$. Also, the monthly rent per apartment will be $500 + 40x$. (There are x increases of $40, for a total increase of $40x$.) The monthly income, $I(x)$, is given by the number of apartments rented times the rent per apartment, so

$$I(x) = (16 - x)(500 + 40x)$$
$$= 8000 + 640x - 500x - 40x^2$$
$$= 8000 + 140x - 40x^2.$$

Since x represents the number of $40 increases and each $40 increase causes one empty apartment, x must be a whole number. Because there are only 16 apartments, $0 \le x \le 16$. Since there is a small number of possibilities, the value of x that produces maximum income may be found in several ways.

Brute Force Method   Use a scientific calculator or the table feature of a graphing calculator (as in Figure 3.29) to evaluate $I(x)$ when $x = 1, 2, \ldots, 16$ and find the largest value.

X	Y1			X	Y1			X	Y1
0	8000			7	7020			14	2120
1	8100			8	6560			15	1100
2	8120			9	6020			16	0
3	8060			10	5400			17	-1180
4	7920			11	4700			18	-2440
5	7700			12	3920			19	-3780
6	7400			13	3060			20	-5200
X=0				X=7				X=14	

Figure 3.29

The tables show that a maximum income of $8120 occurs when $x = 2$. So the manager should charge rent of $500 + 2(40) = \$580$, leaving two apartments vacant.

Algebraic Method   The graph of $I(x) = 8000 + 140x - 40x^2$ is a downward-opening parabola (why?), and the value of x that produces maximum income occurs at the vertex. The methods of Section 3.4 show that the vertex is $(1.75, 8122.50)$. Since x must be a whole number, evaluate $I(x)$ at $x = 1$ and $x = 2$ to see which one gives the best result:

$$\text{If } x = 1, \text{ then } I(1) = -40(1)^2 + 140(1) + 8000 = 8100.$$
$$\text{If } x = 2, \text{ then } I(2) = -40(2)^2 + 140(2) + 8000 = 8120.$$

So maximum income occurs when $x = 2$. The manager should charge a rent of $500 + 2(40) = \$580$, leaving two apartments vacant.

Quadratic Models

Real-world data can sometimes be used to construct a quadratic function that approximates the data. Such **quadratic models** can then be used (subject to limitations) to predict future behavior.

Example 9   **Business**   The number of physical compact disks (CDs, in millions of units) shipped are given in the following table for the years 1997 through 2011. (Data from: Recording Industry Association of America.)

Year	1997	1998	1999	2000	2001	2002	2003	2004
CDs shipped	753	847	939	943	882	803	746	767
Year	2005	2006	2007	2008	2009	2010	2011	
CDs shipped	705	620	511	369	293	253	241	

(a) Let $x = 7$ correspond to the year 1997. Display the information graphically.

Solution Plot the points $(7, 753)$, $(8, 847)$, and so on—as in Figure 3.30.

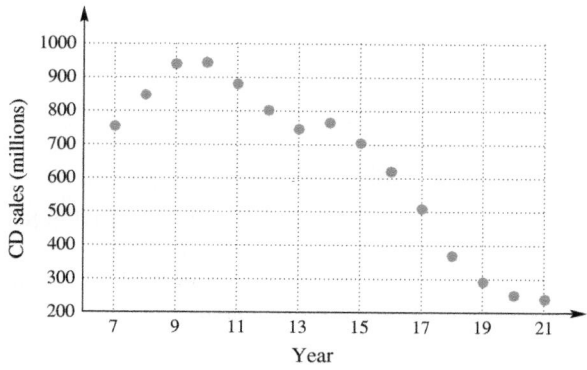

Figure 3.30

(b) The shape of the data points in Figure 3.31 resembles a downward-opening parabola. Using the year 2000 as the maximum, find a quadratic model $f(x) = a(x - h)^2 + k$ for these data.

Solution Recall that when a quadratic function is written in the form $f(x) = a(x - h)^2 + k$, the vertex of its graph is (h, k). On the basis of Figure 3.30, let $(10, 943)$ be the vertex, so that

$$f(x) = a(x - 10)^2 + 943.$$

To find a, choose another data point $(15, 705)$. Assume this point lies on the parabola so that

$$f(x) = a(x - 10)^2 + 943$$
$$705 = a(15 - 10)^2 + 943 \qquad \text{Substitute 15 for } x \text{ and 705 for } f(x).$$
$$705 = 25a + 943 \qquad \text{Subtract inside the parentheses and then square.}$$
$$-238 = 25a \qquad \text{Subtract 943 from both sides.}$$
$$a = -9.52. \qquad \text{Divide both sides by 25.}$$

Therefore, $f(x) = -9.52(x - 10)^2 + 943$ is a quadratic model for these data. If we expand the form into $f(x) = ax^2 + bx + c$, we obtain

$$f(x) = -9.52(x - 10)^2 + 943$$
$$= -9.52(x^2 - 20x + 100) + 943 \qquad \text{Expand inside the parentheses.}$$
$$= -9.52x^2 + 190.4x - 952 + 943 \qquad \text{Distribute the } -9.52.$$
$$= -9.52x^2 + 190.4x - 9. \qquad \text{Add the last two terms together.}$$

✓ **Checkpoint 6**

Find another quadratic model in Example 9(b) by using $(10, 943)$ as the vertex and $(19, 293)$ as the other point.

Figure 3.31, on the following page, shows the original data with the graph of $f(x)$. It appears to fit the data rather well except for the last two points. (We find a better fitting model in Example 10.) ✓6

Figure 3.31

Quadratic Regression

Linear regression was used in Section 2.3 to construct a linear function that modeled a set of data points. When the data points appear to lie on a parabola rather than on a straight line (as in Example 9), a similar least-squares regression procedure is available on most graphing calculators and spreadsheet programs to construct a quadratic model for the data. Simply follow the same steps as in linear regression, with one exception: Choose quadratic, rather than linear, regression. (Both options are on the same menu.)

Example 10   Use a graphing calculator to find a quadratic-regression model for the data in Example 9.

Solution   Enter the first coordinates of the data points as list L_1 and the second coordinates as list L_2. Performing the quadratic regression, as in Figure 3.32, leads to the model

$$g(x) = -5.034x^2 + 90.25x + 461.8.$$

The number R^2 in Figure 3.32 is fairly close to 1, which indicates that this model fits the data fairly well. Figure 3.33 shows the data with the quadratic regression curve.

Figure 3.32

Figure 3.33

3.4 Exercises

The graph of each of the functions in Exercises 1–4 is a parabola. Without graphing, determine whether the parabola opens upward or downward. (See Example 1.)

1. $f(x) = x^2 - 3x - 12$ **2.** $g(x) = -x^2 + 5x + 15$

3. $h(x) = -3x^2 + 14x + 1$ **4.** $f(x) = 6.5x^2 - 7.2x + 4$

Without graphing, determine the vertex of the parabola that is the graph of the given function. State whether the parabola opens upward or downward. (See Examples 2 and 3.)

5. $f(x) = -2(x - 5)^2 + 7$ **6.** $g(x) = -7(x - 8)^2 - 3$

7. $h(x) = 4(x + 1)^2 - 9$ **8.** $f(x) = -8(x + 12)^2 + 9$

Match each function with its graph, which is one of those shown.
(See Examples 1–3.)

9. $f(x) = x^2 + 2$

10. $g(x) = x^2 - 2$

11. $g(x) = (x - 2)^2$

12. $f(x) = -(x + 2)^2$

13. $f(x) = 2(x - 2)^2 + 2$

14. $g(x) = -2(x - 2)^2 - 2$

15. $g(x) = -2(x + 2)^2 + 2$

16. $f(x) = 2(x + 2)^2 - 2$

(a)

(b)

(c)

(d)

(e)

(f)

(g)

(h)

(i)

(j)

(k)

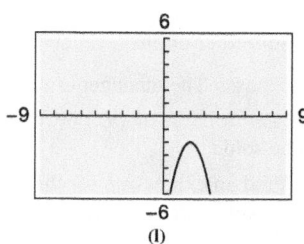
(l)

Find the rule of a quadratic function whose graph has the given
vertex and passes through the given point. (See Example 4.)

17. Vertex $(1, 2)$; point $(5, 6)$

18. Vertex $(-3, 2)$; point $(2, 1)$

19. Vertex $(-1, -2)$; point $(1, 2)$

20. Vertex $(2, -4)$; point $(5, 2)$

Without graphing, find the vertex of the parabola that is the graph
of the given function. (See Examples 5 and 6.)

21. $f(x) = -x^2 - 6x + 3$ **22.** $g(x) = x^2 + 10x + 9$

23. $f(x) = 3x^2 - 12x + 5$ **24.** $g(x) = -4x^2 - 16x + 9$

Without graphing, determine the x- and y-intercepts of each of the
given parabolas. (See Example 6.)

25. $f(x) = 3(x - 2)^2 - 3$ **26.** $f(x) = x^2 - 4x - 1$

27. $g(x) = 2x^2 + 8x + 6$ **28.** $g(x) = x^2 - 10x + 20$

Graph each parabola and find its vertex and axis of symmetry. (See
Examples 1–6.)

29. $f(x) = (x + 2)^2$

30. $f(x) = -(x + 5)^2$

31. $f(x) = x^2 - 4x + 6$

32. $f(x) = x^2 + 6x + 3$

Use a calculator to work these problems.

33. Social Science According to data from the National Safety Council, the fatal-accident rate per 100,000 licensed drivers can be approximated by the function $f(x) = .0328x^2 - 3.55x + 115$, where x is the age of the driver ($16 \le x \le 88$). At what age is the rate the lowest?

34. Social Science Using data from the U.S. Census Bureau, the population (in thousands) of Detroit, Michigan can be approximated by $g(x) = -.422x^2 + 48.84x + 248$, where $x = 0$ corresponds to the year 1900. In what year, according to the given model, did Detroit have its highest population?

35. Natural Science A researcher in physiology has decided that a good mathematical model for the number of impulses fired after a nerve has been stimulated is given by $y = -x^2 + 20x - 60$, where y is the number of responses per millisecond and x is the number of milliseconds since the nerve was stimulated.

(a) When will the maximum firing rate be reached?

(b) What is the maximum firing rate?

36. Physical Science A bullet is fired upward from ground level. Its height above the ground (in feet) at time t seconds is given by

$$H = -16t^2 + 1000t.$$

Find the maximum height of the bullet and the time at which it hits the ground.

37. Business Pat Kan owns a factory that manufactures souvenir key chains. Her weekly profit (in hundreds of dollars) is given by $P(x) = -2x^2 + 60x - 120$, where x is the number of cases of key chains sold.

(a) What is the largest number of cases she can sell and still make a profit?

(b) Explain how it is possible for her to lose money if she sells more cases than your answer in part (a).

(c) How many cases should she make and sell in order to maximize her profits?

38. Business The manager of a bicycle shop has found that, at a price (in dollars) of $p(x) = 150 - \dfrac{x}{4}$ per bicycle, x bicycles will be sold.

(a) Find an expression for the total revenue from the sale of x bicycles. (*Hint:* Revenue = Demand × Price.)

(b) Find the number of bicycle sales that leads to maximum revenue.

(c) Find the maximum revenue.

Work the following problems. (See Example 7.)

39. Business Suppose the supply of and demand for a certain textbook are given by

$$\text{supply:} \ p = \frac{1}{5}q^2 \quad \text{and} \quad \text{demand:} \ p = -\frac{1}{5}q^2 + 40,$$

where p is price and q is quantity. How many books are demanded at a price of

(a) 10? (b) 20? (c) 30? (d) 40?

How many books are supplied at a price of

(e) 5? (f) 10? (g) 20? (h) 30?

(i) Graph the supply and demand functions on the same axes.

40. Business Find the equilibrium quantity and the equilibrium price in Exercise 39.

41. Business Suppose the price p of widgets is related to the quantity q that is demanded by

$$p = 640 - 5q^2,$$

where q is measured in hundreds of widgets. Find the price when the number of widgets demanded is

(a) 0; (b) 5; (c) 10.

Suppose the supply function for widgets is given by $p = 5q^2$, where q is the number of widgets (in hundreds) that are supplied at price p.

(d) Graph the demand function $p = 640 - 5q^2$ and the supply function $p = 5q^2$ on the same axes.

(e) Find the equilibrium quantity.

(f) Find the equilibrium price.

42. Business The supply function for a commodity is given by $p = q^2 + 200$, and the demand function is given by $p = -10q + 3200$

(a) Graph the supply and demand functions on the same axes.

(b) Find the equilibrium point.

(c) What is the equilibrium quantity? the equilibrium price?

Business *Find the equilibrium quantity and equilibrium price for the commodity whose supply and demand functions are given.*

43. Supply: $p = 45q$; demand: $p = -q^2 + 10,000$.

44. Supply: $p = q^2 + q + 10$; demand: $p = -10q + 3060$.

45. Supply: $p = q^2 + 20q$; demand: $p = -2q^2 + 10q + 3000$.

46. Supply: $p = .2q + 51$; demand: $p = \dfrac{3000}{q + 5}$.

Business *The revenue function $R(x)$ and the cost function $C(x)$ for a particular product are given. These functions are valid only for the specified domain of values. Find the number of units that must be produced to break even.*

47. $R(x) = 200x - x^2$; $C(x) = 70x + 2200$; $0 \le x \le 100$

48. $R(x) = 300x - x^2$; $C(x) = 65x + 7000$; $0 \le x \le 150$

49. $R(x) = 400x - 2x^2$; $C(x) = -x^2 + 200x + 1900$; $0 \le x \le 100$

50. $R(x) = 500x - 2x^2$; $C(x) = -x^2 + 270x + 5125$; $0 \le x \le 125$

Business *Work each problem. (See Example 8.)*

51. A charter flight charges a fare of $200 per person, plus $4 per person for each unsold seat on the plane. If the plane holds 100 passengers and if x represents the number of unsold seats, find the following:

(a) an expression for the total revenue received for the flight. (*Hint:* Multiply the number of people flying, $100 - x$, by the price per ticket);

(b) the graph for the expression in part (a);

(c) the number of unsold seats that will produce the maximum revenue;

(d) the maximum revenue.

52. The revenue of a charter bus company depends on the number of unsold seats. If 100 seats are sold, the price is $50 per seat. Each unsold seat increases the price per seat by $1. Let x represent the number of unsold seats.

(a) Write an expression for the number of seats that are sold.

(b) Write an expression for the price per seat.

(c) Write an expression for the revenue.

(d) Find the number of unsold seats that will produce the maximum revenue.

(e) Find the maximum revenue.

53. A hog farmer wants to find the best time to take her hogs to market. The current price is 88 cents per pound, and her hogs weigh an average of 90 pounds. The hogs gain 5 pounds per week, and the market price for hogs is falling each week by 2 cents per pound. How many weeks should the farmer wait before taking her hogs to market in order to receive as much money as possible? At that time, how much money (per hog) will she get?

54. The manager of a peach orchard is trying to decide when to arrange for picking the peaches. If they are picked now, the average yield per tree will be 100 pounds, which can be sold for 40¢ per pound. Past experience shows that the yield per tree will increase about 5 pounds per week, while the price will decrease about 2¢ per pound per week.

(a) Let x represent the number of weeks that the manager should wait. Find the price per pound.

(b) Find the number of pounds per tree.

(c) Find the total revenue from a tree.

(d) When should the peaches be picked in order to produce the maximum revenue?

(e) What is the maximum revenue?

Work these exercises. (See Example 9.)

55. Health The National Center for Catastrophic Sport Injury Research keeps data on the number of fatalities directly related to football each year. These deaths occur in sandlot, pro and semipro, high school, and college-level playing. The following table gives selected years and the number of deaths. (Data from: www.unc.edu/depts/nccsi/FootballAnnual.pdf.)

Year	Deaths
1970	29
1975	15
1980	9
1985	7
1990	0
1995	4
2000	3
2005	3
2010	5

(a) Let $x = 0$ correspond to 1970. Use (20, 0) as the vertex and the data from 2005 to find a quadratic function $g(x) = a(x - h)^2 + k$ that models the data.

(b) Use the model to estimate the number of deaths in 2008.

56. Natural Science The acreage (in millions) consumed by forest fires in the United States is given in the following table. (Data from: National Interagency Fire Center.)

Year	Acres
1985	2.9
1988	5.0
1991	3.0
1994	4.1
1997	2.9
2000	7.4
2003	4.0
2006	9.9
2009	5.9
2012	9.2

(a) Let $x = 5$ correspond to the year 1985. Use (5, 2.9) as the vertex and the data for the year 1994 to find a quadratic function $f(x) = a(x - h)^2 + k$ that models the data.

(b) Use the model to estimate the acreage destroyed by forest fires in the year 2009.

57. Business The following table shows China's gross domestic expenditures on research and development (in billions of U.S. dollars) for the years 2004 through 2010. (Data from: National Science Foundation, *National Patterns of R & D Resources* [annual series].)

Year	Acres
2004	57.8
2005	71.1
2006	86.7
2007	102.4
2008	120.8
2009	154.1
2010	179.0

(a) Let $x = 4$ correspond to the year 2004. Use (4, 57.8) as the vertex and the data from 2008 to find a quadratic function $f(x) = a(x - h)^2 + k$ that models these data.

(b) Use the model to estimate the expenditures in the year 2012.

58. Economics The amount (in billions of dollars) of personal health care expenditures for hospital care for various years is given in the table on the following page. (Data from: U.S. Centers for Medicare and Medicaid Services.)

Year	Expenditures
1990	250
1995	339
2000	416
2005	609
2006	652
2007	693
2008	729
2009	776
2010	814

(a) Let $x = 0$ correspond to the year 1990. Use (0, 250) as the vertex and the data from the year 2007 to find a quadratic function $f(x) = a(x - h)^2 + k$ that models these data.

(b) Use the model to estimate the expenditures in 1997 and 2012.

⚐ *In Exercises 59–62, plot the data points and use quadratic regression to find a function that models the data. (See Example 10.)*

59. Health Use the data in Exercise 55, with $x = 0$ corresponding to 1970. What number of injuries does this model estimate for 2008? Compare your answer with that for Exercise 55.

60. Natural Science Use the data from Exercise 56, with $x = 5$ corresponding to the year 1985. How much acreage does this model estimate for the year 2009? Compare your answer with that for Exercise 56.

61. Business Use the data from Exercise 57, with $x = 4$ corresponding to the year 2004. What is the estimate of the amount of R&D expenditures for China in the year 2012? Compare your answer with that for Exercise 57.

62. Economics Use the data from Exercise 58, with $x = 0$ corresponding to the year 1990. What is the amount of expenditures for hospital care estimated by this model for the years 1997 and 2012? Compare your answers with those for Exercise 58.

Business *Recall that profit equals revenue minus cost. In Exercises 63 and 64, find the following:*

(a) *The break-even point (to the nearest tenth)*

(b) *The x-value that makes profit a maximum*

(c) *The maximum profit*

(d) *For what x-values will a loss occur?*

(e) *For what x-values will a profit occur?*

63. $R(x) = 400x - 2x^2$ and $C(x) = 200x + 2000$, with $0 \le x \le 100$

64. $R(x) = 900x - 3x^2$ and $C(x) = 450x + 5000$, with $20 \le x \le 150$

✓**Checkpoint Answers**

1. (a)

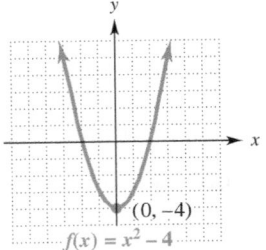

$(0, -4)$
$f(x) = x^2 - 4$

(b)

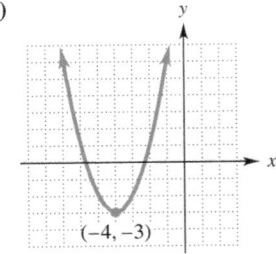

$(0, 4)$
$g(x) = -x^2 + 4$

2. (a)

$(-4, -3)$
$f(x) = (x + 4)^2 - 3$

(b)

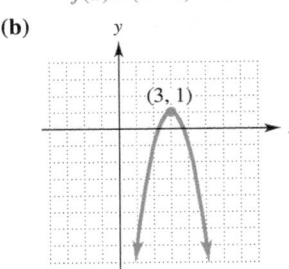

$(3, 1)$
$f(x) = -2(x - 3)^2 + 1$

3. (a) $f(x) = (x + 3)^2 - 4; (-3, -4)$
   (b) $g(x) = (x - 6)^2 - 3; (6, -3)$

4. (a) 10 units   **(b)** $480

5. (a) 4   **(b)** 16

6. $f(x) = -8.02x^2 + 160.4x + 141$

3.5 Polynomial Functions

A **polynomial function of degree** n is a function whose rule is given by a polynomial of degree n.[*] For example

$$f(x) = 3x - 2$$ polynomial function of degree 1;

$$g(x) = 3x^2 + 4x - 6$$ polynomial function of degree 2;

$$h(x) = x^4 + 5x^3 - 6x^2 + x - 3$$ polynomial function of degree 4.

---

[*]The degree of a polynomial was defined on page 13.

Basic Graphs

The simplest polynomial functions are those whose rules are of the form $f(x) = ax^n$ (where a is a constant).

Example 1 Graph $f(x) = x^3$.

Solution First, find several ordered pairs belonging to the graph. Be sure to choose some negative x-values, $x = 0$, and some positive x-values in order to get representative ordered pairs. Find as many ordered pairs as you need in order to see the shape of the graph. Then plot the ordered pairs and draw a smooth curve through them to obtain the graph in Figure 3.34.

✓**Checkpoint 1**

Graph $f(x) = -\dfrac{1}{2}x^3$

x	y
2	8
1	1
0	0
−1	−1
−2	−8

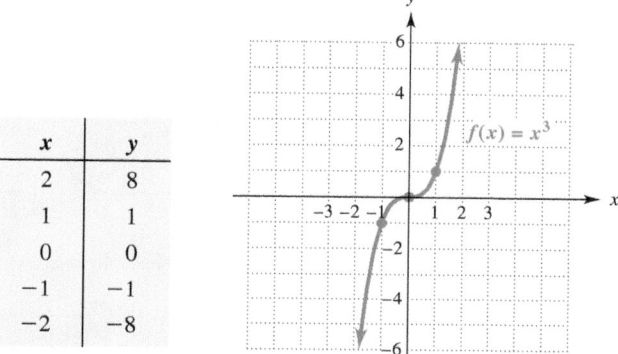

Figure 3.34

Example 2 Graph

$$f(x) = \frac{3}{2}x^4.$$

Solution The following table gives some typical ordered pairs and leads to the graph in Figure 3.35.

✓**Checkpoint 2**

Graph $g(x) = -2x^4$

x	$f(x)$
−2	24
−1	3/2
0	0
1	3/2
2	24

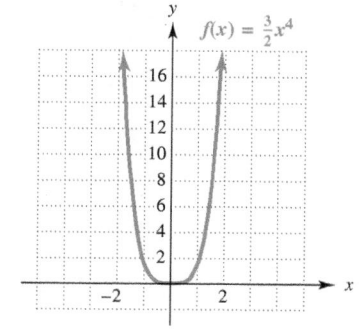

Figure 3.35

The graph of $f(x) = ax^n$ has one of the four basic shapes illustrated in Examples 1 and 2 and in Checkpoints 1 and 2. The basic shapes are summarized on the next page.

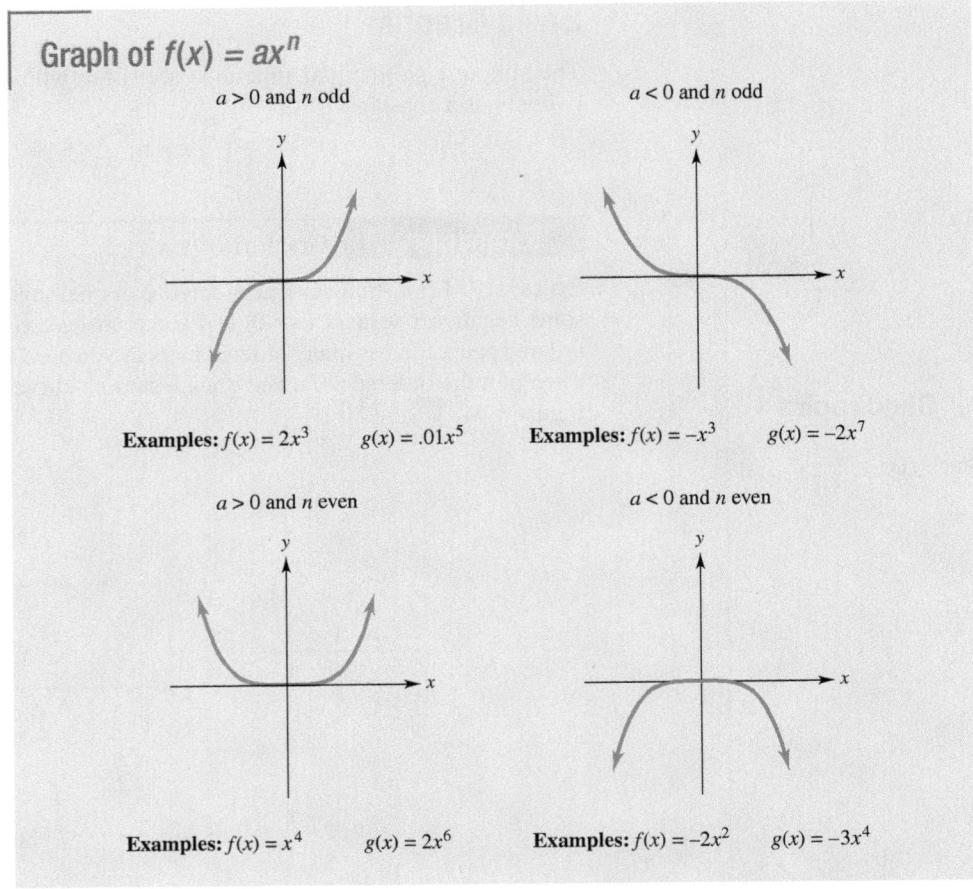

Graph of $f(x) = ax^n$

$a > 0$ and n odd

$a < 0$ and n odd

Examples: $f(x) = 2x^3$ $g(x) = .01x^5$ **Examples:** $f(x) = -x^3$ $g(x) = -2x^7$

$a > 0$ and n even

$a < 0$ and n even

Examples: $f(x) = x^4$ $g(x) = 2x^6$ **Examples:** $f(x) = -2x^2$ $g(x) = -3x^4$

Properties of Polynomial Graphs

Unlike the graphs in the preceding figures, the graphs of more complicated polynomial functions may have several "peaks" and "valleys," as illustrated in Figure 3.36, on the following page. The locations of the peaks and valleys can be accurately approximated by a maximum or minimum finder on a graphing calculator. Calculus is needed to determine their exact location.

The total number of peaks and valleys in a polynomial graph, as well as the number of the graph's x-intercepts, depends on the degree of the polynomial, as shown in Figure 3.36 and summarized here.

Polynomial	Degree	Number of peaks & valleys	Number of x-intercepts
$f(x) = x^3 - 4x + 2$	3	2	3
$f(x) = x^5 - 5x^3 + 4x$	5	4	5
$f(x) = 1.5x^4 + x^3 - 4x^2 - 3x + 4$	4	3	2
$f(x) = -x^6 + x^5 + 2x^4 + 1$	6	3	2

In each case, the number of x-intercepts is *at most* the degree of the polynomial. The total number of peaks and valleys is at most *one less than* the degree of the polynomial. The same thing is true in every case.

1. The total number of peaks and valleys on the graph of a polynomial function of degree n is at most $n - 1$.

2. The number of x-intercepts on the graph of a polynomial function of degree n is at most n.

(a) $f(x) = x^3 - 4x + 2$
1 peak
1 valley $\}$ total 2
3 x-intercepts

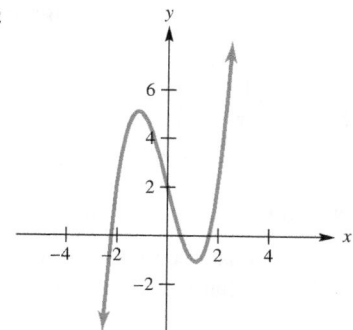

(b) $f(x) = x^5 - 5x^3 + 4x$
2 peaks
2 valleys $\}$ total 4
5 x-intercepts

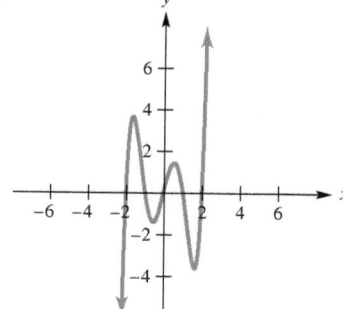

(c) $f(x) = 1.5x^4 + x^3 - 4x^2 - 3x + 4$
1 peak
2 valleys $\}$ total 3
2 x-intercepts

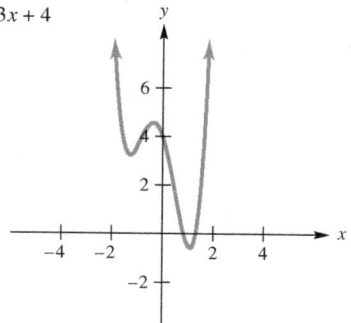

(d) $f(x) = -x^6 + x^5 + 2x^4 + 1$
2 peaks
1 (shallow) valley $\}$ total 3
2 x-intercepts

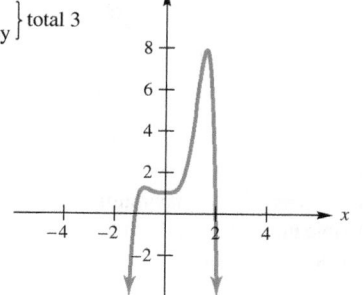

Figure 3.36

The domain of every polynomial function is the set of all real numbers, which means that its graph extends forever to the left and right. We indicate this by the arrows on the ends of polynomial graphs.

Although there may be peaks, valleys, and bends in a polynomial graph, the far ends of the graph are easy to describe: *they look like the graph of the highest-degree term of the polynomial.* Consider, for example, $f(x) = 1.5x^4 + x^3 - 4x^2 - 3x + 4$, whose highest-degree term is $1.5x^4$ and whose graph is shown in Figure 3.36(c). The ends of the graph shoot upward, just as the graph of $y = 1.5x^4$ does in Figure 3.35. When $f(x)$ and $y = 1.5x^4$ are graphed in the same large viewing window of a graphing calculator (Figure 3.37), the graphs look almost identical, except near the origin. This is an illustration of the following facts.

Figure 3.37

> The graph of a polynomial function is a smooth, unbroken curve that extends forever to the left and right. When $|x|$ is large, the graph resembles the graph of its highest-degree term and moves sharply away from the x-axis.

Example 3 Let $g(x) = x^3 - 11x^2 - 32x + 24$, and consider the graph in Figure 3.38.

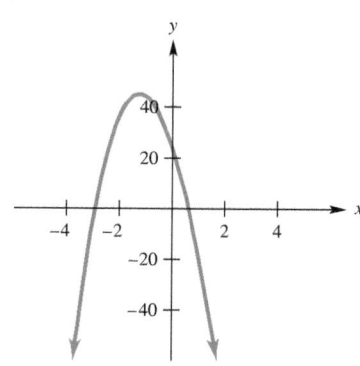

Figure 3.38

(a) Is Figure 3.38, on the previous page, a complete graph of $g(x)$; that is, does it show all the important features of the graph?

Solution   The far ends of the graph of $g(x)$ should resemble the graph of its highest-degree term x^3. The graph of $f(x) = x^3$ in Figure 3.34 moves upward at the far right, but the graph in Figure 3.38 does not. So Figure 3.38 is *not* a complete graph.

(b) Use a graphing calculator to find a complete graph of $g(x)$.

Solution   Since the graph of $g(x)$ must eventually start rising on the right side (as does the graph of x^3), a viewing window that shows a complete graph must extend beyond $x = 4$. By experimenting with various windows, we obtain Figure 3.39. This graph shows a total of two peaks and valleys and three x-intercepts (the maximum possible for a polynomial of degree 3). At the far ends, the graph of $g(x)$ resembles the graph of $f(x) = x^3$. Therefore, Figure 3.39 is a complete graph of $g(x)$.

 Checkpoint 3

Find a viewing window on a graphing calculator that shows a complete graph of
$f(x) = -.7x^4 + 119x^2 + 400.$
(*Hint*: The graph has two x-intercepts and the maximum possible number of peaks and valleys.)

Figure 3.39

Graphing Techniques

Accurate graphs of first- and second-degree polynomial functions (lines and parabolas) are easily found algebraically, as we saw in Sections 2.2 and 3.4. All polynomial functions of degree 3, and some of higher degree, can be accurately graphed by hand by using calculus and algebra to locate the peaks and valleys. When a polynomial can be completely factored, the general shape of its graph can be determined algebraically by using the basic properties of polynomial graphs, as illustrated in Example 4. Obtaining accurate graphs of other polynomial functions generally requires the use of technology.

Example 4   Graph $f(x) = (2x + 3)(x - 1)(x + 2)$.

Checkpoint 4

Multiply out the expression for $f(x)$ in Example 4 and determine its degree.

Solution   Note that $f(x)$ is a polynomial of degree 3. (If you don't see why, do Checkpoint 4.) Begin by finding any x-intercepts. Set $f(x) = 0$ and solve for x:

$$f(x) = 0$$
$$(2x + 3)(x - 1)(x + 2) = 0.$$

Solve this equation by setting each of the three factors equal to 0:

$$2x + 3 = 0 \quad \text{or} \quad x - 1 = 0 \quad \text{or} \quad x + 2 = 0$$
$$x = -\frac{3}{2} \qquad\qquad x = 1 \qquad\qquad x = -2.$$

The three numbers $-3/2$, 1, and -2 divide the x-axis into four intervals:

$$x < -2, \quad -2 < x < -\frac{3}{2}, \quad -\frac{3}{2} < x < 1, \quad \text{and} \quad 1 < x.$$

These intervals are shown in Figure 3.40.

Figure 3.40

Since the graph is an unbroken curve, it can change from above the x-axis to below it only by passing through the x-axis. As we have seen, this occurs only at the x-intercepts: $x = -2, -3/2$, and 1. Consequently, in the interval between two intercepts (or to the left of $x = -2$ or to the right of $x = 1$), the graph of $f(x)$ must lie entirely above or entirely below the x-axis.

We can determine where the graph lies over an interval by evaluating $f(x) = (2x + 3)(x - 1)(x + 2)$ at a number in that interval. For example, $x = -3$ is in the interval where $x < -2$, and

$$f(-3) = (2(-3) + 3)(-3 - 1)(-3 + 2)$$
$$= -12.$$

Therefore, $(-3, -12)$ is on the graph. Since this point lies below the x-axis, all points in this interval (that is, all points with $x < -2$) must lie below the x-axis. By testing numbers in the other intervals, we obtain the following table.

Interval	$x < -2$	$-2 < x < -3/2$	$-3/2 < x < 1$	$x > 1$
Test Number	-3	$-7/4$	0	2
Value of $f(x)$	-12	$11/32$	-6	28
Sign of $f(x)$	Negative	Positive	Negative	Positive
Graph	Below x-axis	Above x-axis	Below x-axis	Above x-axis

Since the graph intersects the x-axis at the intercepts and is above the x-axis between these intercepts, there must be at least one peak there. Similarly, there must be at least one valley between $x = -3/2$ and $x = 1$, because the graph is below the x-axis there. However, a polynomial function of degree 3 can have a total of at most $3 - 1 = 2$ peaks and valleys. So there must be exactly one peak and exactly one valley on this graph.

Furthermore, when $|x|$ is large, the graph must resemble the graph of $y = 2x^3$ (the highest-degree term). The graph of $y = 2x^3$, like the graph of $y = x^3$ in Figure 3.34, moves upward to the right and downward to the left. Using these facts and plotting the x-intercepts shows that the graph must have the general shape shown in Figure 3.41. Plotting additional points leads to the reasonably accurate graph in Figure 3.42. We say "reasonably accurate" because we cannot be sure of the exact locations of the peaks and valleys on the graph without using calculus. ✓5

✓**Checkpoint 5**

Graph $f(x) = .4(x - 2)(x + 3)(x - 4)$.

Figure 3.41

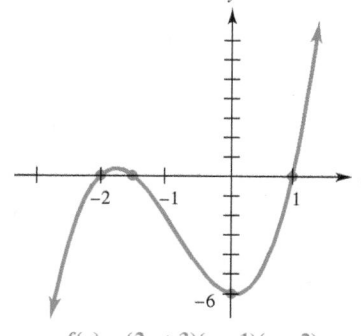

$$f(x) = (2x + 3)(x - 1)(x + 2)$$

Figure 3.42

Polynomial Models

Regression procedures similar to those presented for linear regression in Section 2.3 and quadratic regression in Section 3.5 can be used to find cubic and quartic (degree 4) polynomial models for appropriate data.

Example 5 **Social Science** The following table shows the population of the city of San Francisco, California in selected years.

Year	1950	1960	1970	1980	1990	2000	2010
Population	775,357	740,316	715,674	678,974	723,959	776,733	805,863

(a) Plot the data on a graphing calculator, with $x = 0$ corresponding to the year 1950.

Solution The points in Figure 3.43 suggest the general shape of a fourth-degree (quartic) polynomial.

Figure 3.43

(b) Use quartic regression to obtain a model for these data.

Solution The procedure is the same as for linear regression; just choose "quartic" in place of "linear." It produces the function

$$f(x) = -.137x^4 + 16.07x^3 - 470.34x^2 + 542.65x + 773,944.$$

Its graph, shown in Figure 3.44, appears to fit the data well.

Figure 3.44

(c) Use the model to estimate the population of San Francisco in the years 1985 and 2005.

Solution The years 1985 and 2005 correspond to $x = 35$ and $x = 55$, respectively. Verify that

$$f(35) \approx 700,186 \quad \text{and} \quad f(55) \approx 801,022.$$

Example 6 **Business** The following table shows the revenue and costs (in millions of dollars) for Ford Motor Company for the years 2004–2012. (Data from: www.morningstar.com.)

Year	Revenue	Costs
2004	171,652	168,165
2005	177,089	175,065
2006	160,123	172,736
2007	172,455	175,178
2008	146,277	160,949
2009	118,308	115,346
2010	128,954	122,397
2011	136,264	116,042
2012	134,252	128,588

(a) Let $x = 4$ correspond to the year 2004. Use cubic regression to obtain models for the revenue data $R(x)$ and the costs $C(x)$.

Solution The functions obtained using cubic regression from a calculator or software are

$$R(x) = 551.1x^3 - 12,601x^2 + 82,828x + 7002;$$
$$C(x) = 885.5x^3 - 21,438x^2 + 154,283x - 166,074.$$

(b) Graph $R(x)$ and $C(x)$ on the same set of axes. Did costs ever exceed revenues?

Solution The graph is shown in Figure 3.45. Since the lines cross twice, we can say that costs exceeded revenues in various periods.

(c) Find the profit function $P(x)$ and show its graph.

Solution The profit function is the difference between the revenue function and the cost function. We subtract the coefficients of the cost function from the respective coefficients of the revenue function.

$$\begin{aligned} P(x) &= R(x) - C(x) \\ &= (551.1 - 885.5)x^3 + (-12,601 + 21,438)x^2 \\ &\quad + (82,828 - 154,283)x + (7002 + 166,074) \qquad \text{Subtract like terms.} \\ &= -334.4x^3 + 8837x^2 - 71,455x + 173,076. \end{aligned}$$

The graph of $P(x)$ appears in Figure 3.46.

(d) According to the model of the profit function $P(x)$, in what years was Ford Motor Company profitable?

Solution The motor company was profitable in 2004, 2009, 2010, 2011, and 2012 because that is where the graph is positive.

Figure 3.45

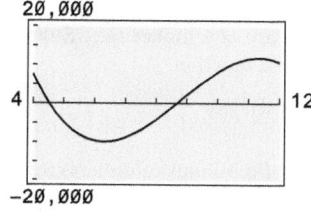

Figure 3.46

3.5 Exercises

Graph each of the given polynomial functions. (See Examples 1 and 2.)

1. $f(x) = x^4$

2. $g(x) = -.5x^6$

3. $h(x) = -.2x^5$

4. $f(x) = x^7$

In Exercises 5–8, state whether the graph could possibly be the graph of (a) some polynomial function; (b) a polynomial function of degree 3; (c) a polynomial function of degree 4; (d) a polynomial function of degree 5. (See Example 3.)

5.

6.

7.

8.

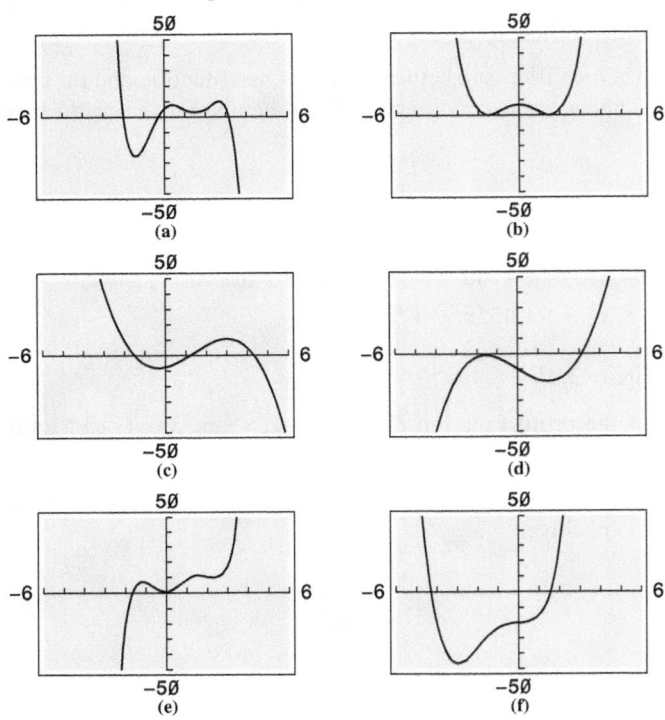

In Exercises 9–14, match the given polynomial function to its graph [(a)–(f)], without using a graphing calculator. (See Example 3 and the two boxes preceding it.)

(a)

(b)

(c)

(d)

(e)

(f)

9. $f(x) = x^3 - 7x - 9$

10. $f(x) = -x^3 + 4x^2 + 3x - 8$

11. $f(x) = x^4 - 5x^2 + 7$

12. $f(x) = x^4 + 4x^3 - 20$

13. $f(x) = .7x^5 - 2.5x^4 - x^3 + 8x^2 + x + 2$

14. $f(x) = -x^5 + 4x^4 + x^3 - 16x^2 + 12x + 5$

Graph each of the given polynomial functions. (See Example 4.)

15. $f(x) = (x + 3)(x - 4)(x + 1)$

16. $f(x) = (x - 5)(x - 1)(x + 1)$

17. $f(x) = x^2(x + 3)(x - 1)$

18. $f(x) = x^2(x + 2)(x - 2)$

19. $f(x) = x^3 - x^2 - 20x$

20. $f(x) = x^3 + 2x^2 - 10x$

21. $f(x) = x^3 + 4x^2 - 7x$

22. $f(x) = x^4 - 6x^2$

Exercises 23–26 require a graphing calculator. Find a viewing window that shows a complete graph of the polynomial function (that is, a graph that includes all the peaks and valleys and that indicates how the curve moves away from the x-axis at the far left and far right). There are many correct answers. Consider your answer correct if it shows all the features that appear in the window given in the answers. (See Example 3.)

23. $g(x) = x^3 - 3x^2 - 4x - 5$

24. $f(x) = x^4 - 10x^3 + 35x^2 - 50x + 24$

25. $f(x) = 2x^5 - 3.5x^4 - 10x^3 + 5x^2 + 12x + 6$

26. $g(x) = x^5 + 8x^4 + 20x^3 + 9x^2 - 27x - 7$

In Exercises 27–31, use a calculator to evaluate the functions. Generate the graph by plotting points or by using a graphing calculator.

27. Finance An idealized version of the Laffer curve (originated by economist Arthur Laffer) is shown in the accompanying graph. According to this theory, decreasing the tax rate, say, from x_2 to x_1, may actually increase the total revenue to the government. The theory is that people will work harder and earn more if they are taxed at a lower rate, which means higher total tax revenues than would be the case at a higher rate. Suppose that the Laffer curve is given by the function

$$f(x) = \frac{x(x - 100)(x - 160)}{240} \quad (0 \le x \le 100),$$

where $f(x)$ is government revenue (in billions of dollars) from a tax rate of x percent. Find the revenue from the given tax rates.

(a) 20% **(b)** 40% **(c)** 50% **(d)** 70%

(e) Graph $f(x)$.

Tax rate (percent)

28. Health A technique for measuring cardiac output depends on the concentration of a dye after a known amount is injected into a vein near the heart. In a normal heart, the concentration of the dye at time x (in seconds) is given by the function defined by

$$g(x) = -.006x^4 + .140x^3 - .053x^2 + 1.79x.$$

(a) Find the following: $g(0); g(1); g(2); g(3)$.

(b) Graph $g(x)$ for $x \ge 0$.

29. Business The revenue for Costco Wholesale Corporation (in millions of dollars) can be approximated by the function

$$R(x) = .141x^3 - 3.11x^2 + 26.98x - 19.99,$$

where $x = 4$ corresponds to the year 2004. (Data from: www.morningstar.com.)

(a) Find the following: $R(5); R(7); R(12)$.

(b) Graph $R(x)$.

(c) Is revenue always increasing in this model?

30. Business The revenue for Target Corporation (in billions of dollars) can be approximated by the function

$$R(x) = .0600x^4 - 1.9766x^3 + 23.155x^2 - 110.22x + 229.42,$$

where $x = 4$ corresponds to the year 2004. (Data from: www.morningstar.com.)

(a) Find the following: $R(6)$; $R(9)$; $R(11)$.

(b) Graph $R(x)$.

31. Business The cost function for Costco Wholesale Corporation (in millions of dollars) can be approximated by the function

$$C(x) = .135x^3 - 2.98x^2 + 25.99x - 18.71,$$

where $x = 4$ corresponds to the year 2004. (Data from: www.morningstar.com.)

(a) Find the following: $C(5)$; $C(7)$; $C(12)$.

(b) Graph $C(x)$.

(c) Are costs always increasing in this model?

32. Business The cost function for Target Corporation (in billions of dollars) can be approximated by the function

$$C(x) = .0697x^4 - 2.296x^3 + 26.947x^2 - 129.49x + 261.86,$$

where $x = 4$ corresponds to the year 2004. (Data from: www.morningstar.com.)

(a) Find the following: $C(6)$; $C(9)$; $C(11)$.

(b) Graph $C(x)$.

33. Business Use the revenue function $R(x)$ from Exercise 29 and the cost function $C(x)$ from Exercise 31 to write the profit function $P(x)$ for Costco Wholesale Corporation. Use your function to find the profit for the year 2012.

34. Business Use the revenue function $R(x)$ from Exercise 30 and the cost function $C(x)$ from Exercise 32 to write the profit function $P(x)$ for Target Corporation. Use your function to find the profit for the year 2011.

⟋ *Use a graphing calculator to do the following problems. (See Example 5.)*

35. Social Science The following table shows the public school enrollment (in millions) in selected years. (Data from: U.S. National Center for Education Statistics.)

Year	Enrollment
1980	50.3
1985	48.9
1990	52.1
1995	55.9
2000	60.0
2005	62.1
2010	64.4

(a) Plot the data with $x = 0$ corresponding to the year 1980.

(b) Use cubic regression to find a third-order polynomial function $g(x)$ that models these data.

(c) Graph $g(x)$ on the same screen as the data points. Does the graph appear to fit the data well?

(d) According to the model, what was the enrollment in the year 2008?

36. Business The following table shows the profit (in billions of dollars) for Intel Corporation. (Data from: www.morningstar.com.)

Year	Profit
2004	7.5
2005	8.7
2006	5.0
2007	7.0
2008	5.3
2009	4.4
2010	11.5
2011	12.9
2012	11.0

(a) Plot the data with $x = 4$ corresponding to the year 2004.

(b) Use quartic regression to find a fourth-order polynomial function $h(x)$ that models these data.

(c) Graph $h(x)$ on the same screen as the data points. Does the graph appear to fit the data well?

(d) According to the model, what were Intel's profits in 2010?

37. Business The accompanying table gives the annual revenue for International Business Machines Corp. (IBM) in billions of dollars for the years 2004–2012. (Data from www.morningstar.com.)

Year	Revenue
2004	96.3
2005	91.1
2006	91.4
2007	98.8
2008	103.6
2009	95.8
2010	99.9
2011	106.9
2012	104.5

(a) Let $x = 4$ correspond to the year 2004. Use cubic regression to find a polynomial function $R(x)$ that models these data.

(b) Graph $R(x)$ on the same screen as the data points. Does the graph appear to fit the data well?

38. Business The accompanying table gives the annual costs for International Business Machines Corp. (IBM) in billions of dollars for the years 2004–2012. (Data from www.morningstar.com.)

Year	Costs
2004	87.9
2005	83.2
2006	81.9
2007	88.4
2008	91.3
2009	82.4
2010	85.1
2011	91.0
2012	87.9

(a) Let $x = 4$ correspond to the year 2004. Use cubic regression to find a polynomial function $C(x)$ that models these data.

(b) Graph $C(x)$ on the screen as the data points. Does the graph appear to fit the data well?

Business *For Exercises 39 and 40, use the functions R(x) and C(x) from the answers to Exercises 37(a) and 38(a).*

39. Find the profit function $P(x)$ for IBM for the years 2004–2012.

40. Find the profits for the year 2008.

✓**Checkpoint Answers**

1.

2.

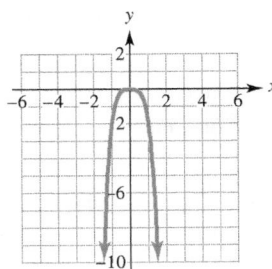

3. Many correct answers, including $-15 \le x \le 15$ and $-2000 \le y \le 6000$.

4. $f(x) = 2x^3 + 5x^2 - x - 6$; degree 3.

5.

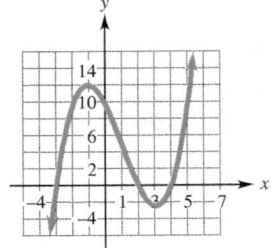

3.6 Rational Functions

A **rational function** is a function whose rule is the quotient of two polynomials, such as

$$f(x) = \frac{2}{1 + x}, \qquad g(x) = \frac{3x + 2}{2x + 4}, \qquad \text{and} \qquad h(x) = \frac{x^2 - 2x - 4}{x^3 - 2x^2 + x}.$$

Thus, a rational function is a function whose rule can be written in the form

$$f(x) = \frac{P(x)}{Q(x)},$$

where $P(x)$ and $Q(x)$ are polynomials, with $Q(x) \neq 0$. The function is undefined for any values of x that make $Q(x) = 0$, so there are breaks in the graph at these numbers.

Linear Rational Functions

We begin with rational functions in which both numerator and denominator are first-degree or constant polynomials. Such functions are sometimes called **linear rational functions.**

Example 1   Graph the rational function defined by

$$y = \frac{2}{1 + x}.$$

Solution   This function is undefined for $x = -1$, since -1 leads to a 0 denominator. For that reason, the graph of this function will not intersect the vertical line $x = -1$. Since x can take on any value except -1, the values of x can approach -1 as closely as desired from either side of -1, as shown in the following table of values.

x approaches −1
↓

x	−1.5	−1.2	−1.1	−1.01	−.99	−.9	−.8	−.5
$1 + x$	−.5	−.2	−.1	−.01	.01	.1	.2	.5
$\dfrac{2}{1 + x}$	−4	−10	−20	−200	200	20	10	4

↑
$|f(x)|$ gets larger and larger

The preceding table suggests that as x gets closer and closer to −1 from either side, $|f(x)|$ gets larger and larger. The part of the graph near $x = -1$ in Figure 3.47 shows this behavior. The vertical line $x = -1$ that is approached by the curve is called a *vertical asymptote*. For convenience, the vertical asymptote is indicated by a dashed line in Figure 3.47, but this line is *not* part of the graph of the function.

As $|x|$ gets larger and larger, so does the absolute value of the denominator $1 + x$. Hence, $y = 2/(1 + x)$ gets closer and closer to 0, as shown in the following table.

x	−101	−11	−2	0	9	99
$1 + x$	−100	−10	−1	1	10	100
$\dfrac{2}{1 + x}$	−.02	−.2	−2	2	.2	.02

✓ **Checkpoint 1**

Graph the following.

(a) $f(x) = \dfrac{3}{5 - x}$

(b) $f(x) = \dfrac{-4}{x + 4}$

The horizontal line $y = 0$ is called a *horizontal asymptote* for this graph. Using the asymptotes and plotting the intercept and other points gives the graph of Figure 3.47. ✓₁

Figure 3.47

Example 1 suggests the following conclusion, which applies to all rational functions.

> If a number c makes the denominator zero, but the numerator nonzero, in the expression defining a rational function, then the line $x = c$ is a **vertical asymptote** for the graph of the function.

If the graph of a function approaches a horizontal line very closely when x is very large or very small, we say that this line is a **horizontal asymptote** of the graph.

In Example 1, the horizontal asymptote was the x-axis. This is not always the case, however, as the next example illustrates.

Example 2   Graph

$$f(x) = \frac{3x + 2}{2x + 4}.$$

Solution Find the vertical asymptote by setting the denominator equal to 0 and then solving for x:

$$2x + 4 = 0$$
$$x = -2.$$

In order to see what the graph looks like when $|x|$ is very large, we rewrite the rule of the function. When $x \neq 0$, dividing both numerator and denominator by x does not change the value of the function:

$$f(x) = \frac{3x + 2}{2x + 4} = \frac{\dfrac{3x + 2}{x}}{\dfrac{2x + 4}{x}}$$

$$= \frac{\dfrac{3x}{x} + \dfrac{2}{x}}{\dfrac{2x}{x} + \dfrac{4}{x}} = \frac{3 + \dfrac{2}{x}}{2 + \dfrac{4}{x}}.$$

Now, when $|x|$ is very large, the fractions $2/x$ and $4/x$ are very close to 0. (For instance, when $x = 200, 4/x = 4/200 = .02$.) Therefore, the numerator of $f(x)$ is very close to $3 + 0 = 3$ and the denominator is very close to $2 + 0 = 2$. Hence, $f(x)$ is very close to $3/2$ when $|x|$ is large, so the line $y = 3/2$ is the horizontal asymptote of the graph, as shown in Figure 3.48. ✔2

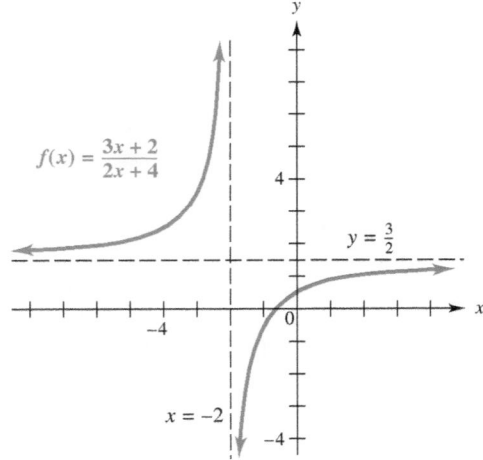

Figure 3.48

✔ **Checkpoint 2**

Graph the following.

(a) $f(x) = \dfrac{2x - 5}{x - 2}$

(b) $f(x) = \dfrac{3 - x}{x + 1}$

Figure 3.49

Figure 3.50

✎ **TECHNOLOGY TIP** Depending on the viewing window, a graphing calculator may not accurately represent the graph of a rational function. For example, the graph of $f(x) = \dfrac{3x + 2}{2x + 4}$ in Figure 3.49, which should look like Figure 3.48, has an erroneous vertical line at the place where the graph has a vertical asymptote. This problem can usually be avoided by using a window that has the vertical asymptote at the center of the x-axis, as in Figure 3.50.

The horizontal asymptotes of a linear rational function are closely related to the coefficients of the x-terms of the numerator and denominator, as illustrated in Examples 1 and 2:

	Function	**Horizontal Asymptote**
Example 2:	$f(x) = \dfrac{3x + 2}{2x + 4}$	$y = \dfrac{3}{2}$
Example 1:	$f(x) = \dfrac{2}{1 + x} = \dfrac{0x + 2}{1x + 1}$	$y = \dfrac{0}{1} = 0 \qquad$ (the x-axis)

The same pattern holds in the general case.

> The graph of $f(x) = \dfrac{ax + b}{cx + d}$ (where $c \neq 0$ and $ad \neq bc$) has a vertical asymptote at the root of the denominator and has horizontal asymptote $y = \dfrac{a}{c}$.

Other Rational Functions

When the numerator or denominator of a rational function has degree greater than 1, the graph of the function can be more complicated than those in Examples 1 and 2. The graph may have several vertical asymptotes, as well as peaks and valleys.

Example 3 Graph

$$f(x) = \frac{2x^2}{x^2 - 4}.$$

Solution Find the vertical asymptotes by setting the denominator equal to 0 and solving for x:

$$x^2 - 4 = 0$$
$$(x + 2)(x - 2) = 0 \qquad \text{Factor.}$$
$$x + 2 = 0 \quad \text{or} \quad x - 2 = 0 \qquad \text{Set each term equal to 0.}$$
$$x = -2 \quad \text{or} \quad x = 2. \qquad \text{Solve for } x.$$

Since neither of these numbers makes the numerator 0, the lines $x = -2$ and $x = 2$ are vertical asymptotes of the graph. The horizontal asymptote can be determined by dividing both the numerator and denominator of $f(x)$ by x^2 (the highest power of x that appears in either one):

$$f(x) = \frac{2x^2}{x^2 - 4}$$
$$= \frac{\dfrac{2x^2}{x^2}}{\dfrac{x^2 - 4}{x^2}}$$
$$= \frac{\dfrac{2x^2}{x^2}}{\dfrac{x^2}{x^2} - \dfrac{4}{x^2}}$$
$$= \frac{2}{1 - \dfrac{4}{x^2}}.$$

When $|x|$ is very large, the fraction $4/x^2$ is very close to 0, so the denominator is very close to 1 and $f(x)$ is very close to 2. Hence, the line $y = 2$ is the horizontal asymptote of the graph. Using this information and plotting several points in each of the three regions determined by the vertical asymptotes, we obtain Figure 3.51. ✓₃

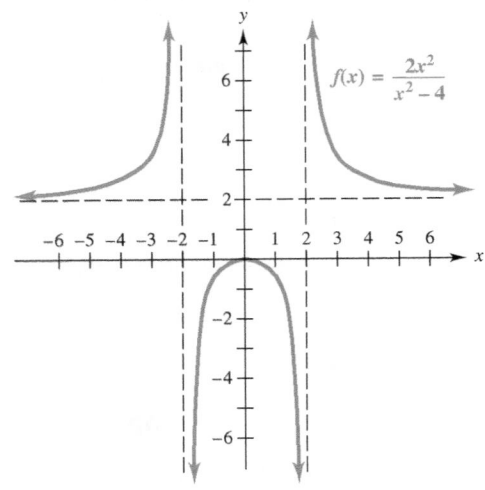

Figure 3.51

✓ **Checkpoint 3**

List the vertical and horizontal asymptotes of the given function.

(a) $f(x) = \dfrac{3x + 5}{x + 5}$

(b) $g(x) = \dfrac{2 - x^2}{x^2 - 4}$

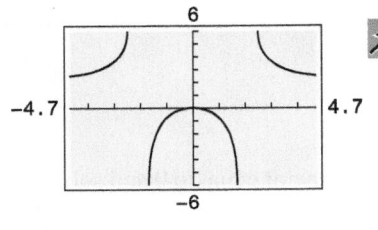

Figure 3.52

TECHNOLOGY TIP When a function whose graph has more than one vertical asymptote (as in Example 3) is graphed on a graphing calculator, erroneous vertical lines can sometimes be avoided by using a *decimal window* (with the *y*-range adjusted to show the graph). On TI, use (Z)DECIMAL in the ZOOM or VIEWS menu. On Casio, use INIT in the V-WINDOW menu. Figure 3.52 shows the function of Example 3 graphed in a decimal window on a TI-84 +. (The *x*-range may be different on other calculators.)

The arguments used to find the horizontal asymptotes in Examples 1–3 work in the general case and lead to the following conclusion.

> If the numerator of a rational function $f(x)$ is of *smaller* degree than the denominator, then the *x*-axis (the line $y = 0$) is the horizontal asymptote of the graph. If the numerator and denominator are of the *same* degree, say, $f(x) = \dfrac{ax^n + \cdots}{cx^n + \cdots}$, then the line $y = \dfrac{a}{c}$ is the horizontal asymptote.*

Applications

Rational functions have a variety of applications, some of which are explored next.

Example 4   **Natural Science**   In many situations involving environmental pollution, much of the pollutant can be removed from the air or water at a fairly reasonable cost, but the minute amounts of the pollutant that remain can be very expensive to remove.

Cost as a function of the percentage of pollutant removed from the environment can be calculated for various percentages of removal, with a curve fitted through the resulting data points. This curve then leads to a function that approximates the situation. Rational functions often are a good choice for these **cost–benefit functions.**

---

*When the numerator is of larger degree than the denominator, the graph has no horizontal asymptote, but may have nonhorizontal lines or other curves as asymptotes; see Exercises 32 and 33 at the end of this section for examples.

For example, suppose a cost–benefit function is given by

$$f(x) = \frac{18x}{106 - x},$$

where $f(x)$, or y, is the cost (in thousands of dollars) of removing x percent of a certain pollutant. The domain of x is the set of all numbers from 0 to 100, inclusive; any amount of pollutant from 0% to 100% can be removed. To remove 100% of the pollutant here would cost

$$y = \frac{18(100)}{106 - 100} = 300,$$

or $300,000. Check that 95% of the pollutant can be removed for about $155,000, 90% for about $101,000, and 80% for about $55,000, as shown in Figure 3.53 (in which the displayed y-coordinates are rounded to the nearest integer).

Figure 3.53

Checkpoint 4

Using the function in Example 4, find the cost to remove the following percentages of pollutants.

(a) 70%

(b) 85%

(c) 98%

In management, **product-exchange functions** give the relationship between quantities of two items that can be produced by the same machine or factory. For example, an oil refinery can produce gasoline, heating oil, or a combination of the two; a winery can produce red wine, white wine, or a combination of the two. The next example discusses a product-exchange function.

Example 5   **Business**   The product-exchange function for the Fruits of the Earth Winery for red wine x and white wine y, in number of cases, is

$$y = \frac{150,000 - 75x}{1200 + x}.$$

Graph the function and find the maximum quantity of each kind of wine that can be produced.

Solution   Only nonnegative values of x and y make sense in this situation, so we graph the function in the first quadrant (Figure 3.54, on the following page). Note that the y-intercept of the graph (found by setting $x = 0$) is 125 and the x-intercept (found by setting $y = 0$ and solving for x) is 2000. Since we are interested only in the portion of the graph in Quadrant I, we can find a few more points in that quadrant and complete the graph as shown in Figure 3.54.

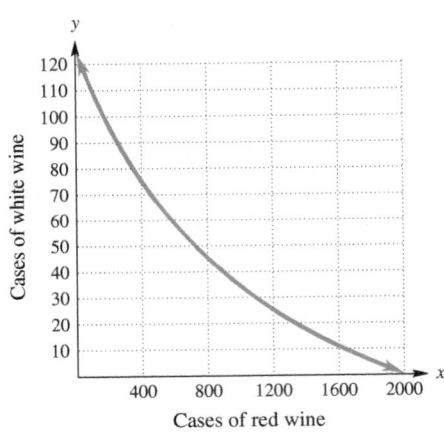

Figure 3.54

The maximum value of y occurs when $x = 0$, so the maximum amount of white wine that can be produced is 125 cases, as given by the y-intercept. The x-intercept gives the maximum amount of red wine that can be produced: 2000 cases. ✓5

Checkpoint 5

Rework Example 5 with the product-exchange function

$$y = \frac{70{,}000 - 10x}{70 + x}$$

to find the maximum amount of each wine that can be produced.

Example 6   **Business**   A retailer buys 2500 specialty lightbulbs from a distributor each year. In addition to the cost of each bulb, there is a fee for each order, so she wants to order as few times as possible. However, storage costs are higher when there are fewer orders (and hence more bulbs per order to store). Past experience shows that the total annual cost (for the bulbs, ordering fees, and storage costs) is given by the rational function.

$$C(x) = \frac{.98x^2 + 1200x + 22{,}000}{x},$$

where x is the number of bulbs ordered each time. How many bulbs should be ordered each time in order to have the smallest possible cost?

Solution   Graph the cost function $C(x)$ in a window with $0 \le x \le 2500$ (because the retailer cannot order a negative number of bulbs and needs only 2500 for the year).

Figure 3.55

Figure 3.56

For each point on the graph in Figure 3.55,

the x-coordinate is the number of bulbs ordered each time;
the y-coordinate is the annual cost when x bulbs are ordered each time.

Use the minimum finder on a graphing calculator to find the point with the smallest y-coordinate, which is approximately (149.83, 1493.67), as shown in Figure 3.56. Since the retailer cannot order part of a lightbulb, she should order 150 bulbs each time, for an approximate annual cost of $1494.

3.6 Exercises

Graph each function. Give the equations of the vertical and horizontal asymptotes. (See Examples 1–3.)

1. $f(x) = \dfrac{1}{x + 5}$

2. $g(x) = \dfrac{-7}{x - 6}$

3. $f(x) = \dfrac{-3}{2x + 5}$

4. $h(x) = \dfrac{-4}{2 - x}$

5. $f(x) = \dfrac{3x}{x - 1}$

6. $g(x) = \dfrac{x - 2}{x}$

7. $f(x) = \dfrac{x + 1}{x - 4}$

8. $f(x) = \dfrac{x - 3}{x + 5}$

9. $f(x) = \dfrac{2 - x}{x - 3}$

10. $g(x) = \dfrac{3x - 2}{x + 3}$

11. $f(x) = \dfrac{3x + 2}{2x + 4}$

12. $f(x) = \dfrac{4x - 8}{8x + 1}$

13. $h(x) = \dfrac{x + 1}{x^2 + 2x - 8}$

14. $g(x) = \dfrac{1}{x(x + 2)^2}$

15. $f(x) = \dfrac{x^2 + 4}{x^2 - 4}$

16. $f(x) = \dfrac{x - 1}{x^2 - 2x - 3}$

Find the equations of the vertical asymptotes of each of the given rational functions.

17. $f(x) = \dfrac{x - 3}{x^2 + x - 2}$

18. $g(x) = \dfrac{x + 2}{x^2 - 1}$

19. $g(x) = \dfrac{x^2 + 2x}{x^2 - 4x - 5}$

20. $f(x) = \dfrac{x^2 - 2x - 4}{x^3 - 2x^2 + x}$

Work these problems. (See Example 4.)

21. Natural Science Suppose a cost–benefit model is given by

$$f(x) = \frac{4.3x}{100 - x},$$

where $f(x)$ is the cost, in thousands of dollars, of removing x percent of a given pollutant. Find the cost of removing each of the given percentages of pollutants.

(a) 50% **(b)** 70% **(c)** 80%

(d) 90% **(e)** 95% **(f)** 98%

(g) 99%

(h) Is it possible, according to this model, to remove *all* the pollutant?

(i) Graph the function.

22. Business Suppose a cost–benefit model is given by

$$f(x) = \frac{6.2x}{112 - x},$$

where $f(x)$ is the cost, in thousands of dollars, of removing x percent of a certain pollutant. Find the cost of removing the given percentages of pollutants.

(a) 0% **(b)** 50%

(c) 80% **(d)** 90%

(e) 95% **(f)** 99%

(g) 100% **(h)** Graph the function.

23. Natural Science The function

$$f(x) = \frac{\lambda x}{1 + (ax)^b}$$

is used in population models to give the size of the next generation $f(x)$ in terms of the current generation x. (See J. Maynard Smith, *Models in Ecology* [Cambridge University Press, 1974].)

(a) What is a reasonable domain for this function, considering what x represents?

(b) Graph the function for $\lambda = a = b = 1$ and $x \geq 0$.

(c) Graph the function for $\lambda = a = 1$ and $b = 2$ and $x \geq 0$.

(d) What is the effect of making b larger?

24. Natural Science The function

$$f(x) = \frac{Kx}{A + x}$$

is used in biology to give the growth rate of a population in the presence of a quantity x of food. This concept is called Michaelis–Menten kinetics. (See Leah Edelstein-Keshet, *Mathematical Models in Biology* [Random House, 1988].)

(a) What is a reasonable domain for this function, considering what x represents?

(b) Graph the function for $K = 5$, $A = 2$, and $x \geq 0$.

(c) Show that $y = K$ is a horizontal asymptote.

(d) What do you think K represents?

(e) Show that A represents the quantity of food for which the growth rate is half of its maximum.

25. Social Science The average waiting time in a line (or queue) before getting served is given by

$$W = \frac{S(S - A)}{A},$$

where A is the average rate at which people arrive at the line and S is the average service time. At a certain fast-food restaurant, the average service time is 3 minutes. Find W for each of the given average arrival times.

(a) 1 minute

(b) 2 minutes

(c) 2.5 minutes

(d) What is the vertical asymptote?

(e) Graph the equation on the interval $(0, 3)$.

(f) What happens to W when $A > 3$? What does this mean?

Business *Sketch the portion of the graph in Quadrant I of each of the functions defined in Exercises 26 and 27, and then estimate the maximum quantities of each product that can be produced. (See Example 5.)*

26. The product-exchange function for gasoline x and heating oil y, in hundreds of gallons per day, is

$$y = \frac{125{,}000 - 25x}{125 + 2x}.$$

27. A drug factory found that the product-exchange function for a red tranquilizer x and a blue tranquilizer y is

$$y = \frac{900{,}000{,}000 - 30{,}000x}{x + 90{,}000}.$$

28. Physical Science The failure of several O-rings in field joints was the cause of the fatal crash of the *Challenger* space shuttle in 1986. NASA data from 24 successful launches prior to *Challenger* suggested that O-ring failure was related to launch temperature by a function similar to

$$N(t) = \frac{600 - 7t}{4t - 100} \quad (50 \le t \le 85),$$

where t is the temperature (in °F) at launch and N is the approximate number of O-rings that fail. Assume that this function accurately models the number of O-ring failures that would occur at lower launch temperatures (an assumption NASA did not make).

(a) Does $N(t)$ have a vertical asymptote? At what value of t does it occur?

(b) Without actually graphing the function, what would you conjecture that the graph would look like just to the right of the vertical asymptote? What does this suggest about the number of O-ring failures that might be expected near that temperature? (The temperature at the *Challenger* launching was 31°.)

(c) Confirm your conjecture by graphing $N(t)$ between the vertical asymptote and $t = 85$.

29. Business A company has fixed costs of $40,000 and a marginal cost of $2.60 per unit.

(a) Find the linear cost function.

(b) Find the average cost function. (Average cost was defined in Section 3.3.)

(c) Find the horizontal asymptote of the graph of the average cost function. Explain what the asymptote means in this situation. (How low can the average cost be?)

Use a graphing calculator to do Exercises 30–33. (See Example 6.)

30. Finance Another model of a Laffer curve (see Exercise 27 of Section 3.5) is given by

$$f(x) = \frac{300x - 3x^2}{10x + 200},$$

where $f(x)$ is government revenue (in billions of dollars) from a tax rate of x percent. Find the revenue from the given tax rates.

(a) 16%   (b) 25%

(c) 40%   (d) 55%

(e) Graph $f(x)$.

(f) What tax rate produces maximum revenue? What is the maximum revenue?

31. Business When no more than 110 units are produced, the cost of producing x units is given by

$$C(x) = .2x^3 - 25x^2 + 1531x + 25{,}000.$$

How many units should be produced in order to have the lowest possible average cost?

32. (a) Graph $f(x) = \dfrac{x^3 + 3x^2 + x + 1}{x^2 + 2x + 1}$.

(b) Does the graph appear to have a horizontal asymptote? Does the graph appear to have some nonhorizontal straight line as an asymptote?

(c) Graph $f(x)$ and the line $y = x + 1$ on the same screen. Does this line appear to be an asymptote of the graph of $f(x)$?

33. (a) Graph $g(x) = \dfrac{x^3 - 2}{x - 1}$ in the window with $-5 \le x \le 5$ and $-6 \le y \le 12$.

(b) Graph $g(x)$ and the parabola $y = x^2 + x + 1$ on the same screen. How do the two graphs compare when $|x| \ge 2$?

✓ **Checkpoint Answers**

1. (a)

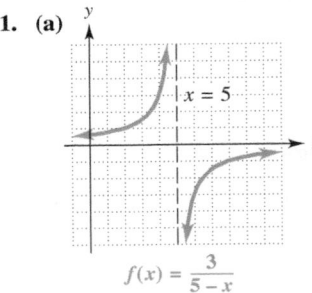

$$f(x) = \frac{3}{5 - x}$$

(b)

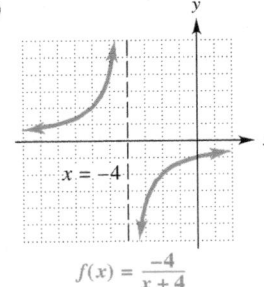

$$f(x) = \frac{-4}{x + 4}$$

2. (a)

(b)

3. (a) Vertical, $x = -5$; horizontal, $y = 3$

(b) Vertical, $x = -2$ and $x = 2$; horizontal, $y = -1$

4. (a) $35,000

(b) About $73,000

(c) About $221,000

5. 7000 cases of red, 1000 cases of white

CHAPTER 3 Summary and Review

Key Terms and Symbols

3.1 function
domain
range
functional notation
piecewise-defined function

3.2 graph
linear function
piecewise linear function
absolute-value function
greatest-integer function
step function

graph reading
vertical-line test

3.3 fixed costs
variable cost
average cost
linear depreciation
rate of change
marginal cost
linear cost function
linear revenue function
break-even point

supply and demand curves
equilibrium point
equilibrium price
equilibrium quantity

3.4 quadratic function
parabola
vertex
axis
quadratic model

3.5 polynomial function
graph of $f(x) = ax^n$

properties of polynomial
graphs
polynomial models

3.6 rational function
linear rational function
vertical asymptote
horizontal asymptote

Chapter 3 Key Concepts

Functions

A **function** consists of a set of inputs called the **domain,** a set of outputs called the **range,** and a rule by which each input determines exactly one output.

If a vertical line intersects a graph in more than one point, the graph is not that of a function.

Linear Functions

A **linear cost function** has equation $C(x) = mx + b$, where m is the **marginal cost** (the cost of producing one more item) and b is the **fixed cost.**

If $p = f(q)$ gives the price per unit when q units can be supplied and $p = g(q)$ gives the price per unit when q units are demanded, then the **equilibrium price** and **equilibrium quantity** occur at the q-value such that $f(q) = g(q)$.

Quadratic Functions

The **quadratic function** defined by $f(x) = a(x - h)^2 + k$ has a graph that is a **parabola** with vertex (h, k) and axis of symmetry $x = h$. The parabola opens upward if $a > 0$ and downward if $a < 0$.

If the equation is in the form $f(x) = ax^2 + bx + c$, the vertex is $\left(-\dfrac{b}{2a}, f\left(-\dfrac{b}{2a}\right)\right)$.

Polynomial Functions

When $|x|$ is large, the graph of a **polynomial function** resembles the graph of its highest-degree term ax^n. The graph of $f(x) = ax^n$ is described on page 160.

On the graph of a polynomial function of degree n,

the total number of peaks and valleys is at most $n - 1$;

the total number of x-intercepts is at most n.

Rational Functions

If a number c makes the denominator of a **rational function** 0, but the numerator nonzero, then the line $x = c$ is a **vertical asymptote** of the graph.

Whenever the values of y approach, but do not equal, some number k as $|x|$ gets larger and larger, the line $y = k$ is a **horizontal asymptote** of the graph.

If the numerator of a rational function is of *smaller* degree than the denominator, then the x-axis is the horizontal asymptote of the graph.

If the numerator and denominator of a rational function are of the *same* degree, say, $f(x) = \dfrac{ax^n + \cdots}{cx^n + \cdots}$, then the line $y = \dfrac{a}{c}$ is the horizontal asymptote of the graph.

Chapter 3 Review Exercises

In Exercises 1–6, state whether the given rule defines a function or not.

1.

x	3	2	1	0	1	2
y	8	5	2	0	−2	−5

2.

x	2	1	0	−1	−2
y	5	3	1	−1	−3

3. $y = \sqrt{x}$

4. $x = |y|$

5. $x = y^2 + 1$

6. $y = 5x - 2$

For the functions in Exercises 7–10, find

(a) $f(6)$;   (b) $f(-2)$;   (c) $f(p)$;   (d) $f(r + 1)$.

7. $f(x) = 4x - 1$ **8.** $f(x) = 3 - 4x$

9. $f(x) = -x^2 + 2x - 4$ **10.** $f(x) = 8 - x - x^2$

11. Let $f(x) = 5x - 3$ and $g(x) = -x^2 + 4x$. Find each of the following:

  (a) $f(-2)$ (b) $g(3)$ (c) $g(-k)$

  (d) $g(3m)$ (e) $g(k - 5)$ (f) $f(3 - p)$

12. Let $f(x) = x^2 + x + 1$. Find each of the following:

  (a) $f(3)$ (b) $f(1)$ (c) $f(4)$

  (d) Based on your answers in parts (a)–(c), is it true that $f(a + b) = f(a) + f(b)$ for all real numbers a and b?

Graph the functions in Exercises 13–24.

13. $f(x) = |x| - 3$ **14.** $f(x) = -|x| - 2$

15. $f(x) = -|x + 1| + 3$ **16.** $f(x) = 2|x - 3| - 4$

17. $f(x) = [x - 3]$ **18.** $f(x) = \left[\frac{1}{2}x - 2\right]$

19. $f(x) = \begin{cases} -4x + 2 & \text{if } x \le 1 \\ 3x - 5 & \text{If } x > 1 \end{cases}$

20. $f(x) = \begin{cases} 3x + 1 & \text{if } x < 2 \\ -x + 4 & \text{if } x \ge 2 \end{cases}$

21. $f(x) = \begin{cases} |x| & \text{if } x < 3 \\ 6 - x & \text{if } x \ge 3 \end{cases}$

22. $f(x) = \sqrt{x^2}$

23. $g(x) = x^2/8 - 3$

24. $h(x) = \sqrt{x} + 2$

25. **Business** Let f be a function that gives the cost to rent a power washer for x hours. The cost is a flat $45 for renting the washer, plus $20 per day or fraction of a day for using the washer.

  (a) Graph f.

  (b) Give the domain and range of f.

  (c) John McDonough wants to rent the washer, but he can spend no more than $90. What is the maximum number of days he can use it?

26. **Business** A tree removal service assesses a $400 fee and then charges $80 per hour for the time on an owner's property.

  (a) Is $750 enough for 5 hours work?

  (b) Graph the ordered pairs (hours, cost).

  (c) Give the domain and range.

27. **Health** The following graph, which tracks the percentage of the female population of the United States who smoke cigarettes, appeared in a report from the Centers for Disease Control and Prevention.

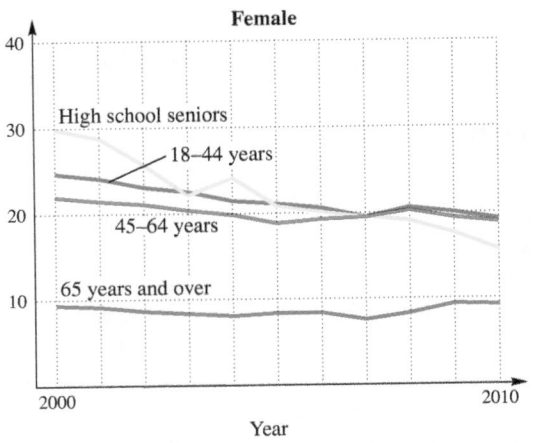

(a) What is the general trend for female high school seniors? What is the general trend for females 65 years and over?

(b) Let $x = 0$ correspond to the year 2000. Approximate a linear function for female high school seniors using the points (0, 30) and (10, 16).

(c) If the trend continues, estimate the percentage of female high school seniors who smoke cigarettes in 2012.

28. **Health** The following graph, which tracks the rate of traumatic brain injury-related deaths per 100,000 people, appeared on a website for the Centers for Disease Control and Prevention.

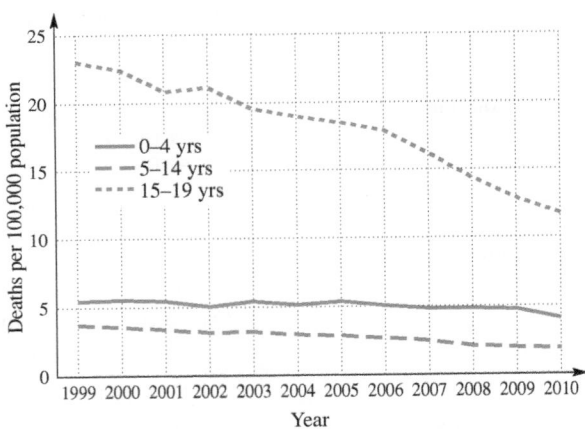

(a) What is the general trend for youth age 15–19 years?

(b) Let $x = 9$ correspond to the year 1999. Approximate a linear function to fit the data using 22 as the number of deaths in 2000 and 11 for 2010.

(c) If the trend continues, estimate the deaths per 100,000 people in the year 2012.

Business *In Exercises 29–32, find the following:*

(a) *the linear cost function;*

(b) *the marginal cost;*

(c) *the average cost per unit to produce 100 units.*

29. Eight units cost $300; fixed cost is $60.

30. Fixed cost is $2000; 36 units cost $8480.

31. Twelve units cost $445; 50 units cost $1585.

32. Thirty units cost $1500; 120 units cost $5640.

33. Business The cost of producing x ink cartridges for a printer is given by $C(x) = 24x + 18,000$. Each cartridge can be sold for $28.

(a) What are the fixed costs?

(b) Find the revenue function.

(c) Find the break-even point.

(d) If the company sells exactly the number of cartridges needed to break even, what is its revenue?

34. Business The cost of producing x laser printers is given by $C(x) = 325x + 2,300,000$. Each printer can be sold for $450.

(a) What are the fixed costs?

(b) Find the revenue function.

(c) Find the break-even point.

(d) If the company sells exactly the number of printers needed to break even, what is its revenue?

35. Business Suppose the demand and price for the HBO cable channel are related by $p = -.5q + 30.95$, where p is the monthly price in dollars and q is measured in millions of subscribers. If the price and supply are related by $p = .3q + 2.15$, what are the equilibrium quantity and price?

36. Business Suppose the supply and price for prescription-strength Tylenol are related by $p = .0015q + 1$, where p is the price (in dollars) of a 30-day prescription. If the demand is related to price by $p = -.0025q + 64.36$, what are the equilibrium quantity and price?

Without graphing, determine whether each of the following parabolas opens upward or downward, and find its vertex.

37. $f(x) = 3(x - 2)^2 + 6$ **38.** $f(x) = 2(x + 3)^2 - 5$

39. $g(x) = -4(x + 1)^2 + 8$ **40.** $g(x) = -5(x - 4)^2 - 6$

Graph each of the following quadratic functions, and label its vertex.

41. $f(x) = x^2 - 9$ **42.** $f(x) = 5 - 2x^2$

43. $f(x) = x^2 + 2x - 6$ **44.** $f(x) = -x^2 + 8x - 1$

45. $f(x) = -x^2 - 6x + 5$ **46.** $f(x) = 5x^2 + 20x - 2$

47. $f(x) = 2x^2 - 12x + 10$ **48.** $f(x) = -3x^2 - 12x - 2$

Determine whether the functions in Exercises 49–52 have a minimum or a maximum value, and find that value.

49. $f(x) = x^2 + 6x - 2$ **50.** $f(x) = x^2 + 4x + 5$

51. $g(x) = -4x^2 + 8x + 3$ **52.** $g(x) = -3x^2 - 6x + 3$

Solve each problem.

53. Business The weekly future price for a barrel of oil can be approximated by the function $f(x) = -.002x^2 + .644x + 45.32$, where x is the number of weeks since the beginning of the year 2009. How many weeks from the beginning of the year 2009 until the peak oil futures price occurs? What is the peak oil futures price with this model? (Data from: U.S. Energy Information Administration.)

54. Social Science The percent of children living below the poverty line can be approximated by the function $f(x) = .096x^2 - 2.40x + 31.7$, where $x = 6$ corresponds to the year 1996. What year saw the lowest percent living in poverty? What was the lowest percent?

55. Social Science The declining birth rate in China has demographers believing that the population of China will soon peak. A model for the population (in millions) for China is $g(x) = -.173x^2 + 12.86x + 1152$, where $x = 0$ corresponds to the year 1990. According to this model, what year will China reach its peak population? What is the estimate of the peak population? (Data from: U.S. Census Bureau.)

56. Business The amount of energy (in kilowatt hours) a new refrigerator typically used for a year of operation can be approximated by the function $h(x) = -1.44x^2 + 220x - 6953$, where $x = 50$ corresponds to the year 1950. According to this model, what year did peak electrical use occur? What was that amount? (Data from: U.S. Energy Information Administration.)

57. Business The following table shows the average cost of tuition and fees at private colleges in various years. (Data from: U.S. Center for Educational Statistics.)

Year	Cost
1975	3672
1980	5470
1985	8885
1990	12,910
1995	17,208
2000	21,373
2005	26,908
2010	32,026

(a) Let $x = 5$ correspond to the year 1975. Find a quadratic function $f(x) = a(x - h)^2 + k$ that models these data using (5, 3672) as the vertex and the data for 2005.

(b) Estimate the average tuition and fees at private colleges in 2015.

58. Social Science According the U.S. Department of Justice, the following table gives the number (in thousands) of violent crimes committed in the given years.

Year	Crimes
2004	1360
2005	1391
2006	1418
2007	1408
2008	1393
2009	1326
2010	1246

(a) Let $x = 4$ correspond to the year 2004. Find a quadratic function $f(x) = a(x - h)^2 + k$ that models these data using (6, 1418) as the vertex and the data for 2009.

(b) Estimate the number of violent crimes in 2012.

59. Business Use the data from Exercise 57 and use quadratic regression to find a function g that models these data.

(a) Give the function.

(b) Graph the function with the data points.

(c) Find the estimated tuition with this model for the year 2015.

60. Business Use the data from Exercise 58 and use quadratic regression to find a function g that models these data.

(a) Give the function.

(b) Graph the function with the data points.

(c) Find the estimated number of violent crimes with this model for the year 2012.

Graph each of the following polynomial functions.

61. $f(x) = x^4 - 5$ **62.** $g(x) = x^3 - 4x$

63. $f(x) = x(x - 4)(x + 1)$

64. $f(x) = (x - 1)(x + 2)(x - 3)$

65. $f(x) = x^4 - 5x^2 - 6$

66. $f(x) = x^4 - 7x^2 - 8$

Use a graphing calculator to do Exercises 67–70.

67. Business The demand equation for automobile oil filters is

$$p = -.000012q^3 - .00498q^2 + .1264q + 1508,$$

where p is in dollars and q is in thousands of items. The supply equation is

$$p = -.000001q^3 + .00097q^2 + 2q.$$

Find the equilibrium quantity and the equilibrium price.

68. Business The average cost (in dollars) per item of manufacturing x thousand cans of spray paint is given by

$$A(x) = -.000006x^4 + .0017x^3 + .03x^2 - 24x + 1110.$$

How many cans should be manufactured if the average cost is to be as low as possible? What is the average cost in that case?

69. Business The revenue (in millions of dollars) for the Exxon Mobil Corporation can be approximated by the function $R(x) = 1558x^3 - 36,587x^2 + 283,469x - 329,027$ where $x = 3$ corresponds to the year 2003. The cost function is approximated by $C(x) = 1261x^3 - 29,686x^2 + 233,069x - 249,868$ again with $x = 3$ corresponding to the year 2003. (Data from: www.morningstar.com.)

(a) Find the revenue for the year 2010.

(b) Find the costs for the year 2010.

(c) Find the profit function $P(x)$.

(d) Find the profit for the years 2010 and 2012.

70. Health The following table shows the average remaining life expectancy (in years) for a person in the United States at selected ages. (Data from: National Center for Health Statistics.)

Current Age	Birth	20	40	60	80	90	100
Life Expectancy	77.8	58.8	39.9	22.6	9.2	5.0	2.6

(a) Let birth $= 0$, and plot the data points.

(b) Use quartic regression to find a fourth-degree polynomial $f(x)$ that models the data.

(c) What is the remaining life expectancy of a person of age 25? age 35? age 50?

(d) What is the life expectancy of a person who is exactly your age?

List the vertical and horizontal asymptotes of each function, and sketch its graph.

71. $f(x) = \dfrac{1}{x - 3}$ **72.** $f(x) = \dfrac{-2}{x + 4}$

73. $f(x) = \dfrac{-3}{2x - 4}$ **74.** $f(x) = \dfrac{5}{3x + 7}$

75. $g(x) = \dfrac{5x - 2}{4x^2 - 4x - 3}$ **76.** $g(x) = \dfrac{x^2}{x^2 - 1}$

77. Business The average cost per carton of producing x cartons of cocoa is given by

$$A(x) = \frac{650}{2x + 40}.$$

Find the average cost per carton to make the given number of cartons.

(a) 10 cartons   (b) 50 cartons   (c) 70 cartons

(d) 100 cartons   (e) Graph $C(x)$.

78. Business The cost and revenue functions (in dollars) for a frozen-yogurt shop are given by

$$C(x) = \frac{400x + 400}{x + 4} \quad \text{and} \quad R(x) = 100x,$$

where x is measured in hundreds of units.

(a) Graph $C(x)$ and $R(x)$ on the same set of axes.

(b) What is the break-even point for this shop?

(c) If the profit function is given by $P(x)$, does $P(1)$ represent a profit or a loss?

(d) Does $P(4)$ represent a profit or a loss?

79. Business The supply and demand functions for the yogurt shop in Exercise 78 are

$$\text{supply: } p = \frac{q^2}{4} + 25 \quad \text{and} \quad \text{demand: } p = \frac{500}{q},$$

where p is the price in dollars for q hundred units of yogurt.

(a) Graph both functions on the same axes, and from the graph, estimate the equilibrium point.

(b) Give the q-intervals where supply exceeds demand.

(c) Give the q-intervals where demand exceeds supply.

80. Business A cost–benefit curve for pollution control is given by

$$y = \frac{9.2x}{106 - x},$$

where y is the cost, in thousands of dollars, of removing x percent of a specific industrial pollutant. Find y for each of the given values of x.

(a) $x = 50$ (b) $x = 98$

(c) What percent of the pollutant can be removed for $22,000?

Case Study 3 Architectural Arches

From ancient Roman bridges to medieval cathedrals, modern high-way tunnels, and fast-food restaurants, arches are everywhere. For centuries builders and architects have used them for both structural and aesthetic reasons. There are arches of almost every material, from stone to steel. Some of the most common arch shapes are the parabolic arch, the semicircular arch, and the Norman arch (a semi-circular arch set atop a rectangle, as shown here).

Parabolic   Semicircular   Norman

Note that every arch is symmetric around a vertical line through its center. The part of the arch on the left side of the line is mirror image of the part on the right side, with the line being the mirror. To describe these arches mathematically, suppose that each one is located on a coordinate plane with the origin at the intersection of the verticle symmetry line and a horizontal line at the base of the arch. For a parabolic arch, the situation looks like this, for some numbers k and c:

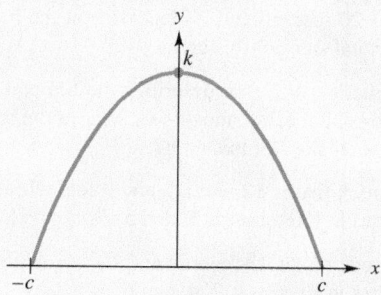

Since $(0, k)$ is the vertex, the arch is the graph of a function of the form

$$f(x) = a(x - 0)^2 + k,$$

or

$$f(x) = ax^2 + k.$$

Note that the point $(c, 0)$ is on the arch, which means that $f(c) = 0$. Therefore, we can make the following derivation:

$$f(x) = ax^2 + k$$
$$f(c) = ac^2 + k \qquad \text{Let } x = c.$$
$$0 = ac^2 + k \qquad f(c) = 0.$$
$$-k = ac^2 \qquad \text{Subtract } k \text{ from both sides.}$$
$$a = \frac{-k}{c^2} \qquad \text{Divide both sides by } c^2.$$

So the function whose graph is the shape of the parabolic arch is

$$f(x) = \frac{-k}{c^2}x^2 + k \qquad (-c \le x \le c),$$

where k is the height of the arch at its highest point and $2c$ (the distance from $-c$ to c) is the width of the arch at its base. For example, a 12-foot-high arch that is 14 feet wide at its base has $k = 12$ and $c = 7$, so it is the graph of

$$f(x) = \frac{-12}{49}x^2 + 12.$$

In order to describe semicircular and Norman arches, we must first find the equation of a circle of radius r with center at the origin. Consider a point (x, y) on the graph and the right triangle it determines:[*]

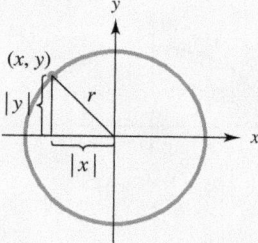

The horizontal side of the triangle has length $|x|$ (the distance from x to 0 on the x-axis), and the vertical side has length $|y|$ (the distance from y to 0 on the y-axis). The hypotenuse has length r (the radius of the circle). By the Pythagorean theorem,

$$|x|^2 + |y|^2 = r^2,$$

which is equivalent to

$$x^2 + y^2 = r^2,$$

because the absolute value of x is either x or $-x$ (see the definition on page 8), so $|x|^2 = (\pm x)^2 = x^2$, and similarly for y. Solving this equation for y shows that

$$y^2 = r^2 - x^2$$
$$y = \sqrt{r^2 - x^2} \quad \text{or} \quad y = -\sqrt{r^2 - x^2}.$$

In the first equation, y is always positive or 0 (because square roots are nonnegative), so its graph is the top half of the circle. Similarly, the second equation gives the bottom half of the circle.

Now consider a semicircle arch of radius r:

---
[*]The figure shows a point in the second quadrant, where x is negative and y is positive, but the same argument will work for points in other quadrants.

The arch is the top half of a circle with center at the origin. By the preceding paragraph, it is the graph of the function

$$g(x) = \sqrt{r^2 - x^2} \quad (-r \le x \le r).$$

For instance, a semicircular arch that is 8 feet high has $r = 8$ and is the graph of

$$g(x) = \sqrt{8^2 - x^2} = \sqrt{64 - x^2} \quad (-8 \le x \le 8).$$

A Norman arch is not the graph of a function (since its sides are vertical lines), but we can describe the semicircular top of the arch.

For example, consider a Norman arch whose top has radius 8 and whose sides are 10 feet high. If the top of the arch were at ground level, then its equation would be $g(x) = \sqrt{64 - x^2}$, as we just saw. But in the actual arch, this semicircular part is raised 10 feet, so it is the graph of

$$h(x) = g(x) + 10 = \sqrt{64 - x^2} + 10 \quad (-8 \le x \le 8),$$

as shown below.

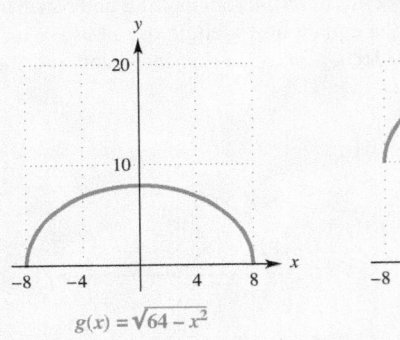

$g(x) = \sqrt{64 - x^2}$

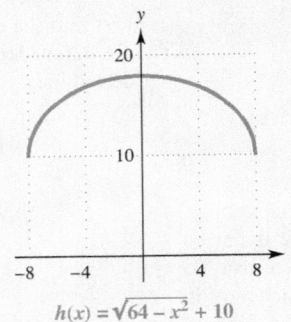

$h(x) = \sqrt{64 - x^2} + 10$

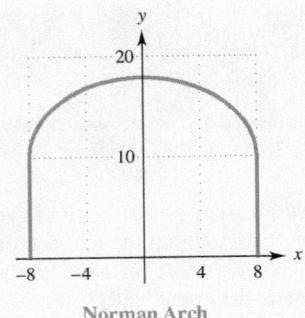

Norman Arch

Exercises

1. Write a function $f(x)$ that describes a parabolic arch which is 20 feet tall and 14 feet wide at the base.

2. Write a function $f(x)$ that describes a parabolic arch that is 25 feet tall and 30 feet wide at its base.

3. Write a function $g(x)$ that describes a semicircular arch that is 25 feet tall. How wide is the arch at its base?

4. Write a function $g(x)$ that describes a semicircular arch that is 40 feet tall. How wide is the arch at its base?

5. Write a function $h(x)$ that describes the top part of a Norman arch that is 20 feet tall and 24 feet wide at the base. How high are the vertical sides of this arch?

6. Write a function $h(x)$ that describes the top part of a Norman arch which is 32 feet tall and 44 feet wide at the base. How high are the vertical sides of this arch?

7. Would a truck that is 12 feet tall and 9 feet wide fit through all of the arches in Exercises 1, 3, and 5?

8. Would a truck that is 13 feet tall and 10 feet wide fit through all of the arches in Exercises 2, 4, and 6?

Extended Projects

1. Find an example of a parabolic, circular, or Norman arch (or all three) on your campus. Measure the dimensions and then write the equation for the arch in a manner similar to Exercises 1–8.

2. Find the dimensions of the fleet of Good Year Blimps that are currently in use. Determine the equation of a semicircular arch that would need to be built for the entrance to a facility that would house the blimps when not in use.

Exponential and Logarithmic Functions

4

CHAPTER

Population growth (of humans, fish, bacteria, etc.), compound interest, radioactive decay, and a host of other phenomena can be described by exponential functions. See Exercises 42–50 on page 191. Archeologists sometimes use carbon-14 dating to determine the approximate age of an artifact (such as a dinosaur skeleton or a mummy). This procedure involves using logarithms to solve an exponential equation. See Exercises 70–72 on page 217. The Richter scale for measuring the magnitude of an earthquake is a logarithmic function. See Exercises 73–74 on page 217.

Exponential and logarithmic functions play a key role in management, economics, the social and physical sciences, and engineering. We begin with exponential growth and exponential decay functions.

4.1 Exponential Functions

In polynomial functions such as $f(x) = x^2 + 5x - 4$, the variable is raised to various constant exponents. In **exponential functions,** such as

$$f(x) = 10^x, \quad g(x) = 750(1.05^x), \quad h(x) = 3^{.6x}, \quad \text{and} \quad k(x) = 2^{-x^2},$$

the variable is in the exponent and the **base** is a positive constant. We begin with the simplest type of exponential function, whose rule is of the form $f(x) = a^x$, with $a > 0$.

Example 1 Graph $f(x) = 2^x$, and estimate the height of the graph when $x = 50$.

Solution Either use a graphing calculator or graph by hand: Make a table of values, plot the corresponding points, and join them by a smooth curve, as in Figure 4.1. The graph has y-intercept 1 and rises steeply to the right. Note that the graph gets very close to the x-axis on the left, but always lies *above* the axis (because *every* power of 2 is positive).

x	y
-3	$1/8$
-2	$1/4$
-1	$1/2$
0	1
1	2
2	4
3	8

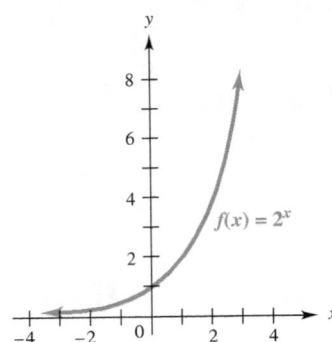

Figure 4.1

The graph illustrates **exponential growth,** which is far more explosive than polynomial growth. At $x = 50$, the graph would be 2^{50} units high. Since there are approximately 6 units to the inch in Figure 4.1, and since there are 12 inches to the foot and 5280 feet to the mile, the height of the graph at $x = 50$ would be approximately

$$\frac{2^{50}}{6 \times 12 \times 5280} \approx 2,961,647,482 \text{ miles!} \quad \boxed{\checkmark_1}$$

When $a > 1$, the graph of the exponential function $h(x) = a^x$ has the same basic shape as the graph of $f(x) = 2^x$, as illustrated in Figure 4.2 and summarized in the next box.

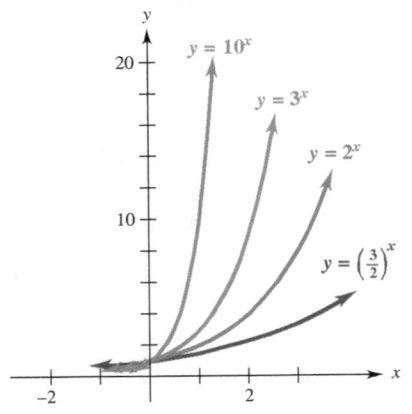

Figure 4.2

When $a > 1$, the function $f(x) = a^x$ has the set of all real numbers as its domain. Its graph has the shape shown on the following page and all five of the properties listed below.

✓**Checkpoint 1**

(a) Fill in this table:

x	$g(x) = 3^x$
-3	
-2	
-1	
0	
1	
2	
3	

(b) Sketch the graph of $g(x) = 3^x$.

Answers to Checkpoint exercises are found at the end of the section.

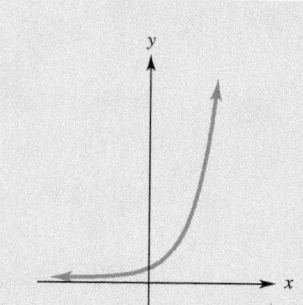

1. The graph is above the x-axis.
2. The y-intercept is 1.
3. The graph climbs steeply to the right.
4. The negative x-axis is a horizontal asymptote.
5. The larger the base a, the more steeply the graph rises to the right.

Example 2   Consider the function $g(x) = 2^{-x}$.

(a) Rewrite the rule of g so that no minus signs appear in it.

Solution   By the definition of negative exponents,

$$g(x) = 2^{-x} = \frac{1}{2^x} = \left(\frac{1}{2}\right)^x.$$

(b) Graph $g(x)$.

Solution   Either use a graphing calculator or graph by hand in the usual way, as shown in Figure 4.3.

x	$y = 2^{-x}$
-3	8
-2	4
-1	2
0	1
1	1/2
2	1/4
3	1/8

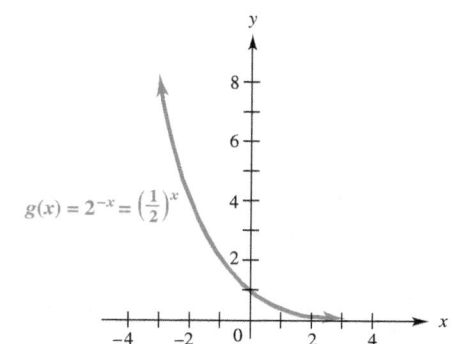

Figure 4.3

✓ **Checkpoint 2**

Graph $h(x) = (1/3)^x$.

The graph falls sharply to the right, but never touches the x-axis, because every power of $\frac{1}{2}$ is positive. This is an example of **exponential decay.**

When $0 < a < 1$, the graph of $k(x) = a^x$ has the same basic shape as the graph of $g(x) = (1/2)^x$, as illustrated in Figure 4.4 and summarized in the next box, on the following page.

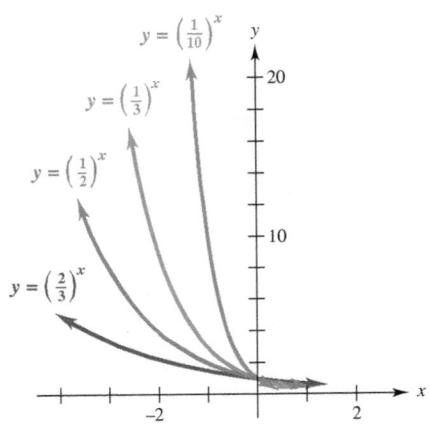

Figure 4.4

When $0 < a < 1$, the function $f(x) = a^x$ has the set of all real numbers as its domain. Its graph has the shape shown here and all five of the properties listed.

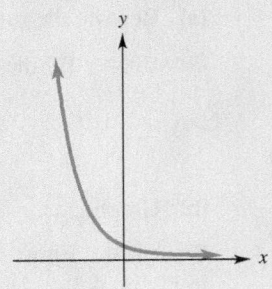

1. The graph is above the x-axis.
2. The y-intercept is 1.
3. The graph falls sharply to the right.
4. The positive x-axis is a horizontal asymptote.
5. The smaller the base a, the more steeply the graph falls to the right.

Checkpoint 3

Use a graphing calculator to graph $f(x) = 4^x$ and $g(x) = \left(\frac{1}{4}\right)^x$ on the same screen.

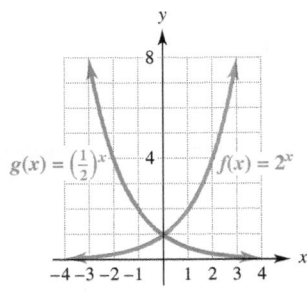

Figure 4.5

Example 3 In each case, graph $f(x)$ and $g(x)$ on the same set of axes and explain how the graphs are related.

(a) $f(x) = 2^x$ and $g(x) = (1/2)^x$

Solution The graphs of f and g are shown in Figures 4.1 and 4.3, above. Placing them on the same set of axes, we obtain Figure 4.5. It shows that the graph of $g(x) = (1/2)^x$ is the mirror image of the graph of $f(x) = 2^x$, with the y-axis as the mirror. ✓3

(b) $f(x) = 3^{1-x}$ and $g(x) = 3^{-x}$

Solution Choose values of x that make the exponent positive, zero, and negative, and plot the corresponding points. The graphs are shown in Figure 4.6, on the following page. The graph of $f(x) = 3^{1-x}$ has the same shape as the graph of $g(x) = 3^{-x}$, but is shifted 1 unit to the right, making the y-intercept $(0, 3)$ rather than $(0, 1)$.

(c) $f(x) = 2^{.6x}$ and $g(x) = 2^x$

Solution Comparing the graphs of $f(x) = 2^{.6x}$ and $g(x) = 2^x$ in Figure 4.7, we see that the graphs are both increasing, but the graph of $f(x)$ rises at a slower rate. This happens because of the .6 in the exponent. If the coefficient of x were greater than 1, the graph would rise at a faster rate than the graph of $g(x) = 2^x$. ✓4

✓**Checkpoint 4**

Graph $f(x) = 2^{x+1}$.

Figure 4.6

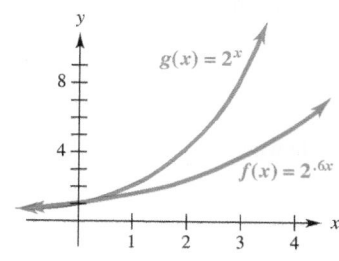

Figure 4.7

When the exponent involves a nonlinear expression in x, the graph of an exponential function may have a much different shape than the preceding ones have.

Example 4   Graph $f(x) = 2^{-x^2}$.

Solution   Either use a graphing calculator or plot points and connect them with a smooth curve, as in Figure 4.8. The graph is symmetric about the y-axis; that is, if the figure were folded on the y-axis, the two halves would match. This graph has the x-axis as a horizontal asymptote. The domain is still all real numbers, but here the range is $0 < y \leq 1$. Graphs such as this are important in probability, where the normal curve has an equation similar to $f(x)$ in this example. ✓5

✓**Checkpoint 5**

Graph $f(x) = (\frac{1}{2})^{-x^2}$.

x	y
-2	1/16
-1.5	.21
-1	1/2
$-.5$	.84
0	1
.5	.84
1	1/2
1.5	.21
2	1/16

Figure 4.8

The Number *e*

In Case 5, we shall see that a certain irrational number, denoted e, plays an important role in the compounding of interest. This number e also arises naturally in a variety of other mathematical and scientific contexts. To 12 decimal places,

$$e \approx 2.718281828459.$$

Perhaps the single most useful exponential function is the function defined by $f(x) = e^x$.

Figure 4.9

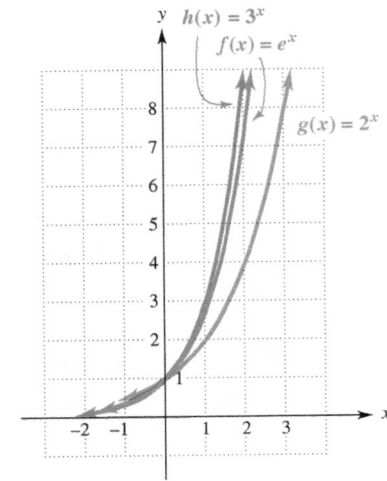 **TECHNOLOGY TIP** To evaluate powers of *e* with a calculator, use the e^x key, as in Figure 4.9. The figure also shows how to display the decimal expansion of *e* by calculating e^1. ✔ 6

In Figure 4.10, the functions defined by

$$g(x) = 2^x, \qquad f(x) = e^x, \qquad \text{and} \qquad h(x) = 3^x$$

are graphed for comparison.

✔ **Checkpoint 6**

Evaluate the following powers of *e*.

(a) $e^{.06}$

(b) $e^{-.06}$

(c) $e^{2.30}$

(d) $e^{-2.30}$

Figure 4.10

Example 5 **Business** The amount of wine (in millions of gallons) consumed in the United States can be approximated by the function

$$f(x) = 139.6e^{.031x},$$

where $x = 0$ corresponds to the year 1950. (Data from: www.wineinstitute.org.)

(a) How much wine was consumed in the year 1970?

Solution Since 1970 corresponds to $x = 20$, we evaluate $f(20)$:

$$f(20) = 139.6e^{.031(20)} \approx 260 \text{ million gallons.}$$

So the consumption was approximately 260 million gallons.

(b) How much wine was consumed in the year 2010?

Solution Since 2010 corresponds to $x = 60$, we evaluate $f(60)$:

$$f(60) = 139.6e^{.031(60)} \approx 897 \text{ million gallons.}$$

So the consumption was approximately 897 million gallons.

 (c) Use a graphing calculator to determine when consumption will reach 1000 million gallons.

Solution Since *f* measures consumption in millions of gallons, we must solve the equation $f(x) = 1000$, that is

$$139.6e^{.031x} = 1000.$$

Figure 4.11

✓ **Checkpoint 7**

Per-person wine consumption (in gallons) can be approximated by $g(x) = .875e^{.019x}$, where $x = 0$ corresponds to the year 1950.

(a) Estimate the per-person wine consumption in 1990.

(b) Determine when the per-person consumption reached 2.0 gallons.

Figure 4.12

One way to do this is to find the intersection point of the graphs of $y = 139.6e^{.031x}$ and $y = 1000$. (The calculator's intersection finder is in the same menu as its root [or zero] finder.) Figure 4.11 shows that this point is approximately (63.5, 1000). Hence, consumption reached 1000 million gallons when $x \approx 63.5$, that is, in 2013. ✓7

Example 6 **Health** When a patient is given a 300-mg dose of the drug cimetidine intravenously, the amount C of the drug in the bloodstream t hours later is given by $C(t) = 300e^{-.3466t}$.

(a) How much of the drug is in the bloodstream after 3 hours and after 10 hours?

Solution Evaluate the function at $t = 3$ and $t = 10$:

$$C(3) = 300e^{-.3466*3} \approx 106.1 \text{ mg};$$
$$C(10) = 300e^{-.3466*10} \approx 9.4 \text{ mg}.$$

(b) Doctors want to give a patient a second 300-mg dose of cimetidine when its level in her bloodstream decreases to 75 mg. Use graphing technology to determine when this should be done.

Solution The second dose should be given when $C(t) = 75$, so we must solve the equation

$$300e^{-.3466t} = 75.$$

Using the method of Example 5(c), we graph $y = 300e^{-.3466t}$ and $y = 75$ and find their intersection point. Figure 4.12 shows that this point is approximately (4, 75). So the second dose should be given 4 hours after the first dose.

4.1 Exercises

Classify each function as linear, quadratic, or exponential.

1. $f(x) = 6^x$

2. $g(x) = -5x$

3. $h(x) = 4x^2 - x + 5$

4. $k(x) = 4^{x+3}$

5. $f(x) = 675(1.055^x)$

6. $g(x) = 12e^{x^2+1}$

Without graphing,

(a) *describe the shape of the graph of each function;*

(b) *find the second coordinates of the points with first coordinates 0 and 1. (See Examples 1–3.)*

7. $f(x) = .6^x$

8. $g(x) = 4^{-x}$

9. $h(x) = 2^{.5x}$

10. $k(x) = 5(3^x)$

11. $f(x) = e^{-x}$

12. $g(x) = 3(16^{x/4})$

Graph each function. (See Examples 1–3.)

13. $f(x) = 3^x$

14. $g(x) = 3^{.5x}$

15. $f(x) = 2^{x/2}$

16. $g(x) = e^{x/4}$

17. $f(x) = (1/5)^x$

18. $g(x) = 2^{3x}$

19. Graph these functions on the same axes.

(a) $f(x) = 2^x$ (b) $g(x) = 2^{x+3}$ (c) $h(x) = 2^{x-4}$

(d) If c is a positive constant, explain how the graphs of $y = 2^{x+c}$ and $y = 2^{x-c}$ are related to the graph of $f(x) = 2^x$.

20. Graph these functions on the same axes.

(a) $f(x) = 3^x$ (b) $g(x) = 3^x + 2$ (c) $h(x) = 3^x - 4$

(d) If c is a positive constant, explain how the graphs of $y = 3^x + c$ and $y = 3^x - c$ are related to the graph of $f(x) = 3^x$.

The accompanying figure shows the graphs of $y = a^x$ for $a = 1.8, 2.3, 3.2, .4, .75,$ and $.31$. They are identified by letter, but not necessarily in the same order as the values just given. Use your knowledge of how the exponential function behaves for various powers of a to match each lettered graph with the correct value of a.

21. A

22. B

23. C

24. D

25. E

26. F

In Exercises 27 and 28, the graph of an exponential function with base a is given. Follow the directions in parts (a)–(f) in each exercise.

27.

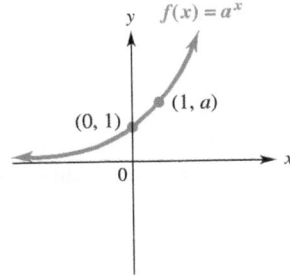

(a) Is $a > 1$ or is $0 < a < 1$?

(b) Give the domain and range of f.

(c) Sketch the graph of $g(x) = -a^x$.

(d) Give the domain and range of g.

(e) Sketch the graph of $h(x) = a^{-x}$.

(f) Give the domain and range of h.

28.

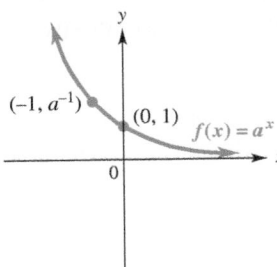

(a) Is $a > 1$ or is $0 < a < 1$?

(b) Give the domain and range of f.

(c) Sketch the graph of $g(x) = a^x + 2$.

(d) Give the domain and range of g.

(e) Sketch the graph of $h(x) = a^{x+2}$.

(f) Give the domain and range of h.

29. If $f(x) = a^x$ and $f(3) = 27$, find the following values of $f(x)$.

(a) $f(1)$ (b) $f(-1)$ (c) $f(2)$ (d) $f(0)$

30. Give a rule of the form $f(x) = a^x$ to define the exponential function whose graph contains the given point.

(a) $(3, 8)$ (b) $(-3, 64)$

Graph each function. (See Example 4.)

31. $f(x) = 2^{-x^2+2}$ **32.** $g(x) = 2^{x^2-2}$

33. $f(x) = x \cdot 2^x$ **34.** $f(x) = x^2 \cdot 2^x$

Work the following exercises.

35. Finance If $1 is deposited into an account paying 6% per year compounded annually, then after t years the account will contain

$$y = (1 + .06)^t = (1.06)^t$$

dollars.

(a) Use a calculator to complete the following table:

t	0	1	2	3	4	5	6	7	8	9	10
y	1					1.34					1.79

(b) Graph $y = (1.06)^t$.

36. Finance If money loses value at the rate of 3% per year, the value of $1 in t years is given by

$$y = (1 - .03)^t = (.97)^t.$$

(a) Use a calculator to complete the following table:

t	0	1	2	3	4	5	6	7	8	9	10
y	1					.86					.74

(b) Graph $y = (.97)^t$.

Work these problems. (See Example 5.)

37. Finance If money loses value, then as time passes, it takes more dollars to buy the same item. Use the results of Exercise 36(a) to answer the following questions.

(a) Suppose a house costs $105,000 today. Estimate the cost of the same house in 10 years. (*Hint:* Solve the equation $.74t = \$105,000$.)

(b) Estimate the cost of a $50 textbook in 8 years.

38. Natural Science Biologists have found that the oxygen consumption of yearling salmon is given by $g(x) = 100e^{.7x}$, where x is the speed in feet per second. Find each of the following.

(a) the oxygen consumption when the fish are still;

(b) the oxygen consumption when the fish are swimming at a speed of 2 feet per second.

39. Business The number of cell phone subscribers (in millions) can be approximated by

$$f(x) = 116.75e^{.101x},$$

where $x = 0$ corresponds to the year 2000. Estimate the number of cell phone subscribers in the following years. (Data from: CTIA-The Wireless Association.)

(a) 2004   (b) 2010   (c) 2011

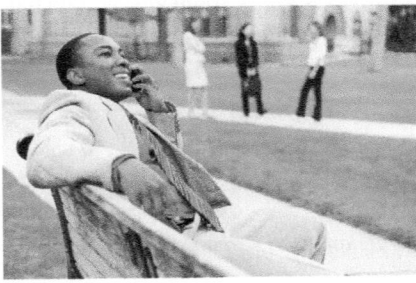

40. Business The monthly payment on a car loan at 12% interest per year on the unpaid balance is given by

$$f(n) = \frac{P}{\dfrac{1 - 1.01^{-n}}{.01}},$$

where P is the amount borrowed and n is the number of months over which the loan is paid back. Find the monthly payment for each of the following loans.

(a) $8000 for 48 months   (b) $8000 for 24 months

(c) $6500 for 36 months   (d) $6500 for 60 months

41. Natural Science The amount of plutonium remaining from 1 kilogram after x years is given by the function $W(x) = 2^{-x/24,360}$. How much will be left after

(a) 1000 years?   (b) 10,000 years?   (c) 15,000 years?

(d) Estimate how long it will take for the 1 kilogram to decay to half its original weight. Your answer may help to explain why nuclear waste disposal is a serious problem.

Business *The scrap value of a machine is the value of the machine at the end of its useful life. By one method of calculating scrap value, where it is assumed that a constant percentage of value is lost annually, the scrap value is given by*

$$S = C(1 - r)^n,$$

where C is the original cost, n is the useful life of the machine in years, and r is the constant annual percentage of value lost. Find the scrap value for each of the following machines.

42. Original cost, $68,000; life, 10 years; annual rate of value loss, 8%

43. Original cost, $244,000; life, 12 years; annual rate of value loss, 15%

44. Use the graphs of $f(x) = 2^x$ and $g(x) = 2^{-x}$ (not a calculator) to explain why $2^x + 2^{-x}$ is approximately equal to 2^x when x is very large.

Work the following problems. (See Examples 5 and 6.)

45. Social Science There were fewer than a billion people on Earth when Thomas Jefferson died in 1826, and there are now more than 6 billion. If the world population continues to grow as expected, the population (in billions) in year t will be given by the function $P(t) = 4.834(1.01^{(t-1980)})$. (Data from: U.S. Census Bureau.) Estimate the world population in the following years.

(a) 2005   (b) 2010   (c) 2030

(d) What will the world population be when you reach 65 years old?

46. Business The number of unique monthly visitors (in thousands) for Pinterest.com can be approximated by the function

$$g(x) = 325(1.29^x),$$

where $x = 1$ corresponds to the month of May, 2011. Estimate the number of unique monthly visitors for the following months. (Data from: cnet.com and techcrunch.com.)

(a) September 2011   (b) May 2012

(c) If the model remains accurate, find the month in which the number of unique visitors surpasses 40,000,000.

47. Economics Projections of the gross domestic product (GDP—in trillions of U.S. dollars), adjusted for purchasing power parity, are approximated as follows.

$$\text{China:} \quad f(x) = 10.21(1.103)^x$$
$$\text{United States:} \quad g(x) = 14.28(1.046)^x,$$

where $x = 1$ corresponds to the year 2011. (Data from: International Monetary Fund.) Find the projected GDP for the given years.

(a) 2012   (b) 2020   (c) 2050

(d) Use technology to determine when the Chinese GDP surpasses the U.S. GDP according to these projections. (*Hint:* Either graph both functions and find their intersection point or use the table feature of a graphing calculator.)

48. Business The amount of electricity (in trillion kilowatt hours) generated by natural gas in the United States can be approximated by the function

$$f(x) = .10(1.05)^x,$$

where $x = 0$ corresponds to the year 1960. (Data from: Energy Information Administration.) How many kilowatt hours were generated in the given years?

(a) 1990

(b) 2002

(c) In what year did the kilowatt hours hit 1 trillion?

49. Business The number of total subscribers (in millions) to Netflix, Inc. can be approximated by the function

$$g(x) = 9.78(1.07)^x,$$

where $x = 1$ corresponds to the first quarter of the year 2009, $x = 2$ corresponds to the second quarter of the year 2009, etc. Find the number of subscribers for the following quarters. (Data from: The *Wall Street Journal* and The *Associated Press.*)

(a) First quarter of 2010

(b) Fourth quarter of 2012

(c) Find the quarter and year when total subscribers surpassed 25 million.

50. Business The monthly rate for basic cable (in dollars) can be approximated by the function

$$h(x) = 8.71e^{.06x}, \quad (5 \le x \le 30)$$

where $x = 5$ corresponds to the year 1985. (Data from: ProQuest Statistical Abstract of the United States: 2013.)

(a) Find the rate in the year 2000 and the year 2009.

(b) When did spending reach $40 a month.

51. Business The amount of music (in billions of hours) listened to on the on-line streaming site Pandora can be approximated by the function

$$f(x) = .54e^{.191x},$$

where $x = 1$ corresponds to the first quarter of the year 2011, $x = 2$ corresponds to the second quarter of the year 2011, etc. Find the hours listened for the following quarters. (Data from: The *Wall Street Journal.*)

(a) Fourth quarter of 2011

(b) Third quarter of 2012

(c) When did the hours exceed 2.5 billion hours?

52. Business The stock price (in dollars) for Apple, Inc. can be approximated by the function

$$g(x) = 2.23e^{.404x} \quad (4 \le x \le 13),$$

where $x = 4$ corresponds to the year 2004. Use this model to approximate the price in the following years. (Data from: www. morningstar.com.)

(a) 2007   **(b)** 2013

(c) In what year, according to the model, did the price reach $300?

53. Health When a patient is given a 20-mg dose of aminophylline intravenously, the amount C of the drug in the bloodstream t hours later is given by $C(t) = 20e^{-.1155t}$. How much aminophylline remains in the bloodstream after the given numbers of hours?

(a) 4 hours

(b) 8 hours

(c) Approximately when does the amount of aminophylline decrease to 3.5 mg?

54. The accompanying figure shows the graph of an exponential growth function $f(x) = Pa^x$.

(a) Find P. [*Hint:* What is $f(0)$?]

(b) Find a. [*Hint:* What is $f(2)$?]

(c) Find $f(5)$.

Checkpoint Answers

1. **(a)** The entries in the second column are 1/27, 1/9, 1/3, 1, 3, 9, 27, respectively.

(b)

2.

3.

4.

$f(x) = 2^{x+1}$

5.

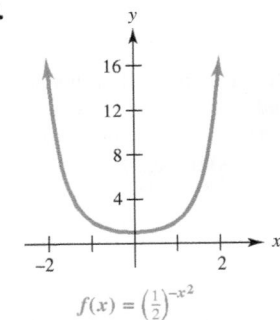

$f(x) = \left(\frac{1}{2}\right)^{-x^2}$

6. **(a)** 1.06184   **(b)** .94176

     (c) 9.97418   **(d)** .10026

7. **(a)** About 1.87 gallons per person

     (b) 1993

4.2   Applications of Exponential Functions

In many situations in biology, economics, and the social sciences, a quantity changes at a rate proportional to the quantity present. For example, a country's population might be increasing at a rate of 1.3% a year. In such cases, the amount present at time t is given by an **exponential growth function.**

It is understood that growth can involve either growing larger or growing smaller.

Exponential Growth Function

Under normal conditions, growth can be described by a function of the form

$$f(t) = y_0 e^{kt} \quad \text{or} \quad f(t) = y_0 b^t,$$

where $f(t)$ is the amount present at time t, y_0 is the amount present at time $t = 0$, and k and b are constants that depend on the rate of growth.

When $f(t) = y_0 e^{kt}$, and $k > 0$, we describe $f(t)$ as modeling exponential growth, and when $k < 0$, we describe $f(t)$ as modeling exponential decay. When $f(t) = y_0 b^t$, and $b > 1$, we describe $f(t)$ as modeling exponential growth, and when $0 < b < 1$, we describe $f(t)$ as modeling exponential decay.

Example 1   **Finance**   Since the early 1970s, the amount of the total credit market (debt owed by the government, companies, or individuals) as a percentage of gross domestic product (GDP) can be approximated by the exponential function

$$f(t) = y_0 e^{.02t},$$

where t is time in years, $t = 0$ corresponds to the year 1970, and $f(t)$ is a percent. (Data from: Federal Reserve.)

(a) If the amount of total credit market was 155% of the GDP in 1970, find the percent in the year 2005.

Solution   Since y_0 represents the percent when $t = 0$ (that is, in 1970) we have $y_0 = 155$. So the growth function is $f(t) = 155e^{.02t}$. To find the percent of the total credit market in the year 2005, evaluate $f(t)$ at $t = 35$ (which corresponds to the year 2005):

$$f(t) = 155e^{.02t}$$
$$f(35) = 155e^{.02(35)} \approx 312.$$

Hence, the percent of the total credit market in the year 2005 was approximately 312% of GDP.

(b) If the model remains accurate, what percent of GDP will the total credit market be in the year 2015?

Solution   Since 2015 corresponds to $t = 45$, evaluate the function at $t = 45$:

$$f(45) = 155e^{.02(45)} \approx 381\%.$$

✓**Checkpoint 1**

Suppose the number of bacteria in a culture at time t is

$$y = 500e^{.4t},$$

where t is measured in hours.

(a) How many bacteria are present initially?

(b) How many bacteria are present after 10 hours?

Example 2   **Business**   Cigarette consumption in the United States has been decreasing for some time. Based on data from the Centers for Disease Control and Prevention, the number (in billions) of cigarettes consumed can be approximated by the function

$$g(x) = 436e^{-.036x},$$

with $x = 0$ corresponding to the year 2000.

(a) Find the number of cigarettes consumed in the years 2005 and 2010.

Solution   The years 2005 and 2010 correspond to $x = 5$ and $x = 10$, respectively. We can evaluate $g(x)$ at these values for x:

$$g(5) = 436e^{-.036(5)} \approx 364 \text{ billion in the year 2005;}$$
$$g(10) = 436e^{-.036(10)} \approx 304 \text{ billion in the year 2010.}$$

Figure 4.13

 (b) If this model remains accurate, when will cigarette consumption fall to 250 billion?

Solution   Graph $y = 436e^{-.036x}$ and $y = 250$ on the same screen and find the x-coordinate of their intersection point. Figure 4.13 shows that consumption is expected to be 250 billion in the year 2015 ($x = 15$).

When a quantity is known to grow exponentially, it is sometimes possible to find a function that models its growth from a small amount of data.

Example 3   **Finance**   When money is placed in a bank account that pays compound interest, the amount in the account grows exponentially, as we shall see in Chapter 5. Suppose such an account grows from $1000 to $1316 in 7 years.

(a) Find a growth function of the form $f(t) = y_0b^t$ that gives the amount in the account at time t years.

Solution   The values of the account at time $t = 0$ and $t = 7$ are given; that is, $f(0) = 1000$ and $f(7) = 1316$. Solve the first of these equations for y_0:

$$f(0) = 1000$$
$$y_0b^0 = 1000 \qquad \text{Rule of } f$$
$$y_0 = 1000. \qquad b^0 = 1$$

So the rule of f has the form $f(t) = 1000b^t$. Now solve the equation $f(7) = 1316$ for b:

$$f(7) = 1316$$
$$1000b^7 = 1316 \qquad \text{Rule of } f$$
$$b^7 = 1.316 \qquad \text{Divide both sides by 1000.}$$
$$b = (1.316)^{1/7} \approx 1.04. \qquad \text{Take the seventh root of each side.}$$

So the rule of the function is $f(t) = 1000(1.04)^t$.

(b) How much is in the account after 12 years?

Solution $f(12) = 1000(1.04)^{12} = \$1601.03$.

 Checkpoint 2

Suppose an investment grows exponentially from $500 to $587.12 in three years.

(a) Find a function of the form $f(t) = y_0b^t$ that gives the value of the investment after t years.

(b) How much is the investment worth after 10 years?

Example 4   **Health**   Infant mortality rates in the United States are shown in the following table. (Data from: U.S. National Center for Health Statistics.)

Year	Rate	Year	Rate
1920	76.7	1980	12.6
1930	60.4	1990	9.2
1940	47.0	1995	7.6
1950	29.2	2000	6.9
1960	26.0	2005	6.9
1970	20.0	2008	6.6

(a) Let $t = 0$ correspond to 1920. Use the data for 1920 and 2008 to find a function of the form $f(t) = y_0b^t$ that models these data.

Solution   Since the rate is 76.7 when $t = 0$, we have $y_0 = 76.7$. Hence, $f(t) = 76.7b^t$. Because 2008 corresponds to $t = 88$, we have $f(88) = 6.6$; that is,

$$76.7b^{88} = 6.6 \qquad \text{Rule of } f$$

$$b^{88} = \frac{6.6}{76.7} \qquad \text{Divide both sides by 76.7.}$$

$$b = \left(\frac{6.6}{76.7}\right)^{\frac{1}{88}} \approx .97251 \qquad \text{Take } 88^{th} \text{ roots on both sides.}$$

Therefore, the function is $f(t) = 76.7(.97251^t)$.

Figure 4.14

(b) Use exponential regression on a graphing calculator to find another model for the data.

Solution   The procedure for entering the data and finding the function is the same as that for linear regression (just choose "exponential" instead of "linear"), as explained in Section 2.3. Depending on the calculator, one of the following functions will be produced:

$$g(t) = 79.2092*.9708^t \qquad \text{or} \qquad h(t) = 79.2092e^{-.0296t}.$$

Both functions give the same values (except for slight differences due to rounding of the coefficients). They fit the data reasonably well, as shown in Figure 4.14.

(c) Use the preceding models, and assume they continue to remain accurate, to estimate the infant mortality rate in the years 2012 and 2015.

Solution   Evaluating each of the models in parts (a) and (b) at $t = 92$ and $t = 95$ shows that the models give slightly different results.

t	$f(t)$	$g(t)$
92	5.9	5.2
95	5.4	4.7

Other Exponential Models

When a quantity changes exponentially, but does not either grow very large or decrease practically to 0, as in Examples 1–3, different functions are needed.

Example 5   **Business**   Sales of a new product often grow rapidly at first and then begin to level off with time. Suppose the annual sales of an inexpensive can opener are given by

$$S(x) = 10{,}000(1 - e^{-.5x}),$$

where $x = 0$ corresponds to the time the can opener went on the market.

(a) What were the sales in each of the first three years?

Solution   At the end of one year ($x = 1$), sales were

$$S(1) = 10{,}000(1 - e^{-.5(1)}) \approx 3935.$$

Sales in the next two years were

$$S(2) = 10{,}000(1 - e^{-.5(2)}) \approx 6321 \qquad \text{and} \qquad S(3) = 10{,}000(1 - e^{-.5(3)}) \approx 7769.$$

(b) What were the sales at the end of the 10th year?

Solution $S(10) = 10{,}000(1 - e^{-.5(10)}) \approx 9933.$

Figure 4.15

(c) Graph the function S. What does it suggest?

Solution   The graph can be obtained by plotting points and connecting them with a smooth curve or by using a graphing calculator, as in Figure 4.15. The graph indicates that sales will level off after the 12th year, to around 10,000 can openers per year.

A variety of activities can be modeled by **logistic functions,** whose rules are of the form

$$f(x) = \frac{c}{1 + ae^{kx}}.$$

The logistic function in the next example is sometimes called a **forgetting curve.**

✓ **Checkpoint 3**

Suppose the value of the assets (in thousands of dollars) of a certain company after t years is given by

$$V(t) = 100 - 75e^{-.2t}.$$

(a) What is the initial value of the assets?

(b) What is the limiting value of the assets?

(c) Find the value after 10 years.

(d) Graph $V(t)$.

Example 6   **Social Science**   Psychologists have measured people's ability to remember facts that they have memorized. In one such experiment, it was found that the number of facts, $N(t)$, remembered after t days was given by

$$N(t) = \frac{10.003}{1 + .0003e^{.8t}}.$$

(a) How many facts were remembered at the beginning of the experiment?

Solution   When $t = 0$,

$$N(0) = \frac{10.003}{1 + .0003e^{.8(0)}} = \frac{10.003}{1.0003} = 10.$$

So 10 facts were remembered at the beginning.

(b) How many facts were remembered after one week? after two weeks?

Solution   One and two weeks respectively correspond to $t = 7$ and $t = 14$:

$$N(7) = \frac{10.003}{1 + .0003e^{.8(7)}} = \frac{10.003}{1.0811} \approx 9.25;$$

$$N(14) = \frac{10.003}{1 + .0003e^{.8(14)}} = \frac{10.003}{22.9391} \approx .44.$$

So 9 facts were remembered after one week, but effectively none were remembered after two weeks (because .44 is less than "half a fact"). The graph of the function in Figure 4.16 gives a picture of this forgetting process.

✓ **Checkpoint 4**

In Example 6,

(a) find the number of facts remembered after 10 days;

(b) use the graph to estimate when just one fact will be remembered.

 TECHNOLOGY TIP

Many graphing calculators can find a logistic model for appropriate data.

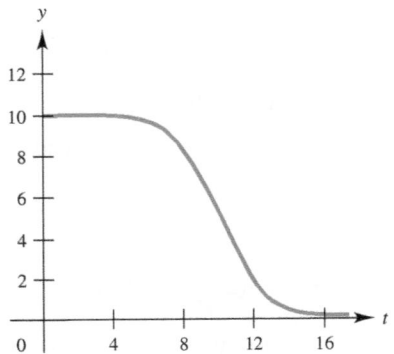

Figure 4.16

4.2 Exercises

1. **Finance** Suppose you owe $800 on your credit card and you decide to make no new purchases and to make the minimum monthly payment on the account. Assuming that the interest rate on your card is 1% per month on the unpaid balance and that the minimum payment is 2% of the total (balance plus interest), your balance after t months is given by

$$B(t) = 800(.9898^t).$$

Find your balance at each of the given times.

(a) six months

(b) one year (remember that t is in months)

(c) five years

(d) eight years

(e) On the basis of your answers to parts (a)–(d), what advice would you give to your friends about minimum payments?

2. **Finance** Suppose you owe $1500 on your credit card and you decide to make no new purchases and to make the minimum monthly payment on the account. Assuming the interest rate on the card is 1.1% per month on the unpaid balance, and the minimum payment is 5% of the total (balance plus interest), your balance after t months is given by

$$B(t) = 1500(.9604)^t.$$

Find the balance at each of the given times.

(a) five months

(b) one year (remember that t is in months)

(c) Is the balance paid off in two years?

3. **Business** The amount (in megawatts) of energy generated in the United States from wind power can be modeled by the function

$$W(t) = w_0(1.30)^t,$$

where $t = 0$ corresponds to the year 2000. (Data from: www.windpoweringamerica.gov.)

(a) The amount generated in the year 2000 was 2540 megawatts. Find w_0.

(b) Estimate the amount of energy generated by wind power in the years 2005 and 2012.

4. **Finance** The percent that public pension funds with assets over $1 billion hold in private-equity investments can be modeled by the function

$$f(t) = 2.214(1.142)^t,$$

where $t = 0$ corresponds to the year 2000. (Data from: The *Wall Street Journal.*)

Find the percent held in private-equity investments in the years:

(a) 2008

(b) 2011

(c) If the model continues to be accurate, project the percent for the year 2015.

In each of the following problems, find an exponential function of the form $f(t) = y_0 b^t$ to model the data. (See Examples 3 and 4.)

5. **Business** The average asking price for rent in San Francisco was $1000 a month in the year 1990 and $2663 in the year 2012. (Data from: The *Wall Street Journal.*)

(a) Find a model for these data in which $t = 0$ corresponds to the year 1990.

(b) If this model remains accurate, what is the predicted average rent in the year 2015?

(c) By experimenting with different values (or using a graphing calculator to solve an appropriate equation), estimate the year in which the average rent hit $2000 a month.

6. **Social Science** The U.S. Census Bureau predicts that the African-American population will increase from 35.3 million in 2000 to 61.8 million in 2060.

(a) Find a model for these data, in which $t = 0$ corresponds to 2000.

(b) What is the projected African-American population in 2020? in 2030?

(c) By experimenting with different values of t (or by using a graphing calculator to solve an appropriate equation), estimate the year in which the African-American population will reach 55 million.

7. **Business** Sales of video and audio equipment, computers, and related services in the United States were about $81.1 billion in the year 1990 and $296 billion in the year 2010.

(a) Let $t = 0$ correspond to the year 1990 and find a model for these data.

(b) According to the model, what were sales in the year 2008?

(c) If the model remains accurate, estimate sales for the year 2015.

8. **Health** Medicare expenditures were $110 billion in the year 1990 and increased to $554 billion in the year 2011.

(a) Find a model for these data in which $t = 0$ corresponds to the year 1990 and expenditures are in billions of dollars.

(b) Estimate Medicare expenditures in 2010.

(c) If the model remains accurate, estimate Medicare expenditures for the year 2016.

In the following exercises, find the exponential model as follows: If you do not have suitable technology, use the first and last data points to find a function. (See Examples 3 and 4.) If you have a graphing calculator or other suitable technology, use exponential regression to find a function. (See Example 4.)

9. **Finance** The table shows the purchasing power of a dollar in recent years, with the year 2000 being the base year. For example, the entry .88 for 2005 means that a dollar in 2005 bought what $.88 did in the year 2000. (Data from: Bureau of Labor Statistics.)

Year	Purchasing Power of $1
2000	$1.00
2001	.97
2002	.96
2003	.94
2004	.91
2005	.88
2006	.85
2007	.83
2008	.79
2009	.80
2010	.79
2011	.77
2012	.75

(a) Find an exponential model for these data, where $t = 0$ corresponds to the year 2000.

(b) Assume the model remains accurate and predict the purchasing power of a dollar in 2015 and 2018.

(c) Use a graphing calculator (or trial and error) to determine the year in which the purchasing power of the 2000 dollar will drop to $.40.

10. **Physical Science** The table shows the atmospheric pressure (in millibars) at various altitudes (in meters).

Altitude	Pressure
0	1,013
1000	899
2000	795
3000	701
4000	617
5000	541
6000	472
7000	411
8000	357
9000	308
10,000	265

(a) Find an exponential model for these data, in which t is measured in thousands. (For instance, $t = 2$ is 2000 meters.)

(b) Use the function in part (a) to estimate the atmospheric pressure at 1500 meters and 11,000 meters. Compare your results with the actual values of 846 millibars and 227 millibars, respectively.

11. **Health** The table shows the age-adjusted death rates per 100,000 Americans for heart disease. (Data from: U.S. Center for Health Statistics.)

Year	Death Rate
2000	257.6
2002	240.8
2004	217.0
2006	210.2
2008	186.5
2010	178.5

(a) Find an exponential model for these data, where $t = 0$ corresponds to the year 2000.

(b) Assuming the model remains accurate, estimate the death rate in 2012 and 2016.

(c) Use a graphing calculator (or trial and error) to determine the year in which the death rate will fall to 100.

12. **Business** The table shows outstanding consumer credit (in billions of dollars) at the beginning of various years. (Data from: U.S. Federal Reserve.)

Year	Credit
1980	350.5
1985	524.0
1990	797.7
1995	1010.4
2000	1543.7
2005	2200.1
2010	2438.7

(a) Find an exponential model for these data, where $t = 0$ corresponds to the year 1980.

(b) If this model remains accurate, what will the outstanding consumer credit be in 2013 and 2016?

(c) In what year will consumer credit reach $6000 billion?

Work the following problems. (See Example 5.)

13. **Business** Assembly-line operations tend to have a high turnover of employees, forcing the companies involved to spend much time and effort in training new workers. It has been found that a worker who is new to the operation of a certain task on the assembly line will produce $P(t)$ items on day t, where

$$P(t) = 25 - 25e^{-.3t}.$$

(a) How many items will be produced on the first day?

(b) How many items will be produced on the eighth day?

(c) According to the function, what is the maximum number of items the worker can produce?

14. **Social Science** The number of words per minute that an average person can type is given by

$$W(t) = 60 - 30e^{-.5t},$$

where t is time in months after the beginning of a typing class. Find each of the following.

(a) $W(0)$ (b) $W(1)$

(c) $W(4)$ (d) $W(6)$

Natural Science *Newton's law of cooling says that the rate at which a body cools is proportional to the difference in temperature between the body and an environment into which it is introduced. Using calculus, we can find that the temperature F(t) of the body at time t after being introduced into an environment having constant temperature T_0 is*

$$F(t) = T_0 + Cb^t,$$

where C and b are constants. Use this result in Exercises 15 and 16.

15. Boiling water at 100° Celsius is placed in a freezer at −18° Celsius. The temperature of the water is 50° Celsius after 24 minutes. Find the temperature of the water after 76 minutes.

16. Paisley refuses to drink coffee cooler than 95°F. She makes coffee with a temperature of 170°F in a room with a temperature of 70°F. The coffee cools to 120°F in 10 minutes. What is the longest amount of time she can let the coffee sit before she drinks it?

17. Social Science A sociologist has shown that the fraction $y(t)$ of people in a group who have heard a rumor after t days is approximated by

$$y(t) = \frac{y_0 e^{kt}}{1 - y_0(1 - e^{kt})},$$

where y_0 is the fraction of people who heard the rumor at time $t = 0$ and k is a constant. A graph of $y(t)$ for a particular value of k is shown in the figure.

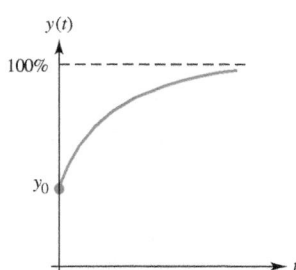

(a) If $k = .1$ and $y_0 = .05$, find $y(10)$.

(b) If $k = .2$ and $y_0 = .10$, find $y(5)$.

(c) Assume the situation in part (b). How many *weeks* will it take for 65% of the people to have heard the rumor?

18. Social Science Data from the National Highway Traffic Safety Administration indicate that, in year t, the approximate percentage of people in the United States who wear seat belts when driving is given by

$$g(t) = \frac{97}{1 + .823e^{-.1401t}},$$

where $t = 0$ corresponds to the year 1994. What percentage used seat belts in

(a) 2000?

(b) 2003?

(c) 2004?

Assuming that this function is accurate after 2004, estimate seat belt use for the following years.

(d) 2011?

(e) 2013?

(f) 2015?

(g) Graph the function. Does the graph suggest that seat belt usage will ever reach 100%?

Use a graphing calculator or other technology to do the following problems. (See Example 6.)

19. Economics The amount of U.S. expenditures on national defense (in billions of dollars) can by approximated by the function

$$f(x) = \frac{1084}{1 + 1.94e^{-.171x}},$$

where $x = 0$ corresponds to the year 2000. (Data from: U.S. Bureau of Economic Analysis.)

(a) Estimate the expenditures in the years 2005 and 2010.

(b) Assume the model remains accurate and graph the function from the year 2000 to the year 2020.

(c) Use the graph to determine the year in which expenditures reach $850 billion.

20. Natural Science The population of fish in a certain lake at time t months is given by the function

$$p(t) = \frac{20,000}{1 + 24(2^{-.36t})}.$$

(a) Graph the population function from $t = 0$ to $t = 48$ (a four-year period).

(b) What was the population at the beginning of the period?

(c) Use the graph to estimate the one-year period in which the population grew most rapidly.

(d) When do you think the population will reach 25,000? What factors in nature might explain your answer?

21. Business The amount (in billions of dollars) spent on legal services in the United States can be approximated by the function

$$g(x) = \frac{99.85}{1 + .527e^{-.258x}},$$

where $x = 0$ corresponds to the year 2000. (Data from: U.S. Bureau of Economic Analysis.)

(a) Estimate the amount spent on legal services in 2007 and 2011.

(b) Assume the model remains accurate and graph $g(x)$ from the year 2000 to the year 2025.

(c) Does the graph ever go over $110 billion dollars?

22. Social Science The probability P percent of having an automobile accident is related to the alcohol level t of the driver's blood by the function $P(t) = e^{21.459t}$.

(a) Graph $P(t)$ in a viewing window with $0 \le t \le .2$ and $0 \le P(t) \le 100$.

(b) At what blood alcohol level is the probability of an accident at least 50%? What is the legal blood alcohol level in your state?

✓**Checkpoint Answers**

1. (a) 500
   (b) About 27,300

2. (a) $f(t) = 500(1.055)^t$
   (b) $854.07

3. (a) $25,000
   (b) $100,000
   (c) $89,850

(d)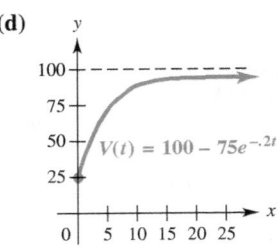

4. (a) 5
   (b) After about 12 days

4.3 Logarithmic Functions

Until the development of computers and calculators, logarithms were the only effective tool for large-scale numerical computations. They are no longer needed for this purpose, but logarithmic functions still play a crucial role in calculus and in many applications.

Common Logarithms

Logarithms are simply *a new language for old ideas*—essentially, a special case of exponents.

> **Definition of Common (Base 10) Logarithms**
>
> $$y = \log x \qquad \text{means} \qquad 10^y = x.$$

Log x, which is read "the logarithm of x," is the answer to the question,

> To what exponent must 10 be raised to produce x?

✓**Checkpoint 1**

Find each common logarithm.

(a) $\log 100$

(b) $\log 1000$

(c) $\log .1$

```
log(359)
            2.555094449
10^(2.5551)
            359.004589
log(.026)
            -1.585026652
```

Figure 4.17

✓**Checkpoint 2**

Find each common logarithm.

(a) $\log 27$

(b) $\log 1089$

(c) $\log .00426$

Example 1   To find $\log 10{,}000$, ask yourself, "To what exponent must 10 be raised to produce $10{,}000$?" Since $10^4 = 10{,}000$, we see that $\log 10{,}000 = 4$. Similarly,

$$\log 1 = 0 \qquad \text{because} \qquad 10^0 = 1;$$

$$\log .01 = -2 \qquad \text{because} \qquad 10^{-2} = \frac{1}{10^2} = \frac{1}{100} = .01;$$

$$\log \sqrt{10} = 1/2 \qquad \text{because} \qquad 10^{1/2} = \sqrt{10}. \qquad ✓_1$$

Example 2   Log (-25) is the exponent to which 10 must be raised to produce -25. But every power of 10 is positive! So there is no exponent that will produce -25. *Logarithms of negative numbers and 0 are not defined.*

Example 3   (a) We know that $\log 359$ must be a number between 2 and 3 because $10^2 = 100$ and $10^3 = 1000$. By using the "log" key on a calculator, we find that $\log 359$ (to four decimal places) is 2.5551. You can verify this statement by computing $10^{2.5551}$; the result (rounded) is 359. See the first two lines in Figure 4.17.

(b) When 10 is raised to a negative exponent, the result is a number less than 1. Consequently, the logarithms of numbers between 0 and 1 are negative. For instance, $\log .026 = -1.5850$, as shown in the third line in Figure 4.17. ✓_2

📄 **NOTE** On most scientific calculators, enter the number followed by the log key. On graphing calculators, press the log key followed by the number, as in Figure 4.17.

Natural Logarithms

Although common logarithms still have some uses (one of which is discussed in Section 4.4), the most widely used logarithms today are defined in terms of the number e (whose decimal expansion begins 2.71828 . . .) rather than 10. They have a special name and notation.

Definition of Natural (Base e) Logarithms

$$y = \ln x \qquad \text{means} \qquad e^y = x.$$

Thus, the number $\ln x$ (which is sometimes read "el-en x") is the exponent to which e must be raised to produce the number x. For instance, $\ln 1 = 0$ because $e^0 = 1$. Although logarithms to the base e may not seem as "natural" as common logarithms, there are several reasons for using them, some of which are discussed in Section 4.4.

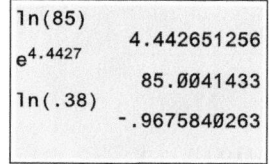

```
ln(85)
               4.442651256
e^4.4427
               85.0041433
ln(.38)
               -.9675840263
```

Figure 4.18

✓ **Checkpoint 3**

Find the following.

(a) $\ln 6.1$

(b) $\ln 20$

(c) $\ln .8$

(d) $\ln .1$

Example 4 **(a)** To find $\ln 85$, use the ⬚LN⬚ key of your calculator, as in Figure 4.18. The result is 4.4427. Thus, 4.4427 is the exponent (to four decimal places) to which e must be raised to produce 85. You can verify this result by computing $e^{4.4427}$; the answer (rounded) is 85. See Figure 4.18.

(b) A calculator shows that $\ln .38 = -.9676$ (rounded), which means that $e^{-.9676} \approx .38$. See Figure 4.18. ✓3

Example 5 You don't need a calculator to find $\ln e^8$. Just ask yourself, "To what exponent must e be raised to produce e^8?" The answer, obviously, is 8. So $\ln e^8 = 8$.

Other Logarithms

The procedure used to define common and natural logarithms can be carried out with any positive number $a \neq 1$ as the base in place of 10 or e.

Definition of Logarithms to the Base a

$$y = \log_a x \qquad \text{means} \qquad a^y = x.$$

Read $y = \log_a x$ as "y is the logarithm of x to the base a." As was the case with common and natural logarithms, $\log_a x$ is an *exponent*; it is the answer to the question,

To what power must a be raised to produce x?

For example, suppose $a = 2$ and $x = 16$. Then $\log_2 16$ is the answer to the question,

To what power must 2 be raised to produce 16?

It is easy to see that $2^4 = 16$, so $\log_2 16 = 4$. In other words, the exponential statement $2^4 = 16$ is equivalent to the logarithmic statement $4 = \log_2 16$.

In the definition of a logarithm to base a, note carefully the relationship between the base and the exponent:

$$\text{Logarithmic form:} \quad y = \log_a x$$

Exponent ↓ ... ↑ Base

$$\text{Exponential form:} \quad a^y = x$$

Exponent ↓ ... ↑ Base

Common and natural logarithms are the special cases when $a = 10$ and when $a = e$, respectively. Both $\log u$ and $\log_{10} u$ mean the same thing. Similarly, $\ln u$ and $\log_e u$ mean the same thing.

Example 6   This example shows several statements written in both exponential and logarithmic form.

Exponential Form	Logarithmic Form
(a) $3^2 = 9$	$\log_3 9 = 2$
(b) $(1/5)^{-2} = 25$	$\log_{1/5} 25 = -2$
(c) $10^5 = 100{,}000$	$\log_{10} 100{,}000 \text{ (or } \log 100{,}000) = 5$
(d) $4^{-3} = 1/64$	$\log_4 (1/64) = -3$
(e) $2^{-4} = 1/16$	$\log_2 (1/16) = -4$
(f) $e^0 = 1$	$\log_e 1 \text{ (or } \ln 1) = 0$

✓ **Checkpoint 4**

Write the logarithmic form of

(a) $5^3 = 125$;

(b) $3^{-4} = 1/81$;

(c) $8^{2/3} = 4$.

✓ **Checkpoint 5**

Write the exponential form of

(a) $\log_{16} 4 = 1/2$;

(b) $\log_3 (1/9) = -2$;

(c) $\log_{16} 8 = 3/4$.

Properties of Logarithms

Some of the important properties of logarithms arise directly from their definition.

Let x and a be any positive real numbers, with $a \neq 1$, and r be any real number. Then

(a) $\log_a 1 = 0$;   (b) $\log_a a = 1$;

(c) $\log_a a^r = r$;   (d) $a^{\log_a x} = x$.

```
10^(log(45))
                    45
e^(ln(350))
                   350
```

Figure 4.19

Property (a) was discussed in Example 1 (with $a = 10$). Property (c) was illustrated in Example 5 (with $a = e$ and $r = 8$). Property (b) is property (c) with $r = 1$. To understand property (d), recall that $\log_a x$ is the exponent to which a must be raised to produce x. Consequently, when you raise a to this exponent, the result is x, as illustrated for common and natural logarithms in Figure 4.19.

The following properties are part of the reason that logarithms are so useful. They will be used in the next section to solve exponential and logarithmic equations.

The Product, Quotient, and Power Properties

Let x, y, and a be any positive real numbers, with $a \neq 1$. Let r be any real number. Then

$$\log_a xy = \log_a x + \log_a y \qquad \text{Product property}$$

$$\log_a \frac{x}{y} = \log_a x - \log_a y \qquad \text{Quotient property}$$

$$\log_a x^r = r \log_a x \qquad \text{Power property}$$

Each of these three properties is illustrated on a calculator in Figure 4.20.

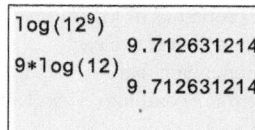

Figure 4.20

To prove the product property, let

$$m = \log_a x \qquad \text{and} \qquad n = \log_a y.$$

Then, by the definition of logarithm,

$$a^m = x \qquad \text{and} \qquad a^n = y.$$

Multiply to get

$$a^m \cdot a^n = x \cdot y,$$

or, by a property of exponents,

$$a^{m+n} = xy.$$

Use the definition of logarithm to rewrite this last statement as

$$\log_a xy = m + n.$$

Replace m with $\log_a x$ and n with $\log_a y$ to get

$$\log_a xy = \log_a x + \log_a y.$$

The quotient and power properties can be proved similarly.

✓ **Checkpoint 6**

Write each expression as a single logarithm, using the properties of logarithms.

(a) $\log_a 5x + \log_a 3x^4$

(b) $\log_a 3p - \log_a 5q$

(c) $4 \log_a k - 3 \log_a m$

Example 7 Using the properties of logarithms, we can write each of the following as a single logarithm:*

(a) $\log_a x + \log_a (x - 1) = \log_a x(x - 1);$ Product property

(b) $\log_a (x^2 + 4) - \log_a (x + 6) = \log_a \dfrac{x^2 + 4}{x + 6};$ Quotient property

(c) $\log_a 9 + 5 \log_a x = \log_a 9 + \log_a x^5 = \log_a 9x^5.$ Product and power properties

---

*Here and elsewhere, we assume that variable expressions represent positive numbers and that the base a is positive, with $a \neq 1$.

> ⚠ **CAUTION** There is no logarithm property that allows you to simplify the logarithm of a sum, such as $\log_a (x^2 + 4)$. In particular, $\log_a (x^2 + 4)$ is *not* equal to $\log_a x^2 + \log_a 4$. The product property of logarithms shows that $\log_a x^2 + \log_a 4 = \log_a 4x^2$.

Example 8   Assume that $\log_6 7 \approx 1.09$ and $\log_6 5 \approx .90$. Use the properties of logarithms to find each of the following:

(a) $\log_6 35 = \log_6 (7 \cdot 5) = \log_6 7 + \log_6 5 \approx 1.09 + .90 = 1.99;$

(b) $\log_6 5/7 = \log_6 5 - \log_6 7 \approx .90 - 1.09 = -.19;$

(c) $\log_6 5^3 = 3 \log_6 5 \approx 3(.90) = 2.70;$

(d) $\log_6 6 = 1;$

(e) $\log_6 1 = 0.$ ✓₇

✓ **Checkpoint 7**

Use the properties of logarithms to rewrite and evaluate each expression, given that $\log_3 7 \approx 1.77$ and $\log_3 5 \approx 1.46$.

(a) $\log_3 35$

(b) $\log_3 7/5$

(c) $\log_3 25$

(d) $\log_3 3$

(e) $\log_3 1$

In Example 8, several logarithms to the base 6 were given. However, they could have been found by using a calculator and the following formula.

Change-of-Base Theorem

For any positive numbers a and x (with $a \neq 1$),

$$\log_a x = \frac{\ln x}{\ln a}.$$

Example 9   To find $\log_7 3$, use the theorem with $a = 7$ and $x = 3$:

$$\log_7 3 = \frac{\ln 3}{\ln 7} \approx \frac{1.0986}{1.9459} \approx .5646.$$

You can check this result on your calculator by verifying that $7^{.5646} \approx 3$.

Example 10 **Natural Science** Environmental scientists who study the diversity of species in an ecological community use the *Shannon index* to measure diversity. If there are k different species, with n_1 individuals of species 1, n_2 individuals of species 2, and so on, then the Shannon index H is defined as

$$H = \frac{N \log_2 N - [n_1 \log_2 n_1 + n_2 \log_2 n_2 + \cdots + n_k \log_2 n_k]}{N},$$

where $N = n_1 + n_2 + n_3 + \cdots + n_k$. A study of the species that barn owls in a particular region typically eat yielded the following data:

Species	Number
Rats	143
Mice	1405
Birds	452

Find the index of diversity of this community.

Solution   In this case, $n_1 = 143, n_2 = 1405, n_3 = 452$, and

$$N = n_1 + n_2 + n_3 = 143 + 1405 + 452 = 2000.$$

So the index of diversity is

$$H = \frac{N \log_2 N - [n_1 \log_2 n_1 + n_2 \log_2 n_2 + \cdots + n_k \log_2 n_k]}{N}$$

$$= \frac{2000 \log_2 2000 - [143 \log_2 143 + 1405 \log_2 1405 + 452 \log_2 452]}{2000}.$$

To compute H, we use the change-of-base theorem:

$$H = \frac{2000 \dfrac{\ln 2000}{\ln 2} - \left[143 \dfrac{\ln 143}{\ln 2} + 1405 \dfrac{\ln 1405}{\ln 2} + 452 \dfrac{\ln 452}{\ln 2}\right]}{2000}$$

$$\approx 1.1149.$$

Logarithmic Functions

For a given *positive* value of x, the definition of logarithm leads to exactly one value of y, so that $y = \log_a x$ defines a function.

> If $a > 0$ and $a \neq 1$, the **logarithmic function** with base a is defined as
>
> $$f(x) = \log_a x.$$

The most important logarithmic function is the natural logarithmic function.

Example 11   Graph $f(x) = \ln x$ and $g(x) = e^x$ on the same axes.

Solution   For each function, use a calculator to compute some ordered pairs. Then plot the corresponding points and connect them with a curve to obtain the graphs in Figure 4.21.

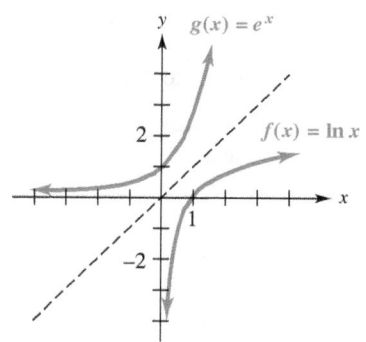

Figure 4.21

The dashed line in Figure 4.21 is the graph of $y = x$. Observe that the graph of $f(x) = \ln x$ is the mirror image of the graph of $g(x) = e^x$, with the line $y = x$ being the mirror. A pair of functions whose graphs are related in this way are said to be **inverses** of each other. A more complete discussion of inverse functions is given in many college algebra books. ☑ 8

✓ **Checkpoint 8**

Verify that $f(x) = \log x$ and $g(x) = 10^x$ are inverses of each other by graphing $f(x)$ and $g(x)$ on the same axes.

When the base $a > 1$, the graph of $f(x) = \log_a x$ has the same basic shape as the graph of the natural logarithmic function in Figure 4.21, as summarized on the following page.

As the information in the box suggests, the functions $f(x) = \log_a x$ and $g(x) = a^x$ are inverses of each other. (Their graphs are mirror images of each other, with the line $y = x$ being the mirror.)

Applications

Logarithmic functions are useful for, among other things, describing quantities that grow, but do so at a slower rate as time goes on.

> **Example 12**   **Health**   The life expectancy at birth of a person born in year x is approximated by the function
>
> $$f(x) = 17.6 + 12.8 \ln x,$$
>
> where $x = 10$ corresponds to 1910. (Data from: U.S. National Center for Health Statistics.)
>
> **(a)** Find the life expectancy of persons born in 1910, 1960, and 2010.
>
> **Solution**   Since these years correspond to $x = 10$, $x = 60$, and $x = 110$, respectively, use a calculator to evaluate $f(x)$ at these numbers:
>
> $$f(10) = 17.6 + 12.8 \ln(10) \approx 47.073;$$
> $$f(60) = 17.6 + 12.8 \ln(60) \approx 70.008;$$
> $$f(110) = 17.6 + 12.8 \ln(110) \approx 77.766.$$
>
> So in the half-century from 1910 to 1960, life expectancy at birth increased from about 47 to 70 years, an increase of 23 years. But in the half-century from 1960 to 2010, it increased less than 8 years, from about 70 to 77.8 years.
>
> **(b)** If this function remains accurate, when will life expectancy at birth be 80.2 years?
>
> **Solution**   We must solve the equation $f(x) = 80.2$, that is,
>
> $$17.6 + 12.8 \ln x = 80.2$$
>
> In the next section, we shall see how to do this algebraically. For now, we solve the equation graphically by graphing $f(x)$ and $y = 80.2$ on the same screen and finding their intersection point. Figure 4.22 shows that the x-coordinate of this point is approximately 133. So life expectancy will be 80.2 years in 2033.

Figure 4.22

4.3 Exercises

Complete each statement in Exercises 1–4.

1. $y = \log_a x$ means $x = $ _____.

2. The statement $\log_5 125 = 3$ tells us that _____ is the power of _____ that equals _____.

3. What is wrong with the expression $y = \log_b$?

4. Logarithms of negative numbers are not defined because _____.

Translate each logarithmic statement into an equivalent exponential statement. (See Examples 1, 5, and 6.)

5. $\log 100{,}000 = 5$

6. $\log .001 = -3$

7. $\log_9 81 = 2$

8. $\log_2 (1/8) = -3$

Translate each exponential statement into an equivalent logarithmic statement. (See Examples 5 and 6.)

9. $10^{1.9823} = 96$

10. $e^{3.2189} = 25$

11. $3^{-2} = 1/9$

12. $16^{1/2} = 4$

Without using a calculator, evaluate each of the given expressions. (See Examples 1, 5, and 6.)

13. $\log 1000$

14. $\log .0001$

15. $\log_6 36$

16. $\log_3 81$

17. $\log_4 64$

18. $\log_5 125$

19. $\log_2 \dfrac{1}{4}$

20. $\log_3 \dfrac{1}{27}$

21. $\ln \sqrt{e}$

22. $\ln(1/e)$

23. $\ln e^{8.77}$

24. $\log 10^{74.3}$

Use a calculator to evaluate each logarithm to three decimal places. (See Examples 3 and 4.)

25. $\log 53$

26. $\log .005$

27. $\ln .0068$

28. $\ln 354$

29. Why does $\log_a 1$ always equal 0 for any valid base a?

Write each expression as the logarithm of a single number or expression. Assume that all variables represent positive numbers. (See Example 7.)

30. $\log 20 - \log 5$

31. $\log 6 + \log 8 - \log 2$

32. $3 \ln 2 + 2 \ln 3$

33. $2 \ln 5 - \frac{1}{2} \ln 25$

34. $5 \log x - 2 \log y$

35. $2 \log u + 3 \log w - 6 \log v$

36. $\ln(3x + 2) + \ln(x + 4)$

37. $2 \ln(x + 2) - \ln(x + 3)$

Write each expression as a sum and/or a difference of logarithms, with all variables to the first degree.

38. $\log 5x^2 y^3$

39. $\ln \sqrt{6m^4 n^2}$

40. $\ln \dfrac{3x}{5y}$

41. $\log \dfrac{\sqrt{xz}}{z^3}$

42. The calculator-generated table in the figure is for $y_1 = \log(4 - x)$. Why do the values in the y_1 column show ERROR for $x \geq 4$?

X	Y1	
0	.60206	
1	.47712	
2	.30103	
3	0	
5	ERROR	
6	ERROR	
	ERROR	
X=4		

Express each expression in terms of u and v, where $u = \ln x$ and $v = \ln y$. For example, $\ln x^3 = 3(\ln x) = 3u$.

43. $\ln(x^2 y^5)$

44. $\ln(\sqrt{x} \cdot y^2)$

45. $\ln(x^3/y^2)$

46. $\ln(\sqrt{x}/y)$

Evaluate each expression. (See Example 9.)

47. $\log_6 384$

48. $\log_{30} 78$

49. $\log_{35} 5646$

50. $\log_6 60 - \log_{60} 6$

Find numerical values for b and c for which the given statement is FALSE.

51. $\log(b + c) = \log b + \log c$

52. $\dfrac{\ln b}{\ln c} = \ln\left(\dfrac{b}{c}\right)$

Graph each function. (See Example 11.)

53. $y = \ln(x + 2)$

54. $y = \ln x + 2$

55. $y = \log(x - 3)$

56. $y = \log x - 3$

57. Graph $f(x) = \log x$ and $g(x) = \log(x/4)$ for $-2 \leq x \leq 8$. How are these graphs related? How does the quotient rule support your answer?

In Exercises 58 and 59, the coordinates of a point on the graph of the indicated function are displayed at the bottom of the screen. Write the logarithmic and exponential equations associated with the display.

58.

59.

60. Match each equation with its graph. Each tick mark represents one unit.

(a) $y = \log x$

(b) $y = 10^x$

(c) $y = \ln x$

(d) $y = e^x$

(A)

(B)

(C)

(D)

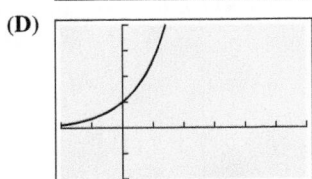

61. Finance The doubling function

$$D(r) = \frac{\ln 2}{\ln(1 + r)}$$

gives the number of years required to double your money when it is invested at interest rate r (expressed as a decimal), compounded annually. How long does it take to double your money at each of the following rates?

(a) 4% (b) 8% (c) 18% (d) 36%

(e) Round each of your answers in parts (a)–(d) to the nearest year, and compare them with these numbers: 72/4, 72/8, 72/18, and 72/36. Use this evidence to state a "rule of thumb" for determining approximate doubling time without employing the function D. This rule, which has long been used by bankers, is called the *rule of 72*.

62. Health Two people with the flu visited a college campus. The number of days, T, that it took for the flu virus to infect n people is given by

$$T = -1.43 \ln\left(\frac{10{,}000 - n}{4998n}\right).$$

How many days will it take for the virus to infect

(a) 500 people? (b) 5000 people?

63. Business The average annual expenditure (in dollars) for a consumer of gasoline and motor oil can be approximated by the function

$$g(x) = -771.9 + 1035 \ln x,$$

where $x = 5$ corresponds to the year 1995. (Data from: U.S. Bureau of Labor Statistics.)

(a) Estimate the average expenditure in 2008.

(b) Graph the function g for the period 1995 to 2011.

(c) Assuming the graph remains accurate, what does the shape of the graph suggest regarding the average expenditure on gasoline and motor oil?

64. Physical Science The barometric pressure p (in inches of mercury) is related to the height h above sea level (in miles) by the equation

$$h = -5 \ln\left(\frac{p}{29.92}\right).$$

The pressure readings given in parts (a)–(c) were made by a weather balloon. At what heights were they made?

(a) 29.92 in. (b) 20.05 in. (c) 11.92 in.

(d) Use a graphing calculator to determine the pressure at a height of 3 miles.

65. Social Science The number of residents (in millions) of the United States age 65 or older can be approximated by the function

$$h(x) = 1.58 + 10.15 \ln x,$$

where $x = 10$ corresponds to the year 1980. (Data from: U.S. Census Bureau.)

(a) Give the number of residents age 65 or older for the years 1990 and 2005.

(b) Graph the function h for $10 \leq x \leq 50$.

(c) What does the graph suggest regarding the number of older people as time goes on?

Natural Science *These exercises deal with the Shannon index of diversity. (See Example 10.) Note that in two communities with the same number of species, a larger index indicates greater diversity.*

66. A study of barn owl prey in a particular area produced the following data:

Species	Number
Rats	662
Mice	907
Birds	531

Find the index of diversity of this community. Is this community more or less diverse than the one in Example 10?

67. An eastern forest is composed of the following trees:

Species	Number
Beech	2754
Birch	689
Hemlock	4428
Maple	629

What is the index of diversity of this community?

68. A community has high diversity when all of its species have approximately the same number of individuals. It has low diversity when a few of its species account for most of the total population. Illustrate this fact for the following two communities:

Community 1	Number
Species A	1000
Species B	1000
Species C	1000

Community 2	Number
Species A	2500
Species B	200
Species C	300

69. Business The total assets (in billions of dollars) held by credit unions can be approximated by the function

$$f(x) = -1237 + 580.6 \ln x,$$

where $x = 10$ corresponds to the year 1990. (Data from: U.S. Census Bureau.)

(a) What were the assets held by credit unions in 1998 and 2010?

↗ **(b)** If the model remains accurate, find the year the assets reach $1000 billion.

70. Finance The amount (in billions of dollars) held in private pension funds can be approximated by the function

$$h(x) = -11,052 + 5742 \ln x,$$

where $x = 10$ corresponds to the year 1990. (Data from: Board of Governors of the Federal Reserve System.)

(a) What was the amount in private pension funds in 2001 and 2009?

(b) If the model remains accurate, when will the amount reach $9000 billion?

71. Business The amount of milk (in gallons) consumed per person annually can be approximated by the function

$$g(x) = 28.29 - 1.948 \ln(x + 1),$$

where $x = 0$ corresponds to the year 1980. (Data from: U.S. Department of Agriculture.)

(a) How many gallons per person were consumed in the years 1985 and 2005?

(b) Assuming the model remains accurate, when will the per-person consumption be at 21 gallons?

72. Economics The median family income is the "middle income"—half the families have this income or more, and half have a lesser income. The median family income can be approximated by

$$f(x) = 22,751 + 8217 \ln(x + 1),$$

where $x = 0$ corresponds to the year 1990. (Data from: U.S. Census Bureau.)

(a) What is the median income in the years 2000 and 2010?

(b) If this model remains accurate, when will the median income reach $52,000?

✓**Checkpoint Answers**

1. (a) 2   **(b)** 3   **(c)** -1

2. (a) 1.4314   **(b)** 3.0370   **(c)** -2.3706

3. (a) 1.8083   **(b)** 2.9957   **(c)** $-.2231$
   (d) -2.3026

4. (a) $\log_5 125 = 3$ **(b)** $\log_3 (1/81) = -4$ **(c)** $\log_8 4 = 2/3$

5. (a) $16^{1/2} = 4$ **(b)** $3^{-2} = 1/9$ **(c)** $16^{3/4} = 8$

6. (a) $\log_a 15x^5$ **(b)** $\log_a (3p/5q)$ **(c)** $\log_a (k^4/m^3)$

7. (a) 3.23   **(b)** .31   **(c)** 2.92
   (d) 1   **(e)** 0

8.

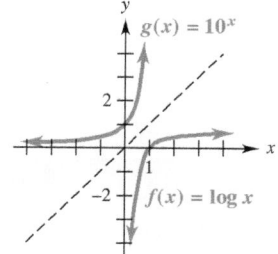

4.4 Logarithmic and Exponential Equations

Many applications involve solving logarithmic and exponential equations, so we begin with solution methods for such equations.

Logarithmic Equations

When an equation involves only logarithmic terms, use the logarithm properties to write each side as a single logarithm. Then use the following fact.

Let u, v, and a be positive real numbers, with $a \neq 1$.

If $\log_a u = \log_a v$, then $u = v$.

Example 1 Solve $\log x = \log(x + 3) - \log(x - 1)$.

Solution First, use the quotient property of logarithms to write the right side as a single logarithm:

$$\log x = \log(x + 3) - \log(x - 1)$$
$$\log x = \log\left(\frac{x + 3}{x - 1}\right). \qquad \text{Quotient property of logarithms}$$

The fact in the preceding box now shows that

$$x = \frac{x + 3}{x - 1}$$
$$x(x - 1) = x + 3 \qquad \text{Cross multiply.}$$
$$x^2 - x = x + 3$$
$$x^2 - 2x - 3 = 0$$
$$(x - 3)(x + 1) = 0 \qquad \text{Factor.}$$
$$x = 3 \quad \text{or} \quad x = -1.$$

Since $\log x$ is not defined when $x = -1$, the only possible solution is $x = 3$. Use a calculator to verify that 3 actually is a solution.

✓ **Checkpoint 1**

Solve each equation.

(a) $\log_2 (p + 9) - \log_2 p = \log_2 (p + 1)$

(b) $\log_3 (m + 1) - \log_3 (m - 1) = \log_3 m$

When an equation involves constants and logarithmic terms, use algebra and the logarithm properties to write one side as a single logarithm and the other as a constant. Then use the following property of logarithms, which was discussed on pages 202–203.

If a and u are positive real numbers, with $a \neq 1$, then

$$a^{\log_a u} = u.$$

Example 2 Solve each equation.

(a) $\log_5 (2x - 3) = 2$

Solution Since the base of the logarithm is 5, raise 5 to the exponents given by the equation:

$$5^{\log_5 (2x - 3)} = 5^2$$

On the left side, use the fact in the preceding box (with $a = 5$ and $u = 2x - 3$) to conclude that

$$2x - 3 = 25$$
$$2x = 28$$
$$x = 14.$$

Verify that 14 is a solution of the original equation.

(b) $\log(x - 16) = 2 - \log(x - 1)$

Solution First rearrange the terms to obtain a single logarithm on the left side:

$$\log(x - 16) + \log(x - 1) = 2$$
$$\log[(x - 16)(x - 1)] = 2 \qquad \text{Product property of logarithms}$$
$$\log(x^2 - 17x + 16) = 2.$$

Since the base of the logarithm is 10, raise 10 to the given powers:

$$10^{\log(x^2 - 17x + 16)} = 10^2.$$

On the left side, apply the logarithm property in the preceding box (with $a = 10$ and $u = x^2 - 17x + 16$):

$$x^2 - 17x + 16 = 100$$
$$x^2 - 17x - 84 = 0$$
$$(x + 4)(x - 21) = 0$$
$$x = -4 \qquad \text{or} \qquad x = 21.$$

In the original equation, when $x = -4$, $\log(x - 16) = \log(-20)$, which is not defined. So -4 is not a solution. You should verify that 21 is a solution of the original equation.

(c) $\log_2 x - \log_2 (x - 1) = 1$

Solution Proceed as before, with 2 as the base of the logarithm:

$$\log_2 \frac{x}{x - 1} = 1 \qquad \text{Quotient property of logarithms}$$
$$2^{\log_2 x/(x-1)} = 2^1 \qquad \text{Exponentiate to the base 2.}$$
$$\frac{x}{x - 1} = 2 \qquad \text{Use the fact in the preceding box.}$$
$$x = 2(x - 1) \qquad \text{Multiply both sides by } x - 1.$$
$$x = 2x - 2$$
$$-x = -2$$
$$x = 2.$$

Verify that 2 is a solution of the original equation.

✓ Checkpoint 2

Solve each equation.

(a) $\log_5 x + 2 \log_5 x = 3$

(b) $\log_6 (a + 2) - \log_6 \frac{a - 7}{5} = 1$

Exponential Equations

An equation in which all the variables are exponents is called an exponential equation. When such an equation can be written as two powers of the same base, it can be solved by using the following fact.

Let a be a positive real number, with $a \neq 1$.

If $a^u = a^v$, then $u = v$.

Example 3 Solve $9^x = 27$.

Solution First, write both sides as powers of the same base. Since $9 = 3^2$ and $27 = 3^3$, we have

$$9^x = 27$$
$$(3^2)^x = 3^3$$
$$3^{2x} = 3^3.$$

Apply the fact in the preceding box (with $a = 3$, $u = 2x$, and $v = 3$):

$$2x = 3$$

$$x = \frac{3}{2}.$$

✓ **Checkpoint 3**

Solve each equation.

(a) $8^{2x} = 4$

(b) $5^{3x} = 25^4$

(c) $36^{-2x} = 6$

Verify that $x = 3/2$ is a solution of the original equation. ✓₃

Exponential equations involving different bases can often be solved by using the power property of logarithms, which is repeated here for natural logarithms.

If u and r are real numbers, with u positive, then

$$\ln u^r = r \ln u.$$

Although natural logarithms are used in the following examples, logarithms to any base will produce the same solutions.

Example 4   Solve $3^x = 5$.

Solution   Take natural logarithms on both sides:

$$\ln 3^x = \ln 5.$$

Apply the power property of logarithms in the preceding box (with $r = x$) to the left side:

$$x \ln 3 = \ln 5$$

$$x = \frac{\ln 5}{\ln 3} \approx 1.465. \qquad \text{Divide both sides by the constant ln 3.}$$

To check, evaluate $3^{1.465}$; the answer should be approximately 5, which verifies that the solution of the given equation is 1.465 (to the nearest thousandth). ✓₄

✓ **Checkpoint 4**

Solve each equation. Round solutions to the nearest thousandth.

(a) $2^x = 7$

(b) $5^m = 50$

(c) $3^y = 17$

⊘ **CAUTION**   Be careful: $\dfrac{\ln 5}{\ln 3}$ is *not* equal to $\ln\left(\dfrac{5}{3}\right)$ or $\ln 5 - \ln 3$.

Example 5   Solve $3^{2x-1} = 4^{x+2}$.

Solution   Taking natural logarithms on both sides gives

$$\ln 3^{2x-1} = \ln 4^{x+2}.$$

Now use the power property of logarithms and the fact that $\ln 3$ and $\ln 4$ are constants to rewrite the equation:

$$(2x - 1)(\ln 3) = (x + 2)(\ln 4) \qquad \text{Power property}$$

$$2x(\ln 3) - 1(\ln 3) = x(\ln 4) + 2(\ln 4) \qquad \text{Distributive property}$$

$$2x(\ln 3) - x(\ln 4) = 2(\ln 4) + 1(\ln 3). \qquad \text{Collect terms with } x \text{ on one side.}$$

Factor out x on the left side to get

$$[2(\ln 3) - \ln 4]x = 2(\ln 4) + \ln 3.$$

Divide both sides by the coefficient of x:

$$x = \frac{2(\ln 4) + \ln 3}{2(\ln 3) - \ln 4}.$$

Using a calculator to evaluate this last expression, we find that

$$x = \frac{2\ln 4 + \ln 3}{2\ln 3 - \ln 4} \approx 4.774.$$ ✓5

Recall that $\ln e = 1$ (because 1 is the exponent to which e must be raised to produce e). This fact simplifies the solution of equations involving powers of e.

Example 6   Solve $3e^{x^2} = 600$.

Solution   First divide each side by 3 to get

$$e^{x^2} = 200.$$

Now take natural logarithms on both sides; then use the power property of logarithms:

$$e^{x^2} = 200$$
$$\ln e^{x^2} = \ln 200$$
$$x^2 \ln e = \ln 200 \qquad \text{Power property}$$
$$x^2 = \ln 200 \qquad \ln e = 1.$$
$$x = \pm\sqrt{\ln 200}$$
$$x \approx \pm 2.302.$$

Verify that the solutions are ± 2.302, rounded to the nearest thousandth. (The symbol $\pm$ is used as a shortcut for writing the two solutions 2.302 and −2.302.) ✓6

Applications

Some of the most important applications of exponential and logarithmic functions arise in banking and finance. They will be thoroughly discussed in Chapter 5. The applications here are from other fields.

Example 7   **Business** The number of total subscribers (in millions) to Netflix, Inc. can be approximated by the function

$$g(x) = 9.78(1.07)^x,$$

where $x = 1$ corresponds to the first quarter of the year 2009, $x = 2$ corresponds to the second quarter of the year 2009, etc. Assume the model remains accurate and determine when the number of subscribers reached 28 million. (Data from: The *Wall Street Journal* and The *Associated Press*.)

Solution   You are being asked to find the value of x for which $g(x) = 28$—that is, to solve the following equation:

$$9.78(1.07)^x = 28$$
$$1.07^x = \frac{28}{9.78} \qquad \text{Divide both sides by 9.78.}$$
$$\ln(1.07^x) = \ln\left(\frac{28}{9.78}\right) \qquad \text{Take logarithms on both sides.}$$
$$x\ln(1.07) = \ln\left(\frac{28}{9.78}\right) \qquad \text{Power property of logarithms}$$
$$x = \frac{\ln(28/9.78)}{\ln(1.07)} \qquad \text{Divide both sides by ln(1.07).}$$
$$x \approx 15.5.$$

The 15th quarter corresponds to the third quarter of the year 2012. Hence, according to this model, Netflix, Inc., reached 28 million subscribers in the third quarter of 2012. ✓7

✓ **Checkpoint 5**

Solve each equation. Round solutions to the nearest thousandth.
(a) $6^m = 3^{2m-1}$
(b) $5^{6a-3} = 2^{4a+1}$

✓ **Checkpoint 6**

Solve each equation. Round solutions to the nearest thousandth.
(a) $e^{.1x} = 11$
(b) $e^{3+x} = .893$
(c) $e^{2x^2-3} = 9$

📍 **TECHNOLOGY TIP**
Logarithmic and exponential equations can be solved on a graphing calculator. To solve $3^x = 5^{2x-1}$, for example, graph $y = 3^x$ and $y = 5^{2x-1}$ on the same screen. Then use the intersection finder to determine the x-coordinates of their intersection points. Alternatively, graph $y = 3^x - 5^{2x-1}$ and use the root finder to determine the x-intercepts of the graph.

✓ **Checkpoint 7**

Use the function in Example 7 to determine when Netflix reached 35 million subscribers.

The **half-life** of a radioactive substance is the time it takes for a given quantity of the substance to decay to one-half its original mass. The half-life depends only on the substance, not on the size of the sample. It can be shown that the amount of a radioactive substance at time t is given by the function

$$f(t) = y_0\left(\frac{1}{2}\right)^{t/h} = y_0(.5^{t/h}),$$

where y_0 is the initial amount (at time $t = 0$) and h is the half-life of the substance.

Radioactive carbon-14 is found in every living plant and animal. After the plant or animal dies, its carbon-14 decays exponentially, with a half-life of 5730 years. This fact is the basis for a technique called *carbon dating* for determining the age of fossils.

Example 8   **Natural Science**   A round wooden table hanging in Winchester Castle (England) was alleged to have belonged to King Arthur, who lived in the fifth century. A recent chemical analysis showed that the wood had lost 9% of its carbon-14.[*] How old is the table?

Solution   The decay function for carbon-14 is

$$f(t) = y_0(.5^{t/5730}),$$

where $t = 0$ corresponds to the time the wood was cut to make the table. (That is when the tree died.) Since the wood has lost 9% of its carbon-14, the amount in the table now is 91% of the initial amount y_0 (that is, $.91y_0$). We must find the value of t for which $f(t) = .91y_0$. So we must solve the equation

$y_0(.5^{t/5730}) = .91y_0$	Definition of $f(t)$
$.5^{t/5730} = .91$	Divide both sides by y_0.
$\ln .5^{t/5730} = \ln .91$	Take logarithms on both sides.
$\left(\dfrac{t}{5730}\right)\ln .5 = \ln .91$	Power property of logarithms
$t \ln .5 = 5730 \ln .91$	Multiply both sides by 5730.
$t = \dfrac{5730 \ln .91}{\ln .5} \approx 779.63.$	Divide both sides by $\ln .5$.

The table is about 780 years old and therefore could not have belonged to King Arthur. ✓8

Checkpoint 8

How old is a skeleton that has lost 65% of its carbon-14?

Earthquakes are often in the news. The standard method of measuring their size, the **Richter scale,** is a logarithmic function (base 10).

Example 9   **Physical Science**   The intensity $R(i)$ of an earthquake, measured on the Richter scale, is given by

$$R(i) = \log\left(\frac{i}{i_0}\right),$$

where i is the intensity of the ground motion of the earthquake and i_0 is the intensity of the ground motion of the so-called *zero earthquake* (the smallest detectable earthquake, against which others are measured). The underwater earthquake that caused the disastrous 2004 tsunami in Southeast Asia measured 9.1 on the Richter scale.

---

[*]This is done by measuring the ratio of carbon-14 to nonradioactive carbon-12 in the table (a ratio that is approximately constant over long periods) and comparing it with the ratio in living wood.

(a) How did the ground motion of this tsunami compare with that of the zero earthquake?

Solution   In this case,

$$R(i) = 9.1$$
$$\log\left(\frac{i}{i_0}\right) = 9.1.$$

By the definition of logarithms, 9.1 is the exponent to which 10 must be raised to produce i/i_0, which means that

$$10^{9.1} = \frac{i}{i_0}, \quad \text{or equivalently,} \quad i = 10^{9.1} i_0.$$

So the earthquake that produced the tsunami had $10^{9.1}$ (about 1.26 *billion*) times more ground motion than the zero earthquake.

(b) What is the Richter-scale intensity of an earthquake with 10 times as much ground motion as the 2004 tsunami earthquake?

Solution   From (a), the ground motion of the tsunami quake was $10^{9.1} i_0$. So a quake with 10 times that motion would satisfy

$$i = 10(10^{9.1} i_0) = 10^1 \cdot 10^{9.1} i_0 = 10^{10.1} i_0.$$

Therefore, its Richter scale measure would be

$$R(i) = \log\left(\frac{i}{i_0}\right) = \log\left(\frac{10^{10.1} i_0}{i_0}\right) = \log 10^{10.1} = 10.1.$$

Thus, a tenfold increase in ground motion increases the Richter scale measure by only 1. ✓9

✓ Checkpoint 9

Find the Richter-scale intensity of an earthquake whose ground motion is 100 times greater than the ground motion of the 2004 tsunami earthquake discussed in Example 9.

Example 10   **Economics**   One action that government could take to reduce carbon emissions into the atmosphere is to place a tax on fossil fuels. This tax would be based on the amount of carbon dioxide that is emitted into the air when such a fuel is burned. The *cost–benefit* equation $\ln(1 - P) = -.0034 - .0053T$ describes the approximate relationship between a tax of T dollars per ton of carbon dioxide and the corresponding percent reduction P (in decimals) in emissions of carbon dioxide.[*]

(a) Write P as a function of T.

Solution   We begin by writing the cost–benefit equation in exponential form:

$$\ln(1 - P) = -.0034 - .0053T$$
$$1 - P = e^{-.0034 - .0053T}$$
$$P = P(T) = 1 - e^{-.0034 - .0053T}.$$

A calculator-generated graph of $P(T)$ is shown in Figure 4.23.

(b) Discuss the benefit of continuing to raise taxes on carbon dioxide emissions.

Solution   From the graph, we see that initially there is a rapid reduction in carbon dioxide emissions. However, after a while, there is little benefit in raising taxes further.

Figure 4.23

---

[*]"To Slow or Not to Slow: The Economics of The Greenhouse Effect," William D. Nordhaus, *The Economic Journal*, Vol. 101, No. 407 (July, 1991), pp. 920–937.

4.4 Exercises

Solve each logarithmic equation. (See Example 1.)

1. $\ln(x + 3) = \ln(2x - 5)$

2. $\ln(8k - 7) - \ln(3 + 4k) = \ln(9/11)$

3. $\ln(3x + 1) - \ln(5 + x) = \ln 2$

4. $\ln(5x + 2) = \ln 4 + \ln(x + 3)$

5. $2\ln(x - 3) = \ln(x + 5) + \ln 4$

6. $\ln(k + 5) + \ln(k + 2) = \ln 18k$

Solve each logarithmic equation. (See Example 2.)

7. $\log_3(6x - 2) = 2$

8. $\log_5(3x - 4) = 1$

9. $\log x - \log(x + 4) = -1$

10. $\log m - \log(m + 4) = -2$

11. $\log_3(y + 2) = \log_3(y - 7) + \log_3 4$

12. $\log_8(z - 6) = 2 - \log_8(z + 15)$

13. $\ln(x + 9) - \ln x = 1$

14. $\ln(2x + 1) - 1 = \ln(x - 2)$

15. $\log x + \log(x - 9) = 1$

16. $\log(x - 1) + \log(x + 2) = 1$

Solve each equation for c.

17. $\log(3 + b) = \log(4c - 1)$

18. $\ln(b + 7) = \ln(6c + 8)$

19. $2 - b = \log(6c + 5)$

20. $8b + 6 = \ln(2c) + \ln c$

21. Suppose you overhear the following statement: "I must reject any negative answer when I solve an equation involving logarithms." Is this correct? Write an explanation of why it is or is not correct.

22. What values of x cannot be solutions of the following equation?
$$\log_a(4x - 7) + \log_a(x^2 + 4) = 0.$$

Solve these exponential equations without using logarithms. (See Example 3.)

23. $2^{x-1} = 8$

24. $16^{-x+2} = 8$

25. $25^{-3x} = 3125$

26. $81^{-2x} = 3^{x-1}$

27. $6^{-x} = 36^{x+6}$

28. $16^x = 64$

29. $\left(\dfrac{3}{4}\right)^x = \dfrac{16}{9}$

30. $2^{x^2 - 4x} = \dfrac{1}{16}$

Use logarithms to solve these exponential equations. (See Examples 4–6.)

31. $2^x = 5$

32. $5^x = 8$

33. $2^x = 3^{x-1}$

34. $4^{x+2} = 5^{x-1}$

35. $3^{1-2x} = 5^{x+5}$

36. $4^{3x-1} = 3^{x-2}$

37. $e^{3x} = 6$

38. $e^{-3x} = 5$

39. $2e^{5a+2} = 8$

40. $10e^{3z-7} = 5$

Solve each equation for c.

41. $10^{4c-3} = d$

42. $3 \cdot 10^{2c+1} = 4d$

43. $e^{2c-1} = b$

44. $3e^{5c-7} = b$

Solve these equations. (See Examples 1–6.)

45. $\log_7(r + 3) + \log_7(r - 3) = 1$

46. $\log_4(z + 3) + \log_4(z - 3) = 2$

47. $\log_3(a - 3) = 1 + \log_3(a + 1)$

48. $\log w + \log(3w - 13) = 1$

49. $\log_2 \sqrt{2y^2} - 1 = 3/2$ 50. $\log_2(\log_2 x) = 1$

51. $\log_2(\log_3 x) = 1$

52. $\dfrac{\ln(2x + 1)}{\ln(3x - 1)} = 2$

53. $5^{-2x} = \dfrac{1}{25}$

54. $5^{x^2+x} = 1$

55. $2^{|x|} = 16$

56. $5^{-|x|} = \dfrac{1}{25}$

57. $2^{x^2-1} = 10$

58. $3^{2-x^2} = 8$

59. $2(e^x + 1) = 10$

60. $5(e^{2x} - 2) = 15$

61. Explain why the equation $4^{x^2+1} = 2$ has no solutions.

62. Explain why the equation $\log(-x) = -4$ does have a solution, and find that solution.

Work these problems. (See Example 7.)

63. **Business** Gambling revenues (in billions of U.S. dollars) generated in Macau, China can be approximated by the function $g(x) = 1.104(1.346)^x$, where $x = 2$ corresponds to the year 2002. Assume the model remains accurate and find the years in which the gambling revenues reached the indicated amounts. (Data from: The *Wall Street Journal*.)

   (a) $20 billion   (b) $45 billion

64. **Social Science** The number of centenarians (in thousands) in the United States can be approximated by the function $h(x) = 2(1.056)^x$, where $x = 0$ corresponds to the year 1950. Find the year in which the number of centenarians reached the following levels. (Data from: U.S. Census Bureau.)

   (a) 30,000   (b) 50,000

65. **Health** As we saw in Example 12 of Section 4.3, the life expectancy at birth of a person born in year x is approximately
$$f(x) = 17.6 + 12.8 \ln x,$$
where $x = 10$ corresponds to the year 1910. Find the birth year of a person whose life expectancy at birth was

   (a) 75.5 years;   (b) 77.5 years;   (c) 81 years.

66. Health A drug's effectiveness decreases over time. If, each hour, a drug is only 90% as effective as during the previous hour, at some point the patient will not be receiving enough medication and must receive another dose. This situation can be modeled by the exponential function $y = y_0(.90)^{t-1}$. In this equation, y_0 is the amount of the initial dose and y is the amount of medication still available t hours after the drug was administered. Suppose 200 mg of the drug is administered. How long will it take for this initial dose to reach the dangerously low level of 50 mg?

67. Economics The percentage of the U.S. income earned by the top one percent of earners can be approximated by the function $f(x) = 7.9e^{.0254x}$, where $x = 0$ corresponds to the year 1970. (Data from: The *New York Times*.)

(a) When did the percentage reach 15%?

(b) If the model remains accurate, when will the percentage reach 30%?

68. Health The probability P percent of having an accident while driving a car is related to the alcohol level t of the driver's blood by the equation $P = e^{kt}$, where k is a constant. Accident statistics show that the probability of an accident is 25% when the blood alcohol level is $t = .15$.

(a) Use the equation and the preceding information to find k (to three decimal places). *Note:* Use $P = 25$, and not .25.

(b) Using the value of k from part (a), find the blood alcohol level at which the probability of having an accident is 50%.

Work these exercises. (See Example 8.)

69. Natural Science The amount of cobalt-60 (in grams) in a storage facility at time t is given by

$$C(t) = 25e^{-.14t},$$

where time is measured in years.

(a) How much cobalt-60 was present initially?

(b) What is the half-life of cobalt-60? (*Hint:* For what value of t is $C(t) = 12.5$?)

70. Natural Science A Native American mummy was found recently. It had 73.6% of the amount of radiocarbon present in living beings. Approximately how long ago did this person die?

71. Natural Science How old is a piece of ivory that has lost 36% of its radiocarbon?

72. Natural Science A sample from a refuse deposit near the Strait of Magellan had 60% of the carbon-14 of a contemporary living sample. How old was the sample?

Natural Science ***Work these problems. (See Example 9.)***

73. In May 2008, Sichuan province, China suffered an earthquake that measured 7.9 on the Richter scale.

(a) Express the intensity of this earthquake in terms of i_0.

(b) In July of the same year, a quake measuring 5.4 on the Richter scale struck Los Angeles. Express the intensity of this earthquake in terms of i_0.

(c) How many times more intense was the China earthquake than the one in Los Angeles?

74. Find the Richter-scale intensity of earthquakes whose ground motion is

(a) $1000i_0$; (b) $100,000i_0$;

(c) $10,000,000i_0$.

(d) Fill in the blank in this statement: Increasing the ground motion by a factor of 10^k increases the Richter intensity by _____ units.

75. The loudness of sound is measured in units called decibels. The decibel rating of a sound is given by

$$D(i) = 10 \cdot \log\left(\frac{i}{i_0}\right),$$

where i is the intensity of the sound and i_0 is the minimum intensity detectable by the human ear (the so-called *threshold sound*). Find the decibel rating of each of the sounds with the given intensities. Round answers to the nearest whole number.

(a) Whisper, $115i_0$

(b) Average sound level in the movie *Godzilla*, $10^{10}i_0$

(c) Jackhammer, $31,600,000,000i_0$

(d) Rock music, $895,000,000,000i_0$

(e) Jetliner at takeoff, $109,000,000,000,000i_0$

76. (a) How much more intense is a sound that measures 100 decibels than the threshold sound?

(b) How much more intense is a sound that measures 50 decibels than the threshold sound?

(c) How much more intense is a sound measuring 100 decibels than one measuring 50 decibels?

77. Natural Science Refer to Example 10.

(a) Determine the percent reduction in carbon dioxide when the tax is $60.

(b) What tax will cause a 50% reduction in carbon dioxide emissions?

78. Business The revenue (in billions of dollars) for Walt Disney Company can be approximated by the function $R(x) = 16.20 + 9.992 \ln x$, where $x = 3$ corresponds to the year 2003. Find each of the following. (Data from: www.morningstar.com.)

(a) $R(9)$ (b) $R(12)$

(c) If the model remains accurate, in what year will revenue reach $50 billion?

79. Business Annual box office revenue (in billions of dollars) generated in North America can be approximated by the function $g(x) = 2.0 + 2.768 \ln x$, where $x = 2$ corresponds to the year 1992. (Data from: www.boxofficemojo.com.)

(a) Graph the function g for the years 1992 through 2012.

(b) According to the model, in what year did revenue reach $9 billion?

80. Physical Science The table on the following page gives some of the planets' average distances D from the sun and their period P of revolution around the sun in years. The distances have been normalized so that Earth is one unit from the sun. Thus, Jupiter's distance of 5.2 means that Jupiter's distance from the sun is 5.2 times farther than Earth's.[*]

Planet	D	P
Earth	1	1
Jupiter	5.2	11.9
Saturn	9.54	29.5
Uranus	19.2	84.0

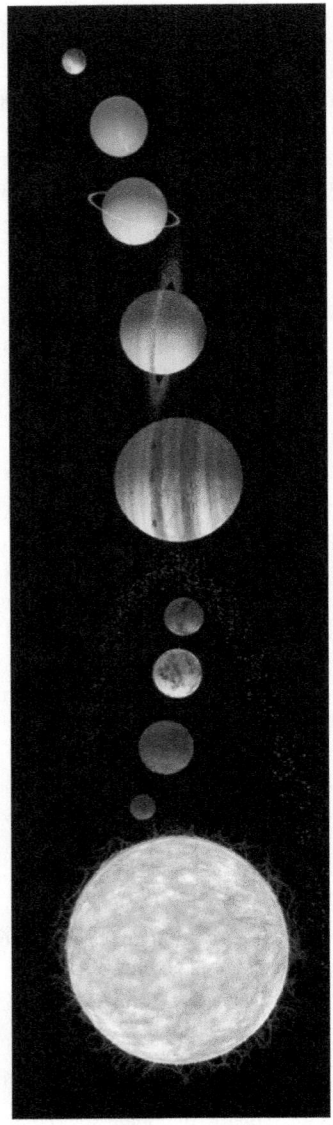

(a) Plot the points (D, P) for these planets. Would a straight line or an exponential curve fit these points best?

(b) Plot the points $(\ln D, \ln P)$ for these planets. Do these points appear to lie on a line?

(c) Determine a linear equation that approximates the data points, with $x = \ln D$ and $y = \ln P$. Use the first and last data points (rounded to 2 decimal places). Graph your line and the data on the same coordinate axes.

(d) Use the linear equation to predict the period of the planet Pluto if its distance is 39.5. Compare your answer with the true value of 248.5 years.

✓ Checkpoint Answers

1. (a) 3   (b) $1 + \sqrt{2} \approx 2.414$

2. (a) 5   (b) 52

3. (a) 1/3   (b) 8/3   (c) −1/4

4. (a) 2.807   (b) 2.431   (c) 2.579

5. (a) 2.710   (b) .802

6. (a) 23.979   (b) −3.113   (c) ±1.612

7. Second quarter of 2013.

8. About 8679 years

9. 11.1

---

[*]C. Ronan, *The Natural History of the Universe.* New York: Macmillan Publishing Co., 1991.

CHAPTER 4 Summary and Review

Key Terms and Symbols

4.1 exponential function
exponential growth and decay
the number
$e \approx 2.71828\ldots$

4.2 exponential growth function
logistic function

4.3 $\log x$ common (base-10) logarithm of x
$\ln x$ natural (base-e) logarithm of x
$\log_a x$ base-a logarithm of x

product, quotient, and power properties of logarithms
change-of-base theorem
Inverse logarithmic functions

4.4 logarithmic equations
exponential equations
half-life
Richter scale

Chapter 4 Key Concepts

Exponentialic Functions

An important application of exponents is the **exponential growth function,** defined as $f(t) = y_0 e^{kt}$ or $f(t) = y_0 b^t$, where y_0 is the amount of a quantity present at time $t = 0$, $e \approx 2.71828$, and k and b are constants.

Logarithmic Functions

The **logarithm** of x to the base a is defined as follows: For $a > 0$ and $a \neq 1$, $y = \log_a x$ means $a^y = x$. Thus, $\log_a x$ is an *exponent*, the power to which a must be raised to produce x.

Properties of Logarithms

Let x, y, and a be positive real numbers, with $a \neq 1$, and let r be any real number. Then

$$\log_a 1 = 0; \quad \log_a a = 1;$$
$$\log_a a^r = r; \quad a^{\log_a x} = x.$$

Product property $\log_a xy = \log_a x + \log_a y$

Quotient property $\log_a \dfrac{x}{y} = \log_a x - \log_a y$

Power property $\log_a x^r = r \log_a x$

Solving Exponential and Logarithmic Equations

Let $a > 0$, with $a \neq 1$.

If $\log_a u = \log_a v$, then $u = v$.

If $a^u = a^v$, then $u = v$.

Chapter 4 Review Exercises

Match each equation with the letter of the graph that most closely resembles the graph of the equation. Assume that $a > 1$.

1. $y = a^{x+2}$

2. $y = a^x + 2$

3. $y = -a^x + 2$

4. $y = a^{-x} + 2$

(a)

(b)

(c)

(d)

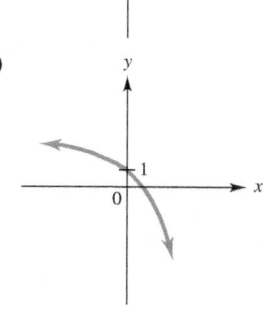

Consider the exponential function $y = f(x) = a^x$ graphed here. Answer each question on the basis of the graph.

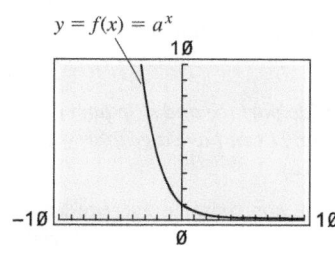

5. What is true about the value of a in comparison to 1?

6. What is the domain of f?

7. What is the range of f?

8. What is the value of $f(0)$?

Graph each function.

9. $f(x) = 4^x$

10. $g(x) = 4^{-x}$

11. $f(x) = \ln x + 5$

12. $g(x) = \log x - 3$

Work these problems.

13. Economics The cumulative number of retail jobs (in thousands) added each month to the U.S. economy can be approximated by the function $f(x) = 39.61(1.118)^x$, where $x = 1$ corresponds to January, 2011. (Data from: U.S. Bureau of Labor Statistics.)

(a) Estimate the cumulative number of jobs added in September, 2012.

(b) In what month, according to the model, did the cumulative number of jobs hit 300,000?

14. Economics The cumulative number of construction jobs (in thousands) added each month to the U.S. economy can be approximated by the function $f(x) = 28.7(1.120)^x$, where $x = 1$ corresponds to January, 2011. (Data from: U.S. Bureau of Labor Statistics.)

(a) Estimate the cumulative number of jobs added in June, 2012.

(b) In what month, according to the model, did the cumulative number of jobs hit 250,000?

Translate each exponential statement into an equivalent logarithmic one.

15. $10^{2.53148} = 340$

16. $5^4 = 625$

17. $e^{3.8067} = 45$

18. $7^{1/2} = \sqrt{7}$

Translate each logarithmic statement into an equivalent exponential one.

19. $\log 10{,}000 = 4$

20. $\log 26.3 = 1.4200$

21. $\ln 81.1 = 4.3957$

22. $\log_2 4096 = 12$

Evaluate these expressions without using a calculator.

23. $\ln e^5$

24. $\log \sqrt[3]{10}$

25. $10^{\log 8.9}$

26. $\ln e^{3t^2}$

27. $\log_8 2$

28. $\log_8 32$

Write these expressions as a single logarithm. Assume all variables represent positive quantities.

29. $\log 4x + \log 5x^5$

30. $4 \log u - 5 \log u^6$

31. $3 \log b - 2 \log c$

32. $7 \ln x - 3(\ln x^3 + 5 \ln x)$

Solve each equation. Round to the nearest thousandth.

33. $\ln(m + 8) - \ln m = \ln 3$

34. $2 \ln(y + 1) = \ln(y^2 - 1) + \ln 5$

35. $\log(m + 3) = 2$

36. $\log x^3 = 2$

37. $\log_2 (3k + 1) = 4$

38. $\log_5 \left(\dfrac{5z}{z - 2} \right) = 2$

39. $\log x + \log(x - 3) = 1$

40. $\log_2 r + \log_2 (r - 2) = 3$

41. $2^{3x} = \dfrac{1}{64}$

42. $\left(\dfrac{9}{16} \right)^x = \dfrac{3}{4}$

43. $9^{2y+1} = 27^y$

44. $\dfrac{1}{2} = \left(\dfrac{b}{4} \right)^{1/4}$

45. $8^p = 19$

46. $3^z = 11$

47. $5 \cdot 2^{-m} = 35$

48. $2 \cdot 15^{-k} = 18$

49. $e^{-5-2x} = 5$

50. $e^{3x-1} = 12$

51. $6^{2-m} = 2^{3m+1}$

52. $5^{3r-1} = 6^{2r+5}$

53. $(1 + .003)^k = 1.089$

54. $(1 + .094)^z = 2.387$

Work these problems.

55. A population is increasing according to the growth law $y = 4e^{.03t}$, where y is in thousands and t is in months. Match each of the questions (a), (b), (c), and (d) with one of the solution (A), (B), (C), or (D).

  (a) How long will it take for the population to double?

  (A) Solve $4e^{.03t} = 12$ for t.

  (b) When will the population reach 12 thousand?

  (B) Evaluate $4e^{.03(72)}$.

  (c) How large will the population be in 6 months?

  (C) Solve $4e^{.03t} = 2 \cdot 4$ for t.

  (d) How large will the population be in 6 years?

  (D) Evaluate $4e^{.03(6)}$.

56. **Natural Science** A population is increasing according to the growth law $y = 2e^{.02t}$, where y is in millions and t is in

years. Match each of the questions (a), (b), (c), and (d) with one of the solutions (A), (B), (C), or (D).

  (a) How long will it take for the population to triple?

  (A) Evaluate $2e^{.02(1/3)}$.

  (b) When will the population reach 3 million?

  (B) Solve $2e^{.02t} = 3 \cdot 2$ for t.

  (c) How large will the population be in 3 years?

  (C) Evaluate $2e^{.02(3)}$.

  (d) How large will the population be in 4 months?

  (D) Solve $2e^{.02t} = 3$ for t.

57. **Natural Science** The amount of polonium (in grams) present after t days is given by

$$A(t) = 10e^{-.00495t}.$$

  (a) How much polonium was present initially?

  (b) What is the half-life of polonium?

  (c) How long will it take for the polonium to decay to 3 grams?

58. **Business** The annual average natural gas price (in dollars per million BTUs) can be approximated by the function $h(x) = 69.54e^{-.264x}$, where $x = 8$ corresponds to the year 2008. (Data from: Energy Information Administration.)

  (a) What was the average price per million BTUs in the year 2010?

  (b) According to the model, in what year did the average price per million BTUs hit \$3.00?

59. **Natural Science** In April, 2013, Enarotali, Indonesia suffered an earthquake that measured 7.0 on the Richter scale.

  (a) Express the intensity of this earthquake in terms of i_0.

  (b) In March, 2013, Papua New Guinea suffered an earthquake that registered 6.5 on the Richter scale. Express the intensity of this earthquake in terms of i_0.

  (c) How many times more intense was the earthquake in Indonesia than the one in Papua New Guinea?

60. **Natural Science** One earthquake measures 4.6 on the Richter scale. A second earthquake has ground motion 1000 times greater than the first. What does the second one measure on the Richter scale?

📐 **Natural Science** *Another form of Newton's law of cooling (see Section 4.2, Exercises 15 and 16) is $F(t) = T_0 + Ce^{-kt}$, where C and k are constants.*

61. A piece of metal is heated to 300° Celsius and then placed in a cooling liquid at 50° Celsius. After 4 minutes, the metal has cooled to 175° Celsius. Find its temperature after 12 minutes.

62. A frozen pizza has a temperature of 3.4° Celsius when it is taken from the freezer and left out in a room at 18° Celsius. After half an hour, its temperature is 7.2° Celsius. How long will it take for the pizza to thaw to 10° Celsius?

In Exercises 63–66, do part (a) and skip part (b) if you do not have a graphing calculator. If you have a graphing calculator, then skip part (a) and do part (b).

63. **Business** The approximate average times (in minutes per month) spent on Facebook per unique visitor in the United

States on a mobile device are given in the following table for the last six months of 2012 and first two months of 2013. (Data from: www.comScore.com.)

Month	July 2012	Aug. 2012	Sept. 2012	Oct. 2012	Nov. 2012	Dec. 2012	Jan. 2013	Feb. 2013
Minutes	500	510	520	580	615	700	760	785

(a) Let $x = 0$ correspond to July, 2012. Use the data points from July, 2012 and February, 2013 to find a function of the form $f(x) = a(b^x)$ that models these data.

(b) Use exponential regression to find a function g that models these data, with $x = 0$ corresponding to July, 2012.

(c) Assume the model remains accurate and estimate the minutes per month in April, 2013.

(d) According to this model, when will the minutes per month reach 1000?

64. Physical Science The atmospheric pressure (in millibars) at a given altitude (in thousands of meters) is listed in the table:

Altitude	0	2000	4000	6000	8000	10,000
Pressure	1013	795	617	472	357	265

(a) Use the data points for altitudes 0 and 10,000 to find a function of the form $f(x) = a(b^x)$ that models these data, where altitude x is measured in thousands of meters. (For example, $x = 4$ means 4000 meters.)

(b) Use exponential regression to find a function $g(x)$ that models these data, with x measured in thousands of meters.

(c) Estimate the pressure at 1500 m and 11,000 m, and compare the results with the actual values of 846 and 227 millibars, respectively.

(d) At what height is the pressure 500 millibars?

65. Business The table shows the approximate digital share (in percent) of recorded music sales in the United States in recent years. (Data from: www.statista.com.)

Year	2006	2007	2008	2009	2010	2011	2012
Percent	18	25	39	43	47	50	59

(a) Let $x = 1$ correspond to the year 2006. Use the data points for 2006 and 2012 to find a function of the form $f(x) = a + b \ln x$ that models these data. [*Hint:* Use (1, 18) to find a; then use (7, 59) to find b.]

(b) Use logarithmic regression to find a function g that models these data, with $x = 1$ corresponding to the year 2006.

(c) Assume the model remains accurate and predict the percentage for 2014.

(d) According to the model, when will the share of digital music reach 70%?

66. Health The number of kidney transplants (in thousands) in selected years is shown in the table. (Data from: National Network for Organ Sharing.)

Year	1991	1995	2000	2005	2011
Transplants	9.678	11.083	13.613	16.481	16.813

(a) Let $x = 1$ correspond to 1991. Use the data points for 1991 and 2011 to find a function of the form $f(x) = a + b \ln x$ that models these data. [See Exercise 65(a).]

(b) Use logarithmic regression to find a function $g(x)$ that models these data, with $x = 1$ corresponding to 1991.

(c) Estimate the number of kidney transplants in 2013.

(d) If the model remains accurate, when will the number of kidney transplants reach 17,500?

Case Study 4 Gapminder.org

The website www.gapminder.org is committed to displaying economic and health data for countries around the world in a visually compelling way. The goal is to make publicly available data easy for citizens of the world to understand so individuals and policy makers can comprehend trends and make data-driven conclusions. For example, the website uses the size of the bubble on a plot to indicate the population of the country, and the color indicates the region in which the country lies:

Yellow	America
Orange	Europe and Central Asia
Green	Middle East and Northern Africa
Dark Blue	Sub-Saharan Africa
Red	East Asia and the Pacific

Additionally, the website also uses animation to show how variables change over time.

Let's look at an example of two variables of interest as best we can on a printed page. We will use income per-person (in U.S. dollars and measured as gross domestic product per capita) as a measure of a country's wealth as the x-axis variable and life expectancy (in years) at birth as a measure of the health of a country on the y–axis. In Figure 4.24 on the following page we see a bubble for each country in the year 1800.

We see that all the countries are bunched together with quite low income per-person and average life expectancy ranging from 25–40 years. The two large bubbles you see are for the two most populous countries: China (red) and India (light blue). When you visit the website (please do so, it is very cool!) and press the "Play" button at the bottom left, you can see how income per-person and life expectancy change over time for each country. At its conclusion, you obtain Figure 4.25 on the following page, which shows the relationship between income per-person and average life expectancy in the year 2011.

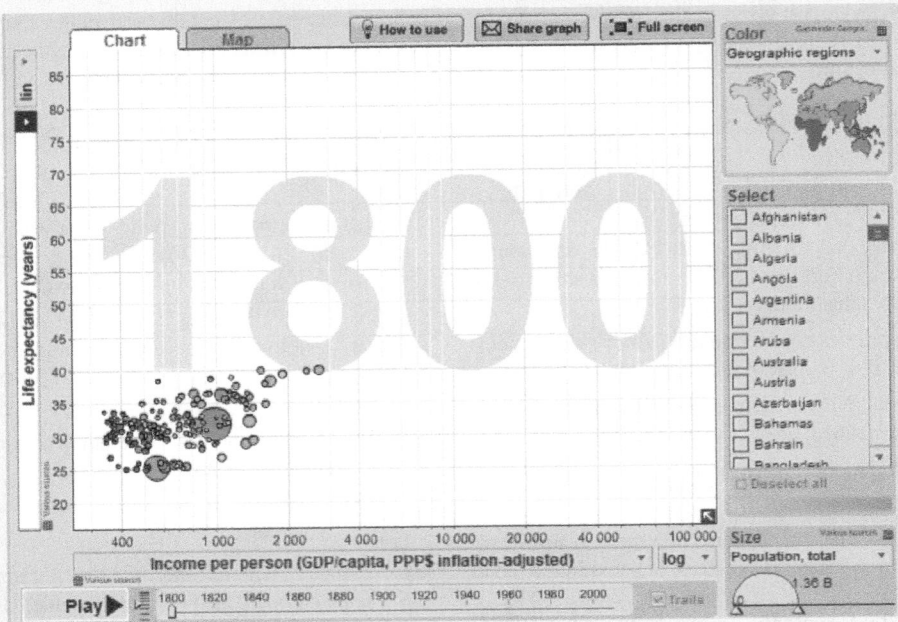

Figure 4.24 Relationship Between Income per Person and Average Life Expectancy in 1800 from Gapminder Foundation. Reproduced by permission of Gapminder Foundation.

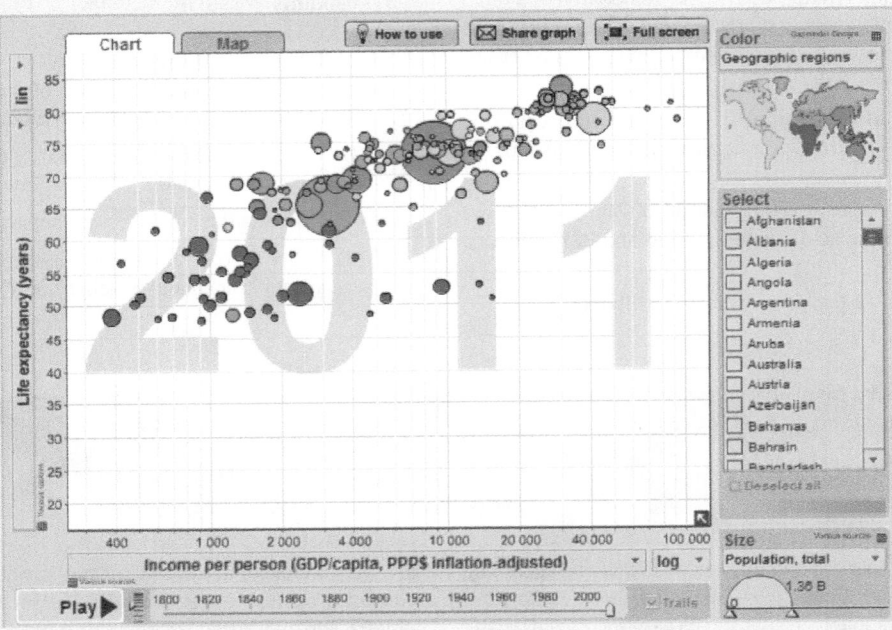

Figure 4.25 Relationship Between Income per Person and Average Life Expectancy in 2011 from Gapminder Foundation. Reproduced by permission of Gapminder Foundation.

We can see that a great deal has changed in 200 years! One great thing is that all countries now have average life expectancy that is over 45 years. This is simply incredible. Also, we see there is a great range of income per-person values for a variety of countries. The country to the far right (the little green dot) is the Middle Eastern country of Qatar. We see that many of the Sub-Sahara countries on the left (in dark blue) have the lowest per-person income and the lowest average life expectancy. The wealthier countries—for example, countries whose per-person income is greater than $20,000—all have life expectancy over 70 years.

We can actually use the per-person income x to predict the average life expectancy $f(x)$. Note that Gapminder.org has its default showing the income per-person on a logarithmic scale. When we see a linear pattern such as this where the x-axis is on a logarithmic scale and the y-axis is on the regular scale, a model of the form $f(x) = a + b \ln x$ often fits the data well. Since Gapminder.org makes all the data for their graphs available, we can fit a model to find values for a and b. Using regression, we obtain the following model:

$$f(x) = 15.32 + 6.178 \ln x. \tag{1}$$

Gapminder.org will also show the economic development for an individual country. Figure 4.26 shows per capita GDP on the y-axis for the country of Brazil over time. We can see that economic gains began close to the year 1900. The graph shows per-person income on the y-axis (again on a logarithmic scale) and the trend seems approx- imately linear since 1900. When this is the case, a model of the form $a(b^x)$ usually fits the data well. Letting $x = 0$ correspond to the year 1900, we obtain the following:

$$g(x) = 510.3(1.029)^x \tag{2}$$

Figure 4.26 Relationship Between Time and per Capita GDP in 2011 from Gapminder Foundation. Reproduced by permission of Gapminder Foundation.

The trajectory of the United States (Figure 4.27) is a bit different, with rising incomes starting in the early 1800s and continuing to the present. Notice the dips that occur in the mid-1930s (the Great Depression) and the early 1940s (World War II). Fitting a model to the data for the United States (again with $x = 0$ corresponding to the year 1900) yields the model:

$$h(x) = 6229.2(1.018)^x \tag{3}$$

Figure 4.27 Trajectory of United States from Gapminder Foundation. Reproduced by permission of Gapminder Foundation.

Exercises

For Exercises 1–6, use Equation (1) that provides a model using per-person income as the x-variable to predict life expectancy as the y-variable.

1. Create a graph of the function given in Equation (1) from $x = 0$ to 100,000.

2. Describe the shape of the graph.

3. The country farthest to the left in Figure 4.25 is the Democratic Republic of the Congo. In 2011, its income per-person was $387 and its life expectancy was 48. Suppose that the economic development improved so that the Democratic Republic of the Congo had a per-person income level of $4000. What does the model of Equation (1) predict for life expectancy?

4. In 2011, Russia had per-person income of $14,738 and life expectancy of 69 years. What does the model predict for life expectancy if the per-person income improved to $25,000?

5. According to the model, what per-person income level predicts a life expectancy of 60 years?

6. According to the model, what per-person income level predicts a life expectancy of 75 years?

For Exercises 7–10, use the model in Equation (2) that uses year (with $x = 0$ corresponding to the year 1900) to predict the per-person income for Brazil.

7. Graph the model of Equation (2) from $x = 0$ to 111.

8. Describe the shape of the model.

9. According to the model, what was the per-person income for Brazil in the year 1950? In the year 2000?

10. What year does the model indicate that per-person income reached $4000?

For Exercises 11–14, use the model in Equation (3) that uses year (with $x = 0$ corresponding to the year 1900) to predict the per-person income for the United States.

11. Graph the model of Equation (3) from $x = 0$ to 111.

12. Describe the shape of the model.

13. According to the model, what was the per-person income for the United States in the year 1960? In the year 2010?

14. What year does the model indicate that per-person income reached $20,000?

⬈ Extended Project

Go to the website www.gapminder.org and explore different relationships. Examine the relationship between a variety of variables that look at relationships among health, climate, disasters, economy, education, family, global trends, HIV, and poverty. (*Hint:* When you have the graphic display showing, click on the button for "Open Graph Menu" to see a list of options in these areas all ready to be viewed.) When observing the different graphs, notice when the x-axis, the y-axis, or both are on a logarithmic scale.

1. Find a relationship that appears linear when the x-axis is on the logarithmic scale and the y-axis is not. Now click on the button to the right of the x-axis and observe the graph on a linear scale (rather than the logarithmic scale). Describe the shape.

2. Find a relationship that appears linear when the x-axis is not on the logarithmic scale, but the y-axis is on the logarithmic scale. Now click on the button above the y-axis and observe the graph on a linear scale (rather than the logarithmic scale). Describe the shape.

3. Find a relationship that appears linear when the x-axis is on the logarithmic scale, and the y-axis is on the logarithmic scale. Now click on the button to the right of the x-axis and click on the button above the y-axis and observe the graph on a linear scale (rather than the logarithmic scale) for both axes. Describe the shape.

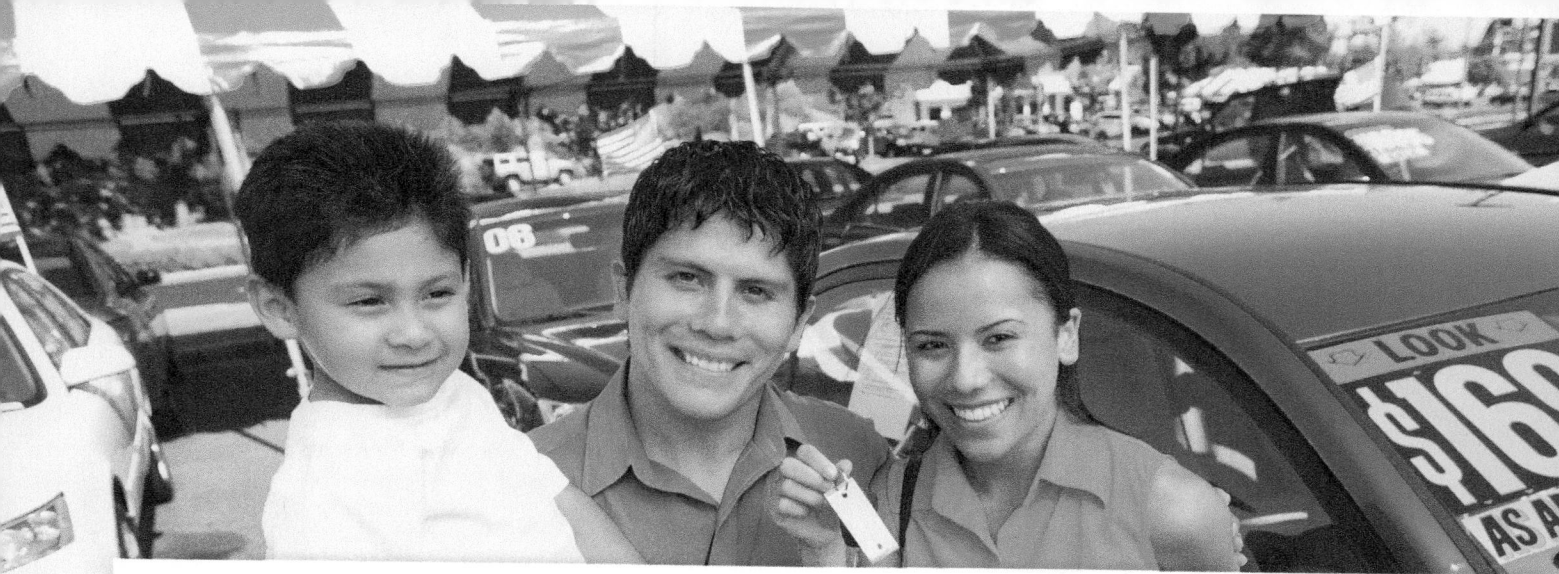

Mathematics of Finance

5

CHAPTER

Most people must take out a loan for a big purchase, such as a car, a major appliance, or a house. People who carry a balance on their credit cards are, in effect, also borrowing money. Loan payments must be accurately determined, and it may take some work to find the "best deal." See Exercise 54 on page 262 and Exercise 57 on page 242. We must all plan for eventual retirement, which usually involves savings accounts and investments in stocks, bonds, and annuities to fund 401K accounts or individual retirement accounts (IRAs). See Exercises 40 and 41 on page 250.

It is important for both businesspersons and consumers to understand the mathematics of finance in order to make sound financial decisions. Interest formulas for borrowing and investing money are introduced in this chapter.

📄 **NOTE** We try to present realistic, up-to-date applications in this text. Because interest rates change so frequently, however, it is very unlikely that the rates in effect when this chapter was written are the same as the rates today when you are reading it. Fortunately, the mathematics of finance is the same regardless of the level of interest rates. So we have used a variety of rates in the examples and exercises. Some will be realistic and some won't by the time you see them—but all of them have occurred in the past several decades.

5.1 Simple Interest and Discount

Interest is the fee paid to use someone else's money. Interest on loans of a year or less is frequently calculated as **simple interest,** which is paid only on the amount borrowed or invested and not on past interest. The amount borrowed or deposited is called the

225

principal. The **rate** of interest is given as a percent per year, expressed as a decimal. For example, $6\% = .06$ and $11\frac{1}{2}\% = .115$. The **time** during which the money is accruing interest is calculated in years. Simple interest is the product of the principal, rate, and time.

Simple Interest

The simple interest I on P dollars at a rate of interest r per year for t years is

$$I = Prt.$$

It is customary in financial problems to round interest to the nearest cent.

Example 1　To furnish her new apartment, Maggie Chan borrowed $4000 at 3% interest from her parents for 9 months. How much interest will she pay?

Solution　Use the formula $I = Prt$, with $P = 4000$, $r = 0.03$, and $t = 9/12 = 3/4$ years:

$$I = Prt$$

$$I = 4000 * .03 * \frac{3}{4} = 90.$$

✓Checkpoint 1

Thus, Maggie pays a total of $90 in interest. ✓₁

Find the simple interest for each loan.

(a) $2000 at 8.5% for 10 months

(b) $3500 at 10.5% for $1\frac{1}{2}$ years

Answers to Checkpoint exercises are found at the end of the section.

　　Simple interest is normally used only for loans with a term of a year or less. A significant exception is the case of **corporate bonds** and similar financial instruments. A typical bond pays simple interest twice a year for a specified length of time, at the end of which the bond **matures.** At maturity, the company returns your initial investment to you.

Example 2　**Finance**　On January 8, 2013, Bank of America issued 10-year bonds at an annual simple interest rate of 3.3%, with interest paid twice a year. John Altiere buys a $10,000 bond. (Data from: www.finra.org.)

(a) How much interest will he earn every six months?

✓Checkpoint 2

For the given bonds, find the semiannual interest payment and the total interest paid over the life of the bond.

(a) $7500 Time Warner Cable, Inc. 30-year bond at 7.3% annual interest.

(b) $15,000 Clear Channel Communications 10-year bond at 9.0% annual interest.

Solution　Use the interest formula, $I = Prt$, with $P = 10,000$, $r = .033$, and $t = \frac{1}{2}$:

$$I = Prt = 10,000 * .033 * \frac{1}{2} = \$165.$$

(b) How much interest will he earn over the 10-year life of the bond?

Solution　Either use the interest formula with $t = 10$, that is,

$$I = Prt = 10,000 * .033 * 10 = \$3300,$$

or take the answer in part (a), which will be paid out every six months for 10 years for a total of twenty times. Thus, John would obtain $165 * 20 = $3300. ✓₂

Future Value

If you deposit P dollars at simple interest rate r for t years, then the **future value** (or **maturity value**) A of this investment is the sum of the principal P and the interest I it has earned:

$$A = \text{Principal} + \text{Interest}$$
$$= P + I$$
$$= P + Prt \qquad I = Prt.$$
$$= P(1 + rt). \qquad \text{Factor out } P.$$

The following box summarizes this result.

Future Value (or Maturity Value) for Simple Interest

The future value (maturity value) A of P dollars for t years at interest rate r per year is

$$A = P + I, \qquad \text{or} \qquad A = P(1 + rt).$$

Example 3   Find each maturity value and the amount of interest paid.

(a) Rick borrows $20,000 from his parents at 5.25% to add a room on his house. He plans to repay the loan in 9 months with a bonus he expects to receive at that time.

Solution   The loan is for 9 months, or $9/12$ of a year, so $t = .75, P = 20,000$, and $r = .0525$. Use the formula to obtain

$$A = P(1 + rt)$$
$$= 20,000[1 + .0525(.75)]$$
$$\approx 20,787.5, \qquad \text{Use a calculator.}$$

or $20,787.50. The maturity value A is the sum of the principal P and the interest I, that is, $A = P + I$. To find the amount of interest paid, rearrange this equation:

$$I = A - P$$
$$I = \$20,787.50 - \$20,000 = \$787.50.$$

(b) A loan of $11,280 for 85 days at 9% interest.

Solution   Use the formula $A = P(1 + rt)$, with $P = 11,280$ and $r = .09$. Unless stated otherwise, we assume a 365-day year, so the period in years is $t = 85/365$. The maturity value is

$$A = P(1 + rt)$$
$$A = 11,280\left(1 + .09 * \frac{85}{365}\right)$$
$$\approx 11,280(1.020958904) \approx \$11,516.42.$$

As in part (a), the interest is

$$I = A - P = \$11,516.42 - \$11,280 = \$236.42. \quad \boxed{\checkmark_3}$$

✓ **Checkpoint 3**

Find each future value.

(a) $1000 at 4.6% for 6 months

(b) $8970 at 11% for 9 months

(c) $95,106 at 9.8% for 76 days

Example 4   Suppose you borrow $15,000 and are required to pay $15,315 in 4 months to pay off the loan and interest. What is the simple interest rate?

Solution   One way to find the rate is to solve for r in the future-value formula when $P = 15,000, A = 15,315$, and $t = 4/12 = 1/3$:

$$P(1 + rt) = A$$

$$15{,}000\left(1 + r * \frac{1}{3}\right) = 15{,}315$$

$$15{,}000 + \frac{15{,}000r}{3} = 15{,}315 \qquad \text{Multiply out left side.}$$

$$\frac{15{,}000r}{3} = 315 \qquad \text{Subtract 15,000 from both sides.}$$

$$15{,}000r = 945 \qquad \text{Multiply both sides by 3.}$$

$$r = \frac{945}{15{,}000} = .063. \qquad \text{Divide both sides by 15,000.}$$

Therefore, the interest rate is 6.3%. ✔️4

Checkpoint 4

You lend a friend $500. She agrees to pay you $520 in 6 months. What is the interest rate?

Present Value

A sum of money that can be deposited today to yield some larger amount in the future is called the **present value** of that future amount. Present value refers to the principal to be invested or loaned, so we use the same variable P as we did for principal. In interest problems, P always represents the amount at the beginning of the period, and A always represents the amount at the end of the period. To find a formula for P, we begin with the future-value formula:

$$A = P(1 + rt).$$

Dividing each side by $1 + rt$ gives the following formula for the present value.

Present Value for Simple Interest

The **present value** P of a future amount of A dollars at a simple interest rate r for t years is

$$P = \frac{A}{1 + rt}.$$

Example 5   Find the present value of $32,000 in 4 months at 9% interest.

Solution

$$P = \frac{A}{1 + rt} = \frac{32{,}000}{1 + (.09)\left(\dfrac{4}{12}\right)} = \frac{32{,}000}{1.03} = 31{,}067.96.$$

Checkpoint 5

Find the present value of the given future amounts. Assume 6% interest.

(a) $7500 in 1 year

(b) $89,000 in 5 months

(c) $164,200 in 125 days

A deposit of $31,067.96 today at 9% interest would produce $32,000 in 4 months. These two sums, $31,067.96 today and $32,000.00 in 4 months, are equivalent (at 9%) because the first amount becomes the second amount in 4 months. ✔️5

Example 6 Because of a court settlement, Jeff Weidenaar owes $5000 to Chuck Synovec. The money must be paid in 10 months, with no interest. Suppose Weidenaar wants to pay the money today and that Synovec can invest it at an annual rate of 5%. What amount should Synovec be willing to accept to settle the debt?

Solution The $5000 is the future value in 10 months. So Synovec should be willing to accept an amount that will grow to $5000 in 10 months at 5% interest. In other words, he should accept the present value of $5000 under these circumstances. Use the present-value formula with $A = 5000$, $r = .05$, and $t = 10/12 = 5/6$:

$$P = \frac{A}{1 + rt} = \frac{5000}{1 + .05 * \frac{5}{6}} = 4800.$$

Synovec should be willing to accept $4800 today in settlement of the debt.

✓ **Checkpoint 6**

Jerrell Davis is owed $19,500 by Christine O'Brien. The money will be paid in 11 months, with no interest. If the current interest rate is 10%, how much should Davis be willing to accept today in settlement of the debt?

Example 7 Larry Parks owes $6500 to Virginia Donovan. The loan is payable in one year at 6% interest. Donovan needs cash to pay medical bills, so four months before the loan is due, she sells the note (loan) to the bank. If the bank wants a return of 9% on its investment, how much should it pay Donovan for the note?

Solution First find the maturity value of the loan—the amount (with interest) that Parks must pay Donovan:

$$A = P(1 + rt) \qquad \text{Maturity-value formula}$$
$$= 6500(1 + .06 * 1) \qquad \text{Let } P = 6500, r = .06, \text{ and } t = 1.$$
$$= 6500(1.06) = \$6890.$$

In four months, the bank will receive $6890. Since the bank wants a 9% return, compute the present value of this amount at 9% for four months:

$$P = \frac{A}{1 + rt} \qquad \text{Present-value formula}$$
$$= \frac{6890}{1 + .09\left(\frac{4}{12}\right)} = \$6689.32. \qquad \text{Let } A = 6890, r = .09, \text{ and } t = 4/12.$$

The bank pays Donovan $6689.32 and four months later collects $6890 from Parks.

✓ **Checkpoint 7**

A firm accepts a $21,000 note due in 8 months, with interest of 10.5%. Two months before it is due, the firm sells the note to a broker. If the broker wants a 12.5% return on his investment, how much should he pay for the note?

Discount

The preceding examples dealt with loans in which money is borrowed and simple interest is charged. For most loans, both the principal (amount borrowed) and the interest are paid at the end of the loan period. With a corporate bond (which is a loan to a company by the investor who buys the bond), interest is paid during the life of the bond and the principal is paid back at maturity. In both cases,

the borrower receives the principal,

but pays back the principal *plus* the interest.

In a **simple discount loan,** however, the interest is deducted in advance from the amount of the loan and the *balance* is given to the borrower. The *full value* of the loan must be paid back at maturity. Thus,

the borrower receives the principal *less* the interest,

but pays back the principal.

The most common examples of simple discount loans are U.S. Treasury bills (T-bills), which are essentially short-term loans to the U.S. government by investors. T-bills are sold at a **discount** from their face value and the Treasury pays back the face value of the T-bill at maturity. The discount amount is the interest deducted in advance from the face value. The Treasury receives the face value less the discount, but pays back the full face value.

> **Example 8** **Finance** An investor bought a six-month $8000 treasury bill on February 28, 2013 that sold at a discount rate of .135%. What is the amount of the discount? What is the price of the T-bill? (Data from: www.treasurydirect.gov.)
>
> **Solution** The discount rate on a T-bill is always a simple *annual* interest rate. Consequently, the discount (interest) is found with the simple interest formula, using $P = 8000$ (face value), $r = .00135$ (discount rate), and $t = .5$ (because 6 months is half a year):
>
> $$\text{Discount} = Prt = 8000 * .00135 * .5 = \$5.40.$$
>
> So the price of the T-bill is
>
> $$\text{Face Value} - \text{Discount} = 8000 - 5.40 = \$7994.60.\ ✓_8$$

✓ **Checkpoint 8**

The maturity times and discount rates for $10,000 T-bills sold on March 7, 2013, are given. Find the discount amount and the price of each T-bill.

(a) one year; .15%

(b) six months; .12%

(c) three months; .11%

In a simple discount loan, such as a T-bill, the discount rate is not the actual interest rate the borrower pays. In Example 8, the discount rate .135% was applied to the face value of $8000, rather than the $7994.60 that the Treasury (the borrower) received.

> **Example 9** **Finance** Find the actual interest rate paid by the Treasury in Example 8.
>
> **Solution** Use the formula for simple interest, $I = Prt$ with r as the unknown. Here, $P = 7994.60$ (the amount the Treasury received) and $I = 5.40$ (the discount amount). Since this is a six-month T-bill, $t = .5$, and we have
>
> $$I = Prt$$
> $$5.40 = 7994.60(r)(.5)$$
> $$5.40 = 3997.3r \qquad \text{Multiply out right side.}$$
> $$r = \frac{5.40}{3997.3} \approx .0013509. \qquad \text{Divide both sides by 3997.3.}$$
>
> So the actual interest rate is .13509%. ✓_9

✓ **Checkpoint 9**

Find the actual interest rate paid by the Treasury for each T-bill in Checkpoint 8.

5.1 Exercises

Unless stated otherwise, "interest" means simple interest, and "interest rate" and "discount rate" refer to annual rates. Assume 365 days in a year.

1. What factors determine the amount of interest earned on a fixed principal?

Find the interest on each of these loans. (See Example 1.)

2. $35,000 at 6% for 9 months

3. $2850 at 7% for 8 months

4. $1875 at 5.3% for 7 months

5. $3650 at 6.5% for 11 months

6. $5160 at 7.1% for 58 days

7. $2830 at 8.9% for 125 days

8. $8940 at 9%; loan made on May 7 and due September 19

9. $5328 at 8%; loan made on August 16 and due December 30

10. $7900 at 7%; loan made on July 7 and due October 25

Finance *For each of the given corporate bonds, whose interest rates are provided, find the semiannual interest payment and the total interest earned over the life of the bond. (See Example 2, Data from: www.finra.org.)*

11. $5000 IBM, 3-year bond; 1.25%

12. $9000 Barrick Gold Corp., 10-year bond; 3.85%

13. $12,500 Morgan Stanley, 10-year bond; 3.75%

14. $4500 Goldman Sachs, 3-year bond; 6.75%

15. $6500 Amazon.com Corp, 10-year bond; 2.5%

16. $10,000 Wells Fargo, 10-year bond; 3.45%

Find the future value of each of these loans. (See Example 3.)

17. $12,000 loan at 3.5% for 3 months

18. $3475 loan at 7.5% for 6 months

19. $6500 loan at 5.25% for 8 months

20. $24,500 loan at 9.6% for 10 months

21. What is meant by the *present value* of money?

22. In your own words, describe the *maturity value* of a loan.

Find the present value of each future amount. (See Examples 5 and 6.)

23. $15,000 for 9 months; money earns 6%

24. $48,000 for 8 months; money earns 5%

25. $15,402 for 120 days; money earns 6.3%

26. $29,764 for 310 days; money earns 7.2%

Finance   *The given treasury bills were sold on April 4, 2013. Find (a) the price of the T-bill, and (b) the actual interest rate paid by the Treasury. (See Examples 8 and 9. Data from: www.treasurydirect.gov.)*

27. Three-month $20,000 T-bill with discount rate of .075%

28. One-month $12,750 T-bill with discount rate of .070%

29. Six-month $15,500 T-bill with discount rate of .105%

30. One-year $7000 T-bill with discount rate of .140%

Finance   *Historically, treasury bills offered higher rates. On March 9, 2007 the discount rates were substantially higher than in April, 2013. For the following treasury bills bought in 2007, find (a) the price of the T-bill, and (b) the actual interest rate paid by the Treasury. (See Examples 8 and 9. Data from: www.treasury.gov.)*

31. Three-month $20,000 T-bill with discount rate of 4.96%

32. One-month $12,750 T-bill with discount rate of 5.13%

33. Six-month $15,500 T-bill with discount rate of 4.93%

34. Six-month $9000 T-bill with discount rate of 4.93%

Finance   *Work the following applied problems.*

35. In March 1868, Winston Churchill's grandfather, L.W. Jerome, issued $1000 bonds (to pay for a road to a race track he owned in what is now the Bronx). The bonds carried a 7% annual interest rate payable semiannually. Mr. Jerome paid the interest until March 1874, at which time New York City assumed responsibility for the bonds (and the road they financed). (Data from: *New York Times,* February 13, 2009.)

    (a) The first of these bonds matured in March 2009. At that time, how much interest had New York City paid on this bond?

    (b) Another of these bonds will not mature until March 2147! At that time, how much interest will New York City have paid on it?

36. An accountant for a corporation forgot to pay the firm's income tax of $725,896.15 on time. The government charged a penalty of 9.8% interest for the 34 days the money was late. Find the total amount (tax and penalty) that was paid.

37. Mike Branson invested his summer earnings of $3000 in a savings account for college. The account pays 2.5% interest. How much will this amount to in 9 months?

38. To pay for textbooks, a student borrows $450 from a credit union at 6.5% simple interest. He will repay the loan in 38 days, when he expects to be paid for tutoring. How much interest will he pay?

39. An account invested in a money market fund grew from $67,081.20 to $67,359.39 in a month. What was the interest rate, to the nearest tenth?

40. A $100,000 certificate of deposit held for 60 days is worth $101,133.33. To the nearest tenth of a percent, what interest rate was earned?

41. Dave took out a $7500 loan at 7% and eventually repaid $7675 (principal and interest). What was the time period of the loan?

42. What is the time period of a $10,000 loan at 6.75%, in which the total amount of interest paid was $618.75?

43. Tuition of $1769 will be due when the spring term begins in 4 months. What amount should a student deposit today, at 3.25%, to have enough to pay the tuition?

44. A firm of accountants has ordered 7 new computers at a cost of $5104 each. The machines will not be delivered for 7 months. What amount could the firm deposit in an account paying 6.42% to have enough to pay for the machines?

45. John Sun Yee needs $6000 to pay for remodeling work on his house. A contractor agrees to do the work in 10 months. How much should Yee deposit at 3.6% to accumulate the $6000 at that time?

46. Lorie Reilly decides to go back to college. For transportation, she borrows money from her parents to buy a small car for $7200. She plans to repay the loan in 7 months. What amount can she deposit today at 5.25% to have enough to pay off the loan?

47. A six-month $4000 Treasury bill sold for $3930. What was the discount rate?

48. A three-month $7600 Treasury bill carries a discount of $80.75. What is the discount rate for this T-bill?

Finance   *Work the next set of problems, in which you are to find the annual simple interest rate. Consider any fees, dividends, or profits as part of the total interest.*

49. A stock that sold for $22 at the beginning of the year was selling for $24 at the end of the year. If the stock paid a dividend of $.50 per share, what is the simple interest rate on an investment in this stock? (*Hint:* Consider the interest to be the increase in value plus the dividend.)

50. Jerry Ryan borrowed $8000 for nine months at an interest rate of 7%. The bank also charges a $100 processing fee. What is the actual interest rate for this loan?

51. You are due a tax refund of $760. Your tax preparer offers you a no-interest loan to be repaid by your refund check, which will arrive in four weeks. She charges a $60 fee for this service. What actual interest rate will you pay for this loan? (*Hint:* The time period of this loan is not 4/52, because a 365-day year is 52 weeks and 1 day. So use days in your computations.)

52. Your cousin is due a tax refund of $400 in six weeks. His tax preparer has an arrangement with a bank to get him the $400 now. The bank charges an administrative fee of $29 plus interest at 6.5%. What is the actual interest rate for this loan? (See the hint for Exercise 51.)

Finance *Work these problems. (See Example 7.)*

53. A building contractor gives a $13,500 promissory note to a plumber who has loaned him $13,500. The note is due in nine months with interest at 9%. Three months after the note is signed, the plumber sells it to a bank. If the bank gets a 10% return on its investment, how much will the plumber receive? Will it be enough to pay a bill for $13,650?

54. Shalia Johnson owes $7200 to the Eastside Music Shop. She has agreed to pay the amount in seven months at an interest rate of 10%. Two months before the loan is due, the store needs $7550 to pay a wholesaler's bill. The bank will buy the note, provided that its return on the investment is 11%. How much will the store receive? Is it enough to pay the bill?

55. Let y_1 be the future value after t years of $100 invested at 8% annual simple interest. Let y_2 be the future value after t years of $200 invested at 3% annual simple interest.

(a) Think of y_1 and y_2 as functions of t and write the rules of these functions.

(b) Without graphing, describe the graphs of y_1 and y_2.

(c) Verify your answer to part (b) by graphing y_1 and y_2 in the first quadrant.

(d) What do the slopes and y-intercepts of the graphs represent (in terms of the investment situation that they describe)?

56. If $y = 16.25t + 250$ and y is the future value after t years of P dollars at interest rate r, what are P and r? (*Hint:* See Exercise 55.)

✓**Checkpoint Answers**

1. (a) $141.67   **(b)** $551.25

2. (a) $273.75; $16,425   **(b)** $675; $13,500

3. (a) $1023   **(b)** $9710.03   **(c)** $97,046.68

4. 8%

5. (a) $7075.47   **(b)** $86,829.27   **(c)** $160,893.96

6. $17,862.60

7. $22,011.43

8. (a) $15; $9985   **(b)** $6; $9994
    (c) $2.75; $9997.25

9. (a) About .15023%   **(b)** About .12007%
    (c) About .11003%

5.2 Compound Interest

With annual simple interest, you earn interest each year on your original investment. With annual **compound interest,** however, you earn interest both on your original investment *and* on any previously earned interest. To see how this process works, suppose you deposit $1000 at 5% annual interest. The following chart shows how your account would grow with both simple and compound interest:

End of Year	SIMPLE INTEREST		COMPOUND INTEREST	
	Interest Earned	Balance	Interest Earned	Balance
	Original Investment: $1000		*Original Investment: $1000*	
1	1000(.05) = $50	$1050	1000(.05) = $50	$1050
2	1000(.05) = $50	$1100	1050(.05) = $52.50	$1102.50
3	1000(.05) = $50	$1150	1102.50(.05) = $55.13*	$1157.63

As the chart shows, simple interest is computed each year on the original investment, but compound interest is computed on the entire balance at the end of the preceding year. So simple interest always produces $50 per year in interest, whereas compound interest

*Rounded to the nearest cent.

✓ Checkpoint 1

Extend the chart in the text by finding the interest earned and the balance at the end of years 4 and 5 for **(a)** simple interest and **(b)** compound interest.

produces $50 interest in the first year and increasingly larger amounts in later years (because you earn interest on your interest). ✓₁

Example 1   If $7000 is deposited in an account that pays 4% interest compounded annually, how much money is in the account after nine years?

Solution   After one year, the account balance is

$$7000 + 4\% \text{ of } 7000 = 7000 + (.04)7000$$
$$= 7000(1 + .04) \qquad \text{Distributive property}$$
$$= 7000(1.04) = \$7280.$$

The initial balance has grown by a factor of 1.04. At the end of the second year, the balance is

$$7280 + 4\% \text{ of } 7280 = 7280 + (.04)7280$$
$$= 7280(1 + .04) \qquad \text{Distributive property}$$
$$= 7280(1.04) = 7571.20.$$

Once again, the balance at the beginning of the year has grown by a factor of 1.04. This is true in general: If the balance at the beginning of a year is P dollars, then the balance at the end of the year is

$$P + 4\% \text{ of } P = P + .04P$$
$$= P(1 + .04)$$
$$= P(1.04).$$

So the account balance grows like this:

Year 1	**Year 2**	**Year 3**

$$7000 \rightarrow 7000(1.04) \rightarrow \underbrace{[7000(1.04)](1.04)}_{7000(1.04)^2} \rightarrow \underbrace{[7000(1.04)(1.040)](1.04)}_{7000(1.04)^3} \rightarrow \cdots.$$

At the end of nine years, the balance is

$$7000(1.04)^9 = \$9963.18 \qquad \text{(rounded to the nearest penny)}.$$

The argument used in Example 1 applies in the general case and leads to this conclusion.

Compound Interest

If P dollars are invested at interest rate i per period, then the **compound amount** (future value) A after n compounding periods is

$$A = P(1 + i)^n.$$

In Example 1, for instance, we had $P = 7000$, $n = 9$, and $i = .04$ (so that $1 + i = 1 + .04 = 1.04$).

NOTE Compare this future value formula for compound interest with the one for simple interest from the previous section, using t as the number of years:

Compound interest $A = P(1 + r)^t$;

Simple interest $A = P(1 + rt)$.

The important distinction between the two formulas is that, in the compound interest formula, the number of years, t, is an *exponent*, so that money grows much more rapidly when interest is compounded.

Example 2   Suppose $1000 is deposited for six years in an account paying 8.31% per year compounded annually.

(a) Find the compound amount.

Solution In the formula above, $P = 1000, i = .0831$, and $n = 6$. The compound amount is

$$A = P(1 + i)^n$$
$$A = 1000(1.0831)^6$$
$$A = \$1614.40.$$

(b) Find the amount of interest earned.

Solution Subtract the initial deposit from the compound amount:

$$\text{Amount of interest} = \$1614.40 - \$1000 = \$614.40. \quad \checkmark_2$$

✓**Checkpoint 2**

Suppose $17,000 is deposited at 4% compounded annually for 11 years.

(a) Find the compound amount.

(b) Find the amount of interest earned.

✈ **TECHNOLOGY TIP**
Spreadsheets are ideal for performing financial calculations. Figure 5.1 shows a Microsoft Excel spreadsheet with the formulas for compound and simple interest used to create columns B and C, respectively, when $1000 is invested at an annual rate of 10%. Notice how rapidly the compound amount increases compared with the maturity value with simple interest. For more details on the use of spreadsheets in the mathematics of finance, see the *Spreadsheet Manual* that is available with this text.

	A	B	C
1	period	compound	simple
2	1	1100	1100
3	2	1210	1200
4	3	1331	1300
5	4	1464.1	1400
6	5	1610.51	1500
7	6	1771.561	1600
8	7	1948.7171	1700
9	8	2143.58881	1800
10	9	2357.947691	1900
11	10	2593.74246	2000
12	11	2853.116706	2100
13	12	3138.428377	2200
14	13	3452.271214	2300
15	14	3797.498336	2400
16	15	4177.248169	2500
17	16	4594.972986	2600
18	17	5054.470285	2700
19	18	5559.917313	2800
20	19	6115.909045	2900
21	20	6727.499949	3000

Figure 5.1

Example 3   If a $16,000 investment grows to $50,000 in 18 years, what is the interest rate (assuming annual compounding)?

Solution   Use the compound interest formula, with $P = 16,000, A = 50,000$, and $n = 18$, and solve for i:

$$P(1 + i)^n = A$$
$$16,000(1 + i)^{18} = 50,000$$
$$(1 + i)^{18} = \frac{50,000}{16,000} = 3.125 \qquad \text{Divide both sides by 16,000.}$$
$$\sqrt[18]{(1 + i)^{18}} = \sqrt[18]{3.125} \qquad \text{Take 18th roots on both sides.}$$
$$1 + i = \sqrt[18]{3.125}$$
$$i = \sqrt[18]{3.125} - 1 \approx .06535. \qquad \text{Subtract 1 from both sides.}$$

So the interest rate is about 6.535%.

Interest can be compounded more than once a year. Common **compounding periods** include

semiannually (2 periods per year),

quarterly (4 periods per year),

monthly (12 periods per year), and

daily (usually 365 periods per year).

When the annual interest i is compounded m times per year, the interest rate per period is understood to be i/m.

Example 4   **Finance**   In April 2013, www.bankrate.com advertised a one-year certificate of deposit (CD) for GE Capital Retail Bank at an interest rate of 1.05%. Find the value of the CD if $10,000 is invested for one year and interest is compounded according to the given periods.

(a) Annually

Solution   Apply the formula $A = P(1 + i)^n$ with $P = 10,000$, $i = .0105$, and $n = 1$:

$$A = P(1 + i)^n = 10,000(1 + .0105)^1 = 10,000(1.0105) = \$10,105.$$

(b) Semiannually

Solution   Use the same formula and value of P. Here interest is compounded twice a year, so the number of periods is $n = 2$ and the interest rate per period is $i = \dfrac{.0105}{2}$:

$$A = P(1 + i)^n = 10,000\left(1 + \frac{.0105}{2}\right)^2 = \$10,105.28.$$

(c) Quarterly

Solution   Proceed as in part (b), but now interest is compounded 4 times a year, and so $n = 4$ and the interest rate per period is $i = \dfrac{.0105}{4}$:

$$A = P(1 + i)^n = 10,000\left(1 + \frac{.0105}{4}\right)^4 = \$10,105.41.$$

(d) Monthly

Solution   Interest is compounded 12 times a year, so $n = 12$ and $i = \dfrac{.0105}{12}$:

$$A = P(1 + i)^n = 10,000\left(1 + \frac{.0105}{12}\right)^{12} = \$10,105.51.$$

(e) Daily

Solution   Interest is compounded 365 times a year, so $n = 365$ and $i = \dfrac{.0105}{365}$:

$$A = P(1 + i)^n = 10,000\left(1 + \frac{.0105}{365}\right)^{365} = \$10,105.55.$$

Example 5   **Finance**   The given CDs were advertised online by various banks in April 2013. Find the future value of each one. (Data from: cdrates.bankaholic.com.)

(a) Nationwide Bank: $100,000 for 5 years at 1.73% compounded daily.

Solution   Use the compound interest formula with $P = 100,000$. Interest is compounded 365 times a year, so the interest rate per period is $i = \dfrac{.0173}{365}$. Since there are five years, the number of periods in 5 years is $n = 365(5) = 1825$. The future value is

$$A = P(1 + i)^n = 100,000\left(1 + \frac{.0173}{365}\right)^{1825} = \$109,034.91.$$

(b) California First National Bank: $5000 for 2 years at 1.06% compounded monthly.

Solution   Use the compound interest formula with $P = 5000$. Interest is compounded 12 times a year, so the interest rate per period is $i = \dfrac{.0106}{12}$. Since there are two years, the number of periods in 2 years is $n = 12(2) = 24$. The future value is

$$A = P(1 + i)^n = 5000\left(1 + \frac{.0106}{12}\right)^{24} = \$5107.08. \quad ✓_3$$

Checkpoint 3

Find the future value for these CDs.

(a) National Republic Bank of Chicago: $1000 at 1.3% compounded monthly for 3 years.

(b) Discover Bank: $2500 at .8% compounded daily for 9 months (assume 30 days in each month).

Example 4 shows that the more often interest is compounded, the larger is the amount of interest earned. Since interest is rounded to the nearest penny, however, there is a limit on how much can be earned. In Example 4, part (e), for instance, that limit of $10,105.55 has been reached. Nevertheless, the idea of compounding more and more frequently leads to a method of computing interest called **continuous compounding** that is used in certain financial situations The formula for continuous compounding is developed in Case 5, but the formula is given in the following box where $e = 2.7182818\ldots$, which was introduced in Chapter 4.

Continuous Compound Interest

The compound amount A for a deposit of P dollars at an interest rate r per year compounded continuously for t years is given by

$$A = Pe^{rt}.$$

Example 6   Suppose that $5000 is invested at an annual interest rate of 3.1% compounded continuously for 4 years. Find the compound amount.

Solution   In the formula for continuous compounding, let $P = 5000, r = .031$, and $t = 4$. Then a calculator with an e^x key shows that

$$A = Pe^{rt} = 5000e^{.031(4)} = \$5660.08. \quad ✓_4$$

Checkpoint 4

Find the compound amount for $7500 invested at an annual interest rate of 2.07% compounded continuously for 3 years.

```
N=365
I%=1.05
PV=-10000
PMT=0
•FV=10105.55166
P/Y=365
C/Y=365
PMT:END BEGIN
```

Figure 5.2

TECHNOLOGY TIP   TI-84+ and most Casios have a "TVM solver" for financial computations (in the TI APPS/financial menu or the Casio main menu); a similar one can be downloaded for TI-89. Figure 5.2 shows the solution of Example 4(e) on such a solver (FV means future value). The use of these solvers is explained in the next section. Most of the problems in this section can be solved just as quickly with an ordinary calculator.

Ordinary corporate or municipal bonds usually make semiannual simple interest payments. With a **zero-coupon bond,** however, there are no interest payments during the life of the bond. The investor receives a single payment when the bond matures, consisting of his original investment and the interest (compounded semiannually) that it has earned. Zero-coupon bonds are sold at a substantial discount from their face value, and the buyer receives the face value of the bond when it matures. The difference between the face value and the price of the bond is the interest earned.

Example 7   Doug Payne bought a 15-year zero-coupon bond paying 4.5% interest (compounded semiannually) for $12,824.50. What is the face value of the bond?

Solution   Use the compound interest formula with $P = 12,824.50$. Interest is paid twice a year, so the rate per period is $i = .045/2$, and the number of periods in 15 years is $n = 30$. The compound amount will be the face value:

$$A = P(1 + i)^n = 12,824.50(1 + .045/2)^{30} = 24,999.99618.$$

Rounding to the nearest cent, we see that the face value of the bond in $25,000.

✓ **Checkpoint 5**

Find the face value of the zero coupon.

(a)   30-year bond at 6% sold for $2546

(b)   15-year bond at 5% sold for $16,686

Example 8   Suppose that the inflation rate is 3.5% (which means that the overall level of prices is rising 3.5% a year). How many years will it take for the overall level of prices to double?

Solution   We want to find the number of years it will take for $1 worth of goods or services to cost $2. Think of $1 as the present value and $2 as the future value, with an interest rate of 3.5%, compounded annually. Then the compound amount formula becomes

$$P(1 + i)^n = A$$
$$1(1 + .035)^n = 2,$$

which simplifies as

$$1.035^n = 2.$$

We must solve this equation for n. There are several ways to do this.

Graphical   Use a graphing calculator (with x in place of n) to find the intersection point of the graphs of $y_1 = 1.035^x$ and $y_2 = 2$. Figure 5.3 shows that the intersection point has (approximate) x-coordinate 20.14879. So it will take about 20.15 years for prices to double.

3

Ø	25
Intersection
X=20.148792   Y=2

Figure 5.3

Algebraic   The same answer can be obtained by using natural logarithms, as in Section 4.4:

$$1.035^n = 2$$
$$\ln 1.035^n = \ln 2 \qquad \text{Take the logarithm of each side.}$$
$$n \ln 1.035 = \ln 2 \qquad \text{Power property of logarithms.}$$
$$n = \frac{\ln 2}{\ln 1.035} \qquad \text{Divide both sides by ln 1.035.}$$
$$n \approx 20.14879. \qquad \text{Use a calculator.}$$

✓ **Checkpoint 6**

Using a calculator, find the number of years it will take for $500 to increase to $750 in an account paying 6% interest compounded semiannually.

Effective Rate (APY)

If you invest $100 at 9%, compounded monthly, then your balance at the end of one year is

$$A = P(1 + i)^n = 100\left(1 + \frac{.09}{12}\right)^{12} = \$109.38.$$

You have earned $9.38 in interest, which is 9.38% of your original $100. In other words, $100 invested at 9.38% compounded *annually* will produce the same amount of interest (namely, $100 * .0938 = \$9.38$) as does 9% compounded monthly. In this situation, 9% is called the **nominal** or **stated rate,** while 9.38% is called the **effective rate** or **annual percentage yield (APY).**

In the discussion that follows, the nominal rate is denoted r and the APY (effective rate) is denoted r_E.

Effective Rate (r_E) or Annual Percentage Yield (APY)

The *APY* r_E is the annual compounding rate needed to produce the same amount of interest in one year, as the nominal rate does with more frequent compounding.

Example 9   **Finance**   In April 2013, Nationwide Bank offered its customers a 5-year $100,000 CD at 1.73% interest, compounded daily. Find the APY. (Data from: cdrates.bankaholic.com.)

Solution   The box given previously means that we must have the following:

$$\begin{array}{c} \$100{,}000 \text{ at rate } r_E \\ \text{compounded annually} \end{array} = \begin{array}{c} \$100{,}000 \text{ at } 1.73\%, \\ \text{compounded daily} \end{array}$$

$$100{,}000(1 + r_E)^1 = 100{,}000\left(1 + \frac{.0173}{365}\right)^{365} \qquad \text{Compound interest formula.}$$

$$(1 + r_E) = \left(1 + \frac{.0173}{365}\right)^{365} \qquad \text{Divide both sides by 100,000.}$$

$$r_E = \left(1 + \frac{.0173}{365}\right)^{365} - 1 \qquad \text{Subtract 1 from both sides.}$$

$$r_E \approx .0175.$$

So the APY is about 1.75%.

The argument in Example 9 can be carried out with 100,000 replaced by P, .0173 by r, and 365 by m. The result is the effective-rate formula.

Effective Rate (APY)

The effective rate (APY) corresponding to a stated rate of interest r compounded m times per year is

$$r_E = \left(1 + \frac{r}{m}\right)^m - 1.$$

Example 10   **Finance**   When interest rates are low (as they were when this text went to press), the interest rate and the APY are insignificantly different. To see when the difference is more pronounced, we will find the APY for each of the given money market checking accounts (with balances between $50,000 and $100,000), which were advertised in October 2008 when offered rates were higher.

(a) Imperial Capital Bank: 3.35% compounded monthly.

Solution   Use the effective-rate formula with $r = .0335$ and $m = 12$:

$$r_E = \left(1 + \frac{r}{m}\right)^m - 1 = \left(1 + \frac{.0335}{12}\right)^{12} - 1 = .034019.$$

So the APY is about 3.40%, a slight increase over the nominal rate of 3.35%.

(b) U.S. Bank: 2.33% compounded daily.

Solution   Use the formula with $r = .0233$ and $m = 365$:

$$r_E = \left(1 + \frac{r}{m}\right)^m - 1 = \left(1 + \frac{.0233}{365}\right)^{365} - 1 = .023572.$$

The APY is about 2.36%.

✓ **Checkpoint 7**

Find the APY corresponding to a nominal rate of

(a) 12% compounded monthly;

(b) 8% compounded quarterly.

↗ **TECHNOLOGY TIP**

Effective rates (APYs) can be computed on TI-84+ by using "Eff" in the APPS financial menu, as shown in Figure 5.4 for Example 11.

```
▶Eff(10.1)
                10
▶Eff(9.6,12)
        10.03386937
▶Eff(9.7,4)
        10.05857629
```

Figure 5.4

✓ **Checkpoint 8**

Find the APY corresponding to a nominal rate of

(a) 4% compounded quarterly;

(b) 7.9% compounded daily.

Example 11   Bank A is now lending money at 10% interest compounded annually. The rate at Bank B is 9.6% compounded monthly, and the rate at Bank C is 9.7% compounded quarterly. If you need to borrow money, at which bank will you pay the least interest?

Solution   Compare the APYs:

$$\text{Bank } A: \quad \left(1 + \frac{.10}{1}\right)^1 - 1 = .10 = 10\%;$$

$$\text{Bank } B: \quad \left(1 + \frac{.096}{12}\right)^{12} - 1 \approx .10034 = 10.034\%;$$

$$\text{Bank } C: \quad \left(1 + \frac{.097}{4}\right)^4 - 1 \approx .10059 = 10.059\%.$$

The lowest APY is at Bank A, which has the highest nominal rate.

📄 **NOTE** Although you can find both the stated interest rate and the APY for most certificates of deposit and other interest-bearing accounts, most bank advertisements mention only the APY.

Present Value for Compound Interest

The formula for compound interest, $A = P(1 + i)^n$, has four variables: A, P, i, and n. Given the values of any three of these variables, the value of the fourth can be found. In particular, if A (the future amount), i, and n are known, then P can be found. Here, P is the amount that should be deposited today to produce A dollars in n periods.

Example 12   Keisha Jones must pay a lump sum of $6000 in 5 years. What amount deposited today at 6.2% compounded annually will amount to $6000 in 5 years?

Solution   Here, $A = 6000$, $i = .062$, $n = 5$, and P is unknown. Substituting these values into the formula for the compound amount gives

$$6000 = P(1.062)^5$$

$$P = \frac{6000}{(1.062)^5} = 4441.49,$$

or $4441.49. If Jones leaves $4441.49 for 5 years in an account paying 6.2% compounded annually, she will have $6000 when she needs it. To check your work, use the compound interest formula with $P = \$4441.49$, $i = .062$, and $n = 5$. You should get $A = \$6000.00$.

✓ **Checkpoint 9**

Find P in Example 12 if the interest rate is

(a) 6%;

(b) 10%.

As Example 12 shows, $6000 in 5 years is (approximately) the same as $4441.49 today (if money can be deposited at 6.2% annual interest). An amount that can be deposited today to yield a given amount in the future is called the *present value* of the future amount. By solving $A = P(1 + i)^n$ for P, we get the following general formula for present value.

> ## Present Value for Compound Interest
>
> The **present value** of A dollars compounded at an interest rate i per period for n periods is
>
> $$P = \frac{A}{(1 + i)^n}, \qquad \text{or} \qquad P = A(1 + i)^{-n}.$$

Example 13   A zero-coupon bond with face value $15,000 and a 6% interest rate (compounded semiannually) will mature in 9 years. What is a fair price to pay for the bond today?

Solution   Think of the bond as a 9-year investment paying 6%, compounded semiannually, whose future value is $15,000. Its present value (what it is worth today) would be a fair price. So use the present value formula with $A = 15,000$. Since interest is compounded twice a year, the interest rate per period is $i = .06/2 = .03$ and the number of periods in nine years is $n = 9(2) = 18$. Hence,

$$P = \frac{A}{(1 + i)^n} = \frac{15,000}{(1 + .03)^{18}} \approx 8810.919114.$$

✓ **Checkpoint 10**

Find the fair price (present value) in Example 13 if the interest rate is 7.5%.

So a fair price would be the present value of $8810.92. ✓10

Example 14   **Economics**   The average annual inflation rate for the years 2010–2012 was 2.29%. How much did an item that sells for $1000 in early 2013 cost three years before? (Data from: inflationdata.com.)

Solution   Think of the price three years prior as the present value P and $1000 as the future value A. Then $i = .0229$, $n = 3$, and the present value is

$$P = \frac{A}{(1 + i)^n} = \frac{1000}{(1 + .0229)^3} = \$934.33.$$

✓ **Checkpoint 11**

What did a $1000 item sell for 5 years prior if the annual inflation rate has been 3.2%?

So the item cost $934.33 three years prior. ✓11

Summary

At this point, it seems helpful to summarize the notation and the most important formulas for simple and compound interest. We use the following variables:

P = principal or present value;

A = future or maturity value;

r = annual (stated or nominal) interest rate;

t = number of years;

m = number of compounding periods per year;

i = interest rate per period;

n = total number of compounding periods;

r_E = effective rate (APY).

Simple Interest	Compound Interest	Continuous Compounding
$A = P(1 + rt)$	$A = P(1 + i)^n$	$A = Pe^{rt}$
$P = \dfrac{A}{1 + rt}$	$P = \dfrac{A}{(1 + i)^n} = A(1 + i)^{-n}$	$P = \dfrac{A}{e^{rt}}$
	$r_E = \left(1 + \dfrac{r}{m}\right)^m - 1$	

5.2 Exercises

Interest on the zero-coupon bonds here is compounded semiannually.

1. In the preceding summary what is the difference between r and i? between t and n?

2. Explain the difference between simple interest and compound interest.

3. What factors determine the amount of interest earned on a fixed principal?

4. In your own words, describe the *maturity value* of a loan.

5. What is meant by the *present value* of money?

6. If interest is compounded more than once per year, which rate is higher, the stated rate or the effective rate?

Find the compound amount and the interest earned for each of the following deposits. (See Examples 1, 2, 4, and 5.)

7. $1000 at 4% compounded annually for 6 years

8. $1000 at 6% compounded annually for 10 years

9. $470 at 8% compounded semiannually for 12 years

10. $15,000 at 4.6% compounded semiannually for 11 years

11. $6500 at 4.5% compounded quarterly for 8 years

12. $9100 at 6.1% compounded quarterly for 4 years

Finance *The following CDs were available on www.bankrate.com on April 13, 2013. Find the compound amount and the interest earned for each of the following. (See Example 5.)*

13. Virtual Bank: $10,000 at .9% compounded daily for 1 year

14. AloStar Bank of Commerce: $1000 at .85% compounded daily for 1 year

15. USAA: $5000 at .81% compounded monthly for 2 years

16. Centennial Bank: $20,000 at .45% compounded monthly for 2 years

17. E-LOAN: $100,000 at 1.52% compounded daily for 5 years

18. Third Federal Savings and Loans: $150,000 at 1.15% compounded quarterly for 5 years

Find the interest rate (with annual compounding) that makes the statement true. (See Example 3.)

19. $3000 grows to $3606 in 5 years

20. $2550 grows to $3905 in 11 years

21. $8500 grows to $12,161 in 7 years

22. $9000 grows to $17,118 in 16 years

Find the compound amount and the interest earned when the following investments have continuous compounding. (See Example 6.)

23. $20,000 at 3.5% for 5 years

24. $15,000 at 2.9% for 10 years

25. $30,000 at 1.8% for 3 years

26. $100,000 at 5.1% for 20 years

Find the face value (to the nearest dollar) of the zero-coupon bond. (See Example 7.)

27. 15-year bond at 5.2%; price $4630

28. 10-year bond at 4.1%; price $13,328

29. 20-year bond at 3.5%; price $9992

30. How do the nominal, or stated, interest rate and the effective interest rate (APY) differ?

Find the APY corresponding to the given nominal rates. (See Examples 9–11).

31. 4% compounded semiannually

32. 6% compounded quarterly

33. 5% compounded quarterly

34. 4.7% compounded semiannually

Find the present value of the given future amounts. (See Example 12.)

35. $12,000 at 5% compounded annually for 6 years

36. $8500 at 6% compounded annually for 9 years

37. $17,230 at 4% compounded quarterly for 10 years

38. $5240 at 6% compounded quarterly for 8 years

What price should you be willing to pay for each of these zero-coupon bonds? (See Example 13.)

39. 5-year $5000 bond; interest at 3.5%

40. 10-year $10,000 bond; interest at 4%

41. 15-year $20,000 bond; interest at 4.7%

42. 20-year $15,000 bond; interest at 5.3%

Finance *For Exercises 43 and 44, assume an annual inflation rate of 2.07% (the annual inflation rate of 2012 according to www.InflationData.com). Find the previous price of the following items. (See Example 14.)*

43. How much did an item that costs $5000 now cost 4 years prior?

44. How much did an item that costs $7500 now cost 5 years prior?

45. If the annual inflation rate is 3.6%, how much did an item that costs $500 now cost 2 years prior?

46. If the annual inflation rate is 1.18%, how much did an item that costs $1250 now cost 6 years prior?

47. If money can be invested at 8% compounded quarterly, which is larger, $1000 now or $1210 in 5 years? Use present value to decide.

48. If money can be invested at 6% compounded annually, which is larger, $10,000 now or $15,000 in 6 years? Use present value to decide.

Finance *Work the following applied problems.*

49. A small business borrows $50,000 for expansion at 9% compounded monthly. The loan is due in 4 years. How much interest will the business pay?

50. A developer needs $80,000 to buy land. He is able to borrow the money at 10% per year compounded quarterly. How much will the interest amount to if he pays off the loan in 5 years?

51. Lora Reilly has inherited $10,000 from her uncle's estate. She will invest the money for 2 years. She is considering two investments: a money market fund that pays a guaranteed 5.8% interest compounded daily and a 2-year Treasury note at 6% annual interest. Which investment pays the most interest over the 2-year period?

52. Which of these 20-year zero-coupon bonds will be worth more at maturity: one that sells for $4510, with a 6.1% interest rate, or one that sells for $5809, with a 4.8% interest rate?

53. As the prize in a contest, you are offered $1000 now or $1210 in 5 years. If money can be invested at 6% compounded annually, which is larger?

54. Two partners agree to invest equal amounts in their business. One will contribute $10,000 immediately. The other plans to contribute an equivalent amount in 3 years, when she expects to acquire a large sum of money. How much should she contribute at that time to match her partner's investment now, assuming an interest rate of 6% compounded semiannually?

55. In the Capital Appreciation Fund, a mutual fund from T. Rowe Price, a $10,000 investment grew to $11,115 over the 3-year period 2010–2013. Find the annual interest rate, compounded yearly, that this investment earned.

56. In the Vanguard Information Technology Index Fund, a $10,000 investment grew to $16,904.75 over the 10-year period 2003–2013. Find the annual interest rate, compounded yearly, that this investment earned.

57. The Flagstar Bank in Michigan offered a 5-year certificate of deposit (CD) at 4.38% interest compounded quarterly in June 2005. On the same day on the Internet, Principal Bank offered a 5-year CD at 4.37% interest compounded monthly. Find the APY for each CD. Which bank paid a higher APY?

58. The Westfield Bank in Ohio offered the CD rates shown in the accompanying table in October 2008. The APY rates shown assume monthly compounding. Find the corresponding nominal rates to the nearest hundredth. (*Hint:* Solve the effective-rate equation for r.)

Term	6 mo	1 yr	2 yr	3 yr	5 yr
APY (%)	2.25	2.50	3.00	3.25	3.75

59. A company has agreed to pay $2.9 million in 5 years to settle a lawsuit. How much must it invest now in an account paying 5% interest compounded monthly to have that amount when it is due?

60. Bill Poole wants to have $20,000 available in 5 years for a down payment on a house. He has inherited $16,000. How much of the inheritance should he invest now to accumulate the $20,000 if he can get an interest rate of 5.5% compounded quarterly?

61. If inflation has been running at 3.75% per year and a new car costs $23,500 today, what would it have cost three years ago?

62. If inflation is 2.4% per year and a washing machine costs $345 today, what did a similar model cost five years ago?

Economics *Use the approach in Example 8 to find the time it would take for the general level of prices in the economy to double at the average annual inflation rates in Exercises 63–66.*

63. 3%   **64.** 4%   **65.** 5%   **66.** 5.5%

67. The consumption of electricity has increased historically at 6% per year. If it continues to increase at this rate indefinitely, find the number of years before the electric utility companies will need to double their generating capacity.

68. Suppose a conservation campaign coupled with higher rates causes the demand for electricity to increase at only 2% per year, as it has recently. Find the number of years before the utility companies will need to double their generating capacity.

69. You decide to invest a $16,000 bonus in a money market fund that guarantees a 5.5% annual interest rate compounded monthly for 7 years. A one-time fee of $30 is charged to set up the account. In addition, there is an annual administrative charge of 1.25% of the balance in the account at the end of each year.

(a) How much is in the account at the end of the first year?

(b) How much is in the account at the end of the seventh year?

70. Joe Marusa decides to invest $12,000 in a money market fund that guarantees a 4.6% annual interest rate compounded daily for 6 years. A one-time fee of $25 is charged to set up the account. In addition, there is an annual administration charge of .9% of the balance in the account at the end of each year.

(a) How much is in the account at the end of the first year?

(b) How much is in the account at the end of the sixth year?

The following exercises are from professional examinations.

71. On January 1, 2002, Jack deposited $1000 into Bank X to earn interest at the rate of j per annum compounded semiannually. On January 1, 2007, he transferred his account to Bank Y to earn interest at the rate of k per annum compounded quarterly. On January 1, 2010, the balance at Bank Y was $1990.76. If Jack could have earned interest at the rate of k per annum compounded quarterly from January 1, 2002, through January 1, 2010, his balance would have been $2203.76. Which of the following represents the ratio k/j? (Deposit of Jack in Bank X from Course 140 Examination, Mathematics of Compound Interest. Copyright © Society of Actuaries. Reproduced by permission of Society of Actuaries.)

(a) 1.25   (b) 1.30   (c) 1.35   (d) 1.40   (e) 1.45

72. On January 1, 2009, Tone Company exchanged equipment for a $200,000 non-interest-bearing note due on January 1, 2012. The prevailing rate of interest for a note of this type on January 1, 2009, was 10%. The present value of $1 at 10% for three periods is 0.75. What amount of interest revenue should be included in Tone's 2010 income statement? (Adapted from the Uniform CPA Examination, American Institute of Certified Public Accountants.)

(a) $7500   (b) $15,000

(c) $16,500   (d) $20,000

✓ **Checkpoint Answers**

4. $7980.52

1. (a)

Year	Interest	Balance
4	$50	$1200
5	$50	$1250

(b)

Year	Interest	Balance
4	$57.88	$1215.51
5	$60.78	$1276.29

5. (a) $15,000   (b) $35,000

6. About 7 years ($n = 6.86$)

7. (a) 12.68%   (b) 8.24%

8. (a) 4.06%   (b) 8.220%

9. (a) $4483.55   (b) $3725.53

10. $7732.24   **11.** $854.28

2. (a) $26,170.72   (b) $9170.72

3. (a) $1039.75   (b) $2514.84

5.3 Annuities, Future Value, and Sinking Funds

So far in this chapter, only lump-sum deposits and payments have been discussed. Many financial situations, however, involve a sequence of payments at regular intervals, such as weekly deposits in a savings account or monthly payments on a mortgage or car loan. Such periodic payments are the subject of this section and the next.

The analysis of periodic payments will require an algebraic technique that we now develop. Suppose x is a real number. For reasons that will become clear later, we want to find the product

$$(x - 1)(1 + x + x^2 + x^3 + \cdots + x^{11}).$$

Using the distributive property to multiply this expression out, we see that all but two of the terms cancel:

$$x(1 + x + x^2 + x^3 + \cdots + x^{11}) - 1(1 + x + x^2 + x^3 + \cdots + x^{11})$$
$$= (x + x^2 + x^3 + \cdots + x^{11} + x^{12}) - 1 - x - x^2 - x^3 - \cdots - x^{11}$$
$$= x^{12} - 1.$$

Hence, $(x - 1)(1 + x + x^2 + x^3 + \cdots + x^{11}) = x^{12} - 1$. Dividing both sides by $x - 1$, we have

$$1 + x + x^2 + x^3 + \cdots + x^{11} = \frac{x^{12} - 1}{x - 1}.$$

The same argument, with any positive integer n in place of 12 and $n - 1$ in place of 11, produces the following result:

> If x is a real number and n is a positive integer, then
> $$1 + x + x^2 + x^3 + \cdots + x^{n-1} = \frac{x^n - 1}{x - 1}.$$

```
1+5+5²+5³+5⁴+5⁵+5⁶
                    19531
 5⁷-1
 ‾‾‾‾
 5-1
                    19531
```

Figure 5.5

For example, when $x = 5$ and $n = 7$, we see that

$$1 + 5 + 5^2 + 5^3 + 5^4 + 5^5 + 5^6 = \frac{5^7 - 1}{5 - 1} = \frac{78,124}{4} = 19,531.$$

A calculator can easily add up the terms on the left side, but it is faster to use the formula (Figure 5.5).

Ordinary Annuities

A sequence of equal payments made at equal periods of time is called an **annuity.** The time between payments is the **payment period,** and the time from the beginning of the first payment period to the end of the last period is called the **term of the annuity.** Annuities can be used to accumulate funds—for example, when you make regular deposits in a savings account. Or they can be used to pay out funds—as when you receive regular payments from a pension plan after you retire.

Annuities that pay out funds are considered in the next section. This section deals with annuities in which funds are accumulated by regular payments into an account or investment that earns compound interest. The **future value** of such an annuity is the final sum on deposit—that is, the total amount of all deposits and all interest earned by them.

We begin with **ordinary annuities**—ones where the payments are made at the *end* of each period and the frequency of payments is the same as the frequency of compounding the interest.

Example 1 $1500 is deposited at the end of each year for the next 6 years in an account paying 8% interest compounded annually. Find the future value of this annuity.

Solution   Figure 5.6 shows the situation schematically.

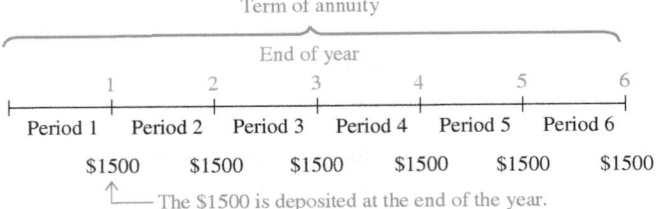

Figure 5.6

To find the future value of this annuity, look separately at each of the $1500 payments. The first $1500 is deposited at the end of period 1 and earns interest for the remaining 5 periods. From the formula in the box on page 233, the compound amount produced by this payment is

$$1500(1 + .08)^5 = 1500(1.08)^5.$$

The second $1500 payment is deposited at the end of period 2 and earns interest for the remaining 4 periods. So the compound amount produced by the second payment is

$$1500(1 + .08)^4 = 1500(1.08)^4.$$

Continue to compute the compound amount for each subsequent payment, as shown in Figure 5.7. Note that the last payment earns no interest.

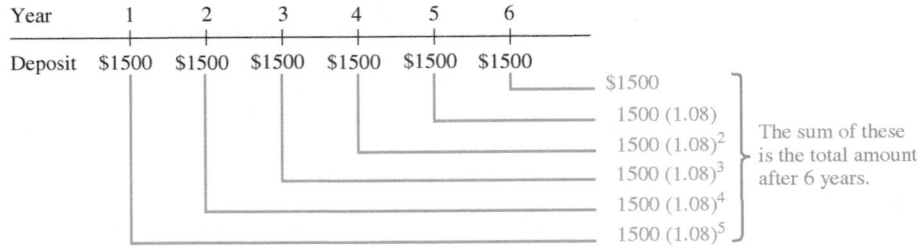

Figure 5.7

The last column of Figure 5.7 shows that the total amount after 6 years is the sum

$$1500 + 1500 \cdot 1.08 + 1500 \cdot 1.08^2 + 1500 \cdot 1.08^3 + 1500 \cdot 1.08^4 + 1500 \cdot 1.08^5$$
$$= 1500(1 + 1.08 + 1.08^2 + 1.08^3 + 1.08^4 + 1.08^5). \tag{1}$$

Now apply the algebraic fact in the box on page 243 to the expression in parentheses (with $x = 1.08$ and $n = 6$). It shows that the sum (the future value of the annuity) is

$$1500 \cdot \frac{1.08^6 - 1}{1.08 - 1} = \$11,003.89.$$

Example 1 is the model for finding a formula for the future value of any annuity. Suppose that a payment of R dollars is deposited at the end of each period for n periods, at an interest rate of i per period. Then the future value of this annuity can be found by using the procedure in Example 1, with these replacements:

1500	.08	1.08	6	5
↓	↓	↓	↓	↓
R	i	$1 + i$	n	$n - 1$

The future value S in Example 1—call it S—is the sum (**1**), which now becomes

$$S = R[1 + (1 + i) + (1 + i)^2 + \cdots + (1 + i)^{n-2} + (1 + i)^{n-1}].$$

Apply the algebraic fact in the box on page 243 to the expression in brackets (with $x = 1 + i$). Then we have

$$S = R\left[\frac{(1 + i)^n - 1}{(1 + i) - 1}\right] = R\left[\frac{(1 + i)^n - 1}{i}\right].$$

The quantity in brackets in the right-hand part of the preceding equation is sometimes written $s_{\overline{n}|i}$ (read "*s*-angle-*n* at *i*"). So we can summarize as follows.*

Future Value of an Ordinary Annuity

The future value S of an ordinary annuity used to accumulate funds is given by

$$S = R\left[\frac{(1 + i)^n - 1}{i}\right], \quad \text{or} \quad S = R \cdot s_{\overline{n}|i},$$

where

R is the payment at the end of each period,

i is the interest rate per period, and

n is the number of periods.

✔ TECHNOLOGY TIP Most computations with annuities can be done quickly with a spreadsheet program or a graphing calculator. On a calculator, use the TVM solver if there is one (see the Technology Tip on page 236); otherwise, use the programs in the Program Appendix.

Figure 5.8 shows how to do Example 1 on a TI-84+ TVM solver. First, enter the known quantities: N = number of payments, I% = annual interest rate, PV = present value, PMT = payment per period (entered as a negative amount), P/Y = number of payments per year, and C/Y = number of compoundings per year. At the bottom of the screen, set PMT: to "END" for ordinary annuities. Then put the cursor next to the unknown amount FV (future value), and press SOLVE.

Note: P/Y and C/Y should always be the same for problems in this text. If you use the solver for ordinary compound interest problems, set PMT = 0 and enter either PV or FV (whichever is known) as a negative amount.

✔Checkpoint 1

Complete these steps for an annuity of $2000 at the end of each year for 3 years. Assume interest of 6% compounded annually.

(a) The first deposit of $2000 produces a total of _____.

(b) The second deposit becomes _____.

(c) No interest is earned on the third deposit, so the total in the account is _____.

```
N=6
I%=8
PV=0
PMT=-1500
•FV=11003.89356
P/Y=1
C/Y=1
PMT:END BEGIN
```

Figure 5.8

Example 2 A rookie player in the National Football League just signed his first 7-year contract. To prepare for his future, he deposits $150,000 at the end of each year for 7 years in an account paying 4.1% compounded annually. How much will he have on deposit after 7 years?

*We use S for the future value here instead of A, as in the compound interest formula, to help avoid confusing the two formulas.

Solution His payments form an ordinary annuity with $R = 150,000, n = 7$, and $i = .041$. The future value of this annuity (by the previous formula) is

$$S = 150,000\left[\frac{(1.041)^7 - 1}{.041}\right] = \$1,188,346.11. \checkmark_2$$

✓ Checkpoint 2

Johnson Building Materials deposits $2500 at the end of each year into an account paying 8% per year compounded annually. Find the total amount on deposit after

(a) 6 years;

(b) 10 years.

Example 3 Allyson, a college professor, contributed $950 a month to the CREF stock fund (an investment vehicle available to many college and university employees). For the past 10 years this fund has returned 4.25%, compounded monthly.

(a) How much did Allyson earn over the course of the last 10 years?

Solution Allyson's payments form an ordinary annuity, with monthly payment $R = 950$. The interest per month is $i = \dfrac{.0425}{12}$, and the number of months in 10 years is $n = 10 * 12 = 120$. The future value of this annuity is

$$S = R\left[\frac{(1 + i)^n - 1}{i}\right] = 950\left[\frac{(1 + .0425/12)^{120} - 1}{.0425/12}\right] = \$141,746.90.$$

(b) As of April 14, 2013, the year to date return was 9.38%, compounded monthly. If this rate were to continue, and Allyson continues to contribute $950 a month, how much would the account be worth at the end of the next 15 years?

Solution Deal separately with the two parts of her account (the $950 contributions in the future and the $141,746.90 already in the account). The contributions form an ordinary annuity as in part (a). Now we have $R = 950, i = .0938/12$, and $n = 12 * 15 = 180$. So the future value is

$$S = R\left[\frac{(1 + i)^n - 1}{i}\right] = 950\left[\frac{(1 + .0938/12)^{180} - 1}{.0938/12}\right] = \$372,068.65.$$

Meanwhile, the $141,746.90 from the first 10 years is also earning interest at 9.38%, compounded monthly. By the compound amount formula (Section 5.2), the future value of this money is

$$141,746.90(1 + .0938/12)^{180} = \$575,691.85.$$

So the total amount in Allyson's account after 25 years is the sum

$$\$372,068.65 + \$575,691.85 = \$947,760.50. \checkmark_3$$

✓ Checkpoint 3

Find the total value of the account in part (b) of Example 3 if the fund's return for the last 15 years is 8.72%, compounded monthly.

Sinking Funds

A **sinking fund** is a fund set up to receive periodic payments. Corporations and municipalities use sinking funds to repay bond issues, to retire preferred stock, to provide for replacement of fixed assets, and for other purposes. If the payments are equal and are made at the end of regular periods, they form an ordinary annuity.

Example 4 A business sets up a sinking fund so that it will be able to pay off bonds it has issued when they mature. If it deposits $12,000 at the end of each quarter in an account that earns 5.2% interest, compounded quarterly, how much will be in the sinking fund after 10 years?

Solution The sinking fund is an annuity, with $R = 12,000, i = .052/4$, and $n = 4(10) = 40$. The future value is

$$S = R\left[\frac{(1 + i)^n - 1}{i}\right] = 12,000\left[\frac{(1 + .052/4)^{40} - 1}{.052/4}\right] = \$624,369.81.$$

So there will be about $624,370 in the sinking fund.

Example 5   A firm borrows $6 million to build a small factory. The bank requires it to set up a $200,000 sinking fund to replace the roof after 15 years. If the firm's deposits earn 6% interest, compounded annually, find the payment it should make at the end of each year into the sinking fund.

Solution   This situation is an annuity with future value $S = 200{,}000$, interest rate $i = .06$, and $n = 15$. Solve the future-value formula for R:

$$S = R\left[\frac{(1 + i)^n - 1}{i}\right]$$

$$200{,}000 = R\left[\frac{(1 + .06)^{15} - 1}{.06}\right] \qquad \text{Let } S = 200{,}000, \; i = .06, \text{ and } n = 15.$$

$$200{,}000 = R[23.27597] \qquad \text{Compute the quantity in brackets.}$$

$$R = \frac{200{,}000}{23.27597} = \$8592.55. \qquad \text{Divide both sides by 23.27597.}$$

So the annual payment is about $8593.

✓ Checkpoint 4

Francisco Arce needs $8000 in 6 years so that he can go on an archaeological dig. He wants to deposit equal payments at the end of each quarter so that he will have enough to go on the dig. Find the amount of each payment if the bank pays

(a) 12% interest compounded quarterly;

(b) 8% interest compounded quarterly.

500,000

Intersection
X=.06660938   Y=100000

0.2

Figure 5.9

N=240
• I%=6.660938285
PV=0
PMT=-200
FV=100000
P/Y=12
C/Y=12
PMT:**END** BEGIN

Figure 5.10

✓ Checkpoint 5

Pete's Pizza deposits $5800 at the end of each quarter for 4 years.

(a) Find the final amount on deposit if the money earns 6.4% compounded quarterly.

(b) Pete wants to accumulate $110,000 in the 4-year period. What interest rate (to the nearest tenth) will be required?

Example 6   As an incentive for a valued employee to remain on the job, a company plans to offer her a $100,000 bonus, payable when she retires in 20 years. If the company deposits $200 a month in a sinking fund, what interest rate must it earn, with monthly compounding, in order to guarantee that the fund will be worth $100,000 in 20 years?

Solution   The sinking fund is an annuity with $R = 200$, $n = 12(20) = 240$, and future value $S = 100{,}000$. We must find the interest rate. If x is the annual interest rate in decimal form, then the interest rate per month is $i = x/12$. Inserting these values into the future-value formula, we have

$$R\left[\frac{(1 + i)^n - 1}{i}\right] = S$$

$$200\left[\frac{(1 + x/12)^{240} - 1}{x/12}\right] = 100{,}000.$$

This equation is hard to solve algebraically. You can get a rough approximation by using a calculator and trying different values for x. With a graphing calculator, you can get an accurate solution by graphing

$$y_1 = 200\left[\frac{(1 + x/12)^{240} - 1}{x/12}\right] \quad \text{and} \quad y_2 = 100{,}000$$

and finding the x-coordinate of the point where the graphs intersect. Figure 5.9 shows that the company needs an interest rate of about 6.661%. The same answer can be obtained on a TVM solver (Figure 5.10). ✓ 5

Annuities Due

The formula developed previously is for *ordinary annuities*—annuities with payments at the *end* of each period. The results can be modified slightly to apply to **annuities due**—annuities where payments are made at the *beginning* of each period.

An example will illustrate how this is done. Consider an annuity due in which payments of $100 are made for 3 years, and an ordinary annuity in which payments of $100 are made for 4 years, both with 5% interest, compounded annually. Figure 5.11 computes the growth of each payment separately (as was done in Example 1).

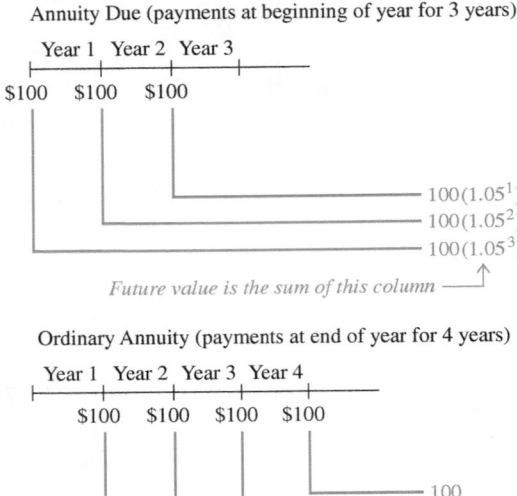

Figure 5.11

Figure 5.11 shows that the future values are the same, *except* for one $100 payment on the ordinary annuity (shown in red). So we can use the formula on page 245 to find the future value of the 4-year ordinary annuity and then subtract one $100 payment to get the future value of the 3-year annuity due:

Future value of $\quad$ = $\quad$ **Future value of** $\quad$ − $\quad$ **One payment**
3-year annuity due $\qquad$ **4-year ordinary annuity**

$$S = 100\left[\frac{1.05^4 - 1}{.05}\right] - 100 = \$331.01.$$

Essentially the same argument works in the general case.

Future Value of an Annuity Due

The future value S of an annuity due used to accumulate funds is given by

$$S = R\left[\frac{(1 + i)^{n+1} - 1}{i}\right] - R$$

S = Future value of an ordinary annuity − One payment, of $n + 1$ payments

where

R is the payment at the beginning of each period,

i is the interest rate per period, and

n is the number of periods.

Example 7 $\quad$ Payments of $500 are made at the beginning of each quarter for 7 years in an account paying 8% interest, compounded quarterly. Find the future value of this annuity due.

✓ Checkpoint 6

(a) Ms. Black deposits $800 at the beginning of each 6-month period for 5 years. Find the final amount if the account pays 6% compounded semiannually.

(b) Find the final amount if this account were an ordinary annuity.

Solution In 7 years, there are $n = 28$ quarterly periods. For an annuity due, add one period to get $n + 1 = 29$, and use the formula with $i = .08/4 = .02$:

$$S = R\left[\frac{(1 + i)^{n+1} - 1}{i}\right] - R = 500\left[\frac{(1 + .02)^{29} - 1}{.02}\right] - 500 = \$18{,}896.12.$$

After 7 years, the account balance will be $18,896.12. ✓ 6

Example 8   Jay Rechtien plans to have a fixed amount from his paycheck directly deposited into an account that pays 5.5% interest, compounded monthly. If he gets paid on the first day of the month and wants to accumulate $13,000 in the next three-and-a-half years, how much should he deposit each month?

Solution Jay's deposits form an annuity due whose future value is $S = 13{,}000$. The interest rate is $i = .055/12$. There are 42 months in three-and-a-half years. Since this is an annuity due, add one period, so that $n + 1 = 43$. Then solve the future-value formula for the payment R:

$$R\left[\frac{(1 + i)^{n+1} - 1}{i}\right] - R = S$$

$$R\left[\frac{(1 + .055/12)^{43} - 1}{.055/12}\right] - R = 13{,}000 \qquad \text{Let } i = .055/12, n = 43, \text{ and } S = 13{,}000.$$

$$R\left(\left[\frac{(1 + .055/12)^{43} - 1}{.055/12}\right] - 1\right) = 13{,}000 \qquad \text{Factor out } R \text{ on left side.}$$

$$R(46.4103) = 13{,}000 \qquad \text{Compute left side.}$$

$$R = \frac{13{,}000}{46.4103} = 280.110. \qquad \text{Divide both sides by 46.4103.}$$

Jay should have $280.11 deposited from each paycheck.

TECHNOLOGY TIP
When a TVM solver is used for annuities due, the PMT: setting at the bottom of the screen should be "BEGIN". See Figure 5.12, which shows the solution of Example 8.

```
N=42
I%=5.5
PV=0
•PMT=-280.110136
FV=13000
P/Y=12
C/Y=12
PMT:END BEGIN
```

Figure 5.12

5.3 Exercises

Note: Unless stated otherwise, all payments are made at the end of the period.

Find each of these sums (to 4 decimal places).

1. $1 + 1.05 + 1.05^2 + 1.05^3 + \cdots + 1.05^{14}$

2. $1 + 1.046 + 1.046^2 + 1.046^3 + \cdots + 1.046^{21}$

Find the future value of the ordinary annuities with the given payments and interest rates. (See Examples 1, 2, 3(a), and 4.)

3. $R = \$12{,}000$, 6.2% interest compounded annually for 8 years

4. $R = \$20{,}000$, 4.5% interest compounded annually for 12 years

5. $R = \$865$, 6% interest compounded semiannually for 10 years

6. $R = \$7300$, 9% interest compounded semiannually for 6 years

7. $R = \$1200$, 8% interest compounded quarterly for 10 years

8. $R = \$20{,}000$, 6% interest compounded quarterly for 12 years

Find the final amount (rounded to the nearest dollar) in each of these retirement accounts, in which the rate of return on the

account and the regular contribution change over time. (See Example 3.)

9. $400 per month invested at 4%, compounded monthly, for 10 years; then $600 per month invested at 6%, compounded monthly, for 10 years.

10. $500 per month invested at 5%, compounded monthly, for 20 years; then $1000 per month invested at 8%, compounded monthly, for 20 years.

11. $1000 per quarter invested at 4.2%, compounded quarterly, for 10 years; then $1500 per quarter invested at 7.4%, compounded quarterly, for 15 years.

12. $1500 per quarter invested at 7.4%, compounded quarterly, for 15 years; then $1000 per quarter invested at 4.2%, compounded quarterly, for 10 years. (Compare with Exercise 11.)

Find the amount of each payment to be made into a sinking fund to accumulate the given amounts. Payments are made at the end of each period. (See Example 5.)

13. $11,000; money earns 5% compounded semiannually for 6 years

14. $65,000; money earns 6% compounded semiannually for $4\frac{1}{2}$ years

15. $50,000; money earns 8% compounded quarterly for $2\frac{1}{2}$ years

16. $25,000; money earns 9% compounded quarterly for $3\frac{1}{2}$ years

17. $6000; money earns 6% compounded monthly for 3 years

18. $9000; money earns 7% compounded monthly for $2\frac{1}{2}$ years

Find the interest rate needed for the sinking fund to reach the required amount. Assume that the compounding period is the same as the payment period. (See Example 6.)

19. $50,000 to be accumulated in 10 years; annual payments of $3940.

20. $100,000 to be accumulated in 15 years; quarterly payments of $1200.

21. $38,000 to be accumulated in 5 years; quarterly payments of $1675.

22. $77,000 to be accumulated in 20 years; monthly payments of $195.

23. What is meant by a sinking fund? List some reasons for establishing a sinking fund.

24. Explain the difference between an ordinary annuity and an annuity due.

Find the future value of each annuity due. (See Example 7.)

25. Payments of $500 for 10 years at 5% compounded annually

26. Payments of $1050 for 8 years at 3.5% compounded annually

27. Payments of $16,000 for 11 years at 4.7% compounded annually

28. Payments of $25,000 for 12 years at 6% compounded annually

29. Payments of $1000 for 9 years at 8% compounded semiannually

30. Payments of $750 for 15 years at 6% compounded semiannually

31. Payments of $100 for 7 years at 9% compounded quarterly

32. Payments of $1500 for 11 years at 7% compounded quarterly

Find the payment that should be used for the annuity due whose future value is given. Assume that the compounding period is the same as the payment period. (See Example 8.)

33. $8000; quarterly payments for 3 years; interest rate 4.4%

34. $12,000; annual payments for 6 years; interest rate 5.1%

35. $55,000; monthly payments for 12 years; interest rate 5.7%

36. $125,000; monthly payments for 9 years; interest rate 6%

Finance *Work the following applied problems.*

37. A typical pack-a-day smoker in Ohio spends about $170 per month on cigarettes. Suppose the smoker invests that amount at the end of each month in an investment fund that pays a return

of 5.3% compounded monthly. What would the account be worth after 40 years? (Data from: www.theawl.com.)

38. A typical pack-a-day smoker in Illinois spends about $307.50 per month on cigarettes. Suppose the smoker invests that amount at the end of each month in an investment fund that pays a return of 4.9% compounded monthly. What would the account be worth after 40 years? (Data from: www.theawl. com.)

39. The Vanguard Explorer Value fund had as of April 2013 a 10-year average return of 10.99%. (Data from: www.vanguard. com.)

    (a) If Becky Anderson deposited $800 a month in the fund for 10 years, find the final value of the amount of her investments. Assume monthly compounding.

    (b) If Becky had invested instead with the Vanguard Growth and Income fund, which had an average annual return of 7.77%, what would the final value of the amount of her investments be? Assume monthly compounding.

    (c) How much more did the Explorer Value fund generate than the Growth and Income fund?

40. The Janus Enterprise fund had as of April 2013 a 10-year average return of 12.54%. (Data from: www.janus.com.)

    (a) If Elaine Chuha deposited $625 a month in the fund for 8 years, find the final value of the amount of her investments. Assume monthly compounding.

    (b) If Elaine had invested instead with the Janus Twenty fund, which had an average annual return of 10.63%, what would the final value of the amount of her investments be? Assume monthly compounding.

    (c) How much more did the Janus Enterprise fund generate than the Janus Twenty fund?

41. Brian Feister, a 25-year-old professional, invests $200 a month in the T. Rowe Price Capital Opportunity fund, which has a 10-year average return of 8.75%. (Data from: www.troweprice.com.)

    (a) Brian wants to estimate what he will have for retirement when he is 60 years old if the rate stays constant. Assume monthly compounding.

    (b) If Brian makes no further deposits and makes no withdrawals after age 60, how much will he have for retirement at age 65?

42. Ian Morrison, a 30-year-old professional, invests $250 a month in the T. Rowe Price Equity Income fund, which has a 10-year average return of 9.04%. (Data from: www.troweprice.com.)

    (a) Ian wants to estimate what he will have for retirement when he is 65 years old if the rate stays constant. Assume monthly compounding.

    (b) If Ian makes no further deposits and makes no withdrawals after age 65, how much will he have for retirement at age 75? Assume monthly compounding.

43. A mother opened an investment account for her son on the day he was born, investing $1000. Each year on his birthday, she deposits another $1000, making the last deposit on his 18th birthday. If the account paid a return rate of 5.6% compounded annually, how much is in the account at the end of the day on the son's 18th birthday?

44. A grandmother opens an investment account for her only grand-daughter on the day she was born, investing $500. Each year on her birthday, she deposits another $500, making the last deposit on her 25th birthday. If the account paid a return rate of 6.2% compounded annually, how much is in the account at the end of the day on the granddaughter's 25th birthday?

45. Chuck Hickman deposits $10,000 at the beginning of each year for 12 years in an account paying 5% compounded annually. He then puts the total amount on deposit in another account paying 6% compounded semi-annually for another 9 years. Find the final amount on deposit after the entire 21-year period.

46. Suppose that the best rate that the company in Example 6 can find is 6.3%, compounded monthly (rather than the 6.661% it wants). Then the company must deposit more in the sinking fund each month. What monthly deposit will guarantee that the fund will be worth $100,000 in 20 years?

47. David Horwitz needs $10,000 in 8 years.

  (a) What amount should he deposit at the end of each quarter at 5% compounded quarterly so that he will have his $10,000?

  (b) Find Horwitz's quarterly deposit if the money is deposited at 5.8% compounded quarterly.

48. Harv's Meats knows that it must buy a new machine in 4 years. The machine costs $12,000. In order to accumulate enough money to pay for the machine, Harv decides to deposit a sum of money at the end of each 6 months in an account paying 6% compounded semiannually. How much should each payment be?

49. Barbara Margolius wants to buy a $24,000 car in 6 years. How much money must she deposit at the end of each quarter in an account paying 5% compounded quarterly so that she will have enough to pay for her car?

50. The Chinns agree to sell an antique vase to a local museum for $19,000. They want to defer the receipt of this money until they retire in 5 years (and are in a lower tax bracket). If the museum can earn 5.8%, compounded annually, find the amount of each annual payment it should make into a sinking fund so that it will have the necessary $19,000 in 5 years.

51. Diane Gray sells some land in Nevada. She will be paid a lump sum of $60,000 in 7 years. Until then, the buyer pays 8% simple interest quarterly.

  (a) Find the amount of each quarterly interest payment.

  (b) The buyer sets up a sinking fund so that enough money will be present to pay off the $60,000. The buyer wants to make semiannual payments into the sinking fund; the account pays 6% compounded semiannually. Find the amount of each payment into the fund.

52. Joe Seniw bought a rare stamp for his collection. He agreed to pay a lump sum of $4000 after 5 years. Until then, he pays 6% simple interest semiannually.

  (a) Find the amount of each semiannual interest payment.

  (b) Seniw sets up a sinking fund so that enough money will be present to pay off the $4000. He wants to make annual payments into the fund. The account pays 8% compounded annually. Find the amount of each payment.

53. To save for retirement, Karla Harby put $300 each month into an ordinary annuity for 20 years. Interest was compounded monthly. At the end of the 20 years, the annuity was worth $147,126. What annual interest rate did she receive?

54. Jennifer Wall made payments of $250 per month at the end of each month to purchase a piece of property. After 30 years, she owned the property, which she sold for $330,000. What annual interest rate would she need to earn on an ordinary annuity for a comparable rate of return?

55. When Joe and Sarah graduate from college, each expects to work a total of 45 years. Joe begins saving for retirement immediately. He plans to deposit $600 at the end of each quarter into an account paying 8.1% interest, compounded quarterly, for 10 years. He will then leave his balance in the account, earning the same interest rate, but make no further deposits for 35 years. Sarah plans to save nothing during the first 10 years and then begin depositing $600 at the end of each quarter in an account paying 8.1% interest, compounded quarterly, for 35 years.

  (a) Without doing any calculations, predict which one will have the most in his or her retirement account after 45 years. Then test your prediction by answering the following questions (calculation required to the nearest dollar).

  (b) How much will Joe contribute to his retirement account?

  (c) How much will be in Joe's account after 45 years?

  (d) How much will Sarah contribute to her retirement account?

  (e) How much will be in Sarah's account after 45 years?

56. In a 1992 Virginia lottery, the jackpot was $27 million. An Australian investment firm tried to buy all possible combinations of numbers, which would have cost $7 million. In fact, the firm ran out of time and was unable to buy all combinations, but ended up with the only winning ticket anyway. The firm received the jackpot in 20 equal annual payments of $1.35 million. Assume these payments meet the conditions of an ordinary annuity. (Data from: *Washington Post*, March 10, 1992, p. A1.)

  (a) Suppose the firm can invest money at 8% interest compounded annually. How many years would it take until the investors would be further ahead than if they had simply invested the $7 million at the same rate? (*Hint:* Experiment with different values of n, the number of years, or use a graphing calculator to plot the value of both investments as a function of the number of years.)

  (b) How many years would it take in part (a) at an interest rate of 12%?

✓**Checkpoint Answers**

1. **(a)** $2247.20   **(b)** $2120.00   **(c)** $6367.20

2. **(a)** $18,339.82   **(b)** $36,216.41

3. $872,354.36

4. **(a)** $232.38   **(b)** $262.97

5. **(a)** $104,812.44   **(b)** 8.9%

6. **(a)** $9446.24   **(b)** $9171.10

5.4 Annuities, Present Value, and Amortization

In the annuities studied previously, regular deposits were made into an interest-bearing account and the value of the annuity increased from 0 at the beginning to some larger amount at the end (the future value). Now we expand the discussion to include annuities that begin with an amount of money and make regular payments each period until the value of the annuity decreases to 0. Examples of such annuities are lottery jackpots, structured settlements imposed by a court in which the party at fault (or his or her insurance company) makes regular payments to the injured party, and trust funds that pay the recipients a fixed amount at regular intervals.

In order to develop the essential formula for dealing with "payout annuities," we need another useful algebraic fact. If x is a nonzero number and n is a positive integer, verify the following equality by multiplying out the right-hand side:[*]

$$x^{-1} + x^{-2} + x^{-3} + \cdots + x^{-(n-1)} + x^{-n} = x^{-n}(x^{n-1} + x^{n-2} + x^{n-3} + \cdots + x^1 + 1).$$

Now use the sum formula in the box on page 243 to rewrite the expression in parentheses on the right-hand side:

$$x^{-1} + x^{-2} + x^{-3} + \cdots + x^{-(n-1)} + x^{-n} = x^{-n}\left(\frac{x^n - 1}{x - 1}\right)$$

$$= \frac{x^{-n}(x^n - 1)}{x - 1} = \frac{x^0 - x^{-n}}{x - 1} = \frac{1 - x^{-n}}{x - 1}.$$

We have proved the following result:

If x is a nonzero real number and n is a positive integer, then

$$x^{-1} + x^{-2} + x^{-3} + \cdots + x^{-n} = \frac{1 - x^{-n}}{x - 1}.$$

Present Value

In Section 5.2, we saw that the present value of A dollars at interest rate i per period for n periods is the amount that must be deposited today (at the same interest rate) in order to produce A dollars in n periods. Similarly, the **present value of an annuity** is the amount that must be deposited today (at the same compound interest rate as the annuity) to provide all the payments for the term of the annuity. It does not matter whether the payments are invested to accumulate funds or are paid out to disperse funds; the amount needed to provide the payments is the same in either case. We begin with ordinary annuities.

Example 1   Your rich aunt has funded an annuity that will pay you $1500 at the end of each year for six years. If the interest rate is 8%, compounded annually, find the present value of this annuity.

Solution   Look separately at each payment you will receive. Then find the present value of each payment—the amount needed now in order to make the payment in the future. The sum of these present values will be the present value of the annuity, since it will provide all of the payments.

---
[*]Remember that powers of x are multiplied by *adding* exponents and that $x^n x^{-n} = x^{n-n} = x^0 = 1$.

To find the first $1500 payment (due in one year), the present value of $1500 at 8% annual interest is needed now. According to the present-value formula for compound interest on page 240 (with $A = 1500$, $i = .08$, and $n = 1$), this present value is

$$\frac{1500}{1 + .08} = \frac{1500}{1.08} = 1500(1.08^{-1}) \approx \$1388.89.$$

This amount will grow to $1500 in one year.

For the second $1500 payment (due in two years), we need the present value of $1500 at 8% interest, compounded annually for two years. The present-value formula for compound interest (with $A = 1500$, $i = .08$, and $n = 2$) shows that this present value is

$$\frac{1500}{(1 + .08)^2} = \frac{1500}{1.08^2} = 1500(1.08^{-2}) \approx \$1286.01.$$

Less money is needed for the second payment because it will grow over two years instead of one.

A similar calculation shows that the third payment (due in three years) has present value $1500(1.08^{-3})$. Continue in this manner to find the present value of each of the remaining payments, as summarized in Figure 5.13.

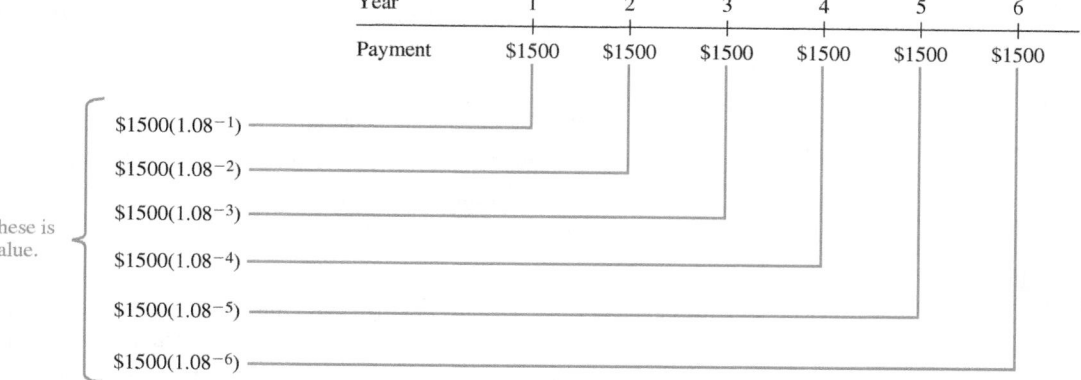

Figure 5.13

The left-hand column of Figure 5.13 shows that the present value is

$$1500 \cdot 1.08^{-1} + 1500 \cdot 1.08^{-2} + 1500 \cdot 1.08^{-3} + 1500 \cdot 1.08^{-4}$$
$$+ 1500 \cdot 1.08^{-5} + 1500 \cdot 1.08^{-6}$$
$$= 1500(1.08^{-1} + 1.08^{-2} + 1.08^{-3} + 1.08^{-4} + 1.08^{-5} + 1.08^{-6}). \qquad \textbf{(1)}$$

Now apply the algebraic fact in the box on page 252 to the expression in parentheses (with $x = 1.08$ and $n = 6$). It shows that the sum (the present value of the annuity) is

$$1500\left[\frac{1 - 1.08^{-6}}{1.08 - 1}\right] = 1500\left[\frac{1 - 1.08^{-6}}{.08}\right] = \$6934.32.$$

This amount will provide for all six payments and leave a zero balance at the end of six years (give or take a few cents due to rounding to the nearest penny at each step). ✓₁

✓ Checkpoint 1

Show that $6934.32 will provide all the payments in Example 1 as follows:

(a) Find the balance at the end of the first year after the interest has been added and the $1500 payment subtracted.

(b) Repeat part (a) to find the balances at the ends of years 2 through 6.

Example 1 is the model for finding a formula for the future value of any ordinary annuity. Suppose that a payment of R dollars is made at the end of each period for n

periods, at interest rate i per period. Then the present value of this annuity can be found by using the procedure in Example 1, with these replacements:

$$
\begin{array}{cccc}
1500 & .08 & 1.08 & 6 \\
\downarrow & \downarrow & \downarrow & \downarrow \\
R & i & 1+i & n
\end{array}
$$

The future value in Example 1 is the sum in equation (**1**), which now becomes

$$P = R[(1 + i)^{-1} + (1 + i)^{-2} + (1 + i)^{-3} + \cdots + (1 + i)^{-n}].$$

Apply the algebraic fact in the box on page 252 to the expression in brackets (with $x = 1 + i$). Then we have

$$P = R\left[\frac{1 - (1 + i)^{-n}}{(1 + i) - 1}\right] = R\left[\frac{1 - (1 + i)^{-n}}{i}\right].$$

The quantity in brackets in the right-hand part of the preceding equation is sometimes written $a_{\overline{n}|i}$ (read "a-angle-n at i"). So we can summarize as follows.

Present Value of an Ordinary Annuity

The present value P of an ordinary annuity is given by

$$P = R\left[\frac{1 - (1 + i)^{-n}}{i}\right], \quad \text{or} \quad P = R \cdot a_{\overline{n}|i},$$

where

R is the payment at the end of each period,

i is the interest rate per period, and

n is the number of periods.

⚠ **CAUTION** Do not confuse the formula for the present value of an annuity with the one for the future value of an annuity. Notice the difference: The numerator of the fraction in the present-value formula is $1 - (1 + i)^{-n}$, but in the future-value formula, it is $(1 + i)^n - 1$.

Example 2   Jim Riles was in an auto accident. He sued the person at fault and was awarded a structured settlement in which an insurance company will pay him $600 at the end of each month for the next seven years. How much money should the insurance company invest now at 4.7%, compounded monthly, to guarantee that all the payments can be made?

Solution   The payments form an ordinary annuity. The amount needed to fund all the payments is the present value of the annuity. Apply the present-value formula with $R = 600, n = 7 \cdot 12 = 84,$ and $i = .047/12$ (the interest rate per month). The insurance company should invest

$$P = R\left[\frac{1 - (1 + i)^{-n}}{i}\right] = 600\left[\frac{1 - (1 + .047/12)^{-84}}{.047/12}\right] = \$42,877.44. \quad ✓_2$$

✓ **Checkpoint 2**

An insurance company offers to pay Jane Parks an ordinary annuity of $1200 per quarter for five years *or* the present value of the annuity now. If the interest rate is 6%, find the present value.

Example 3   To supplement his pension in the early years of his retirement, Ralph Taylor plans to use $124,500 of his savings as an ordinary annuity that will make monthly payments to him for 20 years. If the interest rate is 5.2%, how much will each payment be?

Solution The present value of the annuity is $P = \$124{,}500$, the monthly interest rate is $i = .052/12$, and $n = 12 \cdot 20 = 240$ (the number of months in 20 years). Solve the present-value formula for the monthly payment R:

$$P = R\left[\frac{1 - (1 + i)^{-n}}{i}\right]$$

$$124{,}500 = R\left[\frac{1 - (1 + .052/12)^{-240}}{.052/12}\right]$$

$$R = \frac{124{,}500}{\left[\dfrac{1 - (1 + .052/12)^{-240}}{.052/12}\right]} = \$835.46.$$

✓**Checkpoint 3**

Carl Dehne has $80,000 in an account paying 4.8% interest, compounded monthly. He plans to use up all the money by making equal monthly withdrawals for 15 years. If the interest rate is 4.8%, find the amount of each withdrawal.

Taylor will receive $835.46 a month (about $10,026 per year) for 20 years. ✓3

Example 4 Surinder Sinah and Maria Gonzalez are graduates of Kenyon College. They both agree to contribute to an endowment fund at the college. Sinah says he will give $500 at the end of each year for 9 years. Gonzalez prefers to give a single donation today. How much should she give to equal the value of Sinah's gift, assuming that the endowment fund earns 7.5% interest, compounded annually?

Solution Sinah's gift is an ordinary annuity with annual payments of $500 for 9 years. Its *future* value at 7.5% annual compound interest is

$$S = R\left[\frac{(1 + i)^n - 1}{i}\right] = 500\left[\frac{(1 + .075)^9 - 1}{.075}\right] = 500\left[\frac{1.075^9 - 1}{.075}\right] = \$6114.92.$$

We claim that for Gonzalez to equal this contribution, she should today contribute an amount equal to the *present* value of this annuity, namely,

$$P = R\left[\frac{1 - (1 + i)^{-n}}{i}\right] = 500\left[\frac{1 - (1 + .075)^{-9}}{.075}\right] = 500\left[\frac{1 - 1.075^{-9}}{.075}\right] = \$3189.44.$$

To confirm this claim, suppose the present value $P = \$3189.44$ is deposited today at 7.5% interest, compounded annually for 9 years. According to the compound interest formula on page 233, P will grow to

$$3189.44(1 + .075)^9 = \$6114.92,$$

the future value of Sinah's annuity. So at the end of 9 years, Gonzalez and Sinah will have made identical gifts.

Example 4 illustrates the following alternative description of the present value of an "accumulation annuity."

The present value of an annuity for accumulating funds is the single deposit that would have to be made today to produce the future value of the annuity (assuming the same interest rate and period of time.) ✓4

✓**Checkpoint 4**

What lump sum deposited today would be equivalent to equal payments of

(a) $650 at the end of each year for 9 years at 4% compounded annually?

(b) $1000 at the end of each quarter for 4 years at 4% compounded quarterly?

Corporate bonds, which were introduced in Section 5.1, are routinely bought and sold in financial markets. In most cases, interest rates when a bond is sold differ from the interest rate paid by the bond (known as the **coupon rate**). In such cases, the price of a bond will not be its face value, but will instead be based on current interest rates. The next example shows how this is done.

Example 5 A 15-year $10,000 bond with a 5% coupon rate was issued five years ago and is now being sold. If the current interest rate for similar bonds is 7%, what price should a purchaser be willing to pay for this bond?

Solution According to the simple interest formula (page 226), the interest paid by the bond each half-year is

$$I = Prt = 10{,}000 \cdot .05 \cdot \frac{1}{2} = \$250.$$

Think of the bond as a two-part investment: The first is an annuity that pays $250 every six months for the next 10 years; the second is the $10,000 face value of the bond, which will be paid when the bond matures, 10 years from now. The purchaser should be willing to pay the present value of each part of the investment, assuming 7% interest, compounded semiannually.* The interest rate per period is $i = .07/2$, and the number of six-month periods in 10 years is $n = 20$. So we have:

Present value of annuity

$$P = R\left[\frac{1 - (1 + i)^{-n}}{i}\right]$$

$$= 250\left[\frac{1 - (1 + .07/2)^{-20}}{.07/2}\right]$$

$$= \$3553.10$$

Present value of $10,000 in 10 years

$$P = A(1 + i)^{-n}$$

$$= 10{,}000(1 + .07/2)^{-20}$$

$$= \$5025.66.$$

So the purchaser should be willing to pay the sum of these two present values:

$$\$3553.10 + \$5025.66 = \$8578.76.$$

✓ Checkpoint 5

Suppose the current interest rate for bonds is 4% instead of 7% when the bond in Example 5 is sold. What price should a purchaser be willing to pay for it?

NOTE Example 5 and Checkpoint 5 illustrate the inverse relation between interest rates and bond prices: If interest rates rise, bond prices fall, and if interest rates fall, bond prices rise.

Loans and Amortization

If you take out a car loan or a home mortgage, you repay it by making regular payments to the bank. From the bank's point of view, your payments are an annuity that is paying it a fixed amount each month. The present value of this annuity is the amount you borrowed.

Example 6 **Finance** Chase Bank in April 2013 advertised a new car auto loan rate of 2.23% for a 48-month loan. Shelley Fasulko will buy a new car for $25,000 with a down payment of $4500. Find the amount of each payment. (Data from: www.chase.com.)

Solution After a $4500 down payment, the loan amount is $20,500. Use the present-value formula for an annuity, with $P = 20{,}500$, $n = 48$, and $i = .0223/12$ (the monthly interest rate). Then solve for payment R.

$$P = R\left[\frac{1 - (1 + i)^{-n}}{i}\right]$$

$$20{,}500 = R\left[\frac{1 - (1 + .0223/12)^{-48}}{.0223/12}\right]$$

$$R = \frac{20{,}500}{\left[\frac{1 - (1 + .0223/12)^{-48}}{.0223/12}\right]}$$ Solve for R.

$$R = \$446.81$$

✓ Checkpoint 6

Suzanne Bellini uses a Chase auto loan to purchase a used car priced at $28,750 at an interest rate of 3.64% for a 60-month loan. What is the monthly payment?

A loan is **amortized** if both the principal and interest are paid by a sequence of equal periodic payments. The periodic payment needed to amortize a loan may be found, as in Example 6, by solving the present-value formula for R.

*The analysis here does not include any commissions or fees charged by the financial institution that handles the bond sale.

Amortization Payments

A loan of P dollars at interest rate i per period may be amortized in n equal periodic payments of R dollars made at the end of each period, where

$$R = \frac{P}{\left[\dfrac{1 - (1 + i)^{-n}}{i}\right]} = \frac{Pi}{1 - (1 + i)^{-n}}.$$

Example 7   **Finance**   In April 2013, the average rate for a 30-year fixed mortgage was 3.43%. Assume a down payment of 20% on a home purchase of $272,900. (Data from: Freddie Mac.)

(a)   Find the monthly payment needed to amortize this loan.

Solution   The down payment is .20(272,900) = $54,580. Thus, the loan amount P is $272,900 − 54,580 = $218,320. We can now apply the formula in the preceding box, with $n = 12(30) = 360$ (the number of monthly payments in 30 years), and monthly interest rate $i = .0343/12$.*

$$R = \frac{Pi}{1 - (1 + i)^{-n}} = \frac{(218,320)(.0343/12)}{1 - (1 + .0343/12)^{-360}} = \$971.84$$

Monthly payments of $971.84 are required to amortize the loan.

(b)   After 10 years, approximately how much is owed on the mortgage?

Solution   You may be tempted to say that after 10 years of payments on a 30-year mortgage, the balance will be reduced by a third. However, a significant portion of each payment goes to pay interest. So, much less than a third of the mortgage is paid off in the first 10 years, as we now see.

After 10 years (120 payments), the 240 remaining payments can be thought of as an annuity. The present value for this annuity is the (approximate) remaining balance on the mortgage. Hence, we use the present-value formula with $R = 971.84$, $i = .0343/12$, and $n = 240$:

$$P = 971.84\left[\frac{1 - (1 + .0343/12)^{-240}}{(.0343/12)}\right] = \$168,614.16.$$

So the remaining balance is about $168,614.16. The actual balance probably differs slightly from this figure because payments and interest amounts are rounded to the nearest penny.   ✔ 7

✔ Checkpoint 7

Find the remaining balance after 20 years.

```
N=360
I%=3.43
PV=218320
•PMT=-971.8435089
FV=0
P/Y=12
C/Y=12
PMT:END BEGIN
```

Figure 5.14

📩 **TECHNOLOGY TIP**   A TVM solver on a graphing calculator can find the present value of an annuity or the payment on a loan: Fill in the known information, put the cursor next to the unknown item (PV or PMT), and press SOLVE. Figure 5.14 shows the solution to Example 7(a) on a TVM solver. Alternatively, you can use the program in the Program Appendix.

Example 7(b) illustrates an important fact: Even though equal *payments* are made to amortize a loan, the loan *balance* does not decrease in equal steps. The method used to estimate the remaining balance in Example 7(b) works in the general case. If n payments

---

*Mortgage rates are quoted in terms of annual interest, but it is always understood that the monthly rate is $\frac{1}{12}$ of the annual interest rate and that interest is compounded monthly.

are needed to amortize a loan and x payments have been made, then the remaining payments form an annuity of $n - x$ payments. So we apply the present-value formula with $n - x$ in place of n to obtain this result.

Remaining Balance

If a loan can be amortized by n payments of R dollars each at an interest rate i per period, then the *approximate* remaining balance B after x payments is

$$B = R\left[\frac{1 - (1 + i)^{-(n-x)}}{i}\right].$$

Amortization Schedules

The remaining-balance formula is a quick and convenient way to get a reasonable estimate of the remaining balance on a loan, but it is not accurate enough for a bank or business, which must keep its books exactly. To determine the exact remaining balance after each loan payment, financial institutions normally use an **amortization schedule,** which lists how much of each payment is interest, how much goes to reduce the balance, and how much is still owed after each payment.

Example 8 Beth Hill borrows $1000 for one year at 12% annual interest, compounded monthly.

(a) Find her monthly payment.

Solution Apply the amortization payment formula with $P = 1000, n = 12$, and monthly interest rate $i = .12/12 = .01$. Her payment is

$$R = \frac{Pi}{1 - (1 + i)^{-n}} = \frac{1000(.01)}{1 - (1 + .01)^{-12}} = \$88.85.$$

(b) After making five payments, Hill decides to pay off the remaining balance. Approximately how much must she pay?

Solution Apply the remaining-balance formula just given, with $R = 88.85, i = .01$, and $n - x = 12 - 5 = 7$. Her approximate remaining balance is

$$B = R\left[\frac{1 - (1 + i)^{-(n-x)}}{i}\right] = 88.85\left[\frac{1 - (1 + .01)^{-7}}{.01}\right] = \$597.80.$$

(c) Construct an amortization schedule for Hill's loan.

Solution An amortization schedule for the loan is shown in the table on the next page. It was obtained as follows: The annual interest rate is 12% compounded monthly, so the interest rate per month is $12\%/12 = 1\% = .01$. When the first payment is made, one month's interest, namely, $.01(1000) = \$10$, is owed. Subtracting this from the $88.85 payment leaves $78.85 to be applied to repayment. Hence, the principal at the end of the first payment period is $1000 - 78.85 = \$921.15$, as shown in the "payment 1" line of the table.

When payment 2 is made, one month's interest on the new balance of $921.15 is owed, namely, $.01(921.15) = \$9.21$. Continue as in the preceding paragraph to compute the entries in this line of the table. The remaining lines of the table are found in a similar fashion.

Payment Number	Amount of Payment	Interest for Period	Portion to Principal	Principal at End of Period
0	—	—	—	$1000.00
1	$88.85	$10.00	$78.85	921.15
2	88.85	9.21	79.64	841.51
3	88.85	8.42	80.43	761.08
4	88.85	7.61	81.24	679.84
5	88.85	6.80	82.05	597.79
6	88.85	5.98	82.87	514.92
7	88.85	5.15	83.70	431.22
8	88.85	4.31	84.54	346.68
9	88.85	3.47	85.38	261.30
10	88.85	2.61	86.24	175.06
11	88.85	1.75	87.10	87.96
12	88.84	.88	87.96	0

Note that Hill's remaining balance after five payments differs slightly from the estimate made in part (b).

The final payment in the amortization schedule in Example 8(c) differs from the other payments. It often happens that the last payment needed to amortize a loan must be adjusted to account for rounding earlier and to ensure that the final balance will be exactly 0.

 TECHNOLOGY TIP   Most Casio graphing calculators can produce amortization schedules. For other calculators, use the amortization table program in the Program Appendix. Spreadsheets are another useful tool for creating amortization tables. Microsoft Excel (Microsoft Corporation Excel © 2013) has a built-in feature for calculating monthly payments. Figure 5.15 shows an Excel amortization table for Example 8. For more details, see the *Spreadsheet Manual*, also available with this text.

	A	B	C	D	E	F
1	Prnt#	Payment	Interest	Principal	End Principal	
2	0				1000	
3	1	88.85	10.00	78.85	921.15	
4	2	88.85	9.21	79.64	841.51	
5	3	88.85	8.42	80.43	761.08	
6	4	88.85	7.61	81.24	679.84	
7	5	88.85	6.80	82.05	597.79	
8	6	88.85	5.98	82.87	514.92	
9	7	88.85	5.15	83.70	431.22	
10	8	88.85	4.31	84.54	346.68	
11	9	88.85	3.47	85.38	261.30	
12	10	88.85	2.61	86.24	175.06	
13	11	88.85	1.75	87.10	87.96	
14	12	88.85	0.88	87.97	-0.01	

Figure 5.15

Annuities Due

We want to find the present value of an annuity due in which 6 payments of R dollars are made at the *beginning* of each period, with interest rate i per period, as shown schematically in Figure 5.16.

$$\begin{array}{cccccc} 1 & 2 & 3 & 4 & 5 & 6 \\ | & | & | & | & | & | \\ R & R & R & R & R & R \end{array}$$

Figure 5.16

The present value is the amount needed to fund all 6 payments. Since the first payment earns no interest, R dollars are needed to fund it. Now look at the last 5 payments by themselves in Figure 5.17.

Figure 5.17

If you think of these 5 payments as being made at the end of each period, you see that they form an ordinary annuity. The money needed to fund them is the present value of this ordinary annuity. So the present value of the annuity due is given by

$$R + \text{Present value of the ordinary annuity of 5 payments}$$

$$R + R\left[\frac{1 - (1 + i)^{-5}}{i}\right].$$

Replacing 6 by n and 5 by $n - 1$, and using the argument just given, produces the general result that follows.

Present Value of an Annuity Due

The present value P of an annuity due is given by

$$P = R + R\left[\frac{1 - (1 + i)^{-(n-1)}}{i}\right],$$

$$P = \text{One payment} + \text{Present value of an ordinary annuity of } n - 1 \text{ payments}$$

where

  R is the payment at the beginning of each period,

  i is the interest rate per period, and

  n is the number of periods.

✓ **Checkpoint 8**

What is the cash value for a Lotto jackpot of $25 million if the Illinois Lottery can earn 6.2% annual interest?

```
N=26
 I%=4.88
•PV=7045397.393
 PMT=-461538.46
 FV=0
 P/Y=1
 C/Y=1
 PMT:END BEGIN
```

Figure 5.18

Example 9 **Finance** The *Illinois Lottery Winner's Handbook* discusses the options of how to receive the winnings for a $12 million Lotto jackpot. One option is to take 26 annual payments of approximately $461,538.46, which is $12 million divided into 26 equal payments. The other option is to take a lump-sum payment (which is often called the "cash value"). If the Illinois lottery commission can earn 4.88% annual interest, how much is the cash value?

Solution The yearly payments form a 26-payment annuity due. An equivalent amount now is the present value of this annuity. Apply the present-value formula with $R = 461{,}538.46$, $i = .0488$, and $n = 26$:

$$P = R + R\left[\frac{1 - (1 + i)^{-(n-1)}}{i}\right] = 461{,}538.46 + 461{,}538.46\left[\frac{1 - (1 + .0488)^{-25}}{.0488}\right]$$

$$= \$7{,}045{,}397.39.$$

The cash value is $7,045,397.39.

TECHNOLOGY TIP Figure 5.18 shows the solution of Example 9 on a TVM solver. Since this is an annuity due, the PMT: setting at the bottom of the screen is "BEGIN".

5.4 Exercises

Unless noted otherwise, all payments and withdrawals are made at the end of the period.

1. Explain the difference between the present value of an annuity and the future value of an annuity.

Find the present value of each ordinary annuity. (See Examples 1, 2, and 4.)

2. Payments of $890 each year for 16 years at 6% compounded annually

3. Payments of $1400 each year for 8 years at 6% compounded annually

4. Payments of $10,000 semiannually for 15 years at 7.5% compounded semiannually

5. Payments of $50,000 quarterly for 10 years at 5% compounded quarterly

6. Payments of $15,806 quarterly for 3 years at 6.8% compounded quarterly

Find the amount necessary to fund the given withdrawals. (See Examples 1 and 2.)

7. Quarterly withdrawals of $650 for 5 years; interest rate is 4.9%, compounded quarterly.

8. Yearly withdrawals of $1200 for 14 years; interest rate is 5.6%, compounded annually.

9. Monthly withdrawals of $425 for 10 years; interest rate is 6.1%, compounded monthly.

10. Semiannual withdrawals of $3500 for 7 years; interest rate is 5.2%, compounded semiannually.

Find the payment made by the ordinary annuity with the given present value. (See Example 3.)

11. $90,000; monthly payments for 22 years; interest rate is 4.9%, compounded monthly.

12. $45,000; monthly payments for 11 years; interest rate is 5.3%, compounded monthly.

13. $275,000; quarterly payments for 18 years; interest rate is 6%, compounded quarterly.

14. $330,000; quarterly payments for 30 years; interest rate is 6.1% compounded quarterly.

Find the lump sum deposited today that will yield the same total amount as payments of $10,000 at the end of each year for 15 years at each of the given interest rates. (See Example 4 and the box following it.)

15. 3% compounded annually

16. 4% compounded annually

17. 6% compounded annually

18. What sum deposited today at 5% compounded annually for 8 years will provide the same amount as $1000 deposited at the end of each year for 8 years at 6% compounded annually?

19. What lump sum deposited today at 8% compounded quarterly for 10 years will yield the same final amount as deposits of $4000 at the end of each 6-month period for 10 years at 6% compounded semiannually?

Find the price a purchaser should be willing to pay for the given bond. Assume that the coupon interest is paid twice a year. (See Example 5.)

20. $20,000 bond with coupon rate 4.5% that matures in 8 years; current interest rate is 5.9%.

21. $15,000 bond with coupon rate 6% that matures in 4 years; current interest rate is 5%.

22. $25,000 bond with coupon rate 7% that matures in 10 years; current interest rate is 6%.

23. $10,000 bond with coupon rate 5.4% that matures in 12 years; current interest rate is 6.5%.

24. What does it mean to amortize a loan?

Find the payment necessary to amortize each of the given loans. (See Examples 6, 7(a), and 8(a).)

25. $2500; 8% compounded quarterly; 6 quarterly payments

26. $41,000; 9% compounded semiannually; 10 semiannual payments

27. $90,000; 7% compounded annually; 12 annual payments

28. $140,000; 12% compounded quarterly; 15 quarterly payments

29. $7400; 8.2% compounded semiannually; 18 semiannual payments

30. $5500; 9.5% compounded monthly; 24 monthly payments

Finance *In April 2013, the mortgage interest rates listed in Exercises 31–34 for the given companies were listed at www.hsh.com. Find the monthly payment necessary to amortize the given loans. (See Example 7(a).)*

31. $225,000 at 3.25% for 30 years from Amerisave

32. $330,000 at 3.125% for 20 years from Quicken Loans

33. $140,000 at 2.375% for 15 years from Discover Home Loans

34. $180,000 at 2.25% for 10 years from Roundpoint Mortgage Company

Finance *Find the monthly payment and estimate the remaining balance (to the nearest dollar). Assume interest is on the unpaid balance. The interest rates are from national averages from www.bankrate.com in April 2013. (See Examples 7 and 8.)*

35. Four-year new car loan for $26,799 at 3.13%; remaining balance after 2 years

36. Three-year used car loan for $15,875 at 2.96%; remaining balance after 1 year

37. Thirty-year mortgage for $210,000 at 3.54%; remaining balance after 12 years

38. Fifteen-year mortgage for $195,000 at 2.78%; remaining balance after 4.5 years

Use the amortization table in Example 8(c) to answer the questions in Exercises 39–42.

39. How much of the 5th payment is interest?

40. How much of the 10th payment is used to reduce the debt?

41. How much interest is paid in the first 5 months of the loan?

42. How much interest is paid in the last 5 months of the loan?

Find the cash value of the lottery jackpot (to the nearest dollar). Yearly jackpot payments begin immediately (26 for Mega Millions and 30 for Powerball). Assume the lottery can invest at the given interest rate. (See Example 9.)

43. Powerball: $57.6 million; 5.1% interest

44. Powerball: $207 million; 5.78% interest

45. Mega Millions: $41.6 million; 4.735% interest

46. Mega Millions: $23.4 million; 4.23% interest

Finance *Work the following applied problems.*

47. An auto stereo dealer sells a stereo system for $600 down and monthly payments of $30 for the next 3 years. If the interest rate is 1.25% *per month* on the unpaid balance, find

   (a) the cost of the stereo system;

   (b) the total amount of interest paid.

48. John Kushida buys a used car costing $6000. He agrees to make payments at the end of each monthly period for 4 years. He pays 12% interest, compounded monthly.

   (a) What is the amount of each payment?

   (b) Find the total amount of interest Kushida will pay.

49. A speculator agrees to pay $15,000 for a parcel of land; this amount, with interest, will be paid over 4 years with semiannual payments at an interest rate of 10% compounded semiannually. Find the amount of each payment.

50. Alan Stasa buys a new car costing $26,750. What is the monthly payment if the interest rate is 4.2%, compounded monthly, and the loan is for 60 months? Find the total amount of interest Alan will pay.

Finance *A student education loan has two repayment options. The standard plan repays the loan in 10 years with equal monthly payments. The extended plan allows from 12 to 30 years to repay the loan. A student borrows $35,000 at 7.43% compounded monthly.*

51. Find the monthly payment and total interest paid under the standard plan.

52. Find the monthly payment and total interest paid under the extended plan with 20 years to pay off the loan.

Finance *Use the formula for the approximate remaining balance to work each problem. (See Examples 7(b) and 8(b).)*

53. When Teresa Flores opened her law office, she bought $14,000 worth of law books and $7200 worth of office furniture. She paid $1200 down and agreed to amortize the balance with semiannual payments for 5 years at 12% compounded semiannually.

   (a) Find the amount of each payment.

   (b) When her loan had been reduced below $5000, Flores received a large tax refund and decided to pay off the loan. How many payments were left at this time?

54. Kareem Adams buys a house for $285,000. He pays $60,000 down and takes out a mortgage at 6.9% on the balance. Find his monthly payment and the total amount of interest he will pay if the length of the mortgage is

   (a) 15 years;

   (b) 20 years;

   (c) 25 years.

   (d) When will half the 20-year loan be paid off?

55. Susan Carver will purchase a home for $257,000. She will use a down payment of 20% and finance the remaining portion at 3.9%, compounded monthly for 30 years.

   (a) What will be the monthly payment?

   (b) How much will remain on the loan after making payments for 5 years?

   (c) How much interest will be paid on the total amount of the loan over the course of 30 years?

56. Mohsen Manouchehri will purchase a $230,000 home with a 20-year mortgage. If he makes a down payment of 20% and the interest rate is 3.3%, compounded monthly,

   (a) what will the monthly payment be?

   (b) how much will he owe after making payments for 8 years?

   (c) how much in total interest will he pay over the course of the 20-year loan?

Work each problem.

57. Elizabeth Bernardi and her employer contribute $400 at the end of each month to her retirement account, which earns 7% interest, compounded monthly. When she retires after 45 years, she plans to make monthly withdrawals for 30 years. If her account earns 5% interest, compounded monthly, then when she retires, what is her maximum possible monthly withdrawal (without running out of money)?

58. Jim Milliken won a $15,000 prize. On March 1, he deposited it in an account earning 5.2% interest, compounded monthly. On March 1 one year later, he begins to withdraw the same amount at the beginning of each month for a year. Assuming that he uses up all the money in the account, find the amount of each monthly withdrawal.

59. Catherine Dohanyos plans to retire in 20 years. She will make 20 years of monthly contributions to her retirement account. One month after her last contribution, she will begin the first of 10 years of withdrawals. She wants to withdraw $2500 per month. How large must her monthly contributions be in order to accomplish her goal if the account earns interest of 7.1% compounded monthly for the duration of her contributions and the 120 months of withdrawals?

60. David Turner plans to retire in 25 years. He will make 25 years of monthly contributions to his retirement account. One month after his last contribution, he will begin the first of 10 years of withdrawals. He wants to withdraw $3000 per month. How large must his monthly contributions be in order to accomplish his goal if the account earns interest of 6.8% compounded monthly for the duration of his contributions and the 120 months of withdrawals?

61. William Blake plans to retire in 20 years. William will make 10 years (120 months) of equal monthly payments into his account. Ten years after his last contribution, he will begin the first of 120 monthly withdrawals of $3400 per month. Assume that the retirement account earns interest of 8.2% compounded monthly for the duration of his contributions, the 10 years in between his contributions and the beginning of his withdrawals, and the 10 years of withdrawals. How large must William's monthly contributions be in order to accomplish his goal?

62. Gil Stevens plans to retire in 25 years. He will make 15 years (180 months) of equal monthly payments into his account. Ten years after his last contribution, he will begin the first of 120 monthly withdrawals of $2900 per month. Assume that the retirement account earns interest of 5.4% compounded monthly for the duration of his contributions, the 10 years in between his

contributions and the beginning of his withdrawals, and the 10 years of withdrawals. How large must Gil's monthly contributions be in order to accomplish his goal?

Finance *In Exercises 63–66, prepare an amortization schedule showing the first four payments for each loan. (See Example 8(c).)*

63. An insurance firm pays $4000 for a new printer for its computer. It amortizes the loan for the printer in 4 annual payments at 8% compounded annually.

64. Large semitrailer trucks cost $72,000 each. Ace Trucking buys such a truck and agrees to pay for it by a loan that will be amortized with 9 semiannual payments at 6% compounded semiannually.

65. One retailer charges $1048 for a certain computer. A firm of tax accountants buys 8 of these computers. It makes a down payment of $1200 and agrees to amortize the balance with monthly payments at 12% compounded monthly for 4 years.

66. Joan Varozza plans to borrow $20,000 to stock her small boutique. She will repay the loan with semiannual payments for 5 years at 7% compounded semiannually.

✓ Checkpoint Answers

1. **(a)** $5989.07
   (b) $4968.20; $3865.66; $2674.91; $1388.90; $0.01
2. $20,602.37
3. $624.33
4. **(a)** $4832.97   **(b)** $14,717.87
5. $10,817.57
6. $524.82
7. $98,605.61
8. $13,023,058.46

CHAPTER 5 Summary and Review

Key Terms and Symbols

5.1 simple interest
principal
rate
time
future value (maturity value)
present value
discount and T-bills

5.2 compound interest
compound amount
compounding period
nominal rate (stated rate)
effective rate (APY)
present value

5.3 annuity
payment period

term of an annuity
ordinary annuity
future value of an ordinary annuity
sinking fund
annuity due
future value of an annuity due

5.4 present value of an ordinary annuity
amortization payments
remaining balance
amortization schedule
present value of an annuity due

Chapter 5 Key Concepts

A Strategy for Solving Finance Problems

We have presented a lot of new formulas in this chapter. By answering the following questions, you can decide which formula to use for a particular problem.

1. Is simple or compound interest involved?

 Simple interest is normally used for investments or loans of a year or less; compound interest is normally used in all other cases.

2. If simple interest is being used, what is being sought—interest amount, future value, present value, or discount?

3. If compound interest is being used, does it involve a lump sum (single payment) or an annuity (sequence of payments)?

 (a) For a lump sum,

 (i) is ordinary compound interest involved?

 (ii) what is being sought—present value, future value, number of periods, or effective rate (APY)?

 (b) For an annuity,

 (i) is it an ordinary annuity (payment at the end of each period) or an annuity due (payment at the beginning of each period)?

 (ii) what is being sought—present value, future value, or payment amount?

 Once you have answered these questions, choose the appropriate formula and work the problem. As a final step, consider whether the answer you get makes sense. For instance, the amount of interest or the payments in an annuity should be fairly small compared with the total future value.

Key Formulas

List of Variables

r is the annual interest rate.

m is the number of periods per year.

i is the interest rate per period. $i = \dfrac{r}{m}$

t is the number of years.

n is the number of periods. $n = tm$

P is the principal or present value.

A is the future value of a lump sum.

S is the future value of an annuity.

R is the periodic payment in an annuity.

B is the remaining balance on a loan.

Interest	Simple Interest	Compound Interest
Interest	$I = Prt$	$I = A - P$
Future value	$A = P(1 + rt)$	$A = P(1 + i)^n$
Present value	$P = \dfrac{A}{1 + rt}$	$P = \dfrac{A}{(1 + i)^n} = A(1 + i)^{-n}$
		Effective rate (or APY) $r_E = \left(1 + \dfrac{r}{m}\right)^m - 1$

Discount   If D is the **discount** on a T-bill with face value P at simple interest rate r for t years, then $D = Prt.$

Continuous Interest   If P dollars are deposited for t years at interest rate r per year, compounded continuously, the **compound amount (future value)** is $A = Pe^{rt}.$

The **present value** P of A dollars at interest rate r per year compounded continuously for t years is

$$P = \frac{A}{e^{rt}}.$$

Annuities

Ordinary annuity	Future value	$S = R\left[\dfrac{(1+i)^n - 1}{i}\right] = R \cdot s_{\overline{n}|i}$	
	Present value	$P = R\left[\dfrac{1-(1+i)^{-n}}{i}\right] = R \cdot a_{\overline{n}|i}$	
Annuity due	Future value	$S = R\left[\dfrac{(1+i)^{n+1}-1}{i}\right] - R$	
	Present value	$P = R + R\left[\dfrac{1-(1+i)^{-(n-1)}}{i}\right]$	

Chapter 5 Review Exercises

Find the simple interest for the following loans.

1. $4902 at 6.5% for 11 months

2. $42,368 at 9.22% for 5 months

3. $3478 at 7.4% for 88 days

4. $2390 at 8.7% from May 3 to July 28

Find the semiannual (simple) interest payment and the total interest earned over the life of the bond.

5. $12,000 Merck Company 6-year bond at 4.75% annual interest

6. $20,000 General Electric 9-year bond at 5.25% annual interest

Find the maturity value for each simple interest loan.

7. $7750 at 6.8% for 4 months

8. $15,600 at 8.2% for 9 months

9. What is meant by the present value of an amount A?

Find the present value of the given future amounts; use simple interest.

10. $459.57 in 7 months; money earns 5.5%

11. $80,612 in 128 days; money earns 6.77%

12. A 9-month $7000 Treasury bill sells at a discount rate of 3.5%. Find the amount of the discount and the price of the T-bill.

13. A 6-month $10,000 T-bill sold at a 4% discount. Find the actual rate of interest paid by the Treasury.

14. For a given amount of money at a given interest rate for a given period greater than 1 year, does simple interest or compound interest produce more interest? Explain.

Find the compound amount and the amount of interest earned in each of the given scenarios.

15. $2800 at 6% compounded annually for 12 years

16. $57,809.34 at 4% compounded quarterly for 6 years

17. $12,903.45 at 6.37% compounded quarterly for 29 quarters

18. $4677.23 at 4.57% compounded monthly for 32 months

Find the amount of compound interest earned by each deposit.

19. $22,000 at 5.5%, compounded quarterly for 6 years

20. $2975 at 4.7%, compounded monthly for 4 years

Find the face value (to the nearest dollar) of the zero-coupon bond.

21. 5-year bond at 3.9%; price $12,366

22. 15-year bond at 5.2%; price $11,575

Find the APY corresponding to the given nominal rate.

23. 5% compounded semiannually

24. 6.5% compounded daily

Find the present value of the given amounts at the given interest rate.

25. $42,000 in 7 years; 12% compounded monthly

26. $17,650 in 4 years; 8% compounded quarterly

27. $1347.89 in 3.5 years; 6.2% compounded semiannually

28. $2388.90 in 44 months; 5.75% compounded monthly

Find the price that a purchaser should be willing to pay for these zero-coupon bonds.

29. 10-year $15,000 bond; interest at 4.4%

30. 25-year $30,000 bond; interest at 6.2%

31. What is meant by the future value of an annuity?

Find the future value of each annuity.

32. $1288 deposited at the end of each year for 14 years; money earns 7% compounded annually

33. $4000 deposited at the end of each quarter for 8 years; money earns 6% compounded quarterly

34. $233 deposited at the end of each month for 4 years; money earns 6% compounded monthly

35. $672 deposited at the beginning of each quarter for 7 years; money earns 5% compounded quarterly

36. $11,900 deposited at the beginning of each month for 13 months; money earns 7% compounded monthly

37. What is the purpose of a sinking fund?

Find the amount of each payment that must be made into a sinking fund to accumulate the given amounts. Assume payments are made at the end of each period.

38. $6500; money earns 5% compounded annually; 6 annual payments

39. $57,000; money earns 6% compounded semiannually for $8\frac{1}{2}$ years

40. $233,188; money earns 5.7% compounded quarterly for $7\frac{3}{4}$ years

41. $56,788; money earns 6.12% compounded monthly for $4\frac{1}{2}$ years

Find the present value of each ordinary annuity.

42. Payments of $850 annually for 4 years at 5% compounded annually

43. Payments of $1500 quarterly for 7 years at 8% compounded quarterly

44. Payments of $4210 semiannually for 8 years at 5.6% compounded semiannually

45. Payments of $877.34 monthly for 17 months at 6.4% compounded monthly

Find the amount necessary to fund the given withdrawals (which are made at the end of each period).

46. Quarterly withdrawals of $800 for 4 years with interest rate 4.6%, compounded quarterly

47. Monthly withdrawals of $1500 for 10 years with interest rate 5.8%, compounded monthly

48. Yearly withdrawals of $3000 for 15 years with interest rate 6.2%, compounded annually

Find the payment for the ordinary annuity with the given present value.

49. $150,000; monthly payments for 15 years, with interest rate 5.1%, compounded monthly

50. $25,000; quarterly payments for 8 years, with interest rate 4.9%, compounded quarterly

51. Find the lump-sum deposit today that will produce the same total amount as payments of $4200 at the end of each year for 12 years. The interest rate in both cases is 4.5%, compounded annually.

52. If the current interest rate is 6.5%, find the price (to the nearest dollar) that a purchaser should be willing to pay for a $24,000 bond with coupon rate 5% that matures in 6 years.

Find the amount of the payment necessary to amortize each of the given loans.

53. $32,000 at 8.4% compounded quarterly; 10 quarterly payments

54. $5607 at 7.6% compounded monthly; 32 monthly payments

Find the monthly house payments for the given mortgages.

55. $95,000 at 3.67% for 30 years

56. $167,000 at 2.91% for 15 years

57. Find the approximate remaining balance after 5 years of payments on the loan in Exercise 55.

58. Find the approximate remaining balance after 7.5 years of payments on the loan in Exercise 56.

Finance *According to www.studentaid.ed.gov, in 2013 the interest rate for a direct unsubsidized student loan was 6.8%. A portion of an amortization table is given here for a $15,000 direct unsubsidized student loan compounded monthly to be paid back in 10 years. Use the table to answer Exercises 59–62.*

Payment Number	Amount of Payment	Interest for Period	Portion to Principal	Principal at End of Period
0				15,000.00
1	172.62	85.00	87.62	14,912.38
2	172.62	84.50	88.12	14,824.26
3	172.62	84.00	88.62	14,735.64
4	172.62	83.50	89.12	14,646.52
5	172.62	83.00	89.62	14,556.90
6	172.62	82.49	90.13	14,466.77
7	172.62	81.98	90.64	14,376.13
8	172.62	81.46	91.16	14,284.97

59. How much of the seventh payment is interest?

60. How much of the fourth payment is used to reduce the debt?

61. How much interest is paid in the first 6 months of the loan?

62. How much has the debt been reduced at the end of the first 8 months?

Finance *Work the following applied problems.*

63. In February 2013, a Virginia family won a Powerball lottery prize of $217,000,000.

   (a) If they had chosen to receive the money in 30 yearly payments, beginning immediately, what would have been the amount of each payment?

   (b) The family chose the one-time lump-sum cash option. If the interest rate is 3.58%, approximately how much did they receive?

64. A firm of attorneys deposits $15,000 of profit-sharing money in an account at 6% compounded semiannually for $7\frac{1}{2}$ years. Find the amount of interest earned.

65. Tom, a graduate student, is considering investing $500 now, when he is 23, or waiting until he is 40 to invest $500. How much more money will he have at age 65 if he invests now, given that he can earn 5% interest compounded quarterly?

66. According to a financial Web site, on June 15, 2005, Frontenac Bank of Earth City, Missouri, paid 3.94% interest, compounded quarterly, on a 2-year CD, while E*TRADE Bank of Arlington, Virginia, paid 3.93% compounded daily. What was the effective rate for the two CDs, and which bank paid a higher effective rate? (Data from: www.bankrate.com.)

67. Chalon Bridges deposits semiannual payments of $3200, received in payment of a debt, in an ordinary annuity at 6.8% compounded semiannually. Find the final amount in the account and the interest earned at the end of 3.5 years.

68. Each year, a firm must set aside enough funds to provide employee retirement benefits of $52,000 in 20 years. If the firm can invest money at 7.5% compounded monthly, what amount must be invested at the end of each month for this purpose?

69. A benefactor wants to be able to leave a bequest to the college she attended. If she wants to make a donation of $2,000,000 in 10 years, how much each month does she need to place in an investment account that pays an interest rate of 5.5%, compounded monthly?

70. Suppose you have built up a pension with $12,000 annual payments by working 10 years for a company when you leave to accept a better job. The company gives you the option of collecting half the full pension when you reach age 55 or the full pension at age 65. Assume an interest rate of 8% compounded annually. By age 75, how much will each plan produce? Which plan would produce the larger amount?

71. In 3 years, Ms. Nguyen must pay a pledge of $7500 to her favorite charity. What lump sum can she deposit today at 10% compounded semiannually so that she will have enough to pay the pledge?

72. To finance the $15,000 cost of their kitchen remodeling, the Chews will make equal payments at the end of each month for 36 months. They will pay interest at the rate of 7.2% compounded monthly. Find the amount of each payment.

73. To expand her business, the owner of a small restaurant borrows $40,000. She will repay the money in equal payments at the end of each semiannual period for 8 years at 9% interest compounded semiannually. What payments must she make?

74. The Fix family bought a house for $210,000. They paid $42,000 down and took out a 30-year mortgage for the balance at 3.75%.

(a) Find the monthly payment.

(b) How much of the first payment is interest?

After 15 years, the family sold their house for $255,000.

(c) Estimate the current mortgage balance at the time of the sale.

(d) Find the amount of money they received from the sale after paying off the mortgage.

75. Over a 20-year period, the class A shares of the Davis New York Venture mutual fund increased in value at the rate of 11.2%, compounded monthly. If you had invested $250 at the end of each month in this fund, what would have the value of your account been at the end of those 20 years?

76. Dan Hook deposits $400 a month to a retirement account that has an interest rate of 3.1%, compounded monthly. After making 60 deposits, Dan changes his job and stops making payments for 3 years. After 3 years, he starts making deposits again, but now he deposits $525 per month. What will the value of the retirement account be after Dan makes his $525 monthly deposits for 5 years?

77. The proceeds of a $10,000 death benefit are left on deposit with an insurance company for 7 years at an annual effective interest rate of 5%.* The balance at the end of 7 years is paid to the beneficiary in 120 equal monthly payments of X, with the first payment made immediately. During the payout period, interest is credited at an annual effective interest rate of 3%. Which of the following is the correct value of X?

(a) 117　　(b) 118　　(c) 129　　(d) 135　　(e) 158

78. Eileen Gianiodis wants to retire on $75,000 per year for her life expectancy of 20 years after she retires. She estimates that she will be able to earn an interest rate of 10.1%, compounded annually, throughout her lifetime. To reach her retirement goal, Eileen will make annual contributions to her account for the next 30 years. One year after making her last deposit, she will receive her first retirement check. How large must her yearly contributions be?

---

*The Proceeds of Death Benefit Left on Deposit with an Insurance Company from Course 140 Examination, Mathematics of Compound Interest. Copyright © Society of Actuaries. Reproduced by permission of Society of Actuaries.

Case Study 5   Continuous Compounding

Informally, you can think of *continuous compounding* as a process in which interest is compounded *very* frequently (for instance, every nanosecond). You will occasionally see an ad for a certificate of deposit in which interest is compounded continuously. That's pretty much a gimmick in most cases, because it produces only a few more cents than daily compounding. However, continuous compounding does play a serious role in certain financial situations, notably in the pricing of derivatives.* So let's see what is involved in continuous compounding.

As a general rule, the more often interest is compounded, the better off you are as an investor. (See Example 4 of Section

5.2.) But there is, alas, a limit on the amount of interest, no matter how often it is compounded. To see why this is so, suppose you have $1 to invest. The Exponential Bank offers to pay 100% annual interest, compounded n times per year and rounded to the nearest penny. Furthermore, you may pick any value for n that you want. Can you choose n so large that your $1 will grow to $5 in a year? We will test several values of n in the formula for the compound amount, with $P = 1$. In this case, the annual interest rate (in decimal form) is also 1. If there are n periods in the year, the interest rate per period is $i = 1/n$. So the amount that your dollar grows to is:

$$A = P(1 + i)^n = 1\left(1 + \frac{1}{n}\right)^n.$$

---

*Derivatives are complicated financial instruments. But investors have learned the hard way that they can sometimes cause serious problems—as was the case in the recession that began in 2008, which was blamed in part on the misuse of derivatives.

A computer gives the following results for various values of n:

Interest Is Compounded ...	n	$\left(1 + \dfrac{1}{n}\right)^n$
Annually	1	$\left(1 + \dfrac{1}{1}\right)^1 = 2$
Semiannually	2	$\left(1 + \dfrac{1}{2}\right)^2 = 2.25$
Quarterly	4	$\left(1 + \dfrac{1}{4}\right)^4 \approx 2.4414$
Monthly	12	$\left(1 + \dfrac{1}{12}\right)^{12} \approx 2.6130$
Daily	365	$\left(1 + \dfrac{1}{365}\right)^{365} \approx 2.71457$
Hourly	8760	$\left(1 + \dfrac{1}{8760}\right)^{8760} \approx 2.718127$
Every minute	525,600	$\left(1 + \dfrac{1}{525,600}\right)^{525,600} \approx 2.7182792$
Every second	31,536,000	$\left(1 + \dfrac{1}{31,536,000}\right)^{31,536,000} \approx 2.7182818$

Because interest is rounded to the nearest penny, the compound amount never exceeds $2.72, no matter how big n is. (A computer was used to develop the table, and the figures in it are accurate. If you try these computations with your calculator, however, your answers may not agree exactly with those in the table because of round-off error in the calculator.)

The preceding table suggests that as n takes larger and larger values, the corresponding values of $\left(1 + \dfrac{1}{n}\right)^n$ get closer and closer to a specific real number whose decimal expansion begins $2.71828 \cdots$. This is indeed the case, as is shown in calculus, and the number $2.71828 \cdots$ is denoted e. This fact is sometimes expressed by writing

$$\lim_{n \to \infty} \left(1 + \frac{1}{n}\right)^n = e,$$

which is read "the limit of $\left(1 + \dfrac{1}{n}\right)^n$ as n approaches infinity is e."

The preceding example is typical of what happens when interest is compounded n times per year, with larger and larger values of n. It can be shown that no matter what interest rate or principal is used, there is always an upper limit (involving the number e) on the compound amount, which is called the compound amount from continuous compounding.

Continuous Compounding

The compound amount A for a deposit of P dollars at an interest rate r per year compounded continuously for t years is given by

$$A = Pe^{rt}.$$

Most calculators have an e^x key for computing powers of e. See the Technology Tip on page 188 for details on using a calculator to evaluate e^x.

Example 1   Suppose $5000 is invested at an annual rate of 4% compounded continuously for 5 years. Find the compound amount.

Solution   In the formula for continuous compounding, let $P = 5000$, $r = .04$, and $t = 5$. Then a calculator with an e^x key shows that

$$A = 5000e^{(.04)5} = 5000e^{.2} \approx \$6107.01.$$

You can readily verify that daily compounding would have produced a compound amount about 6¢ less.

Exercises

1. Find the compound amount when $20,000 is invested at 6% compounded continuously for
   (a) 2 years;   (b) 10 years;   (c) 20 years.

2. (a) Find the compound amount when $2500 is invested at 5.5%, compounded monthly for two years.
   (b) Do part (a) when the interest rate is 5.5% compounded continuously.

3. Determine the compounded amount from a deposit of $25,000 when it is invested at 5% for 10 years and compounded in the following time periods:
   (a) annually   (b) quarterly   (c) monthly
   (d) daily   (e) continuously

4. Determine the compounded amount from a deposit of $250,000 when it is invested at 5% for 10 years and compounded in the following time periods:

   (a) annually   (b) quarterly   (c) monthly

   (d) daily   (e) continuously

5. It can be shown that if interest is compounded continuously at nominal rate r, then the effective rate r_E is $e^r - 1$. Find the effective rate of continuously compounded interest if the nominal rate is

   (a) 4.5%;   (b) 5.7%;   (c) 7.4%.

6. Suppose you win a court case and the defendant has up to 8 years to pay you $5000 in damages. Assume that the defendant will wait until the last possible minute to pay you.

   (a) If you can get an interest rate of 3.75% compounded continuously, what is the present value of the $5000? [*Hint:* Solve the continuous-compounding formula for P.]

   (b) If the defendant offers you $4000 immediately to settle his debt, should you take the deal?

Extended Projects

1. Investigate the interest rates for the subsidized and unsubsidized student loans. If you have taken out student loans or plan to take out student loans before graduating, calculate your own monthly payment and how much interest you will pay over the course of the repayment period. If you have not taken out, and you do not plan to take out a student loan, contact the financial aid office of your college and university to determine the median amount borrowed with student loans at your institution. Determine the monthly payment and how much interest is paid during repayment for the typical borrowing student.

2. Determine the best interest rate for a new car purchase for a 48-month loan at a bank near you. If you finance $25,999 with such a loan, determine the payment and the total interest paid over the course of the loan. Also, determine the best interest rate for a new car purchase for a 48-month loan at a credit union near you. Determine the monthly payment and total interest paid if the same auto loan is financed through the credit union. Is it true that the credit union would save you money?

Systems of Linear Equations and Matrices

6

CHAPTER

A variety of resource allocation problems involving many variables can be handled by solving an appropriate system of linear equations. Technology (such as graphing calculators, WolframAlpha.com, computer algebra systems, and smart phone apps) is very helpful for handling large systems. Smaller ones can easily be solved by hand. See Exercises 22 and 23 on page 296.

This chapter deals with **linear** (or **first-degree**) **equations** such as

$$2x + 3y = 14 \qquad \text{linear equation in two variables,}$$

$$4x - 2y + 5z = 8 \qquad \text{linear equation in three variables,}$$

and so on. A **solution** of such an equation is an ordered list of numbers that, when substituted for the variables in the order they appear, produces a true statement. For instance, $(1, 4)$ is a solution of the equation $2x + 3y = 14$ because substituting $x = 1$ and $y = 4$ produces the true statement $2(1) + 3(4) = 14$.

Many applications involve **systems of linear equations,** such as these two:

Two equations in two variables	Three equations in four variables

$$\begin{aligned} &5x - 3y = 7 \\ &2x + 4y = 8 \end{aligned} \qquad \begin{aligned} 2x + y + z \phantom{{}+w} &= 3 \\ x + y + z + w &= 5 \\ -4x + \phantom{y+{}} z + w &= 0. \end{aligned}$$

A **solution of a system** is a solution that satisfies *all* the equations in the system. For instance, in the right-hand system of equations on page 270, (1, 0, 1, 3) is a solution of all three equations (check it) and hence is a solution of the system. By contrast, (1, 1, 0, 3) is a solution of the first two equations, but not the third. Hence, (1, 1, 0, 3) is not a solution of the system.

This chapter presents methods for solving such systems, including matrix methods. Matrix algebra and other applications of matrices are also discussed.

6.1 Systems of Two Linear Equations in Two Variables

The graph of a linear equation in two variables is a straight line. The coordinates of each point on the graph represent a solution of the equation (Section 2.1). Thus, the solution of a system of two such equations is represented by the point or points where the two lines intersect. There are exactly three geometric possibilities for two lines: They intersect at a single point, or they coincide, or they are distinct and parallel. As illustrated in Figure 6.1, each of these geometric possibilities leads to a different number of solutions for the system.

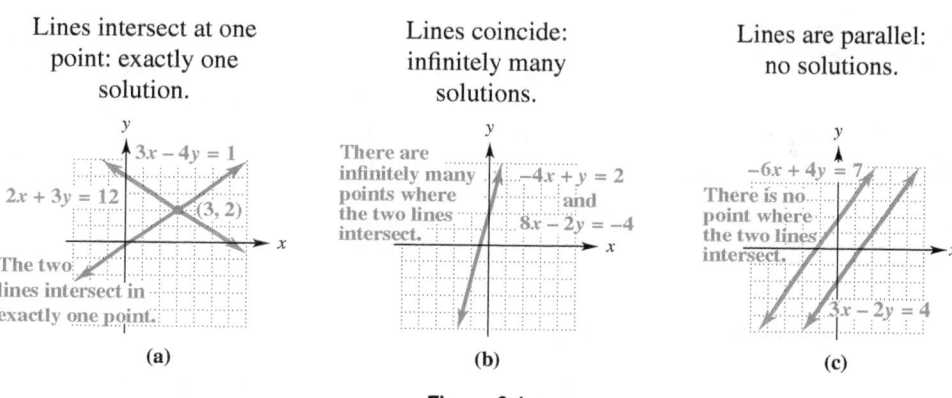

Lines intersect at one point: exactly one solution.

Lines coincide: infinitely many solutions.

Lines are parallel: no solutions.

(a)　　　　　(b)　　　　　(c)

Figure 6.1

The Substitution Method

Example 1 illustrates the substitution method for solving a system of two equations in two variables.

Example 1   Solve the system

$$2x - y = 1$$
$$3x + 2y = 4.$$

Solution   Begin by solving the first equation for y:

$$2x - y = 1$$
$$-y = -2x + 1 \qquad \text{Subtract } 2x \text{ from both sides.}$$
$$y = 2x - 1. \qquad \text{Multiply both sides by } -1.$$

Substitute this expression for y in the second equation and solve for x:

$$3x + 2y = 4$$
$$3x + 2(2x - 1) = 4 \qquad \text{Substitute } 2x - 1 \text{ for } y.$$
$$3x + 4x - 2 = 4 \qquad \text{Multiply out the left side.}$$
$$7x - 2 = 4 \qquad \text{Combine like terms.}$$
$$7x = 6 \qquad \text{Add 2 to both sides.}$$
$$x = 6/7. \qquad \text{Divide both sides by 7.}$$

Therefore, every solution of the system must have $x = 6/7$. To find the corresponding solution for y, substitute $x = 6/7$ in one of the two original equations and solve for y. We shall use the first equation.

$$2x - y = 1$$

$$2\left(\frac{6}{7}\right) - y = 1 \qquad \text{Substitute 6/7 for } x.$$

$$\frac{12}{7} - y = 1 \qquad \text{Multiply out the left side.}$$

$$-y = -\frac{12}{7} + 1 \qquad \text{Subtract 12/7 from both sides.}$$

$$y = \frac{12}{7} - 1 = \frac{5}{7}. \qquad \text{Multiply both sides by } -1.$$

Hence, the solution of the original system is $x = 6/7$ and $y = 5/7$. We would have obtained the same solution if we had substituted $x = 6/7$ in the second equation of the original system, as you can easily verify. ✓1

The substitution method is useful when at least one of the equations has a variable with coefficient 1. That is why we solved for y in the first equation of Example 1. If we had solved for x in the first equation or for x or y in the second, we would have had a lot more fractions to deal with.

TECHNOLOGY TIP A graphing calculator can be used to solve systems of two equations in two variables. Solve each of the given equations for y and graph them on the same screen. In Example 1, for instance we would graph

$$y_1 = 2x - 1 \quad \text{and} \quad y_2 = \frac{-3x + 4}{2}.$$

Use the intersection finder to determine the point where the graphs intersect (the solution of the system), as shown in Figure 6.2. Note that this is an *approximate* solution, rather than the exact solution found algebraically in Example 1.

The Elimination Method

The elimination method of solving systems of linear equations is often more convenient than substitution, as illustrated in the next four examples.

Example 2 Solve the system

$$5x + y = 4$$
$$3x + 2y = 1.$$

Solution Multiply the first equation by -2, so that the coefficients of y in the two equations are negatives of each other:

$$-10x - 2y = -8 \qquad \text{First equation multiplied by } -2.$$
$$3x + 2y = 1. \qquad \text{Second equation as given.}$$

Any solution of this system of equations must also be a solution of the sum of the two equations:

$$-10x - 2y = -8$$
$$\underline{3x + 2y = 1}$$
$$-7x = -7 \qquad \text{Sum; variable } y \text{ is eliminated.}$$
$$x = 1. \qquad \text{Divide both sides by } -7.$$

✓ **Checkpoint 1**

Use the substitution method to solve this system:

$$x - 2y = 3$$
$$2x + 3y = 13.$$

Answers to Checkpoint exercises are found at the end of the section.

Figure 6.2

To find the corresponding value of y, substitute $x = 1$ in one of the original equations, say the first one:

$$5x + y = 4$$
$$5(1) + y = 4 \qquad \text{Substitute 1 for } x.$$
$$y = -1. \qquad \text{Subtract 5 from both sides.}$$

Therefore, the solution of the original system is $(1, -1)$. ✓₂

✓ **Checkpoint 2**

Use the elimination method to solve this system:

$$x + 2y = 4$$
$$3x - 4y = -8.$$

> **Example 3**   Solve the system
>
> $$3x - 4y = 1$$
> $$2x + 3y = 12.$$

Solution   Multiply the first equation by 2 and the second equation by -3 to get

$$6x - 8y = 2 \qquad \text{First equation multiplied by 2.}$$
$$-6x - 9y = -36. \qquad \text{Second equation multiplied by } -3.$$

The multipliers 2 and -3 were chosen so that the coefficients of x in the two equations would be negatives of each other. Any solution of both these equations must also be a solution of their sum:

$$6x - 8y = 2$$
$$\underline{-6x - 9y = -36}$$
$$-17y = -34 \qquad \text{Sum; variable } x \text{ is eliminated.}$$
$$y = 2. \qquad \text{Divide both sides by } -17.$$

To find the corresponding value of x, substitute 2 for y in either of the original equations. We choose the first equation:

$$3x - 4y = 1$$
$$3x - 4(2) = 1 \qquad \text{Substitute 2 for } y.$$
$$3x - 8 = 1 \qquad \text{Simplify.}$$
$$3x = 9 \qquad \text{Add 8 to both sides.}$$
$$x = 3. \qquad \text{Divide both sides by 3.}$$

Therefore, the solution of the system is $(3, 2)$. The graphs of both equations of the system are shown in Figure 6.1(a). They intersect at the point $(3, 2)$, the solution of the system. ✓₃

✓ **Checkpoint 3**

Solve the system of equations

$$3x + 2y = -1$$
$$5x - 3y = 11.$$

Draw the graph of each equation on the same set of axes.

Dependent and Inconsistent Systems

A system of equations that has a unique solution, such as those in Examples 1–3, is called an **independent system.** Now we consider systems that have infinitely many solutions or no solutions at all.

> **Example 4**   Solve the system
>
> $$-4x + y = 2$$
> $$8x - 2y = -4.$$

Solution   If you solve each equation in the system for y, you see that the two equations are actually the same:

$$-4x + y = 2 \qquad\qquad 8x - 2y = -4$$
$$y = 4x + 2 \qquad\qquad -2y = -8x - 4$$
$$y = 4x + 2.$$

So the two equations have the same graph, as shown in Figure 6.1(b), and the system has infinitely many solutions (namely, all solutions of $y = 4x + 2$). A system such as this is said to be **dependent.**

You do not have to analyze a system as was just done in order to find out that the system is dependent. The elimination method will warn you. For instance, if you attempt to eliminate x in the original system by multiplying both sides of the first equation by 2 and adding the results to the second equation, you obtain

$$
\begin{array}{ll}
-8x + 2y = 4 & \text{First equation multiplied by 2.} \\
\underline{8x - 2y = -4} & \text{Second equation as given.} \\
0 = 0. & \text{Both variables are eliminated.}
\end{array}
$$

The equation "$0 = 0$" is an algebraic indication that the system is dependent and has infinitely many solutions. ✔4

✓ **Checkpoint 4**

Solve the following system:
$$3x - 4y = 13$$
$$12x - 16y = 52.$$

Example 5   Solve the system
$$3x - 2y = 4$$
$$-6x + 4y = 7.$$

Solution   The graphs of these equations are parallel lines (each has slope $3/2$), as shown in Figure 6.1(c). Therefore, the system has no solution. However, you do not need the graphs to discover this fact. If you try to solve the system algebraically by multiplying both sides of the first equation by 2 and adding the results to the second equation, you obtain

$$
\begin{array}{ll}
6x - 4y = 8 & \text{First equation multiplied by 2.} \\
\underline{-6x + 4y = 7} & \text{Second equation as given.} \\
0 = 15. & \text{False statement.}
\end{array}
$$

The false statement "$0 = 15$" is the algebraic signal that the system has no solution. A system with no solutions is said to be **inconsistent.** ✔5

✓ **Checkpoint 5**

Solve the system
$$x - y = 4$$
$$2x - 2y = 3.$$

Draw the graph of each equation on the same set of axes.

Applications

In many applications, the answer is the solution of a system of equations. Solving the system is the easy part—*finding* the system, however, may take some thought.

Example 6   **Business**   Eight hundred people attend a basketball game, and total ticket sales are $3102. If adult tickets are $6 and student tickets are $3, how many adults and how many students attended the game?

Solution   Let x be the number of adults and y the number of students. Then

Number of adults + Number of students = Total attendance.

$$x + y = 800.$$

A second equation can be found by considering ticket sales:

Adult ticket sales   +   Student ticket sales   = Total ticket sales

$$
\left(\begin{array}{c}\text{Price}\\\text{per}\\\text{ticket}\end{array}\right) \times \left(\begin{array}{c}\text{Number}\\\text{of}\\\text{adults}\end{array}\right) + \left(\begin{array}{c}\text{Price}\\\text{per}\\\text{ticket}\end{array}\right) \times \left(\begin{array}{c}\text{Number}\\\text{of}\\\text{students}\end{array}\right) = 3102
$$

$$6x + 3y = 3102.$$

✓ **Checkpoint 6**

(a) Use substitution or elimination to solve the system of equations in Example 6.

✎ **(b)** Use technology to solve the system. (*Hint:* Solve each equation for *y*, graph both equations on the same screen, and use the intersection finder.)

To find *x* and *y* we must solve this system of equations:

$$x + y = 800$$
$$6x + 3y = 3102.$$

The system can readily be solved by hand or by using technology. See Checkpoint 6, which shows that 234 adults and 566 students attended the game. ✓ 6

6.1 Exercises

Determine whether the given ordered list of numbers is a solution of the system of equations.

1. $(-1, 3)$
$$2x + y = 1$$
$$-3x + 2y = 9$$

2. $(2, -.5)$
$$.5x + 8y = -3$$
$$x + 5y = -5$$

Use substitution to solve each system. (See Example 1.)

3. $3x - y = 1$
$$x + 2y = -9$$

4. $x + y = 7$
$$x - 2y = -5$$

5. $3x - 2y = 4$
$$2x + y = -1$$

6. $5x - 3y = -2$
$$-x - 2y = 3$$

Use elimination to solve each system. (See Examples 2–5.)

7. $x - 2y = 5$
$$2x + y = 3$$

8. $3x - y = 1$
$$-x + 2y = 4$$

9. $2x - 2y = 12$
$$-2x + 3y = 10$$

10. $3x + 2y = -4$
$$4x - 2y = -10$$

11. $x + 3y = -1$
$$2x - y = 5$$

12. $4x - 3y = -1$
$$x + 2y = 19$$

13. $2x + 3y = 15$
$$8x + 12y = 40$$

14. $2x + 5y = 8$
$$6x + 15y = 18$$

15. $2x - 8y = 2$
$$3x - 12y = 3$$

16. $3x - 2y = 4$
$$6x - 4y = 8$$

In Exercises 17 and 18, multiply both sides of each equation by a common denominator to eliminate the fractions. Then solve the system.

17. $\dfrac{x}{5} + 3y = 31$

$$2x - \dfrac{y}{5} = 8$$

18. $\dfrac{x}{2} + \dfrac{y}{3} = 8$

$$\dfrac{2x}{3} + \dfrac{3y}{2} = 17$$

19. Business When Neil Simon opened a new play, he had to decide whether to open the show on Broadway or off Broadway. For example, he decided to open his play *London Suite* off Broadway. From information provided by Emanuel Azenberg, his producer, the following equations were developed:

$$43,500x - y = 1,295,000$$
$$27,000x - y = 440,000,$$

where *x* represents the number of weeks that the show ran and *y* represents the profit or loss from the show. The first equation is for Broadway, and the second equation is for off Broadway.[*]

(a) Solve this system of equations to determine when the profit or loss from the show will be equal for each venue. What is the amount of that profit or loss?

✎ **(b)** Discuss which venue is favorable for the show.

20. Social Science One of the factors that contribute to the success or failure of a particular army during war is its ability to get new troops ready for service. It is possible to analyze the rate of change in the number of troops of two hypothetical armies with the simplified model

Rate of increase (Red Army) $= 200,000 - .5r - .3b$

Rate of increase (Blue Army) $= 350,000 - .5r - .7b,$

[*]Albert Goetz, "Basic Economics: Calculating against Theatrical Disaster," *Mathematics Teacher* 89, no. 1 (January 1996): 30–32. Reprinted with permission, ©1996 by the National Council of Teachers of Mathematics. All rights reserved.

where r is the number of soldiers in the Red Army at a given time and b is the number of soldiers in the Blue Army at the same time. The factors .5 and .7 represent each army's efficiency at bringing new soldiers into the fight.[*]

(a) Solve this system of equations to determine the number of soldiers in each army when the rate of increase for each is zero.

(b) Describe what might be going on in a war when the rate of increase is zero.

21. **Social Science**   According to U.S. Census Bureau projections through the year 2030, the population y of the given state in year x is approximated by

$$\text{Ohio:} \qquad -5x + y = 11{,}400$$
$$\text{North Carolina:} \quad -140x + y = 8000,$$

where $x = 0$ corresponds to the year 2000 and y is in thousands. In what year do the two states have the same population?

22. **Social Science**   The population y of the given state in year x is approximated by

$$\text{Florida:} \quad 50y - 21x = 800$$
$$\text{New York:} \quad 75y - x = 1425,$$

where $x = 0$ corresponds to the year 2000 and y is in millions. (Data from: U.S. Census Bureau.)

(a) Which state had the larger population in the year 2000?

(b) Which state is projected to have the larger population in the year 2030?

(c) In what year do the two states have the same population?

23. **Finance**   On the basis of data from 2000 and 2010, median weekly earnings y in year x can be approximated for women and men by

$$\text{Women:} \quad 2y - 9x = 1248$$
$$\text{Men:} \quad 10y - 13x = 8110,$$

where $x = 0$ corresponds to the year 2000 and y is in constant 2010 dollars. If these equations remain valid in the future, when will the median weekly earnings for women and men be the same? (Data from: Bureau of Labor Statistics.)

24. **Health**   The number of deaths y in year x can be approximated for diseases of the heart and malignant neoplasms (cancer) by

$$\text{Heart disease:} \quad 58x + 5y = 3555$$
$$\text{Cancer:} \quad -21x + 10y = 5530,$$

where $x = 0$ corresponds to the year 2000 and y is in thousands. According to these models (which are based on data from 2000 and 2010), when were deaths from heart disease equal to cancer deaths? (Data from: Centers for Disease Control and Prevention.)

25. **Business**   A 200-seat theater charges $8 for adults and $5 for children. If all seats were filled and the total ticket income was $1435, how many adults and how many children were in the audience?

26. **Business**   In November 2008, HBO released the complete series of *The Sopranos* on DVD. According to an ad in the *New York Times*, there were 86 episodes on 33 discs. If 5 discs were soundtracks and bonus material and 6 discs each had 4 episodes, how many discs had 2 episodes and how many had 3?

27. **Physical Science**   A plane flies 3000 miles from San Francisco to Boston in 5 hours, with a tailwind all the way. The return trip on the same route, now with a headwind, takes 6 hours. Assuming both remain constant, find the speed of the plane and the speed of the wind. [*Hint:* If x is the plane's speed and y the wind speed (in mph), then the plane travels to Boston at $x + y$ mph because the plane and the wind go in the same direction; on the return trip, the plane travels at $x - y$ mph. (Why?)]

28. **Physical Science**   A plane flying into a headwind travels 2200 miles in 5 hours. The return flight along the same route with a tailwind takes 4 hours. Find the wind speed and the plane's speed (assuming both are constant). (See the hint for Exercise 27.)

29. **Finance**   Shirley Cicero has $16,000 invested in Boeing and GE stock. The Boeing stock currently sells for $30 a share and the GE stock for $70 a share. If GE stock triples in value and Boeing stock goes up 50%, her stock will be worth $34,500. How many shares of each stock does she own?

30. **Business**   An apparel shop sells skirts for $45 and blouses for $35. Its entire stock is worth $51,750, but sales are slow and only half the skirts and two-thirds of the blouses are sold, for a total of $30,600. How many skirts and blouses are left in the store?

31. (a) Find the equation of the straight line through $(1, 2)$ and $(3, 4)$.

(b) Find the equation of the line through $(-1, 1)$ with slope 3.

(c) Find a point that lies on both of the lines in (a) and (b).

32. (a) Find an equation of the straight line through $(0, 9)$ and $(2, 1)$.

(b) Find an equation of the straight line through $(1, 5)$ with slope 2.

(c) Find a point that lies on both of the lines in (a) and (b).

✓ Checkpoint Answers

1. $(5, 1)$ 2. $(0, 2)$

3. $(1, -2)$

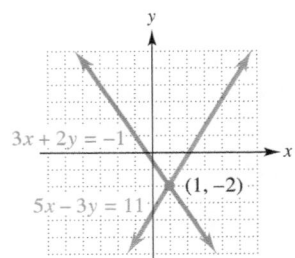

4. All ordered pairs that satisfy the equation $3x - 4y = 13$ (or $12x - 16y = 52$)

5. No solution

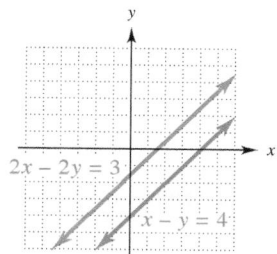

6. (a) $x = 234$ and $y = 566$

(b)

6.2 Larger Systems of Linear Equations

Two systems of equations are said to be **equivalent** if they have the same solutions. The basic procedure for solving a large system of equations is to transform the system into a simpler, equivalent system and then solve this simpler system.

Three operations, called **elementary operations,** are used to transform a system into an equivalent one:

1. **Interchange any two equations in the system.**
   Changing the order of the equations obviously does not affect the solutions of the equations or the system.

2. **Multiply an equation in the system by a nonzero constant.**
   Multiplying an equation by a nonzero constant does not change its solutions. So it does not change the solutions of the system.

3. **Replace an equation in the system by the sum of itself and a constant multiple of another equation.**
   We are not saying here that the replacement equation has the same solutions as the one it replaces—it doesn't—only that the new *system* has the same solutions as the original system (that is, the systems are equivalent).[*]

Example 1 shows how to use elementary operations on a system to eliminate certain variables and produce an equivalent system that is easily solved. The italicized statements provide an outline of the procedure. Here and later on, we use R_1 to denote the first equation in a system, R_2 the second equation, and so on.

Example 1 Solve the system

$$2x + y - z = 2$$
$$x + 3y + 2z = 1$$
$$x + y + z = 2.$$

Solution First, *use elementary operations to produce an equivalent system in which 1 is the coefficient of x in the first equation.* One way to do this is to interchange the first two equations (another would be to multiply both sides of the first equation by $\frac{1}{2}$):

$$x + 3y + 2z = 1 \qquad \text{Interchange } R_1 \text{ and } R_2.$$
$$2x + y - z = 2$$
$$x + y + z = 2.$$

---

[*]This operation was used in a slightly different form in Section 6.1, when the sum of an equation and a constant multiple of another equation was found in order to eliminate one of the variables. See, for instance, Examples 2 and 3 of that section.

Next, *use elementary operations to produce an equivalent system in which the x-term has been eliminated from the second and third equations.* To eliminate the x-term from the second equation, replace the second equation by the sum of itself and -2 times the first equation:

$$
\begin{array}{rl}
-2R_1 & -2x - 6y - 4z = -2 \\
R_2 & \underline{2x + \ y - \ z = \ 2} \\
-2R_1 + R_2 & -5y - 5z = \ 0
\end{array}
$$

$$
\begin{aligned}
x + 3y + 2z &= 1 \\
-5y - 5z &= 0 \qquad -2R_1 + R_2 \\
x + \ y + \ z &= 2.
\end{aligned}
$$

To eliminate the x-term from the third equation of this last system, replace the third equation by the sum of itself and -1 times the first equation:

$$
\begin{array}{rl}
-1R_1 & -x - 3y - 2z = -1 \\
R_3 & \underline{x + \ y + \ z = \ 2} \\
-1R_1 + R_3 & - 2y \ -z = \ 1
\end{array}
$$

$$
\begin{aligned}
x + 3y + 2z &= 1 \\
-5y - 5z &= 0 \\
-2y - \ z &= 1. \qquad -1R_1 + R_3
\end{aligned}
$$

Now that x has been eliminated from all but the first equation, we ignore the first equation and work on the remaining ones. *Use elementary operations to produce an equivalent system in which 1 is the coefficient of y in the second equation.* This can be done by multiplying the second equation in the system by $-\frac{1}{5}$:

$$
\begin{aligned}
x + 3y + 2z &= 1 \\
y + \ z &= 0 \qquad -\tfrac{1}{5}R_2 \\
-2y - \ z &= 1.
\end{aligned}
$$

Then *use elementary operations to obtain an equivalent system in which y has been eliminated from the third equation.* Replace the third equation by the sum of itself and 2 times the second equation:

$$
\begin{aligned}
x + 3y + 2z &= 1 \\
y + \ z &= 0 \\
z &= 1. \qquad 2R_2 + R_3
\end{aligned}
$$

The solution of the third equation is obvious: $z = 1$. Now work backward in the system. Substitute 1 for z in the second equation and solve for y, obtaining $y = -1$. Finally, substitute 1 for z and -1 for y in the first equation and solve for x, obtaining $x = 2$. This process is known as **back substitution.** When it is finished, we have the solution of the original system, namely, $(2, -1, 1)$. It is always wise to check the solution by substituting the values for x, y, and z in *all* equations of the original system.

The procedure used in Example 1 to eliminate variables and produce a system in which back substitution works can be carried out with any system, as summarized below. In this summary, the first variable that appears in an equation with a nonzero coefficient is called the **leading variable** of that equation, and its nonzero coefficient is called the **leading coefficient.**

The Elimination Method for Solving Large Systems of Linear Equations

Use elementary operations to transform the given system into an equivalent one as follows:

1. Make the leading coefficient of the first equation 1 either by interchanging equations or by multiplying the first equation by a suitable constant.

2. Eliminate the leading variable of the first equation from each later equation by replacing the later equation by the sum of itself and a suitable multiple of the first equation.

3. Repeat Steps 1 and 2 for the second equation: Make its leading coefficient 1 and eliminate its leading variable from each later equation by replacing the later equation by the sum of itself and a suitable multiple of the second equation.

4. Repeat Steps 1 and 2 for the third equation, fourth equation, and so on, until it is not possible to go any further.

Then solve the resulting system by back substitution.

At various stages in the elimination process, you may have a choice of elementary operations that can be used. As long as the final result is a system in which back substitution can be used, the choice does not matter. To avoid unnecessary errors, choose elementary operations that minimize the amount of computation and, as far as possible, avoid complicated fractions. ✓₁

Matrix Methods

You may have noticed that the variables in a system of equations remain unchanged during the solution process. So we need to keep track of only the coefficients and the constants. For instance, consider the system in Example 1:

$$2x + y - z = 2$$
$$x + 3y + 2z = 1$$
$$x + y + z = 2.$$

This system can be written in an abbreviated form without listing the variables as

$$\begin{bmatrix} 2 & 1 & -1 & 2 \\ 1 & 3 & 2 & 1 \\ 1 & 1 & 1 & 2 \end{bmatrix}.$$

Such a rectangular array of numbers, consisting of horizontal **rows** and vertical **columns,** is called a **matrix** (plural, **matrices**). Each number in the array is an **element,** or **entry.** To separate the constants in the last column of the matrix from the coefficients of the variables, we sometimes use a vertical line, producing the following **augmented matrix:**

$$\begin{bmatrix} 2 & 1 & -1 & | & 2 \\ 1 & 3 & 2 & | & 1 \\ 1 & 1 & 1 & | & 2 \end{bmatrix}.$$ ✓₂

The rows of the augmented matrix can be transformed in the same way as the equations of the system, since the matrix is just a shortened form of the system. The following **row operations** on the augmented matrix correspond to the elementary operations used on systems of equations.

Performing any one of the following **row operations** on the augmented matrix of a system of linear equations produces the augmented matrix of an equivalent system:

1. Interchange any two rows.

2. Multiply each element of a row by a nonzero constant.

3. Replace a row by the sum of itself and a constant multiple of another row of the matrix.

✓ **Checkpoint 1**

Use the elimination method to solve each system.

(a) $2x + y = -1$
$x + 3y = 2$

(b) $2x - y + 3z = 2$
$x + 2y - z = 6$
$-x - y + z = -5$

✓ **Checkpoint 2**

(a) Write the augmented matrix of the following system:
$4x - 2y + 3z = 4$
$3x + 5y + z = -7$
$5x - y + 4z = 6.$

(b) Write the system of equations associated with the following augmented matrix:
$$\begin{bmatrix} 2 & -2 & | & -2 \\ 1 & 1 & | & 4 \\ 3 & 5 & | & 8 \end{bmatrix}.$$

Row operations on a matrix are indicated by the same notation we used for elementary operations on a system of equations. For example, $2R_3 + R_1$ indicates the sum of 2 times row 3 and row 1.

✓ **Checkpoint 3**

Perform the given row operations on the matrix

$$\begin{bmatrix} -1 & 5 \\ 3 & -2 \end{bmatrix}.$$

(a) Interchange R_1 and R_2.

(b) Find $2R_1$.

(c) Replace R_2 by $-3R_1 + R_2$.

(d) Replace R_1 by $2R_2 + R_1$.

Example 2 Use matrices to solve the system

$$x - 2y = 6 - 4z$$
$$x + 13z = 6 - y$$
$$-2x + 6y - z = -10.$$

Solution First, put the system in the required form, with the constants on the right side of the equals sign and the terms with variables *in the same order* in each equation on the left side of the equals sign. Then write the augmented matrix of the system.

$$\begin{array}{rcr} x - 2y + 4z = & 6 \\ x + y + 13z = & 6 \\ -2x + 6y - z = & -10 \end{array} \qquad \begin{bmatrix} 1 & -2 & 4 & | & 6 \\ 1 & 1 & 13 & | & 6 \\ -2 & 6 & -1 & | & -10 \end{bmatrix}.$$

The matrix method is the same as the elimination method, except that row operations are used on the augmented matrix instead of elementary operations on the corresponding system of equations, as shown in the following side-by-side comparison:

Equation Method	**Matrix Method**

Replace the second equation by the sum of itself and -1 times the first equation:

$$\begin{array}{rcr} x - 2y + 4z = & 6 \\ 3y + 9z = & 0 \\ -2x + 6y - z = & -10. \end{array}$$

Replace the second row by the sum of itself and -1 times the first row:

$$\leftarrow -1R_1 + R_2 \rightarrow \qquad \begin{bmatrix} 1 & -2 & 4 & | & 6 \\ 0 & 3 & 9 & | & 0 \\ -2 & 6 & -1 & | & -10 \end{bmatrix}.$$

Replace the third equation by the sum of itself and 2 times the first equation:

$$\begin{array}{rcr} x - 2y + 4z = & 6 \\ 3y + 9z = & 0 \\ 2y + 7z = & 2. \end{array}$$

Replace the third row by the sum of itself and 2 times the first row:

$$\leftarrow 2R_1 + R_3 \rightarrow \qquad \begin{bmatrix} 1 & -2 & 4 & | & 6 \\ 0 & 3 & 9 & | & 0 \\ 0 & 2 & 7 & | & 2 \end{bmatrix}.$$

Multiply both sides of the second equation by $\frac{1}{3}$:

$$\begin{array}{rcr} x - 2y + 4z = & 6 \\ y + 3z = & 0 \\ 2y + 7z = & 2. \end{array}$$

Multiply each element of row 2 by $\frac{1}{3}$:

$$\leftarrow \frac{1}{3}R_2 \rightarrow \qquad \begin{bmatrix} 1 & -2 & 4 & | & 6 \\ 0 & 1 & 3 & | & 0 \\ 0 & 2 & 7 & | & 2 \end{bmatrix}.$$

Replace the third equation by the sum of itself and -2 times the second equation:

$$\begin{array}{rcr} x - 2y + 4z = & 6 \\ y + 3z = & 0 \\ z = & 2. \end{array}$$

Replace the third row by the sum of itself and -2 times the second row:

$$\leftarrow -2R_2 + R_3 \rightarrow \qquad \begin{bmatrix} 1 & -2 & 4 & | & 6 \\ 0 & 1 & 3 & | & 0 \\ 0 & 0 & 1 & | & 2 \end{bmatrix}.$$

✓ **Checkpoint 4**

Complete the matrix solution of the system with this augmented matrix:

$$\begin{bmatrix} 1 & 1 & 1 & | & 2 \\ 1 & -2 & 1 & | & -1 \\ 0 & 3 & 1 & | & 5 \end{bmatrix}.$$

Now use back substitution:

$$z = 2 \qquad\qquad y + 3(2) = 0 \qquad\qquad x - 2(-6) + 4(2) = 6$$
$$y = -6 \qquad\qquad\qquad x + 20 = 6$$
$$x = -14.$$

The solution of the system is $(-14, -6, 2)$. ✓

A matrix, such as the last one in Example 2, is said to be in **row echelon form** when

all rows consisting entirely of zeros (if any) are at the bottom;

the first nonzero entry in each row is 1 (called a *leading* 1); and

each leading 1 appears to the right of the leading 1s in any preceding rows.

When a matrix in row echelon form is the augmented matrix of a system of equations, as in Example 2, the system can readily be solved by back substitution. So the matrix solution method amounts to transforming the augmented matrix of a system of equations into a matrix in row echelon form.

The Gauss–Jordan Method

The **Gauss–Jordan method** is a variation on the matrix elimination method used in Example 2. It replaces the back substitution used there with additional elimination of variables, as illustrated in the next example.

Example 3   Use the Gauss–Jordan method to solve the system in Example 2.

Solution   First, set up the augmented matrix. Then apply the same row operations used in Example 2 until you reach the final row echelon matrix, which is

$$\left[\begin{array}{ccc|c} 1 & -2 & 4 & 6 \\ 0 & 1 & 3 & 0 \\ 0 & 0 & 1 & 2 \end{array}\right].$$

Now use additional row operations to make the entries (other than the 1s) in columns two and three into zeros. Make the first two entries in column three 0 as follows:

$$\left[\begin{array}{ccc|c} 1 & -2 & 4 & 6 \\ 0 & 1 & 0 & -6 \\ 0 & 0 & 1 & 2 \end{array}\right] \qquad -3R_3 + R_2$$

$$\left[\begin{array}{ccc|c} 1 & -2 & 0 & -2 \\ 0 & 1 & 0 & -6 \\ 0 & 0 & 1 & 2 \end{array}\right] \qquad -4R_3 + R_1$$

Now make the first entry in column two 0.

$$\left[\begin{array}{ccc|c} 1 & 0 & 0 & -14 \\ 0 & 1 & 0 & -6 \\ 0 & 0 & 1 & 2 \end{array}\right]. \qquad 2R_2 + R_1$$

The last matrix corresponds to the system $x = -14, y = -6, z = 2$. So the solution of the original system is $(-14, -6, 2)$. This solution agrees with what we found in Example 2.

The final matrix in the Gauss–Jordan method is said to be in **reduced row echelon form,** meaning that it is in row echelon form *and* every column containing a leading 1 has zeros in all its other entries, as in Example 3. As we saw there, the solution of the system can be read directly from the reduced row echelon matrix.

In the Gauss–Jordan method, row operations may be performed in any order, but it is best to transform the matrix systematically. Either follow the procedure in Example 3 (which first puts the system into a form in which back substitution can be used and then eliminates additional variables) or work column by column from left to right, as in Checkpoint 5.

✓**Checkpoint 5**

Use the Gauss–Jordan method to solve the system

$$x + 2y = 11$$
$$-4x + y = -8$$
$$5x + y = 19$$

as instructed in parts (a)–(g). Give the shorthand notation for the required row operations in parts (b)–(f) and the new matrix in each step.

(a) Set up the augmented matrix.

(b) Get 0 in row 2, column 1.

(c) Get 0 in row 3, column 1.

(d) Get 1 in row 2, column 2.

(e) Get 0 in row 1, column 2.

(f) Get 0 in row 3, column 2.

(g) List the solution of the system.

Technology and Systems of Equations

When working by hand, it is usually better to use the matrix elimination method (Example 2), because errors with back substitution are less likely to occur than errors in performing the additional row operations needed in the Gauss–Jordan method. When you are using technology, however, the Gauss–Jordan method (Example 3) is more efficient: The solution can be read directly from the final reduced row echelon matrix without any "hand work," as illustrated in the next example.

 Example 4   Use a graphing calculator to solve the system in Example 2.

Solution   There are three ways to proceed.

Matrix Elimination Method   Enter the augmented matrix of the system into the calculator (Figure 6.3). Use REF (in the MATH or OPS submenu of the MATRIX menu) to put this matrix in row echelon form (Figure 6.4). The system corresponding to this matrix is

$$x - 3y + .5z = 5$$
$$y + 3.125z = .25$$
$$z = 2.$$

Because the calculator used a different sequence of row operations than was used in Example 2, it produced a different row echelon matrix (and corresponding system). However, back substitution shows that the solutions of this system are the same ones found in Example 2:

$$z = 2 \qquad y + 3.125(2) = .25 \qquad x - 3(-6) + .5(2) = 5$$
$$y + 6.25 = .25 \qquad x + 18 + 1 = 5$$
$$y = -6 \qquad x = -14.$$

As you can see, a significant amount of hand work is involved in this method, so it is not recommended.

Gauss–Jordan Method   Enter the augmented matrix (Figure 6.3). Use RREF (in same menu as REF) to produce the same reduced row echelon matrix obtained in Example 3 (Figure 6.5). The solution of the system can be read directly from the matrix: $x = -14$, $y = -6, z = 2$.

System Solver Method   This is essentially the same as the Gauss–Jordan method, with an extra step at the beginning. Call up the solver (see the Technology Tip on the next page) and enter the number of variables and equations. The solver will display an appropriately sized matrix, with all entries 0. Change the entries so that the matrix becomes the augmented matrix of the system (Figure 6.6). Press SOLVE and the solution will appear (Figure 6.7). The calculator uses the variables x_1, x_2, and x_3 instead of x, y, and z.

Figure 6.3

Figure 6.4

Figure 6.5

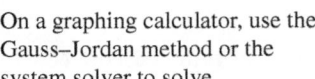

On a graphing calculator, use the Gauss–Jordan method or the system solver to solve

$$x - y + 5z = -6$$
$$4x + 2y + 4z = 4$$
$$x - 5y + 8z = -17$$
$$x + 3y + 2z = 5.$$

Figure 6.6

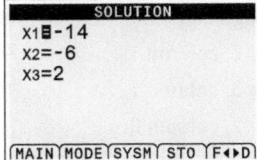

Figure 6.7

TECHNOLOGY TIP   Many graphing calculators have system solvers. Select PLYSMLT2 in the APPS menu of TI-84+, SIMULT on the TI-86 keyboard, or EQUA in the Casio main menu. *Note:* The TI-86 and Casio solvers work only for systems that have the same number of variables as equations *and* have a unique solution (so they cannot be used in Checkpoint 6 or in Examples 5–8).

Example 5   Use a graphing calculator to solve the system

$$x + 2y - z = 0$$
$$3x - y + z = 6$$
$$7x + 28y - 8z = -5$$
$$5x + 3y - z = 6.$$

Solution   Enter the augmented matrix into the calculator (Figure 6.8). Then use RREF to put this matrix in reduced row echelon form (Figure 6.9). In Figure 6.9, you must use the arrow key to scroll over to see the full decimal expansions in the right-hand column. This inconvenience can be avoided on TI calculators by using FRAC (in the MATH menu), as in Figure 6.10.

```
[A]
[1   2   -1   0]
[3  -1    1   6]
[7  28   -8  -5]
[5   3   -1   6]
```

```
rref([A])
[1  0  0   1.571428571]
[0  1  0  -.2857142857]
[0  0  1    1]
[0  0  0    0]
```

```
rref([A])▶Frac
[1  0  0   11/7]
[0  1  0   -2/7]
[0  0  1    1]
[0  0  0    0]
```

Figure 6.8   **Figure 6.9**   **Figure 6.10**

The answers can now be read from the last column of the matrix in Figure 6.10: $x = 11/7$, $y = -2/7, z = 1.$

✓ **Checkpoint 7**

Use a graphing calculator to solve the following system:

$$x + 3y = 4$$
$$4x + 8y = 4$$
$$6x + 12y = 6.$$

Inconsistent and Dependent Systems

Recall that a system of equations in two variables may have exactly one solution, an infinite number of solutions, or no solutions at all. This fact was illustrated geometrically in Figure 6.1. The same thing is true for systems with three or more variables (and the same terminology is used): A system has exactly one solution (an **independent system**), an infinite number of solutions (a **dependent system**), or no solutions at all (an **inconsistent system**).

Example 6   Solve the system

$$2x + 4y = 4$$
$$3x + 6y = 8$$
$$2x + y = 7.$$

Solution   There are several possible ways to proceed.

Manual Method   Write the augmented matrix and perform row operations to obtain a first column whose entries (from top to bottom) are 1, 0, 0:

$$\begin{bmatrix} 2 & 4 & | & 4 \\ 3 & 6 & | & 8 \\ 2 & 1 & | & 7 \end{bmatrix}$$

$$\begin{bmatrix} 1 & 2 & | & 2 \\ 3 & 6 & | & 8 \\ 2 & 1 & | & 7 \end{bmatrix} \qquad \tfrac{1}{2}R_1$$

$$\begin{bmatrix} 1 & 2 & | & 2 \\ 0 & 0 & | & 2 \\ 2 & 1 & | & 7 \end{bmatrix}. \qquad -3R_1 + R_2$$

```
rref([A])
        [1  0  0]
        [0  1  0]
        [0  0  1]
```

Figure 6.11

Stop! The second row of the matrix denotes the equation $0x + 0y = 2$. Since the left side of this equation is always 0 and the right side is 2, it has no solution. Therefore, the original system has no solution.

Calculator Method Enter the augmented matrix into a graphing calculator and use RREF to put it into reduced row echelon form, as in Figure 6.11. The last row of that matrix corresponds to $0x + 0y = 1$, which has no solution. Hence, the original system has no solution. ✓ 8

✓ **Checkpoint 8**

Solve each system.

(a) $\quad x - y = 4$
$\quad -2x + 2y = 1$

(b) $\quad 3x - 4y = 0$
$\quad 2x + y = 0$

Whenever the solution process produces a row whose elements are all 0 *except* the last one, as in Example 6, the system is inconsistent and has no solutions. However, if a row with a 0 for *every* entry is produced, it corresponds to an equation such as $0x + 0y + 0z = 0$, which has infinitely many solutions. So the system may have solutions, as in the next example.

Example 7 Solve the system

$$2x - 3y + 4z = \quad 6$$
$$x - 2y + \quad z = \quad 9$$
$$y + 2z = -12.$$

Solution Use matrix elimination as far as possible, beginning with the augmented matrix of the system:

$$\begin{bmatrix} 2 & -3 & 4 & | & 6 \\ 1 & -2 & 1 & | & 9 \\ 0 & 1 & 2 & | & -12 \end{bmatrix}$$

$$\begin{bmatrix} 1 & -2 & 1 & | & 9 \\ 2 & -3 & 4 & | & 6 \\ 0 & 1 & 2 & | & -12 \end{bmatrix} \qquad \text{Interchange } R_1 \text{ and } R_2.$$

$$\begin{bmatrix} 1 & -2 & 1 & | & 9 \\ 0 & 1 & 2 & | & -12 \\ 0 & 1 & 2 & | & -12 \end{bmatrix} \qquad -2R_1 + R_2$$

$$\begin{bmatrix} 1 & -2 & 1 & | & 9 \\ 0 & 1 & 2 & | & -12 \\ 0 & 0 & 0 & | & 0 \end{bmatrix}. \qquad -R_2 + R_3 \qquad \begin{aligned} x - 2y + z &= 9 \\ y + 2z &= -12. \end{aligned}$$

The last augmented matrix above represents the system shown to its right. Since there are only two rows in the matrix, it is not possible to continue the process. The fact that the corresponding system has one variable (namely, z) that is not the leading variable of an equation indicates a dependent system. To find its solutions, first solve the second equation for y:

$$y = -2z - 12.$$

Now substitute the result for y in the first equation and solve for x:

$$x - 2y + z = 9$$
$$x - 2(-2z - 12) + z = 9$$
$$x + 4z + 24 + z = 9$$
$$x + 5z = -15$$
$$x = -5z - 15.$$

Each choice of a value for z leads to values for x and y. For example,

if $z = 1$,   then $x = -20$ and $y = -14$;

if $z = -6$,   then $x = 15$ and $y = 0$;

if $z = 0$,   then $x = -15$ and $y = -12$.

There are infinitely many solutions of the original system, since z can take on infinitely many values. The solutions are all ordered triples of the form

$$(-5z - 15, -2z - 12, z),$$

where z is any real number.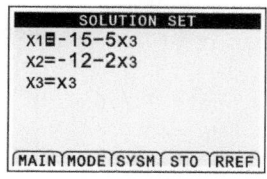

Since both x and y in Example 7 were expressed in terms of z, the variable z is called a **parameter.** If we had solved the system in a different way, x or y could have been the parameter. The system in Example 7 had one more variable than equations. If there are two more variables than equations, there usually will be two parameters, and so on.

Example 8   Row operations were used to reduce the augmented matrix of a system of three equations in four variables $(x, y, z,$ and $w)$ to the reduced row echelon matrix in Figure 6.12. Solve the system.

Solution   First write out the system represented by the matrix:

$$x + \qquad\qquad 9w = -12$$
$$y - \qquad w = \quad 4$$
$$z - 2w = \quad 1.$$

Let w be the parameter. Solve the first equation for x, the second for y, and the third for z:

$$x = -9w - 12; \qquad y = w + 4; \qquad z = 2w + 1.$$

The solutions are given by $(-9w - 12, w + 4, 2w + 1, w)$, where w is any real number.

TECHNOLOGY TIP   When the system solvers on TI-86 and Casio produce an error message, the system might be inconsistent (no solutions) or dependent (infinitely many solutions). You must use RREF or manual methods to solve the system.

The TI-84+ solver usually solves dependent systems directly; Figure 6.13 shows its solutions for Example 7. When the message "no solution found" is displayed, as in Figure 6.14, select RREF at the bottom of the screen to display the reduced row echelon matrix of the system. From that, you can determine the solutions (if there are any) or that no solutions are possible.

✓ Checkpoint 9

Use the following values of z to find additional solutions for the system of Example 7.

(a) $z = 7$

(b) $z = -14$

(c) $z = 5$

```
[A]
⎡1  Ø  Ø   9  -12⎤
⎢Ø  1  Ø  -1   4 ⎥
⎣Ø  Ø  1  -2   1 ⎦
```

Figure 6.12

```
┌──────────────────────┐
│    SOLUTION SET      │
│ X1█-15-5x3           │
│ X2=-12-2x3           │
│ X3=X3                │
│                      │
│                      │
│ MAIN MODE SYSM STO RREF │
└──────────────────────┘
```

Figure 6.13

```
┌──────────────────────┐
│      SOLUTION        │
│                      │
│  ┌──────────────────┐│
│  │ NO SOLUTION FOUND ││
│  └──────────────────┘│
│                      │
│ MAIN MODE SYSM RREF   │
└──────────────────────┘
```

Figure 6.14

6.2 Exercises

Obtain an equivalent system by performing the stated elementary operation on the system. (See Example 1.)

1. Interchange equations 1 and 2.

$$2x - 4y + 5z = 1$$
$$x \quad - 3z = 2$$
$$5x - 8y + 7z = 6$$
$$3x - 4y + 2z = 3$$

2. Interchange equations 1 and 3.

$$2x - 2y + z = -6$$
$$3x + y + 2z = 2$$
$$x + y - 2z = 0$$

3. Multiply the second equation by -1.

$$3x \quad + z + 2w + 18v = 0$$
$$4x - y + \quad w + 24v = 0$$
$$7x - y + z + 3w + 42v = 0$$
$$4x \quad + z + 2w + 24v = 0$$

4. Multiply the third equation by $1/2$.

$$x + 2y + 4z = 3$$
$$x \quad + 2z = 0$$
$$2x + 4y + z = 3$$

5. Replace the second equation by the sum of itself and -2 times the first equation.

$$x + y + 2z + 3w = 1$$
$$2x + y + 3z + 4w = 1$$
$$3x + y + 4z + 5w = 2$$

6. Replace the third equation by the sum of itself and -1 times the first equation.

$$x + 2y + 4z = 6$$
$$y + z = 1$$
$$x + 3y + 5z = 10$$

7. Replace the third equation by the sum of itself and -2 times the second equation.

$$x + 12y - 3z + 4w = 10$$
$$2y + 3z + w = 4$$
$$4y + 5z + 2w = 1$$
$$6y - 2z - 3w = 0$$

8. Replace the third equation by the sum of itself and 3 times the second equation.

$$2x + 2y - 4z + w = -5$$
$$2y + 4z - w = 2$$
$$-6y - 4z + 2w = 6$$
$$2y + 5z - 3w = 7$$

Solve the system by back substitution. (See Example 1.)

9.
$$x + 3y - 4z + 2w = 1$$
$$y + z - w = 4$$
$$2z + 2w = -6$$
$$3w = 9$$

10.
$$x + \quad 5z + 6w = 10$$
$$y + 3z - 2w = 4$$
$$z - 4w = -6$$
$$2w = 4$$

11.
$$2x + 2y - 4z + w = -5$$
$$3y + 4z - w = 0$$
$$2z - 7w = -6$$
$$5w = 15$$

12.
$$3x - 2y - 4z + 2w = 6$$
$$2y + 5z - 3w = 7$$
$$3z + 4w = 0$$
$$3w = 15$$

Write the augmented matrix of each of the given systems. Do not solve the systems. (See Example 2.)

13.
$$2x + y + z = 3$$
$$3x - 4y + 2z = -5$$
$$x + y + z = 2$$

14.
$$3x + 4y - 2z - 3w = 0$$
$$x - 3y + 7z + 4w = 9$$
$$2x \quad + 5z - 6w = 0$$

Write the system of equations associated with each of the given augmented matrices. Do not solve the systems.

15. $\begin{bmatrix} 2 & 3 & 8 & | & 20 \\ 1 & 4 & 6 & | & 12 \\ 0 & 3 & 5 & | & 10 \end{bmatrix}$

16. $\begin{bmatrix} 3 & 2 & 6 & | & 18 \\ 2 & -2 & 5 & | & 7 \\ 1 & 0 & 5 & | & 20 \end{bmatrix}$

Use the indicated row operation to transform each matrix. (See Examples 2 and 3.)

17. Interchange R_2 and R_3.

$\begin{bmatrix} 1 & 2 & 3 & | & -1 \\ 6 & 5 & 4 & | & 6 \\ 2 & 0 & 7 & | & -4 \end{bmatrix}$

18. Replace R_3 by $-3R_1 + R_3$.

$\begin{bmatrix} 1 & 5 & 2 & 0 & | & -1 \\ 8 & 5 & 4 & 6 & | & 6 \\ 3 & 0 & 7 & 1 & | & -4 \end{bmatrix}$

19. Replace R_2 by $2R_1 + R_2$.

$\begin{bmatrix} -4 & -3 & 1 & -1 & | & 2 \\ 8 & 2 & 5 & 0 & | & 6 \\ 0 & -2 & 9 & 4 & | & 5 \end{bmatrix}$

20. Replace R_3 by $\dfrac{1}{4}R_3$.

$\begin{bmatrix} 2 & 5 & 1 & | & -1 \\ -4 & 0 & 4 & | & 6 \\ 6 & 0 & 8 & | & -4 \end{bmatrix}$

In Exercises 21–24, the reduced row echelon form of the augmented matrix of a system of equations is given. Find the solutions of the system. (See Example 3.)

21. $\begin{bmatrix} 1 & 0 & 0 & 0 & | & 3/2 \\ 0 & 1 & 0 & 0 & | & 17 \\ 0 & 0 & 1 & 0 & | & -5 \\ 0 & 0 & 0 & 1 & | & 0 \end{bmatrix}$

22. $\begin{bmatrix} 1 & 0 & 0 & 0 & 0 & | & 6 \\ 0 & 1 & 0 & 0 & 0 & | & 4 \\ 0 & 0 & 1 & 0 & 0 & | & 5 \\ 0 & 0 & 0 & 0 & 1 & | & 2 \\ 0 & 0 & 0 & 0 & 0 & | & 1 \end{bmatrix}$

23. $\begin{bmatrix} 1 & 0 & 0 & 1 & | & 12 \\ 0 & 1 & 0 & 2 & | & -3 \\ 0 & 0 & 1 & 0 & | & -5 \\ 0 & 0 & 0 & 0 & | & 0 \end{bmatrix}$

24. $\begin{bmatrix} 1 & 0 & 0 & 0 & | & 7 \\ 0 & 1 & 0 & 0 & | & 2 \\ 0 & 0 & 1 & 0 & | & -5 \\ 0 & 0 & 0 & 1 & | & 3 \\ 0 & 0 & 0 & 0 & | & 0 \\ 0 & 0 & 0 & 0 & | & 0 \end{bmatrix}$

In Exercises 25–30, perform row operations on the augmented matrix as far as necessary to determine whether the system is independent, dependent, or inconsistent. (See Examples 6–8.)

25.
$x + 2y \quad\quad = 0$
$\quad\quad y - z = 2$
$x + \ y + z = -2$

26.
$x + 2y + \ z = 0$
$\quad\quad y + 2z = 0$
$x + \ y - \ z = 0$

27.
$x + 2y + 4z = 6$
$\quad\quad y + \ z = 1$
$x + 3y + 5z = 10$

28.
$x + y + 2z + 3w = 1$
$2x + y + 3z + 4w = 1$
$3x + y + 4z + 5w = 2$

29.
$a - 3b - 2c = -3$
$3a + 2b - \ c = 12$
$-a - \ b + 4c = 3$

30.
$2x + 2y + 2z = 6$
$3x - 3y - 4z = -1$
$x + \ y + 3z = 11$

Write the augmented matrix of the system and use the matrix method to solve the system. (See Examples 2 and 4.)

31.
$-x + 3y + 2z = 0$
$2x - \ y - \ z = 3$
$x + 2y + 3z = 0$

32.
$3x + 7y + 9z = 0$
$x + 2y + 3z = 2$
$x + 4y + \ z = 2$

33.
$x - 2y + \ 4z = 6$
$x + 2y + 13z = 6$
$-2x + 6y - \ z = -10$

34.
$x - \ 2y + 5z = -6$
$x + \ 2y + 3z = 0$
$x + \ 3y + 2z = 5$

35.
$x + \ y + \ z = 200$
$x - 2y \quad\quad = 0$
$2x + 3y + 5z = 600$
$2x - \ y + \ z = 200$

36.
$2x - \ y + 2z = 3$
$-x + 2y - \ z = 0$
$\quad\quad 3y - 2z = 1$
$x + \ y - \ z = 1$

37.
$x + y + z = 5$
$2x + y - z = 2$
$x - y + z = -2$

38.
$2x + y + 3z = 9$
$-x - y + \ z = 1$
$3x - y + \ z = 9$

Use the Gauss–Jordan method to solve each of the given systems of equations. (See Examples 3–5.)

39.
$x + 2y + \ z = 5$
$2x + \ y - 3z = -2$
$3x + \ y + 4z = -5$

40.
$3x - 2y + \ z = 6$
$3x + \ y - \ z = -4$
$-x + 2y - 2z = -8$

41.
$x + 3y - 6z = 7$
$2x - \ y + 2z = 0$
$x + \ y + 2z = -1$

42.
$x = 1 - y$
$2x = z$
$2z = -2 - y$

43.
$x - 2y + \ 4z = 9$
$x + \ y + 13z = 6$
$-2x + 6y - \ z = -10$

44.
$x - \ y + 5z = -6$
$3x + 3y - \ z = 10$
$x + 2y + 3z = 5$

Solve the system by any method.

45.
$x + 3y + 4z = 14$
$2x - 3y + 2z = 10$
$3x - \ y + \ z = 9$
$4x + 2y + 5z = 9$

46.
$4x - \ y + 3z = -2$
$3x + 5y - \ z = 15$
$-2x + \ y + 4z = 14$
$x + 6y + 3z = 29$

47.
$x + 8y + 8z = 8$
$3x - \ y + 3z = 5$
$-2x - 4y - 6z = 5$

48.
$3x - 2y - \ 8z = 1$
$9x - 6y - 24z = -2$
$x - \ y + \ z = 1$

49.
$5x + 3y + 4z = 19$
$3x - \ y + \ z = -4$

50.
$3x + y - \ z = 0$
$2x - y + 3z = -7$

51.
$x - 2y + \ z = 5$
$2x + \ y - \ z = 2$
$-2x + 4y - 2z = 2$

52.
$2x + 3y + \ z = 9$
$4x + \ y - 3z = -7$
$6x + 2y - 4z = -8$

53.
$-8x - \ 9y = 11$
$24x + 34y = 2$
$16x + 11y = -57$

54.
$2x + \ y = 7$
$x - \ y = 3$
$x + 3y = 4$

55.
$x + 2y = 3$
$2x + 3y = 4$
$3x + 4y = 5$
$4x + 5y = 6$

56.
$x - \ y = 2$
$x + \ y = 4$
$2x + 3y = 9$
$3x - 2y = 6$

57.
$x + y - z = -20$
$2x - y + z = 11$

58.
$4x + 3y + \ z = 1$
$-2x - \ y + 2z = 0$

59.
$2x + \ y + 3z - 2w = -6$
$4x + 3y + \ z - \ w = -2$
$x + \ y + \ z + \ w = -5$
$-2x - 2y - 2z + 2w = -10$

60.
$x + \ y + z + \ w = -1$
$-x + 4y + z - \ w = 0$
$x - 2y + z - 2w = 11$
$-x - 2y + z + 2w = -9$

61.
$x + 2y - z \quad\quad = 3$
$3x + \ y \quad\quad + w = 4$
$2x - \ y + z + w = 2$

62. $x - 2y - z - 3w = -3$
$-x + y + z \quad\quad = 2$
$\quad\quad 4y + 3z - 6w = -2$

63. $\dfrac{3}{x} - \dfrac{1}{y} + \dfrac{4}{z} = -13$

$\dfrac{1}{x} + \dfrac{2}{y} - \dfrac{1}{z} = 12$

$\dfrac{4}{x} - \dfrac{1}{y} + \dfrac{3}{z} = -7$

[*Hint:* Let $u = 1/x, v = 1/y,$ and $w = 1/z,$ and solve the resulting system.]

64. $\dfrac{1}{x + 1} - \dfrac{2}{y - 3} + \dfrac{3}{z - 2} = 4$

$\dfrac{5}{y - 3} - \dfrac{10}{z - 2} = -5$

$\dfrac{-3}{x + 1} + \dfrac{4}{y - 3} - \dfrac{1}{z - 2} = -2$

[*Hint:* Let $u = 1/(x + 1), v = 1/(y - 3),$ and $w = 1/(z - 2).$]

Work these exercises.

65. Social Science The population y in year x of the county listed is approximated by:

Calhoun County, IL: $\quad x + 20y = 102$
Martin County, TX: $\quad -x + 10y = 48$
Schley County, GA: $\quad\quad\quad y = 5,$

where $x = 0$ corresponds to the year 2010 and y is in thousands. When did all three counties have the same population? What was that population? (Data from: U.S. Census Bureau.)

66. Social Science The population y in year x of the greater metropolitan area listed is approximated by the given equation in which $x = 0$ corresponds to the year 2010 and y is in thousands:

Portland, OR: $\quad -32x + y = 2226$
Cambridge, MA: $\quad -22x + y = 2246$
Charlotte, NC: $\quad -73x + 2y = 4434.$

In what year did all three metropolitan areas have the same population? (Data from: U.S. Census Bureau.)

67. Business A band concert is attended by x adults, y teenagers, and z preteen children. These numbers satisfy the following equations:

$x + 1.25y + .25z = 457.5$
$x + .6y + .4z = 390$
$3.16x + 3.48y + .4z = 1297.2.$

How many adults, teenagers, and children were present?

68. Business The owner of a small business borrows money on three separate credit cards: x dollars on Mastercard, y dollars on Visa, and z dollars on American Express. These amounts satisfy the following equations:

$1.18x + 1.15y + 1.09z = 11,244.25$
$3.54x - .55y + .27z = 3,732.75$
$.06x + .05y + .03z = 414.75.$

How much did the owner borrow on each card?

Work these problems.

69. Graph the equations in the given system. Then explain why the graphs show that the system is inconsistent:

$2x + 3y = 8$
$x - y = 4$
$5x + y = 7.$

70. Explain why the graphs of the equations in the given system suggest that the system is independent:

$-x + y = 1$
$-2x + y = 0$
$x + y = 3.$

71. Find constants a, b, and c such that the points $(2, 3)$, $(-1, 0)$, and $(-2, 2)$ lie on the graph of the equation $y = ax^2 + bx + c$. (*Hint:* Since $(2, 3)$ is on the graph, we must have $3 = a(2^2) + b(2) + c$; that is, $4a + 2b + c = 3$. Similarly, the other two points lead to two more equations. Solve the resulting system for a, b, and c.)

72. Explain why a system with more variables than equations cannot have a unique solution (that is, be an independent system). (*Hint:* When you apply the elimination method to such a system, what must happen?)

✓ Checkpoint Answers

1. **(a)** $(-1, 1)$ **(b)** $(3, 1, -1)$

2. **(a)** $\begin{bmatrix} 4 & -2 & 3 & | & 4 \\ 3 & 5 & 1 & | & -7 \\ 5 & -1 & 4 & | & 6 \end{bmatrix}$ **(b)** $2x - 2y = -2$
$x + y = 4$
$3x + 5y = 8$

3. **(a)** $\begin{bmatrix} 3 & -2 \\ -1 & 5 \end{bmatrix}$ **(b)** $\begin{bmatrix} -2 & 10 \\ 3 & -2 \end{bmatrix}$

(c) $\begin{bmatrix} -1 & 5 \\ 6 & -17 \end{bmatrix}$ **(d)** $\begin{bmatrix} 5 & 1 \\ 3 & -2 \end{bmatrix}$

4. $(-1, 1, 2)$

5. **(a)** $\begin{bmatrix} 1 & 2 & | & 11 \\ -4 & 1 & | & -8 \\ 5 & 1 & | & 19 \end{bmatrix}$ **(b)** $4R_1 + R_2 \begin{bmatrix} 1 & 2 & | & 11 \\ 0 & 9 & | & 36 \\ 5 & 1 & | & 19 \end{bmatrix}$

(c) $-5R_1 + R_3 \begin{bmatrix} 1 & 2 & | & 11 \\ 0 & 9 & | & 36 \\ 0 & -9 & | & -36 \end{bmatrix}$

(d) $\frac{1}{9}R_2 \begin{bmatrix} 1 & 2 & | & 11 \\ 0 & 1 & | & 4 \\ 0 & -9 & | & -36 \end{bmatrix}$

(e) $-2R_2 + R_1$ $\begin{bmatrix} 1 & 0 & | & 3 \\ 0 & 1 & | & 4 \\ 0 & -9 & | & -36 \end{bmatrix}$

(f) $\begin{bmatrix} 1 & 0 & | & 3 \\ 0 & 1 & | & 4 \\ 0 & 0 & | & 0 \end{bmatrix}$ $9R_2 + R_3$

(g) $(3, 4)$

6. $(1, 2, -1)$

7. $(-5, 3)$

8. **(a)** No solution   **(b)** $(0, 0)$

9. **(a)** $(-50, -26, 7)$ **(b)** $(55, 16, -14)$
    (c) $(-40, -22, 5)$

6.3 Applications of Systems of Linear Equations

There are no hard and fast rules for solving applied problems, but it is usually best to begin by identifying the unknown quantities and letting each be represented by a variable. Then look at the given data to find one or more relationships among the unknown quantities that lead to equations. If the equations are all linear, use the techniques of the preceding sections to solve the system.

Example 1   **Business**   The U-Drive Rent-a-Truck Company plans to spend $5 million on 200 new vehicles. Each van will cost $20,000, each small truck $25,000, and each large truck $35,000. Past experience shows that U-Drive needs twice as many vans as small trucks. How many of each kind of vehicle can the company buy?

Solution   Let x be the number of vans, y the number of small trucks, and z the number of large trucks. Then

$$\left(\begin{array}{c}\text{Number of} \\ \text{vans}\end{array}\right) + \left(\begin{array}{c}\text{Number of} \\ \text{small trucks}\end{array}\right) + \left(\begin{array}{c}\text{Number of} \\ \text{large trucks}\end{array}\right) = \text{Total number of vehicles}$$

$$x + y + z = 200. \tag{1}$$

Similarly,

$$\left(\begin{array}{c}\text{Cost of } x \\ \text{vans}\end{array}\right) + \left(\begin{array}{c}\text{Cost of } y \\ \text{small trucks}\end{array}\right) + \left(\begin{array}{c}\text{Cost of } z \\ \text{large trucks}\end{array}\right) = \text{Total cost}$$

$$20,000x + 25,000y + 35,000z = 5,000,000.$$

Dividing both sides by 5000 produces the equivalent equation

$$4x + 5y + 7z = 1000. \tag{2}$$

Finally, the number of vans is twice the number of small trucks; that is, $x = 2y$, or equivalently,

$$x - 2y = 0. \tag{3}$$

We must solve the system given by equations (1)–(3):

$$\begin{aligned} x + y + z &= 200 \\ 4x + 5y + 7z &= 1000 \\ x - 2y \phantom{{}+7z} &= 0. \end{aligned}$$

Manual Method Form the augmented matrix and transform it into row echelon form:

$$\left[\begin{array}{ccc|c} 1 & 1 & 1 & 200 \\ 4 & 5 & 7 & 1000 \\ 1 & -2 & 0 & 0 \end{array}\right]$$

$$\left[\begin{array}{ccc|c} 1 & 1 & 1 & 200 \\ 0 & 1 & 3 & 200 \\ 0 & -3 & -1 & -200 \end{array}\right] \quad \begin{array}{l} -4R_1 + R_2 \\ -R_1 + R_3 \end{array}$$

$$\left[\begin{array}{ccc|c} 1 & 1 & 1 & 200 \\ 0 & 1 & 3 & 200 \\ 0 & 0 & 8 & 400 \end{array}\right] \quad \cdot \quad 3R_2 + R_3$$

$$\left[\begin{array}{ccc|c} 1 & 1 & 1 & 200 \\ 0 & 1 & 3 & 200 \\ 0 & 0 & 1 & 50 \end{array}\right]. \quad \frac{1}{8}R_3$$

This row echelon matrix corresponds to the system

$$x + y + z = 200$$
$$y + 3z = 200$$
$$z = 50.$$

Use back substitution to solve this system:

$$z = 50 \qquad y + 3z = 200 \qquad x + y + z = 200$$
$$y + 3(50) = 200 \qquad x + 50 + 50 = 200$$
$$y + 150 = 200 \qquad x + 100 = 200$$
$$y = 50 \qquad x = 100.$$

Therefore, U-Drive should buy 100 vans, 50 small trucks, and 50 large trucks.

Figure 6.15

✓ **Checkpoint 1**

In Example 1, suppose that U-Drive can spend only $2 million on 150 new vehicles and the company needs three times as many vans as small trucks. Write a system of equations to express these conditions.

Calculator Method Enter the augmented matrix of the system into the calculator. Use RREF to change it into reduced row echelon form, as in Figure 6.15. The answers may be read directly from the matrix: $x = 100$ vans, $y = 50$ small trucks, and $z = 50$ large trucks. ✓₁

Example 2 **Finance** Ellen McGillicuddy plans to invest a total of $100,000 in a money market account, a bond fund, an international stock fund, and a domestic stock fund. She wants 60% of her investment to be conservative (money market and bonds). She wants the amount in international stocks to be one-fourth of the amount in domestic stocks. Finally, she needs an annual return of $4000. Assuming she gets annual returns of 2.5% on the money market account, 3.5% on the bond fund, 5% on the international stock fund, and 6% on the domestic stock fund, how much should she put in each investment?

Solution Let x be the amount invested in the money market account, y the amount in the bond fund, z the amount in the international stock fund, and w the amount in the domestic stock fund. Then

$$x + y + z + w = \text{total amount invested} = 100{,}000. \quad \textbf{(4)}$$

Use her annual return to get a second equation:

$$\begin{pmatrix} 2.5\% \text{ return} \\ \text{on money} \\ \text{market} \end{pmatrix} + \begin{pmatrix} 3.5\% \text{ return} \\ \text{on bond} \\ \text{fund} \end{pmatrix} + \begin{pmatrix} 5\% \text{ return on} \\ \text{international} \\ \text{stock fund} \end{pmatrix} + \begin{pmatrix} 6\% \text{ return} \\ \text{on domestic} \\ \text{stock fund} \end{pmatrix} = 4000$$

$$.025x \qquad + \qquad .035y \qquad + \qquad .05z \qquad + \qquad .06w \qquad = 4000. \quad \textbf{(5)}$$

Since Ellen wants the amount in international stocks to be one-fourth of the amount in domestic stocks, we have

$$z = \frac{1}{4}w, \qquad \text{or equivalently,} \qquad z - .25w = 0. \tag{6}$$

Finally, the amount in conservative investments is $x + y$, and this quantity should be equal to 60% of \$100,000—that is,

$$x + y = 60{,}000. \tag{7}$$

Now solve the system given by equations (4)–(7):

$$
\begin{aligned}
x + \quad y + \quad z + \quad w &= 100{,}000 \\
.025x + .035y + .05z + .06w &= \quad 4{,}000 \\
z - .25w &= \quad\quad 0 \\
x + \quad y \qquad\qquad\qquad &= \quad 60{,}000.
\end{aligned}
$$

✓ Checkpoint 2

(a) Write the augmented matrix of the system given by equations (4)–(7) of Example 2.

(b) List a sequence of row operations that transforms this matrix into row echelon form.

(c) Display the final row echelon form matrix.

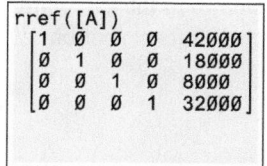

Figure 6.16

Manual Method Write the augmented matrix of the system and transform it into row echelon form, as in Checkpoint 2. ✓2

The final matrix in Checkpoint 2 represented the system

$$
\begin{aligned}
x + y + \quad z + \quad w &= 100{,}000 \\
y + 2.5z + 3.5w &= 150{,}000 \\
z - .25w &= \quad\quad 0 \\
w &= \quad 32{,}000.
\end{aligned}
$$

Back substitution shows that

$$w = 32{,}000 \qquad z = .25w = .25(32{,}000) = 8000$$
$$y = -2.5z - 3.5w + 150{,}000 = -2.5(8000) - 3.5(32{,}000) + 150{,}000 = 18{,}000$$
$$x = -y - z - w + 100{,}000 = -18{,}000 - 8000 - 32{,}000 + 100{,}000 = 42{,}000.$$

Therefore, Ellen should put \$42,000 in the money market account, \$18,000 in the bond fund, \$8000 in the international stock fund, and \$32,000 in the domestic stock fund.

Calculator Method Enter the augmented matrix of the system into the calculator. Use RREF to change it into reduced row echelon form, as in Figure 6.16. The answers can easily be read from this matrix: $x = 42{,}000$, $y = 18{,}000$, $z = 8000$, and $w = 32{,}000$.

Example 3   **Business** An animal feed is to be made from corn, soybeans, and cottonseed. Determine how many units of each ingredient are needed to make a feed that supplies 1800 units of fiber, 2800 units of fat, and 2200 units of protein, given that 1 unit of each ingredient provides the numbers of units shown in the table below. The table states, for example, that a unit of corn provides 10 units of fiber, 30 units of fat, and 20 units of protein.

	Corn	Soybeans	Cottonseed	Totals
Units of Fiber	10	20	30	1800
Units of Fat	30	20	40	2800
Units of Protein	20	40	25	2200

Solution Let x represent the required number of units of corn, y the number of units of soybeans, and z the number of units of cottonseed. Since the total amount of fiber is to be 1800, we have

$$10x + 20y + 30z = 1800.$$

The feed must supply 2800 units of fat, so

$$30x + 20y + 40z = 2800.$$

Finally, since 2200 units of protein are required, we have

$$20x + 40y + 25z = 2200.$$

Thus, we must solve this system of equations:

$$
\begin{aligned}
10x + 20y + 30z &= 1800 \\
30x + 20y + 40z &= 2800 \\
20x + 40y + 25z &= 2200.
\end{aligned}
\tag{8}
$$

Now solve the system, either manually or with technology.

Manual Method   Write the augmented matrix and use row operations to transform it into row echelon form, as in Checkpoint 3. The resulting matrix represents the following system: ✓3

$$
\begin{aligned}
x + 2y + 3z &= 180 \\
y + \frac{5}{4}z &= 65 \\
z &= 40.
\end{aligned}
\tag{9}
$$

Back substitution now shows that

$$z = 40, \quad y = 65 - \frac{5}{4}(40) = 15, \quad \text{and} \quad x = 180 - 2(15) - 3(40) = 30.$$

Thus, the feed should contain 30 units of corn, 15 units of soybeans, and 40 units of cottonseed.

Calculator Method   Enter the augmented matrix of the system into the calculator (top of Figure 6.17). Use RREF to transform it into reduced row echelon form (bottom of Figure 6.17), which shows that $x = 30$, $y = 15$, and $z = 40$.

✓ **Checkpoint 3**

(a) Write the augmented matrix of system (8) of Example 3.

(b) List a sequence of row operations that transforms this matrix into row echelon form.

(c) Display the final row echelon form matrix.

```
[10   20   30   1800]
[30   20   40   2800]
[20   40   25   2200]
rref([A])
         [1   0   0   30]
         [0   1   0   15]
         [0   0   1   40]
```

Figure 6.17

═══════

Example 4   **Social Science**   The table shows Census Bureau projections for the population of the United States (in millions).

Year	2020	2040	2050
U.S. Population	334	380	400

(a) Use the given data to construct a quadratic function that gives the U.S. population (in millions) in year x.

Solution   Let $x = 0$ correspond to the year 2000. Then the table represents the data points $(20,334)$, $(40,380)$, and $(50,400)$. We must find a function of the form

$$f(x) = ax^2 + bx + c$$

whose graph contains these three points. If $(20,334)$ is to be on the graph, we must have $f(20) = 334$; that is,

$$a(20)^2 + b(20) + c = 334$$
$$400a + 20b + c = 334.$$

The other two points lead to these equations:

$$f(40) = 380 \qquad\qquad f(50) = 400$$
$$a(40)^2 + b(40) + c = 380 \qquad a(50)^2 + b(50) + c = 400$$
$$1600a + 40b + c = 380 \qquad 2500a + 50b + c = 400.$$

Now work by hand or use technology to solve the following system:

$$400a + 20b + c = 334$$
$$1600a + 40b + c = 380$$
$$2500a + 50b + c = 400.$$

The reduced row echelon form of the augmented matrix in Figure 6.18 shows that the solution is $a = -.01$, $b = 2.9$, and $c = 280$. So the function is

$$f(x) = -.01x^2 + 2.9x + 280.$$

Figure 6.18

(b) Use this model to estimate the U.S. population in the year 2030.

Solution   The year 2030 corresponds to $x = 30$, so the U.S. population is projected to be

$$f(30) = -.01(30)^2 + 2.9(30) + 280 = 358 \text{ million.}$$

Example 5   **Business**   Kelly Karpet Kleaners sells rug-cleaning machines. The EZ model weighs 10 pounds and comes in a 10-cubic-foot box. The compact model weighs 20 pounds and comes in an 8-cubic-foot box. The commercial model weighs 60 pounds and comes in a 28-cubic-foot box. Each of Kelly's delivery vans has 248 cubic feet of space and can hold a maximum of 440 pounds. In order for a van to be fully loaded, how many of each model should it carry?

Solution   Let x be the number of EZ, y the number of compact, and z the number of commercial models carried by a van. Then we can summarize the given information in this table.

Model	Number	Weight	Volume
EZ	x	10	10
Compact	y	20	8
Commercial	z	60	28
Total for a load		440	248

Since a fully loaded van can carry 440 pounds and 248 cubic feet, we must solve this system of equations:

$$10x + 20y + 60z = 440 \qquad \text{Weight equation}$$
$$10x + 8y + 28z = 248. \qquad \text{Volume equation}$$

The augmented matrix of the system is

$$\begin{bmatrix} 10 & 20 & 60 & | & 440 \\ 10 & 8 & 28 & | & 248 \end{bmatrix}.$$

If you are working by hand, transform the matrix into row echelon form and use back substitution. If you are using a graphing calculator, use RREF to transform the matrix into reduced row echelon form, as in Figure 6.19 (which also uses FRAC in the MATH menu to eliminate long decimals).

Figure 6.19

The system corresponding to Figure 6.19 is

$$x + \frac{2}{3}z = 12$$

$$y + \frac{8}{3}z = 16,$$

which is easily solved: $x = 12 - \frac{2}{3}z$ and $y = 16 - \frac{8}{3}z$.

Hence, all solutions of the system are given by $\left(12 - \frac{2}{3}z, 16 - \frac{8}{3}z, z\right)$. The only solutions that apply in this situation, however, are those given by $z = 0, 3,$ and 6, because all other values of z lead to fractions or negative numbers. (You can't deliver part of a box or a negative number of boxes). Hence, there are three ways to have a fully loaded van:

Solution	Van Load
(12, 16, 0)	12 EZ, 16 compact, 0 commercial
(10, 8, 3)	10 EZ, 8 compact, 3 commercial
(8, 0, 6)	8 EZ, 0 compact, 6 commercial.

6.3 Exercises

Use systems of equations to work these applied problems. (See Examples 1–5.)

1. **Business** The U-Drive Rent-a-Truck Company of Example 1 learns that each van now costs $25,000, each small truck costs $30,000, and each large truck costs $40,000. The company still needs twice as many vans as small trucks and wants to spend $5 million, but it decides to buy only 175 vehicles. How many of each kind should it buy?

2. **Finance** Suppose that Ellen McGillicuddy in Example 2 finds that her annual return on the international stock fund will be only 4%. Now how much should she put in each investment?

3. **Health** To meet consumer demand, the animal feed in Example 3 now supplies only 2400 units of fat. How many units of corn, soybeans, and cottonseed are now needed?

4. **Business** Suppose that Kelly Karpet Kleaners in Example 5 finds a way to pack the EZ model in an 8-cubic-foot box. Now how many of each model should a fully loaded van carry?

5. **Business** Mario took clothes to the cleaners three times last month. First, he brought 3 shirts and 1 pair of slacks and paid $10.96. Then he brought 7 shirts, 2 pairs of slacks, and a sports coat and paid $30.40. Finally, he brought 4 shirts and 1 sports coat and paid $14.45. How much was he charged for each shirt, each pair of slacks, and each sports coat?

6. **Business** A minor league baseball park has 7000 seats. Box seats cost $6, grandstand seats cost $4, and bleacher seats cost $2. When all seats are sold, the revenue is $26,400. If the number of box seats is one-third the number of bleacher seats, how many seats of each type are there?

7. **Business** Tickets to a band concert cost $5 for adults, $3 for teenagers, and $2 for preteens. There were 570 people at the concert, and total ticket receipts were $1950. Three-fourths as many teenagers as preteens attended. How many adults, teenagers, and preteens attended?

8. **Business** Shipping charges at an online bookstore are $4 for one book, $6 for two books, and $7 for three to five books. Last week, there were 6400 orders of five or fewer books, and total shipping charges for these orders were $33,600. The number of shipments with $7 charges was 1000 less than the number with $6 charges. How many shipments were made in each category (one book, two books, three-to-five books)?

9. **Finance** An investor wants to invest $30,000 in corporate bonds that are rated AAA, A, and B. The lower rated ones pay higher interest, but pose a higher risk as well. The average yield is 5% on AAA bonds, 6% on A bonds, and 10% on B bonds. Being conservative, the investor wants to have twice as much in AAA bonds as in B bonds. How much should she invest in each type of bond to have an interest income of $2000?

10. **Finance** Makayla borrows $10,000. Some is from her friend at 8% annual interest, twice as much as that from her bank at 9%, and the remainder from her insurance company at 5%. She pays a total of $830 in interest for the first year. How much did she borrow from each source?

11. **Business** Pretzels cost $3 per pound, dried fruit $4 per pound, and nuts $8 per pound. How many pounds of each should be used to produce 140 pounds of trail mix costing $6 per pound in which there are twice as many pretzels (by weight) as dried fruit?

12. **Business** An auto manufacturer sends cars from two plants, I and II, to dealerships A and B, located in a midwestern city.

Plant I has a total of 28 cars to send, and plant II has 8. Dealer *A* needs 20 cars, and dealer *B* needs 16. Transportation costs based on the distance of each dealership from each plant are $220 from I to *A*, $300 from I to *B*, $400 from II to *A*, and $180 from II to *B*. The manufacturer wants to limit transportation costs to $10,640. How many cars should be sent from each plant to each of the two dealerships?

13. Natural Science An animal breeder can buy four types of tiger food. Each case of Brand *A* contains 25 units of fiber, 30 units of protein, and 30 units of fat. Each case of Brand *B* contains 50 units of fiber, 30 units of protein, and 20 units of fat. Each case of Brand *C* contains 75 units of fiber, 30 units of protein, and 20 units of fat. Each case of Brand *D* contains 100 units of fiber, 60 units of protein, and 30 units of fat. How many cases of each brand should the breeder mix together to obtain a food that provides 1200 units of fiber, 600 units of protein, and 400 units of fat?

14. Physical Science The stopping distance for a car traveling 25 mph is 61.7 feet, and for a car traveling 35 mph it is 106 feet. The stopping distance in feet can be described by the equation $y = ax^2 + bx$, where *x* is the speed in mph. (Data from: *National Traffic Safety Institute Student Workbook*, 1993, p. 7.)

(a) Find the values of *a* and *b*.

(b) Use your answers from part (a) to find the stopping distance for a car traveling 55 mph.

15. Finance An investor plans to invest $70,000 in a mutual fund, corporate bonds, and a fast-food franchise. She plans to put twice as much in bonds as in the mutual fund. On the basis of past performance, she expects the mutual fund to pay a 2% dividend, the bonds 6%, and the franchise 10%. She would like a dividend income of $4800. How much should she put in each of three investments?

16. Business According to data from a Texas agricultural report, the amounts of nitrogen (lb/acre), phosphate (lb/acre), and labor (hr/acre) needed to grow honeydews, yellow onions, and lettuce are given by the following table:*

	Honeydews	Yellow Onions	Lettuce
Nitrogen	120	150	180
Phosphate	180	80	80
Labor	4.97	4.45	4.65

(a) If a farmer has 220 acres, 29,100 pounds of nitrogen, 32,600 pounds of phosphate, and 480 hours of labor, can he use all of his resources completely? If so, how many acres should he allot for each crop?

(b) Suppose everything is the same as in part (a), except that 1061 hours of labor are available. Is it possible to use all of his resources completely? If so, how many acres should he allot for each crop?

17. Health Computer-aided tomography (CAT) scanners take X-rays of a part of the body from different directions and put the information together to create a picture of a cross-section of

the body.† The amount by which the energy of the X-ray decreases, measured in linear-attenuation units, tells whether the X-ray has passed through healthy tissue, tumorous tissue, or bone, on the basis of the following table:

Type of Tissue	**Linear-Attenuation Values**
Healthy tissue	.1625–.2977
Tumorous tissue	.2679–.3930
Bone	.3857–.5108

The part of the body to be scanned is divided into cells. If an X-ray passes through more than one cell, the total linear-attenuation value is the sum of the values for the cells. For example, in the accompanying figure, let *a*, *b*, and *c* be the values for cells *A*, *B*, and *C*, respectively. Then the attenuation value for beam 1 is $a + b$ and for beam 2 is $a + c$.

(a) Find the attenuation value for beam 3.

(b) Suppose that the attenuation values are .8, .55, and .65 for beams 1, 2, and 3, respectively. Set up and solve the system of three equations for *a*, *b*, and *c*. What can you conclude about cells *A*, *B*, and *C*?

18. Health (Refer to Exercise 17.) Four X-ray beams are aimed at four cells, as shown in the following figure:

(a) Suppose the attenuation values for beams 1, 2, 3, and 4 are .60, .75, .65, and .70, respectively. Do we have enough information to determine the values of *a*, *b*, *c*, and *d*? Explain.

(b) Suppose we have the data from part (a), as well as the following values for *d*. Find the values for *a*, *b*, and *c*, and make conclusions about cells *A*, *B*, *C*, and *D* in each case.

(i) .33

(ii) .43

(c) Two X-ray beams are added as shown in the figure. In addition to the data in part (a), we now have attenuation values of .85 and .50 for beams 5 and 6, respectively. Find the values for a, b, c, and d, and make conclusions about cells A, B, C, and D.

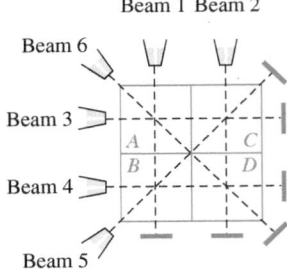

Beam 1 Beam 2
Beam 6
Beam 3
Beam 4
Beam 5

19. **Physical Science** During rush hours, substantial traffic congestion is encountered at the intersections shown in the figure. (The arrows indicate one-way streets.)

 The city wishes to improve the signals at these corners to speed the flow of traffic. The traffic engineers first gather data. As the figure shows, 700 cars per hour come down M Street to intersection A, and 300 cars per hour come down 10th Street to intersection A. x_1 of these cars leave A on M Street, and x_4 cars leave A on 10th Street.

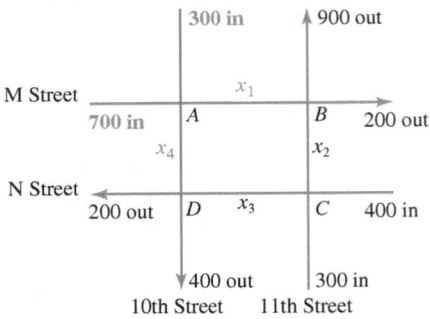

The number of cars entering A must equal the number leaving, so that

$$x_1 + x_4 = 700 + 300,$$

or

$$x_1 + x_4 = 1000.$$

For intersection B, x_1 cars enter on M Street and x_2 on 11th Street. The figure shows that 900 cars leave B on 11th Street and 200 cars leave B on M Street. So, we have

$$x_1 + x_2 = 900 + 200$$
$$x_1 + x_2 = 1100.$$

(a) Write two equations representing the traffic entering and leaving intersections C and D.

(b) Solve the system of four equations, using x_4 as the parameter.

(c) On the basis of your solution to part (b), what are the largest and smallest possible values for the number of cars leaving intersection A on 10th Street?

(d) Answer the question in part (c) for the other three variables.

(e) Verify that you could have discarded any one of the four original equations without changing the solution. What does this tell you about the original problem?

20. **Physical Science** The diagram shows the traffic flow at four intersections during rush hour, as in Exercise 19.

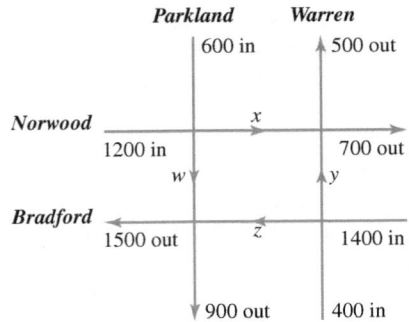

(a) What are the possible values of x, y, z, and w that will avoid any congestion? (Use w as the parameter.)

(b) What are the possible values of w?

⤤ *A graphing calculator or other technology is recommended for the following exercises.*

21. **Health** The table shows the calories, sodium, and protein in one cup of various kinds of soup.

	Progresso™ Hearty Chicken Rotini	Healthy Choice™ Hearty Chicken	Campbell's™ Chunky Chicken Noodle
Calories	100	130	110
Sodium (mg)	960	480	890
Protein (g)	7	9	8

How many cups of each kind of soup should be mixed together to produce 10 servings of soup, each of which provides 171 calories, 1158 milligrams of sodium, and 12.1 grams of protein? What is the serving size (in cups)? (*Hint:* In 10 servings, there must be 1710 calories, 11,580 milligrams of sodium, and 121 grams of protein.)

22. **Health** The table shows the calories, sodium, and fat in 1 ounce of various snack foods (all produced by Planters™):

	Sweet N' Crunchy Peanuts	Dry Roasted Honey Peanuts	Kettle Roasted Honey BBQ Peanuts
Calories	140	160	180
Sodium (mg)	20	110	55
Fat (g)	8	13	15

How many ounces of each kind of snack should be combined to produce 10 servings, each of which provides 284 calories, 93 milligrams of sodium, and 20.6 grams of fat? What is the serving size?

23. **Finance** An investment firm recommends that a client invest in bonds rated AAA, A, and B. The average yield on AAA bonds is 6%, on A bonds 7%, and on B bonds 10%. The client wants to invest twice as much in AAA bonds as in B bonds.

How much should be invested in each type of bond under the following conditions?

   (a)   The total investment is $25,000, and the investor wants an annual return of $1810 on the three investments.

   (b)   The values in part (a) are changed to $30,000 and $2150, respectively.

   (c)   The values in part (a) are changed to $40,000 and $2900, respectively.

24. Business   An electronics company produces transistors, resistors, and computer chips. Each transistor requires 3 units of copper, 1 unit of zinc, and 2 units of glass. Each resistor requires 3, 2, and 1 unit of the three materials, and each computer chip requires 2, 1, and 2 units of these materials, respectively. How many of each product can be made with the following amounts of materials?

   (a)   810 units of copper, 410 of zinc, and 490 of glass

   (b)   765 units of copper, 385 of zinc, and 470 of glass

   (c)   1010 units of copper, 500 of zinc, and 610 of glass

Work these exercises. (See Example 4.)

25. Social Science   The table shows Census Bureau projections for the female population of the United States (in millions).

Year	2015	2035	2040
Female Population	163	187	192

   (a)   Find a quadratic function $f(x) = ax^2 + bx + c$ that gives the female population (in millions) in year x, where $x = 0$ corresponds to the year 2000.

   (b)   Estimate the female population in the year 2020.

26. Social Science   The table shows Census Bureau projections for the male population of the United States (in millions).

Year	2015	2035	2040
Male Population	158	183	188

   (a)   Find a quadratic function $f(x) = ax^2 + bx + c$ that gives the male population (in millions) in year x, where $x = 0$ corresponds to the year 2000.

   (b)   Estimate the male population in the year 2020.

27. Business   At a pottery factory, fuel consumption for heating the kilns varies with the size of the order being fired. In the past, the company recorded the figures in the table.

x = Number of Platters	y = Fuel Cost per Platter
6	$2.80
8	2.48
10	2.24

   (a)   Find an equation of the form $y = ax^2 + bx + c$ whose graph contains the three points corresponding to the data in the table.

   (b)   How many platters should be fired at one time in order to minimize the fuel cost per platter? What is the minimum fuel cost per platter?

28. Health   The number of Alzheimer's cases in people 85 and older was 2 million in 2004 and is projected to be 3 million in 2025 and 8 million in 2050. (Data from: Alzheimer's Association.)

   (a)   Let $x = 0$ correspond to 2000. Find a quadratic function that models the given data.

   (b)   How many people 85 or older will have Alzheimer's disease in 2020 and in 2034?

   (c)   In the year you turn 85, how many people your age or older are expected to have Alzheimer's disease?

29. Physical Science   For certain aircraft, there exists a quadratic relationship between an airplane's maximum speed S (in knots) and its ceiling C—its highest altitude possible (in thousands of feet). (Data from: D. Sanders, *Statistics: A First Course*, Fifth Edition [McGraw Hill, 1995].) The following table lists three airplanes that conform to this relationship:

Airplane	Maximum Speed	Ceiling
Hawkeye	320	33
Corsair	600	40
Tomcat	1283	50

   (a)   If the relationship between C and S is written as $C = aS^2 + bS + c$, use a linear system of equations to determine the constants a, b, and c.

   (b)   A new aircraft of this type has a ceiling of 45,000 feet. Predict its top speed.

30. Natural Science   The concentration (in parts per million) of carbon dioxide (a greenhouse gas) has been measured at Mauna Loa, Hawaii since 1959. The concentrations are known to have increased quadratically. The following table lists readings for three years. (Data from: National Oceanic and Atmospheric Administration.)

Year	1960	1989	2012
Carbon Dioxide	317	353	394

   (a)   Use the given data to construct a quadratic function that gives the concentration in year x. Let $x = 0$ correspond to the year 1959, so the table represents the data points (1,317), (30,353), and (53,394).

   (b)   Use this model to estimate the carbon dioxide concentration in the year 2019.

✓**Checkpoint Answers**

1. $x + y + z = 150$
$4x + 5y + 7z = 400$
$x - 3y \quad\quad = 0$

2.   **(a)** $\begin{bmatrix} 1 & 1 & 1 & 1 & 100{,}000 \\ .025 & .035 & .05 & .06 & 4000 \\ 0 & 0 & 1 & -.25 & 0 \\ 1 & 1 & 0 & 0 & 60{,}000 \end{bmatrix}$

(b) Many sequences are possible, including this one:

Replace R_2 by $-.025R_1 + R_2$;

replace R_4 by $-R_1 + R_4$;

replace R_2 by $\frac{1}{.01}R_2$;

replace R_4 by $R_3 + R_4$;

replace R_4 by $\frac{-1}{1.25}R_4$.

(c) $\begin{bmatrix} 1 & 1 & 1 & 1 & 100{,}000 \\ 0 & 1 & 2.5 & 3.5 & 150{,}000 \\ 0 & 0 & 1 & -.25 & 0 \\ 0 & 0 & 0 & 1 & 32{,}000 \end{bmatrix}$

3. (a) $\begin{bmatrix} 10 & 20 & 30 & 1800 \\ 30 & 20 & 40 & 2800 \\ 20 & 40 & 25 & 2200 \end{bmatrix}$

(b) Many sequences are possible, including this one:

Replace R_1 by $\frac{1}{10}R_1$;

replace R_2 by $\frac{1}{10}R_2$;

replace R_3 by $\frac{1}{5}R_3$;

replace R_2 by $-3R_1 + R_2$;

replace R_3 by $-4R_1 + R_3$;

replace R_2 by $-\frac{1}{4}R_2$;

replace R_3 by $-\frac{1}{7}R_3$.

(c) $\begin{bmatrix} 1 & 2 & 3 & 180 \\ 0 & 1 & \dfrac{5}{4} & 65 \\ 0 & 0 & 1 & 40 \end{bmatrix}$

6.4 Basic Matrix Operations

Until now, we have used matrices only as a convenient shorthand to solve systems of equations. However, matrices are also important in the fields of management, natural science, engineering, and social science as a way to organize data, as Example 1 demonstrates.

Example 1 **Business** The EZ Life Company manufactures sofas and armchairs in three models: *A*, *B*, and *C*. The company has regional warehouses in New York, Chicago, and San Francisco. In its August shipment, the company sends 10 model *A* sofas, 12 model *B* sofas, 5 model *C* sofas, 15 model *A* chairs, 20 model *B* chairs, and 8 model *C* chairs to each warehouse.

These data might be organized by first listing them as follows:

Sofas	10 model *A*	12 model *B*	5 model *C*;
Chairs	15 model *A*	20 model *B*	8 model *C*.

Alternatively, we might tabulate the data:

		MODEL		
		A	*B*	*C*
FURNITURE	Sofa	10	12	5
	Chair	15	20	8

With the understanding that the numbers in each row refer to the type of furniture (sofa or chair) and the numbers in each column refer to the model (*A*, *B*, or *C*), the same information can be given by a matrix as follows:

$$M = \begin{bmatrix} 10 & 12 & 5 \\ 15 & 20 & 8 \end{bmatrix} \quad \boxed{\checkmark_1}$$

✓**Checkpoint 1**

Rewrite matrix *M* in Example 1 in a matrix with three rows and two columns.

A matrix with *m* horizontal rows and *n* vertical columns has **dimension**, or **size**, $m \times n$. The number of rows is always given first.

Example 2

(a) The matrix $\begin{bmatrix} 6 & 5 \\ 3 & 4 \\ 5 & -1 \end{bmatrix}$ is a 3 × 2 matrix.

(b) $\begin{bmatrix} 5 & 8 & 9 \\ 0 & 5 & -3 \\ -4 & 0 & 5 \end{bmatrix}$ is a 3 × 3 matrix.

(c) [1   6   5   −2   5] is a 1 × 5 matrix.

(d) A graphing calculator displays a 4 × 1 matrix like this:

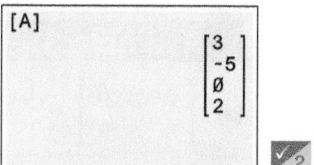

Checkpoint 2

Give the size of each of the following matrices.

(a) $\begin{bmatrix} 2 & 1 & -5 & 6 \\ 3 & 0 & 7 & -4 \end{bmatrix}$

(b) $\begin{bmatrix} 1 & 2 & 3 \\ 4 & 5 & 6 \\ 9 & 8 & 7 \end{bmatrix}$

Checkpoint 3

Use the numbers 2, 5, −8, and 4 to write

(a) a row matrix;

(b) a column matrix;

(c) a square matrix.

A matrix with only one row, as in Example 2(c), is called a **row matrix,** or **row vector.** A matrix with only one column, as in Example 2(d), is called a **column matrix,** or **column vector.** A matrix with the same number of rows as columns is called a **square matrix.** The matrix in Example 2(b) is a square matrix, as are

$$A = \begin{bmatrix} -5 & 6 \\ 8 & 3 \end{bmatrix} \quad \text{and} \quad B = \begin{bmatrix} 0 & 0 & 0 & 0 \\ -2 & 4 & 1 & 3 \\ 0 & 0 & 0 & 0 \\ -5 & -4 & 1 & 8 \end{bmatrix}.$$

When a matrix is denoted by a single letter, such as the matrix A above, the element in row i and column j is denoted a_{ij}. For example, $a_{21} = 8$ (the element in row 2, column 1). Similarly, in matrix B, $b_{42} = -4$ (the element in row 4, column 2).

Addition

The matrix given in Example 1,

$$M = \begin{bmatrix} 10 & 12 & 5 \\ 15 & 20 & 8 \end{bmatrix},$$

shows the August shipment from the EZ Life plant to each of its warehouses. If matrix N below gives the September shipment to the New York warehouse, what is the total shipment for each item of furniture to the New York warehouse for the two months?

$$N = \begin{bmatrix} 45 & 35 & 20 \\ 65 & 40 & 35 \end{bmatrix}$$

If 10 model A sofas were shipped in August and 45 in September, then altogether 55 model A sofas were shipped in the two months. Adding the other corresponding entries gives a new matrix, Q, that represents the total shipment to the New York warehouse for the two months:

$$Q = \begin{bmatrix} 55 & 47 & 25 \\ 80 & 60 & 43 \end{bmatrix}$$

It is convenient to refer to Q as the *sum* of M and N.

The way these two matrices were added illustrates the following definition of addition of matrices:

Matrix Addition

The **sum** of two $m \times n$ matrices X and Y is the $m \times n$ matrix $X + Y$ in which each element is the sum of the corresponding elements of X and Y.

It is important to remember that only matrices that are the same size can be added.

Example 3 Find each sum if possible.

(a) $\begin{bmatrix} 5 & -6 \\ 8 & 9 \end{bmatrix} + \begin{bmatrix} -4 & 6 \\ 8 & -3 \end{bmatrix} = \begin{bmatrix} 5 + (-4) & -6 + 6 \\ 8 + 8 & 9 + (-3) \end{bmatrix} = \begin{bmatrix} 1 & 0 \\ 16 & 6 \end{bmatrix}$.

(b) The matrices

$$A = \begin{bmatrix} 5 & 8 \\ 6 & 2 \end{bmatrix} \quad \text{and} \quad B = \begin{bmatrix} 3 & 9 & 1 \\ 4 & 2 & 5 \end{bmatrix}$$

are of different sizes, so it is not possible to find the sum $A + B$. ✔4

✓Checkpoint 4

Find each sum when possible.

(a) $\begin{bmatrix} 2 & 5 & 7 \\ 3 & -1 & 4 \end{bmatrix}$
$+ \begin{bmatrix} -1 & 2 & 0 \\ 10 & -4 & 5 \end{bmatrix}$

(b) $\begin{bmatrix} 1 \\ 2 \\ 3 \end{bmatrix} + \begin{bmatrix} 2 & -1 \\ 4 & 5 \\ 6 & 0 \end{bmatrix}$

(c) $[5 \quad 4 \quad -1] + [-5 \quad 2 \quad 3]$

TECHNOLOGY TIP Graphing calculators can find matrix sums, as illustrated in Figure 6.20.

Figure 6.20

Example 4 **Business** The September shipments of the three models of sofas and chairs from the EZ Life Company to the New York, San Francisco, and Chicago warehouses are given respectively in matrices N, S, and C as follows:

$$N = \begin{bmatrix} 45 & 35 & 20 \\ 65 & 40 & 35 \end{bmatrix}; \quad S = \begin{bmatrix} 30 & 32 & 28 \\ 43 & 47 & 30 \end{bmatrix}; \quad C = \begin{bmatrix} 22 & 25 & 38 \\ 31 & 34 & 35 \end{bmatrix}.$$

What was the total amount shipped to the three warehouses in September?

Solution The total of the September shipments is represented by the sum of the three matrices N, S, and C:

$$N + S + C = \begin{bmatrix} 45 & 35 & 20 \\ 65 & 40 & 35 \end{bmatrix} + \begin{bmatrix} 30 & 32 & 28 \\ 43 & 47 & 30 \end{bmatrix} + \begin{bmatrix} 22 & 25 & 38 \\ 31 & 34 & 35 \end{bmatrix}$$
$$= \begin{bmatrix} 97 & 92 & 86 \\ 139 & 121 & 100 \end{bmatrix}.$$

✓Checkpoint 5

From the result of Example 4, find the total number of the following shipped to the three warehouses.

(a) Model A chairs

(b) Model B sofas

(c) Model C chairs

For example, from this sum, the total number of model C sofas shipped to the three warehouses in September was 86. ✔5

Example 5 **Health** A drug company is testing 200 patients to see if Painoff (a new headache medicine) is effective. Half the patients receive Painoff and half receive a placebo. The data on the first 50 patients is summarized in this matrix:

$$\begin{array}{cc} & \text{Pain Relief Obtained} \\ & \text{Yes \quad No} \end{array}$$

$$\begin{array}{c} \text{Patient took Painoff} \\ \text{Patient took placebo} \end{array} \begin{bmatrix} 22 & 3 \\ 8 & 17 \end{bmatrix}$$

For example, row 2 shows that, of the people who took the placebo, 8 got relief, but 17 did not. The test was repeated on three more groups of 50 patients each, with the results summarized by these matrices:

$$\begin{bmatrix} 21 & 4 \\ 6 & 19 \end{bmatrix}; \quad \begin{bmatrix} 19 & 6 \\ 10 & 15 \end{bmatrix}; \quad \begin{bmatrix} 23 & 2 \\ 3 & 22 \end{bmatrix}.$$

The total results of the test can be obtained by adding these four matrices:

$$\begin{bmatrix} 22 & 3 \\ 8 & 17 \end{bmatrix} + \begin{bmatrix} 21 & 4 \\ 6 & 19 \end{bmatrix} + \begin{bmatrix} 19 & 6 \\ 10 & 15 \end{bmatrix} + \begin{bmatrix} 23 & 2 \\ 3 & 22 \end{bmatrix} = \begin{bmatrix} 85 & 15 \\ 27 & 73 \end{bmatrix}.$$

Because 85 of 100 patients got relief with Painoff and only 27 of 100 did so with the placebo, it appears that Painoff is effective. ✓₆

✓**Checkpoint 6**

Later, it was discovered that the data in the last group of 50 patients in Example 5 was invalid. Use a matrix to represent the total test results after those data were eliminated.

Subtraction

Subtraction of matrices can be defined in a manner similar to matrix addition.

Matrix Subtraction

The **difference** of two $m \times n$ matrices X and Y is the $m \times n$ matrix $X - Y$ in which each element is the difference of the corresponding elements of X and Y.

Example 6 Find the following.

(a) $\begin{bmatrix} 1 & 2 & 3 \\ 0 & -1 & 5 \end{bmatrix} - \begin{bmatrix} -2 & 3 & 0 \\ 1 & -7 & 2 \end{bmatrix}$

Solution

$$\begin{bmatrix} 1 & 2 & 3 \\ 0 & -1 & 5 \end{bmatrix} - \begin{bmatrix} -2 & 3 & 0 \\ 1 & -7 & 2 \end{bmatrix} = \begin{bmatrix} 1-(-2) & 2-3 & 3-0 \\ 0-1 & -1-(-7) & 5-2 \end{bmatrix}$$
$$= \begin{bmatrix} 3 & -1 & 3 \\ -1 & 6 & 3 \end{bmatrix}.$$

(b) $[8 \quad 6 \quad -4] - [3 \quad 5 \quad -8]$

Solution

$$[8 \quad 6 \quad -4] - [3 \quad 5 \quad -8] = [8-3 \quad 6-5 \quad -4-(-8)]$$
$$= [5 \quad 1 \quad 4].$$

(c) $\begin{bmatrix} -2 & 5 \\ 0 & 1 \end{bmatrix} - \begin{bmatrix} 3 \\ 5 \end{bmatrix}$

Solution The matrices are of different sizes and thus cannot be subtracted. ✓₇

✓**Checkpoint 7**

Find each of the following differences when possible.

(a) $\begin{bmatrix} 2 & 5 \\ -1 & 0 \end{bmatrix} - \begin{bmatrix} 6 & 4 \\ 3 & -2 \end{bmatrix}$

(b) $\begin{bmatrix} 1 & 5 & 6 \\ 2 & 4 & 8 \end{bmatrix} - \begin{bmatrix} 2 & 1 \\ 10 & 3 \end{bmatrix}$

(c) $[5 \quad -4 \quad 1] - [6 \quad 0 \quad -3]$

➤ **TECHNOLOGY TIP**
Graphing calculators can do matrix subtraction, as illustrated in Figure 6.21.

```
[B]
     [-4   5   Ø   2]
     [ 6   3  -7   1]
[C]
     [ 4  12   8  -5]
     [ 2   8   5   Ø]
```

```
[B]-[C]
     [-8  -7  -8   7]
     [ 4  -5 -12   1]
```

Figure 6.21

Example 7 **Business** During September, the Chicago warehouse of the EZ Life Company shipped out the following numbers of each model, where the entries in the matrix have the same meaning as given earlier:

$$K = \begin{bmatrix} 5 & 10 & 8 \\ 11 & 14 & 15 \end{bmatrix}.$$

What was the Chicago warehouse's inventory on October 1, taking into account only the number of items received and sent out during the previous month?

Solution The number of each kind of item received during September is given by matrix C from Example 4; the number of each model sent out during September is given by matrix K. The October 1 inventory is thus represented by the matrix $C - K$:

$$C - K = \begin{bmatrix} 22 & 25 & 38 \\ 31 & 34 & 35 \end{bmatrix} - \begin{bmatrix} 5 & 10 & 8 \\ 11 & 14 & 15 \end{bmatrix} = \begin{bmatrix} 17 & 15 & 30 \\ 20 & 20 & 20 \end{bmatrix}.$$

Scalar Multiplication

Suppose one of the EZ Life Company warehouses receives the following order, written in matrix form, where the entries have the same meaning as given earlier:

$$\begin{bmatrix} 5 & 4 & 1 \\ 3 & 2 & 3 \end{bmatrix}.$$

Later, the store that sent the order asks the warehouse to send six more of the same order. The six new orders can be written as one matrix by multiplying each element in the matrix by 6, giving the product

$$6\begin{bmatrix} 5 & 4 & 1 \\ 3 & 2 & 3 \end{bmatrix} = \begin{bmatrix} 30 & 24 & 6 \\ 18 & 12 & 18 \end{bmatrix}.$$

In work with matrices, a real number, like the 6 in the preceding multiplication, is called a **scalar.**

```
[A]
     [3  -4]
     [5   2]
2[A]
     [ 6  -8]
     [1Ø   4]
```

Figure 6.22

> **Scalar Multiplication**
>
> The **product** of a scalar k and a matrix X is the matrix kX in which each element is k times the corresponding element of X.

✓ **Checkpoint 8**

Find each product.

(a) $-3\begin{bmatrix} 4 & -2 \\ 1 & 5 \end{bmatrix}$

(b) $4\begin{bmatrix} 2 & 4 & 7 \\ 8 & 2 & 1 \\ 5 & 7 & 3 \end{bmatrix}$

Example 8

(a) $(-3)\begin{bmatrix} 2 & -5 \\ 1 & 7 \\ 4 & -6 \end{bmatrix} = \begin{bmatrix} -6 & 15 \\ -3 & -21 \\ -12 & 18 \end{bmatrix}.$

(b) Graphing calculators can also do scalar multiplication (Figure 6.22). ✓₈

↻ Recall that the *negative* of a real number a is the number $-a = (-1)a$. The negative of a matrix is defined similarly.

TECHNOLOGY TIP

To compute the negative of matrix A on a calculator, use the "negative" key (−), as shown in Figure 6.23.

Figure 6.23

 Checkpoint 9

Let A and B be the matrices in Example 9. Find

(a) $A + (-B)$;

(b) $A - B$.

(c) What can you conclude from parts (a) and (b)?

The **negative** (or *additive inverse*) of a matrix A is the matrix $(-1)A$ which is obtained by multiplying each element of A by -1. It is denoted $-A$.

Example 9 Find $-A$ and $-B$ when

$$A = \begin{bmatrix} 1 & 2 & 3 \\ 0 & -1 & 5 \end{bmatrix} \quad \text{and} \quad B = \begin{bmatrix} -2 & 3 & 0 \\ 1 & -7 & 2 \end{bmatrix}.$$

Solution By the preceding definition,

$$-A = \begin{bmatrix} -1 & -2 & -3 \\ 0 & 1 & -5 \end{bmatrix} \quad \text{and} \quad -B = \begin{bmatrix} 2 & -3 & 0 \\ -1 & 7 & -2 \end{bmatrix}. \checkmark_9$$

A matrix consisting only of zeros is called a **zero matrix** and is denoted O. There is an $m \times n$ zero matrix for each pair of values of m and n—for instance,

$$\begin{bmatrix} 0 & 0 \\ 0 & 0 \end{bmatrix}; \qquad \begin{bmatrix} 0 & 0 & 0 & 0 \\ 0 & 0 & 0 & 0 \end{bmatrix}.$$

2×2 zero matrix 2×4 zero matrix

The negative of a matrix and zero matrices have the following properties, as illustrated in Checkpoint 9 and Exercises 28–30.

Let A and B be any $m \times n$ matrices and let O be the $m \times n$ zero matrix. Then

$$A + (-B) = A - B;$$
$$A + (-A) = O = A - A;$$
$$A + O = A = O + A.$$

6.4 Exercises

Find the size of each of the given matrices. Identify any square, column, or row matrices. Give the negative (additive inverse) of each matrix. (See Examples 2 and 9.)

1. $\begin{bmatrix} 7 & -8 & 4 \\ 0 & 13 & 9 \end{bmatrix}$

2. $\begin{bmatrix} -7 & 23 \\ 5 & -6 \end{bmatrix}$

3. $\begin{bmatrix} -3 & 0 & 11 \\ 1 & \frac{1}{4} & -7 \\ 5 & -3 & 9 \end{bmatrix}$

4. $[6 \quad -4 \quad \frac{2}{3} \quad 12 \quad 2]$

5. $\begin{bmatrix} 7 \\ 11 \end{bmatrix}$

6. $[-5]$

7. If A is a 5×3 matrix and $A + B = A$, what do you know about B?

8. If C is a 3×3 matrix and D is a 3×4 matrix, then $C + D$ is _____.

Perform the indicated operations where possible. (See Examples 3–7.)

9. $\begin{bmatrix} 1 & 2 & 7 & -1 \\ 8 & 0 & 2 & -4 \end{bmatrix} + \begin{bmatrix} -8 & 12 & -5 & 5 \\ -2 & -3 & 0 & 0 \end{bmatrix}$

10. $\begin{bmatrix} 1 & 7 \\ 2 & -3 \\ 3 & 7 \end{bmatrix} + \begin{bmatrix} 2 & 8 \\ 6 & 8 \\ -1 & 9 \end{bmatrix}$

11. $\begin{bmatrix} -1 & -5 & 9 \\ 2 & 2 & 3 \end{bmatrix} + \begin{bmatrix} 4 & 4 & -7 \\ 1 & -1 & 2 \end{bmatrix}$

12. $\begin{bmatrix} 2 & 4 \\ -8 & 2 \end{bmatrix} + \begin{bmatrix} 9 & -5 \\ 8 & 5 \end{bmatrix}$

13. $\begin{bmatrix} -3 & -2 & 5 \\ 3 & 9 & 0 \end{bmatrix} - \begin{bmatrix} 1 & 5 & -2 \\ -3 & 6 & 8 \end{bmatrix}$

14. $\begin{bmatrix} 0 & -2 \\ 1 & 9 \\ -5 & -9 \end{bmatrix} - \begin{bmatrix} 8 & 6 \\ 9 & 17 \\ 3 & -1 \end{bmatrix}$

15. $\begin{bmatrix} 9 & 1 \\ 0 & -3 \\ 4 & 10 \end{bmatrix} - \begin{bmatrix} 1 & 9 & -4 \\ -1 & 1 & 0 \end{bmatrix}$

16. $\begin{bmatrix} 3 & -8 & 0 \\ 1 & 5 & -7 \end{bmatrix} - \begin{bmatrix} 2 & 6 \\ 9 & -4 \end{bmatrix}$

Let $A = \begin{bmatrix} -2 & 0 \\ 5 & 3 \end{bmatrix}$ and $B = \begin{bmatrix} 0 & 2 \\ 4 & -6 \end{bmatrix}$. Find each of the following. (See Examples 8 and 9.)

17. $2A$ **18.** $-3B$ **19.** $-4B$

20. $5A$ **21.** $-4A + 5B$ **22.** $3A - 10B$

Let $A = \begin{bmatrix} 1 & -2 \\ 4 & 3 \end{bmatrix}$ and $B = \begin{bmatrix} 2 & -1 \\ 0 & 5 \end{bmatrix}$. Find a matrix X satisfying the given equation.

23. $2X = 2A + 3B$ **24.** $3X = A - 3B$

Using matrices

$$O = \begin{bmatrix} 0 & 0 \\ 0 & 0 \end{bmatrix}, P = \begin{bmatrix} m & n \\ p & q \end{bmatrix}, T = \begin{bmatrix} r & s \\ t & u \end{bmatrix}, and\ X = \begin{bmatrix} x & y \\ z & w \end{bmatrix},$$

verify that the statements in Exercises 25–30 are true.

25. $X + T$ is a 2×2 matrix.

26. $X + T = T + X$ (commutative property of addition of matrices).

27. $X + (T + P) = (X + T) + P$ (associative property of addition of matrices).

28. $X + (-X) = O$ (inverse property of addition of matrices).

29. $P + O = P$ (identity property of addition of matrices).

30. Which of the preceding properties are valid for matrices that are not square?

Work the following exercises. (See Example 1.)

31. **Business** When ticket holders fail to attend, major league sports teams lose the money these fans would have spent on refreshments, souvenirs, etc. The percentage of fans who don't show up is 16% in basketball and hockey, 20% in football, and 18% in baseball. The lost revenue per fan is $18.20 in basketball, $18.25 in hockey, $19 in football, and $15.40 in baseball. The total annual lost revenue is $22.7 million in basketball, $35.8 million in hockey, $51.9 million in football, and $96.3 million in baseball. Express this information in matrix form; specify what the rows and columns represent. (Data from: American Demographics.)

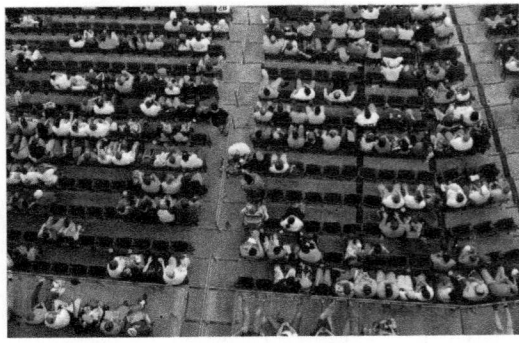

32. **Finance** In both 2010 and 2011, 66% of college graduates had student loan debt. The average debt was $25,250 in 2010 and rose to $26,600 in 2011. The unemployment rate for 2011 graduates was 8.8%, down slightly from 9.1% in 2010. Write

this information as a 3×2 matrix, labeling rows and columns. (Data from: ProjectOnStudentDebt.org.)

33. **Health** The shortage of organs for transplants is a continuing problem in the United States. At the end of 2009, there were 2674 adults waiting for a heart transplant, 1799 for a lung transplant, 15,094 for a liver transplant, and 79,397 for a kidney transplant. Corresponding figures for 2010 were 2874, 1759, 15,394, and 83,919, respectively. In 2011, the figures were 2813, 1630, 15,330, and 86,547, respectively. Express this information as a matrix, labeling rows and columns. (Data from: Organ Procurement and Transplant Network and Scientific Registry of Transplant Recipients.)

34. **Finance** Median household debt varies by age group. Median secured debt (backed by collateral) is $76,500 for individuals under 35 years old, $128,500 for 35–44 year-olds, $99,000 for 45–54 year-olds, $85,000 for 55–64 year olds, and $50,000 for those 65 and older. The corresponding figures for unsecured debt (including credit card debt) are $9700, $8400, $8000, $6000, and $3450. Round all dollar amounts to the nearest thousand and then write this information (in thousands) in matrix form, labeling rows and columns. (Data from: U.S. Census Bureau.)

Work these exercises.

35. **Business** There are three convenience stores in Gambier. This week, Store I sold 88 loaves of bread, 48 quarts of milk, 16 jars of peanut butter, and 112 pounds of cold cuts. Store II sold 105 loaves of bread, 72 quarts of milk, 21 jars of peanut butter, and 147 pounds of cold cuts. Store III sold 60 loaves of bread, 40 quarts of milk, no peanut butter, and 50 pounds of cold cuts.

  (a) Use a 3×4 matrix to express the sales information for the three stores.

  (b) During the following week, sales on these products at Store I increased by 25%, sales at Store II increased by one-third, and sales at Store III increased by 10%. Write the sales matrix for that week.

  (c) Write a matrix that represents total sales over the two-week period.

36. **Social Science** The following table gives educational attainment as a percent of the U.S. population 25 years and older in various years. (Data from: U.S. Census Bureau.)

	MALE		FEMALE	
Year	Four Years of High School or More	Four Years of College or More	Four Years of High School or More	Four Years of College or More
1940	22.7%	5.5%	26.3%	3.8%
1970	55.0%	14.1%	55.4%	8.2%
2000	84.2%	27.8%	84.0%	23.6%
2012	87.3%	31.4%	88.0%	30.6%

  (a) Write a 2×4 matrix for the educational attainment of males.

  (b) Write a 2×4 matrix for the educational attainment of females.

  (c) Use the matrices from parts (a) and (b) to write a matrix showing how much more (or less) males have reached educational attainment than females.

37. Social Science The tables give the death rates (per million person-trips) for male and female drivers for various ages and numbers of passengers:[*]

MALE DRIVERS

Age	Number of Passengers			
	0	1	2	≥3
16	2.61	4.39	6.29	9.08
17	1.63	2.77	4.61	6.92
30–59	.92	.75	.62	.54

FEMALE DRIVERS

Age	Number of Passengers			
	0	1	2	≥3
16	1.38	1.72	1.94	3.31
17	1.26	1.48	2.82	2.28
30–59	.41	.33	.27	.40

(a) Write a matrix A for the death rate of male drivers.

(b) Write a matrix B for the death rate of female drivers.

(c) Use the matrices from parts (a) and (b) to write a matrix showing the difference between the death rates of males and females.

38. Social Science Use matrix operations on the matrices found in Exercise 37(a) and (b) to obtain one matrix that gives the combined death rates for males and females (per million person-trips) of drivers of various ages, with varying numbers of passengers. $\left[\text{Hint: Consider } \frac{1}{2}(A + B). \right]$

[*]Li-Hui Chen, Susan Baker, Elisa Braver, and Guohua Li, "Carrying Passengers as a Risk Factor for Crashes Fatal to 16- and 17-Year-Old Drivers," *JAMA* 283, no. 12 (March 22/29, 2000): 1578–1582.

✓ Checkpoint Answers

1. $\begin{bmatrix} 10 & 15 \\ 12 & 20 \\ 5 & 8 \end{bmatrix}$

2. (a) 2×4 **(b)** 3×3

3. (a) $[2 \quad 5 \quad -8 \quad 4]$

(b) $\begin{bmatrix} 2 \\ 5 \\ -8 \\ 4 \end{bmatrix}$ **(c)** $\begin{bmatrix} 2 & 5 \\ -8 & 4 \end{bmatrix}$ or $\begin{bmatrix} 2 & -8 \\ 5 & 4 \end{bmatrix}$

(Other answers are possible.)

4. (a) $\begin{bmatrix} 1 & 7 & 7 \\ 13 & -5 & 9 \end{bmatrix}$ **(b)** Not possible

(c) $[0 \quad 6 \quad 2]$

5. (a) 139   **(b)** 92   **(c)** 100

6. $\begin{bmatrix} 62 & 13 \\ 24 & 51 \end{bmatrix}$

7. (a) $\begin{bmatrix} -4 & 1 \\ -4 & 2 \end{bmatrix}$ **(b)** Not possible

(c) $[-1 \quad -4 \quad 4]$

8. (a) $\begin{bmatrix} -12 & 6 \\ -3 & -15 \end{bmatrix}$ **(b)** $\begin{bmatrix} 8 & 16 & 28 \\ 32 & 8 & 4 \\ 20 & 28 & 12 \end{bmatrix}$

9. (a) $\begin{bmatrix} 3 & -1 & 3 \\ -1 & 6 & 3 \end{bmatrix}$ **(b)** $\begin{bmatrix} 3 & -1 & 3 \\ -1 & 6 & 3 \end{bmatrix}$

(c) $A + (-B) = A - B$.

6.5 Matrix Products and Inverses

To understand the reasoning behind the definition of matrix multiplication, look again at the EZ Life Company. Suppose sofas and chairs of the same model are often sold as sets, with matrix W showing the number of each model set in each warehouse:

$$\begin{array}{c} \\ \text{New York} \\ \text{Chicago} \\ \text{San Francisco} \end{array} \begin{array}{ccc} A & B & C \\ \begin{bmatrix} 10 & 7 & 3 \\ 5 & 9 & 6 \\ 4 & 8 & 2 \end{bmatrix} \end{array} = W.$$

If the selling price of a model A set is $800, of a model B set is $1000, and of a model C set is $1200, find the total value of the sets in the New York warehouse as follows:

Type	Number of Sets		Price of Set		Total
A	10	×	$ 800	=	$ 8,000
B	7	×	1000	=	7,000
C	3	×	1200	=	3,600
			Total for New York		$18,600

The total value of the three kinds of sets in New York is $18,600.

✓ **Checkpoint 1**

In this example of the EZ Life Company, find the total value of the New York sets if model A sets sell for $1200, model B for $1600, and model C for $1300.

The work done in the preceding table is summarized as

$$10(\$800) + 7(\$1000) + 3(\$1200) = \$18,600.$$

In the same way, the Chicago sets have a total value of

$$5(\$800) + 9(\$1000) + 6(\$1200) = \$20,200,$$

and in San Francisco, the total value of the sets is

$$4(\$800) + 8(\$1000) + 2(\$1200) = \$13,600.$$

The selling prices can be written as a column matrix P and the total value in each location as a column matrix V:

$$P = \begin{bmatrix} 800 \\ 1000 \\ 1200 \end{bmatrix} \quad \text{and} \quad V = \begin{bmatrix} 18,600 \\ 20,200 \\ 13,600 \end{bmatrix}.$$

Consider how the first row of the matrix W and the single column P lead to the first entry of V:

$$\begin{array}{cc} W & P \\ \begin{bmatrix} \mathbf{10} & \mathbf{7} & \mathbf{3} \\ 5 & 9 & 6 \\ 4 & 8 & 2 \end{bmatrix} & \begin{bmatrix} \mathbf{800} \\ \mathbf{1000} \\ \mathbf{1200} \end{bmatrix} \end{array} \quad 10(800) + 7(1000) + 3(1200) = \quad \begin{array}{c} V \\ \begin{bmatrix} 18,600 \\ 20,200 \\ 13,600 \end{bmatrix} \end{array}$$

Product of first entries + Product of second entries + Product of third entries

Similarly, adding the products of corresponding entries in the second row of W and the column P produces the second entry in V. The third entry in V is obtained in the same way by using the third row of W and column P. This suggests that it is reasonable to *define* the product WP to be V:

$$WP = \begin{bmatrix} 10 & 7 & 3 \\ 5 & 9 & 6 \\ 4 & 8 & 2 \end{bmatrix} \begin{bmatrix} 800 \\ 1000 \\ 1200 \end{bmatrix} = \begin{bmatrix} 18,600 \\ 20,200 \\ 13,600 \end{bmatrix} = V$$

Note the sizes of the matrices here: The product of a 3×3 matrix and a 3×1 matrix is a 3×1 matrix.

Multiplying Matrices

In order to define matrix multiplication in the general case, we first define the **product of a row of a matrix and a column of a matrix** (with the same number of entries in each) to be the *number* obtained by multiplying the corresponding entries (first by first, second by second, etc.) and adding the results. For instance,

$$[3 \quad -2 \quad 1] \cdot \begin{bmatrix} 4 \\ 5 \\ 0 \end{bmatrix} = 3 \cdot 4 + (-2) \cdot 5 + 1 \cdot 0 = 12 - 10 + 0 = 2.$$

Now **matrix multiplication** is defined as follows.

Matrix Multiplication

Let A be an $m \times n$ matrix and let B be an $n \times k$ matrix. The **product matrix AB** is the $m \times k$ matrix whose entry in the ith row and jth column is

the product of the ith row of A and the jth column of B.

⚠️ **CAUTION** Be careful when multiplying matrices. Remember that the number of *columns* of A must equal the number of *rows* of B in order to get the product matrix AB. The final product will have as many rows as A and as many columns as B.

Example 1 Suppose matrix A is 2 × 2 and matrix B is 2 × 4. Can the product AB be calculated? If so, what is the size of the product?

Solution The following diagram helps decide the answers to these questions:

The product AB can be calculated because A has two columns and B has two rows. The product will be a 2 × 4 matrix. ✓₂

✓ **Checkpoint 2**

Matrix A is 4 × 6 and matrix B is 2 × 4.

(a) Can AB be found? If so, give its size.

(b) Can BA be found? If so, give its size.

Example 2 Find the product CD when

$$C = \begin{bmatrix} -3 & 4 & 1 \\ 5 & 0 & 4 \end{bmatrix} \quad \text{and} \quad D = \begin{bmatrix} -6 & 4 \\ 2 & 3 \\ 3 & -2 \end{bmatrix}.$$

Solution Here, matrix C is 2 × 3 and matrix D is 3 × 2, so matrix CD can be found and will be 2 × 2.

Step 1 row 1, column 1

$$\begin{bmatrix} \mathbf{-3} & \mathbf{4} & \mathbf{1} \\ 5 & 0 & 4 \end{bmatrix} \begin{bmatrix} \mathbf{-6} & 4 \\ \mathbf{2} & 3 \\ \mathbf{3} & -2 \end{bmatrix} \quad (-3) \cdot (-6) + 4 \cdot 2 + 1 \cdot 3 = 29.$$

Hence, 29 is the entry in row 1, column 1, of CD, as shown in Step 5 below.

Step 2 row 1, column 2

$$\begin{bmatrix} \mathbf{-3} & \mathbf{4} & \mathbf{1} \\ 5 & 0 & 4 \end{bmatrix} \begin{bmatrix} -6 & \mathbf{4} \\ 2 & \mathbf{3} \\ 3 & \mathbf{-2} \end{bmatrix} \quad (-3) \cdot 4 + 4 \cdot 3 + 1 \cdot (-2) = -2.$$

So −2 is the entry in row 1, column 2, of CD, as shown in Step 5. Continue in this manner to find the remaining entries of CD.

Step 3 row 2, column 1

$$\begin{bmatrix} -3 & 4 & 1 \\ \mathbf{5} & \mathbf{0} & \mathbf{4} \end{bmatrix} \begin{bmatrix} \mathbf{-6} & 4 \\ \mathbf{2} & 3 \\ \mathbf{3} & -2 \end{bmatrix} \quad 5 \cdot (-6) + 0 \cdot 2 + 4 \cdot 3 = -18.$$

Step 4 row 2, column 2

$$\begin{bmatrix} -3 & 4 & 1 \\ \mathbf{5} & \mathbf{0} & \mathbf{4} \end{bmatrix} \begin{bmatrix} -6 & \mathbf{4} \\ 2 & \mathbf{3} \\ 3 & \mathbf{-2} \end{bmatrix} \quad 5 \cdot 4 + 0 \cdot 3 + 4 \cdot (-2) = 12.$$

Step 5 The product is

$$CD = \begin{bmatrix} -3 & 4 & 1 \\ 5 & 0 & 4 \end{bmatrix} \begin{bmatrix} -6 & 4 \\ 2 & 3 \\ 3 & -2 \end{bmatrix} = \begin{bmatrix} 29 & -2 \\ -18 & 12 \end{bmatrix}. \quad \checkmark_3$$

✓**Checkpoint 3**

Find the product CD, given that

$$C = \begin{bmatrix} 1 & 3 & 5 \\ 2 & -4 & -1 \end{bmatrix}$$

and

$$D = \begin{bmatrix} 2 & -1 \\ 4 & 3 \\ 1 & -2 \end{bmatrix}.$$

Example 3 Find BA, given that

$$A = \begin{bmatrix} 1 & 7 \\ -3 & 2 \end{bmatrix} \quad \text{and} \quad B = \begin{bmatrix} 1 & 0 & -1 \\ 3 & 1 & 4 \end{bmatrix}.$$

Since B is a 2 × 3 matrix and A is a 2 × 2 matrix, the product BA is not defined. ✓₄

TECHNOLOGY TIP Graphing calculators can find matrix products. However, if you use a graphing calculator to try to find the product in Example 3, the calculator will display an error message.

Matrix multiplication has some similarities to the multiplication of numbers.

✓**Checkpoint 4**

Give the size of each of the following products, if the product can be found.

(a) $\begin{bmatrix} 2 & 4 \\ 6 & 8 \end{bmatrix} \begin{bmatrix} 1 & 2 & 3 \\ 0 & -1 & 2 \end{bmatrix}$

(b) $\begin{bmatrix} 1 & 2 \\ 5 & 10 \\ 12 & 7 \end{bmatrix} \begin{bmatrix} 2 & 4 \\ 3 & 6 \\ 9 & 1 \end{bmatrix}$

(c) $\begin{bmatrix} 5 \\ 2 \\ 4 \end{bmatrix} [1 \quad 0 \quad 6]$

For any matrices A, B, and C such that all the indicated sums and products exist, matrix multiplication is associative and distributive:

$$A(BC) = (AB)C; A(B + C) = AB + AC; (B + C)A = BA + CA.$$

However, there are important differences between matrix multiplication and the multiplication of numbers. (See Exercises 19–22 at the end of this section.) In particular, matrix multiplication is *not* commutative.

If A and B are matrices such that the products AB and BA exist,

$$AB \text{ may not equal } BA.$$

Figure 6.24 shows an example of this situation.

```
[A]                                    [A][B]
              [1  -4]                              [-22   -8]
              [3   2]                              [ 4    18]
[B]                                    [B][A]
              [-2  4]                              [10   16]
              [ 5  3]                              [14  -14]
```

Figure 6.24

Example 4 **Business** A contractor builds three kinds of houses, models A, B, and C, with a choice of two styles, Spanish or contemporary. Matrix P shows the number of each kind of house planned for a new 100-home subdivision:

	Spanish	Contemporary	
Model A	0	30	
Model B	10	20	$= P.$
Model C	20	20	

The amounts for each of the exterior materials used depend primarily on the style of the house. These amounts are shown in matrix Q (concrete is measured in cubic yards, lumber in units of 1000 board feet, brick in thousands, and shingles in units of 100 square feet):

$$
\begin{array}{c}
 \\
\text{Spanish} \\
\text{Contemporary}
\end{array}
\begin{array}{cccc}
\text{Concrete} & \text{Lumber} & \text{Brick} & \text{Shingles} \\
\end{array}
\left[
\begin{array}{cccc}
10 & 2 & 0 & 2 \\
50 & 1 & 20 & 2
\end{array}
\right] = Q.
$$

Matrix R gives the cost for each kind of material:

$$
\begin{array}{c}
 \\
\text{Concrete} \\
\text{Lumber} \\
\text{Brick} \\
\text{Shingles}
\end{array}
\begin{array}{c}
\text{Cost per Unit} \\
\left[
\begin{array}{c}
20 \\
180 \\
60 \\
25
\end{array}
\right]
\end{array} = R.
$$

(a) What is the total cost for each model of house?

Solution   First find the product PQ, which shows the amount of each material needed for each model of house:

$$
PQ = \left[
\begin{array}{cc}
0 & 30 \\
10 & 20 \\
20 & 20
\end{array}
\right]
\left[
\begin{array}{cccc}
10 & 2 & 0 & 2 \\
50 & 1 & 20 & 2
\end{array}
\right]
$$

$$
PQ = \begin{array}{cccc}
\text{Concrete} & \text{Lumber} & \text{Brick} & \text{Shingles} \\
\end{array}
\left[
\begin{array}{cccc}
1500 & 30 & 600 & 60 \\
1100 & 40 & 400 & 60 \\
1200 & 60 & 400 & 80
\end{array}
\right]
\begin{array}{c}
\text{Model } A \\
\text{Model } B. \\
\text{Model } C
\end{array}
$$

Now multiply PQ and R, the cost matrix, to get the total cost for each model of house:

$$
\left[
\begin{array}{cccc}
1500 & 30 & 600 & 60 \\
1100 & 40 & 400 & 60 \\
1200 & 60 & 400 & 80
\end{array}
\right]
\left[
\begin{array}{c}
20 \\
180 \\
60 \\
25
\end{array}
\right] =
\begin{array}{c}
\text{Cost} \\
\left[
\begin{array}{c}
72{,}900 \\
54{,}700 \\
60{,}800
\end{array}
\right]
\end{array}
\begin{array}{c}
\text{Model } A \\
\text{Model } B. \\
\text{Model } C
\end{array}
$$

(b) How much of each of the four kinds of material must be ordered?

Solution   The totals of the columns of matrix PQ will give a matrix whose elements represent the total amounts of each material needed for the subdivision. Call this matrix T and write it as a row matrix:

$$
T = [3800 \quad 130 \quad 1400 \quad 200].
$$

(c) What is the total cost for material?

Solution   Find the total cost of all the materials by taking the product of matrix T, the matrix showing the total amounts of each material, and matrix R, the cost matrix. [To multiply these and get a 1×1 matrix representing total cost, we must multiply a 1×4 matrix by a 4×1 matrix. This is why T was written as a row matrix in (b).] So, we have

$$
TR = [3800 \quad 130 \quad 1400 \quad 200]
\left[
\begin{array}{c}
20 \\
180 \\
60 \\
25
\end{array}
\right] = [188{,}400].
$$

(d) Suppose the contractor builds the same number of homes in five subdivisions. What is the total amount of each material needed for each model in this case?

Let matrix A be

$$\text{Brand} \begin{array}{c} \\ \\ X \\ Y \end{array} \overset{\overset{\text{Vitamin}}{\text{C\quad E\quad K}}}{\begin{bmatrix} 2 & 7 & 5 \\ 4 & 6 & 9 \end{bmatrix}}$$

and matrix B be

$$\text{Vitamin} \begin{array}{c} \\ \\ C \\ E \\ K \end{array} \overset{\overset{\text{Cost}}{X\quad Y}}{\begin{bmatrix} 12 & 14 \\ 18 & 15 \\ 9 & 10 \end{bmatrix}}.$$

(a) What quantities do matrices A and B represent?

(b) What quantities does the product AB represent?

(c) What quantities does the product BA represent?

✓**Checkpoint 6**

Let $A = \begin{bmatrix} 3 & -2 \\ 4 & -1 \end{bmatrix}$ and

$I = \begin{bmatrix} 1 & 0 \\ 0 & 1 \end{bmatrix}$.

Find IA and AI.

Solution Determine the total amount of each material for each model for all five subdivisions. Multiply PQ by the scalar 5 as follows:

$$5 \begin{bmatrix} 1500 & 30 & 600 & 60 \\ 1100 & 40 & 400 & 60 \\ 1200 & 60 & 400 & 80 \end{bmatrix} = \begin{bmatrix} 7500 & 150 & 3000 & 300 \\ 5500 & 200 & 2000 & 300 \\ 6000 & 300 & 2000 & 400 \end{bmatrix}.$$

We can introduce notation to help keep track of the quantities a matrix represents. For example, we can say that matrix P from Example 4 represents models/styles, matrix Q represents styles/materials, and matrix R represents materials/cost. In each case, the meaning of the rows is written first and the columns second. When we found the product PQ in Example 4, the rows of the matrix represented models and the columns represented materials. Therefore, we can say that the matrix product PQ represents models/materials. The common quantity, styles, in both P and Q was eliminated in the product PQ. Do you see that the product $(PQ)R$ represents models/cost?

In practical problems, this notation helps decide in what order to multiply two matrices so that the results are meaningful. In Example 4(c), we could have found either product RT or product TR. However, since T represents subdivisions/materials and R represents materials/cost, the product TR gives subdivisions/cost. ✓₅

Identity Matrices

Recall from Section 1.1 that the real number 1 is the identity element for multiplication of real numbers: For any real number a, $a \cdot 1 = 1 \cdot a = a$. In this section, an **identity matrix** I is defined that has properties similar to those of the number 1.

If I is to be the identity matrix, the products AI and IA must both equal A. The 2×2 identity matrix that satisfies these conditions is

$$I = \begin{bmatrix} 1 & 0 \\ 0 & 1 \end{bmatrix}. \quad ✓₆$$

To check that I is really the 2×2 identity matrix, let

$$A = \begin{bmatrix} a & b \\ c & d \end{bmatrix}.$$

Then AI and IA should both equal A:

$$AI = \begin{bmatrix} a & b \\ c & d \end{bmatrix}\begin{bmatrix} 1 & 0 \\ 0 & 1 \end{bmatrix} = \begin{bmatrix} a(1) + b(0) & a(0) + b(1) \\ c(1) + d(0) & c(0) + d(1) \end{bmatrix} = \begin{bmatrix} a & b \\ c & d \end{bmatrix} = A;$$

$$IA = \begin{bmatrix} 1 & 0 \\ 0 & 1 \end{bmatrix}\begin{bmatrix} a & b \\ c & d \end{bmatrix} = \begin{bmatrix} 1(a) + 0(c) & 1(b) + 0(d) \\ 0(a) + 1(c) & 0(b) + 1(d) \end{bmatrix} = \begin{bmatrix} a & b \\ c & d \end{bmatrix} = A.$$

This verifies that I has been defined correctly. (It can also be shown that I is the only 2×2 identity matrix.)

The identity matrices for 3×3 matrices and 4×4 matrices are, respectively,

$$I = \begin{bmatrix} 1 & 0 & 0 \\ 0 & 1 & 0 \\ 0 & 0 & 1 \end{bmatrix} \text{ and } I = \begin{bmatrix} 1 & 0 & 0 & 0 \\ 0 & 1 & 0 & 0 \\ 0 & 0 & 1 & 0 \\ 0 & 0 & 0 & 1 \end{bmatrix}.$$

By generalizing these findings, an identity matrix can be found for any n by n matrix. This identity matrix will have 1s on the main diagonal from upper left to lower right, with all other entries equal to 0.

Inverse Matrices

Recall that for every nonzero real number a, the equation $ax = 1$ has a solution, namely, $x = 1/a = a^{-1}$. Similarly, for a square matrix A, we consider the matrix equation $AX = I$.

✈ **TECHNOLOGY TIP**

An $n \times n$ identity matrix can be displayed on most graphing calculators by using IDENTITY n or IDENT n or IDENMAT(n). Look in the MATH or OPS submenu of the TI MATRIX menu, or the OPTN MAT menu of Casio.

This equation does not always have a solution, but when it does, we use special terminology. If there is a matrix A^{-1} satisfying

$$AA^{-1} = I,$$

(that is, A^{-1} is a solution of $AX = I$), then A^{-1} is called the **inverse matrix** of A. In this case, it can be proved that $A^{-1}A = I$ and that A^{-1} is unique (that is, a square matrix has no more than one inverse). When a matrix has an inverse, it can be found by using the row operations given in Section 6.2, as we shall see later.

CAUTION Only square matrices have inverses, but not every square matrix has one. A matrix that does not have an inverse is called a **singular matrix.** Note that the symbol A^{-1} (read "A-inverse") does *not* mean $1/A$; the symbol A^{-1} is just the notation for the inverse of matrix A. There is no such thing as matrix division.

Example 5   Given matrices A and B as follows, determine whether B is the inverse of A:

$$A = \begin{bmatrix} 1 & 2 \\ 4 & 6 \end{bmatrix}; \quad B = \begin{bmatrix} -3 & 1 \\ 2 & -\frac{1}{2} \end{bmatrix}.$$

Solution B is the inverse of A if $AB = I$ and $BA = I$, so we find those products:

$$AB = \begin{bmatrix} 1 & 2 \\ 4 & 6 \end{bmatrix}\begin{bmatrix} -3 & 1 \\ 2 & -\frac{1}{2} \end{bmatrix} = \begin{bmatrix} 1 & 0 \\ 0 & 1 \end{bmatrix} = I;$$

$$BA = \begin{bmatrix} -3 & 1 \\ 2 & -\frac{1}{2} \end{bmatrix}\begin{bmatrix} 1 & 2 \\ 4 & 6 \end{bmatrix} = \begin{bmatrix} 1 & 0 \\ 0 & 1 \end{bmatrix} = I.$$

Therefore, B is the inverse of A; that is, $A^{-1} = B$. (It is also true that A is the inverse of B, or $B^{-1} = A$.) ✔ 7

✓ **Checkpoint 7**

Given $A = \begin{bmatrix} 2 & 1 \\ 3 & 8 \end{bmatrix}$ and $B = \begin{bmatrix} -1 & 3 \\ 1 & -2 \end{bmatrix}$, determine whether they are inverses.

Example 6   Find the multiplicative inverse of

$$A = \begin{bmatrix} 2 & 4 \\ 1 & -1 \end{bmatrix}.$$

Solution   Let the unknown inverse matrix be

$$A^{-1} = \begin{bmatrix} x & y \\ z & w \end{bmatrix}.$$

By the definition of matrix inverse, $AA^{-1} = I$, or

$$AA^{-1} = \begin{bmatrix} 2 & 4 \\ 1 & -1 \end{bmatrix}\begin{bmatrix} x & y \\ z & w \end{bmatrix} = \begin{bmatrix} 1 & 0 \\ 0 & 1 \end{bmatrix}.$$

Use matrix multiplication to get

$$\begin{bmatrix} 2x + 4z & 2y + 4w \\ x - z & y - w \end{bmatrix} = \begin{bmatrix} 1 & 0 \\ 0 & 1 \end{bmatrix}.$$

Setting corresponding elements equal to each other gives the system of equations

$$2x + 4z = 1 \qquad \qquad \text{(1)}$$
$$2y + 4w = 0 \qquad \qquad \text{(2)}$$
$$x - z = 0 \qquad \qquad \text{(3)}$$
$$y - w = 1. \qquad \qquad \text{(4)}$$

Since equations (1) and (3) involve only x and z, while equations (2) and (4) involve only y and w, these four equations lead to two systems of equations:

$$\begin{matrix} 2x + 4z = 1 \\ x - z = 0 \end{matrix} \quad \text{and} \quad \begin{matrix} 2y + 4w = 0 \\ y - w = 1. \end{matrix}$$

Writing the two systems as augmented matrices gives

$$\begin{bmatrix} 2 & 4 & | & 1 \\ 1 & -1 & | & 0 \end{bmatrix} \quad \text{and} \quad \begin{bmatrix} 2 & 4 & | & 0 \\ 1 & -1 & | & 1 \end{bmatrix}.$$

Note that the row operations needed to transform both matrices are the same because the first two columns of both matrices are identical. Consequently, we can save time by combining these matrices into the single matrix

$$\begin{bmatrix} 2 & 4 & | & 1 & 0 \\ 1 & -1 & | & 0 & 1 \end{bmatrix}. \tag{5}$$

Columns 1–3 represent the first system and columns 1, 2, and 4 represent the second system. Now use row operations as follows:

$$\begin{bmatrix} 1 & -1 & | & 0 & 1 \\ 2 & 4 & | & 1 & 0 \end{bmatrix} \qquad \text{Interchange } R_1 \text{ and } R_2.$$

$$\begin{bmatrix} 1 & -1 & | & 0 & 1 \\ 0 & 6 & | & 1 & -2 \end{bmatrix} \qquad -2R_1 + R_2$$

$$\begin{bmatrix} 1 & -1 & | & 0 & 1 \\ 0 & 1 & | & \frac{1}{6} & -\frac{1}{3} \end{bmatrix} \qquad \frac{1}{6}R_2$$

$$\begin{bmatrix} 1 & 0 & | & \frac{1}{6} & \frac{2}{3} \\ 0 & 1 & | & \frac{1}{6} & -\frac{1}{3} \end{bmatrix}. \qquad R_2 + R_1 \tag{6}$$

The left half of the augmented matrix in equation (6) is the identity matrix, so the Gauss–Jordan process is finished and the solutions can be read from the right half of the augmented matrix. The numbers in the first column to the right of the vertical bar give the values of x and z. The second column to the right of the bar gives the values of y and w. That is,

$$\begin{bmatrix} 1 & 0 & | & x & y \\ 0 & 1 & | & z & w \end{bmatrix} = \begin{bmatrix} 1 & 0 & | & \frac{1}{6} & \frac{2}{3} \\ 0 & 1 & | & \frac{1}{6} & -\frac{1}{3} \end{bmatrix},$$

so that

$$A^{-1} = \begin{bmatrix} x & y \\ z & w \end{bmatrix} = \begin{bmatrix} \frac{1}{6} & \frac{2}{3} \\ \frac{1}{6} & -\frac{1}{3} \end{bmatrix}.$$

Check by multiplying A and A^{-1}. The result should be I:

$$AA^{-1} = \begin{bmatrix} 2 & 4 \\ 1 & -1 \end{bmatrix}\begin{bmatrix} \frac{1}{6} & \frac{2}{3} \\ \frac{1}{6} & -\frac{1}{3} \end{bmatrix} = \begin{bmatrix} \frac{1}{3}+\frac{2}{3} & \frac{4}{3}-\frac{4}{3} \\ \frac{1}{6}-\frac{1}{6} & \frac{2}{3}+\frac{1}{3} \end{bmatrix} = \begin{bmatrix} 1 & 0 \\ 0 & 1 \end{bmatrix} = I.$$

Thus, the original augmented matrix in equation (5) has A as its left half and the identity matrix as its right half, while the final augmented matrix in equation (6), at the end of the Gauss–Jordan process, has the identity matrix as its left half and the inverse matrix A^{-1} as its right half:

$$[A \mid I] \rightarrow [I \mid A^{-1}]. \quad ✓ 8$$

The procedure in Example 6 can be generalized as follows.

✓ **Checkpoint 8**

Carry out the process in Example 6 on a graphing calculator as follows: Enter matrix (5) in the example as matrix [B] on the calculator. Then find RREF [B]. What is the result?

Inverse Matrix

To obtain an **inverse matrix** A^{-1} for any $n \times n$ matrix A for which A^{-1} exists, follow these steps:

1. Form the augmented matrix $[A \mid I]$, where I is the $n \times n$ identity matrix.
2. Perform row operations on $[A \mid I]$ to get a matrix of the form $[I \mid B]$.
3. Matrix B is A^{-1}.

Example 7 Find A^{-1} if

$$A = \begin{bmatrix} 1 & 0 & 1 \\ 2 & -2 & -1 \\ 5 & 0 & 0 \end{bmatrix}.$$

Solution First write the augmented matrix $[A \mid I]$:

$$[A \mid I] = \begin{bmatrix} 1 & 0 & 1 & 1 & 0 & 0 \\ 2 & -2 & -1 & 0 & 1 & 0 \\ 5 & 0 & 0 & 0 & 0 & 1 \end{bmatrix}.$$

Transform the left side of this matrix into the 3×3 identity matrix:

$$\begin{bmatrix} 1 & 0 & 1 & 1 & 0 & 0 \\ 0 & -2 & -3 & -2 & 1 & 0 \\ 0 & 0 & -5 & -5 & 0 & 1 \end{bmatrix} \quad \begin{array}{l} -2R_1 + R_2 \\ -5R_1 + R_3 \end{array}$$

$$\begin{bmatrix} 1 & 0 & 1 & 1 & 0 & 0 \\ 0 & 1 & \frac{3}{2} & 1 & -\frac{1}{2} & 0 \\ 0 & 0 & 1 & 1 & 0 & -\frac{1}{5} \end{bmatrix} \quad \begin{array}{l} -\frac{1}{2}R_2 \\ -\frac{1}{5}R_3 \end{array}$$

$$\begin{bmatrix} 1 & 0 & 0 & 0 & 0 & \frac{1}{5} \\ 0 & 1 & 0 & -\frac{1}{2} & -\frac{1}{2} & \frac{3}{10} \\ 0 & 0 & 1 & 1 & 0 & -\frac{1}{5} \end{bmatrix}. \quad \begin{array}{l} -1R_3 + R_1 \\ -\frac{3}{2}R_3 + R_2 \end{array}$$

Looking at the right half of the preceding matrix, we see that

$$A^{-1} = \begin{bmatrix} 0 & 0 & \frac{1}{5} \\ -\frac{1}{2} & -\frac{1}{2} & \frac{3}{10} \\ 1 & 0 & -\frac{1}{5} \end{bmatrix}.$$

Verify that AA^{-1} is I.

The best way to find matrix inverses on a graphing calculator is illustrated in the next example.

 Example 8 Use a graphing calculator to find the inverse of the following matrices (if they have inverses):

$$A = \begin{bmatrix} 1 & 0 & 1 \\ 2 & -2 & -1 \\ 5 & 0 & 0 \end{bmatrix} \quad \text{and} \quad B = \begin{bmatrix} 2 & 4 \\ 3 & 6 \end{bmatrix}.$$

Solution Enter matrix A into the calculator [Figure 6.25(a)]. Then use the x^{-1} key to find the inverse matrix, as in Figure 6.25(b). (Using $\wedge$ and -1 for the inverse results in an error message on most calculators.) Note that Figure 6.25(b) agrees with the answer we found working by hand in Example 7.

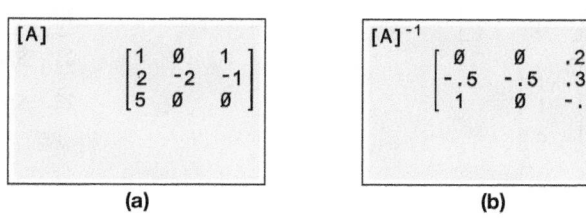

(a)   (b)

Figure 6.25

Now enter matrix B into the calculator and use the x^{-1} key. The result is an error message (Figure 6.26), which indicates that the matrix is singular; it does not have an inverse. (If you were working by hand, you would have found that the appropriate system of equations has no solution.)

Checkpoint 9

Use a graphing calculator to find the inverses of these matrices (if they exist).

(a) $A = \begin{bmatrix} 1 & 2 & 3 \\ 4 & -1 & 0 \\ 5 & 1 & 3 \end{bmatrix}$

(b) $B = \begin{bmatrix} 2 & 3 \\ -1 & 4 \end{bmatrix}$

```
ERR:SINGULAR MAT
1:Quit
2:Goto
```

Figure 6.26

 TECHNOLOGY TIP Because of round-off error, a graphing calculator may sometimes display an "inverse" for a matrix that doesn't actually have one. So always verify your results by multiplying A and A^{-1}. If the product is not the identity matrix, then A does not have an inverse.

6.5 Exercises

In Exercises 1–6, the sizes of two matrices A and B are given. Find the sizes of the product AB and the product BA whenever these products exist. (See Example 1.)

1. A is 2×2 and B is 2×2.

2. A is 3×3 and B is 3×2.

3. A is 3×5 and B is 5×3.

4. A is 4×3 and B is 3×6.

5. A is 4×2 and B is 3×4.

6. A is 7×3 and B is 2×7.

7. To find the product matrix AB, the number of _____ of A must be the same as the number of _____ of B.

8. The product matrix AB has the same number of _____ as A and the same number of _____ as B.

Find each of the following matrix products, if they exist. (See Examples 2 and 3.)

9. $\begin{bmatrix} 1 & 2 \\ 3 & 4 \end{bmatrix} \begin{bmatrix} -1 \\ 3 \end{bmatrix}$

10. $\begin{bmatrix} -2 & 5 \\ 7 & 0 \end{bmatrix} \begin{bmatrix} 2 \\ 6 \end{bmatrix}$

11. $\begin{bmatrix} 2 & 2 & -1 \\ 5 & 0 & 1 \end{bmatrix} \begin{bmatrix} 0 & -2 \\ -1 & 5 \\ 0 & 2 \end{bmatrix}$

12. $\begin{bmatrix} -9 & 3 & 1 \\ 3 & 0 & 0 \end{bmatrix} \begin{bmatrix} 2 \\ -1 \\ 4 \end{bmatrix}$

13. $\begin{bmatrix} -4 & 1 \\ 2 & -3 \end{bmatrix} \begin{bmatrix} 1 & 0 \\ 0 & 1 \end{bmatrix}$

14. $\begin{bmatrix} 1 & 0 \\ 0 & 1 \end{bmatrix} \begin{bmatrix} 3 & -2 \\ 1 & -5 \end{bmatrix}$

15. $\begin{bmatrix} 1 & 0 & 0 \\ 0 & 1 & 0 \\ 0 & 0 & 1 \end{bmatrix} \begin{bmatrix} 3 & -5 & 7 \\ -2 & 1 & 6 \\ 0 & -3 & 4 \end{bmatrix}$

16. $\begin{bmatrix} -8 & 9 \\ 3 & -4 \\ -1 & 6 \end{bmatrix} \begin{bmatrix} 1 & 0 & 0 \\ 0 & 1 & 0 \end{bmatrix}$

17. $\begin{bmatrix} 1 & 2 & 3 \\ 4 & 0 & 6 \\ 7 & 8 & 9 \end{bmatrix} \begin{bmatrix} -1 & 4 \\ 7 & 0 \\ 1 & 2 \end{bmatrix}$

18. $\begin{bmatrix} -2 & 0 & 3 \\ 4 & -3 & -1 \end{bmatrix} \begin{bmatrix} 2 & 0 & -1 & 5 \\ 0 & 1 & 0 & -1 \\ 4 & 2 & 5 & -4 \end{bmatrix}$

In Exercises 19–21, use the matrices

$$A = \begin{bmatrix} -3 & -9 \\ 2 & 6 \end{bmatrix} \quad and \quad B = \begin{bmatrix} 4 & 6 \\ 2 & 3 \end{bmatrix}.$$

19. Show that $AB \neq BA$. Hence, matrix multiplication is not commutative.

20. Show that $(A + B)^2 \neq A^2 + 2AB + B^2$.

21. Show that $(A + B)(A - B) \neq A^2 - B^2$.

22. Show that $D^2 = D$, where

$$D = \begin{bmatrix} 1 & 0 & 0 \\ \frac{1}{2} & 0 & \frac{1}{2} \\ 0 & 0 & 1 \end{bmatrix}.$$

Given matrices

$$P = \begin{bmatrix} m & n \\ p & q \end{bmatrix}, \qquad X = \begin{bmatrix} x & y \\ z & w \end{bmatrix}, \qquad and \qquad T = \begin{bmatrix} r & s \\ t & u \end{bmatrix},$$

verify that the statements in Exercises 23–26 are true.

23. $(PX)T = P(XT)$ (associative property)

24. $P(X + T) = PX + PT$ (distributive property)

25. $k(X + T) = kX + kT$ for any real number k

26. $(k + h)P = kP + hP$ for any real numbers k and h

Determine whether the given matrices are inverses of each other by computing their product. (See Example 5.)

27. $\begin{bmatrix} 5 & 2 \\ 3 & -1 \end{bmatrix}$ and $\begin{bmatrix} -1 & 2 \\ 3 & -4 \end{bmatrix}$ **28.** $\begin{bmatrix} 3 & 2 \\ 7 & 5 \end{bmatrix}$ and $\begin{bmatrix} 5 & 0 \\ -7 & 3 \end{bmatrix}$

29. $\begin{bmatrix} 3 & -1 \\ -4 & 2 \end{bmatrix}$ and $\begin{bmatrix} 1 & \frac{1}{2} \\ 2 & \frac{3}{2} \end{bmatrix}$ **30.** $\begin{bmatrix} 3 & 5 \\ 7 & 9 \end{bmatrix}$ and $\begin{bmatrix} -\frac{9}{8} & \frac{5}{8} \\ \frac{7}{8} & -\frac{3}{8} \end{bmatrix}$

31. $\begin{bmatrix} 1 & 1 & 1 \\ 2 & 3 & 0 \\ 1 & 2 & 1 \end{bmatrix}$ and $\begin{bmatrix} 1.5 & .5 & -1.5 \\ -1 & 0 & 1 \\ .5 & -.5 & .5 \end{bmatrix}$

32. $\begin{bmatrix} 2 & 5 & 4 \\ 1 & 4 & 3 \\ 1 & 3 & 2 \end{bmatrix}$ and $\begin{bmatrix} 1 & 2 & 1 \\ -5 & 8 & 2 \\ 7 & -11 & -3 \end{bmatrix}$

Find the inverse, if it exists, for each of the given matrices. (See Examples 6 and 7.)

33. $\begin{bmatrix} 2 & -3 \\ -1 & 2 \end{bmatrix}$ **34.** $\begin{bmatrix} 2 & 1 \\ 1 & 1 \end{bmatrix}$

35. $\begin{bmatrix} -1 & 2 \\ 1 & -1 \end{bmatrix}$ **36.** $\begin{bmatrix} 1 & 2 \\ 3 & 4 \end{bmatrix}$

37. $\begin{bmatrix} 1 & 2 \\ 3 & 6 \end{bmatrix}$ **38.** $\begin{bmatrix} -3 & -5 \\ 6 & 10 \end{bmatrix}$

39. $\begin{bmatrix} 1 & -1 & 0 \\ -1 & 2 & 3 \\ 1 & 0 & 2 \end{bmatrix}$ **40.** $\begin{bmatrix} 0 & 1 & -1 \\ 2 & -2 & -1 \\ -1 & 1 & 1 \end{bmatrix}$

41. $\begin{bmatrix} 1 & 4 & 3 \\ 1 & -3 & -2 \\ 2 & 5 & 4 \end{bmatrix}$ **42.** $\begin{bmatrix} 1 & -1 & 4 \\ 0 & 1 & 3 \\ 2 & -3 & 4 \end{bmatrix}$

43. $\begin{bmatrix} 1 & 2 & 0 \\ 3 & -1 & 2 \\ -2 & 3 & -2 \end{bmatrix}$ **44.** $\begin{bmatrix} 1 & 0 & -5 \\ 4 & -7 & 3 \\ 3 & -7 & 8 \end{bmatrix}$

📝 *Use a graphing calculator to find the inverse of each matrix. (See Example 8.)*

45. $\begin{bmatrix} 1 & 2 & 3 \\ 1 & 4 & 2 \\ 0 & 1 & -1 \end{bmatrix}$ **46.** $\begin{bmatrix} 2 & 2 & -4 \\ 2 & 6 & 0 \\ -3 & -3 & 5 \end{bmatrix}$

47. $\begin{bmatrix} 1 & 0 & -2 & 0 \\ -2 & 1 & 2 & 2 \\ 3 & -1 & -2 & -3 \\ 0 & 1 & 4 & 1 \end{bmatrix}$ **48.** $\begin{bmatrix} 1 & 1 & 0 & 2 \\ 2 & -1 & 1 & -1 \\ 3 & 3 & 2 & -2 \\ 1 & 2 & 1 & 0 \end{bmatrix}$

A graphing calculator or other technology is recommended for part (c) of Exercises 49–51.

49. Social Science Population estimates and projections (in millions) for several regions of the world and the average birth and death rates per million people for those regions are shown in the tables below. (Data from: United Nations Population Fund.)

	Asia	Europe	Latin America	North America
2000	3719	727	521	313
2010	4164	738	590	345
2020	4566	744	652	374

	Births	Deaths
Asia	.019	.007
Europe	.011	.011
Latin America	.019	.006
North America	.024	.008

(a) Write the information in the first table as a 3×4 matrix A.

(b) Write the information in the second table as a 4×2 matrix B.

(c) Find the matrix product AB.

(d) Explain what AB represents.

(e) According to matrix AB, what was the total number of births in these four regions combined in 2010? What total number of deaths is projected for 2020?

50. Business A restaurant has a main location and a traveling food truck. The first matrix A shows the number of managers and associates employed. The second matrix B shows the average annual cost of salary and benefits (in thousands of dollars).

$$\begin{array}{c} \\ \text{Restaurant} \\ \text{Food Truck} \end{array} \begin{array}{cc} \text{Managers} & \text{Associates} \end{array} \\ \begin{bmatrix} 5 & 25 \\ 1 & 4 \end{bmatrix} = A$$

$$\begin{array}{c} \\ \text{Managers} \\ \text{Associates} \end{array} \begin{array}{cc} \text{Salary} & \text{Benefits} \end{array} \\ \begin{bmatrix} 41 & 6 \\ 20 & 2 \end{bmatrix} = B$$

(a) Find the matrix product AB.

(b) Explain what AB represents.

(c) According to matrix AB, what is the total cost of salaries for all employees (managers and associates) at the restaurant? What is the total cost of benefits for all employees at the food truck?

51. Social Science Population estimates and projections (in millions) for the BRIC countries (Brazil, Russia, India, China) and birth and death rates per million people for those countries are shown in the tables on the next page. (Data from: United Nations Population Fund.)

	2010	2020
Brazil	195	210
Russia	143	141
India	1225	1387
China	1341	1388

	Births	Deaths
Brazil	.016	.006
Russia	.011	.014
India	.023	.008
China	.013	.007

(a) Write the information in the first table as a 2 × 4 matrix A.

(b) Write the information in the second table as a 4 × 2 matrix B.

(c) Find the matrix product AB.

(d) Explain what AB represents.

(e) According to matrix AB, what was the total number of deaths in the BRIC countries in 2010? What total number of births is projected for 2020?

52. Business The first table shows the number of employees (in millions) in various sectors of the U.S. economy over a 3-year period. The second table gives the average weekly wage per employee (in dollars) in each sector over the same period. (Data from: Bureau of Labor Statistics.)

	2007	2008	2009
Private	114.0	113.2	106.9
Local Government	14.0	14.2	14.2
State Government	4.6	4.6	4.6
Federal Government	2.7	2.8	2.8

	2007	2008	2009
Private	853	873	868
Local Government	784	813	830
State Government	883	923	937
Federal Government	1248	1275	1303

(a) Write the information in the first table as a 4 × 3 matrix A.

(b) Write the information in the second table as a 3 × 4 matrix B.

(c) Explain what each of the following entries in AB represents: row 1, column 1; row 2, column 2; row 3, column 3; row 4, column 4. Do any of the other entries represent anything meaningful?

(d) What was the total weekly payroll (in dollars) for the federal government over the 3-year period?

53. Business The four departments of Stagg Enterprises need to order the following amounts of the same products:

	Paper	Tape	Ink Cartridges	Memo Pads	Pens
Department 1	10	4	3	5	6
Department 2	7	2	2	3	8
Department 3	4	5	1	0	10
Department 4	0	3	4	5	5

The unit price (in dollars) of each product is as follows for two suppliers:

Product	Supplier A	Supplier B
Paper	9	12
Tape	6	6
Ink Cartridges	24	18
Memo Pads	4	4
Pens	8	12

(a) Use matrix multiplication to get a matrix showing the comparative costs for each department for the products from the two suppliers.

(b) Find the total cost to buy products from each supplier. From which supplier should the company make the purchase?

54. Health The first table shows the number of live births (in thousands). The second table shows infant mortality rates (deaths per 1000 live births). (Data from: U.S. Center for Health Statistics.)

	2008	2009	2010
Black	671	658	636
White	3274	3173	3069

	2008	2009	2010
Black	12.7	12.6	11.6
White	5.6	5.3	5.2

(a) Write the information in the first table as a 3 × 2 matrix C.

(b) Write the information in the second table as a 2 × 3 matrix D.

(c) Find the matrix product DC.

(d) Which entry in DC gives the total number of black infant deaths from 2008 to 2010?

(e) Which entry in DC gives the total number of white infant deaths from 2008 to 2010?

55. Business Burger Barn's three locations sell hamburgers, fries, and soft drinks. Barn I sells 900 burgers, 600 orders of fries, and 750 soft drinks each day. Barn II sells 1500 burgers a day and Barn III sells 1150. Soft drink sales number 900 a day at Barn II and 825 a day at Barn III. Barn II sells 950 orders of fries per day and Barn III sells 800.

(a) Write a 3 × 3 matrix S that displays daily sales figures for all locations.

(b) Burgers cost $3.00 each, fries $1.80 an order, and soft drinks $1.20 each. Write a 1×3 matrix P that displays the prices.

(c) What matrix product displays the daily revenue at each of the three locations?

(d) What is the total daily revenue from all locations?

56. **Business** The Perulli Candy Company makes three types of chocolate candy: Cheery Cherry, Mucho Mocha, and Almond Delight. The company produces its products in San Diego, Mexico City, and Managua, using two main ingredients: chocolate and sugar.

(a) Each kilogram of Cheery Cherry requires .5 kilogram of sugar and .2 kilogram of chocolate; each kilogram of Mucho Mocha requires .4 kilogram of sugar and .3 kilogram of chocolate; and each kilogram of Almond Delight requires .3 kilogram of sugar and .3 kilogram of chocolate. Put this information into a 2×3 matrix, labeling the rows and columns.

(b) The cost of 1 kilogram of sugar is $3 in San Diego, $2 in Mexico City, and $1 in Managua. The cost of 1 kilogram of chocolate is $3 in San Diego, $3 in Mexico City, and $4 in Managua. Put this information into a matrix in such a way that when you multiply it with your matrix from part (a), you get a matrix representing the cost by ingredient of producing each type of candy in each city.

(c) Multiply the matrices in parts (a) and (b), labeling the product matrix.

(d) From part (c), what is the combined cost of sugar and chocolate required to produce 1 kilogram of Mucho Mocha in Managua?

(e) Perulli Candy needs to quickly produce a special shipment of 100 kilograms of Cheery Cherry, 200 kilograms of Mucho Mocha, and 500 kilograms of Almond Delight, and it decides to select one factory to fill the entire order. Use matrix multiplication to determine in which city the total cost of sugar and chocolate combined required to produce the order is the smallest.

✓**Checkpoint Answers**

1. $27,100

2. (a) No   (b) Yes; 2×6

3. $CD = \begin{bmatrix} 19 & -2 \\ -13 & -12 \end{bmatrix}$

4. (a) 2×3 (b) Not possible   (c) 3×3

5. (a) $A = $ brand/vitamin;
   $B = $ vitamin/cost.
   (b) $AB = $ brand/cost.
   (c) Not meaningful, although the product BA can be found.

6. $IA = \begin{bmatrix} 3 & -2 \\ 4 & -1 \end{bmatrix} = A$, and $AI = \begin{bmatrix} 3 & -2 \\ 4 & -1 \end{bmatrix} = A$.

7. No, because $AB \neq I$.

8. RREF [B] is matrix (6) in the example.

9. (a) No inverse
   (b) Use the FRAC key (if you have one) to simplify the answer, which is
   $B^{-1} = \begin{bmatrix} 4/11 & -3/11 \\ 1/11 & 2/11 \end{bmatrix}$.

6.6 Applications of Matrices

This section gives a variety of applications of matrices.

Solving Systems with Matrices

Consider this system of linear equations:

$$2x - 3y = 4$$
$$x + 5y = 2.$$

Let

$$A = \begin{bmatrix} 2 & -3 \\ 1 & 5 \end{bmatrix}, \qquad X = \begin{bmatrix} x \\ y \end{bmatrix}, \qquad \text{and} \qquad B = \begin{bmatrix} 4 \\ 2 \end{bmatrix}.$$

Since

$$AX = \begin{bmatrix} 2 & -3 \\ 1 & 5 \end{bmatrix} \begin{bmatrix} x \\ y \end{bmatrix} = \begin{bmatrix} 2x - 3y \\ x + 5y \end{bmatrix} \quad \text{and} \quad B = \begin{bmatrix} 4 \\ 2 \end{bmatrix},$$

the original system is equivalent to the single matrix equation $AX = B$. Similarly, any system of linear equations can be written as a matrix equation $AX = B$. The matrix A is called the **coefficient matrix.** ✓₁

A matrix equation $AX = B$ can be solved if A^{-1} exists. Assuming that A^{-1} exists and using the facts that $A^{-1}A = I$ and $IX = X$, along with the associative property of multiplication of matrices, gives

$$AX = B$$
$$A^{-1}(AX) = A^{-1}B \qquad \text{Multiply both sides by } A^{-1}.$$
$$(A^{-1}A)X = A^{-1}B \qquad \text{Associative property}$$
$$IX = A^{-1}B \qquad \text{Inverse property}$$
$$X = A^{-1}B. \qquad \text{Identity property}$$

✓ **Checkpoint 1**

Write the matrix of coefficients, the matrix of variables, and the matrix of constants for the system

$$2x + 6y = -14$$
$$-x - 2y = 3.$$

When multiplying by matrices on both sides of a matrix equation, be careful to multiply in the same order on both sides, since multiplication of matrices is not commutative (unlike the multiplication of real numbers). This discussion is summarized below.

Suppose that a system of equations with the same number of equations as variables is written in matrix form as $AX = B$, where A is the square matrix of coefficients, X is the column matrix of variables, and B is the column matrix of constants. If A has an inverse, then the unique solution of the system is $X = A^{-1}B$.*

Example 1 Consider this system of equations:

$$x + y + z = 2$$
$$2x + 3y \quad\;\; = 5$$
$$x + 2y + z = -1.$$

(a) Write the system as a matrix equation.

Solution We have these three matrices:

Coefficient Matrix	Matrix of Variables	Matrix of Constants
$A = \begin{bmatrix} 1 & 1 & 1 \\ 2 & 3 & 0 \\ 1 & 2 & 1 \end{bmatrix},$	$X = \begin{bmatrix} x \\ y \\ z \end{bmatrix},$ and	$B = \begin{bmatrix} 2 \\ 5 \\ -1 \end{bmatrix}.$

So the matrix equation is

$$AX = B$$

$$\begin{bmatrix} 1 & 1 & 1 \\ 2 & 3 & 0 \\ 1 & 2 & 1 \end{bmatrix} \begin{bmatrix} x \\ y \\ z \end{bmatrix} = \begin{bmatrix} 2 \\ 5 \\ -1 \end{bmatrix}.$$

---

*If A does not have an inverse, then the system either has no solution or has an infinite number of solutions. Use the methods of Sections 6.1 or 6.2.

(b) Find A^{-1} and solve the equation.

Solution Use Exercise 31 of Section 6.5, technology, or the method of Section 6.5 to find that

$$A^{-1} = \begin{bmatrix} 1.5 & .5 & -1.5 \\ -1 & 0 & 1 \\ .5 & -.5 & .5 \end{bmatrix}.$$

Hence,

$$X = A^{-1}B = \begin{bmatrix} 1.5 & .5 & -1.5 \\ -1 & 0 & 1 \\ .5 & -.5 & .5 \end{bmatrix}\begin{bmatrix} 2 \\ 5 \\ -1 \end{bmatrix} = \begin{bmatrix} 7 \\ -3 \\ -2 \end{bmatrix}.$$

Thus, the solution of the original system is $(7, -3, -2)$. ✓2

✓Checkpoint 2

Use the inverse matrix to solve the system in Example 1 if the constants for the three equations are 12, 0, and 8, respectively.

Example 2 Use the inverse of the coefficient matrix to solve the system

$$x + 1.5y = 8$$
$$2x + 3y = 10.$$

Solution The coefficient matrix is $A = \begin{bmatrix} 1 & 1.5 \\ 2 & 3 \end{bmatrix}$. A graphing calculator will indicate that A^{-1} does not exist. If we try to carry out the row operations, we see why:

$$\begin{bmatrix} 1 & 1.5 & | & 1 & 0 \\ 2 & 3 & | & 0 & 1 \end{bmatrix}$$
$$\begin{bmatrix} 1 & 1.5 & | & 1 & 0 \\ 0 & 0 & | & -2 & 1 \end{bmatrix}. \quad -2R_1 + R_2$$

The next step cannot be performed because of the zero in the second row, second column. Verify that the original system has no solution. ✓3

✓Checkpoint 3

Solve the system in Example 2 if the constants are, respectively, 3 and 6.

Input–Output Analysis

An interesting application of matrix theory to economics was developed by Nobel Prize winner Wassily Leontief. His application of matrices to the interdependencies in an economy is called **input–output analysis.** In practice, input–output analysis is very complicated, with many variables. We shall discuss only simple examples with just a few variables.

Input–output models are concerned with the production and flow of goods and services. A typical economy is composed of a number of different sectors (such as manufacturing, energy, transportation, agriculture, etc.). Each sector requires input from other sectors (and possibly from itself) to produce its output. For instance, manufacturing output requires energy, transportation, and manufactured items (such as tools and machinery). If an economy has n sectors, then the inputs required by the various sectors from each other to produce their outputs can be described by an $n \times n$ matrix called the **input–output matrix** (or the **technological matrix**).

Example 3 **Economics** Suppose a simplified economy involves just three sectors—agriculture, manufacturing, and transportation—all in appropriate units. The production of 1 unit of agriculture requires $\frac{1}{2}$ unit of manufacturing and $\frac{1}{4}$ unit of transportation. The production of 1 unit of manufacturing requires $\frac{1}{4}$ unit of agriculture and $\frac{1}{4}$ unit of transportation. The production of 1 unit of transportation requires $\frac{1}{3}$ unit of agriculture and $\frac{1}{4}$ unit of manufacturing. Write the input–output matrix of this economy.

Solution   Since there are three sectors in the economy, the input–output matrix A is 3×3. Each row and each column is labeled by a sector of the economy, as shown below. The first column lists the units from each sector of the economy that are required to produce one unit of agriculture. The second column lists the units required from each sector to produce 1 unit of manufacturing, and the last column lists the units required from each sector to produce 1 unit of transportation.

Output

| | Agriculture | Manufacturing | Transportation |

$$\text{Input}\quad \begin{matrix} \text{Agriculture} \\ \text{Manufacturing} \\ \text{Transportation} \end{matrix} \begin{bmatrix} 0 & \frac{1}{4} & \frac{1}{3} \\ \frac{1}{2} & 0 & \frac{1}{4} \\ \frac{1}{4} & \frac{1}{4} & 0 \end{bmatrix} = A. \quad \boxed{✓}_4$$

✓**Checkpoint 4**

Write a 2×2 input–output matrix in which 1 unit of electricity requires $\frac{1}{2}$ unit of water and $\frac{1}{3}$ unit of electricity, while 1 unit of water requires no water but $\frac{1}{4}$ unit of electricity.

Example 3 is a bit unrealistic in that no sector of the economy requires any input from itself. In an actual economy, most sectors require input from themselves as well as from other sectors to produce their output (as discussed in the paragraph preceding Example 3). Nevertheless, it is easier to learn the basic concepts from simplified examples, so we shall continue to use them.

The input–output matrix gives only a partial picture of an economy. We also need to know the amount produced by each sector and the amount of the economy's output that is used up by the sectors themselves in the production process. The remainder of the total output is available to satisfy the needs of consumers and others outside the production system.

Example 4   **Economics**   Consider the economy whose input–output matrix A was found in Example 3.

(a) Suppose this economy produces 60 units of agriculture, 52 units of manufacturing, and 48 units of transportation. Write this information as a column matrix.

Solution   Listing the sectors in the same order as the rows of input–output matrix, we have

$$X = \begin{bmatrix} 60 \\ 52 \\ 48 \end{bmatrix}.$$

The matrix X is called the **production matrix.**

(b) How much from each sector is used up in the production process?

Solution   Since $\frac{1}{4}$ unit of agriculture is used to produce each unit of manufacturing and there are 52 units of manufacturing output, the amount of agriculture used up by manufacturing is $\frac{1}{4} \times 52 = 13$ units. Similarly $\frac{1}{3}$ unit of agriculture is used to produce a unit of transportation, so $\frac{1}{3} \times 48 = 16$ units of agriculture are used up by transportation. Therefore $13 + 16 = 29$ units of agriculture are used up in the economy's production process.

A similar analysis shows that the economy's production process uses up

$$\underset{\substack{\text{agricul-} \\ \text{ture}}}{\frac{1}{2} \times 60} + \underset{\substack{\text{transpor-} \\ \text{tation}}}{\frac{1}{4} \times 48} = 30 + 12 = 42 \text{ units of manufacturing}$$

and

$$\underset{\substack{\text{agricul-} \\ \text{ture}}}{\frac{1}{4} \times 60} + \underset{\substack{\text{manufac-} \\ \text{turing}}}{\frac{1}{4} \times 52} = 15 + 13 = 28 \text{ units of transportation.}$$

(c) Describe the conclusions of part (b) in terms of the input–output matrix A and the production matrix X.

Solution The matrix product AX gives the amount from each sector that is used up in the production process, as shown here [with selected entries color coded as in part (b)]:

$$AX = \begin{bmatrix} 0 & \frac{1}{4} & \frac{1}{3} \\ \frac{1}{2} & 0 & \frac{1}{4} \\ \frac{1}{4} & \frac{1}{4} & 0 \end{bmatrix} \begin{bmatrix} 60 \\ 52 \\ 48 \end{bmatrix} = \begin{bmatrix} 0\cdot 60 + \frac{1}{4}\cdot 52 + \frac{1}{3}\cdot 48 \\ \frac{1}{2}\cdot 60 + 0\cdot 52 + \frac{1}{4}\cdot 48 \\ \frac{1}{4}\cdot 60 + \frac{1}{4}\cdot 52 + 0\cdot 48 \end{bmatrix}$$

$$= \begin{bmatrix} \frac{1}{4}\cdot 52 + \frac{1}{3}\cdot 48 \\ \frac{1}{2}\cdot 60 + \frac{1}{4}\cdot 48 \\ \frac{1}{4}\cdot 60 + \frac{1}{4}\cdot 52 \end{bmatrix} = \begin{bmatrix} 29 \\ 42 \\ 28 \end{bmatrix}.$$

(d) Find the matrix $D = X - AX$ and explain what its entries represent.

Solution From parts (a) and (c), we have

$$D = X - AX = \begin{bmatrix} 60 \\ 52 \\ 48 \end{bmatrix} - \begin{bmatrix} 29 \\ 42 \\ 28 \end{bmatrix} = \begin{bmatrix} 31 \\ 10 \\ 20 \end{bmatrix}.$$

The matrix D lists the amount of each sector that is *not* used up in the production process and hence is available to groups outside the production process (such as consumers). For example, 60 units of agriculture are produced and 29 units are used up in the process, so the difference $60 - 29 = 31$ is the amount of agriculture that is available to groups outside the production process. Similar remarks apply to manufacturing and transportation. The matrix D is called the **demand matrix.** Matrices A and D show that the production of 60 units of agriculture, 52 units of manufacturing, and 48 units of transportation would satisfy an outside demand of 31 units of agriculture, 10 units of manufacturing, and 20 units of transportation. ✓5

✓**Checkpoint 5**

(a) Write a 2 × 1 matrix X to represent the gross production of 9000 units of electricity and 12,000 units of water.

(b) Find AX, using A from Checkpoint 4.

(c) Find D, using $D = X - AX$.

Example 4 illustrates the general situation. In an economy with n sectors, the input–output matrix A is $n \times n$. The production matrix X is a column matrix whose n entries are the outputs of each sector of the economy. The demand matrix D is also a column matrix with n entries. This matrix is defined by

$$D = X - AX.$$

D lists the amount from each sector that is available to meet the demands of consumers and other groups outside the production process.

In Example 4, we knew the input–output matrix A and the production matrix X and used them to find the demand matrix D. In practice, however, this process is reversed: The input–output matrix A and the demand matrix D are known, and we must find the production matrix X needed to satisfy the required demands. Matrix algebra can be used to solve the equation $D = X - AX$ for X:

$$D = X - AX$$
$$D = IX - AX \qquad \text{Identity property}$$
$$D = (I - A)X. \qquad \text{Distributive property}$$

If the matrix $I - A$ has an inverse, then

$$X = (I - A)^{-1}D.$$

Example 5 **Economics** Suppose, in the three-sector economy of Examples 3 and 4, there is a demand for 516 units of agriculture, 258 units of manufacturing, and 129 units of transportation. What should production be for each sector?

Solution The demand matrix is

$$D = \begin{bmatrix} 516 \\ 258 \\ 129 \end{bmatrix}.$$

Find the production matrix by first calculating $I - A$:

$$I - A = \begin{bmatrix} 1 & 0 & 0 \\ 0 & 1 & 0 \\ 0 & 0 & 1 \end{bmatrix} - \begin{bmatrix} 0 & \frac{1}{4} & \frac{1}{3} \\ \frac{1}{2} & 0 & \frac{1}{4} \\ \frac{1}{4} & \frac{1}{4} & 0 \end{bmatrix} = \begin{bmatrix} 1 & -\frac{1}{4} & -\frac{1}{3} \\ -\frac{1}{2} & 1 & -\frac{1}{4} \\ -\frac{1}{4} & -\frac{1}{4} & 1 \end{bmatrix}.$$

Using a calculator with matrix capability or row operations, find the inverse of $I - A$:

$$(I - A)^{-1} = \begin{bmatrix} 1.3953 & .4961 & .5891 \\ .8372 & 1.3643 & .6202 \\ .5581 & .4651 & 1.3023 \end{bmatrix}.$$

(The entries are rounded to four decimal places.[*]) Since $X = (I - A)^{-1}D.$

$$X = \begin{bmatrix} 1.3953 & .4961 & .5891 \\ .8372 & 1.3643 & .6202 \\ .5581 & .4651 & 1.3023 \end{bmatrix} \begin{bmatrix} 516 \\ 258 \\ 129 \end{bmatrix} = \begin{bmatrix} 924 \\ 864 \\ 576 \end{bmatrix}$$

(rounded to the nearest whole numbers).

From the last result, we see that the production of 924 units of agriculture, 864 units of manufacturing, and 576 units of transportation is required to satisfy demands of 516, 258, and 129 units, respectively.

Example 6 **Economics** An economy depends on two basic products: wheat and oil. To produce 1 metric ton of wheat requires .25 metric ton of wheat and .33 metric ton of oil. The production of 1 metric ton of oil consumes .08 metric ton of wheat and .11 metric ton of oil. Find the production that will satisfy a demand of 500 metric tons of wheat and 1000 metric tons of oil.

Solution The input–output matrix is

$$\begin{array}{cc} & \text{Wheat} \quad \text{Oil} \end{array}$$
$$A = \begin{bmatrix} .25 & .08 \\ .33 & .11 \end{bmatrix} \begin{array}{l} \text{Wheat} \\ \text{Oil} \end{array},$$

and we also have

$$I - A = \begin{bmatrix} 1 & 0 \\ 0 & 1 \end{bmatrix} - \begin{bmatrix} .25 & .08 \\ .33 & .11 \end{bmatrix} = \begin{bmatrix} .75 & -.08 \\ -.33 & .89 \end{bmatrix}.$$

Next, use technology or the methods of Section 6.5 to calculate $(I - A)^{-1}$:

$$(I - A)^{-1} = \begin{bmatrix} 1.3882 & .1248 \\ .5147 & 1.1699 \end{bmatrix} \quad \text{(rounded)}.$$

The demand matrix is

$$D = \begin{bmatrix} 500 \\ 1000 \end{bmatrix}.$$

---

[*]Although we show the matrix $(I - A)^{-1}$ with entries rounded to four decimal places, we did not round off in calculating $(I - A)^{-1}D$. If the rounded figures are used, the numbers in the product may vary slightly in the last digit.

Consequently, the production matrix is

$$X = (I - A)^{-1}D = \begin{bmatrix} 1.3882 & .1248 \\ .5147 & 1.1699 \end{bmatrix}\begin{bmatrix} 500 \\ 1000 \end{bmatrix} = \begin{bmatrix} 819 \\ 1427 \end{bmatrix},$$

where the production numbers have been rounded to the nearest whole numbers. The production of 819 metric tons of wheat and 1427 metric tons of oil is required to satisfy the indicated demand.

✓ Checkpoint 6

A simple economy depends on just two products: beer and pretzels.

(a) Suppose $\frac{1}{2}$ unit of beer and $\frac{1}{2}$ unit of pretzels are needed to make 1 unit of beer, and $\frac{3}{4}$ unit of beer is needed to make 1 unit of pretzels. Write the technological matrix A for the economy.

(b) Find $I - A$.

(c) Find $(I - A)^{-1}$.

(d) Find the gross production X that will be needed to get a net production of
$$D = \begin{bmatrix} 100 \\ 1000 \end{bmatrix}.$$

TECHNOLOGY TIP If you are using a graphing calculator to determine X, you can calculate $(I - A)^{-1}D$ in one step without finding the intermediate matrices $I - A$ and $(I - A)^{-1}$.

Code Theory

Governments need sophisticated methods of coding and decoding messages. One example of such an advanced code uses matrix theory. This code takes the letters in the words and divides them into groups. (Each space between words is treated as a letter; punctuation is disregarded.) Then, numbers are assigned to the letters of the alphabet. For our purposes, let the letter a correspond to 1, b to 2, and so on. Let the number 27 correspond to a space.

For example, the message

mathematics is for the birds

can be divided into groups of three letters each:

mat   hem   ati   cs−   is−   for   −th   e−b   ird   s−−

(We used − to represent a space.) We now write a column matrix for each group of three symbols, using the corresponding numbers instead of letters. For example, the first four groups can be written as

$$\overset{mat}{\begin{bmatrix} 13 \\ 1 \\ 20 \end{bmatrix}}, \overset{hem}{\begin{bmatrix} 8 \\ 5 \\ 13 \end{bmatrix}}, \overset{ati}{\begin{bmatrix} 1 \\ 20 \\ 9 \end{bmatrix}}, \overset{cs-}{\begin{bmatrix} 3 \\ 19 \\ 27 \end{bmatrix}}.$$

The entire message consists of ten 3×1 column matrices:

$$\begin{bmatrix} 13 \\ 1 \\ 20 \end{bmatrix}, \begin{bmatrix} 8 \\ 5 \\ 13 \end{bmatrix}, \begin{bmatrix} 1 \\ 20 \\ 9 \end{bmatrix}, \begin{bmatrix} 3 \\ 19 \\ 27 \end{bmatrix}, \begin{bmatrix} 9 \\ 19 \\ 27 \end{bmatrix}, \begin{bmatrix} 6 \\ 15 \\ 18 \end{bmatrix}, \begin{bmatrix} 27 \\ 20 \\ 8 \end{bmatrix}, \begin{bmatrix} 5 \\ 27 \\ 2 \end{bmatrix}, \begin{bmatrix} 9 \\ 18 \\ 4 \end{bmatrix}, \begin{bmatrix} 19 \\ 27 \\ 27 \end{bmatrix}.$$

✓ Checkpoint 7

Write the message *"when"* using 2×1 matrices.

Although you could transmit these matrices, a simple substitution code such as this is very easy to break.

To get a more reliable code, we choose a 3×3 matrix M that has an inverse. Suppose we choose

$$M = \begin{bmatrix} 1 & 3 & 3 \\ 1 & 4 & 3 \\ 1 & 3 & 4 \end{bmatrix}.$$

Then encode each message group by multiplying by M—that is,

$$\begin{bmatrix} 1 & 3 & 3 \\ 1 & 4 & 3 \\ 1 & 3 & 4 \end{bmatrix}\begin{bmatrix} 13 \\ 1 \\ 20 \end{bmatrix} = \begin{bmatrix} 76 \\ 77 \\ 96 \end{bmatrix}, \quad \begin{bmatrix} 1 & 3 & 3 \\ 1 & 4 & 3 \\ 1 & 3 & 4 \end{bmatrix}\begin{bmatrix} 8 \\ 5 \\ 13 \end{bmatrix} = \begin{bmatrix} 62 \\ 67 \\ 75 \end{bmatrix},$$

$$\begin{bmatrix} 1 & 3 & 3 \\ 1 & 4 & 3 \\ 1 & 3 & 4 \end{bmatrix}\begin{bmatrix} 1 \\ 20 \\ 9 \end{bmatrix} = \begin{bmatrix} 88 \\ 108 \\ 97 \end{bmatrix},$$

and so on. The coded message consists of the ten 3×1 column matrices

$$\begin{bmatrix} 76 \\ 77 \\ 96 \end{bmatrix}, \begin{bmatrix} 62 \\ 67 \\ 75 \end{bmatrix}, \begin{bmatrix} 88 \\ 108 \\ 97 \end{bmatrix}, \ldots, \begin{bmatrix} 181 \\ 208 \\ 208 \end{bmatrix}.$$

The message would be sent as a string of numbers:

$$76, 77, 96, 62, 67, 75, 88, 108, 97, \ldots, 181, 208, 208.$$

Note that the same letter may be encoded by different numbers. For instance, the first a in "mathematics" is 77 and the second a is 88. This makes the code harder to break. ✔8

The receiving agent rewrites the message as the ten 3×1 column matrices shown in color previously. The agent then decodes the message by multiplying each of these column matrices by the matrix M^{-1}. Verify that

$$M^{-1} = \begin{bmatrix} 7 & -3 & -3 \\ -1 & 1 & 0 \\ -1 & 0 & 1 \end{bmatrix}.$$

So the first two matrices of the coded message are decoded as

$$\begin{bmatrix} 7 & -3 & -3 \\ -1 & 1 & 0 \\ -1 & 0 & 1 \end{bmatrix}\begin{bmatrix} 76 \\ 77 \\ 96 \end{bmatrix} = \begin{bmatrix} 13 \\ 1 \\ 20 \end{bmatrix} \begin{matrix} m \\ a \\ t \end{matrix}$$

and

$$\begin{bmatrix} 7 & -3 & -3 \\ -1 & 1 & 0 \\ -1 & 0 & 1 \end{bmatrix}\begin{bmatrix} 62 \\ 67 \\ 75 \end{bmatrix} = \begin{bmatrix} 8 \\ 5 \\ 13 \end{bmatrix} \begin{matrix} h \\ e \\ m \end{matrix}.$$

The other blocks are decoded similarly.

✓ Checkpoint 8

Use the following matrix to find the 2×1 matrices to be transmitted for the message in Checkpoint 7:

$$\begin{bmatrix} 2 & 1 \\ 5 & 0 \end{bmatrix}.$$

Routing

The diagram in Figure 6.27 shows the pathways connecting five buildings on a college campus. We can represent the pathways via matrix A, where the entries represent the number of pathways connecting two buildings without passing through another building. From the diagram, we see that there are two pathways connecting building 1 to building 2 without passing through buildings 3, 4, or 5. This information is entered in row one, column two, and again in row two, column one of matrix A:

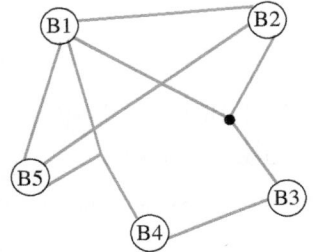

Figure 6.27

$$A = \begin{bmatrix} 0 & 2 & 1 & 1 & 2 \\ 2 & 0 & 1 & 0 & 1 \\ 1 & 1 & 0 & 1 & 0 \\ 1 & 0 & 1 & 0 & 1 \\ 2 & 1 & 0 & 1 & 0 \end{bmatrix}.$$

Note that there are no pathways connecting each building to itself, so the main diagonal of the matrix from upper left to lower right consists entirely of zeros.

We can also investigate the number of ways to go from building 1 to building 3 by going through exactly one other building. This can happen by going from building 1 to building 2 two ways, and then from building 2 to building 3. Another way is to go from building 1 to building 4 and then from building 4 to building 3. Thus, there are three total ways to go from building 1 to building 3 by going through exactly one other building.

The matrix A^2 shows the number of ways to travel between any two buildings by going through exactly one other building.

$$A^2 = \begin{bmatrix} 10 & 3 & 3 & 3 & 3 \\ 3 & 6 & 2 & 4 & 4 \\ 3 & 2 & 3 & 1 & 4 \\ 3 & 4 & 1 & 3 & 2 \\ 3 & 4 & 4 & 2 & 6 \end{bmatrix}.$$

We ignore the values down the main diagonal for travel from one building into itself. We notice that the entry in row one, column three has a value of 3. This coincides with what we learned earlier—that there are three ways to go from building 1 to building 3 that go through exactly one other building.

We can also find the number of ways to walk between any two buildings by passing through exactly two other buildings by calculating A^3. Additionally, $A + A^2$ gives the number of ways to walk between two buildings with at most one intermediate building.

The diagram can be given many other interpretations. For example, the lines could represent lines of mutual influence between people or nations, or they could represent communication lines, such as telephone lines.

✓**Checkpoint 9**

Use a graphing calculator to find the following.

(a) A^3

(b) $A + A^2$

6.6 Exercises

Solve the matrix equation AX = B for X. (See Example 1.)

1. $A = \begin{bmatrix} 1 & -1 \\ 5 & 6 \end{bmatrix}, B = \begin{bmatrix} 4 \\ -2 \end{bmatrix}$

2. $A = \begin{bmatrix} 1 & 2 \\ 1 & 5 \end{bmatrix}, B = \begin{bmatrix} -3 \\ 5 \end{bmatrix}$

3. $A = \begin{bmatrix} 3 & 1 \\ 4 & 2 \end{bmatrix}, B = \begin{bmatrix} 3 & 4 \\ 5 & 6 \end{bmatrix}$

4. $A = \begin{bmatrix} 1 & 4 \\ 2 & 7 \end{bmatrix}, B = \begin{bmatrix} 0 & 8 \\ 4 & 1 \end{bmatrix}$

5. $A = \begin{bmatrix} 2 & 1 & 0 \\ -4 & -1 & 3 \\ 3 & 1 & -2 \end{bmatrix}, B = \begin{bmatrix} 1 \\ 4 \\ 0 \end{bmatrix}$

6. $A = \begin{bmatrix} 3 & -1 & 0 \\ 0 & 1 & 2 \\ 9 & 0 & 5 \end{bmatrix}, B = \begin{bmatrix} -3 \\ 6 \\ 12 \end{bmatrix}$

Use the inverse of the coefficient matrix to solve each system of equations. (See Example 1.)

7. $x + 2y + 3z = 10$
   $2x + 3y + 2z = 6$
   $-x - 2y - 4z = -1$

8. $-x + y - 3z = 3$
   $2x + 4y - 4z = 6$
   $-x + y + 4z = -1$

9. $x + 4y + 3z = -12$
   $x - 3y - 2z = 0$
   $2x + 5y + 4z = 7$

10. $5x + 2z = 3$
    $2x + 2y + z = 4$
    $-3x + y - z = 5$

11. $x + 2y + 3z = 4$
    $x + 4y + 2z = 8$
    $y - z = -4$

12. $2x + 2y - 4z = 12$
    $2x + 6y = 16$
    $-3x - 3y + 5z = -20$

13. $x + y + 2w = 3$
    $2x - y + z - w = 3$
    $3x + 3y + 2z - 2w = 5$
    $x + 2y + z = 3$

14. $x - 2z = 4$
    $-2x + y + 2z + 2w = -8$
    $3x - y - 2z - 3w = 12$
    $y + 4z + w = -4$

Use matrix algebra to solve the given matrix equations for X. Check your work.

15. $N = X - MX; N = \begin{bmatrix} 8 \\ -12 \end{bmatrix}, M = \begin{bmatrix} 0 & 1 \\ -2 & 1 \end{bmatrix}$

16. $A = BX + X; A = \begin{bmatrix} 4 & 6 \\ -2 & 2 \end{bmatrix}, B = \begin{bmatrix} -2 & -2 \\ 3 & 3 \end{bmatrix}$

To complete these exercises, write a system of equations and use the inverse of the coefficient matrix to solve the system.

17. **Business** Donovan's Dandy Furniture makes dining room furniture. A buffet requires 15 hours for cutting, 20 hours for assembly, and 5 hours for finishing. A chair requires 5 hours for cutting, 8 hours for assembly, and 5 hours for finishing. A table requires 10 hours for cutting, 6 hours for assembly, and 6 hours for finishing. The cutting department has 4900 hours of labor available each

week, the assembly department has 6600 hours available, and the finishing department has 3900 hours available. How many pieces of each type of furniture should be produced each week if the factory is to run at full capacity?

18. **Natural Science** A hospital dietician is planning a special diet for a certain patient. The total amount per meal of food groups A, B, and C must equal 400 grams. The diet should include one-third as much of group A as of group B, and the sum of the amounts of group A and group C should equal twice the amount of group B.

   (a) How many grams of each food group should be included?

   (b) Suppose we drop the requirement that the diet include one-third as much of group A as of group B. Describe the set of all possible solutions.

   (c) Suppose that, in addition to the conditions given in part (a), foods A and B cost 2 cents per gram, food C costs 3 cents per gram, and a meal must cost $8. Is a solution possible?

19. **Natural Science** Three species of bacteria are fed three foods: I, II, and III. A bacterium of the first species consumes 1.3 units each of foods I and II and 2.3 units of food III each day. A bacterium of the second species consumes 1.1 units of food I, 2.4 units of food II, and 3.7 units of food III each day. A bacterium of the third species consumes 8.1 units of I, 2.9 units of II, and 5.1 units of III each day. If 16,000 units of I, 28,000 units of II, and 44,000 units of III are supplied each day, how many of each species can be maintained in this environment?

20. **Business** A company produces three combinations of mixed vegetables, which sell in 1-kilogram packages. Italian style combines .3 kilogram of zucchini, .3 of broccoli, and .4 of carrots. French style combines .6 kilogram of broccoli and .4 of carrots. Oriental style combines .2 kilogram of zucchini, .5 of broccoli, and .3 of carrots. The company has a stock of 16,200 kilograms of zucchini, 41,400 kilograms of broccoli, and 29,400 kilograms of carrots. How many packages of each style should the company prepare in order to use up its supplies?

21. **Business** A national chain of casual clothing stores recently sent shipments of jeans, jackets, sweaters, and shirts to its stores in various cities. The number of items shipped to each city and their total wholesale cost are shown in the table. Find the wholesale price of one pair of jeans, one jacket, one sweater, and one shirt.

City	Jeans	Jackets	Sweaters	Shirts	Total Cost
Cleveland	3000	3000	2200	4200	$507,650
St. Louis	2700	2500	2100	4300	459,075
Seattle	5000	2000	1400	7500	541,225
Phoenix	7000	1800	600	8000	571,500

22. **Health** A 100-bed nursing home provides two levels of long-term care: regular and maximum. Patients at each level have a choice of a private room or a less expensive semiprivate room. The tables show the number of patients in each category at various times last year. The total daily costs for all patients were

$24,040 in January, $23,926 in April, $23,760 in July, and $24,042 in October. Find the daily cost of each of the following: a private room (regular care), a private room (maximum care), a semiprivate room (regular care), and a semiprivate room (maximum care).

	REGULAR-CARE PATIENTS	
Month	Semiprivate	Private
January	22	8
April	26	8
July	24	14
October	20	10

	MAXIMUM-CARE PATIENTS	
Month	Semiprivate	Private
January	60	10
April	54	12
July	56	6
October	62	8

Find the production matrix for the given input–output and demand matrices. (See Examples 3–6.).

23. $A = \begin{bmatrix} .1 & .03 \\ .07 & .6 \end{bmatrix}, D = \begin{bmatrix} 5 \\ 10 \end{bmatrix}$

24. $A = \begin{bmatrix} \frac{1}{2} & \frac{2}{5} \\ \frac{1}{4} & \frac{1}{5} \end{bmatrix}, D = \begin{bmatrix} 2 \\ 4 \end{bmatrix}$

Exercises 25 and 26 refer to Example 6.

25. **Business** If the demand is changed to 690 metric tons of wheat and 920 metric tons of oil, how many units of each commodity should be produced?

26. **Business** Change the technological matrix so that the production of 1 metric ton of wheat requires $\frac{1}{5}$ metric ton of oil (and no wheat) and the production of 1 metric ton of oil requires $\frac{1}{3}$ metric ton of wheat (and no oil). To satisfy the same demand matrix, how many units of each commodity should be produced?

Work these problems. (See Examples 3–6.)

27. **Business** A simplified economy has only two industries: the electric company and the gas company. Each dollar's worth of the electric company's output requires $.40 of its own output and $.50 of the gas company's output. Each dollar's worth of the gas company's output requires $.25 of its own output and $.60 of the electric company's output. What should the production of electricity and gas be (in dollars) if there is a $12 million demand for gas and a $15 million demand for electricity?

28. **Business** A two-segment economy consists of manufacturing and agriculture. To produce 1 unit of manufacturing output requires .40 unit of its own output and .20 unit of agricultural output. To produce 1 unit of agricultural output

requires .30 unit of its own output and .40 unit of manufacturing output. If there is a demand of 240 units of manufacturing and 90 units of agriculture, what should be the output of each segment?

29. Business A primitive economy depends on two basic goods: yams and pork. The production of 1 bushel of yams requires $\frac{1}{4}$ bushel of yams and $\frac{1}{2}$ of a pig. To produce 1 pig requires $\frac{1}{6}$ bushel of yams. Find the amount of each commodity that should be produced to get

(a) 1 bushel of yams and 1 pig;

(b) 100 bushels of yams and 70 pigs.

30. Business A simplified economy is based on agriculture, manufacturing, and transportation. Each unit of agricultural output requires .4 unit of its own output, .3 unit of manufacturing output, and .2 unit of transportation output. One unit of manufacturing output requires .4 unit of its own output, .2 unit of agricultural output, and .3 unit of transportation output. One unit of transportation output requires .4 unit of its own output, .1 unit of agricultural output, and .2 unit of manufacturing output. There is demand for 35 units of agricultural, 90 units of manufacturing, and 20 units of transportation output. How many units should each segment of the economy produce?

31. Business In his work *Input–Output Economics*, Leontief provides an example of a simplified economy with just three sectors: agriculture, manufacturing, and households (that is, the sector of the economy that produces labor).[*] It has the following input–output matrix:

	Agriculture	Manufacturing	Households
Agriculture	.25	.40	.133
Manufacturing	.14	.12	.100
Households	.80	3.60	.133

(a) How many units from each sector does the manufacturing sector require to produce 1 unit?

(b) What production levels are needed to meet a demand of 35 units of agriculture, 38 units of manufacturing, and 40 units of households?

(c) How many units of agriculture are used up in the economy's production process?

32. Business A much simplified version of Leontief's 42-sector analysis of the 1947 American economy has the following input–output matrix:[†]

	Agriculture	Manufacturing	Households
Agriculture	.245	.102	.051
Manufacturing	.099	.291	.279
Households	.433	.372	.011

(a) What information about the needs of agricultural production is given by column 1 of the matrix?

(b) Suppose the demand matrix (in billions of dollars) is

$$D = \begin{bmatrix} 2.88 \\ 31.45 \\ 30.91 \end{bmatrix}.$$

Find the amount of each commodity that should be produced.

33. Business An analysis of the 1958 Israeli economy is simplified here by grouping the economy into three sectors, with the following input–output matrix:[‡]

	Agriculture	Manufacturing	Energy
Agriculture	.293	0	0
Manufacturing	.014	.207	.017
Energy	.044	.010	.216

(a) How many units from each sector does the energy sector require to produce one unit?

(b) If the economy's production (in thousands of Israeli pounds) is 175,000 of agriculture, 22,000 of manufacturing, and 12,000 of energy, how much is available from each sector to satisfy the demand from consumers and others outside the production process?

(c) The actual 1958 demand matrix is

$$D = \begin{bmatrix} 138,213 \\ 17,597 \\ 1786 \end{bmatrix}.$$

How much must each sector produce to meet this demand?

34. Business The 1981 Chinese economy can be simplified to three sectors: agriculture, industry and construction, and transportation and commerce.[§] The input–output matrix is

	Agri.	Industry/Constr.	Trans./Commerce
Agri.	.158	.156	.009
Industry/Constr.	.136	.432	.071
Trans./Commerce	.013	.041	.011

The demand [in 100,000 *renminbi* (RMB), the unit of money in China] is

$$D = \begin{bmatrix} 106,674 \\ 144,739 \\ 26,725 \end{bmatrix}.$$

(a) Find the amount each sector should produce.

(b) Interpret the economic value of an increase in demand of 1 RMB in agriculture exports.

35. Business The 1987 economy of the state of Washington has been simplified to four sectors: natural resource, manufacturing,

[*]Wassily Leontief, *Input–Output Economics*, 2d ed. (Oxford University Press, 1986), pp. 19–27.

[†]Ibid., pp. 6–9.

[‡]Ibid., pp. 174–175.

[§]*Input–Output Tables of China: 1981*, China Statistical Information and Consultancy Service Centre, 1987, pp. 17–19.

trade and services, and personal consumption. The input–output matrix is as follows:[*]

	Natural Resources	Manufacturing	Trade and Services	Personal Consumption
Natural Resources	.1045	.0428	.0029	.0031
Manufacturing	.0826	.1087	.0584	.0321
Trade and Services	.0867	.1019	.2032	.3555
Personal Consumption	.6253	.3448	.6106	.0798

Suppose the demand (in millions of dollars) is

$$D = \begin{bmatrix} 450 \\ 300 \\ 125 \\ 100 \end{bmatrix}.$$

Find the amount each sector should produce.

36. Business The 1963 economy of the state of Nebraska has been condensed to six sectors; livestock, crops, food products, mining and manufacturing, households, and other. The input–output matrix is as follows:[†]

$$\begin{bmatrix} .178 & .018 & .411 & 0 & .005 & 0 \\ .143 & .018 & .088 & 0 & .001 & 0 \\ .089 & 0 & .035 & 0 & .060 & .003 \\ .001 & .010 & .012 & .063 & .007 & .014 \\ .141 & .252 & .088 & .089 & .402 & .124 \\ .188 & .156 & .103 & .255 & .008 & .474 \end{bmatrix}.$$

(a) Find the matrix $(I - A)^{-1}$ and interpret the value in row two, column one, of this matrix.

(b) Suppose the demand (in millions of dollars) is

$$D = \begin{bmatrix} 1980 \\ 650 \\ 1750 \\ 1000 \\ 2500 \\ 3750 \end{bmatrix}.$$

Find the dollar amount each sector should produce.

37. Business Input–output analysis can also be used to model how changes in one city can affect cities that are connected with it in some way. For example, if a large manufacturing company shuts down in one city, it is very likely that the economic welfare of all of the cities around it will suffer. Consider three Pennsylvania communities: Sharon, Farrell, and Hermitage.

Due to their proximity to each other, residents of these three communities regularly spend time and money in the other communities. Suppose that we have gathered information in the form of an input–output matrix

$$\begin{bmatrix} .2 & .1 & .1 \\ .1 & .1 & 0 \\ .5 & .6 & .7 \end{bmatrix}.$$

This matrix can be thought of as the likelihood that a person from a particular community will spend money in each of the communities.[‡]

(a) Treat this matrix like an input–output matrix and calculate $(I - A)^{-1}$, where A is the given input–output matrix.

(b) Interpret the entries of this inverse matrix.

38. Social Science Use the method discussed in this section to encode the message

Anne is home.

Break the message into groups of two letters and use the matrix

$$M = \begin{bmatrix} 1 & 3 \\ 2 & 7 \end{bmatrix}.$$

39. Social Science Use the matrix of Exercise 38 to encode the message

Head for the hills!

40. Social Science Decode the following message, which was encoded by using the matrix M of Exercise 38:

$$\begin{bmatrix} 90 \\ 207 \end{bmatrix}, \begin{bmatrix} 39 \\ 87 \end{bmatrix}, \begin{bmatrix} 26 \\ 57 \end{bmatrix}, \begin{bmatrix} 66 \\ 145 \end{bmatrix}, \begin{bmatrix} 61 \\ 142 \end{bmatrix}, \begin{bmatrix} 89 \\ 205 \end{bmatrix}.$$

Work these routing problems.

41. Social Science Use matrix A in the discussion on routing (pages 324–325) to find A^2. Then answer the following questions: How many ways are there to travel from

(a) city 1 to city 3 by passing through exactly one city?

(b) city 2 to city 4 by passing through exactly one city?

(c) city 1 to city 3 by passing through at most one city?

(d) city 2 to city 4 by passing through at most one city?

42. Social Science The matrix A^3 (see Exercise 41) was found in Checkpoint 9 of the text. Use it to answer the following questions.

(a) How many ways are there to travel between cities 1 and 4 by passing through exactly two cities?

(b) How many ways are there to travel between cities 1 and 4 by passing through at most two cities?

43. Business A small telephone system connects three cities. There are four lines between cities 3 and 2, three lines connecting city 3 with city 1, and two lines between cities 1 and 2.

(a) Write a matrix B to represent this information.

(b) Find B^2.

[*]Robert Chase, Philip Bourque, and Richard Conway, Jr., *The 1987 Washington State Input–Output Study*, Report to the Graduate School of Business Administration, University of Washington, September 1993.

[†]F. Charles Lamphear and Theodore Roesler, "1970 Nebraska Input–Output Tables," *Nebraska Economic and Business Report No. 10*, Bureau of Business Research, University of Nebraska, Lincoln.

[‡]The idea for this problem came from an example created by Thayer Watkins, Department of Economics, San Jose State University.

(c) How many lines that connect cities 1 and 2 go through exactly one other city (city 3)?

(d) How many lines that connect cities 1 and 2 go through at most one other city?

44. Business The figure shows four southern cities served by Supersouth Airlines.

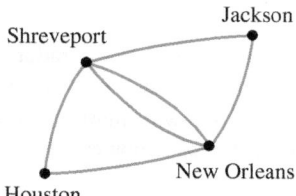

(a) Write a matrix to represent the number of nonstop routes between cities.

(b) Find the number of one-stop flights between Houston and Jackson.

(c) Find the number of flights between Houston and Shreveport that require at most one stop.

(d) Find the number of one-stop flights between New Orleans and Houston.

45. Natural Science The figure shows a food web. The arrows indicate the food sources of each population. For example, cats feed on rats and on mice.

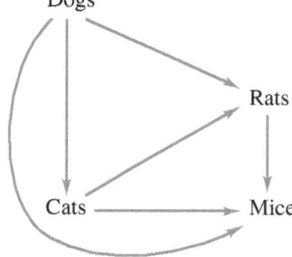

(a) Write a matrix C in which each row and corresponding column represent a population in the food chain. Enter a 1 when the population in a given row feeds on the population in the given column.

(b) Calculate and interpret C^2.

✓ **Checkpoint Answers**

1. $A = \begin{bmatrix} 2 & 6 \\ -1 & -2 \end{bmatrix}$, $X = \begin{bmatrix} x \\ y \end{bmatrix}$, and $B = \begin{bmatrix} -14 \\ 3 \end{bmatrix}$.

2. $(6, -4, 10)$

3. $(3 - 1.5y, y)$ for all real numbers y

4.
	Elec.	Water
Elec.	$\frac{1}{3}$	$\frac{1}{4}$
Water	$\frac{1}{2}$	0

5. **(a)** $\begin{bmatrix} 9000 \\ 12{,}000 \end{bmatrix}$ **(b)** $\begin{bmatrix} 6000 \\ 4500 \end{bmatrix}$ **(c)** $\begin{bmatrix} 3000 \\ 7500 \end{bmatrix}$

6. **(a)** $\begin{bmatrix} \frac{1}{2} & \frac{3}{4} \\ \frac{1}{2} & 0 \end{bmatrix}$ **(b)** $\begin{bmatrix} \frac{1}{2} & -\frac{3}{4} \\ -\frac{1}{2} & 1 \end{bmatrix}$

(c) $\begin{bmatrix} 8 & 6 \\ 4 & 4 \end{bmatrix}$ **(d)** $\begin{bmatrix} 6800 \\ 4400 \end{bmatrix}$

7. $\begin{bmatrix} 23 \\ 8 \end{bmatrix}, \begin{bmatrix} 5 \\ 14 \end{bmatrix}$

8. $\begin{bmatrix} 54 \\ 115 \end{bmatrix}, \begin{bmatrix} 24 \\ 25 \end{bmatrix}$

9. **(a)**
```
[A]³
[18  26  16  16  26]
[26  12  13   9  16]
[16  13   6  10   9]
[16   9  10   6  13]
[26  16   9  13  12]
```
(b)
```
[A]+[A]²
[10  5  4  4  5]
[ 5  6  3  4  5]
[ 4  3  2  2  4]
[ 4  4  2  3  3]
[ 5  5  4  3  6]
```

CHAPTER 6 Summary and Review

Key Terms and Symbols

6.1
linear equation
system of linear equations
solution of a system
substitution method
elimination method
independent system
dependent system
inconsistent system

6.2
equivalent systems
elementary operations
elimination method
row

column
matrix (matrices)
element (entry)
augmented matrix
row operations
row echelon form
Gauss–Jordan method
reduced row echelon form
independent system
inconsistent system
dependent system
parameter

6.3
applications of systems of linear equations

6.4
row matrix (row vector)
column matrix (column vector)
square matrix
additive inverse of a matrix
zero matrix
scalar
product of a scalar and a matrix

6.5
product matrix
identity matrix
inverse matrix
singular matrix

6.6
coefficient matrix
input–output analysis
input–output matrix
production matrix
demand matrix
code theory
routing theory

Chapter 6 Key Concepts

Solving Systems of Equations

The following **elementary operations** are used to transform a system of equations into a simpler equivalent system:

1. Interchange any two equations.

2. Multiply both sides of an equation by a nonzero constant.

3. Replace an equation by the sum of itself and a constant multiple of another equation in the system.

The **elimination method** is a systematic way of using elementary operations to transform a system into an equivalent one that can be solved by **back substitution.** See Section 6.2 for details.

The matrix version of the elimination method uses the following **matrix row operations,** which correspond to using elementary row operations with back substitution on a system of equations:

1. Interchange any two rows.

2. Multiply each element of a row by a nonzero constant.

3. Replace a row by the sum of itself and a constant multiple of another row in the matrix.

The **Gauss–Jordan method** is an extension of the elimination method for solving a system of linear equations. It uses row operations on the augmented matrix of the system. See Section 6.2 for details.

Operations on Matrices

The **sum** of two $m \times n$ matrices X and Y is the $m \times n$ matrix $X + Y$ in which each element is the sum of the corresponding elements of X and Y. The **difference** of two $m \times n$ matrices X and Y is the $m \times n$ matrix $X - Y$ in which each element is the difference of the corresponding elements of X and Y.

The **product** of a scalar k and a matrix X is the matrix kX, with each element being k times the corresponding element of X.

The **product matrix** AB of an $m \times n$ matrix A and an $n \times k$ matrix B is the $m \times k$ matrix whose entry in the ith row and jth column is the product of the ith row of A and the jth column of B.

The **inverse matrix** A^{-1} for any $n \times n$ matrix A for which A^{-1} exists is found as follows: Form the augmented matrix $[A|I]$, and perform row operations on $[A|I]$ to get the matrix $[I|A^{-1}]$.

Chapter 6 Review Exercises

Solve each of the following systems.

1. $-5x - 3y = -3$
   $2x + y = 4$

2. $3x - y = 8$
   $2x + 3y = 6$

3. $3x - 5y = 16$
   $2x + 3y = -2$

4. $\dfrac{1}{4}x - \dfrac{1}{3}y = -\dfrac{1}{4}$

   $\dfrac{1}{10}x + \dfrac{2}{5}y = \dfrac{2}{5}$

5. Business Abigail Henderson plans to buy shares of two stocks. One costs $32 per share and pays dividends of $1.20 per share. The other costs $23 per share and pays dividends of $1.40 per share. She has $10,100 to spend and wants to earn dividends of $540. How many shares of each stock should she buy?

6. Business Emma Henderson has money in two investment funds. Last year, the first fund paid a dividend of 8% and the second a dividend of 2%, and she received a total of $780. This year, the first fund paid a 10% dividend and the second only 1%, and she received $810. How much does she have invested in each fund?

Solve each of the following systems.

7. $x - 2y = 1$
   $4x + 4y = 2$
   $10x + 8y = 4$

8. $4x - y - 2z = 4$

   $x - y - \dfrac{1}{2}z = 1$

   $2x - y - z = 8$

9. $3x + y - z = 3$
   $x + 2z = 6$
   $-3x - y + 2z = 9$

10. $x + y - 4z = 0$
   $2x + y - 3z = 2$

Solve each of the following systems by using matrix methods.

11. $x + z = -3$
   $y - z = 6$
   $2x + 3z = 5$

12. $2x + 3y + 4z = 8$
   $-x + y - 2z = -9$
   $2x + 2y + 6z = 16$

13. $x - 2y + 5z = 3$
   $4x + 3y - 4z = 1$
   $3x + 5y - 9z = 7$

14. $5x - 8y + z = 1$
   $3x - 2y + 4z = 3$
   $10x - 16y + 2z = 3$

15. $x - 2y + 3z = 4$
   $2x + y - 4z = 3$
   $-3x + 4y - z = -2$

16. $3x + 2y - 6z = 3$
   $x + y + 2z = 2$
   $2x + 2y + 5z = 0$

17. Finance You are given $144 in one-, five-, and ten-dollar bills. There are 35 bills. There are two more ten-dollar bills than five-dollar bills. How many bills of each type are there?

18. Social Science A social service agency provides counseling, meals, and shelter to clients referred by sources I, II, and III. Clients from source I require an average of $100 for food, $250 for shelter, and no counseling. Source II clients require an average of $100 for counseling, $200 for food, and nothing for shelter. Source III clients require an average of $100 for counseling, $150 for food, and $200 for shelter. The agency has funding of $25,000 for counseling, $50,000 for food, and $32,500 for shelter. How many clients from each source can be served?

19. **Business** A small business makes woven blankets, rugs, and skirts. Each blanket requires 24 hours for spinning the yarn, 4 hours for dying the yarn, and 15 hours for weaving. Rugs require 30, 5, and 18 hours, and skirts require 12, 3, and 9 hours, respectively. If there are 306, 59, and 201 hours available for spinning, dying, and weaving, respectively, how many of each item can be made? (*Hint:* Simplify the equations you write, if possible, before solving the system.)

20. **Business** Each week at a furniture factory, 2000 work hours are available in the construction department, 1400 work hours in the painting department, and 1300 work hours in the packing department. Producing a chair requires 2 hours of construction, 1 hour of painting, and 2 hours for packing. Producing a table requires 4 hours of construction, 3 hours of painting, and 3 hours for packing. Producing a chest requires 8 hours of construction, 6 hours of painting, and 4 hours for packing. If all available time is used in every department, how many of each item are produced each week?

For each of the following, find the dimensions of the matrix and identify any square, row, or column matrices.

21. $\begin{bmatrix} 2 & 3 \\ 5 & 9 \end{bmatrix}$

22. $\begin{bmatrix} 2 & -1 \\ 4 & 6 \\ 5 & 7 \end{bmatrix}$

23. $[12 \quad 4 \quad -8 \quad -1]$

24. $\begin{bmatrix} -7 & 5 & 6 & 4 \\ 3 & 2 & -1 & 2 \\ -1 & 12 & 8 & -1 \end{bmatrix}$

25. $\begin{bmatrix} 6 & 8 & 10 \\ 5 & 3 & -2 \end{bmatrix}$

26. $\begin{bmatrix} -9 \\ 15 \\ 4 \end{bmatrix}$

27. **Finance** The closing stock price, change in price, and volume of stocks traded for the following companies were reported on January 3, 2013: Apple Inc.: $542.10; −$6.93; and 12,605,900. Nike Inc.: $52.37; $.53; and 3,616,100. Verizon Communications Inc.: $44.06; −$.21; and 11,227,700. Write these data as a 3 × 3 matrix. (Data from: www.morningstar.com.)

28. **Natural Science** The activities of a grazing animal can be classified roughly into three categories: grazing, moving, and resting. Suppose horses spend 8 hours grazing, 8 moving, and 8 resting; cattle spend 10 grazing, 5 moving, and 9 resting; sheep spend 7 grazing, 10 moving, and 7 resting; and goats spend 8 grazing, 9 moving, and 7 resting. Write this information as a 4 × 3 matrix.

Given the matrices

$$A = \begin{bmatrix} 4 & 6 \\ -2 & -2 \\ 5 & 9 \end{bmatrix}, \quad B = \begin{bmatrix} 1 & 2 & -3 \\ 2 & 3 & 0 \\ 0 & 1 & 4 \end{bmatrix}, \quad C = \begin{bmatrix} 5 & 0 \\ -1 & 3 \\ 4 & 7 \end{bmatrix},$$

$$D = \begin{bmatrix} 6 \\ 1 \\ 0 \end{bmatrix}, \quad E = [1 \quad 3 \quad -4], \quad F = \begin{bmatrix} -1 & 2 \\ 6 & 7 \end{bmatrix}, \quad and$$

$$G = \begin{bmatrix} 2 & 5 \\ 1 & 6 \end{bmatrix},$$

find each of the following (if possible).

29. $-B$ 30. $-D$ 31. $A + 2C$ 32. $F + 3G$

33. $2B - 5C$ 34. $D + E$ 35. $3A - 2C$ 36. $G - 2F$

37. **Finance** Refer to Exercise 27. Write a 3 × 2 matrix giving just the change in price and volume data for the three companies. The next day's changes in price and volume for the same three companies were: −$15.10 and 21,226,200; $.51 and 3,397,000; $.24 and 14,930,400. Write a 3 × 2 matrix to represent these new price change and volume figures. Use matrix addition to find the total change in price and volume of stock traded for the two days. (Data from: www.morningstar.com.)

38. **Business** An oil refinery in Tulsa sent 110,000 gallons of oil to a Chicago distributor, 73,000 to a Dallas distributor, and 95,000 to an Atlanta distributor. Another refinery in New Orleans sent the following respective amounts to the same three distributors: 85,000, 108,000, and 69,000. The next month, the two refineries sent the same distributors new shipments of oil as follows: from Tulsa, 58,000 to Chicago, 33,000 to Dallas, and 80,000 to Atlanta; from New Orleans, 40,000, 52,000, and 30,000, respectively.

(a) Write the monthly shipments from the two distributors to the three refineries as 3 × 2 matrices.

(b) Use matrix addition to find the total amounts sent to the refineries from each distributor.

Use the matrices shown before Exercise 29 to find each of the following (if possible).

39. AG 40. EB 41. GA

42. CA 43. AGF 44. EBD

45. **Health** In a study, the numbers of head and neck injuries among hockey players wearing full face shields and half face shields were compared. Injury rates were recorded per 1000 athlete exposures for specific injuries that caused a player to miss one or more events.[*]

Players wearing a half shield had the following rates of injury:

Head and face injuries, excluding concussions: 3.54;
Concussions: 1.53;
Neck injuries: .34;
Other injuries: 7.53.

Players wearing a full shield had the following injury rates:

Head and face injuries, excluding concussions: 1.41;
Concussions: 1.57;
Neck injuries: .29;
Other injuries: 6.21.

---

[*]Brian Benson, Nicholas Nohtadi, Sarah Rose, and Willem Meeuwisse, "Head and Neck Injuries among Ice Hockey Players Wearing Full Face Shields vs. Half Face Shields," *JAMA*, 282, no. 24, (December 22/29, 1999): 2328–2332.

If an equal number of players in a large league wear each type of shield and the total number of athlete exposures for the league in a season is 8000, use matrix operations to estimate the total number of injuries of each type.

46. **Business** An office supply manufacturer makes two kinds of paper clips: standard and extra large. To make a unit of standard paper clips requires $\frac{1}{4}$ hour on a cutting machine and $\frac{1}{2}$ hour on a machine that shapes the clips. A unit of extra-large paper clips requires $\frac{1}{3}$ hour on each machine.

    (a) Write this information as a 2 × 2 matrix (size/machine).

    (b) If 48 units of standard and 66 units of extra-large clips are to be produced, use matrix multiplication to find out how many hours each machine will operate. (*Hint:* Write the units as a 1 × 2 matrix.)

47. **Finance** The cost per share of stock was $61.17 for Coca-Cola Bottling Co. Consolidated, $60.50 for Starbucks Corporation, and $96.21 for Anheuser-Busch, as reported on April 26, 2013. The dividend per share was $1.00, $.84, and $1.88, respectively. Your stock portfolio consists of 100 shares of Coca-Cola, 500 shares of Starbucks, and 200 shares of Anheuser-Busch. (Data from: www.morningstar.com.)

    (a) Write the cost per share and dividend per share data as a 3 × 2 matrix.

    (b) Write the number of shares of each stock as a 1 × 3 matrix.

    (c) Use matrix multiplication to find the total cost and total dividend earnings of this portfolio.

48. **Finance** Matthew's stock portfolio consists of 4000 shares of The New York Times Company, 1000 shares of Coffee Holding Co. Inc., 5000 shares of Barnes & Noble Inc., and 2000 shares of Columbia Sportswear Company. On April 26, 2013, the cost per share for each of these stocks was $9.45, $6.59, $18.21, and $60.70, respectively, and the dividend per share for each of these stocks was $0, $.24, $0, and $.88, respectively. (Data from: www.morningstar.com.)

    (a) Write the cost per share and dividend per share data as a 4 × 2 matrix.

    (b) Write the number of shares of each stock as a 1 × 4 matrix.

    (c) Use matrix multiplication to find the total cost and total dividend earnings of this portfolio.

49. If $A = \begin{bmatrix} 3 & 0 \\ 2 & 1 \end{bmatrix}$, find a matrix B such that both AB and BA are defined and $AB \neq BA$.

50. Is it possible to do Exercise 49 if $A = \begin{bmatrix} 4 & 0 \\ 0 & 4 \end{bmatrix}$? Explain.

Find the inverse of each of the following matrices, if an inverse exists for that matrix.

51. $\begin{bmatrix} -2 & 2 \\ 0 & 5 \end{bmatrix}$

52. $\begin{bmatrix} 3 & -1 \\ -5 & 2 \end{bmatrix}$

53. $\begin{bmatrix} 6 & 4 \\ 3 & 2 \end{bmatrix}$

54. $\begin{bmatrix} 15 & -12 \\ 5 & -4 \end{bmatrix}$

55. $\begin{bmatrix} 2 & 0 & 6 \\ 1 & -1 & 0 \\ 0 & 1 & -3 \end{bmatrix}$

56. $\begin{bmatrix} 2 & -1 & 0 \\ 1 & 0 & 2 \\ 1 & -4 & 0 \end{bmatrix}$

57. $\begin{bmatrix} 2 & 3 & 5 \\ -2 & -3 & -5 \\ 1 & 4 & 2 \end{bmatrix}$

58. $\begin{bmatrix} 1 & 3 & 6 \\ 4 & 0 & 9 \\ 5 & 15 & 30 \end{bmatrix}$

59. $\begin{bmatrix} 1 & 3 & -2 & -1 \\ 0 & 1 & 1 & 2 \\ -1 & -1 & 1 & -1 \\ 1 & -1 & -3 & -2 \end{bmatrix}$

60. $\begin{bmatrix} 3 & 2 & 0 & -1 \\ 2 & 0 & 1 & 2 \\ 1 & 2 & -1 & 0 \\ 2 & -1 & 1 & 1 \end{bmatrix}$

Refer again to the matrices shown before Exercise 29 to find each of the following (if possible).

61. F^{-1}

62. G^{-1}

63. $(G - F)^{-1}$

64. $(F + G)^{-1}$

65. B^{-1}

66. Explain why the matrix $\begin{bmatrix} a & 0 \\ c & 0 \end{bmatrix}$, where a and c are nonzero constants, cannot have an inverse.

Solve each of the following matrix equations AX = B for X.

67. $A = \begin{bmatrix} -3 & 4 \\ -1 & 2 \end{bmatrix}$, $B = \begin{bmatrix} 3 \\ -1 \end{bmatrix}$

68. $A = \begin{bmatrix} 1 & 3 \\ -2 & 4 \end{bmatrix}$, $B = \begin{bmatrix} 9 \\ 6 \end{bmatrix}$

69. $A = \begin{bmatrix} 1 & 0 & 2 \\ -1 & 1 & 0 \\ 3 & 0 & 4 \end{bmatrix}$, $B = \begin{bmatrix} 8 \\ 4 \\ -6 \end{bmatrix}$

70. $A = \begin{bmatrix} 2 & 4 & 0 \\ 1 & -2 & 0 \\ 0 & 0 & 3 \end{bmatrix}$, $B = \begin{bmatrix} 72 \\ -24 \\ 48 \end{bmatrix}$

Use the method of matrix inverses to solve each of the following systems.

71. $x + y = -2$
    $2x + 5y = 2$

72. $5x - 3y = -2$
    $2x + 7y = -9$

73. $2x + y = 10$
    $3x - 2y = 8$

74. $x - 2y = 7$
    $3x + y = 7$

75. $x + y + z = 1$
    $2x - y = -2$
    $3y + z = 2$

76. $x = -3$
    $y + z = 6$
    $2x - 3z = -9$

77. $3x - 2y + 4z = 4$
    $4x + y - 5z = 2$
    $-6x + 4y - 8z = -2$

78. $-2x + 3y - z = 1$
    $5x - 7y + 8z = 4$
    $6x - 9y + 3z = 2$

Solve each of the following problems by any method.

79. **Business** A wine maker has two large casks of wine. One is 9% alcohol and the other is 14% alcohol. How many liters of

each wine should be mixed to produce 40 liters of wine that is 12% alcohol?

80. Business A gold merchant has some 12-carat gold (12/24 pure gold) and some 22-carat gold (22/24 pure). How many grams of each could be mixed to get 25 grams of 15-carat gold?

81. Natural Science A chemist has a 40% acid solution and a 60% solution. How many liters of each should be used to get 40 liters of a 45% solution?

82. Business How many pounds of tea worth $4.60 a pound should be mixed with tea worth $6.50 a pound to get 10 pounds of a mixture worth $5.74 a pound?

83. Business A machine in a pottery factory takes 3 minutes to form a bowl and 2 minutes to form a plate. The material for a bowl costs $.25, and the material for a plate costs $.20. If the machine runs for 8 hours and exactly $44 is spent for material, how many bowls and plates can be produced?

84. Physical Science A boat travels at a constant speed a distance of 57 kilometers downstream in 3 hours and then turns around and travels 55 kilometers upstream in 5 hours. What are the speeds of the boat and the current?

85. Business Henry Miller invests $50,000 three ways—at 8%, $8\frac{1}{2}$%, and 11%. In total, he receives $4436.25 per year in interest. The interest on the 11% investment is $80 more than the interest on the 8% investment. Find the amount he has invested at each rate.

86. Business Tickets to the homecoming football game cost $4 for students, $10 for alumni, $12 for other adults, and $6 for children. The total attendance was 3750, and the ticket receipts were $29,100. Six times more students than children attended. The number of alumni was $\frac{4}{5}$ of the number of students. How many students, alumni, other adults, and children were at the game?

87. Given the input–output matrix $A = \begin{bmatrix} 0 & \frac{1}{4} \\ \frac{1}{2} & 0 \end{bmatrix}$ and the demand matrix $D = \begin{bmatrix} 2100 \\ 1400 \end{bmatrix}$, find each of the following.

(a) $I - A$

(b) $(I - A)^{-1}$

(c) The production matrix X

88. Business An economy depends on two commodities: goats and cheese. It takes $\frac{2}{3}$ unit of goats to produce 1 unit of cheese and $\frac{1}{2}$ unit of cheese to produce 1 unit of goats.

(a) Write the input–output matrix for this economy.

(b) Find the production required to satisfy a demand of 400 units of cheese and 800 units of goats.

⬈ *Use technology to do Exercises 89–91.*

89. Business In a simple economic model, a country has two industries: agriculture and manufacturing. To produce $1 of agricultural output requires $.10 of agricultural output and $.40 of manufacturing output. To produce $1 of manufacturing output

requires $.70 of agricultural output and $.20 of manufacturing output. If agricultural demand is $60,000 and manufacturing demand is $20,000, what must each industry produce? (Round answers to the nearest whole number.)

90. Business Here is the input–output matrix for a small economy:

	Agriculture	Services	Mining	Manufacturing
Agriculture	.02	.9	0	.001
Services	0	.4	0	.06
Mining	.01	.02	.06	.07
Manufacturing	.25	.9	.9	.4

(a) How many units from each sector does the service sector require to produce 1 unit?

(b) What production levels are needed to meet a demand for 760 units of agriculture, 1600 units of services, 1000 units of mining, and 2000 units of manufacturing?

(c) How many units of manufacturing production are used up in the economy's production process?

91. Use this input–output matrix to answer the questions below.

	Agriculture	Construction	Energy	Manufacturing	Transportation
Agriculture	.18	.017	.4	.005	0
Construction	.14	.018	.09	.001	0
Energy	.9	0	.4	.06	.002
Manufacturing	.19	.16	.1	.008	.5
Transportation	.14	.25	.9	.4	.12

(a) How many units from each sector does the energy sector require to produce 1 unit?

(b) If the economy produces 28,067 units of agriculture, 9383 units of construction, 51,372 units of energy, 61,364 units of manufacturing, and 90,403 units of transportation, how much is available from each sector to satisfy the demand from consumers and others outside the production system?

(c) A new demand matrix for the economy is

$$\begin{bmatrix} 2400 \\ 850 \\ 1400 \\ 3200 \\ 1800 \end{bmatrix}.$$

How much must each sector produce to meet this demand?

92. Business The following matrix represents the number of direct flights between four cities:

$$
\begin{array}{c}
\quad\quad A\ \ B\ \ C\ \ D \\
\begin{array}{c} A \\ B \\ C \\ D \end{array}
\left[
\begin{array}{cccc}
0 & 1 & 0 & 1 \\
1 & 0 & 0 & 1 \\
0 & 0 & 0 & 1 \\
1 & 1 & 1 & 0
\end{array}
\right].
\end{array}
$$

(a) Find the number of one-stop flights between cities A and C.

(b) Find the total number of flights between cities B and C that are either direct or one stop.

(c) Find the matrix that gives the number of two-stop flights between these cities.

93. Social Science Use the matrix $M = \begin{bmatrix} 2 & 6 \\ 1 & 4 \end{bmatrix}$ to encode the message "leave now."

94. What matrix should be used to decode the answer to the previous exercise?

Case Study 6 Matrix Operations and Airline Route Maps

Airline route maps are usually published on airline Web sites, as well as in in-flight magazines. The purpose of these maps is to show what cities are connected to each other by nonstop flights provided by the airline. We can think of these maps as another type of **graph,** and we can use matrix operations to answer questions of interest about the graph. To study these graphs, a bit of terminology will be helpful. In this context, a **graph** is a set of points called **vertices** or **nodes** and a set of lines called **edges** connecting some pairs of vertices. Two vertices connected by an edge are said to be **adjacent.** Suppose, for example, that Stampede Air is a short-haul airline serving the state of Texas whose route map is shown in Figure 1 below. The vertices are the cities to which Stampede Air flies, and two vertices are connected if there is a nonstop flight between them.

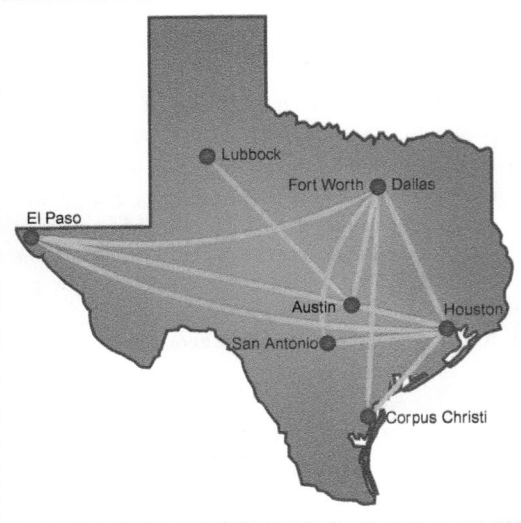

Figure 1 Stampede Air route map

Some natural questions arise about graphs. It might be important to know if two vertices are connected by a sequence of two edges, even if they are not connected by a single edge. In the route map, Huston and Lubbock are connected by a two-edge sequence, meaning that a passenger would have to stop in Austin while flying between those cities on Stampede Air. It might be important to know if it is possible to get from a vertex to another vertex in a given number of flights. In the example, a passenger on Stampede Air can get from any city in the company's network to any other city, given enough flights. But how many flights are enough? This is another issue of interest: What is the minimum number of steps required to get from one vertex to another? What is the minimum number of steps required to get from any vertex on the graph to any other? While these questions are relatively easy to answer for a small graph, as the number of vertices and edges grows, it becomes harder to keep track of all the different ways the vertices are connected. Matrix notation and computation can help to answer these questions.

The **adjacency matrix** for a graph with n vertices is an $n \times n$ matrix whose (i, j) entry is 1 if the ith and jth vertices are connected and 0 if they are not. If the vertices in the Stampede Air graph respectively correspond to Austin (A), El Paso (E), Houston (H), Dallas-Fort Worth (D), San Antonio (S), Corpus Christi (C), and Lubbock (L), then the adjacency matrix for Stampede Air is as follows.

$$
A =
\begin{array}{c}
\quad\quad\ A\ \ E\ \ H\ \ D\ \ S\ \ C\ \ L \\
\left[
\begin{array}{ccccccc}
0 & 1 & 1 & 1 & 0 & 0 & 1 \\
1 & 0 & 1 & 1 & 0 & 0 & 0 \\
1 & 1 & 0 & 1 & 1 & 1 & 0 \\
1 & 1 & 1 & 0 & 1 & 1 & 0 \\
0 & 0 & 1 & 1 & 0 & 0 & 0 \\
0 & 0 & 1 & 1 & 0 & 0 & 0 \\
1 & 0 & 0 & 0 & 0 & 0 & 0
\end{array}
\right]
\begin{array}{c} A \\ E \\ H \\ D^\cdot \\ S \\ C \\ L \end{array}
\end{array}
$$

Adjacency matrices can be used to address the questions about graphs raised earlier. Which vertices are connected by a two-edge sequence? How many different two-edge sequences connect each pair of vertices? Consider the matrix A^2, which is A multiplied by itself. For example, let the $(6, 2)$ entry in the matrix A^2 be named b_{62}. This entry in A^2 is the product of the 6th row of A and the 2nd column of A, or

$$b_{62} = a_{61}a_{12} + a_{62}a_{22} + a_{63}a_{32} + a_{64}a_{42} + a_{65}a_{52} + a_{66}a_{62} + a_{67}a_{72}$$
$$= 0 \cdot 1 + 0 \cdot 0 + 1 \cdot 1 + 1 \cdot 1 + 0 \cdot 0 + 0 \cdot 0 + 0 \cdot 0$$
$$= 2,$$

which happens to be the number of two-flight sequences that connect city 6 (Corpus Christi) and city 2 (El Paso). A careful look at Figure 1 confirms this fact. This calculation works because, in order for a two-flight sequence to occur between Corpus Christi and El Paso, Corpus Christi and El Paso must each connect to an intermediate city. Since Corpus Christi connects to Houston and Houston connects to El Paso, $a_{63}a_{32} = 1 \cdot 1 = 1$. Thus, there is one two-flight sequence between Corpus Christi and El Paso that passes through Houston. Since Corpus Christi does not connect to Austin (city 1), but Austin does connect with El Paso, $a_{61}a_{12} = 0 \cdot 1 = 0$. Hence, there is no two-flight sequence from Corpus Christi to El Paso that passes through Austin. To find the total number of two-flight sequences between Corpus Christi and El Paso, simply sum over all intermediate points. Notice that this sum, which is

$$a_{61}a_{12} + a_{62}a_{22} + a_{63}a_{32} + a_{64}a_{42} + a_{65}a_{52} + a_{66}a_{62} + a_{67}a_{72},$$

is just b_{62}, the $(6, 2)$ entry in the matrix A^2. So we see that the number of two-step sequences between vertex i and vertex j in a graph with adjacency matrix A is the (i, j) entry in A^2. A more general result is the following:

The number of k-step sequences between vertex i and vertex j in a graph with adjacency matrix A is the (i, j) entry in A^k.

If A is the adjacency matrix for Figure 1, then

$$A^2 = \begin{bmatrix} 4 & 2 & 2 & 2 & 2 & 2 & 0 \\ 2 & 3 & 2 & 2 & 2 & 2 & 1 \\ 2 & 2 & 5 & 4 & 1 & 1 & 1 \\ 2 & 2 & 4 & 5 & 1 & 1 & 1 \\ 2 & 2 & 1 & 1 & 2 & 2 & 0 \\ 2 & 2 & 1 & 1 & 2 & 2 & 0 \\ 0 & 1 & 1 & 1 & 0 & 0 & 1 \end{bmatrix} \begin{matrix} A \\ E \\ H \\ D \\ S \\ C \\ L \end{matrix}$$

and

$$A^3 = \begin{bmatrix} 6 & 8 & 12 & 12 & 4 & 4 & 4 \\ 8 & 6 & 11 & 11 & 4 & 4 & 2 \\ 12 & 11 & 10 & 11 & 9 & 9 & 2 \\ 12 & 11 & 11 & 10 & 9 & 9 & 2 \\ 4 & 4 & 9 & 9 & 2 & 2 & 2 \\ 4 & 4 & 9 & 9 & 2 & 2 & 2 \\ 4 & 2 & 2 & 2 & 2 & 2 & 0 \end{bmatrix} \begin{matrix} A \\ E \\ H \\ D \\ S \\ C \\ L \end{matrix}$$

Since the $(6, 3)$ entry in A^2 is 1, there is one two-step sequence from Corpus Christi to Houston. Likewise, there are four three-step

sequences between El Paso and San Antonio, since the $(2, 5)$ entry in A^3 is 4.

In observing the figure, note that some two-step or three-step sequences may not be meaningful. On the Stampede Air route map, Dallas-Fort Worth is reachable in two steps from Austin (via El Paso or Houston), but in reality this does not matter, since there is a non-stop flight between the two cities. A better question to ask of a graph might be, "What is the least number of edges that must be traversed to go from vertex i to vertex j?"

To answer this question, consider the matrix $S_k = A + A^2 + \cdots + A^k$. The (i, j) entry in this matrix tallies the number of ways to get from vertex i to vertex j in k steps or less. If such a trip is impossible, this entry will be zero. Thus, to find the shortest number of steps between the vertices, continue to compute S_k as k increases; the first k for which the (i, j) entry in S_k is nonzero is the shortest number of steps between i and j. Note that although the shortest number of steps may be computed, the method does not determine what those steps are.

Exercises

1. Which Stampede Air cities may be reached by a two-flight sequence from San Antonio? Which may be reached by a three-flight sequence?

2. It was shown previously that there are four three-step sequences between El Paso and San Antonio. Describe these three-step sequences.

3. Which trips in the Stampede Air network take the greatest number of flights?

4. Suppose that Vacation Air is an airline serving Jacksonville, Orlando, West Palm Beach, Miami, and Tampa, Florida. The route map is given in Figure 2. Produce an adjacency matrix B for this map, listing the cities in the order given.

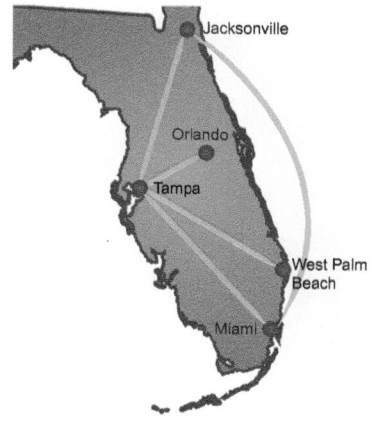

Figure 2 Vacation Air route map

5. Find B^2, the square of the adjacency matrix found in Exercise 4. What does this matrix tell you?

6. Find $B + B^2$. What can you conclude from this calculation?

Extended Project

Visit the website dir.yahoo.com/business_and_economy/shopping_ and_services/travel_and_transportation/airlines/. This site includes links to many obscure and smaller airlines, as well as the more well-known carriers. Find a small regional airline that serves your area and use their route map to produce an adjacency matrix. Determine which trips using this airline take the largest number of flights. How many flights did these trips take? Prepare a report that includes an overview of the airline, the route map, an explanation of the adjacency matrix, and your findings about which trips take the largest number of flights.

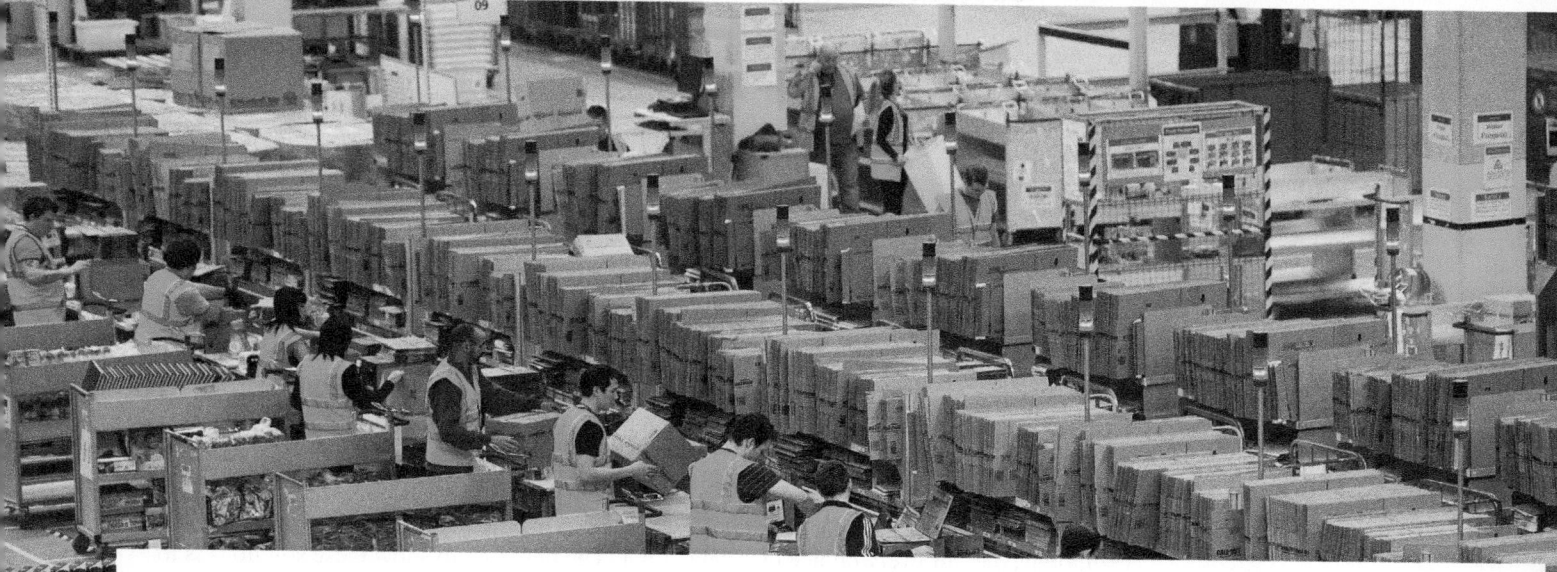

Linear Programming

CHAPTER OUTLINE

Linear programming is one of the most remarkable (and useful) mathematical techniques developed in the last 65 years. It is used to deal with a variety of issues faced by businesses, financial planners, medical personnel, sports leagues, and others. Typical applications include maximizing company profits by adjusting production schedules, minimizing shipping costs by locating warehouses efficiently, and maximizing pension income by choosing the best mix of financial products. See Exercise 17 on page 377, Exercise 33 on page 398, and Exercise 19 on page 357.

Many real-world problems involve inequalities. For example, a factory may have no more than 200 workers on a shift and must manufacture at least 3000 units at a cost of no more than $35 each. How many workers should it have per shift in order to produce the required number of units at minimal cost? *Linear programming* is a method for finding the optimal (best possible) solution for such problems—if there is one.

In this chapter, we shall study two methods of solving linear programming problems: the graphical method and the simplex method. The graphical method requires a knowledge of **linear inequalities,** which are inequalities involving only first-degree polynomials in x and y. So we begin with a study of such inequalities.

7.1 Graphing Linear Inequalities in Two Variables

Examples of linear inequalities in two variables include

$$x + 2y < 4, \qquad 3x + 2y > 6, \qquad \text{and} \qquad 2x - 5y \geq 10.$$

A solution of a linear inequality is an ordered pair that satisfies the inequality. For example (4, 4) is a solution of

$$3x - 2y \leq 6.$$

(Check by substituting 4 for x and 4 for y.) A linear inequality has an infinite number of solutions, one for every choice of a value for x. The best way to show these solutions is to sketch the **graph of the inequality,** which consists of all points in the plane whose coordinates satisfy the inequality.

Example 1   Graph the inequality $3x - 2y \leq 6$.

Solution   First, solve the inequality for y:

$$3x - 2y \leq 6$$
$$-2y \leq -3x + 6$$
$$y \geq \frac{3}{2}x - 3 \qquad \text{Multiply by } -\tfrac{1}{2}; \text{ reverse the inequality.}$$
$$y \geq 1.5x - 3.$$

This inequality has the same solutions as the original one. To solve it, note that the points on the line $y = 1.5x - 3$ certainly satisfy $y \geq 1.5x - 3$. Plot some points, and graph this line, as in Figure 7.1.

The points on the line satisfy "y *equals* $1.5x - 3$." The points satisfying "y is *greater than* $1.5x - 3$" are the points *above* the line (because they have larger second coordinates than the points on the line; see Figure 7.2). Similarly, the points satisfying

$$y < 1.5x - 3$$

lie below the line (because they have smaller second coordinates), as shown in Figure 7.2. The line $y = 1.5x - 3$ is the **boundary line.**

Thus, the solutions of $y \geq 1.5x - 3$ are all points *on or above* the line $y = 1.5x - 3$. The line and the shaded region of Figure 7.3 make up the graph of the inequality $y \geq 1.5x - 3$. ✓₁

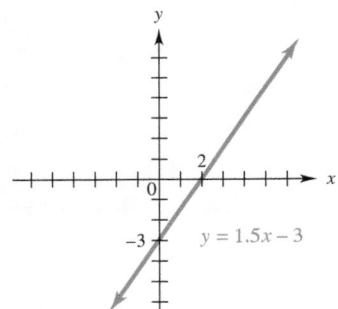

Figure 7.1

✓ **Checkpoint 1**

Graph the given inequalities.

(a) $2x + 5y \leq 10$

(b) $x - y \geq 4$

Answers to Checkpoint exercises are found at the end of the section.

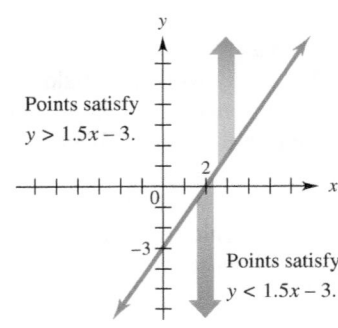

Points satisfy $y > 1.5x - 3$.

Points satisfy $y < 1.5x - 3$.

Figure 7.2

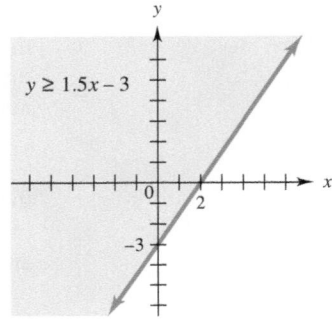

$y \geq 1.5x - 3$

Figure 7.3

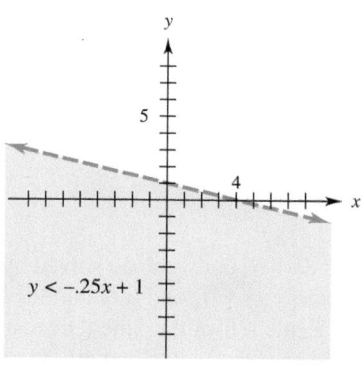

Figure 7.4

✓ **Checkpoint 2**

Graph the given inequalities.

(a) $2x + 3y > 12$

(b) $3x - 2y < 6$

Example 2   Graph $x + 4y < 4$.

Solution   First obtain an equivalent inequality by solving for y:

$$4y < -x + 4$$

$$y < -\frac{1}{4}x + 1$$

$$y < -.25x + 1.$$

The boundary line is $y = -.25x + 1$, but it is *not* part of the solution, since points *on* the line do not satisfy $y < -.25x + 1$. To indicate this, the line is drawn dashed in Figure 7.4. The points *below* the boundary line are the solutions of $y < -.25x + 1$, because they have smaller second coordinates than the points on the line $y = -.25x + 1$. The shaded region in Figure 7.4 (excluding the dashed line) is the graph of the inequality $y < -.25x + 1$.

Examples 1 and 2 show that the solutions of a linear inequality form a **half-plane** consisting of all points on one side of the boundary line (and possibly the line itself). When an inequality is solved for y, the inequality symbol immediately tells whether the points above ($>$), on ($=$), or below ($<$) the boundary line satisfy the inequality, as summarized here.

Inequality	Solution Consists of All Points
$y \geq mx + b$	*on or above* the line $y = mx + b$
$y > mx + b$	*above* the line $y = mx + b$
$y \leq mx + b$	*on or below* the line $y = mx + b$
$y < mx + b$	*below* the line $y = mx + b$

When graphing by hand, draw the boundary line $y = mx + b$ solid when it is included in the solution ($\geq$ or $\leq$ inequalities) and dashed when it is not part of the solution ($>$ or $<$ inequalities).

🡕 **TECHNOLOGY TIP** To shade the area above or below the graph of Y_1 on TI-84+, go to the Y = menu and move the cursor to the left of Y_1. Press ENTER until the correct shading pattern appears (🡔 for above the line and 🡖 for below the line). Then press GRAPH. On TI-86/89, use the STYLE key in the Y = menu instead of the ENTER key. For other calculators, consult your instruction manual.

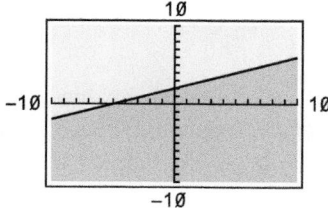

Figure 7.5

✓ **Checkpoint 3** 🡕

Use a graphing calculator to graph $2x < y$.

Example 3   Graph $5y - 2x \leq 10$.

Solution   Solve the inequality for y:

$$5y \leq 2x + 10$$

$$y \leq \frac{2}{5}x + 2$$

$$y \leq .4x + 2.$$

The graph consists of all points on or below the boundary line $y \leq .4x + 2$, as shown in Figure 7.5. (See the Technology Tip.)

🛇 **CAUTION** You cannot tell from a calculator-produced graph whether the boundary line is included. It is included in Figure 7.5, but not in the answer to Checkpoint 3.

Figure 7.6

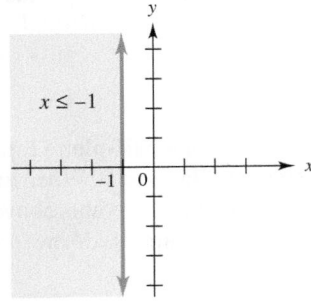

Figure 7.7

✓ **Checkpoint 4**

Graph each of the following.

(a) $x \geq 3$

(b) $y - 3 \leq 0$

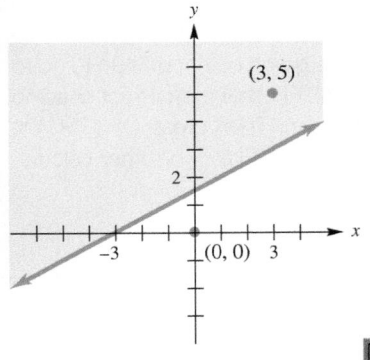

Figure 7.8

Example 4 Graph each of the given inequalities.

(a) $y \geq 2$

Solution The boundary line is the horizontal line $y = 2$. The graph consists of all points on or above this line (Figure 7.6).

(b) $x \leq -1$

Solution This inequality does not fit the pattern discussed earlier, but it can be solved by a similar technique. Here, the boundary line is the vertical line $x = -1$, and it is included in the solution. The points satisfying $x < -1$ are all points to the left of this line (because they have x-coordinates smaller than -1). So the graph consists of the points that are *on or to the left of* the vertical line $x = -1$, as shown in Figure 7.7. ✓ 4

An alternative technique for solving inequalities that does not require solving for y is illustrated in the next example. Feel free to use it if you find it easier than the technique presented in Examples 1–4.

Example 5 Graph $4y - 2x \geq 6$.

Solution The boundary line is $4y - 2x = 6$, which can be graphed by finding its intercepts:

x-intercept: Let $y = 0$. y-intercept: Let $x = 0$.

$$4(0) - 2x = 6 \qquad\qquad 4y - 2(0) = 6$$

$$x = -3. \qquad\qquad y = \frac{6}{4} = 1.5.$$

The graph contains the half-plane above or below this line. To determine which, choose a test point—any point not on the boundary line, say, $(0, 0)$. Letting $x = 0$ and $y = 0$ in the inequality produces

$$4(0) - 2(0) \geq 6, \qquad \text{a } \textit{false} \text{ statement.}$$

Therefore, $(0, 0)$ is not in the solution. So the solution is the half-plane that does *not* include $(0, 0)$, as shown in Figure 7.8. If a different test point is used, say, $(3, 5)$, then substituting $x = 3$ and $y = 5$ in the inequality produces

$$4(5) - 2(3) \geq 6, \qquad \text{a } \textit{true} \text{ statement.}$$

Therefore, the solution of the inequality is the half-plane containing $(3, 5)$, as shown in Figure 7.8.

📄 **NOTE** When using the method of Example 5, $(0, 0)$ is the best choice for the test point because it makes the calculation very easy. The only time that $(0, 0)$ cannot be used is for inequalities of the form $ax + by \geq 0$ (or $>$ or $<$ or $\leq$); in such cases, $(0, 0)$ is on the line $ax + by = 0$.

Systems of Inequalities

Real-world problems often involve many inequalities. For example, a manufacturing problem might produce inequalities resulting from production requirements, as well as inequalities about cost requirements. A set of at least two inequalities is called a **system of inequalities.** The **graph** of a system of inequalities is made up of all those points which satisfy *all* the inequalities of the system.

Example 6 Graph the system

$$3x + y \le 12$$
$$x \le 2y.$$

Solution First, solve each inequality for y:

$$3x + y \le 12 \qquad\qquad x \le 2y$$
$$y \le -3x + 12 \qquad y \ge \frac{x}{2}.$$

Then the original system is equivalent to this one:

$$y \le -3x + 12$$
$$y \ge \frac{x}{2}.$$

Checkpoint 5

Graph the system

$$x + y \le 6$$
$$2x + y \ge 4.$$

The solutions of the first inequality are the points *on or below* the line $y = -3x + 12$ (Figure 7.9). The solutions of the second inequality are the points *on or above* the line $y = x/2$ (Figure 7.10). So the solutions of the *system* are the points that satisfy both of these conditions, as shown in Figure 7.11. ✓5

Figure 7.9

Figure 7.10

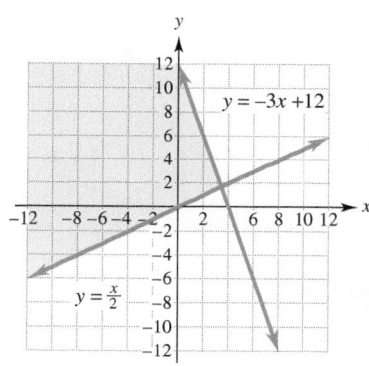

Figure 7.11

The shaded region in Figure 7.11 is sometimes called the **region of feasible solutions,** or just the **feasible region,** since it consists of all the points that satisfy (are feasible for) every inequality of the system.

Example 7 Graph the feasible region for the system

$$2x - 5y \le 10$$
$$x + 2y \le 8$$
$$x \ge 0, y \ge 0.$$

Solution Begin by solving the first two inequalities for y:

$$2x - 5y \le 10 \qquad\qquad x + 2y \le 8$$
$$-5y \le -2x + 10 \qquad\qquad 2y \le -x + 8$$
$$y \ge .4x - 2 \qquad\qquad y \le -.5x + 4.$$

Then the original system is equivalent to this one:

$$y \ge .4x - 2$$
$$y \le -.5x + 4$$
$$x \ge 0, y \ge 0.$$

The inequalities $x \geq 0$ and $y \geq 0$ restrict the graph to the first quadrant. So the feasible region consists of all points in the first quadrant that are on or above the line $y = .4x - 2$ *and* on or below the line $y = -.5x + 4$. In the calculator-generated graph of Figure 7.12, the feasible region is the region with both vertical and horizontal shading. This is confirmed by the hand-drawn graph of the feasible region in Figure 7.13. ✓6

✓**Checkpoint 6**

Graph the feasible region of the system

$$x + 4y \leq 8$$
$$x - y \geq 3$$
$$x \geq 0, y \geq 0.$$

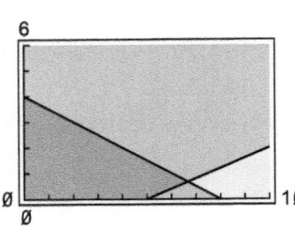

Figure 7.12   **Figure 7.13**

Example 8   Graph the feasible region for the system

$$5y - 2x \leq 10$$
$$x \geq 3, y \geq 2.$$

Solution   Solve the first inequality for y (as in Example 3) to obtain an equivalent system:

$$y \leq .4x + 2$$
$$x \geq 3, y \geq 2.$$

As shown in Example 3, Checkpoint 4, and Example 4(a), the feasible region consists of all points that lie

on or below the line $y \leq .4x + 2$ *and*

on or to the right of the vertical line $x = 3$ *and*

on or above the horizontal line $y = 2$,

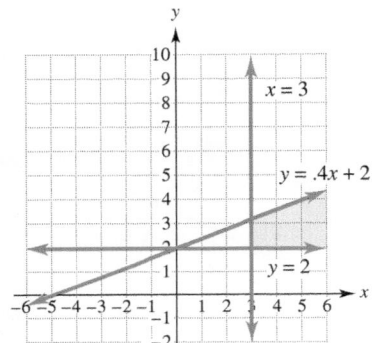

Figure 7.14

as shown in Figure 7.14.

Example 9   **Health**   A bodybuilder wishes to supplement his regular meals with protein shakes and protein bars. The protein shake contains 30 grams of protein and 325 calories. The protein bar contains 25 grams of protein and 275 calories. During a 5-day work week, the bodybuilder wants to achieve at least 350 grams of protein, but fewer than or equal to 7150 calories. Write a system of inequalities expressing these conditions, and graph the feasible region.

Solution   Let x represent the number of protein shakes to be consumed and y the number of protein bars. Then make a chart that summarizes the given information.

	Number of Units	Grams of Protein	Number of Calories
Protein Shakes	x	30	325
Protein Bars	y	25	275
Maximum or Minimum		350	7150

We must have $x \geq 0$ and $y \geq 0$, because the bodybuilder cannot consume a negative number of protein shakes or bars. In terms of consuming at least 350 grams of protein, we have

$$30x + 25y \geq 350$$
$$y \geq -\frac{6}{5}x + 14. \qquad \text{Solve for } y.$$

Similarly, the 7150 calorie requirement has that

$$325x + 275y \leq 7150$$

$$y \leq -\frac{13}{11}x + 26. \qquad \text{Solve for } y.$$

So we must solve the system

$$y \geq -\frac{6}{5}x + 14$$

$$y \leq -\frac{13}{11}x + 26$$

$$x \geq 0, y \geq 0.$$

✓ **Checkpoint 7**

Mylene wishes to invest up to $40,000 in two bond products. Bond A has an annual return of 4% and Bond B has an annual return of 5.2%. She wants to earn at least $1800 annually. Write a system of inequalities expressing these conditions, and graph the feasible region.

The feasible region is shown in Figure 7.15. ✓ 7

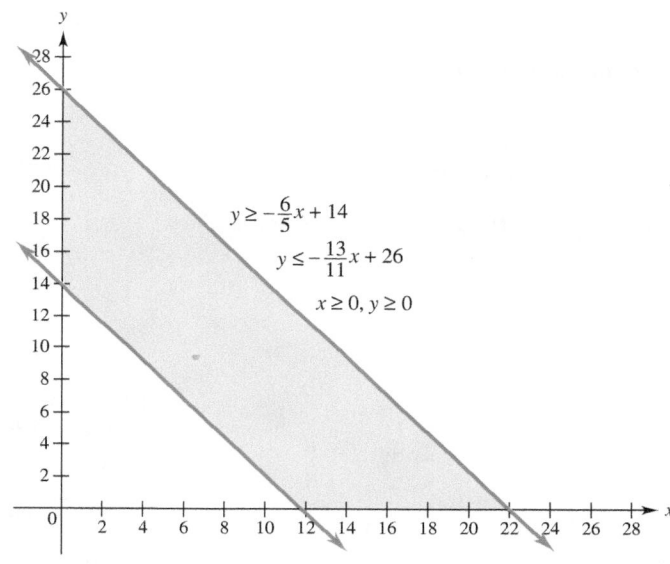

Figure 7.15

7.1 Exercises

Match the inequality with its graph, which is one of the ones shown.

1. $y \geq -x - 2$ **2.** $y \leq 2x - 2$ **3.** $y \leq x + 2$

4. $y \geq x + 1$ **5.** $6x + 4y \geq -12$ **6.** $3x - 2y \geq -4$

A.

B.

C.

D.

E.

F.

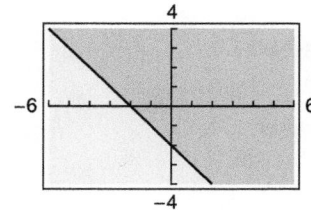

Graph each of the given linear inequalities. (See Examples 1–5.)

7. $y < 5 - 2x$

8. $y < x + 3$

9. $3x - 2y \geq 18$

10. $2x + 5y \geq 10$

11. $2x - y \leq 4$

12. $4x - 3y \leq 24$

13. $y \leq -4$

14. $x \geq -2$

15. $3x - 2y \geq 18$

16. $3x + 2y \geq -4$

17. $3x + 4y \geq 12$

18. $4x - 3y > 9$

19. $2x - 4y \leq 3$

20. $4x - 3y < 12$

21. $x \leq 5y$

22. $2x \geq y$

23. $-3x \leq y$

24. $-x \geq 6y$

25. $y \leq x$

26. $y > -2x$

27. In your own words, explain how to determine whether the boundary line of an inequality should be solid or dashed.

28. When graphing $y \leq 3x - 6$, would you shade above or below the line $y = 3x - 6$? Explain your answer.

Graph the feasible region for the given systems of inequalities. (See Examples 6 and 7.)

29. $y \geq 3x - 6$
$y \geq -x + 1$

30. $x + y \leq 4$
$x - y \geq 2$

31. $2x + y \leq 5$
$x + 2y \leq 5$

32. $x - y \geq 1$
$x \leq 3$

33. $2x + y \geq 8$
$4x - y \leq 3$

34. $4x + y \geq 9$
$2x + 3y \leq 7$

35. $2x - y \leq 1$
$3x + y \leq 6$

36. $x + 3y \leq 6$
$2x + 4y \geq 7$

37. $-x - y \leq 5$
$2x - y \leq 4$

38. $6x - 4y \geq 8$
$3x + 2y \geq 4$

39. $3x + y \geq 6$
$x + 2y \geq 7$
$x \geq 0$
$y \geq 0$

40. $2x + 3y \geq 12$
$x + y \geq 4$
$x \geq 0$
$y \geq 0$

41. $-2 \leq x \leq 3$
$-1 \leq y \leq 5$
$2x + y \leq 6$

42. $-2 \leq x \leq 2$
$y \geq 1$
$x - y \geq 0$

43. $2y - x \geq -5$
$y \leq 3 + x$
$x \geq 0$
$y \geq 0$

44. $2x + 3y \leq 12$
$2x + 3y \geq -6$
$3x + y \leq 4$
$x \geq 0$
$y \geq 0$

45. $3x + 4y \geq 12$
$2x - 3y \leq 6$
$0 \leq y \leq 2$
$x \geq 0$

46. $0 \leq x \leq 9$
$x - 2y \geq 4$
$3x + 5y \leq 30$
$y \geq 0$

Find a system of inequalities that has the given graph.

47.

48.

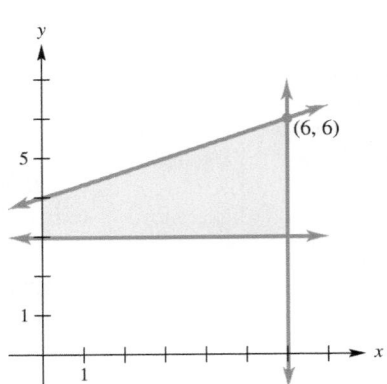

In Exercises 49 and 50, find a system of inequalities whose feasible region is the interior of the given polygon.

49. Rectangle with vertices $(2, 3)$, $(2, -1)$, $(7, 3)$, and $(7, -1)$

50. Triangle with vertices $(2, 4)$, $(-4, 0)$, and $(2, -1)$

51. Business Cindi Herring and Kent Merrill produce handmade shawls and afghans. They spin the yarn, dye it, and then weave it. A shawl requires 1 hour of spinning, 1 hour of dyeing, and 1 hour of weaving. An afghan needs 2 hours of spinning, 1 of dyeing, and 4 of weaving. Together, they spend at most 8 hours spinning, 6 hours dyeing, and 14 hours weaving.

(a) Complete the following table.

	Number	Hours Spinning	Hours Dyeing	Hours Weaving
Shawls	x			
Afghans	y			
Maximum Number of Hours Available		8	6	14

(b) Use the table to write a system of inequalities that describes the situation.

(c) Graph the feasible region of this system of inequalities.

52. Business A manufacturer of electric shavers makes two models: the regular and the flex. Because of demand, the number of regular shavers made is never more than half the number of flex shavers. The factory's production cannot exceed 1200 shavers per week.

(a) Write a system of inequalities that describes the possibilities for making x regular and y flex shavers per week.

(b) Graph the feasible region of this system of inequalities.

In each of the following, write a system of inequalities that describes all the given conditions, and graph the feasible region of the system. (See Example 9.)

53. **Finance** As of April 2013, a New York, NY Development Corp. municipal bond fund yielded an annual return of 3.6% and the Florida Village Community Development District No. 8 municipal bond fund yielded an annual return of 5.0%. You would like to invest up to $50,000 and obtain at least $2100 in interest. Let x be the amount invested in the New York fund and let y be the amount invested in the Florida fund. (Data from: Financial Industry Regulatory Authority.)

54. **Finance** As of April 2013, a Sanilac County, Michigan municipal bond fund yielded an annual return of 6.0% and the Mandan North Dakota municipal bond fund yielded an annual return of 4.7%. You would like to invest up to $40,000 and earn at least $2250 in interest. Let x be the amount invested in the Michigan fund and let y be the amount invested in the North Dakota fund. (Data from: Financial Industry Regulatory Authority.)

55. **Business** Joyce Blake is the marketing director for a new company selling a fashion collection for young women and she wishes to place ads in two magazines: *Vogue* and *Elle*. Joyce estimates that each one-page ad in *Vogue* will be read by 1.3 million people and each one-page ad in *Elle* will be read by 1.1 million people. Joyce wants to reach at least 8 million readers and to place at least 2 ads in each magazine. (Data from: www.nyjobsource.com.)

56. **Business** Corey Steinbruner is the marketing director for a new vitamin supplement and he wants to place ads in two magazines: *Sports Illustrated* and *Men's Health*. Corey estimates that each one-page ad in *Sports Illustrated* will be read by 3.2 million people and each one-page ad in *Men's Health* will be read by 1.9 million people. Corey wants to reach at least 20 million readers and to place at least 3 ads in each magazine. (Data from: www.nyjobsource.com.)

✓**Checkpoint Answers**

1. (a)

(b)

2. (a)

(b)

3.

4. (a)   **(b)**

5.

6.

7.

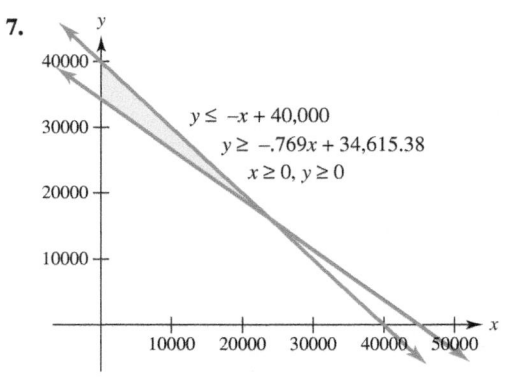

7.2 Linear Programming: The Graphical Method

Many problems in business, science, and economics involve finding the optimal value of a function (for instance, the maximum value of the profit function or the minimum value of the cost function), subject to various **constraints** (such as transportation costs, environmental protection laws, availability of parts, and interest rates). **Linear programming** deals with such situations. In linear programming, the function to be optimized, called the **objective function,** is linear and the constraints are given by linear inequalities. Linear programming problems that involve only two variables can be solved by the graphical method, explained in Example 1.

Example 1 Find the maximum and minimum values of the objective function $z = 2x + 5y$, subject to the following constraints:

$$3x + 2y \le 6$$
$$-2x + 4y \le 8$$
$$x + y \ge 1$$
$$x \ge 0, y \ge 0.$$

Solution First, graph the feasible region of the system of inequalities (Figure 7.16). The points in this region or on its boundaries are the only ones that satisfy all the constraints. However, each such point may produce a different value of the objective function. For instance, the points $(.5, 1)$ and $(1, 0)$ in the feasible region lead to the respective values

$$z = 2(.5) + 5(1) = 6 \quad \text{and} \quad z = 2(1) + 5(0) = 2.$$

We must find the points that produce the maximum and minimum values of z.

To find the maximum value, consider various possible values for z. For instance, when $z = 0$, the objective function is $0 = 2x + 5y$, whose graph is a straight line. Similarly, when z is 5, 10, and 15, the objective function becomes (in turn)

$$5 = 2x + 5y, \quad 10 = 2x + 5y, \quad \text{and} \quad 15 = 2x + 5y.$$

These four lines are graphed in Figure 7.17. (All the lines are parallel because they have the same slope.) The figure shows that z cannot take on the value 15, because the graph for $z = 15$ is entirely outside the feasible region. The maximum possible value of z will be obtained from a line parallel to the others and between the lines representing the objective

Figure 7.16

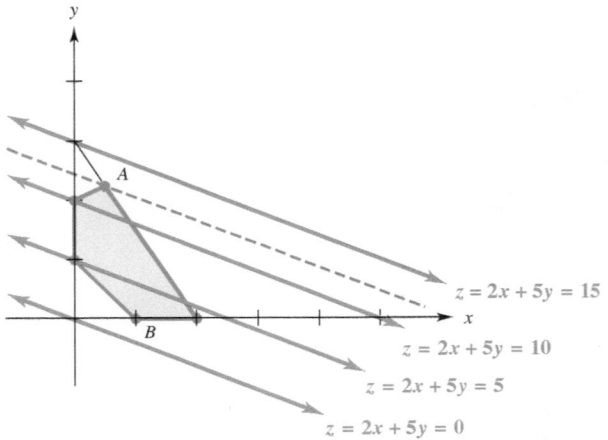

Figure 7.17

function when $z = 10$ and $z = 15$. The value of z will be as large as possible, and all constraints will be satisfied, if this line just touches the feasible region. This occurs with the green line through point A.

The point A is the intersection of the graphs of $3x + 2y = 6$ and $-2x + 4y = 8$. (See Figure 7.16.) Its coordinates can be found either algebraically or graphically (using a graphing calculator).

Algebraic Method	**Graphical Method**

Algebraic Method

Solve the system

$$3x + 2y = 6$$
$$-2x + 4y = 8,$$

as in Section 6.1, to get $x = \frac{1}{2}$ and $y = \frac{9}{4}$. Hence, A has coordinates $\left(\frac{1}{2}, \frac{9}{4}\right) = (.5, 2.25)$.

The value of z at point A is

$$z = 2x + 5y = 2(.5) + 5(2.25) = 12.25.$$

Thus, the maximum possible value of z is 12.25. Similarly, the minimum value of z occurs at point B, which has coordinates $(1, 0)$. The minimum value of z is $2(1) + 5(0) = 2$. ✓

Graphical Method

Solve the two equations for y:

$$y = -1.5x + 3$$
$$y = .5x + 2.$$

Graph both equations on the same screen and use the intersection finder to find that the coordinates of the intersection point A are $(.5, 2.25)$.

✓ **Checkpoint 1**

Suppose the objective function in Example 1 is changed to $z = 5x + 2y$.

(a) Sketch the graphs of the objective function when $z = 0$, $z = 5$, and $z = 10$ on the region of feasible solutions given in Figure 7.16.

(b) From the graph, decide what values of x and y will maximize the objective function.

Points such as A and B in Example 1 are called corner points. A **corner point** is a point in the feasible region where the boundary lines of two constraints cross. The feasible region in Figure 7.16 is **bounded** because the region is enclosed by boundary lines on all sides. Linear programming problems with bounded regions always have solutions. However, if Example 1 did not include the constraint $3x + 2y \le 6$, the feasible region would be **unbounded,** and there would be no way to *maximize* the value of the objective function.

Some general conclusions can be drawn from the method of solution used in Example 1. Figure 7.18 shows various feasible regions and the lines that result from various values of z. (Figure 7.18 shows the situation in which the lines are in order from left to right as z increases.) In part (a) of Figure 7.18, the objective function takes on its minimum value at corner point Q and its maximum value at corner point P. The minimum is again at Q in part (b), but the maximum occurs at P_1 or P_2, or any point on the line segment connecting them. Finally, in part (c), the minimum value occurs at Q, but the objective function has no maximum value because the feasible region is unbounded.

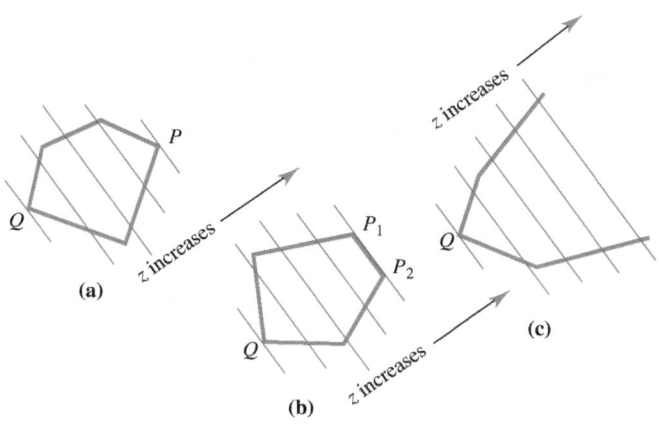

Figure 7.18

The preceding discussion suggests the **corner point theorem.**

Corner Point Theorem

If the feasible region is bounded, then the objective function has both a maximum and a minimum value, and each occurs at one or more corner points.

If the feasible region is unbounded, the objective function may not have a maximum or minimum. But if a maximum or minimum value exists, it will occur at one or more corner points.

This theorem simplifies the job of finding an optimum value. First, graph the feasible region and find all corner points. Then test each point in the objective function. Finally, identify the corner point producing the optimum solution.

With the theorem, the problem in Example 1 could have been solved by identifying the five corner points of Figure 7.16: $(0, 1)$, $(0, 2)$, $(.5, 2.25)$, $(2, 0)$, and $(1, 0)$. Then, substituting each of these points into the objective function $z = 2x + 5y$ would identify the corner points that produce the maximum and minimum values of z.

Corner Point	Value of $z = 2x + 5y$	
$(0, 1)$	$2(0) + 5(1) = 5$	
$(0, 2)$	$2(0) + 5(2) = 10$	
$(.5, 2.25)$	$2(.5) + 5(2.25) = 12.25$	(maximum)
$(2, 0)$	$2(2) + 5(0) = 4$	
$(1, 0)$	$2(1) + 5(0) = 2$	(minimum)

From these results, the corner point $(.5, 2.25)$ yields the maximum value of 12.25 and the corner point $(1, 0)$ gives the minimum value of 2. These are the same values found earlier. ✔2

A summary of the steps for solving a linear programming problem by the graphical method is given here.

✓**Checkpoint 2**

(a) Identify the corner points in the given graph.

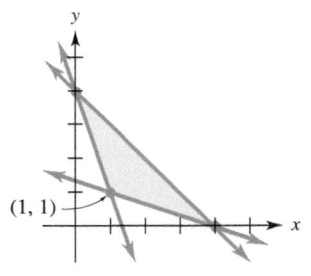

(1, 1)

(b) Which corner point would minimize $z = 2x + 3y$?

Solving a Linear Programming Problem Graphically

1. Write the objective function and all necessary constraints.

2. Graph the feasible region.

3. Determine the coordinates of each of the corner points.

4. Find the value of the objective function at each corner point.

5. If the feasible region is bounded, the solution is given by the corner point producing the optimum value of the objective function.

6. If the feasible region is an unbounded region in the first quadrant and both coefficients of the objective function are positive,* then the minimum value of the objective function occurs at a corner point and there is no maximum value.

---

*This is the only case of an unbounded region that occurs in the applications considered here.

Example 2   Sketch the feasible region for the following set of constraints:

$$3y - 2x \geq 0$$
$$y + 8x \leq 52$$
$$y - 2x \leq 2$$
$$x \geq 3.$$

Then find the maximum and minimum values of the objective function $z = 5x + 2y$.

Solution   Graph the feasible region, as in Figure 7.19. To find the corner points, you must solve these four systems of equations:

A	B	C	D
$y - 2x = 2$	$3y - 2x = 0$	$3y - 2x = 0$	$y - 2x = 2$
$x = 3$	$x = 3$	$y + 8x = 52$	$y + 8x = 52$

The first two systems are easily solved by substitution, which shows that $A = (3, 8)$ and $B = (3, 2)$. The other two systems can be solved either graphically (as in Figure 7.20) or algebraically (see Checkpoint 3). Hence, $C = (6, 4)$ and $D = (5, 12)$. ✔3

Figure 7.19   **Figure 7.20**

✓ **Checkpoint 3**

Use the elimination method (see Section 6.1) to solve the last system and find the coordinates of D in Example 2.

Use the corner points from the graph to find the maximum and minimum values of the objective function.

Corner Point	Value of $z = 5x + 2y$	
$(3, 8)$	$5(3) + 2(8) = 31$	
$(3, 2)$	$5(3) + 2(2) = 19$	(minimum)
$(6, 4)$	$5(6) + 2(4) = 38$	
$(5, 12)$	$5(5) + 2(12) = 49$	(maximum)

The minimum value of $z = 5x + 2y$ is 19, at the corner point $(3, 2)$. The maximum value is 49, at $(5, 12)$. ✔4

✓ **Checkpoint 4**

Use the region of feasible solutions in the accompanying sketch to find the given values.

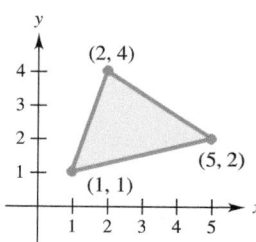

(a) The values of x and y that maximize $z = 2x - y$

(b) The maximum value of $z = 2x - y$

(c) The values of x and y that minimize $z = 4x + 3y$

(d) The minimum value of $z = 4x + 3y$

Example 3   Solve the following linear programming problem:

$$\text{Minimize} \quad z = x + 2y$$
$$\text{subject to} \quad x + y \leq 10$$
$$3x + 2y \geq 6$$
$$x \geq 0, y \geq 0.$$

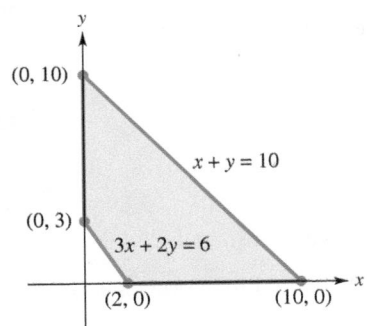

Figure 7.21

Solution   The feasible region is shown in Figure 7.21.

From the figure, the corner points are (0, 3), (0, 10), (10, 0), and (2, 0). These corner points give the following values of z.

Corner Point	Value of $z = x + 2y$	
(0, 3)	$0 + 2(3) = 6$	
(0, 10)	$0 + 2(10) = 20$	
(10, 0)	$10 + 2(0) = 10$	
(2, 0)	$2 + 2(0) = 2$	(minimum)

The minimum value of z is 2; it occurs at (2, 0). ✔5

✓ Checkpoint 5

The given sketch shows a feasible region. Let $z = x + 3y$. Use the sketch to find the values of x and y that

(a) minimize z;

(b) maximize z.

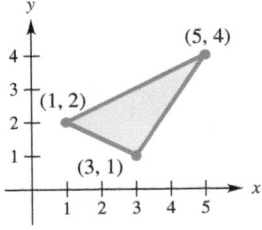

Example 4   Solve the following linear programming problem:

$$\text{Minimize}\qquad z = 2x + 4y$$
$$\text{subject to}\qquad x + 2y \geq 10$$
$$3x + \ y \geq 10$$
$$x \geq 0, y \geq 0.$$

Solution   Figure 7.22 shows the hand-drawn graph with corner points (0, 10), (2, 4), and (10, 0), as well as the calculator graph with the corner point (2, 4). Find the value of z for each point.

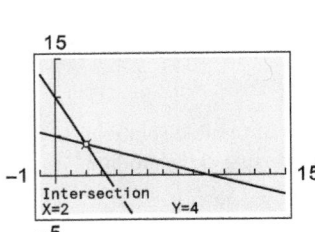

Figure 7.22

✓ Checkpoint 6

The sketch shows a region of feasible solutions. From the sketch, decide what ordered pair would minimize $z = 2x + 4y$.

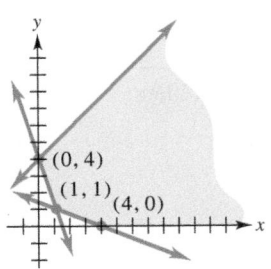

Corner Point	Value of $z = 2x + 4y$	
(0, 10)	$2(0) + 4(10) = 40$	
(2, 4)	$2(2) + 4(4) = 20$	(minimum)
(10, 0)	$2(10) + 4(0) = 20$	(minimum)

In this case, both (2, 4) and (10, 0), as well as all the points on the boundary line between them, give the same optimum value of z. So there is an infinite number of equally "good" values of x and y that give the same minimum value of the objective function $z = 2x + 4y$. The minimum value is 20. ✔6

7.2 Exercises

Exercises 1–6 show regions of feasible solutions. Use these regions to find maximum and minimum values of each given objective function. (See Examples 1 and 2.)

1. $z = 6x + y$

2. $z = 4x + y$

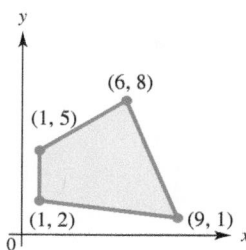

3. $z = .3x + .5y$

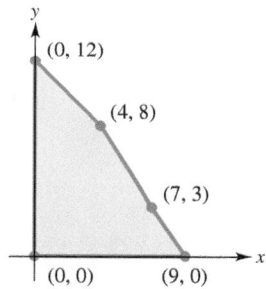

4. $z = .35x + 1.25y$

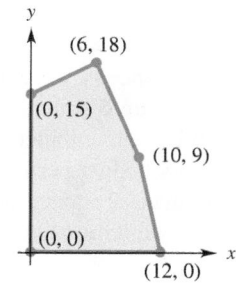

5. (a) $z = x + 5y$
   (b) $z = 2x + 3y$
   (c) $z = 2x + 4y$
   (d) $z = 4x + y$

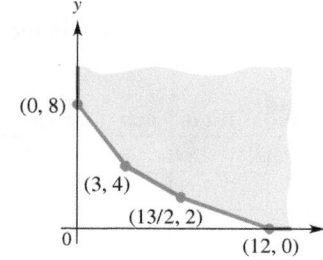

6. (a) $z = 5x + 2y$
   (b) $z = 5x + 6y$
   (c) $z = x + 2y$
   (d) $z = x + y$

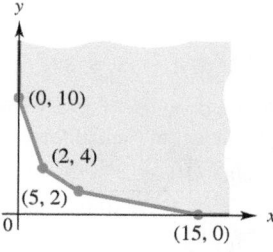

Use graphical methods to solve Exercises 7–12. (See Examples 2–4.)

7. Maximize $z = 4x + 3y$
   subject to $2x + 3y \le 6$
   $4x + y \le 6$
   $x \ge 0, y \ge 0.$

8. Minimize $z = x + 3y$
   subject to $2x + y \le 10$
   $5x + 2y \ge 20$
   $-x + 2y \ge 0$
   $x \ge 0, y \ge 0.$

9. Minimize $z = 2x + y$
   subject to $3x - y \ge 12$
   $x + y \le 15$
   $x \ge 2, y \ge 3.$

10. Maximize $z = x + 3y$
   subject to $2x + 3y \le 100$
   $5x + 4y \le 200$
   $x \ge 10, y \ge 20.$

11. Maximize $z = 5x + y$
   subject to $x - y \le 10$
   $5x + 3y \le 75$
   $x \ge 0, y \ge 0.$

12. Maximize $z = 4x + 5y$
   subject to $10x - 5y \le 100$
   $20x + 10y \ge 150$
   $x \ge 0, y \ge 0.$

Find the minimum and maximum values of $z = 3x + 4y$ (if possible) for each of the given sets of constraints. (See Examples 2–4.)

13. $3x + 2y \ge 6$
   $x + 2y \ge 4$
   $x \ge 0, y \ge 0$

14. $2x + y \le 20$
   $10x + y \ge 36$
   $2x + 5y \ge 36$

15. $x + y \le 6$
   $-x + y \le 2$
   $2x - y \le 8$

16. $-x + 2y \le 6$
   $3x + y \ge 3$
   $x \ge 0, y \ge 0$

17. Find values of $x \ge 0$ and $y \ge 0$ that maximize $z = 10x + 12y$, subject to each of the following sets of constraints.

(a) $x + y \leq 20$

$\quad x + 3y \leq 24$

(c) $\quad x + 2y \geq 10$

$\quad\quad 2x + y \geq 12$

$\quad\quad\quad x - y \leq 8$

(b) $3x + y \leq 15$

$\quad\quad x + 2y \leq 18$

18. Find values of $x \geq 0$ and $y \geq 0$ that minimize $z = 3x + 2y$, subject to each of the following sets of constraints.

(a) $10x + 7y \leq 42$

$\quad\quad 4x + 10y \geq 35$

(b) $6x + 5y \geq 25$

$\quad\quad 2x + 6y \geq 15$

(c) $2x + 5y \geq 22$

$\quad\quad 4x + 3y \leq 28$

$\quad\quad 2x + 2y \leq 17$

19. Explain why it is impossible to maximize the function $z = 3x + 4y$ subject to the constraints

$\quad x + y \geq 8$

$\quad 2x + y \leq 10$

$\quad x + 2y \leq 8$

$\quad x \geq 0, y \geq 0.$

20. You are given the following multiple-choice linear programming problem.*

$$\text{Maximize} \quad z = c_1 x_1 + c_2 x_2$$
$$\text{subject to} \quad 2x_1 + x_2 \leq 11$$
$$\quad\quad -x_1 + 2x_2 \leq 2$$
$$\quad\quad x_1 \geq 0, x_2 \geq 0.$$

---

*Problem from "Course 130 Examination Operations Research" of the *Education and Examination Committee of the Society of Actuaries*. Reprinted by permission of the Society of Actuaries.

If $c_2 > 0$, determine the range of c_1/c_2 for which $(x_1, x_2) = (4, 3)$ is an optimal solution.

(a) $[-2, 1/2]$

(b) $[-1/2, 2]$

(c) $[-11, -1]$

(d) $[1, 11]$

(e) $[-11, 11]$

 Checkpoint Answers

1. (a)

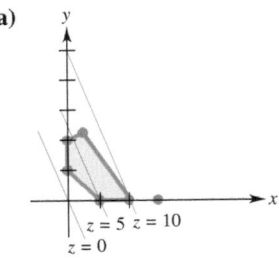

(b) $(2, 0)$

2. (a) $(0, 4), (1, 1), (4, 0)$

(b) $(1, 1)$

3. $D = (5, 12)$

4. (a) $(5, 2)$ **(b)** 8

(c) $(1, 1)$ **(d)** 7

5. (a) $(3, 1)$ **(b)** $(5, 4)$

6. $(1, 1)$

7.3 Applications of Linear Programming

In this section, we show several applications of linear programming with two variables.

> **Example 1** **Business** An office manager needs to purchase new filing cabinets. He knows that Ace cabinets cost $40 each, require 6 square feet of floor space, and hold 8 cubic feet of files. On the other hand, each Excello cabinet costs $80, requires 8 square feet of floor space, and holds 12 cubic feet. His budget permits him to spend no more than $560, while the office has room for no more than 72 square feet of cabinets. The manager desires the greatest storage capacity within the limitations imposed by funds and space. How many of each type of cabinet should he buy?
>
> **Solution** Let x represent the number of Ace cabinets to be bought, and let y represent the number of Excello cabinets. The information given in the problem can be summarized as follows.

	Number	Cost of Each	Space Required	Storage Capacity
Ace	x	$40	6 sq ft	8 cu ft
Excello	y	$80	8 sq ft	12 cu ft
Maximum Available		$560	72 sq ft	

The constraints imposed by cost and space are

$$40x + 80y \le 560 \qquad \text{Cost}$$
$$6x + 8y \le 72. \qquad \text{Floor space}$$

The number of cabinets cannot be negative, so $x \ge 0$ and $y \ge 0$. The objective function to be maximized gives the amount of storage capacity provided by some combination of Ace and Excello cabinets. From the information in the chart, the objective function is

$$z = \text{Storage capacity} = 8x + 12y.$$

In sum, the given problem has produced the following linear programming problem:

$$\begin{aligned} \text{Maximize} \quad & z = 8x + 12y \\ \text{subject to} \quad & 40x + 80y \le 560 \\ & 6x + 8y \le 72 \\ & x \ge 0, y \ge 0. \end{aligned}$$

A graph of the feasible region is shown in Figure 7.23. Three of the corner points can be identified from the graph as $(0, 0)$, $(0, 7)$, and $(12, 0)$. The fourth corner point, labeled Q in the figure, can be found algebraically or with a graphing calculator to be $(8, 3)$. ✓₁

✓ Checkpoint 1

Find the corner point labeled P on the region of feasible solutions in the given graph.

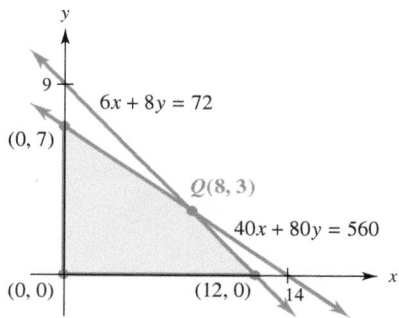

Figure 7.23

Use the corner point theorem to find the maximum value of z.

Corner Point	Value of $z = 8x + 12y$	
$(0, 0)$	0	
$(0, 7)$	84	
$(8, 3)$	100	(maximum)
$(12, 0)$	96	

The objective function, which represents storage space, is maximized when $x = 8$ and $y = 3$. The manager should buy 8 Ace cabinets and 3 Excello cabinets. ✓₂

✓ Checkpoint 2

A popular cereal combines oats and corn. At least 27 tons of the cereal are to be made. For the best flavor, the amount of corn should be no more than twice the amount of oats. Oats cost $300 per ton, and corn costs $200 per ton. How much of each grain should be used to minimize the cost?

(a) Make a chart to organize the information given in the problem.

(b) Write an equation for the objective function.

(c) Write four inequalities for the constraints.

Example 2 **Health** Certain laboratory animals must have at least 30 grams of protein and at least 20 grams of fat per feeding period. These nutrients come from food A, which costs 18¢ per unit and supplies 2 grams of protein and 4 of fat, and food B, with 6 grams of protein and 2 of fat, costing 12¢ per unit. Food B is bought under a long-term contract requiring that at least 2 units of B be used per serving. How much of each food must be bought to produce the minimum cost per serving?

Solution Let x represent the amount of food A needed and y the amount of food B. Use the given information to produce the following table.

Food	Number of Units	Grams of Protein	Grams of Fat	Cost
A	x	2	4	18¢
B	y	6	2	12¢
Minimum Required		30	20	

Use the table to develop the linear programming problem. Since the animals must have *at least* 30 grams of protein and 20 grams of fat, use $\geq$ in the constraint inequalities for protein and fat. The long-term contract provides a constraint not shown in the table, namely, $y \geq 2$. So we have the following problem:

$$\begin{array}{lll} \text{Minimize} & z = .18x + .12y & \text{Cost} \\ \text{subject to} & 2x + 6y \geq 30 & \text{Protein} \\ & 4x + 2y \geq 20 & \text{Fat} \\ & y \geq 2 & \text{Contract} \\ & x \geq 0, y \geq 0. & \end{array}$$

(The constraint $y \geq 0$ is redundant because of the constraint $y \geq 2$.) A graph of the feasible region with the corner points identified is shown in Figure 7.24.

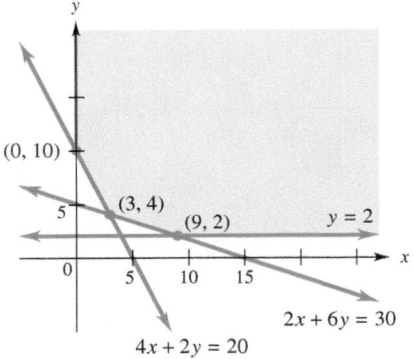

Figure 7.24

Use the corner point theorem to find the minimum value of z as shown in the table.

Corner Points	$z = .18x + .12y$
(0, 10)	$.18(0) + .12(10) = 1.20$
(3, 4)	$.18(3) + .12(4) = 1.02$ **(minimum)**
(9, 2)	$.18(9) + .12(2) = 1.86$

The minimum value of 1.02 occurs at (3, 4). Thus, 3 units of food A and 4 units of food B will produce a minimum cost of $1.02 per serving. ✓₃

✓ **Checkpoint 3**

Use the information in Checkpoint 2 to do the following.

(a) Graph the feasible region and find the corner points.

(b) Determine the minimum value of the objective function and the point where it occurs.

(c) Is there a maximum cost?

The feasible region in Figure 7.24 is an unbounded one: The region extends indefinitely to the upper right. With this region, it would not be possible to *maximize* the objective function, because the total cost of the food could always be increased by encouraging the animals to eat more.

One measure of the risk involved in investing in a stock or mutual fund is called the standard deviation. The standard deviation measures the volatility of investment returns relative to an historical average. If the return of an investment tool fluctuates a great deal from the historical average return, then there will be a higher standard deviation value for that stock. If an investment tool's value stays near the historical average, then it will have a small standard deviation value. Thus, a higher standard deviation for an investment tool can be one measure of higher risk. Investors often wish to obtain the highest profit while minimizing risk.

Example 3   **Finance**   Carolyn Behr-Jerome wants to invest up to $5000 in stocks. The share price for the Costco Whole Corporation (COST) is $108, and it has a standard deviation value of 15.9. The share price for CVS Caremark Corporation (CVS) is $59, and the standard deviation value is 19.5. Based on the average of 10-year returns, Costco would produce in a year a profit of $15 per share and CVS would produce a profit of $10 a share. Carolyn would like to obtain at least $800 in profit. How many shares of each stock should she purchase to minimize the risk as measured by the standard deviation? What is the minimum value of the risk? (Data from: www.morningstar.com and www.abg-analytics.com as of April 2013.)

Solution   Let x represent the number of shares of Costco stock to be purchased, and let y be the number of shares of CVS stock to be purchased. The information in the problem can be summarized as follows:

	Number of Shares	Cost of Each	Profit	Risk
Costco	x	$108	$15	15.9
CVS	y	$59	$10	19.5
Constraints		$5000	$800	

The constraints imposed by the cost of the shares and the profits are

$$108x + 59y \le 5000$$
$$15x + 10y \ge 800.$$

The number of stocks to be purchased cannot be negative, so $x \ge 0$ and $y \ge 0$. The objective function to be minimized gives the amount of risk provided by some combination of shares in Costco and CVS stocks. From the information in the chart, the objective function is

$$z = \text{standard deviation} = 15.9x + 19.5y.$$

In sum, the given problem has produced the following linear programming problem:

$$\text{Minimize} \quad z = 15.9x + 19.5y$$
$$\text{subject to} \quad 108x + 59y \le 5000$$
$$15x + 10y \ge 800$$
$$x \ge 0, y \ge 0.$$

A graph of the feasible region with the corner points identified is shown in Figure 7.25.

Figure 7.25

Use the corner point theorem to find the minimum value of z as shown in the table.

Corner Points	$z = 15.9x + 19.5y$
(0, 84.7)	$15.9(0) + 19.5(84.7) = 1651.65$
(0, 80)	$15.9(0) + 19.5(80) = 1560.0$
(14.4, 58.4)	$15.9(14.4) + 19.5(58.4) = 1367.76$

The minimum value of 1367.76 occurs at (14.4, 58.4). Since Carolyn must buy a whole share of stock, she would buy 14 shares of Costco stock and 58 shares of CVS stock.

7.3 Exercises

Write the constraints in Exercises 1–4 as linear inequalities and identify all variables used. In some instances, not all of the information is needed to write the constraints. (See Examples 1–3.)

1. A canoe requires 8 hours of fabrication and a rowboat 5 hours. The fabrication department has at most 110 hours of labor available each week.

2. Doug Gilbert needs at least 2800 milligrams of vitamin C per day. Each Supervite pill provides 250 milligrams, and each Vitahealth pill provides 350 milligrams.

3. A candidate can afford to spend no more than $9500 on radio and TV advertising. Each radio spot costs $250, and each TV ad costs $750.

4. A hospital dietician has two meal choices: one for patients on solid food that costs $2.75 and one for patients on liquids that costs $3.75. There is a maximum of 600 patients in the hospital.

Solve these linear programming problems, which are somewhat simpler than the examples in the text.

5. **Business** A chain saw requires 4 hours of assembly and a wood chipper 6 hours. A maximum of 48 hours of assembly time is available. The profit is $150 on a chain saw and $220 on a chipper. How many of each should be assembled for maximum profit?

6. **Health** Mark Donovan likes to snack frequently during the day, but he wants his snacks to provide at least 24 grams of protein per day. Each Snack-Pack provides 4 grams of protein, and each Minibite provides 1 gram. Snack-Packs cost 50 cents each and Minibites 12 cents. How many of each snack should he use to minimize his daily cost?

7. **Business** Deluxe coffee is to be mixed with regular coffee to make at least 50 pounds of a blended coffee. The mixture must contain at least 10 pounds of deluxe coffee. Deluxe coffee costs $6 per pound and regular coffee $5 per pound. How many pounds of each kind of coffee should be used to minimize costs?

8. **Business** The company in Exercise 1 cannot sell more than 10 canoes each week and always sells at least 6 rowboats. The profit on a canoe is $400, and the profit on a rowboat is $225. Assuming the same situation as in Exercise 1, how many of each should be made per week to maximize profits?

9. Kevin Chagin is an auto mechanic. He spends 3 hours when he replaces the shocks on a car and 2 hours when he replaces the brakes. He works no more than 48 hours a week. He routinely completes at least 2 shocks replacements and 6 brake replacements a week. If he charges $500 for labor replacing shocks and $300 in labor for replacing brakes, how many jobs of each type should he complete a week to maximize his income?

10. **Health** Doug Gilbert of Exercise 2 pays 3 cents for each Supervite pill and 4 cents for each Vitahealth pill. Because of its other ingredients, he cannot take more than 7 Supervite pills per day. Assuming the same conditions as in Example 2, how many of each pill should he take to provide the desired level of vitamin C at minimum cost?

11. **Social Science** The candidate in Exercise 3 wants to have at least 8 radio spots and at least 3 TV ads. A radio spot reaches 600 people, and a TV ad reaches 2000 people. Assuming the monetary facts given in Exercise 3, how many of each kind should be used to reach the largest number of people?

12. **Health** The hospital in Exercise 4 always has at least 100 patients on solid foods and at least 100 on liquids. Assuming the facts in Exercise 4, what number of each type of patient would minimize food costs?

Solve the following linear programming problems. (See Examples 1–3.)

13. **Health** Mike May has been told that each day he needs at least 16 units of vitamin A, at least 5 units of vitamin B-1, and at least 20 units of vitamin C. Each Brand X pill contain 8 units of vitamin A, 1 of vitamin B-1, and 2 of vitamin C, while each Brand Z pill contains 2 units of vitamin A, 1 of vitamin B-1, and 7 of vitamin C. A Brand X pill costs 15 cents, and a Brand Z pill costs 30 cents. How many pills of each brand should he buy to minimize his daily cost? What is the minimum cost?

14. **Business** The manufacturing process requires that oil refineries manufacture at least 2 gallons of gasoline for every gallon of fuel oil. To meet the winter demand for fuel oil, at least 3 million gallons a day must be produced. The demand for gasoline is no more than 12 million gallons per day. It takes .25 hour to ship each million gallons of gasoline and 1 hour to ship each million gallons of fuel oil out of the warehouse. No more than 6.6 hours are available for shipping. If the refinery sells gasoline

for $1.25 per gallon and fuel oil for $1 per gallon, how much of each should be produced to maximize revenue? Find the maximum revenue.

15. Business A machine shop manufactures two types of bolts. The bolts require time on each of three groups of machines, but the time required on each group differs, as shown in the table:

		MACHINE GROUP		
		I	II	III
Bolts	Type 1	.1 min	.1 min	.1 min
	Type 2	.1 min	.4 min	.02 min

Production schedules are made up one day at a time. In a day, there are 240, 720, and 160 minutes available, respectively, on these machines. Type 1 bolts sell for 10¢ and type 2 bolts for 12¢. How many of each type of bolt should be manufactured per day to maximize revenue? What is the maximum revenue?

16. Health Kim Walrath has a nutritional deficiency and is told to take at least 2400 mg of iron, 2100 mg of vitamin B-1, and 1500 mg of vitamin B-2. One Maxivite pill contains 40 mg of iron, 10 mg of vitamin B-1, and 5 mg of vitamin B-2 and costs 6¢. One Healthovite pill provides 10 mg of iron, 15 mg of vitamin B-1, and 15 mg of vitamin B-2 and costs 8¢.

(a) What combination of Maxivite and Healthovite pills will meet Kim's requirements at lowest cost? What is the lowest cost?

(b) In your solution for part (a), does Kim receive more than the minimum amount she needs of any vitamin? If so, which vitamin is it?

(c) Is there any way that Kim can avoid receiving more than the minimum she needs and still meet the other constraints and minimize the cost? Explain.

17. Business A greeting card manufacturer has 500 boxes of a particular card in warehouse I and 290 boxes of the same card in warehouse II. A greeting card shop in San Jose orders 350 boxes of the card, and another shop in Memphis orders 250 boxes. The shipping costs per box to these shops from the two warehouses are shown in the following table:

		DESTINATION	
		San Jose	Memphis
Warehouse	I	$.25	$.22
	II	$.23	$.21

How many boxes should be shipped to each city from each warehouse to minimize shipping costs? What is the minimum cost? (*Hint:* Use x, $350 - x$, y, and $250 - y$ as the variables.)

18. Business *Hotnews Magazine* publishes a U.S. and a Canadian edition each week. There are 30,000 subscribers in the United States and 20,000 in Canada. Other copies are sold at newsstands. Postage and shipping costs average $80 per thousand copies for the United States and $60 per thousand copies for Canada. Surveys show that no more than 120,000 copies of

each issue can be sold (including subscriptions) and that the number of copies of the Canadian edition should not exceed twice the number of copies of the U.S. edition. The publisher can spend at most $8400 a month on postage and shipping. If the profit is $200 for each thousand copies of the U.S. edition and $150 for each thousand copies of the Canadian edition, how many copies of each version should be printed to earn as large a profit as possible? What is that profit?

19. Finance A pension fund manager decides to invest at most $50 million in U.S. Treasury Bonds paying 4% annual interest and in mutual funds paying 6% annual interest. He plans to invest at least $20 million in bonds and at least $6 million in mutual funds. Bonds have an initial fee of $300 per million dollars, while the fee for mutual funds is $100 per million. The fund manager is allowed to spend no more than $8400 on fees. How much should be invested in each to maximize annual interest? What is the maximum annual interest?

20. Natural Science A certain predator requires at least 10 units of protein and 8 units of fat per day. One prey of Species I provides 5 units of protein and 2 units of fat; one prey of Species II provides 3 units of protein and 4 units of fat. Capturing and digesting each Species II prey requires 3 units of energy, and capturing and digesting each Species I prey requires 2 units of energy. How many of each prey would meet the predator's daily food requirements with the least expenditure of energy? Are the answers reasonable? How could they be interpreted?

21. Social Science Students at Upscale U. are required to take at least 4 humanities and 4 science courses. The maximum allowable number of science courses is 12. Each humanities course carries 4 credits and each science course 5 credits. The total number of credits in science and humanities cannot exceed 92. Quality points for each course are assigned in the usual way: the number of credit hours times 4 for an A grade, times 3 for a B grade, and times 2 for a C grade. Susan Katz expects to get B's in all her science courses. She expects to get C's in half her humanities courses, B's in one-fourth of them, and A's in the rest. Under these assumptions, how many courses of each kind should she take in order to earn the maximum possible number of quality points?

22. Social Science In Exercise 21, find Susan's grade point average (the total number of quality points divided by the total number of credit hours) at each corner point of the feasible region. Does the distribution of courses that produces the highest number of quality points also yield the highest grade point average? Is this a contradiction?

23. Finance The ClearBridge Aggressive Growth Fund sells at $162 a share and has a 3-year average annual return of $30 per share. The risk measure of standard deviation is 19.4. The American Century Mid Cap Fund sells at $12 a share and has a 3-year average annual return of $2 a share. The risk measure of standard deviation is 13.7. Joe Burke wants to spend no more than $9000 investing in these two funds, but he wants to obtain at least $1600 in annual revenue. Joe also wants to minimize his risk. Determine how many shares of each stock Joe should buy. (Data from: www.morningstar.com as of May 2013.)

24. Finance The John Hancock III Disciplined Value Mid Cap A Fund sells at $15 a share and has a 3-year average annual return of $2 per share. The risk measure of standard deviation is 17.6. The HighMark Geneva Small Cap Fund sells at $36 a share and has a 3-year average annual return of $6 a share. The risk measure of standard deviation is 16.7. Sandy Grady wants to spend no more than $6000 investing in these two funds, but she wants to obtain at least $600 in annual revenue. Sandy also wants to minimize her risk. Determine how many shares of each stock Sandy should buy. (Data from: www.morningstar.com as of May 2013.)

25. **Finance** The Franklin MicroCap Value ADV Fund sells at $36 a share and has a 3-year average annual return of $3 per share. The risk measure of standard deviation is 17.1. The Delaware Select Growth Fund sells at $46 a share and has a 3-year average annual return of $8 a share. The risk measure of standard deviation is 15.5. Sally Burkhardt wants to spend no more than $8000 investing in these two funds, but she wants to obtain at least $800 in annual revenue. Sally also wants to minimize her risk. Determine how many shares of each stock Sally should buy. (Data from: www.morningstar. com as of May 2013.)

26. **Finance** The Wells Fargo Advantage Growth A Fund sells at $43 a share and has a 3-year average annual return of $7 per share. The risk measure of standard deviation is 17.4. The Nuveen Symphony Optimized Alpha Fund sells at $24 a share and has a 3-year average annual return of $3 a share. The risk measure of standard deviation is 13.0. Robert Cenni wants to spend no more than $75,000 investing in these two funds, but he wants to obtain at least $11,000 in annual revenue. Robert also wants to minimize his risk. Determine how many shares of each stock Robert should buy. (Data from: www.morningstar.com as of May 2013.)

*The importance of linear programming is shown by the inclusion of linear programming problems on most qualification examinations for Certified Public Accountants. Exercises 27–29 are reprinted from one such examination.**

The Random Company manufactures two products: Zeta and Beta. Each product must pass through two processing operations. All materials are introduced at the start of Process No. 1. There are no work-in-process inventories. Random may produce either one product exclusively or various combinations of both products, subject to the following constraints:

	Process No. 1	Process No. 2	Contribution Margin per Unit
Hours required to produce 1 unit of:			
Zeta	1 hour	1 hour	$4.00
Beta	2 hours	3 hours	$5.25
Total capacity in hours per day	1000 hours	1275 hours	

A shortage of technical labor has limited Beta production to 400 units per day. There are no constraints on the production of Zeta other than the hour constraints shown in the schedule. Assume that all the relationships between capacity and production are linear.

27. Given the objective to maximize total contribution margin, what is the production constraint for Process No. 1?

   (a) Zeta + Beta ≤ 1000

   (b) Zeta + 2 Beta ≤ 1000

   (c) Zeta + Beta ≥ 1000

   (d) Zeta + 2 Beta ≥ 1000

28. Given the objective to maximize total contribution margin, what is the labor constraint for production of Beta?

   (a) Beta ≤ 400

   (b) Beta ≥ 400

   (c) Beta ≤ 425

   (d) Beta ≥ 425

29. What is the objective function of the data presented?

   (a) Zeta + 2 Beta = $9.25

   (b) $4.00 Zeta + 3($5.25) Beta = total contribution margin

   (c) $4.00 Zeta + $5.25 Beta = total contribution margin

   (d) 2($4.00) Zeta + 3($5.25) Beta = total contribution margin

✓Checkpoint Answers

1. $\left(\frac{8}{3}, \frac{4}{3}\right)$

2. (a)

	Number of Tons	Cost/ Ton
Oats	x	$300
Corn	y	$200
	27	

   (b) $z = 300x + 200y$

   (c) $x + y \geq 27$

   $y \leq 2x$

   $x \geq 0$

   $y \geq 0$

3. (a)

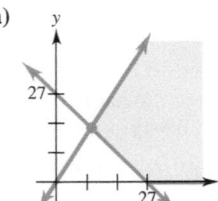

   Corner points: (27, 0), (9, 18)

   (b) $6300 at (9, 18)

   (c) No

7.4 The Simplex Method: Maximization

For linear programming problems with more than two variables or with two variables and many constraints, the graphical method is usually inefficient or impossible, so the **simplex method** is used. This method, which is introduced in this section, was developed for the U.S. Air Force by George B. Danzig in 1947. It is now used in industrial planning, factory design, product distribution networks, sports scheduling, truck routing, resource allocation, and a variety of other ways.

Because the simplex method is used for problems with many variables, it usually is not convenient to use letters such as x, y, z, or w as variable names. Instead, the symbols x_1 (read "x-sub-one"), x_2, x_3, and so on, are used. In the simplex method, all constraints must be expressed in the linear form

$$a_1x_1 + a_2x_2 + a_3x_3 + \cdots \leq b,$$

where $x_1, x_2, x_3, \ldots$ are variables, $a_1, a_2, a_3, \ldots$ are coefficients, and b is a constant.

We first discuss the simplex method for linear programming problems such as the following:

$$\begin{aligned}
\text{Maximize} \quad & z = 2x_1 + 3x_2 + x_3 \\
\text{subject to} \quad & x_1 + x_2 + 4x_3 \leq 100 \\
& x_1 + 2x_2 + x_3 \leq 150 \\
& 3x_1 + 2x_2 + x_3 \leq 320, \\
\text{with} \quad & x_1 \geq 0, x_2 \geq 0, x_3 \geq 0.
\end{aligned}$$

This example illustrates *standard maximum form*, which is defined as follows.

Standard Maximum Form

A linear programming problem is in **standard maximum form** if
1. the objective function is to be maximized;
2. all variables are nonnegative ($x_i \geq 0, i = 1, 2, 3, \ldots$);
3. all constraints involve $\leq$;
4. the constants on the right side in the constraints are all nonnegative ($b \geq 0$).

Problems that do not meet all of these conditions are considered in Sections 7.6 and 7.7.

The "mechanics" of the simplex method are demonstrated in Examples 1–5. Although the procedures to be followed will be made clear, as will the fact that they result in an optimal solution, the reasons these procedures are used may not be immediately apparent. Examples 6 and 7 will supply these reasons and explain the connection between the simplex method and the graphical method used in Section 7.3.

Setting up the Problem

The first step is to convert each constraint, a linear inequality, into a linear equation. This is done by adding a nonnegative variable, called a **slack variable,** to each constraint. For example, convert the inequality $x_1 + x_2 \leq 10$ into an equation by adding the slack variable s_1, to get

$$x_1 + x_2 + s_1 = 10, \qquad \text{where } s_1 \geq 0.$$

The inequality $x_1 + x_2 \leq 10$ says that the sum $x_1 + x_2$ is less than or equal to 10. The variable s_1 "takes up any slack" and represents the amount by which $x_1 + x_2$ fails to equal 10. For example, if $x_1 + x_2$ equals 8, then s_1 is 2. If $x_1 + x_2 = 10$, the value of s_1 is 0.

⊘ **CAUTION** A different slack variable must be used for each constraint.

Example 1 Restate the following linear programming problem by introducing slack variables:

$$\text{Maximize} \quad z = 2x_1 + 3x_2 + x_3$$
$$\text{subject to} \quad x_1 + x_2 + 4x_3 \leq 100$$
$$x_1 + 2x_2 + x_3 \leq 150$$
$$3x_1 + 2x_2 + x_3 \leq 320,$$
$$\text{with} \quad x_1 \geq 0, x_2 \geq 0, x_3 \geq 0.$$

Solution Rewrite the three constraints as equations by introducing nonnegative slack variables s_1, s_2, and s_3, one for each constraint. Then the problem can be restated as

$$\text{Maximize} \quad z = 2x_1 + 3x_2 + x_3$$
$$\text{subject to} \quad x_1 + x_2 + 4x_3 + s_1 \qquad\qquad = 100 \qquad \text{Constraint 1}$$
$$x_1 + 2x_2 + x_3 \qquad + s_2 \qquad = 150 \qquad \text{Constraint 2}$$
$$3x_1 + 2x_2 + x_3 \qquad\qquad + s_3 = 320, \qquad \text{Constraint 3}$$
$$\text{with} \quad x_1 \geq 0, x_2 \geq 0, x_3 \geq 0, s_1 \geq 0, s_2 \geq 0, s_3 \geq 0. \quad ☑_1$$

✓ **Checkpoint 1**

Rewrite the following set of constraints as equations by adding nonnegative slack variables:

$$x_1 + x_2 + x_3 \leq 12$$
$$2x_1 + 4x_2 \qquad \leq 15$$
$$x_2 + 3x_3 \leq 10.$$

Adding slack variables to the constraints converts a linear programming problem into a system of linear equations. These equations should have all variables on the left of the equals sign and all constants on the right. All the equations of Example 1 satisfy this condition except for the objective function, $z = 2x_1 + 3x_2 + x_3$, which may be written with all variables on the left as

$$-2x_1 - 3x_2 - x_3 + z = 0. \qquad \text{Objective Function}$$

Now the equations of Example 1 (with the constraints listed first and the objective function last) can be written as the following augmented matrix.

$$
\begin{array}{ccccccc}
x_1 & x_2 & x_3 & s_1 & s_2 & s_3 & z \\
\end{array}
$$

$$
\left[
\begin{array}{ccccccc|c}
1 & 1 & 4 & 1 & 0 & 0 & 0 & 100 \\
1 & 2 & 1 & 0 & 1 & 0 & 0 & 150 \\
3 & 2 & 1 & 0 & 0 & 1 & 0 & 320 \\
\hline
-2 & -3 & -1 & 0 & 0 & 0 & 1 & 0
\end{array}
\right]
\begin{array}{l}
\text{Constraint 1} \\
\text{Constraint 2} \\
\text{Constraint 3} \\
\text{Objective Function}
\end{array}
$$

Indicators

✓ **Checkpoint 2**

Set up the initial simplex tableau for the following linear programming problem:

$$\text{Maximize} \quad z = 2x_1 + 3x_2$$
$$\text{subject to} \quad x_1 + 2x_2 \leq 85$$
$$2x_1 + x_2 \leq 92$$
$$x_1 + 4x_2 \leq 104,$$
$$\text{with} \quad x_1 \geq 0 \text{ and } x_2 \geq 0.$$

Locate and label the indicators.

This matrix is the initial **simplex tableau.** Except for the last entries—the 1 and 0 on the right end—the numbers in the bottom row of a simplex tableau are called **indicators.** ☑_2

This simplex tableau represents a system of four linear equations in seven variables. Since there are more variables than equations, the system is dependent and has infinitely many solutions. Our goal is to find a solution in which all the variables are nonnegative and z is as large as possible. This will be done by using row operations to replace the given system by an equivalent one in which certain variables are eliminated from some of the equations. The process will be repeated until the optimum solution can be read from the matrix, as explained next.

Selecting the Pivot

Recall how row operations are used to eliminate variables in the Gauss–Jordan method: A particular nonzero entry in the matrix is chosen and changed to a 1; then all other entries in that column are changed to zeros. A similar process is used in the simplex method. The chosen entry is called the **pivot.** If we were interested only in solving the system, we could choose the various pivots in many different ways, as in Chapter 6. Here, however, it is not enough just to find a solution. We must find one that is nonnegative, satisfies all the constraints, *and* makes z as a large as possible. Consequently, the pivot must be chosen carefully, as explained in the next example. The reasons this procedure is used and why it works are discussed in Example 7.

Example 2   Determine the pivot in the simplex tableau for the problem in Example 1.

Solution   Look at the indicators (the last row of the tableau) and choose the most negative one:

$$
\begin{array}{ccccccc}
x_1 & x_2 & x_3 & s_1 & s_2 & s_3 & z \\
\end{array}
$$

$$
\left[
\begin{array}{ccccccc|c}
1 & 1 & 4 & 1 & 0 & 0 & 0 & 100 \\
1 & 2 & 1 & 0 & 1 & 0 & 0 & 150 \\
3 & 2 & 1 & 0 & 0 & 1 & 0 & 320 \\
\hline
-2 & \mathbf{-3} & -1 & 0 & 0 & 0 & 1 & 0 \\
\end{array}
\right]
$$

Most negative indicator

The most negative indicator identifies the variable that is to be eliminated from all but one of the equations (rows)—in this case, x_2. The column containing the most negative indicator is called the **pivot column.** Now, for each *positive* entry in the pivot column, divide the number in the far right column of the same row by the positive number in the pivot column:

$$
\begin{array}{ccccccc}
x_1 & x_2 & x_3 & s_1 & s_2 & s_3 & z \\
\end{array}
$$

$$
\left[
\begin{array}{ccccccc|c}
1 & \mathbf{1} & 4 & 1 & 0 & 0 & 0 & \mathbf{100} \\
1 & \mathbf{2} & 1 & 0 & 1 & 0 & 0 & \mathbf{150} \\
3 & \mathbf{2} & 1 & 0 & 0 & 1 & 0 & \mathbf{320} \\
\hline
-2 & -3 & -1 & 0 & 0 & 0 & 1 & 0 \\
\end{array}
\right]
$$

Quotients
$100/1 = 100$
$150/2 = 75 \leftarrow$ Smallest
$320/2 = 160$

The row with the smallest quotient (in this case, the second row) is called the **pivot row.** The entry in the pivot row and pivot column is the pivot:

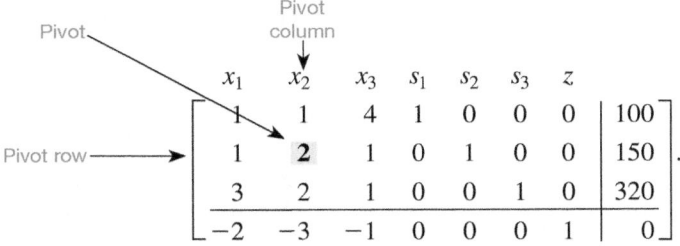

Pivot   Pivot column

Pivot row

$$
\begin{array}{ccccccc}
x_1 & x_2 & x_3 & s_1 & s_2 & s_3 & z \\
\end{array}
$$

$$
\left[
\begin{array}{ccccccc|c}
1 & 1 & 4 & 1 & 0 & 0 & 0 & 100 \\
1 & \mathbf{2} & 1 & 0 & 1 & 0 & 0 & 150 \\
3 & 2 & 1 & 0 & 0 & 1 & 0 & 320 \\
\hline
-2 & -3 & -1 & 0 & 0 & 0 & 1 & 0 \\
\end{array}
\right]
$$

⚠ **CAUTION** In some simplex tableaus, the pivot column may contain zeros or negative entries. Only the positive entries in the pivot column should be used to form the quotients and determine the pivot row. If there are no positive entries in the pivot column (so that a pivot row cannot be chosen), then no maximum solution exists. ✓3

✓**Checkpoint 3**

Find the pivot for the following tableau:

$$
\begin{array}{cccccc}
x_1 & x_2 & s_1 & s_2 & s_3 & z \\
\end{array}
$$

$$
\left[
\begin{array}{cccccc|c}
0 & 1 & 1 & 0 & 0 & 0 & 50 \\
-2 & 3 & 0 & 1 & 0 & 0 & 78 \\
2 & 4 & 0 & 0 & 1 & 0 & 65 \\
\hline
-5 & -3 & 0 & 0 & 0 & 1 & 0 \\
\end{array}
\right]
$$

Pivoting

Once the pivot has been selected, row operations are used to replace the initial simplex tableau by another simplex tableau in which the pivot column variable is eliminated from all but one of the equations. Since this new tableau is obtained by row operations, it represents an equivalent system of equations (that is, a system with the same solutions as the original system). This process, which is called **pivoting,** is explained in the next example.

Example 3   Use the indicated pivot, 2, to perform the pivoting on the simplex tableau of Example 2:

$$
\begin{array}{ccccccc}
x_1 & x_2 & x_3 & s_1 & s_2 & s_3 & z \\
\end{array}
$$

$$
\left[
\begin{array}{ccccccc|c}
1 & 1 & 4 & 1 & 0 & 0 & 0 & 100 \\
1 & \mathbf{2} & 1 & 0 & 1 & 0 & 0 & 150 \\
3 & 2 & 1 & 0 & 0 & 1 & 0 & 320 \\
\hline
-2 & -3 & -1 & 0 & 0 & 0 & 1 & 0 \\
\end{array}
\right].
$$

Solution   Start by multiplying each entry of row 2 by $\frac{1}{2}$ in order to change the pivot to 1:

$$
\begin{array}{ccccccc}
x_1 & x_2 & x_3 & s_1 & s_2 & s_3 & z \\
\end{array}
$$

$$
\left[
\begin{array}{ccccccc|c}
1 & 1 & 4 & 1 & 0 & 0 & 0 & 100 \\
\frac{1}{2} & \mathbf{1} & \frac{1}{2} & 0 & \frac{1}{2} & 0 & 0 & 75 \\
3 & 2 & 1 & 0 & 0 & 1 & 0 & 320 \\
\hline
-2 & -3 & -1 & 0 & 0 & 0 & 1 & 0 \\
\end{array}
\right]. \qquad \frac{1}{2}R_2
$$

Now use row operations to make the entry in row 1, column 2, a 0:

$$
\begin{array}{ccccccc}
x_1 & x_2 & x_3 & s_1 & s_2 & s_3 & z \\
\end{array}
$$

$$
\left[
\begin{array}{ccccccc|c}
\frac{1}{2} & 0 & \frac{7}{2} & 1 & -\frac{1}{2} & 0 & 0 & 25 \\
\frac{1}{2} & 1 & \frac{1}{2} & 0 & \frac{1}{2} & 0 & 0 & 75 \\
3 & 2 & 1 & 0 & 0 & 1 & 0 & 320 \\
\hline
-2 & -3 & -1 & 0 & 0 & 0 & 1 & 0 \\
\end{array}
\right]. \qquad -R_2 + R_1
$$

Change the 2 in row 3, column 2, to a 0 by a similar process:

$$
\begin{array}{ccccccc}
x_1 & x_2 & x_3 & s_1 & s_2 & s_3 & z \\
\end{array}
$$

$$
\left[
\begin{array}{ccccccc|c}
\frac{1}{2} & 0 & \frac{7}{2} & 1 & -\frac{1}{2} & 0 & 0 & 25 \\
\frac{1}{2} & 1 & \frac{1}{2} & 0 & \frac{1}{2} & 0 & 0 & 75 \\
2 & 0 & 0 & 0 & -1 & 1 & 0 & 170 \\
\hline
-2 & -3 & -1 & 0 & 0 & 0 & 1 & 0 \\
\end{array}
\right]. \qquad -2R_2 + R_3
$$

Finally, add 3 times row 2 to the last row in order to change the indicator -3 to 0:

$$
\begin{array}{ccccccc}
x_1 & x_2 & x_3 & s_1 & s_2 & s_3 & z \\
\end{array}
$$

$$
\left[
\begin{array}{ccccccc|c}
\frac{1}{2} & 0 & \frac{7}{2} & 1 & -\frac{1}{2} & 0 & 0 & 25 \\
\frac{1}{2} & 1 & \frac{1}{2} & 0 & \frac{1}{2} & 0 & 0 & 75 \\
2 & 0 & 0 & 0 & -1 & 1 & 0 & 170 \\
\hline
-\frac{1}{2} & 0 & \frac{1}{2} & 0 & \frac{3}{2} & 0 & 1 & 225 \\
\end{array}
\right]. \qquad 3R_2 + R_4
$$

The pivoting is now complete, because the pivot column variable x_2 has been eliminated from all equations except the one represented by the pivot row. The initial simplex tableau has been replaced by a new simplex tableau, which represents an equivalent system of equations.

✓ **Checkpoint 4**

For the given simplex tableau,

(a) find the pivot;

(b) perform the pivoting and write the new tableau.

$$
\begin{array}{cccccc}
x_1 & x_2 & x_3 & s_1 & s_2 & z \\
\end{array}
$$

$$
\left[
\begin{array}{cccccc|c}
1 & 2 & 6 & 1 & 0 & 0 & 16 \\
1 & 3 & 0 & 0 & 1 & 0 & 25 \\
\hline
-1 & -4 & -3 & 0 & 0 & 1 & 0 \\
\end{array}
\right]
$$

⊘ CAUTION During pivoting, do not interchange rows of the matrix. Make the pivot entry 1 by multiplying the pivot row by an appropriate constant, as in Example 3. ✓₄

When at least one of the indicators in the last row of a simplex tableau is negative (as is the case with the tableau obtained in Example 3), the simplex method requires that a new pivot be selected and the pivoting be performed again. This procedure is repeated until a simplex tableau with no negative indicators in the last row is obtained or a tableau is reached in which no pivot row can be chosen.

Example 4   In the simplex tableau obtained in Example 3, select a new pivot and perform the pivoting.

Solution   First, locate the pivot column by finding the most negative indicator in the last row. Then locate the pivot row by computing the necessary quotients and finding the smallest one, as shown here:

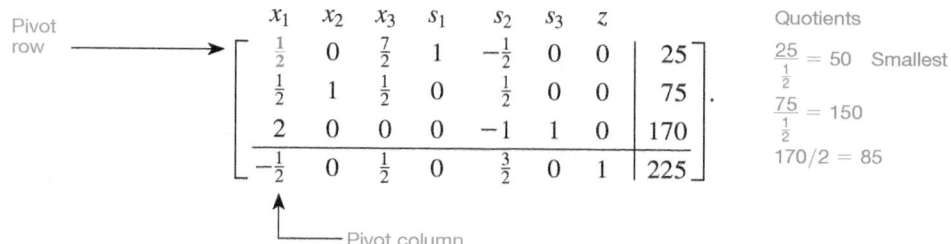

So the pivot is the number $\frac{1}{2}$ in row 1, column 1. Begin the pivoting by multiplying every entry in row 1 by 2. Then continue as indicated to obtain the following simplex tableau:

$$
\begin{array}{ccccccc|c}
x_1 & x_2 & x_3 & s_1 & s_2 & s_3 & z & \\
1 & 0 & 7 & 2 & -1 & 0 & 0 & 50 \\
0 & 1 & -3 & -1 & 1 & 0 & 0 & 50 \\
0 & 0 & -14 & -4 & 1 & 1 & 0 & 70 \\
\hline
0 & 0 & 4 & 1 & 1 & 0 & 1 & 250
\end{array}
\qquad
\begin{array}{l}
2R_1 \\
-\frac{1}{2}R_1 + R_2 \\
-2R_1 + R_3 \\
\frac{1}{2}R_1 + R_4
\end{array}
$$

Since there are no negative indicators in the last row, no further pivoting is necessary, and we call this the **final simplex tableau.**

Reading the Solution

The next example shows how to read an optimal solution of the original linear programming problem from the final simplex tableau.

Example 5   Solve the linear programming problem introduced in Example 1.

Solution   Look at the final simplex tableau for this problem, which was obtained in Example 4:

$$
\begin{array}{ccccccc|c}
x_1 & x_2 & x_3 & s_1 & s_2 & s_3 & z & \\
1 & 0 & 7 & 2 & -1 & 0 & 0 & 50 \\
0 & 1 & -3 & -1 & 1 & 0 & 0 & 50 \\
0 & 0 & -14 & -4 & 1 & 1 & 0 & 70 \\
\hline
0 & 0 & 4 & 1 & 1 & 0 & 1 & 250
\end{array}
$$

The last row of this matrix represents the equation

$$4x_3 + s_1 + s_2 + z = 250, \qquad \text{or equivalently,} \qquad z = 250 - 4x_3 - s_1 - s_2.$$

If x_3, s_1, and s_2 are all 0, then the value of z is 250. If any one of x_3, s_1, or s_2 is positive, then z will have a smaller value than 250. (Why?) Consequently, since we want a solution for this system in which all the variables are nonnegative and z is as large as possible, we must have

$$x_3 = 0, \qquad s_1 = 0, \qquad s_2 = 0.$$

When these values are substituted into the first equation (represented by the first row of the final simplex tableau), the result is

$$x_1 + 7 \cdot 0 + 2 \cdot 0 - 1 \cdot 0 = 50; \quad \text{that is,} \quad x_1 = 50.$$

Similarly, substituting 0 for x_3, s_1, and s_2 in the last three equations represented by the final simplex tableau shows that

$$x_2 = 50, \quad s_3 = 70, \quad \text{and} \quad z = 250.$$

Therefore, the maximum value of $z = 2x_1 + 3x_2 + x_3$ occurs when

$$x_1 = 50, \quad x_2 = 50, \quad \text{and} \quad x_3 = 0,$$

in which case $z = 2 \cdot 50 + 3 \cdot 50 + 0 = 250$. (The values of the slack variables are irrelevant in stating the solution of the original problem.)

In any simplex tableau, some columns look like columns of an identity matrix (one entry is 1 and the rest are 0). The variables corresponding to these columns are called **basic variables** and the variables corresponding to the other columns are referred to as **nonbasic variables.** In the tableau of Example 5, for instance, the basic variables are x_1, x_2, s_3, and z (shown in blue), and the nonbasic variables are x_3, s_1, and s_2:

$$\begin{array}{ccccccc} x_1 & x_2 & x_3 & s_1 & s_2 & s_3 & z \\ \left[\begin{array}{ccccccc|c} 1 & 0 & 7 & 2 & -1 & 0 & 0 & 50 \\ 0 & 1 & -3 & -1 & 1 & 0 & 0 & 50 \\ 0 & 0 & -14 & -4 & 1 & 1 & 0 & 70 \\ 0 & 0 & 4 & 1 & 1 & 0 & 1 & 250 \end{array} \right] \end{array}.$$

The optimal solution in Example 5 was obtained from the final simplex tableau by setting the nonbasic variables equal to 0 and solving for the basic variables. Furthermore, the values of the basic variables are easy to read from the matrix: Find the 1 in the column representing a basic variable; the last entry in that row is the value of that basic variable in the optimal solution. In particular, *the entry in the lower right-hand corner of the final simplex tableau is the maximum value of z.* ✓5

✓ Checkpoint 5

A linear programming problem with slack variables s_1 and s_2 has the following final simplex tableau:

$$\begin{array}{cccccc} x_1 & x_2 & x_3 & s_1 & s_2 & z \\ \left[\begin{array}{cccccc|c} 0 & 3 & 1 & 5 & 2 & 0 & 9 \\ 1 & -2 & 0 & 4 & 1 & 0 & 6 \\ 0 & 5 & 0 & 1 & 0 & 1 & 21 \end{array} \right] \end{array}.$$

What is the optimal solution?

⓵ **CAUTION** If there are two identical columns in a tableau, each of which is a column in an identity matrix, only one of the variables corresponding to these columns can be a basic variable. The other is treated as a nonbasic variable. You may choose either one to be the basic variable, unless one of them is z, in which case z must be the basic variable.

The steps involved in solving a standard maximum linear programming problem by the simplex method have been illustrated in Examples 1–5 and are summarized here.

Simplex Method

1. Determine the objective function.
2. Write down all necessary constraints.
3. Convert each constraint into an equation by adding a slack variable.
4. Set up the initial simplex tableau.

5. Locate the most negative indicator. If there are two such indicators, choose one. This indicator determines the pivot column.

6. Use the positive entries in the pivot column to form the quotients necessary for determining the pivot. If there are no positive entries in the pivot column, no maximum solution exists. If two quotients are equally the smallest, let either determine the pivot.[*]

7. Multiply every entry in the pivot row by the reciprocal of the pivot to change the pivot to 1. Then use row operations to change all other entries in the pivot column to 0 by adding suitable multiples of the pivot row to the other rows.

8. If the indicators are all positive or 0, you have found the final tableau. If not, go back to Step 5 and repeat the process until a tableau with no negative indicators is obtained.[†]

9. In the final tableau, the *basic* variables correspond to the columns that have one entry of 1 and the rest 0. The *nonbasic* variables correspond to the other columns. Set each nonbasic variable equal to 0 and solve the system for the basic variables. The maximum value of the objective function is the number in the lower right-hand corner of the final tableau.

The solution found by the simplex method may not be unique, especially when choices are possible in steps 5, 6, or 9. There may be other solutions that produce the same maximum value of the objective function. (See Exercises 37 and 38 at the end of this section.) ✔6

✔ Checkpoint 6

A linear programming problem has the following initial tableau:

$$\begin{bmatrix} 1 & 1 & 1 & 0 & 0 & | & 40 \\ 2 & 1 & 0 & 1 & 0 & | & 24 \\ \hline -300 & -200 & 0 & 0 & 1 & | & 0 \end{bmatrix}.$$

Use the simplex method to solve the problem.

📌 The Simplex Method with Technology

Unless indicated otherwise, the simplex method is carried out by hand in the examples and exercises of this chapter, so you can see how and why it works. Once you are familiar with the method, however,

we strongly recommend that you use technology to apply the simplex method.

Doing so will eliminate errors that occur in manual computations. It will also give you a better idea of how the simplex method is used in the real world, where applications involve so many variables and constraints that the manual approach is impractical. Readily available technology includes the following:

Graphing Calculators As noted in the Graphing Calculator Appendix of this book, a simplex program exists. It pauses after each round of pivoting, so you can examine the intermediate simplex tableau.

Spreadsheets Most spreadsheets have a built-in simplex method program. Figure 7.26, on the next page, shows the Solver of Microsoft Excel (Microsoft Corporation Excel © 2013). Spreadsheets also provide a sensitivity analysis, which allows you to see how much the constraints can be varied without changing the maximal solution.

Other Computer Programs A variety of simplex method programs, many of which are free, can be downloaded on the Internet. Google "simplex method program" for some possibilities.

---

[*]It may be that the first choice of a pivot does not produce a solution. In that case, try the other choice.
[†]Some special circumstances are noted at the end of Section 7.7.

Figure 7.26

Geometric Interpretation of the Simplex Method

Although it may not be immediately apparent, the simplex method is based on the same geometrical considerations as the graphical method. This can be seen by looking at a problem that can be readily solved by both methods.

Example 6 In Example 1 of Section 7.3, the following problem was solved graphically (using x and y instead of x_1 and x_2, respectively):

$$\text{Maximize} \quad z = 8x_1 + 12x_2$$
$$\text{subject to} \quad 40x_1 + 80x_2 \leq 560$$
$$6x_1 + 8x_2 \leq 72$$
$$x_1 \geq 0, x_2 \geq 0.$$

Graphing the feasible region (Figure 7.27) and evaluating z at each corner point shows that the maximum value of z occurs at $(8, 3)$.

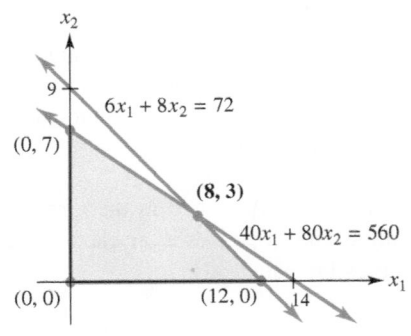

Corner Point	Value of $z = 8x_1 + 12x_2$	
$(0,0)$	0	
$(0,7)$	84	
$(8,3)$	100	(maximum)
$(12,0)$	96	

Figure 7.27

To solve the same problem by the simplex method, add a slack variable to each constraint:

$$40x_1 + 80x_2 + s_1 \qquad = 560$$
$$6x_1 + 8x_2 \qquad + s_2 = 72.$$

Then write the initial simplex tableau:

$$\begin{array}{ccccc} x_1 & x_2 & s_1 & s_2 & z \end{array}$$
$$\begin{bmatrix} 40 & 80 & 1 & 0 & 0 & | & 560 \\ 6 & 8 & 0 & 1 & 0 & | & 72 \\ \hline -8 & -12 & 0 & 0 & 1 & | & 0 \end{bmatrix}.$$

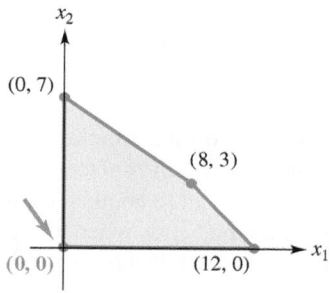

Figure 7.28

In this tableau, the basic variables are s_1, s_2, and z. (Why?) By setting the nonbasic variables (namely, x_1 and x_2) equal to 0 and solving for the basic variables, we obtain the following solution (which will be called a **basic feasible solution**):

$$x_1 = 0, \quad x_2 = 0, \quad s_1 = 560, \quad s_2 = 72, \quad \text{and} \quad z = 0.$$

Since $x_1 = 0$ and $x_2 = 0$, this solution corresponds to the corner point at the origin in the graphical solution (Figure 7.28).

The basic feasible solution $(0, 0)$ given by the initial simplex tableau has $z = 0$, which is obviously not maximal. Each round of pivoting in the simplex method will produce another corner point, with a larger value of z, until we reach a corner point that provides the maximum solution.

The most negative indicator in the initial tableau is -12, and it determines the pivot column. Then we form the necessary quotients and determine the pivot row:

Thus, the pivot is 80 in row 1, column 2. Performing the pivoting leads to this tableau:

$$\begin{bmatrix} x_1 & x_2 & s_1 & s_2 & z & \\ \frac{1}{2} & 1 & \frac{1}{80} & 0 & 0 & 7 \\ 2 & 0 & -\frac{1}{10} & 1 & 0 & 16 \\ -2 & 0 & \frac{3}{20} & 0 & 1 & 84 \end{bmatrix} \quad \begin{matrix} \frac{1}{80} R_1 \\ -8R_1 + R_2 \\ 12R_1 + R_3 \end{matrix}$$

The basic variables here are x_2, s_2, and z, and the basic feasible solution (found by setting the nonbasic variables equal to 0 and solving for the basic variables) is

$$x_1 = 0, \quad x_2 = 7, \quad s_1 = 0, \quad s_2 = 16, \quad \text{and} \quad z = 84,$$

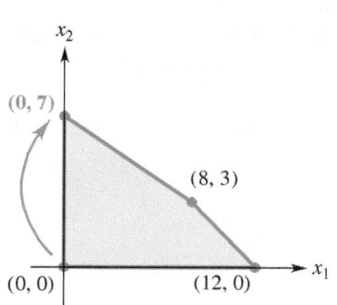

Figure 7.29

which corresponds to the corner point $(0, 7)$ in Figure 7.29. Note that the new value of the pivot variable x_2 is precisely the smallest quotient, 7, that was used to select the pivot row. Although this value of z is better, further improvement is possible.

Now the most negative indicator is -2. We form the necessary quotients and determine the pivot as usual:

The pivot is 2 in row 2, column 1. Pivoting now produces the final tableau:

$$\begin{bmatrix} x_1 & x_2 & s_1 & s_2 & z & \\ 0 & 1 & \frac{3}{80} & -\frac{1}{4} & 0 & 3 \\ 1 & 0 & -\frac{1}{20} & \frac{1}{2} & 0 & 8 \\ 0 & 0 & \frac{1}{20} & 1 & 1 & 100 \end{bmatrix} \quad \begin{matrix} -\frac{1}{2}R_2 + R_1 \\ \frac{1}{2}R_2 \\ 2R_2 + R_3 \end{matrix}$$

Here, the basic feasible solution is

$$x_1 = 8, \quad x_2 = 3, \quad s_1 = 0, \quad s_2 = 0, \quad \text{and} \quad z = 100,$$

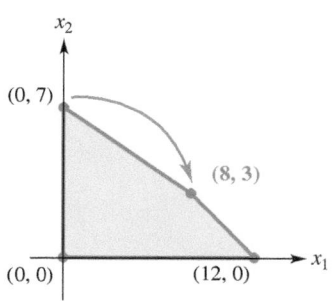

Figure 7.30

which corresponds to the corner point $(8, 3)$ in Figure 7.30. Once again, the new value of the pivot variable x_1 is the smallest quotient, 8, that was used to select the pivot. Because all the indicators in the last row of the final tableau are nonnegative, $(8, 3)$ is the maximum solution according to the simplex method. We know that this is the case, since this is the maximum solution found by the graphical method. An algebraic argument similar to the one in Example 5 could also be made.

As illustrated in Example 6, the basic feasible solution obtained from a simplex tableau corresponds to a corner point of the feasible region. Pivoting, which replaces one tableau with another, is a systematic way of moving from one corner point to another, each time improving the value of the objective function. The simplex method ends when a corner point that produces the maximum value of the objective function is reached (or when it becomes clear that the problem has no maximum solution).

When there are three or more variables in a linear programming problem, it may be difficult or impossible to draw a picture, but it can be proved that the optimal value of the objective function occurs at a basic feasible solution (corresponding to a corner point in the two-variable case). The simplex method provides a means of moving from one basic feasible solution to another until one that produces the optimal value of the objective function is reached.

Explanation of Pivoting

The rules for selecting the pivot in the simplex method can be understood by examining how the first pivot was chosen in Example 6.

Example 7 The initial simplex tableau of Example 6 provides a basic feasible solution with $x_1 = 0$ and $x_2 = 0$:

$$\begin{array}{ccccc} x_1 & x_2 & s_1 & s_2 & z \\ \left[\begin{array}{ccccc|c} 40 & 80 & 1 & 0 & 0 & 560 \\ 6 & 8 & 0 & 1 & 0 & 72 \\ \hline -8 & -12 & 0 & 0 & 1 & 0 \end{array}\right]. \end{array}$$

This solution certainly does not give a maximum value for the objective function $z = 8x_1 + 12x_2$. Since x_2 has the largest coefficient, z will be increased most if x_2 is increased. In other words, the most negative indicator in the tableau (which corresponds to the largest coefficient in the objective function) identifies the variable that will provide the greatest change in the value of z.

To determine how much x_2 can be increased without leaving the feasible region, look at the first two equations,

$$40x_1 + 80x_2 + s_1 \qquad = 560$$
$$6x_1 + \ 8x_2 \qquad + s_2 = 72,$$

and solve for the basic variables s_1 and s_2:

$$s_1 = 560 - 40x_1 - 80x_2$$
$$s_2 = 72 - 6x_1 - 8x_2.$$

Now x_2 is to be increased while x_1 is to keep the value 0. Hence,

$$s_1 = 560 - 80x_2$$
$$s_2 = 72 - 8x_2.$$

Since $s_1 \geq 0$ and $s_2 \geq 0$, we must have

$$0 \leq s_1 \qquad\qquad 0 \leq s_2$$
$$0 \leq 560 - 80x_2 \quad \text{and} \quad 0 \leq 72 - 8x_2$$
$$80x_2 \leq 560 \qquad\qquad 8x_2 \leq 72$$
$$x_2 \leq \frac{560}{80} = 7 \qquad\qquad x_2 \leq \frac{72}{8} = 9.$$

The right sides of these last inequalities are the quotients used to select the pivot row. Since x_2 must satisfy both inequalities, x_2 can be at most 7. In other words, the smallest quotient formed from positive entries in the pivot column identifies the value of x_2 that produces the largest change in z while remaining in the feasible region. By pivoting with the pivot determined in this way, we obtain the second tableau and a basic feasible solution in which $x_2 = 7$, as was shown in Example 6.

An analysis similar to that in Example 7 applies to each occurrence of pivoting in the simplex method. The idea is to improve the value of the objective function by adjusting one variable at a time. The most negative indicator identifies the variable that will account for the largest increase in z. The smallest quotient determines the largest value of that variable which will produce a feasible solution. Pivoting leads to a solution in which the selected variable has this largest value.

7.4 Exercises

In Exercises 1–4, (a) determine the number of slack variables needed; (b) name them; (c) use the slack variables to convert each constraint into a linear equation. (See Example 1.)

1. Maximize $z = 32x_1 + 9x_2$
   subject to $4x_1 + 2x_2 \le 20$
   $5x_1 + x_2 \le 50$
   $2x_1 + 3x_2 \le 25$
   $x_1 \ge 0, x_2 \ge 0.$

2. Maximize $z = 3.7x_1 + 4.3x_2$
   subject to $2.4x_1 + 1.5x_2 \le 10$
   $1.7x_1 + 1.9x_2 \le 15$
   $x_1 \ge 0, x_2 \ge 0.$

3. Maximize $z = 8x_1 + 3x_2 + x_3$
   subject to $3x_1 - x_2 + 4x_3 \le 95$
   $7x_1 + 6x_2 + 8x_3 \le 118$
   $4x_1 + 5x_2 + 10x_3 \le 220$
   $x_1 \ge 0, x_2 \ge 0, x_3 \ge 0.$

4. Maximize $z = 12x_1 + 15x_2 + 10x_3$
   subject to $2x_1 + 2x_2 + x_3 \le 8$
   $x_1 + 4x_2 + 3x_3 \le 12$
   $x_1 \ge 0, x_2 \ge 0, x_3 \ge 0.$

Introduce slack variables as necessary and then write the initial simplex tableau for each of these linear programming problems.

5. Maximize $z = 5x_1 + x_2$
   subject to $2x_1 + 5x_2 \le 6$
   $4x_1 + x_2 \le 6$
   $5x_1 + 3x_2 \le 15$
   $x_1 \ge 0, x_2 \ge 0.$

6. Maximize $z = 5x_1 + 3x_2 + 7x_3$
   subject to $4x_1 + 3x_2 + 2x_3 \le 60$
   $3x_1 + 4x_2 + x_3 \le 24$
   $x_1 \ge 0, x_2 \ge 0, x_3 \ge 0.$

7. Maximize $z = x_1 + 5x_2 + 10x_3$
   subject to $x_1 + 2x_2 + 3x_3 \le 10$
   $2x_1 + x_2 + x_3 \le 8$
   $3x_1 + 4x_3 \le 6$
   $x_1 \ge 0, x_2 \ge 0, x_3 \ge 0.$

8. Maximize $z = 5x_1 - x_2 + 3x_3$
   subject to $3x_1 + 2x_2 + x_3 \le 36$
   $x_1 + 6x_2 + x_3 \le 24$
   $x_1 - x_2 - x_3 \le 32$
   $x_1 \ge 0, x_2 \ge 0, x_3 \ge 0.$

Find the pivot in each of the given simplex tableaus. (See Example 2.)

9.

x_1	x_2	x_3	s_1	s_2	z	
2	2	0	3	1	0	15
3	4	1	6	0	0	20
−2	−3	0	1	0	1	10

10.

x_1	x_2	x_3	s_1	s_2	z	
0	2	1	1	3	0	5
1	−5	0	1	2	0	8
0	−2	0	−3	1	1	10

11.

x_1	x_2	x_3	s_1	s_2	s_3	z	
6	2	1	3	0	0	0	8
0	2	0	1	0	1	0	7
6	1	0	3	1	0	0	6
−3	−2	0	2	0	0	1	12

12.

x_1	x_2	x_3	s_1	s_2	s_3	z	
0	2	0	1	2	2	0	3
0	3	1	0	1	2	0	4
1	4	0	0	3	5	0	5
0	−4	0	0	4	3	1	20

In Exercises 13–16, use the indicated entry as the pivot and perform the pivoting. (See Examples 3 and 4.)

13.

$$
\begin{array}{cccccc}
x_1 & x_2 & x_3 & s_1 & s_2 & z \\
\end{array}
$$

$$
\left[\begin{array}{cccccc|c}
1 & 2 & 4 & 1 & 0 & 0 & 56 \\
2 & 2 & 1 & 0 & 1 & 0 & 40 \\
\hline
-1 & -3 & -2 & 0 & 0 & 1 & 0
\end{array}\right]
$$

14.

$$
\begin{array}{ccccccc}
x_1 & x_2 & x_3 & s_1 & s_2 & s_3 & z \\
\end{array}
$$

$$
\left[\begin{array}{ccccccc|c}
2 & 2 & 1 & 1 & 0 & 0 & 0 & 12 \\
1 & 2 & 3 & 0 & 1 & 0 & 0 & 45 \\
3 & 1 & 1 & 0 & 0 & 1 & 0 & 20 \\
\hline
-2 & -1 & -3 & 0 & 0 & 0 & 1 & 0
\end{array}\right]
$$

15.

$$
\begin{array}{ccccccc}
x_1 & x_2 & x_3 & s_1 & s_2 & s_3 & z \\
\end{array}
$$

$$
\left[\begin{array}{ccccccc|c}
1 & 1 & 1 & 1 & 0 & 0 & 0 & 60 \\
3 & 1 & 2 & 0 & 1 & 0 & 0 & 100 \\
1 & 2 & 3 & 0 & 0 & 1 & 0 & 200 \\
\hline
-1 & -1 & -2 & 0 & 0 & 0 & 1 & 0
\end{array}\right]
$$

16.

$$
\begin{array}{ccccccc}
x_1 & x_2 & x_3 & s_1 & s_2 & s_3 & z \\
\end{array}
$$

$$
\left[\begin{array}{ccccccc|c}
4 & 2 & 3 & 1 & 0 & 0 & 0 & 22 \\
2 & 2 & 5 & 0 & 1 & 0 & 0 & 28 \\
1 & 3 & 2 & 0 & 0 & 1 & 0 & 45 \\
\hline
-3 & -2 & -4 & 0 & 0 & 0 & 1 & 0
\end{array}\right]
$$

For each simplex tableau in Exercises 17–20, (a) list the basic and the nonbasic variables, (b) find the basic feasible solution determined by setting the nonbasic variables equal to 0, and (c) decide whether this is a maximum solution. (See Examples 5 and 6.)

17.

$$
\begin{array}{cccccc}
x_1 & x_2 & x_3 & s_1 & s_2 & z \\
\end{array}
$$

$$
\left[\begin{array}{cccccc|c}
3 & 2 & 0 & -3 & 1 & 0 & 29 \\
4 & 0 & 1 & -2 & 0 & 0 & 16 \\
\hline
-5 & 0 & 0 & -1 & 0 & 1 & 11
\end{array}\right]
$$

18.

$$
\begin{array}{ccccccc}
x_1 & x_2 & x_3 & s_1 & s_2 & s_3 & z \\
\end{array}
$$

$$
\left[\begin{array}{ccccccc|c}
-3 & 0 & \frac{1}{2} & 1 & -2 & 0 & 0 & 22 \\
2 & 0 & -3 & 0 & 1 & 1 & 0 & 10 \\
4 & 1 & 4 & 0 & \frac{3}{4} & 0 & 0 & 17 \\
\hline
-1 & 0 & 0 & 0 & 1 & 0 & 1 & 120
\end{array}\right]
$$

19.

$$
\begin{array}{ccccccc}
x_1 & x_2 & x_3 & s_1 & s_2 & s_3 & z \\
\end{array}
$$

$$
\left[\begin{array}{ccccccc|c}
1 & 0 & 2 & \frac{1}{2} & 0 & \frac{1}{3} & 0 & 6 \\
0 & 1 & -1 & 5 & 0 & -1 & 0 & 13 \\
0 & 0 & 1 & \frac{3}{2} & 1 & -\frac{1}{3} & 0 & 21 \\
\hline
0 & 0 & 2 & \frac{1}{2} & 0 & 3 & 1 & 18
\end{array}\right]
$$

20.

$$
\begin{array}{cccccccc}
x_1 & x_2 & x_3 & x_4 & s_1 & s_2 & s_3 & z \\
\end{array}
$$

$$
\left[\begin{array}{cccccccc|c}
-1 & 0 & 0 & 1 & 0 & 3 & -2 & 0 & 47 \\
2 & 0 & 1 & 0 & 0 & 2 & -\frac{1}{2} & 0 & 37 \\
3 & 5 & 0 & 0 & 1 & -1 & 6 & 0 & 43 \\
\hline
4 & 1 & 0 & 0 & 0 & 6 & 0 & 1 & 86
\end{array}\right]
$$

Use the simplex method to solve Exercises 21–36.

21. Maximize $z = x_1 + 3x_2$
subject to $x_1 + x_2 \le 10$
$5x_1 + 2x_2 \le 20$
$x_1 + 2x_2 \le 36$
$x_1 \ge 0, x_2 \ge 0.$

22. Maximize $z = 5x_1 + x_2$
subject to $2x_1 + 3x_2 \le 8$
$4x_1 + 8x_2 \le 12$
$5x_1 + 2x_2 \le 30$
$x_1 \ge 0, x_2 \ge 0.$

23. Maximize $z = 2x_1 + x_2$
subject to $x_1 + 3x_2 \le 12$
$2x_1 + x_2 \le 10$
$x_1 + x_2 \le 4$
$x_1 \ge 0, x_2 \ge 0.$

24. Maximize $z = 4x_1 + 2x_2$
subject to $-x_1 - x_2 \le 12$
$3x_1 - x_2 \le 15$
$x_1 \ge 0, x_2 \ge 0.$

25. Maximize $z = 5x_1 + 4x_2 + x_3$
subject to $-2x_1 + x_2 + 2x_3 \le 3$
$x_1 - x_2 + x_3 \le 1$
$x_1 \ge 0, x_2 \ge 0, x_3 \ge 0.$

26. Maximize $z = 3x_1 + 2x_2 + x_3$
subject to $2x_1 + 2x_2 + x_3 \le 10$
$x_1 + 2x_2 + 3x_3 \le 15$
$x_1 \ge 0, x_2 \ge 0, x_3 \ge 0.$

27. Maximize $z = 2x_1 + x_2 + x_3$
subject to $x_1 - 3x_2 + x_3 \le 3$
$x_1 - 2x_2 + 2x_3 \le 12$
$x_1 \ge 0, x_2 \ge 0, x_3 \ge 0.$

28. Maximize $z = 4x_1 + 5x_2 + x_3$
subject to $x_1 + 2x_2 + 4x_3 \le 10$
$2x_1 + 2x_2 + x_3 \le 10$
$x_1 \ge 0, x_2 \ge 0, x_3 \ge 0.$

29. Maximize $z = 2x_1 + 2x_2 - 4x_3$
subject to $3x_1 + 3x_2 - 6x_3 \le 51$
$5x_1 + 5x_2 + 10x_3 \le 99$
$x_1 \ge 0, x_2 \ge 0, x_3 \ge 0.$

30. Maximize $z = 4x_1 + x_2 + 3x_3$
subject to $x_1 + 3x_3 \le 6$
$6x_1 + 3x_2 + 12x_3 \le 40$
$x_1 \ge 0, x_2 \ge 0, x_3 \ge 0.$

31. Maximize $z = 300x_1 + 200x_2 + 100x_3$

subject to $x_1 + x_2 + x_3 \le 100$

$2x_1 + 3x_2 + 4x_3 \le 320$

$2x_1 + x_2 + x_3 \le 160$

$x_1 \ge 0, x_2 \ge 0, x_3 \ge 0.$

32. Maximize $z = x_1 + 5x_2 - 10x_3$

subject to $8x_1 + 4x_2 + 12x_3 \le 18$

$x_1 + 6x_2 + 2x_3 \le 45$

$5x_1 + 7x_2 + 3x_3 \le 60$

$x_1 \ge 0, x_2 \ge 0, x_3 \ge 0.$

33. Maximize $z = 4x_1 - 3x_2 + 2x_3$

subject to $2x_1 - x_2 + 8x_3 \le 40$

$4x_1 - 5x_2 + 6x_3 \le 60$

$2x_1 - 2x_2 + 6x_3 \le 24$

$x_1 \ge 0, x_2 \ge 0, x_3 \ge 0.$

34. Maximize $z = 3x_1 + 2x_2 - 4x_3$

subject to $x_1 - x_2 + x_3 \le 10$

$2x_1 - x_2 + 2x_3 \le 30$

$-3x_1 + x_2 + 3x_3 \le 40$

$x_1 \ge 0, x_2 \ge 0, x_3 \ge 0.$

35. Maximize $z = x_1 + 2x_2 + x_3 + 5x_4$

subject to $x_1 + 2x_2 + x_3 + x_4 \le 50$

$3x_1 + x_2 + 2x_3 + x_4 \le 100$

$x_1 \ge 0, x_2 \ge 0, x_3 \ge 0, x_4 \ge 0.$

36. Maximize $z = x_1 + x_2 + 4x_3 + 5x_4$

subject to $x_1 + 2x_2 + 3x_3 + x_4 \le 115$

$2x_1 + x_2 + 8x_3 + 5x_4 \le 200$

$x_1 + x_3 \le 50$

$x_1 \ge 0, x_2 \ge 0, x_3 \ge 0, x_4 \ge 0.$

37. The initial simplex tableau of a linear programming problem is

$$\begin{array}{cccccc} x_1 & x_2 & x_3 & s_1 & s_2 & z \\ \left[\begin{array}{cccccc|c} 1 & 1 & 1 & 1 & 0 & 0 & 12 \\ 2 & 1 & 2 & 0 & 1 & 0 & 30 \\ \hline -2 & -2 & -1 & 0 & 0 & 1 & 0 \end{array}\right]. \end{array}$$

(a) Use the simplex method to solve the problem with column 1 as the first pivot column.

(b) Now use the simplex method to solve the problem with column 2 as the first pivot column.

(c) Does this problem have a unique maximum solution? Why?

38. The final simplex tableau of a linear programming problem is

$$\begin{array}{ccccc} x_1 & x_2 & s_1 & s_2 & z \\ \left[\begin{array}{ccccc|c} 1 & 1 & 2 & 0 & 0 & 24 \\ 2 & 0 & 2 & 1 & 0 & 8 \\ \hline 4 & 0 & 0 & 0 & 1 & 40 \end{array}\right]. \end{array}$$

(a) What is the solution given by this tableau?

(b) Even though all the indicators are nonnegative, perform one more round of pivoting on this tableau, using column 3 as the pivot column and choosing the pivot row by forming quotients in the usual way.

(c) Show that there is more than one solution to the linear programming problem by comparing your answer in part (a) with the basic feasible solution given by the tableau found in part (b). Does it give the same value of z as the solution in part (a)?

✓**Checkpoint Answers**

1. $x_1 + x_2 + x_3 + s_1 = 12$

$2x_1 + 4x_2 + s_2 = 15$

$x_2 + 3x_3 + s_3 = 10$

2.
$$\begin{array}{cccccc} x_1 & x_2 & s_1 & s_2 & s_3 & z \\ \left[\begin{array}{cccccc|c} 1 & 2 & 1 & 0 & 0 & 0 & 85 \\ 2 & 1 & 0 & 1 & 0 & 0 & 92 \\ 1 & 4 & 0 & 0 & 1 & 0 & 104 \\ \hline -2 & -3 & 0 & 0 & 0 & 1 & 0 \end{array}\right] \end{array}$$

Indicators

3. 2 (in first column)

4. (a) 2

(b)
$$\begin{array}{cccccc} x_1 & x_2 & x_3 & s_1 & s_2 & z \\ \left[\begin{array}{cccccc|c} \frac{1}{2} & 1 & 3 & \frac{1}{2} & 0 & 0 & 8 \\ -\frac{1}{2} & 0 & -9 & -\frac{3}{2} & 1 & 0 & 1 \\ \hline 1 & 0 & 9 & 2 & 0 & 1 & 32 \end{array}\right] \end{array}$$

5. $z = 21$ when $x_1 = 6, x_2 = 0,$ and $x_3 = 9.$

6. $x_1 = 0, x_2 = 24, s_1 = 16, s_2 = 0, z = 4800$

7.5 Maximization Applications

Applications of the simplex method are considered in this section. First, however, we make a slight change in notation. You have noticed that the column representing the variable z in a simplex tableau never changes during pivoting. (Since all the entries except the last one in this column are 0, performing row operations has no effect on these entries—

they remain 0.) Consequently, this column is unnecessary and can be omitted without causing any difficulty.

> Hereafter in this text, the column corresponding to the variable z (representing the objective function) will be omitted from all simplex tableaus.

Example 1   **Business**   A farmer has 110 acres of available land he wishes to plant with a mixture of potatoes, corn, and cabbage. It costs him $400 to produce an acre of potatoes, $160 to produce an acre of corn, and $280 to produce an acre of cabbage. He has a maximum of $20,000 to spend. He makes a profit of $120 per acre of potatoes, $40 per acre of corn, and $60 per acre of cabbage.

(a) How many acres of each crop should he plant to maximize his profit?

Solution   Let the number of acres alloted to each of potatoes, corn, and cabbage be x_1, x_2, and x_3, respectively. Then summarize the given information as follows:

Crop	Number of Acres	Cost per Acre	Profit per Acre
Potatoes	x_1	$400	$120
Corn	x_2	$160	$40
Cabbage	x_3	$280	$60
Maximum Available	110	$20,000	

The constraints can be expressed as

$$x_1 + x_2 + x_3 \leq 110 \qquad \text{Number of acres}$$
$$400x_1 + 160x_2 + 280x_3 \leq 20,000, \qquad \text{Production costs}$$

where x_1, x_2, and x_3 are all nonnegative. The first of these constraints says that $x_1 + x_2 + x_3$ is less than or perhaps equal to 110. Use s_1 as the slack variable, giving the equation

$$x_1 + x_2 + x_3 + s_1 = 110.$$

Here, s_1 represents the amount of the farmer's 110 acres that will not be used. (s_1 may be 0 or any value up to 110.)

In the same way, the constraint $400x_1 + 160x_2 + 280x_3 \leq 20,000$ can be converted into an equation by adding a slack variable s_2:

$$400x_1 + 160x_2 + 280x_3 + s_2 = 20,000.$$

The slack variable s_2 represents any unused portion of the farmer's $20,000 capital. (Again, s_2 may have any value from 0 to 20,000.)

The farmer's profit on potatoes is the product of the profit per acre ($120) and the number x_1 of acres, that is, $120x_1$. His profits on corn and cabbage are computed similarly. Hence, his total profit is given by

$$z = \text{profit on potatoes} + \text{profit on corn} + \text{profit on cabbage}$$
$$z = 120x_1 + 40x_2 + 60x_3.$$

The linear programming problem can now be stated as follows:

$$\text{Maximize} \quad z = 120x_1 + 40x_2 + 60x_3$$
$$\text{subject to} \quad x_1 + x_2 + x_3 + s_1 = 110$$
$$400x_1 + 160x_2 + 280x_3 + s_2 = 20,000,$$
$$\text{with} \quad x_1 \geq 0, x_2 \geq 0, x_3 \geq 0, s_1 \geq 0, s_2 \geq 0.$$

The initial simplex tableau (without the z column) is

$$
\begin{array}{c}
\begin{array}{ccccc} x_1 & x_2 & x_3 & s_1 & s_2 \end{array}\\
\left[\begin{array}{ccccc|c}
1 & 1 & 1 & 1 & 0 & 110\\
400 & 160 & 280 & 0 & 1 & 20{,}000\\
\hline
-120 & -40 & -60 & 0 & 0 & 0
\end{array}\right]
\end{array} \; .
$$

The most negative indicator is -120; column 1 is the pivot column. The quotients needed to determine the pivot row are $110/1 = 110$ and $20{,}000/400 = 50$. So the pivot is 400 in row 2, column 1. Multiplying row 2 by $1/400$ and completing the pivoting leads to the final simplex tableau:

$$
\begin{array}{c}
\begin{array}{ccccc} x_1 & x_2 & x_3 & s_1 & s_2 \end{array}\\
\left[\begin{array}{ccccc|c}
0 & .6 & .3 & 1 & -.0025 & 60\\
1 & .4 & .7 & 0 & .0025 & 50\\
\hline
0 & 8 & 24 & 0 & .3 & 6000
\end{array}\right]
\end{array}
\begin{array}{l}
-1R_2 + R_1\\[4pt]
\tfrac{1}{400}R_2\\[4pt]
120R_2 + R_3
\end{array} \; .
$$

Setting the nonbasic variables x_2, x_3, and s_2 equal to 0, solving for the basic variables x_1 and s_1, and remembering that the value of z is in the lower right-hand corner leads to this maximum solution:

$$x_1 = 50, \qquad x_2 = 0, \qquad x_3 = 0, \qquad s_1 = 60, \qquad s_2 = 0, \qquad \text{and} \qquad z = 6000.$$

Therefore, the farmer will make a maximum profit of \$6000 by planting 50 acres of potatoes and no corn or cabbage.

(b) If the farmer maximizes his profit, how much land will remain unplanted? What is the explanation for this?

Solution   Since 50 of 110 acres are planted, 60 acres will remain unplanted. Alternatively, note that the unplanted acres of land are represented by s_1, the slack variable in the "number of acres" constraint. In the maximal solution found in part (a), $s_1 = 60$, which means that 60 acres are left unplanted.

The amount of unused cash is represented by s_2, the slack variable in the "production costs" constraint. Since $s_2 = 0$, all the available money has been used. By using the maximal solution in part (a), the farmer has used his \$20,000 most effectively. If he had more cash, he would plant more crops and make a larger profit.

Example 2   **Business**   Ana Pott, who is a candidate for the state legislature, has \$96,000 to buy TV advertising time. Ads cost \$400 per minute on a local cable channel, \$4000 per minute on a regional independent channel, and \$12,000 per minute on a national network channel. Because of existing contracts, the TV stations can provide at most a total of 30 minutes of advertising time, with a maximum of 6 minutes on the national network channel. At any given time during the evening, approximately 100,000 people watch the cable channel, 200,000 the independent channel, and 600,000 the network channel. To get maximum exposure, how much time should Ana buy from each station?

(a) Set up the initial simplex tableau for this problem.

Solution   Let x_1 be the number of minutes of ads on the cable channel, x_2 the number of minutes on the independent channel, and x_3 the number of minutes on the network channel. Exposure is measured in viewer-minutes. For instance, 100,000 people watching x_1 minutes of ads on the cable channel produces $100{,}000x_1$ viewer-minutes. The amount of exposure is given by the total number of viewer-minutes for all three channels, namely,

$$100{,}000x_1 + 200{,}000x_2 + 600{,}000x_3.$$

Since 30 minutes are available,

$$x_1 + x_2 + x_3 \leq 30.$$

The fact that only 6 minutes can be used on the network channel means that

$$x_3 \leq 6.$$

Expenditures are limited to $96,000, so

$$\text{Cable cost} + \text{independent cost} + \text{network cost} \leq 96,000$$
$$400x_1 + 4000x_2 + 12,000x_3 \leq 96,000.$$

Therefore, Ana must solve the following linear programming problem:

$$\text{Maximize} \quad z = 100,000x_1 + 200,000x_2 + 600,000x_3$$
$$\text{subject to} \quad x_1 + x_2 + x_3 \leq 30$$
$$x_3 \leq 6$$
$$400x_1 + 4000x_2 + 12,000x_3 \leq 96,000,$$
$$\text{with} \quad x_1 \geq 0, x_2 \geq 0, x_3 \geq 0.$$

Introducing slack variables s_1, s_2, and s_3 (one for each constraint), rewriting the constraints as equations, and expressing the objective function as

$$-100,000x_1 - 200,000x_2 - 600,000x_3 + z = 0$$

leads to the initial simplex tableau:

$$
\begin{array}{cccccc}
x_1 & x_2 & x_3 & s_1 & s_2 & s_3 \\
\end{array}
$$
$$
\left[
\begin{array}{cccccc|c}
1 & 1 & 1 & 1 & 0 & 0 & 30 \\
0 & 0 & 1 & 0 & 1 & 0 & 6 \\
400 & 4000 & 12,000 & 0 & 0 & 1 & 96,000 \\
\hline
-100,000 & -200,000 & -600,000 & 0 & 0 & 0 & 0
\end{array}
\right].
$$

(b) Use the simplex method to find the final simplex tableau.

Solution Work by hand, or use a graphing calculator's simplex program or a spreadsheet, to obtain this final tableau:

$$
\begin{array}{cccccc}
x_1 & x_2 & x_3 & s_1 & s_2 & s_3 \\
\end{array}
$$
$$
\left[
\begin{array}{cccccc|c}
1 & 0 & 0 & \frac{10}{9} & \frac{20}{9} & -\frac{25}{90,000} & 20 \\
0 & 0 & 1 & 0 & 1 & 0 & 6 \\
0 & 1 & 0 & -\frac{1}{9} & -\frac{29}{9} & \frac{25}{90,000} & 4 \\
\hline
0 & 0 & 0 & \frac{800,000}{9} & \frac{1,600,000}{9} & \frac{250}{9} & 6,400,000
\end{array}
\right].
$$

Therefore, the optimal solution is

$$x_1 = 20, \quad x_2 = 4, \quad x_3 = 6, \quad s_1 = 0, \quad s_2 = 0, \quad \text{and} \quad s_3 = 0.$$

Ana should buy 20 minutes of time on the cable channel, 4 minutes on the independent channel, and 6 minutes on the network channel.

(c) What do the values of the slack variables in the optimal solution tell you?

Solution All three slack variables are 0. This means that all the available minutes have been used ($s_1 = 0$ in the first constraint), the maximum possible 6 minutes on the national network have been used ($s_2 = 0$ in the second constraint), and all of the $96,000 has been spent ($s_3 = 0$ in the third constraint). ✓₁

✓ **Checkpoint 1**

In Example 2, what is the number of viewer-minutes in the optimal solution?

Example 3 **Business** A chemical plant makes three products—glaze, solvent, and clay—each of which brings in different revenue per truckload. Production is limited, first by the number of air pollution units the plant is allowed to produce each day and second by the time available in the evaporation tank. The plant manager wants to maximize the daily revenue. Using information not given here, he sets up an initial simplex tableau and uses the simplex method to produce the following final simplex tableau:

$$
\begin{array}{ccccc}
x_1 & x_2 & x_3 & s_1 & s_2 \\
\end{array}
$$

$$
\left[
\begin{array}{ccccc|c}
-10 & -25 & 0 & 1 & -1 & 60 \\
3 & 4 & 1 & 0 & .1 & 24 \\
\hline
7 & 13 & 0 & 0 & .4 & 96
\end{array}
\right].
$$

The three variables represent the number of truckloads of glaze, solvent, and clay, respectively. The first slack variable comes from the air pollution constraint and the second slack variable from the time constraint on the evaporation tank. The revenue function is given in hundreds of dollars.

(a) What is the optimal solution?

Solution

$$x_1 = 0, \qquad x_2 = 0, \qquad x_3 = 24, \qquad s_1 = 60, \qquad s_2 = 0, \qquad \text{and} \qquad z = 96.$$

(b) Interpret this solution. What do the variables represent, and what does the solution mean?

Solution   The variable x_1 is the number of truckloads of glaze, x_2 the number of truckloads of solvent, x_3 the number of truckloads of clay to be produced, and z the revenue produced (in hundreds of dollars). The plant should produce 24 truckloads of clay and no glaze or solvent, for a maximum revenue of $9600. The first slack variable, s_1, represents the number of air pollution units below the maximum number allowed. Since $s_1 = 60$, the number of air pollution units will be 60 less than the allowable maximum. The second slack variable, s_2, represents the unused time in the evaporation tank. Since $s_2 = 0$, the evaporation tank is fully used.

7.5 Exercises

Set up the initial simplex tableau for each of the given problems. You will be asked to solve these problems in Exercises 19–22.

1. **Business**   A cat breeder has the following amounts of cat food: 90 units of tuna, 80 units of liver, and 50 units of chicken. To raise a Siamese cat, the breeder must use 2 units of tuna, 1 of liver, and 1 of chicken per day, while raising a Persian cat requires 1, 2, and 1 units, respectively, per day. If a Siamese cat sells for $12 while a Persian cat sells for $10, how many of each should be raised in order to obtain maximum gross income? What is the maximum gross income?

2. **Business**   Banal, Inc., produces art for motel rooms. Its painters can turn out mountain scenes, seascapes, and pictures of clowns. Each painting is worked on by three different artists: *T*, *D*, and *H*. Artist *T* works only 25 hours per week, while *D* and *H* work 45 and 40 hours per week, respectively. Artist *T* spends 1 hour on a mountain scene, 2 hours on a seascape, and 1 hour on a clown. Corresponding times for *D* and *H* are 3, 2, and 2 hours and 2, 1, and 4 hours, respectively. Banal makes $20 on a mountain scene, $18 on a seascape, and $22 on a clown. The head painting packer can't stand clowns, so that no more than 4 clown paintings may be done in a week. Find the number of each type of painting that should be made weekly in order to maximize profit. Find the maximum possible profit.

3. **Health**   A biologist has 500 kilograms of nutrient A, 600 kilograms of nutrient B, and 300 kilograms of nutrient C. These nutrients will be used to make 4 types of food—*P*, *Q*, *R*, and *S*—whose contents (in percent of nutrient per kilogram of food) and whose "growth values" are as shown in the following table:

	P	*Q*	*R*	*S*
A	0	0	37.5	62.5
B	0	75	50	37.5
C	100	25	12.5	0
Growth Value	90	70	60	50

How many kilograms of each food should be produced in order to maximize total growth value? Find the maximum growth value.

4. **Natural Science**   A lake is stocked each spring with three species of fish: A, B, and C. The average weights of the fish are 1.62, 2.12, and 3.01 kilograms for the three species, respectively. Three foods—I, II, and III—are available in the lake. Each fish of species A requires 1.32 units of food I, 2.9 units of food II, and 1.75 units of food III, on the average, each day. Species B fish require 2.1 units of food I, .95 units of food II,

and .6 units of food III daily. Species *C* fish require .86, 1.52, and 2.01 units of I, II, and III per day, respectively. If 490 units of food I, 897 units of food II, and 653 units of food III are available daily, how should the lake be stocked to maximize the weight of the fish it supports?

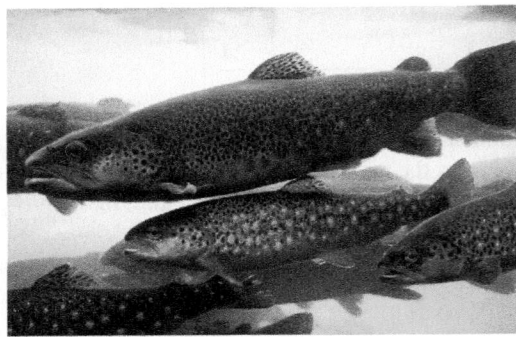

In each of the given exercises, (a) use the simplex method to solve the problem and (b) explain what the values of the slack variables in the optimal solution mean in the context of the problem. (See Examples 1–3).

5. **Business** A manufacturer of bicycles builds 1-, 3-, and 10-speed models. The bicycles are made of both aluminum and steel. The company has available 91,800 units of steel and 42,000 units of aluminum. The 1-, 3-, and 10-speed models need, respectively, 20, 30, and 40 units of steel and 12, 21, and 16 units of aluminum. How many of each type of bicycle should be made in order to maximize profit if the company makes $8 per 1-speed bike, $12 per 3-speed bike, and $24 per 10-speed bike? What is the maximum possible profit?

6. **Business** Liz is working to raise money for breast cancer research by sending informational letters to local neighborhood organizations and church groups. She discovered that each church group requires 2 hours of letter writing and 1 hour of follow-up, while each neighborhood group needs 2 hours of letter writing and 3 hours of follow-up. Liz can raise $1000 from each church group and $2000 from each neighborhood organization, and she has a maximum of 16 hours of letter-writing time and a maximum of 12 hours of follow-up time available per month. Determine the most profitable mixture of groups she should contact and the most money she can raise in a month.

7. **Business** A local news channel plans a 27-minute Saturday morning news show. The show will be divided into three segments involving sports, news, and weather. Market research has shown that the sports segment should be twice as long as the weather segment. The total time taken by the sports and weather segments should be twice the time taken by the news segment. On the basis of the market research, it is believed that 40, 60, and 50 (in thousands) viewers will watch the program for each minute the sports, news, and weather segments, respectively, are on the air. Find the time that should be allotted to each segment in order to get the maximum number of viewers. Find the number of viewers.

8. **Business** A food wholesaler has three kinds of individual bags of potato chips: regular, barbeque, and salt and vinegar. She wants to sells the bags of chips in bulk packages. The bronze package consists of 20 bags of regular and 10 bags of barbeque. The silver package contains 20 bags of regular, 10 bags of barbeque, and 10 bags of salt and vinegar. The gold package consists of 30 bags of regular, 10 bags of barbeque, and 10 bags of salt and vinegar. The profit is $30 on each bronze package, $40 on each silver package, and $60 on each gold package. The food wholesaler has a total of 8000 bags of regular chips, 4000 bags of barbeque, and 2000 bags of salt and vinegar. Assuming all the packages will be sold, how many gold, silver, and bronze packages should be made up in order to maximize profit? What is the maximum profit?

9. **Business** Mario Cekada owns a tree nursery business. Mario can sell a weeping Japanese maple of a certain size for $350 in profit. He can sell tri-color beech trees of a certain size for $500 profit. The travel time to acquire the Japanese maple trees is 5 hours while the travel time for the beech trees is 7 hours. The digging process takes 1 hour for the Japanese maple trees and 2 hours for the beech trees. Both kinds of trees require 4 hours of time to deliver to the client. In a particular season, Mario has available 3600 work hours for travel time to acquire the trees, 900 work-hours for digging, and 2600 work-hours for delivery to the clients. How many trees of each kind should he acquire to make a maximum profit? What is the maximum profit?

10. **Business** The Texas Poker Company assembles three different poker sets. Each Royal Flush poker set contains 1000 poker chips, 4 decks of cards, 10 dice, and 2 dealer buttons. Each Deluxe Diamond poker set contains 600 poker chips, 2 decks of cards, 5 dice, and 1 dealer button. The Full House poker set contains 300 poker chips, 2 decks of cards, 5 dice, and 1 dealer button. The Texas Poker Company has 2,800,000 poker chips, 10,000 decks of cards, 25,000 dice, and 6000 dealer buttons in stock. It earns a profit of $38 for each Royal Flush poker set, $22 for each Deluxe Diamond poker set, and $12 for each Full House poker set. How many of each type of poker set should it assemble to maximize profit? What is the maximum profit?

Use the simplex method to solve the given problems. (See Examples 1–3.)

11. **Business** The Fancy Fashions Store has $8000 available each month for advertising. Newspaper ads cost $400 each, and no more than 20 can be run per month. Radio ads cost $200 each, and no more than 30 can run per month. TV ads cost $1200 each, with a maximum of 6 available each month. Approximately 2000 women will see each newspaper ad, 1200 will hear each radio commercial, and 10,000 will see each TV ad. How much of each type of advertising should be used if the store wants to maximize its ad exposure?

12. **Business** Caroline's Quality Candy Confectionery is famous for fudge, chocolate cremes, and pralines. Its candy-making equipment is set up to make 100-pound batches at a time. Currently there is a chocolate shortage, and the company can get only 120 pounds of chocolate in the next shipment. On a week's run, the confectionery's cooking and processing equipment is available for a total of 42 machine hours. During the same period, the employees have a total of 56 work hours available for packaging. A batch of fudge requires 20 pounds of chocolate, while a batch of cremes uses 25 pounds of chocolate. The cooking and processing take 120 minutes for fudge, 150 minutes for chocolate cremes, and 200 minutes for pralines. The packaging times, measured in minutes per 1-pound box, are 1, 2, and 3, respectively, for fudge, cremes, and pralines. Determine how many batches of each type of candy the confectionery

should make, assuming that the profit per 1-pound box is 50¢ on fudge, 40¢ on chocolate cremes, and 45¢ on pralines. Also, find the maximum profit for the week.

13. **Finance** A political party is planning its fund-raising activities for a coming election. It plans to raise money through large fund-raising parties, letters requesting funds, and dinner parties where people can meet the candidate personally. Each large fund-raising party costs $3000, each mailing costs $1000, and each dinner party costs $12,000. The party can spend up to $102,000 for these activities. From experience, it is known that each large party will raise $200,000, each letter campaign will raise $100,000, and each dinner party will raise $600,000. The party is able to carry out as many as 25 of these activities.

    (a) How many of each should the party plan to raise the maximum amount of money? What is the maximum amount?

    ✎ **(b)** Dinner parties are more expensive than letter campaigns, yet the optimum solution found in part (a) includes dinner parties, but no letter campaigns. Explain how this is possible.

14. **Business** A baker has 60 units of flour, 132 units of sugar, and 102 units of raisins. A loaf of raisin bread requires 1 unit of flour, 1 unit of sugar, and 2 units of raisins, while a raisin cake needs 2, 4, and 1 units, respectively. If raisin bread sells for $3 a loaf and a raisin cake for $4, how many of each should be baked so that the gross income is maximized? What is the maximum gross income?

15. **Health** Rachel Reeve, a fitness trainer, has an exercise regimen that includes running, biking, and walking. She has no more than 15 hours per week to devote to exercise, including at most 3 hours for running. She wants to walk at least twice as many hours as she bikes. A 130-pound person like Rachel will burn on average 531 calories per hour running, 472 calories per hour biking, and 354 calories per hour walking. How many hours per week should Rachel spend on each exercise to maximize the number of calories she burns? What is the maximum number of calories she will burn? (*Hint:* Write the constraint involving walking and biking in the form ≤ 0.)

16. **Health** Joe Vetere's exercise regimen includes light calisthenics, swimming, and playing the drums. He has at most 10 hours per week to devote to these activities. He wants the total time he does calisthenics and plays the drums to be at least twice as long as he swims. His neighbors, however, will tolerate no more than 4 hours per week on the drums. A 190-pound person like Joe will burn an average of 388 calories per hour doing calisthenics, 518 calories per hour swimming, and 345 calories per hour playing the drums. How many hours per week should Joe spend on each exercise to maximize the number of calories he burns? What is the maximum number of calories he will burn?

Business *The next two problems come from past CPA examinations.*[*] *Select the appropriate answer for each question.*

17. The Ball Company manufactures three types of lamps, labeled A, B, and C. Each lamp is processed in two departments: I and

---
[*]Problem No. 17, The Ball Company Manufactures from Uniform CPA Examinations and Unofficial Answers. Copyright © 1973 American Institute of Certified Public Accountants, Inc. (AICPA). Reproduced by permission of American Institute of Certified Public Accountants, Inc. (AICPA).

II. Total available person-hours per day for departments I and II are 400 and 600, respectively. No additional labor is available. Time requirements and profit per unit for each type of lamp are as follows:

	A	**B**	**C**
Person-Hours in I	2	3	1
Person-Hours in II	4	2	3
Profit per Unit	$5	$4	$3

The company has assigned you as the accounting member of its profit-planning committee to determine the numbers of types of A, B, and C lamps that it should produce in order to maximize its total profit from the sale of lamps. The following questions relate to a linear programming model that your group has developed:

    (a) The coefficients of the objective function would be
      (1) 4, 2, 3;
      (2) 2, 3, 1;
      (3) 5, 4, 3;
      (4) 400,600.

    (b) The constraints in the model would be
      (1) 2, 3, 1;
      (2) 5, 4, 3;
      (3) 4, 2, 3;
      (4) 400,600.

    (c) The constraint imposed by the available number of person-hours in department I could be expressed as
      (1) $4X_1 + 2X_2 + 3X_3 \leq 400$;
      (2) $4X_1 + 2X_2 + 3X_3 \geq 400$;
      (3) $2X_1 + 3X_2 + 1X_3 \leq 400$;
      (4) $2X_1 + 3X_2 + 1X_3 \geq 400$.

18. The Golden Hawk Manufacturing Company wants to maximize the profits on products A, B, and C. The contribution margin for each product is as follows:

Product	Contribution Margin
A	$2
B	5
C	4

The production requirements and the departmental capacities are as follows:

Department	Production Requirements by Product (Hours)			Departmental Capacity (Total Hours)
	A	**B**	**C**	
Assembling	2	3	2	30,000
Painting	1	2	2	38,000
Finishing	2	3	1	28,000

    (a) What is the profit-maximization formula for the Golden Hawk Company?
      (1) $2A + $5B + $4C = X$ (where X = profit)
      (2) $5A + 8B + 5C \leq 96,000$

(3) $2A + \$5B + \$4C \le X$
(4) $2A + \$5B + \$4C = 96{,}000$

(b) What is the constraint for the Painting Department of the Golden Hawk Company?
(1) $1A + 2B + 2C \ge 38{,}000$
(2) $\$2A + \$5B + \$4C \ge 38{,}000$
(3) $1A + 2B + 2C \le 38{,}000$
(4) $2A + 3B + 2C \le 30{,}000$

19. Solve the problem in Exercise 1.

✈ *Use a graphing calculator or a computer program for the simplex method to solve the given linear programming problems.*

20. Exercise 2. Your final answer should consist of whole numbers (because Banal can't sell half a painting).

21. Exercise 3

22. Exercise 4

✓**Checkpoint Answer**

1. $z = 6{,}400{,}000$

7.6 The Simplex Method: Duality and Minimization

📄 **NOTE** Sections 7.6 and 7.7 are independent of each other and may be read in either order.

Here, we present a method of solving *minimization* problems in which all constraints involve $\ge$ and all coefficients of the objective function are positive. When it applies, this method may be more efficient than the method discussed in Section 7.7. However, the method in Section 7.7 applies to a wider variety of problems—both minimization and maximization problems, even those that involve *mixed constraints* ($\le$, $=$, or $\ge$)—and it has no restrictions on the objective function.

We begin with a necessary tool from matrix algebra: if A is a matrix, then the **transpose** of A is the matrix obtained by interchanging the rows and columns of A.

Example 1   Find the transpose of each matrix.

(a) $A = \begin{bmatrix} 2 & -1 & 5 \\ 6 & 8 & 0 \\ -3 & 7 & -1 \end{bmatrix}$.

Solution   Write the rows of matrix A as the columns of the transpose:

$$\text{Transpose of } A = \begin{bmatrix} 2 & 6 & -3 \\ -1 & 8 & 7 \\ 5 & 0 & -1 \end{bmatrix}.$$

(b) $A = \begin{bmatrix} 1 & 2 & 4 & 0 \\ 2 & 1 & 7 & 6 \end{bmatrix}$.

Solution   The transpose of $\begin{bmatrix} 1 & 2 & 4 & 0 \\ 2 & 1 & 7 & 6 \end{bmatrix}$ is $\begin{bmatrix} 1 & 2 \\ 2 & 1 \\ 4 & 7 \\ 0 & 6 \end{bmatrix}$. ✓₁

✓**Checkpoint 1**

Give the transpose of each matrix.

(a) $\begin{bmatrix} 2 & 4 \\ 6 & 3 \\ 1 & 5 \end{bmatrix}$

(b) $\begin{bmatrix} 4 & 7 & 10 \\ 3 & 2 & 6 \\ 5 & 8 & 12 \end{bmatrix}$

Figure 7.31

✈ **TECHNOLOGY TIP** Most graphing calculators can find the transpose of a matrix. Look for this feature in the MATRIX MATH menu (TI) or the OPTN MAT menu (Casio). The transpose of matrix A from Example 1(a) is shown in Figure 7.31.

We now consider linear programming problems satisfying the following conditions:

1. The objective function is to be minimized.
2. All the coefficients of the objective function are nonnegative.
3. All constraints involve $\geq$.
4. All variables are nonnegative.

The method of solving minimization problems presented here is based on an interesting connection between maximization and minimization problems: Any solution of a maximizing problem produces the solution of an associated minimizing problem, and vice versa. Each of the associated problems is called the **dual** of the other. Thus, duals enable us to solve minimization problems of the type just described by the simplex method introduced in Section 7.4.

When dealing with minimization problems, we use y_1, y_2, y_3, etc., as variables and denote the objective function by w. The next two examples show how to construct the dual problem. Later examples will show how to solve both the dual problem and the original one.

Example 2   Construct the dual of this problem:

$$\text{Minimize} \quad w = 8y_1 + 16y_2$$
$$\text{subject to} \quad y_1 + 5y_2 \geq 9$$
$$2y_1 + 2y_2 \geq 10$$
$$y_1 \geq 0, y_2 \geq 0.$$

Solution   Write the augmented matrix of the system of inequalities *and* include the coefficients of the objective function (not their negatives) as the last row of the matrix:

Constants

$$\begin{bmatrix} 1 & 5 & | & 9 \\ 2 & 2 & | & 10 \\ \hline 8 & 16 & | & 0 \end{bmatrix}.$$

Objective function

Now form the transpose of the preceding matrix:

$$\begin{bmatrix} 1 & 2 & | & 8 \\ 5 & 2 & | & 16 \\ \hline 9 & 10 & | & 0 \end{bmatrix}.$$

In this last matrix, think of the first two rows as constraints and the last row as the objective function. Then the dual maximization problem is as follows:

$$\text{Maximize} \quad z = 9x_1 + 10x_2$$
$$\text{subject to} \quad x_1 + 2x_2 \leq 8$$
$$5x_1 + 2x_2 \leq 16$$
$$x_1 \geq 0, x_2 \geq 0.$$

Example 3   Write the duals of the given minimization linear programming problems.

(a) Minimize $\quad w = 10y_1 + 8y_2$
subject to $\quad y_1 + 2y_2 \geq 2$
$$y_1 + y_2 \geq 5$$
$$y_1 \geq 0, y_2 \geq 0.$$

Solution Begin by writing the augmented matrix for the given problem:

$$\begin{bmatrix} 1 & 2 & | & 2 \\ 1 & 1 & | & 5 \\ 10 & 8 & | & 0 \end{bmatrix}.$$

Form the transpose of this matrix to get

$$\begin{bmatrix} 1 & 1 & | & 10 \\ 2 & 1 & | & 8 \\ 2 & 5 & | & 0 \end{bmatrix}.$$

The dual problem is stated from this second matrix as follows (using x instead of y):

$$\begin{aligned} \text{Maximize} \quad & z = 2x_1 + 5x_2 \\ \text{subject to} \quad & x_1 + x_2 \le 10 \\ & 2x_1 + x_2 \le 8 \\ & x_1 \ge 0, x_2 \ge 0. \end{aligned}$$

(b) Minimize $\quad w = 7y_1 + 5y_2 + 8y_3$

subject to $\quad 3y_1 + 2y_2 + y_3 \ge 10$
$$y_1 + y_2 + y_3 \ge 8$$
$$4y_1 + 5y_2 \qquad \ge 25$$
$$y_1 \ge 0, y_2 \ge 0, y_3 \ge 0.$$

Solution Find the augmented matrix for this problem, as in part (a). Form the dual matrix, which represents the following problem:

$$\begin{aligned} \text{Maximize} \quad & z = 10x_1 + 8x_2 + 25x_3 \\ \text{subject to} \quad & 3x_1 + x_2 + 4x_3 \le 7 \\ & 2x_1 + x_2 + 5x_3 \le 5 \\ & x_1 + x_2 \qquad \le 8 \\ & x_1 \ge 0, x_2 \ge 0, x_3 \ge 0. \quad \boxed{2} \end{aligned}$$

✓ **Checkpoint 2**

Write the dual of the following linear programming problem:

Minimize $w = 2y_1 + 5y_2 + 6y_3$
subject to $\quad 2y_1 + 3y_2 + y_3 \ge 15$
$$y_1 + y_2 + 2y_3 \ge 12$$
$$5y_1 + 3y_2 \qquad \ge 10$$
$$y_1 \ge 0, y_2 \ge 0, y_3 \ge 0.$$

In Example 3, all the constraints of the minimization problems were $\ge$ inequalities, while all those in the dual maximization problems were $\le$ inequalities. This is generally the case; inequalities are reversed when the dual problem is stated.

The following table shows the close connection between a problem and its dual.

Given Problem	Dual Problem
m variables	n variables
n constraints	m constraints (m slack variables)
Coefficients from objective function	Constraint constants
Constraint constants	Coefficients from objective function

Now that you know how to construct the dual problem, we examine how it is related to the original problem and how both may be solved.

Example 4 Solve this problem and its dual:

$$\begin{aligned} \text{Minimize} \quad & w = 8y_1 + 16y_2 \\ \text{subject to} \quad & y_1 + 5y_2 \ge 9 \\ & 2y_1 + 2y_2 \ge 10 \\ & y_1 \ge 0, y_2 \ge 0. \end{aligned}$$

Solution In Example 2, we saw that the dual problem is

$$\text{Maximize} \quad z = 9x_1 + 10x_2$$
$$\text{subject to} \quad x_1 + 2x_2 \leq 8$$
$$5x_1 + 2x_2 \leq 16$$
$$x_1 \geq 0, x_2 \geq 0.$$

In this case, both the original problem and the dual may be solved geometrically, as in Section 7.2. Figure 7.32(a) shows the region of feasible solutions for the original minimization problem, and Checkpoint 3 shows that

the minimum value of w is 48 at the vertex (4, 1).

Figure 7.32(b) shows the region of feasible solutions for the dual maximization problem, and Checkpoint 4 shows that

the maximum value of z is 48 at the vertex (2, 3).

Even though the regions and the corner points are different, the minimization problem and its dual have the same solution, 48.

Checkpoint 3

Use the corner points in Figure 7.32(a) to find the minimum value of $w = 8y_1 + 16y_2$ and where it occurs.

Checkpoint 4

Use Figure 7.32(b) to find the maximum value of $z = 9x_1 + 10x_2$ and where it occurs.

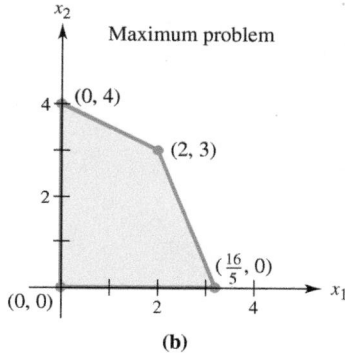

Figure 7.32

The next theorem, whose proof requires advanced methods, guarantees that what happened in Example 4 happens in the general case as well.

Theorem of Duality

The objective function w of a minimizing linear programming problem takes on a minimum value if, and only if, the objective function z of the corresponding dual maximizing problem takes on a maximum value. The maximum value of z equals the minimum value of w.

Geometric solution methods were used in Example 4, but the simplex method can also be used. In fact, the final simplex tableau shows the solutions for both the original minimization problem and the dual maximization problem, as illustrated in the next example.

Example 5 Use the simplex method to solve the minimization problem in Example 4.

Solution First, set up the dual problem, as in Example 4:

$$\text{Maximize} \quad z = 9x_1 + 10x_2$$
$$\text{subject to} \quad x_1 + 2x_2 \leq 8$$
$$5x_1 + 2x_2 \leq 16$$
$$x_1 \geq 0, x_2 \geq 0.$$

This is a maximization problem in standard form, so it can be solved by the simplex method. Use slack variables to write the inequalities and the objective function as equations:

$$
\begin{aligned}
x_1 + 2x_2 + s_1 &= 8 \\
5x_1 + 2x_2 + s_2 &= 16 \\
-9x_1 - 10x_2 + z &= 0,
\end{aligned}
$$

with $x_1 \geq 0, x_2 \geq 0, s_1 \geq 0$, and $s_2 \geq 0$. So the initial tableau is

$$
\begin{array}{cccc}
x_1 & x_2 & s_1 & s_2 \\
\end{array}
\qquad \text{Quotients}
$$

$$
\left[
\begin{array}{cccc|c}
1 & 2 & 1 & 0 & 8 \\
5 & 2 & 0 & 1 & 16 \\
\hline
-9 & -10 & 0 & 0 & 0
\end{array}
\right]
\begin{array}{l}
8/2 = 4 \\
16/2 = 8 \\
\end{array}
$$

The quotients show that the first pivot is the 2 shaded in blue. Pivoting is done as follows:

$$
\begin{array}{cccc}
x_1 & x_2 & s_1 & s_2 \\
\end{array}
$$

$$
\left[
\begin{array}{cccc|c}
\frac{1}{2} & 1 & \frac{1}{2} & 0 & 4 \\
4 & 0 & -1 & 1 & 8 \\
\hline
-4 & 0 & 5 & 0 & 40
\end{array}
\right]
\begin{array}{l}
\frac{1}{2}R_1 \\
-2R_1 + R_2 \\
10R_1 + R_3
\end{array}
$$

✓ **Checkpoint 5**

In the second tableau, find the next pivot.

Checkpoint 5 shows that the new pivot is the 4 in row 2, column 1. ☑5 Pivoting leads to the final simplex tableau:

$$
\begin{array}{cccc}
x_1 & x_2 & s_1 & s_2 \\
\end{array}
$$

$$
\left[
\begin{array}{cccc|c}
0 & 1 & \frac{5}{8} & -\frac{1}{8} & 3 \\
1 & 0 & -\frac{1}{4} & \frac{1}{4} & 2 \\
\hline
0 & 0 & 4 & 1 & 48
\end{array}
\right]
\begin{array}{l}
-\frac{1}{2}R_2 + R_1 \\
\frac{1}{4}R_2 \\
4R_2 + R_3
\end{array}
$$

The final simplex tableau shows that the maximum value of 48 occurs when $x_1 = 2$ and $x_2 = 3$. In Example 4, we saw that the minimum value of 48 occurs when $y_1 = 4$ and $y_2 = 1$. Note that this information appears in the last row (shown in blue). The minimum value of 48 is in the lower right-hand corner, and the values where this occurs ($y_1 = 4$ and $y_2 = 1$) are in the last row at the bottom of the slack-variable columns.

A minimization problem that meets the conditions listed after Example 1 can be solved by the method used in Example 5 and summarized here.

Solving Minimization Problems with Duals

1. Find the dual standard maximization problem.[*]
2. Use the simplex method to solve the dual maximization problem.
3. Read the optimal solution of the original minimization problem from the final simplex tableau:

   y_1 is the last entry in the column corresponding to the first slack variable;

   y_2 is the last entry in the column corresponding to the second slack variable; and so on.

   These values of y_1, y_2, y_3, etc., produce the minimum value of w, which is the entry in the lower right-hand corner of the tableau.

---

[*]The coefficients of the objective function in the minimization problem are the constants on the right side of the constraints in the dual maximization problem. So when all these coefficients are nonnegative (condition 2), the dual problem is in standard maximum form.

Example 6

$$\text{Minimize} \quad w = 3y_1 + 2y_2$$
$$\text{subject to} \quad y_1 + 3y_2 \geq 6$$
$$2y_1 + y_2 \geq 3$$
$$y_1 \geq 0, y_2 \geq 0.$$

Solution   Use the given information to write the matrix:

$$\begin{bmatrix} 1 & 3 & | & 6 \\ 2 & 1 & | & 3 \\ \hline 3 & 2 & | & 0 \end{bmatrix}.$$

Transpose to get the following matrix for the dual problem:

$$\begin{bmatrix} 1 & 2 & | & 3 \\ 3 & 1 & | & 2 \\ \hline 6 & 3 & | & 0 \end{bmatrix}.$$

Write the dual problem from this matrix as follows:

$$\text{Maximize} \quad z = 6x_1 + 3x_2$$
$$\text{subject to} \quad x_1 + 2x_2 \leq 3$$
$$3x_1 + x_2 \leq 2$$
$$x_1 \geq 0, x_2 \geq 0.$$

Solve this standard maximization problem by the simplex method. Start by introducing slack variables, giving the system

$$x_1 + 2x_2 + s_1 \qquad\quad = 3$$
$$3x_1 + x_2 \qquad + s_2 \quad = 2$$
$$-6x_1 - 3x_2 - 0s_1 - 0s_2 + z = 0,$$

with $x_1 \geq 0, x_2 \geq 0, s_1 \geq 0,$ and $s_2 \geq 0.$

The initial tableau for this system is

$$\begin{array}{cccc} x_1 & x_2 & s_1 & s_2 \end{array}$$
$$\begin{bmatrix} 1 & 2 & 1 & 0 & | & 3 \\ \mathbf{3} & 1 & 0 & 1 & | & 2 \\ \hline -6 & -3 & 0 & 0 & | & 0 \end{bmatrix}, \qquad \begin{array}{l} \text{Quotients} \\ 3/1 = 3 \\ 2/3 \end{array}$$

with the pivot as indicated. Two rounds of pivoting produce the following final tableau:

$$\begin{array}{cccc} x_1 & x_2 & s_1 & s_2 \end{array}$$
$$\begin{bmatrix} 0 & 1 & \frac{3}{5} & -\frac{1}{5} & | & \frac{7}{5} \\ 1 & 0 & -\frac{1}{5} & \frac{2}{5} & | & \frac{1}{5} \\ \hline 0 & 0 & \frac{3}{5} & \frac{9}{5} & | & \frac{27}{5} \end{bmatrix}.$$
$$\qquad\qquad\quad y_1 \quad\; y_2 \quad\; w$$

As indicated in blue below the final tableau, the last entries in the columns corresponding to the slack variables (s_1 and s_2) give the values of the original variables y_1 and y_2 that produce the minimal value of w. This minimal value of w appears in the lower right-hand corner (and is the same as the maximal value of z in the dual problem). So the solution of the given minimization problem is as follows:

The minimum value of $w = 3y_1 + 2y_2$, subject to the given constraints, is $\frac{27}{5}$ and occurs when $y_1 = \frac{3}{5}$ and $y_2 = \frac{9}{5}$. ✓ 6

✓ **Checkpoint 6**

$$\text{Minimize} \quad w = 10y_1 + 8y_2$$
$$\text{subject to} \quad y_1 + 2y_2 \geq 2$$
$$y_1 + y_2 \geq 5$$
$$y_1 \geq 0, y_2 \geq 0.$$

Example 7   A minimization problem in three variables was solved by the use of duals. The final simplex tableau for the dual maximization problem is shown here:

$$
\begin{array}{cccccc}
x_1 & x_2 & x_3 & s_1 & s_2 & s_3 \\
\end{array}
$$

$$
\left[
\begin{array}{cccccc|c}
3 & 1 & 1 & 0 & 9 & 0 & 1 \\
13 & -1 & 0 & 1 & -2 & 0 & 10 \\
9 & 10 & 0 & 0 & 7 & 1 & 7 \\
\hline
5 & 1 & 0 & 4 & 1 & 7 & 28
\end{array}
\right].
$$

(a) What is the optimal solution of the dual minimization problem?

Solution   Looking at the bottom of the columns corresponding to the slack variables s_1, s_2, and s_3, we see that the solution of the minimization problem is

$$y_1 = 4, \qquad y_2 = 1, \qquad \text{and} \qquad y_3 = 7, \qquad \text{with a minimal value of } w = 28.$$

(b) What is the optimal solution of the dual maximization problem?

Solution   Since s_1, s_2, and s_3 are slack variables by part (a), the variables in the dual problem are x_1, x_2, and x_3. Read the solution from the final tableau, as in Sections 7.4 and 7.5:

$$x_1 = 0, \qquad x_2 = 0, \qquad \text{and} \qquad x_3 = 1, \qquad \text{with a maximal value of } z = 28.$$

Further Uses of the Dual

The dual is useful not only in solving minimization problems, but also in seeing how small changes in one variable will affect the value of the objective function. For example, suppose an animal breeder needs at least 6 units per day of nutrient A and at least 3 units of nutrient B and that the breeder can choose between two different feeds: feed 1 and feed 2. Find the minimum cost for the breeder if each bag of feed 1 costs \$3 and provides 1 unit of nutrient A and 2 units of B, while each bag of feed 2 costs \$2 and provides 3 units of nutrient A and 1 of B.

If y_1 represents the number of bags of feed 1 and y_2 represents the number of bags of feed 2, the given information leads to the following minimization problem:

$$
\begin{aligned}
\text{Minimize} \quad & w = 3y_1 + 2y_2 \\
\text{subject to} \quad & y_1 + 3y_2 \geq 6 \\
& 2y_1 + y_2 \geq 3 \\
& y_1 \geq 0, y_2 \geq 0.
\end{aligned}
$$

This minimization linear programming problem is the one we solved in Example 6 of this section. In that example, we formed the dual and reached the following final tableau:

$$
\begin{array}{cccc}
x_1 & x_2 & s_1 & s_2 \\
\end{array}
$$

$$
\left[
\begin{array}{cccc|c}
0 & 1 & \frac{3}{5} & -\frac{1}{5} & \frac{7}{5} \\
1 & 0 & -\frac{1}{5} & \frac{2}{5} & \frac{1}{5} \\
\hline
0 & 0 & \frac{3}{5} & \frac{9}{5} & \frac{27}{5}
\end{array}
\right].
$$

This final tableau shows that the breeder will obtain minimum feed costs by using $\frac{3}{5}$ bag of feed 1 and $\frac{9}{5}$ bags of feed 2 per day, for a daily cost of $\frac{27}{5} = 5.40$ dollars.

Now look at the data from the feed problem shown in the following table:

	Units of Nutrient (per Bag)		Cost per Bag
	A	B	
Feed 1	1	2	\$3
Feed 2	3	1	\$2
Minimum Nutrient Needed	6	3	

If x_1 and x_2 are the cost *per unit* of nutrients A and B, the constraints of the dual problem can be stated as follows (see pages 383–384):

$$\text{Cost of feed 1:} \qquad x_1 + 2x_2 \leq 3$$
$$\text{Cost of feed 2:} \qquad 3x_1 + x_2 \leq 2.$$

The solution of the dual problem, which maximizes nutrients, also can be read from the final tableau above:

$$x_1 = \frac{1}{5} = .20 \qquad \text{and} \qquad x_2 = \frac{7}{5} = 1.40.$$

This means that a unit of nutrient A costs $\frac{1}{5}$ of a dollar $= \$.20$, while a unit of nutrient B costs $\frac{7}{5}$ dollars $= \$1.40$. The minimum daily cost, $\$5.40$, is found as follows.

$$(\$.20 \text{ per unit of } A) \times (6 \text{ units of } A) = \$1.20$$
$$\underline{+ \ (\$1.40 \text{ per unit of } B) \times (3 \text{ units of } B) = \$4.20}$$
$$\text{Minimum daily cost} = \$5.40.$$

The numbers .20 and 1.40 are called the **shadow costs** of the nutrients. These two numbers from the dual, $\$.20$ and $\$1.40$, also allow the breeder to estimate feed costs for "small" changes in nutrient requirements. For example, an increase of 1 unit in the requirement for each nutrient would produce a total cost as follows:

$5.40	6 units of A, 3 of B
.20	1 extra unit of A
1.40	1 extra unit of B
$7.00.	Total cost per day

7.6 Exercises

Find the transpose of each matrix. (See Example 1.)

1. $\begin{bmatrix} 3 & -4 & 5 \\ 1 & 10 & 7 \\ 0 & 3 & 6 \end{bmatrix}$

2. $\begin{bmatrix} 3 & -5 & 9 & 4 \\ 1 & 6 & -7 & 0 \\ 4 & 18 & 11 & 9 \end{bmatrix}$

3. $\begin{bmatrix} 3 & 0 & 14 & -5 & 3 \\ 4 & 17 & 8 & -6 & 1 \end{bmatrix}$

4. $\begin{bmatrix} 15 & -6 & -2 \\ 13 & -1 & 11 \\ 10 & 12 & -3 \\ 24 & 1 & 0 \end{bmatrix}$

State the dual problem for each of the given problems, but do not solve it. (See Examples 2 and 3.)

5. Minimize $w = 3y_1 + 5y_2$
subject to $\quad 3y_1 + y_2 \geq 4$
$\qquad\qquad -y_1 + 2y_2 \geq 6$
$\qquad\qquad y_1 \geq 0, y_2 \geq 0.$

6. Minimize $w = 4y_1 + 7y_2$
subject to $\quad y_1 + y_2 \geq 17$
$\qquad\qquad 3y_1 + 6y_2 \geq 21$
$\qquad\qquad 2y_1 + 4y_2 \geq 19$
$\qquad\qquad y_1 \geq 0, y_2 \geq 0.$

7. Minimize $w = 2y_1 + 8y_2$
subject to $\quad y_1 + 7y_2 \geq 18$
$\qquad\qquad 4y_1 + y_2 \geq 15$
$\qquad\qquad 5y_1 + 3y_2 \geq 20$
$\qquad\qquad y_1 \geq 0, y_2 \geq 0.$

8. Minimize $w = y_1 + 2y_2 + 6y_3$
subject to $\quad 3y_1 + 4y_2 + 6y_3 \geq 8$
$\qquad\qquad y_1 + 5y_2 + 2y_3 \geq 12$
$\qquad\qquad y_1 \geq 0, y_2 \geq 0, y_3 \geq 0.$

9. Minimize $w = 5y_1 + y_2 + 3y_3$
subject to $\quad 7y_1 + 6y_2 + 8y_3 \geq 18$
$\qquad\qquad 4y_1 + 5y_2 + 10y_3 \geq 20$
$\qquad\qquad y_1 \geq 0, y_2 \geq 0, y_3 \geq 0.$

10. Minimize $w = 4y_1 + 3y_2 + y_3$
subject to $\quad y_1 + 2y_2 + 3y_3 \geq 115$
$\qquad\qquad 2y_1 + y_2 + 8y_3 \geq 200$
$\qquad\qquad y_1 \qquad - y_3 \geq 50$
$\qquad\qquad y_1 \geq 0, y_2 \geq 0, y_3 \geq 0.$

11. Minimize $\quad w = 8y_1 + 9y_2 + 3y_3$

subject to $\quad y_1 + y_2 + \;\; y_3 \geq 5$

$y_1 + y_2 \qquad\quad \geq 4$

$2y_1 + y_2 + 3y_3 \geq 15$

$y_1 \geq 0, y_2 \geq 0, y_3 \geq 0.$

12. Minimize $\quad w = y_1 + 2y_2 + y_3 + 5y_4$

subject to $\quad y_1 + y_2 + \;\; y_3 + y_4 \geq 50$

$3y_1 + y_2 + 2y_3 + y_4 \geq 100$

$y_1 \geq 0, y_2 \geq 0, y_3 \geq 0, y_4 \geq 0.$

Use duality to solve the problem that was set up in the given exercise.

13. Exercise 9 $\qquad$ **14.** Exercise 8

15. Exercise 11 $\qquad$ **16.** Exercise 12

Use duality to solve the given problems. (See Examples 5 and 6.)

17. Minimize $\quad w = 2y_1 + y_2 + 3y_3$

subject to $\quad y_1 + y_2 + y_3 \geq 100$

$2y_1 + y_2 \qquad \geq 50$

$y_1 \geq 0, y_2 \geq 0, y_3 \geq 0.$

18. Minimize $\quad w = 2y_1 + 4y_2$

subject to $\quad 4y_1 + 2y_2 \geq 10$

$4y_1 + \;\; y_2 \geq 8$

$2y_1 + \;\; y_2 \geq 12$

$y_1 \geq 0, y_2 \geq 0.$

19. Minimize $\quad w = 3y_1 + y_2 + 4y_3$

subject to $\quad 2y_1 + \;\; y_2 + \;\; y_3 \geq 6$

$y_1 + 2y_2 + \;\; y_3 \geq 8$

$2y_1 + \;\; y_2 + 2y_3 \geq 12$

$y_1 \geq 0, y_2 \geq 0, y_3 \geq 0.$

20. Minimize $\quad w = y_1 + y_2 + 3y_3$

subject to $\quad 2y_1 + 6y_2 + \;\; y_3 \geq 8$

$y_1 + 2y_2 + 4y_3 \geq 12$

$y_1 \geq 0, y_2 \geq 0, y_3 \geq 0.$

21. Minimize $\quad w = 6y_1 + 4y_2 + 2y_3$

subject to $\quad 2y_1 + 2y_2 + \;\; y_3 \geq 2$

$y_1 + 3y_2 + 2y_3 \geq 3$

$y_1 + \;\; y_2 + 2y_3 \geq 4$

$y_1 \geq 0, y_2 \geq 0, y_3 \geq 0.$

22. Minimize $\quad w = 12y_1 + 10y_2 + 7y_3$

subject to $\quad 2y_1 + \;\; y_2 + y_3 \geq 7$

$y_1 + 2y_2 + y_3 \geq 4$

$y_1 \geq 0, y_2 \geq 0, y_3 \geq 0.$

23. Minimize $\quad w = 20y_1 + 12y_2 + 40y_3$

subject to $\quad y_1 + y_2 + 5y_3 \geq 20$

$2y_1 + y_2 + \;\; y_3 \geq 30$

$y_1 \geq 0, y_2 \geq 0, y_3 \geq 0.$

24. Minimize $\quad w = 4y_1 + 5y_2$

subject to $\quad 10y_1 + \;\; 5y_2 \geq 100$

$20y_1 + 10y_2 \geq 150$

$y_1 \geq 0, y_2 \geq 0.$

25. Minimize $\quad w = 4y_1 + 2y_2 + y_3$

subject to $\quad y_1 + y_2 + \;\; y_3 \geq 4$

$3y_1 + y_2 + 3y_3 \geq 6$

$y_1 + y_2 + 3y_3 \geq 5$

$y_1 \geq 0, y_2 \geq 0, y_3 \geq 0.$

26. Minimize $\quad w = 3y_1 + 2y_2$

subject to $\quad 2y_1 + 3y_2 \geq 60$

$y_1 + 4y_2 \geq 40$

$y_1 \geq 0, y_2 \geq 0.$

27. **Health** Glenn Russell, who is dieting, requires two food supplements: I and II. He can get these supplements from two different products—A and B—as shown in the following table:

		Supplement (Grams per Serving)	
		I	II
Product	A	4	2
	B	2	5

Glenn's physician has recommended that he include at least 20 grams of supplement I and 18 grams of supplement II in his diet. If product A costs 24¢ per serving and product B costs 40¢ per serving, how can he satisfy these requirements most economically?

28. **Business** An animal food must provide at least 54 units of vitamins and 60 calories per serving. One gram of soybean meal provides at least 2.5 units of vitamins and 5 calories. One gram of meat by-products provides at least 4.5 units of vitamins and 3 calories. One gram of grain provides at least 5 units of vitamins and 10 calories. If a gram of soybean meal costs 8¢, a gram of meat by-products 9¢, and a gram of grain 10¢, what mixture of these three ingredients will provide the required vitamins and calories at minimum cost?

29. **Business** A brewery produces regular beer and a lower-carbohydrate "light" beer. Steady customers of the brewery buy 12 units of regular beer and 10 units of light beer monthly. While setting up the brewery to produce the beers, the management decides to produce extra beer, beyond the need to satisfy the steady customers. The cost per unit of regular beer is $36,000, and the cost per unit of light beer is $48,000. Every unit of regular beer brings in $100,000 in revenue, while every unit of light beer brings in $300,000. The brewery wants at least $7,000,000 in revenue. At least 20 additional units of beer can be sold. How much of each type of beer should be made so as to minimize total production costs?

30. **Business** Joan McKee has a part-time job conducting public-opinion interviews. She has found that a political interview takes 45 minutes and a market interview takes 55 minutes. To allow more time for her full-time job, she needs to minimize the time she spends doing interviews. Unfortunately, to keep her part-time job, she must complete at least 8 interviews each week. Also, she must earn at least $60 per week at this job, at which she earns $8 for each political interview and $10 for each market interview. Finally, to stay in good standing with her supervisor, she must earn at least 40 bonus points per week; she receives 6 bonus points for each political interview and 5 points for each market interview. How many of each interview should she do each week to minimize the time spent?

31. You are given the following linear programming problem (P)[*]:

$$\text{Maximize} \quad z = x_1 + 2x_2$$
$$\text{subject to} \quad -2x_1 + x_2 \geq 1$$
$$x_1 - 2x_2 \geq 1$$
$$x_1 \geq 0, x_2 \geq 0.$$

The dual of (P) is (D). Which of the following statements is true?

(a) (P) has no feasible solution and the objective function of (D) is unbounded.

(b) (D) has no feasible solution and the objective function of (P) is unbounded.

(c) The objective functions of both (P) and (D) are unbounded.

(d) Both (P) and (D) have optimal solutions.

(e) Neither (P) nor (D) has a feasible solution.

32. Business Refer to the end of this section in the text, on minimizing the daily cost of feeds.

(a) Find a combination of feeds that will cost $7.00 and give 7 units of A and 4 units of B.

(b) Use the dual variables to predict the daily cost of feed if the requirements change to 5 units of A and 4 units of B. Find a combination of feeds to meet these requirements at the predicted price.

33. Business A small toy-manufacturing firm has 200 squares of felt, 600 ounces of stuffing, and 90 feet of trim available to make two types of toys: a small bear and a monkey. The bear requires 1 square of felt and 4 ounces of stuffing. The monkey requires 2 squares of felt, 3 ounces of stuffing, and 1 foot of trim. The firm makes $1 profit on each bear and $1.50 profit on

[*]Problem 2 from "November 1989 course 130 Examination Operations Research" of the *Education and Examination Committee of the Society of Actuaries.* Reprinted by permission of the Society of Actuaries.

each monkey. The linear programming problem to maximize profit is

$$\text{Maximize} \quad z = x_1 + 1.5x_2$$
$$\text{subject to} \quad x_1 + 2x_2 \leq 200$$
$$4x_1 + 3x_2 \leq 600$$
$$x_2 \leq 90$$
$$x_1 \geq 0, x_2 \geq 0.$$

The final simplex tableau is

$$\begin{bmatrix} 1 & 0 & -.6 & .4 & 0 & | & 120 \\ 0 & 0 & -.8 & .2 & 1 & | & 50 \\ 0 & 1 & .8 & -.2 & 0 & | & 40 \\ \hline 0 & 0 & .6 & .1 & 0 & | & 180 \end{bmatrix}.$$

(a) What is the corresponding dual problem?

(b) What is the optimal solution to the dual problem?

(c) Use the shadow values to estimate the profit the firm will make if its supply of felt increases to 210 squares.

(d) How much profit will the firm make if its supply of stuffing is cut to 590 ounces and its supply of trim is cut to 80 feet?

34. Refer to Example 1 in Section 7.5.

(a) Give the dual problem.

(b) Use the shadow values to estimate the farmer's profit if land is cut to 90 acres, but capital increases to $21,000.

(c) Suppose the farmer has 110 acres, but only $19,000. Find the optimal profit and the planting strategy that will produce this profit.

✓ **Checkpoint Answers**

1. (a) $\begin{bmatrix} 2 & 6 & 1 \\ 4 & 3 & 5 \end{bmatrix}$ **(b)** $\begin{bmatrix} 4 & 3 & 5 \\ 7 & 2 & 8 \\ 10 & 6 & 12 \end{bmatrix}$

2. Maximize $z = 15x_1 + 12x_2 + 10x_3$
subject to $2x_1 + x_2 + 5x_3 \leq 2$
$3x_1 + x_2 + 3x_3 \leq 5$
$x_1 + 2x_2 \leq 6$
$x_1 \geq 0, x_2 \geq 0, x_3 \geq 0.$

3. 48 when $y_1 = 4$ and $y_2 = 1$ **4.** 48 when $x_1 = 2$ and $x_2 = 3$

5. The 4 in row 2, column 1

6. $y_1 = 0$ and $y_2 = 5$, for a minimum of 40

7.7 The Simplex Method: Nonstandard Problems

📄 **NOTE** Section 7.7 is independent of Section 7.6 and may be read first, if desired.

So far, the simplex method has been used to solve problems in which the variables are nonnegative and all the other constraints are of one type (either all $\leq$ or all $\geq$). Now we extend the simplex method to linear programming problems with nonnegative variables and mixed constraints ($\leq$, $=$, and $\geq$).

The solution method to be used here requires that all inequality constraints be written so that the constant on the right side is nonnegative. For instance, the inequality

$$4x_1 + 5x_2 - 12x_3 \leq -30$$

can be replaced by the equivalent one obtained by multiplying both sides by -1 and reversing the direction of the inequality sign:

$$-4x_1 - 5x_2 + 12x_3 \geq 30.$$

Maximization with $\leq$ and $\geq$ Constraints

As is always the case when the simplex method is involved, each inequality constraint must be written as an equation. Constraints involving $\leq$ are converted to equations by adding a nonnegative slack variable, as in Section 7.4. Similarly, constraints involving $\geq$ are converted to equations by *subtracting* a nonnegative **surplus variable**. For example, the inequality $2x_1 - x_2 + 5x_3 \geq 12$ is written as

$$2x_1 - x_2 + 5x_3 - s_1 = 12,$$

where $s_1 \geq 0$. The surplus variable s_1 represents the amount by which $2x_1 - x_2 + 5x_3$ exceeds 12.

Example 1   Restate the following problem in terms of equations, and write its initial simplex tableau:

$$\begin{aligned} \text{Maximize} \quad & z = 4x_1 + 10x_2 + 6x_3 \\ \text{subject to} \quad & x_1 + 4x_2 + 4x_3 \geq 8 \\ & x_1 + 3x_2 + 2x_3 \leq 6 \\ & 3x_1 + 4x_2 + 8x_3 \leq 22 \\ & x_1 \geq 0, x_2 \geq 0, x_3 \geq 0. \end{aligned}$$

Solution   In order to write the constraints as equations, subtract a surplus variable from the $\geq$ constraint and add a slack variable to each $\leq$ constraint. So the problem becomes

$$\begin{aligned} \text{Maximize} \quad & z = 4x_1 + 10x_2 + 6x_3 \\ \text{subject to} \quad & x_1 + 4x_2 + 4x_3 - s_1 \qquad\qquad = 8 \\ & x_1 + 3x_2 + 2x_3 \qquad + s_2 \qquad = 6 \\ & 3x_1 + 4x_2 + 8x_3 \qquad\qquad + s_3 = 22 \\ & x_1 \geq 0, x_2 \geq 0, x_3 \geq 0, s_1 \geq 0, s_2 \geq 0, s_3 \geq 0. \end{aligned}$$

Write the objective function as $-4x_1 - 10x_2 - 6x_3 + z = 0$ and use the coefficients of the four equations to write the initial simplex tableau (omitting the z column):

✓ **Checkpoint 1**

(a) Restate this problem in terms of equations:

$$\begin{aligned} \text{Maximize} \quad & z = 3x_1 - 2x_2 \\ \text{subject to} \quad & 2x_1 + 3x_2 \leq 8 \\ & 6x_1 - 2x_2 \geq 3 \\ & x_1 + 4x_2 \geq 1 \\ & x_1 \geq 0, x_2 \geq 0. \end{aligned}$$

(b) Write the initial simplex tableau.

$$\begin{array}{cccccc} x_1 & x_2 & x_3 & s_1 & s_2 & s_3 \\ \left[\begin{array}{cccccc|c} 1 & 4 & 4 & -1 & 0 & 0 & 8 \\ 1 & 3 & 2 & 0 & 1 & 0 & 6 \\ \hline 3 & 4 & 8 & 0 & 0 & 1 & 22 \\ -4 & -10 & -6 & 0 & 0 & 0 & 0 \end{array}\right] \end{array}$$

The tableau in Example 1 resembles those which have appeared previously, and similar terminology is used. The variables whose columns have one entry that is ± 1 and the rest that are 0 will be called **basic variables**; the other variables are nonbasic. A solution obtained by setting the nonbasic variables equal to 0 and solving for the basic variables (by looking at the constants in the right-hand column) will be called a **basic solution**. A basic solution that is feasible is called a **basic feasible solution**. In the tableau of Example 1, for instance, the basic variables are s_1, s_2, and s_3, and the basic solution is

$$x_1 = 0, \quad x_2 = 0, \quad x_3 = 0, \quad s_1 = -8, \quad s_2 = 6, \quad \text{and} \quad s_3 = 22.$$

However, because one variable is negative, this solution is not feasible. ✔2

The solution method for problems such as the one in Example 1 consists of two stages. **Stage I** consists of finding a basic *feasible* solution that can be used as the starting point for the simplex method. (This stage is unnecessary in a standard maximization problem, because the solution given by the initial tableau is always feasible.) There are many systematic ways of finding a feasible solution, all of which depend on the fact that row operations produce a tableau that represents a system with the same solutions as the original one. One such technique is explained in the next example. Since the immediate goal is to find a feasible solution, not necessarily an optimal one, the procedures for choosing pivots differ from those in the ordinary simplex method.

✓**Checkpoint 2**

State the basic solution given by each tableau. Is it feasible?

(a)

x_1	x_2	s_1	s_2	s_3	
3	−5	1	0	0	12
4	7	0	1	0	6
1	3	0	0	−1	5
−7	4	0	0	0	0

(b)

x_1	x_2	x_3	s_1	s_2	
9	8	−1	1	0	12
−5	3	0	0	1	7
4	2	3	0	0	0

Example 2   Find a basic feasible solution for the problem in Example 1, whose initial tableau is

x_1	x_2	x_3	s_1	s_2	s_3	
1	4	4	−1	0	0	8
1	3	2	0	1	0	6
3	4	8	0	0	1	22
−4	−10	−6	0	0	0	0

Solution   In the basic solution given by this tableau, s_1 has a negative value. The only nonzero entry in its column is the −1 in row 1. Choose any *positive* entry in row 1 except the entry on the far right. The column that the chosen entry is in will be the pivot column. We choose the first positive entry in row 1: the 1 in column 1. The pivot row is determined in the usual way by considering quotients (the constant at the right end of the row, divided by the positive entry in the pivot column) in each row except the objective row:

$$\frac{8}{1} = 8, \qquad \frac{6}{1} = 6, \qquad \frac{22}{3} = 7\frac{1}{3}.$$

The smallest quotient is 6, so the pivot is the 1 in row 2, column 1. Pivoting in the usual way leads to the tableau

x_1	x_2	x_3	s_1	s_2	s_3		
0	1	2	−1	−1	0	2	$-R_2 + R_1$
1	3	2	0	1	0	6	
0	−5	2	0	−3	1	4	$-3R_2 + R_3$
0	2	2	0	4	0	24	$4R_2 + R_4$

and the basic solution

$$x_1 = 6, \quad x_2 = 0, \quad x_3 = 0, \quad s_1 = -2, \quad s_2 = 0, \quad \text{and} \quad s_3 = 4.$$

Since the basic variable s_1 is negative, this solution is not feasible. So we repeat the pivoting process. The s_1 column has a −1 in row 1, so we choose a positive entry in that row, namely, the 1 in row 1, column 2. This choice makes column 2 the pivot column. The pivot row is determined by the quotients $\frac{2}{1} = 2$ and $\frac{6}{3} = 2$. (Negative entries in the pivot column and the entry in the objective row are not used.) Since there is a tie, we can choose either row 1 or row 2. We choose row 1 and use the 1 in row 1, column 2, as the pivot. Pivoting produces the tableau

$$
\begin{array}{cccccc}
x_1 & x_2 & x_3 & s_1 & s_2 & s_3 \\
\end{array}
$$

$$
\begin{bmatrix}
0 & 1 & 2 & -1 & -1 & 0 & 2 \\
1 & 0 & -4 & 3 & 4 & 0 & 0 \\
0 & 0 & 12 & -5 & -8 & 1 & 14 \\
0 & 0 & -2 & 2 & 6 & 0 & 20
\end{bmatrix}
\quad
\begin{array}{l}
\\
-3R_1 + R_2 \\
5R_1 + R_3 \\
-2R_1 + R_4
\end{array}
$$

and the basic *feasible* solution

$$x_1 = 0, \qquad x_2 = 2, \qquad x_3 = 0, \qquad s_1 = 0, \qquad s_2 = 0, \qquad \text{and} \qquad s_3 = 14.$$

Once a basic feasible solution has been found, Stage I is ended. The procedures used in Stage I are summarized here.[*]

Finding a Basic Feasible Solution

1. If any basic variable has a negative value, locate the -1 in that variable's column and note the row it is in.

2. In the row determined in Step 1, choose a positive entry (other than the one at the far right) and note the column it is in. This is the pivot column.

3. Use the positive entries in the pivot column (except in the objective row) to form quotients and select the pivot.

4. Pivot as usual, which results in the pivot column having one entry that is 1 and the rest that are 0's.

5. Repeat Steps 1–4 until every basic variable is nonnegative, so that the basic solution given by the tableau is feasible. If it ever becomes impossible to continue, then the problem has no feasible solution.

One way to make the required choices systematically is to choose the first possibility in each case (going from the top for rows and from the left for columns). However, any choice meeting the required conditions may be used. For maximum efficiency, it is usually best to choose the pivot column in Step 2, so that the pivot is in the same row chosen in Step 1, if this is possible. ✔3

In **Stage II**, the simplex method is applied as usual to the tableau that produced the basic feasible solution in Stage I. Just as in Section 7.4, each round of pivoting replaces the basic feasible solution of one tableau with the basic feasible solution of a new tableau in such a way that the value of the objective function is increased, until an optimal value is obtained (or it becomes clear that no optimal solution exists).

✓ **Checkpoint 3**

The initial tableau of a maximization problem is shown. Use column 1 as the pivot column for carrying out Stage I, and state the basic feasible solution that results.

$$
\begin{array}{cccc}
x_1 & x_2 & s_1 & s_2 \\
\end{array}
$$

$$
\begin{bmatrix}
1 & 3 & 1 & 0 & 70 \\
2 & 4 & 0 & -1 & 50 \\
-8 & -10 & 0 & 0 & 0
\end{bmatrix}
$$

Example 3   Solve the linear programming problem in Example 1 of this section.

Solution   A basic feasible solution for this problem was found in Example 2 by using the tableau shown below. However, this solution is not maximal, because there is a negative indicator in the objective row. So we use the simplex method. The most negative

---

[*]Except in rare cases that do not occur in this book, this method either eventually produces a basic feasible solution or shows that one does not exist. The *two-phase method* using artificial variables, which is discussed in more advanced texts, works in all cases and often is more efficient.

indicator determines the pivot column, and the usual quotients determine that the number 2 in row 1, column 3, is the pivot:

x_1	x_2	x_3	s_1	s_2	s_3		Quotients
0	1	**2**	-1	-1	0	2	$2/2 \leftarrow$ Smallest
1	0	-4	3	4	0	0	
0	0	12	-5	-8	1	14	14/12
0	0	-2	2	6	0	20	

↑ —— Most negative indicator

Pivoting leads to the final tableau:

x_1	x_2	x_3	s_1	s_2	s_3		
0	$\frac{1}{2}$	1	$-\frac{1}{2}$	$-\frac{1}{2}$	0	1	$\frac{1}{2}R_1$
1	0	-4	3	4	0	0	
0	0	12	-5	-8	1	14	
0	0	-2	2	6	0	20	

x_1	x_2	x_3	s_1	s_2	s_3		
0	$\frac{1}{2}$	1	$-\frac{1}{2}$	$-\frac{1}{2}$	0	1	
1	2	0	1	2	0	4	$4R_1 + R_2$
0	-6	0	1	-2	1	2	$-12R_1 + R_3$
0	1	0	1	5	0	22	$2R_1 + R_4$

Therefore, the maximum value of z occurs when $x_1 = 4$, $x_2 = 0$, and $x_3 = 1$, in which case $z = 22$.

✓ **Checkpoint 4**

Complete Stage II and find an optimal solution for Checkpoint 3 on page 390. What is the optimal value of the objective function z?

Minimization Problems

When dealing with minimization problems, we use y_1, y_2, y_3, etc., as variables and denote the objective function by w. The two-stage method for maximization problems illustrated in Examples 1–3 also provides a means of solving minimization problems. To see why, consider this simple fact: When a number t gets smaller, $-t$ gets larger, and vice versa. For instance, if t goes from 6 down to -8, then $-t$ goes from -6 up to 8. Thus, if w is the objective function of a linear programming problem, the feasible solution that produces the minimum value of w also produces the maximum value of $-w$, and vice versa. Therefore, to solve a minimization problem with objective function w, we need only solve the maximization problem with the same constraints and objective function $z = -w$.

Example 4

Minimize $w = 2y_1 + y_2 - y_3$

subject to $\quad -y_1 - y_2 + y_3 \leq -4$

$y_1 + 3y_2 + 3y_3 \geq 6$

$y_1 \geq 0, y_2 \geq 0, y_3 \geq 0.$

Solution Make the constant in the first constraint positive by multiplying both sides by -1. Then solve this maximization problem:

Maximize $z = -w = -2y_1 - y_2 + y_3$

subject to $\quad y_1 + y_2 - y_3 \geq 4$

$y_1 + 3y_2 + 3y_3 \geq 6$

$y_1 \geq 0, y_2 \geq 0, y_3 \geq 0.$

Convert the constraints to equations by subtracting surplus variables, and set up the first tableau:

$$\begin{array}{ccccc} y_1 & y_2 & y_3 & s_1 & s_2 \\ \left[\begin{array}{ccccc|c} 1 & 1 & -1 & -1 & 0 & 4 \\ 1 & 3 & 3 & 0 & -1 & 6 \\ \hline 2 & 1 & -1 & 0 & 0 & 0 \end{array}\right]. \end{array}$$

The basic solution given by this tableau, namely, $y_1 = 0$, $y_2 = 0$, $y_3 = 0$, $s_1 = -4$, and $s_2 = -6$, is not feasible, so the procedures of Stage I must be used to find a basic feasible solution. In the column of the negative basic variable s_1, there is a -1 in row 1; we choose the first positive entry in that row, so that column 1 will be the pivot column. The quotients $\frac{4}{1} = 4$ and $\frac{6}{1} = 6$ show that the pivot is the 1 in row 1, column 1. Pivoting produces this tableau:

$$\begin{array}{ccccc} y_1 & y_2 & y_3 & s_1 & s_2 \\ \left[\begin{array}{ccccc|c} 1 & 1 & -1 & -1 & 0 & 4 \\ 0 & 2 & 4 & 1 & -1 & 2 \\ \hline 0 & -1 & 1 & 2 & 0 & -8 \end{array}\right]. \end{array} \quad \begin{array}{l} \\ -R_1 + R_2 \\ -2R_1 + R_3 \end{array}$$

The basic solution $y_1 = 4$, $y_2 = 0$, $y_3 = 0$, $s_1 = 0$, and $s_2 = -2$ is not feasible because s_2 is negative, so we repeat the process. We choose the first positive entry in row 2 (the row containing the -1 in the s_2 column), which is in column 2, so that column 2 is the pivot column. The relevant quotients are $\frac{4}{1} = 4$ and $\frac{2}{2} = 1$, so the pivot is the 2 in row 2, column 2. Pivoting produces a new tableau:

$$\begin{array}{ccccc} y_1 & y_2 & y_3 & s_1 & s_2 \\ \left[\begin{array}{ccccc|c} 1 & 1 & -1 & -1 & 0 & 4 \\ 0 & 1 & 2 & \frac{1}{2} & -\frac{1}{2} & 1 \\ \hline 0 & -1 & 1 & 2 & 0 & -8 \end{array}\right] \end{array} \quad \begin{array}{l} \\ \frac{1}{2}R_2 \\ \\ \end{array}$$

$$\begin{array}{ccccc} y_1 & y_2 & y_3 & s_1 & s_2 \\ \left[\begin{array}{ccccc|c} 1 & 0 & -3 & -\frac{3}{2} & \frac{1}{2} & 3 \\ 0 & 1 & 2 & \frac{1}{2} & -\frac{1}{2} & 1 \\ \hline 0 & 0 & 3 & \frac{5}{2} & -\frac{1}{2} & -7 \end{array}\right]. \end{array} \quad \begin{array}{l} -R_2 + R_1 \\ \\ R_2 + R_3 \end{array}$$

The basic solution $y_1 = 3$, $y_2 = 1$, $y_3 = 0$, $s_1 = 0$, and $s_2 = 0$ is feasible, so Stage I is complete. However, this solution is not optimal, because the objective row contains the negative indicator $-\frac{1}{2}$ in column 5. According to the simplex method, column 5 is the next pivot column. The only positive ratio, $3/\frac{1}{2} = 6$, is in row 1, so the pivot is $\frac{1}{2}$ in row 1, column 5. Pivoting produces the final tableau:

$$\begin{array}{ccccc} y_1 & y_2 & y_3 & s_1 & s_2 \\ \left[\begin{array}{ccccc|c} 2 & 0 & -6 & -3 & 1 & 6 \\ 0 & 1 & 2 & \frac{1}{2} & -\frac{1}{2} & 1 \\ \hline 0 & 0 & 3 & \frac{5}{2} & -\frac{1}{2} & -7 \end{array}\right] \end{array} \quad \begin{array}{l} 2R_1 \\ \\ \\ \end{array}$$

$$\begin{array}{ccccc} y_1 & y_2 & y_3 & s_1 & s_2 \\ \left[\begin{array}{ccccc|c} 2 & 0 & -6 & -3 & 1 & 6 \\ 1 & 1 & -1 & -1 & 0 & 4 \\ \hline 1 & 0 & 0 & 1 & 0 & -4 \end{array}\right]. \end{array} \quad \begin{array}{l} \\ \frac{1}{2}R_1 + R_2 \\ \frac{1}{2}R_1 + R_3 \end{array}$$

✓**Checkpoint 5**

Minimize $w = 2y_1 + 3y_2$
subject to $y_1 + y_2 \geq 10$
$2y_1 + y_2 \geq 16$
$y_1 \geq 0, y_2 \geq 0$.

Since there are no negative indicators, the solution given by this tableau ($y_1 = 0$, $y_2 = 4$, $y_3 = 0$, $s_1 = 0$, and $s_2 = 6$) is optimal. The maximum value of $z = -w$ is -4. Therefore, the minimum value of the original objective function w is $-(-4) = 4$, which occurs when $y_1 = 0$, $y_2 = 4$, and $y_3 = 0$. ✓5

Equation Constraints

Recall that, for any real numbers a and b,

$$a = b \quad \text{exactly when } a \geq b \text{ and simultaneously } a \leq b.$$

Thus, an equation such as $y_1 + 3y_2 + 3y_3 = 6$ is equivalent to this pair of inequalities:

$$y_1 + 3y_2 + 3y_3 \geq 6$$
$$y_1 + 3y_2 + 3y_3 \leq 6.$$

In a linear programming problem, each equation constraint should be replaced in this way by a pair of inequality constraints. Then the problem can be solved by the two-stage method.

Example 5

Minimize $\quad w = 2y_1 + y_2 - y_3$

subject to $\quad -y_1 - y_2 + y_3 \leq -4$

$\qquad\qquad\quad y_1 + 3y_2 + 3y_3 = 6$

$\qquad\qquad\quad y_1 \geq 0, y_2 \geq 0, y_3 \geq 0.$

Solution   Multiply the first inequality by -1 and replace the equation by an equivalent pair of inequalities, as just explained, to obtain this problem:

Maximize $\quad z = -w = -2y_1 - y_2 + y_3$

subject to $\quad y_1 + y_2 - y_3 \geq 4$

$\qquad\qquad\quad y_1 + 3y_2 + 3y_3 \geq 6$

$\qquad\qquad\quad y_1 + 3y_2 + 3y_3 \leq 6$

$\qquad\quad y_1 \geq 0, y_2 \geq 0, y_3 \geq 0.$

Convert the constraints to equations by subtracting surplus variables s_1 and s_2 from the first two inequalities and adding a slack variable s_3 to the third. Then the first tableau is

$$
\begin{array}{cccccc}
y_1 & y_2 & y_3 & s_1 & s_2 & s_3 \\
\end{array}
$$
$$
\left[
\begin{array}{cccccc|c}
1 & 1 & -1 & -1 & 0 & 0 & 4 \\
1 & 3 & 3 & 0 & -1 & 0 & 6 \\
1 & 3 & 3 & 0 & 0 & 1 & 6 \\
\hline
2 & 1 & -1 & 0 & 0 & 0 & 0 \\
\end{array}
\right].
$$

The basic solution given by this tableau is $y_1 = 0, y_2 = 0, y_3 = 0, s_1 = -4, s_2 = -6$, and $s_3 = 6$, which is not feasible. So we begin Stage I. The basic variable s_1 has a negative value because of the -1 in row 1. We choose the first positive entry in that row. So column 1 will be the pivot column. The quotients are $\frac{4}{1} = 4$ in row 1 and $\frac{6}{1} = 6$ in rows 2 and 3, which means that the pivot is the 1 in row 1, column 1. Pivoting produces this tableau:

$$
\begin{array}{cccccc}
y_1 & y_2 & y_3 & s_1 & s_2 & s_3 \\
\end{array}
$$
$$
\left[
\begin{array}{cccccc|c}
1 & 1 & -1 & -1 & 0 & 0 & 4 \\
0 & 2 & 4 & 1 & -1 & 0 & 2 \\
0 & 2 & 4 & 1 & 0 & 1 & 2 \\
\hline
0 & -1 & 1 & 2 & 0 & 0 & -8 \\
\end{array}
\right].
$$

Now the basic variable s_2 has a negative value because of the -1 in row 2. We choose the first nonzero entry in this row and form the quotients $\frac{4}{1} = 4$ in row 1 and $\frac{2}{2} = 1$ in rows 2 and 3. Thus, there are two choices for the pivot, and we take the 2 in row 2, column 2. Pivoting produces the tableau

$$
\begin{array}{c}
\begin{array}{cccccc} y_1 & y_2 & y_3 & s_1 & s_2 & s_3 \end{array} \\
\left[\begin{array}{cccccc|c}
1 & 0 & -3 & -1.5 & .5 & 0 & 3 \\
0 & 1 & 2 & .5 & -.5 & 0 & 1 \\
0 & 0 & 0 & 0 & 1 & 1 & 0 \\
\hline
0 & 0 & 3 & 2.5 & -.5 & 0 & -7
\end{array}\right].
\end{array}
$$

This tableau gives the basic feasible solution $y_1 = 3, y_2 = 1, y_3 = 0, s_1 = 0, s_2 = 0$, and $s_3 = 0$, so Stage I is complete. Now apply the simplex method. One round of pivoting produces the final tableau:

$$
\begin{array}{c}
\begin{array}{cccccc} y_1 & y_2 & y_3 & s_1 & s_2 & s_3 \end{array} \\
\left[\begin{array}{cccccc|c}
1 & 0 & -3 & -1.5 & 0 & -.5 & 3 \\
0 & 1 & 2 & .5 & 0 & .5 & 1 \\
0 & 0 & 0 & 0 & 1 & 1 & 0 \\
\hline
0 & 0 & 3 & 2.5 & 0 & .5 & -7
\end{array}\right].
\end{array}
$$

Therefore, the minimum value of $w = -z$ is $w = -(-7) = 7$, which occurs when $y_1 = 3, y_2 = 1$, and $y_3 = 0$.

You may have noticed that Example 5 is just Example 4 with the last inequality constraint replaced by an equation constraint. Note, however, that the optimal solutions are different in the two examples. The minimal value of w found in Example 4 is smaller than the one found in Example 5, but does not satisfy the equation constraint in Example 5.

The two-stage method used in Examples 1–5 is summarized here.

Solving Nonstandard Problems

1. Replace each equation constraint by an equivalent pair of inequality constraints.
2. If necessary, write each constraint with a positive constant.
3. Convert a minimization problem to a maximization problem by letting $z = -w$.
4. Add slack variables and subtract surplus variables as needed to convert the constraints into equations.
5. Write the initial simplex tableau.
6. Find a basic feasible solution for the problem if such a solution exists (Stage I).
7. When a basic feasible solution is found, use the simplex method to solve the problem (Stage II).

NOTE It may happen that the tableau which gives the basic feasible solution in Stage I has no negative indicators in its last row. In this case, the solution found is already optimal and Stage II is not necessary.

Applications

Many real-world applications of linear programming involve mixed constraints. Since they typically include a large number of variables and constraints, technology is normally required to solve such problems.

Example 6 **Business** A college textbook publisher has received orders from two colleges: C_1 and C_2. C_1 needs 500 books, and C_2 needs 1000. The publisher can supply the books from either of two warehouses. Warehouse W_1 has 900 books available, and warehouse W_2 has 700. The costs to ship a book from each warehouse to each college are as follows:

		To	
		C_1	C_2
From	W_1	$1.20	$1.80
	W_2	$2.10	$1.50

How many books should be sent from each warehouse to each college to minimize the shipping costs?

Solution To begin, let

$$y_1 = \text{the number of books shipped from } W_1 \text{ to } C_1;$$
$$y_2 = \text{the number of books shipped from } W_2 \text{ to } C_1;$$
$$y_3 = \text{the number of books shipped from } W_1 \text{ to } C_2;$$
$$y_4 = \text{the number of books shipped from } W_2 \text{ to } C_2.$$

C_1 needs 500 books, so $y_1 + y_2 = 500$, which is equivalent to this pair of inequalities:

$$y_1 + y_2 \geq 500$$
$$y_1 + y_2 \leq 500.$$

Similarly, $y_3 + y_4 = 1000$, which is equivalent to

$$y_3 + y_4 \geq 1000$$
$$y_3 + y_4 \leq 1000.$$

Since W_1 has 900 books available and W_2 has 700 available,

$$y_1 + y_3 \leq 900 \quad \text{and} \quad y_2 + y_4 \leq 700.$$

The company wants to minimize shipping costs, so the objective function is

$$w = 1.20y_1 + 2.10y_2 + 1.80y_3 + 1.50y_4.$$

Now write the problem as a system of linear equations, adding slack or surplus variables as needed, and let $z = -w$:

$$
\begin{aligned}
y_1 + \quad y_2 \qquad\qquad\qquad\quad - s_1 \qquad\qquad\qquad\qquad &= 500 \\
y_1 + \quad y_2 + \qquad\qquad\qquad\qquad s_2 \qquad\qquad\qquad &= 500 \\
y_3 + \quad y_4 \qquad - s_3 \qquad\qquad\qquad &= 1000 \\
y_3 + \quad y_4 + \qquad\qquad s_4 \qquad\qquad &= 1000 \\
y_1 + \qquad y_3 + \qquad\qquad\qquad s_5 \qquad &= 900 \\
y_2 \qquad\qquad y_4 + \qquad\qquad\qquad s_6 &= 700 \\
1.20y_1 + 2.10y_2 + 1.80y_3 + 1.50y_4 \qquad\qquad\qquad\qquad + z &= 0.
\end{aligned}
$$

Set up the initial simplex tableau:

y_1	y_2	y_3	y_4	s_1	s_2	s_3	s_4	s_5	s_6	
1	1	0	0	−1	0	0	0	0	0	500
1	1	0	0	0	1	0	0	0	0	500
0	0	1	1	0	0	−1	0	0	0	1000
0	0	1	1	0	0	0	1	0	0	1000
1	0	1	0	0	0	0	0	1	0	900
0	1	0	1	0	0	0	0	0	1	700
1.20	2.10	1.80	1.50	0	0	0	0	0	0	0

The basic solution here is not feasible, because $s_1 = -500$ and $s_3 = -1000$. Stages I and II could be done by hand here, but because of the large size of the matrix, it is more efficient to use technology, such as the program in the Graphing Calculator Appendix. Stage I takes four rounds of pivoting and produces the feasible solution in Figure 7.33.

$$
\begin{array}{cccccc}
y_1 & y_2 & y_3\,y_4 & s_1 & s_2 \\
\end{array}
$$

$$
\left[\begin{array}{cccccc}
1 & 1 & 0\ 0 & -1 & 0 \\
0 & 0 & 0\ 0 & 1 & 1 \\
0 & 1 & 0\ 1 & 0 & 0 \\
0 & 0 & 0\ 0 & 0 & 0 \\
0 & -1 & 1\ 0 & 0 & 0 \\
0 & 0 & 0\ 0 & 1 & 0 \\
0 & 1.2 & 0\ 0 & 1.2 & 0
\end{array}\right]
$$

$$
\begin{array}{cccccc}
y_1 & y_2\,y_3\,y_4 & s_1 & s_2 \\
\end{array}
$$

$$
\left[\begin{array}{cccccc}
1 & 1\ 0\ 0 & -1 & 0 \\
0 & 0\ 0\ 0 & 1 & 1 \\
-1 & 0\ 0\ 1 & 0 & 0 \\
0 & 0\ 0\ 0 & 0 & 0 \\
1 & 0\ 1\ 0 & 0 & 0 \\
0 & 0\ 0\ 0 & 1 & 0 \\
-1.2 & 0\ 0\ 0 & 2.1 & 0
\end{array}\right]
$$

$$
\begin{array}{cccc}
s_3 & s_4\,s_5 & s_6 \\
\end{array}
$$

$$
\left[\begin{array}{cccc}
0 & 0\ 0 & 0 & 500 \\
0 & 0\ 0 & 1 & 0 \\
-1 & 0\ -1 & 0 & 100 \\
1 & 1\ 0 & 0 & 0 \\
0 & 0\ 1 & 0 & 900 \\
1 & 0\ 1 & 1 & 100 \\
1.5 & 0\ -.3 & 0 & -2820
\end{array}\right]
$$

Figure 7.33

$$
\begin{array}{cccc}
s_3 & s_4\,s_5 & s_6 \\
\end{array}
$$

$$
\left[\begin{array}{cccc}
0 & 0\ 0 & 0 & 500 \\
0 & 0\ 0 & 0 & 0 \\
0 & 0\ 0 & 1 & 700 \\
1 & 1\ 0 & 0 & 0 \\
-1 & 0\ 0 & -1 & 300 \\
1 & 0\ 1 & 1 & 100 \\
1.8 & 0\ 0 & .3 & -2190
\end{array}\right]
$$

Figure 7.34

Because of the small size of a calculator screen, you must scroll to the right to see the entire matrix. Now Stage II begins. Two rounds of pivoting produce the final tableau (Figure 7.34).

The optimal solution is $y_1 = 500$, $y_2 = 0$, $y_3 = 300$, and $y_4 = 700$, which results in a minimum shipping cost of \$2190. (Remember that the optimal value for the original minimization problem is the negative of the optimal value of the associated maximization problem.)

7.7 Exercises

In Exercises 1–4, (a) restate the problem in terms of equations by introducing slack and surplus variables and (b) write the initial simplex tableau. (See Example 1.)

1. Maximize $z = -5x_1 + 4x_2 - 2x_3$
   subject to $\quad -2x_2 + 5x_3 \geq 8$
   $$4x_1 - x_2 + 3x_3 \leq 12$$
   $$x_1 \geq 0, x_2 \geq 0, x_3 \geq 0.$$

2. Maximize $z = -x_1 + 4x_2 - 2x_3$
   subject to $\quad 2x_1 + 2x_2 + 6x_3 \leq 10$
   $$-x_1 + 2x_2 + 4x_3 \geq 7$$
   $$x_1 \geq 0, x_2 \geq 0, x_3 \geq 0.$$

3. Maximize $z = 2x_1 - 3x_2 + 4x_3$
   subject to $\quad x_1 + x_2 + x_3 \leq 100$
   $$x_1 + x_2 + x_3 \geq 75$$
   $$x_1 + x_2 \qquad \geq 27$$
   $$x_1 \geq 0, x_2 \geq 0, x_3 \geq 0.$$

4. Maximize $z = -x_1 + 5x_2 + x_3$
   subject to $\quad 2x_1 \qquad + x_3 \leq 40$
   $$x_1 + x_2 \qquad \geq 18$$
   $$x_1 \qquad + x_3 = 20$$
   $$x_1 \geq 0, x_2 \geq 0, x_3 \geq 0.$$

Convert Exercises 5–8 into maximization problems with positive constants on the right side of each constraint, and write the initial simplex tableau. (See Examples 4 and 5.)

5. Minimize $w = 2y_1 + 5y_2 - 3y_3$
   subject to $\quad y_1 + 2y_2 + 3y_3 \geq 115$
   $$2y_1 + y_2 + y_3 \leq 200$$
   $$y_1 \qquad + y_3 \geq 50$$
   $$y_1 \geq 0, y_2 \geq 0, y_3 \geq 0.$$

6. Minimize $w = 7y_1 + 6y_2 + y_3$
   subject to $\quad y_1 + y_2 + y_3 \geq 5$
   $$-y_1 + y_2 \qquad \leq -4$$
   $$2y_1 + y_2 + 3y_3 \geq 15$$
   $$y_1 \geq 0, y_2 \geq 0, y_3 \geq 0.$$

7. Minimize $w = 10y_1 + 8y_2 + 15y_3$
   subject to $\quad y_1 + y_2 + y_3 \geq 12$
   $$5y_1 + 4y_2 + 9y_3 \geq 48$$
   $$y_1 \geq 0, y_2 \geq 0, y_3 \geq 0.$$

8. Minimize $w = y_1 + 2y_2 + y_3 + 5y_4$
   subject to $\quad -y_1 - y_2 + y_3 - y_4 \leq -50$
   $$3y_1 + y_2 + 2y_3 + y_4 = 100$$
   $$y_1 \geq 0, y_2 \geq 0, y_3 \geq 0, y_4 \geq 0.$$

Use the two-stage method to solve Exercises 9–20. (See Examples 1–5.)

9. Maximize $z = 12x_1 + 10x_2$

subject to $x_1 + 2x_2 \geq 24$

$x_1 + x_2 \leq 40$

$x_1 \geq 0, x_2 \geq 0.$

10. Find $x_1 \geq 0, x_2 \geq 0,$ and $x_3 \geq 0$ such that

$x_1 + x_2 + x_3 \leq 150$

$x_1 + x_2 + x_3 \geq 100$

and $z = 2x_1 + 5x_2 + 3x_3$ is maximized.

11. Find $x_1 \geq 0, x_2 \geq 0,$ and $x_3 \geq 0$ such that

$x_1 + x_2 + 2x_3 \leq 38$

$2x_1 + x_2 + x_3 \geq 24$

and $z = 3x_1 + 2x_2 + 2x_3$ is maximized.

12. Maximize $z = 6x_1 + 8x_2$

subject to $3x_1 + 12x_2 \geq 48$

$2x_1 + 4x_2 \leq 60$

$x_1 \geq 0, x_2 \geq 0.$

13. Find $x_1 \geq 0$ and $x_2 \geq 0$ such that

$x_1 + 2x_2 \leq 18$

$x_1 + 3x_2 \geq 12$

$2x_1 + 2x_2 \leq 30$

and $z = 5x_1 + 10x_2$ is maximized.

14. Find $y_1 \geq 0, y_2 \geq 0$ such that

$10y_1 + 5y_2 \geq 100$

$20y_1 + 10y_2 \geq 160$

and $w = 4y_1 + 5y_2$ is minimized.

15. Minimize $w = 3y_1 + 2y_2$

subject to $2y_1 + 3y_2 \geq 60$

$y_1 + 4y_2 \geq 40$

$y_1 \geq 0, y_2 \geq 0.$

16. Minimize $w = 3y_1 + 4y_2$

subject to $y_1 + 2y_2 \geq 10$

$y_1 + y_2 \geq 8$

$2y_1 + y_2 \leq 22$

$y_1 \geq 0, y_2 \geq 0.$

17. Maximize $z = 3x_1 + 2x_2$

subject to $x_1 + x_2 = 50$

$4x_1 + 2x_2 \geq 120$

$5x_1 + 2x_2 \leq 200$

with $x_1 \geq 0, x_2 \geq 0.$

18. Maximize $z = 10x_1 + 9x_2$

subject to $x_1 + x_2 = 30$

$x_1 + x_2 \geq 25$

$2x_1 + x_2 \leq 40$

with $x_1 \geq 0, x_2 \geq 0.$

19. Minimize $w = 32y_1 + 40y_2$

subject to $20y_1 + 10y_2 = 200$

$25y_1 + 40y_2 \leq 500$

$18y_1 + 24y_2 \geq 300$

with $y_1 \geq 0, y_2 \geq 0.$

20. Minimize $w = 15y_1 + 12y_2$

subject to $y_1 + 2y_2 \leq 12$

$3y_1 + y_2 \geq 18$

$y_1 + y_2 = 10$

with $y_1 \geq 0, y_2 \geq 0.$

Use the two-stage method to solve the problem that was set up in the given exercise.

21. Exercise 1   **22.** Exercise 2

23. Exercise 3   **24.** Exercise 4

25. Exercise 5   **26.** Exercise 6

27. Exercise 7   **28.** Exercise 8

In Exercises 29–32, set up the initial simplex tableau, but do not solve the problem. (See Example 6.)

29. Business A company is developing a new additive for gasoline. The additive is a mixture of three liquid ingredients: I, II, and III. For proper performance, the total amount of additive must be at least 10 ounces per barrel of gasoline. However, for safety reasons, the amount of additive should not exceed 15 ounces per barrel of gasoline. At least $\frac{1}{4}$ ounce of ingredient I must be used for every ounce of ingredient II, and at least 1 ounce of ingredient III must be used for every ounce of ingredient I. If the costs of I, II, and III are \$.30, \$.09, and \$.27 per ounce, respectively, find the mixture of the three ingredients that produces the minimum cost of the additive. What is the minimum cost?

30. Business A popular soft drink called Sugarlo, which is advertised as having a sugar content of no more than 10%, is blended from five ingredients, each of which has some sugar content. Water may also be added to dilute the mixture. The sugar content of the ingredients and their costs per gallon are given in the table:

	Ingredient					
	1	**2**	**3**	**4**	**5**	**Water**
Sugar content (%)	.28	.19	.43	.57	.22	0
Cost ($/gal.)	.48	.32	.53	.28	.43	.04

At least .01 of the content of Sugarlo must come from ingredient 3 or 4, .01 must come from ingredient 2 or 5, and .01 from ingredient 1 or 4. How much of each ingredient should be used in preparing at least 15,000 gallons of Sugarlo to minimize the cost? What is the minimum cost?

31. Business The manufacturer of a popular personal computer has orders from two dealers. Dealer D_1 wants 32 computers, and dealer D_2 wants 20 computers. The manufacturer can fill the orders from either of two warehouses, W_1 or W_2. W_1 has 25 of the computers on hand, and W_2 has 30. The costs (in dollars) to ship one computer to each dealer from each warehouse are as follows:

		To	
		D_1	D_2
From	W_1	$14	$22
	W_2	$12	$10

How should the orders be filled to minimize shipping costs? What is the minimum cost?

32. Natural Science Mark, who is ill, takes vitamin pills. Each day, he must have at least 16 units of vitamin A, 5 units of vitamin B_1, and 20 units of vitamin C. He can choose between pill 1, which costs 10¢ and contains 8 units of vitamin A, 1 unit of vitamin B_1, and 2 units of vitamin C, and pill 2, which costs 20¢ and contains 2 units of vitamin A, 1 unit of vitamin B_1, and 7 units of vitamin C. How many of each pill should he buy in order to minimize his cost?

Use the two-stage method to solve Exercises 33–40. (See Examples 5 and 6.)

33. Business Southwestern Oil supplies two distributors in the Northwest from two outlets: S_1 and S_2. Distributor D_1 needs at least 3000 barrels of oil, and distributor D_2 needs at least 5000 barrels. The two outlets can each furnish up to 5000 barrels of oil. The costs per barrel to ship the oil are given in the table:

		Distributors	
		D_1	D_2
Outlets	S_1	$30	$20
	S_2	$25	$22

There is also a shipping tax per barrel as given in the table below.

	D_1	D_2
S_1	$2	$6
S_2	$5	$4

Southwestern Oil is determined to spend no more than $40,000 on shipping tax. How should the oil be supplied to minimize shipping costs?

34. Business Change Exercise 33 so that the two outlets each furnish exactly 5000 barrels of oil, with everything else the same. Solve the problem as in Example 5.

35. Business Topgrade Turf lawn seed mixture contains three types of seeds: bluegrass, rye, and Bermuda. The costs per pound of the three types of seed are 12¢, 15¢, and 5¢, respectively. In each batch, there must be at least 20% bluegrass seed, and the amount of Bermuda seed must be no more than two-thirds the amount of rye seed. To fill current orders, the company must make at least 5000 pounds of the mixture. How much of each kind of seed should be used to minimize costs?

36. Business Change Exercise 35 so that the company must make exactly 5000 pounds of the mixture. Solve the problem as in Example 5.

37. Finance A bank has set aside a maximum of $25 million for commercial and home loans. Every million dollars in commercial loans requires 2 lengthy application forms, while every million dollars in home loans requires 3 lengthy application forms. The bank cannot process more than 72 application forms at this time. The bank's policy is to loan at least four times as much for home loans as for commercial loans. Because of prior commitments, at least $10 million will be used for these two types of loans. The bank earns 12% on home loans and 10% on commercial loans. What amount of money should be allotted for each type of loan to maximize the interest income?

38. Finance Virginia Keleske has decided to invest a $100,000 inheritance in government securities that earn 7% per year, municipal bonds that earn 6% per year, and mutual funds that earn an average of 10% per year. She will spend at least $40,000 on government securities, and she wants at least half the inheritance to go to bonds and mutual funds. Government securities have an initial fee of 2%, municipal bonds an initial fee of 1%, and mutual funds an initial fee of 3%. Virginia has $2400 available to pay initial fees. How much money should go into each type of investment to maximize the interest while meeting the constraints? What is the maximum interest she can earn?

39. Business A brewery produces regular beer and a lower-carbohydrate "light" beer. Steady customers of the brewery buy 12 units of regular beer and 10 units of light beer. While setting up the brewery to produce the beers, the management decides to produce extra beer, beyond that needed to satisfy the steady customers. The cost per unit of regular beer is $36,000, and the cost per unit of light beer is $48,000. The number of units of light beer should not exceed twice the number of units of regular beer. At least 20 additional units of beer can be sold. How much of each type of beer should be made so as to minimize total production costs?

40. Business The chemistry department at a local college decides to stock at least 800 small test tubes and 500 large test tubes. It wants to buy at least 1500 test tubes to take advantage of a special price. Since the small tubes are broken twice as often as the large, the department will order at least twice as many small tubes as large. If the small test tubes cost 15¢ each and the large ones, made of a cheaper glass, cost 12¢ each, how many of each size should the department order to minimize cost?

Business *Use technology to solve the following exercises, whose initial tableaus were set up in Exercises 29–31.*

41. Exercise 29   **42.** Exercise 30

43. Exercise 31

✓ Checkpoint Answers

1. (a) Maximize $z = 3x_1 - 2x_2$

   subject to
   $$2x_1 + 3x_2 + s_1 = 8$$
   $$6x_1 - 2x_2 - s_2 = 3$$
   $$x_1 + 4x_2 - s_3 = 1$$
   $$x_1 \geq 0, x_2 \geq 0, s_1 \geq 0, s_2 \geq 0, s_3 \geq 0.$$

(b) $\begin{bmatrix} x_1 & x_2 & s_1 & s_2 & s_3 & \\ 2 & 3 & 1 & 0 & 0 & 8 \\ 6 & -2 & 0 & -1 & 0 & 3 \\ 1 & 4 & 0 & 0 & -1 & 1 \\ \hline -3 & 2 & 0 & 0 & 0 & 0 \end{bmatrix}$

3. $\begin{bmatrix} x_1 & x_2 & s_1 & s_2 & \\ 0 & 1 & 1 & \frac{1}{2} & 45 \\ 1 & 2 & 0 & -\frac{1}{2} & 25 \\ \hline 0 & 6 & 0 & -4 & 200 \end{bmatrix}$

$x_1 = 25, x_2 = 0, s_1 = 45,$ and $s_2 = 0.$

2. (a) $x_1 = 0, x_2 = 0, s_1 = 12, s_2 = 6, s_3 = -5;$ no

(b) $x_1 = 0, x_2 = 0, x_3 = 0, s_1 = 12, s_2 = 7;$ yes

4. The optimal value $z = 560$ occurs when $x_1 = 70, x_2 = 0,$ $s_1 = 0,$ and $s_2 = 90$

5. $y_1 = 10$ and $y_2 = 0; w = 20$

CHAPTER 7 Summary and Review

Key Terms and Symbols

7.1 linear inequality
graphs of linear
  inequalities
boundary
half-plane
system of inequalities
region of feasible solutions
  (feasible region)

7.2 linear programming
objective function

constraints
corner point
bounded feasible region
unbounded feasible region
corner point theorem

7.3 applications of linear
  programming

7.4 standard maximum form
slack variable
simplex tableau

indicator
pivot and pivoting
final simplex tableau
basic variables
nonbasic variables
basic feasible solution

7.6 transpose of a matrix
dual
theorem of duality
shadow costs

7.7 surplus variable
basic variables
basic solution
basic feasible solution
Stage I
Stage II

Chapter 7 Key Concepts

Graphing a Linear Inequality

Graph the boundary line as a solid line if the inequality includes "or equal to," and as a dashed line otherwise. Shade the half-plane for which the inequality is true. The graph of a system of inequalities, called the **region of feasible solutions**, includes all points that satisfy all the inequalities of the system at the same time.

Solving Linear Programming Problems

Graphical Method: Determine the objective function and all necessary constraints. Graph the region of feasible solutions. The maximum or minimum value will occur at one or more of the corner points of this region.

Simplex Method: Determine the objective function and all necessary constraints. Convert each constraint into an equation by adding slack variables. Set up the initial simplex tableau. Locate the most negative indicator. Form the quotients to determine the pivot. Use row operations to change the pivot to 1 and all other numbers in that column to 0. If the indicators are all positive or 0, this is the final tableau. If not, choose a new pivot and repeat the process until no indicators are negative. Read the solution from the final tableau. The optimum value of the objective function is the number in the lower right corner of the final tableau. For problems with **mixed constraints**, replace each equation constraint by a pair of inequality constraints. Then add slack variables and subtract surplus variables as needed to convert each constraint into an equation. In Stage I, use row operations to transform the matrix until the solution is feasible. In Stage II, use the simplex method as just described. For **minimization** problems, let the objective function be w and set $-w = z$. Then proceed as with mixed constraints.

Solving Minimization Problems with Duals

Find the dual maximization problem. Solve the dual problem with the simplex method. The minimum value of the objective function w is the maximum value of the dual objective function z. The optimal solution is found in the entries in the bottom row of the columns corresponding to the slack variables.

Chapter 7 Review Exercises

Graph each of the given linear inequalities.

1. $y \le 3x + 2$

2. $2x - y \ge 6$

3. $3x + 4y \ge 12$

4. $y \le 4$

Graph the solution of each of the given systems of inequalities.

5. $x + y \le 6$
$2x - y \ge 3$

6. $4x + y \ge 8$
$2x - 3y \le 6$

7. $2 \le x \le 5$
$1 \le y \le 6$
$x - y \le 3$

8. $x + 2y \le 4$
$2x - 3y \le 6$
$x \ge 0, y \ge 0$

Set up a system of inequalities for each of the given problems, and then graph the region of feasible solutions.

9. Business Linda Quinn is a statistical consultant who creates two kind of reports: summary reports and inference reports. Each summary report requires 2 hours of analysis time and 1.5 hours to write the report. Each inference report needs 4 hours of analysis time and 2 hours of writing time. Suppose Linda has only 15 hours available for analysis and 9 hours for writing.

10. Business A company makes two kinds of pizza: basic (cheese and tomatoes) and margherita (cheese, tomatoes, and basil). The company sells at least 60 units a day of the pizza margherita and 40 units a day of the basic. The cost of the tomatoes and basil is $2 per unit for the pizza margherita and the cost of tomatoes is $1 per unit for the basic. No more than $320 a day can be spent on tomatoes and basil together. The cheese used for the pizza margherita is $5 per unit, and the cheese for the basic is $4 per unit. The company spends no more than $1000 a day on cheese.

Use the given regions to find the maximum and minimum values of the objective function $z = 3x + 4y$.

11.

12.

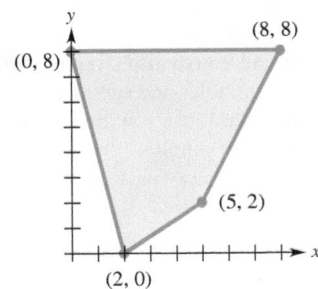

Use the graphical method to solve Exercises 13–16.

13. Maximize $z = 6x + 2y$

subject to $2x + 7y \le 14$
$2x + 3y \le 10$
$x \ge 0, y \ge 0.$

14. Find $x \ge 0$ and $y \ge 0$ such that

$$8x + 9y \ge 72$$
$$6x + 8y \ge 72$$

and $w = 2x + 10y$ is minimized.

15. Find $x \ge 0$ and $y \ge 0$ such that

$$x + y \le 50$$
$$2x + y \ge 20$$
$$x + 2y \ge 30$$

and $w = 5x + 2y$ is minimized.

16. Maximize $z = 5x - 2y$

subject to $3x + 2y \le 12$
$5x + y \ge 5$
$x \ge 0, y \ge 0.$

17. Business How many of each kind of statistical report (summary or inference) should Linda Quinn create in Exercise 9 in order to maximize profit if the summary reports earn a profit of $500 and the inference reports produce a profit of $750? (Assume it is possible to complete a fractional part of a project.)

18. How many units of each pizza in Exercise 10 should the company make in order to maximize revenue if the basic pizza sells for $15 per unit and the pizza margherita sells for $20 per unit.

19. Finance The BlackRock Equity Dividend Fund sells at $22 a share and has a 3-year average annual return of $3 per share. The risk measure of standard deviation is 13.2. The Columbia Dividend Income Fund sells for $17 a share and has a 3-year average annual return of $2 a share. The risk measure of standard deviation is 12.8. Donald Hackett wants to spend no more than $10,000 investing in these two funds, but he wants to obtain at least $1200 in annual revenue. Donald also wants to minimize his risk. Determine how many shares of each stock Donald should buy. (Data from: www.morningstar.com as of May 2013.)

20. Finance The Alger Spectra Z Fund sells at $15 a share and has a 3-year average annual return of $2 per share. The risk measure of standard deviation is 17. The Dynamic US Growth Fund sells for $22 a share and has a 3-year average annual return of $3.50 a share. The risk measure of standard deviation is 20. Kimberly Bramer wants to spend no more than $5016 investing in these two funds, but she wants to obtain at least $700 in annual revenue. Kimberly also wants to minimize her risk. Determine how many shares of each stock Kimberly should buy. (Data from: www.morningstar.com as of May 2013.)

For each of the following problems, (a) add slack variables and (b) set up the initial simplex tableau.

21. Maximize $z = 5x_1 + 6x_2 + 3x_3$

subject to $x_1 + x_2 + x_3 \leq 100$

$2x_1 + 3x_2 \qquad \leq 500$

$x_1 \qquad + 2x_3 \leq 350$

$x_1 \geq 0, x_2 \geq 0, x_3 \geq 0.$

22. Maximize $z = 2x_1 + 9x_2$

subject to $3x_1 + 5x_2 \leq 47$

$x_1 + x_2 \leq 25$

$5x_1 + 2x_2 \leq 35$

$2x_1 + x_2 \leq 30$

$x_1 \geq 0, x_2 \geq 0.$

23. Maximize $z = x_1 + 8x_2 + 2x_3$

subject to $x_1 + x_2 + x_3 \leq 90$

$2x_1 + 5x_2 + x_3 \leq 120$

$x_1 + 3x_2 \qquad \leq 80$

$x_1 \geq 0, x_2 \geq 0, x_3 \geq 0.$

24. Maximize $z = 15x_1 + 12x_2$

subject to $2x_1 + 5x_2 \leq 50$

$x_1 + 3x_2 \leq 25$

$4x_1 + x_2 \leq 18$

$x_1 + x_2 \leq 12$

$x_1 \geq 0, x_2 \geq 0.$

For each of the following, use the simplex method to solve the maximization linear programming problems with initial tableaus as given.

25.
x_1	x_2	x_3	s_1	s_2	
1	2	3	1	0	28
2	4	8	0	1	32
−5	−2	−3	0	0	0

26.
x_1	x_2	s_1	s_2	
2	1	1	0	10
9	3	0	1	15
−2	−3	0	0	0

27.
x_1	x_2	x_3	s_1	s_2	s_3	
1	2	2	1	0	0	50
4	24	0	0	1	0	20
1	0	2	0	0	1	15
−5	−3	−2	0	0	0	0

28.
x_1	x_2	s_1	s_2	s_3	
1	−2	1	0	0	38
1	−1	0	1	0	12
2	1	0	0	1	30
−1	−2	0	0	0	0

Use the simplex method to solve the problem that was set up in the given exercise.

29. Exercise 21   **30.** Exercise 22

31. Exercise 23   **32.** Exercise 24

For Exercises 33–36, (a) select appropriate variables, (b) write the objective function, and (c) write the constraints as inequalities.

33. Business Roberta Hernandez sells three items—A, B, and C—in her gift shop. Each unit of A costs her $2 to buy, $1 to sell, and $2 to deliver. For each unit of B, the costs are $3, $2, and $2, respectively, and for each unit of C, the costs are $6, $2, and $4, respectively. The profit on A is $4, on B it is $3, and on C it is $3. How many of each item should she order to maximize her profit if she can spend $1200 to buy, $800 to sell, and $500 to deliver?

34. Business An investor is considering three types of investment: a high-risk venture into oil leases with a potential return of 15%, a medium-risk investment in bonds with a 9% return, and a relatively safe stock investment with a 5% return. He has $50,000 to invest. Because of the risk, he will limit his investment in oil leases and bonds to 30% and his investment in oil leases and stock to 50%. How much should he invest in each to maximize his return, assuming investment returns are as expected?

35. Business The Aged Wood Winery makes two white wines—Fruity and Crystal—from two kinds of grapes and sugar. The wines require the amounts of each ingredient per gallon and produce a profit per gallon as shown in the following table:

	Grape A (bushels)	Grape B (bushels)	Sugar (pounds)	Profit (dollars)
Fruity	2	2	2	12
Crystal	1	3	1	15

The winery has available 110 bushels of grape A, 125 bushels of grape B, and 90 pounds of sugar. How much of each wine should be made to maximize profit?

36. Business A company makes three sizes of plastic bags: 5 gallon, 10 gallon, and 20 gallon. The production time in hours for cutting, sealing, and packaging a unit of each size is as follows:

Size	Cutting	Sealing	Packaging
5 gallon	1	1	2
10 gallon	1.1	1.2	3
20 gallon	1.5	1.3	4

There are at most 8 hours available each day for each of the three operations. If the profit per unit is $1 for 5-gallon bags, $.90 for 10-gallon bags, and $.95 for 20-gallon bags, how many of each size should be made per day to maximize the profit?

37. When is it necessary to use the simplex method rather than the graphical method?

38. What types of problems can be solved with the use of slack variables and surplus variables?

39. What kind of problem can be solved with the method of duals?

40. In solving a linear programming problem, you are given the following initial tableau:

$$\begin{bmatrix} 4 & 2 & 3 & 1 & 0 & | & 9 \\ 5 & 4 & 1 & 0 & 1 & | & 10 \\ \hline -6 & -7 & -5 & 0 & 0 & | & 0 \end{bmatrix}.$$

(a) What is the problem being solved?

(b) If the 1 in row 1, column 4, were a -1 rather than a 1, how would it change your answer to part (a)?

(c) After several steps of the simplex algorithm, the following tableau results:

$$\begin{bmatrix} .6 & 0 & 1 & .4 & -.2 & | & 1.6 \\ 1.1 & 1 & 0 & -.1 & .3 & | & 2.1 \\ \hline 4.7 & 0 & 0 & 1.3 & 1.1 & | & 22.7 \end{bmatrix}.$$

What is the solution? (List only the values of the original variables and the objective function. Do not include slack or surplus variables.)

(d) What is the dual of the problem you found in part (a)?

(e) What is the solution of the dual you found in part (d)? [Do not perform any steps of the simplex algorithm; just examine the tableau given in part (c).]

The tableaus in Exercises 41–43 are the final tableaus of minimization problems solved by the method of duals. State the solution and the minimum value of the objective function for each problem.

41. $\begin{bmatrix} 1 & 0 & 0 & 3 & 1 & 2 & | & 12 \\ 0 & 0 & 1 & 4 & 5 & 3 & | & 5 \\ 0 & 1 & 0 & -2 & 7 & -6 & | & 8 \\ \hline 0 & 0 & 0 & 5 & 7 & 3 & | & 172 \end{bmatrix}$

42. $\begin{bmatrix} 0 & 0 & 1 & 6 & 3 & 1 & | & 2 \\ 1 & 0 & 0 & 4 & -2 & 2 & | & 8 \\ 0 & 1 & 0 & 10 & 7 & 0 & | & 12 \\ \hline 0 & 0 & 0 & 9 & 5 & 8 & | & 62 \end{bmatrix}$

43. $\begin{bmatrix} 1 & 0 & 7 & -1 & | & 100 \\ 0 & 1 & 1 & 3 & | & 27 \\ \hline 0 & 0 & 7 & 2 & | & 640 \end{bmatrix}$

Use the method of duals to solve these minimization problems.

44. Minimize $w = 5y_1 + 2y_2$
subject to $2y_1 + 3y_2 \geq 6$
$2y_1 + y_2 \geq 7$
$y_1 \geq 0, y_2 \geq 0.$

45. Minimize $w = 18y_1 + 10y_2$
subject to $y_1 + y_2 \geq 17$
$5y_1 + 8y_2 \geq 42$
$y_1 \geq 0, y_2 \geq 0.$

46. Minimize $w = 4y_1 + 5y_2$
subject to $10y_1 + 5y_2 \geq 100$
$20y_1 + 10y_2 \geq 150$
$y_1 \geq 0, y_2 \geq 0.$

Write the initial simplex tableau for each of these mixed-constraint problems.

47. Maximize $z = 20x_1 + 30x_2$
subject to $5x_1 + 10x_2 \leq 120$
$10x_1 + 15x_2 \geq 200$
$x_1 \geq 0, x_2 \geq 0.$

48. Minimize $w = 4y_1 + 2y_2$
subject to $y_1 + 3y_2 \geq 6$
$2y_1 + 8y_2 \leq 21$
$y_1 \geq 0, y_2 \geq 0.$

49. Minimize $w = 12y_1 + 20y_2 - 8y_3$
subject to $y_1 + y_2 + 2y_3 \geq 48$
$y_1 + y_2 \leq 12$
$y_3 \geq 10$
$3y_1 + y_3 \geq 30$
$y_1 \geq 0, y_2 \geq 0, y_3 \geq 0.$

50. Maximize $w = 6x_1 - 3x_2 + 4x_3$
subject to $2x_1 + x_2 + x_3 \leq 112$
$x_1 + x_2 + x_3 \geq 80$
$x_1 + x_2 \leq 45$
$x_1 \geq 0, x_2 \geq 0, x_3 \geq 0.$

The given tableaus are the final tableaus of minimization problems solved by letting $w = -z$. Give the solution and the minimum value of the objective function for each problem.

51. $\begin{bmatrix} 0 & 1 & 0 & 2 & 5 & 0 & | & 17 \\ 0 & 0 & 1 & 3 & 1 & 1 & | & 25 \\ 1 & 0 & 0 & 4 & 2 & \frac{1}{2} & | & 8 \\ \hline 0 & 0 & 0 & 2 & 5 & 0 & | & -427 \end{bmatrix}$

52. $\begin{bmatrix} 0 & 0 & 2 & 1 & 0 & 6 & 6 & | & 92 \\ 1 & 0 & 3 & 0 & 0 & 0 & 2 & | & 47 \\ 0 & 1 & 0 & 0 & 0 & 1 & 0 & | & 68 \\ 0 & 0 & 4 & 0 & 1 & 0 & 3 & | & 35 \\ \hline 0 & 0 & 5 & 0 & 0 & 2 & 9 & | & -1957 \end{bmatrix}$

Use the two-stage method to solve these mixed-constraint problems.

53. Exercise 47   **54.** Exercise 48

55. Minimize $w = 4y_1 - 8y_2$
subject to $y_1 + y_2 \leq 50$
$2y_1 - 4y_2 \geq 20$
$y_1 - y_2 \leq 22$
$y_1 \geq 0, y_2 \geq 0.$

56. Maximize $z = 2x_1 + 4x_2$
   subject to $3x_1 + 2x_2 \leq 12$
   $5x_1 + x_2 \geq 5$
   $x_1 \geq 0, x_2 \geq 0.$

Business   *Solve the following maximization problems, which were begun in Exercises 33–36.*

57. Exercise 33   **58.** Exercise 34

59. Exercise 35   **60.** Exercise 36

Business   *Solve the following minimization problems.*

61. Cauchy Canners produces canned corn, beans, and carrots. Demand for vegetables requires the company to produce at least 1000 cases per month. Based on past sales, it should produce at least twice as many cases of corn as of beans and at least 340 cases of carrots. It costs \$10 to produce a case of corn, \$15 to produce a case of beans, and \$25 to produce a case of carrots. How many cases of each vegetable should be produced to minimize costs? What is the minimum cost?

62. A contractor builds boathouses in two basic models: the Atlantic and the Pacific. Each Atlantic model requires 1000 feet of framing lumber, 3000 cubic feet of concrete, and \$2000 for advertising. Each Pacific model requires 2000 feet of framing lumber, 3000 cubic feet of concrete, and \$3000 for advertising. Contracts call for using at least 8000 feet of framing lumber, 18,000 cubic feet of concrete, and \$15,000 worth of advertising. If the total spent on each Atlantic model is \$3000 and the total spent on each Pacific model is \$4000, how many of each model should be built to minimize costs?

Business   *Solve these mixed-constraint problems.*

63. Brand X Cannery produces canned whole tomatoes and tomato sauce. This season, the company has available 3,000,000 kilograms of tomatoes for these two products. To meet the demands of regular customers, it must produce at least 80,000 kilograms of sauce and 800,000 kilograms of whole tomatoes. The cost per kilogram is \$4 to produce canned whole tomatoes and \$3.25 to produce tomato sauce. Labor agreements require that at least 110,000 person-hours be used. Each 1-kilogram can of sauce requires 3 minutes for one worker to produce, and each 1-kilogram can of whole tomatoes requires 6 minutes for one worker. How many kilograms of tomatoes should Brand X use for each product to minimize cost? (For simplicity, assume that the production of y_1 kilograms of canned whole tomatoes and y_2 kilograms of tomato sauce requires $y_1 + y_2$ kilograms of tomatoes.)

64. A steel company produces two types of alloys. A run of type I requires 3000 pounds of molybdenum and 2000 tons of iron ore pellets, as well as \$2000 in advertising. A run of type II requires 3000 pounds of molybdenum and 1000 tons of iron ore pellets, as well as \$3000 in advertising. Total costs are \$15,000 on a run of type I and \$6000 on a run of type II. The company has on hand 18,000 pounds of molybdenum and 7000 tons of iron ore pellets and wants to use all of it. It plans to spend at least \$14,000 on advertising. How much of each type should be produced to minimize cost? What is the minimum cost?

Case Study 7 Cooking with Linear Programming

Constructing a nutritious recipe can be a difficult task. The recipe must produce food that tastes good, and it must also balance the nutrients that each ingredient brings to the dish. This balancing of nutrients is very important in several diet plans that are currently popular. Many of these plans restrict the intake of certain nutrients (usually fat) while allowing for large amounts of other nutrients (protein and carbohydrates are popular choices). The number of calories in the dish is also often minimized. Linear programming can be used to help create recipes that balance nutrients.

In order to develop solutions to this type of problem, we will need to have nutritional data for the ingredients in our recipes. This data can be found in the U.S. Department of Agriculture's USDA Nutrient Database for Standard Reference, available at www.ndb.nal.usda.gov. This database contains the nutrient levels for hundreds of basic foods. The nutrient levels are given per 100 grams of food. Unfortunately, grams are not often used in recipes; instead, kitchen measures like cups, tablespoons, and fractions of vegetables are used. Table 1 shows the conversion factors from grams to more familiar kitchen units and gives serving sizes for various food.

Table 1   Serving Sizes of Various Food

Food	Serving Size
Beef	$6\,oz = 170\,g$
Egg	$1\,egg = 61\,g$
Feta Cheese	$\frac{1}{4}\,cup = 38\,g$
Lettuce	$\frac{1}{2}\,cup = 28\,g$
Milk	$1\,cup = 244\,g$
Oil	$1\,Tbsp = 13.5\,g$
Onion	$1\,onion = 110\,g$
Salad Dressing	$1\,cup = 250\,g$
Soy Sauce	$1\,Tbsp = 18\,g$
Spinach	$1\,cup = 180\,g$
Tomato	$1\,tomato = 123\,g$

Consider creating a recipe for a spinach omelet from eggs, milk, vegetable oil, and spinach. The nutrients of interest will be protein, fat, and carbohydrates. Calories will also be monitored. The amounts of the nutrients and calories for these ingredients are given in Table 2.

Table 2   Nutritional Values per 100 g of Food

Nutrient (units)	Eggs	Milk	Oil	Spinach
Calories (kcal)	152	61.44	884	23
Protein (g)	10.33	3.29	0	2.9
Fat (g)	11.44	3.34	100	.26
Carbohydrates (g)	1.04	4.66	0	3.75

Let x_1 be the number of 100-gram units of eggs to use in the recipe, x_2 be the number of 100-gram units of milk, x_3 be the number of 100-gram units of oil, and x_4 be the number of 100-gram units of spinach. We will want to minimize the number of calories in the dish while providing at least 15 grams of protein, 4 grams of carbohydrates, and 20 grams of fat. The cooking technique specifies that at least $\frac{1}{8}$ of a cup of milk (30.5 grams) must be used in the recipe. We should thus minimize the objective function (using 100-gram units of food)

$$z = 152x_1 + 61.44x_2 + 884x_3 + 23x_4$$

subject to

$$10.33x_1 + 3.29x_2 + 0x_3 + 2.90x_4 \geq 15$$
$$11.44x_1 + 3.34x_2 + 100x_3 + .26x_4 \geq 20$$
$$1.04x_1 + 4.66x_2 + 0x_3 + 3.75x_4 \geq 4$$
$$0x_1 + 1x_2 + 0x_3 + 0x_4 \geq .305.$$

Of course, all variables are subject to nonnegativity constraints:

$$x_1 \geq 0, \quad x_2 \geq 0, \quad x_3 \geq 0, \quad \text{and} \quad x_4 \geq 0.$$

Using a graphing calculator or a computer with linear programming software, we get the following solution:

$$x_1 = 1.2600, \quad x_2 = .3050, \quad x_3 = .0448, \quad \text{and} \quad x_4 = .338.$$

This recipe produces an omelet with 257.63 calories. The amounts of each ingredient are 126 grams of eggs, 30.5 grams of milk, 4.48 grams of oil, and 33.8 grams of spinach. Converting to kitchen units using Table 1, we find the recipe to be approximately 2 eggs, $\frac{1}{8}$ cup milk, 1 teaspoon oil, and $\frac{1}{4}$ cup spinach.

Exercises

1. Consider preparing a high-carbohydrate Greek salad using feta cheese, lettuce, salad dressing, and tomato. The amount of carbohydrates in the salad should be maximized. In addition, the salad should have less than 260 calories, over 210 milligrams of calcium, and over 6 grams of protein. The salad should also weigh less than 400 grams and be dressed with at least 2 tablespoons ($\frac{1}{8}$ cup) of salad dressing. The amounts of the nutrients and calories for these ingredients are given in Table 3.

Table 3   Nutritional Values per 100 g of Food

Nutrient (units)	Feta Cheese	Lettuce	Salad Dressing	Tomato
Calories (kcal)	263	14	448.8	21
Calcium (mg)	492.5	36	0	5
Protein (g)	10.33	1.62	0	.85
Carbohydrates (g)	4.09	2.37	2.5	4.64

Use linear programming to find the number of 100-gram units of each ingredient in such a Greek salad, and convert to kitchen units by using Table 1. (*Hint:* Since the ingredients are measured in 100-gram units, the constant in the weight contraint is 4, not 400.)

2. Consider preparing a stir-fry using beef, oil, onion, and soy sauce. A low-calorie stir-fry is desired, which contains less than 10 grams of carbohydrates, more than 50 grams of protein, and more than 3.5 grams of vitamin C. In order for the wok to function correctly, at least one teaspoon (or 4.5 grams) of oil must be used in the recipe. The amounts of the nutrients and calories for these ingredients are given in Table 4.

Table 4   Nutritional Values per 100 g of Food

Nutrient (units)	Beef	Oil	Onion	Soy Sauce
Calories (kcal)	215	884	38	60
Protein (g)	26	0	1.16	10.51
Carbohydrates (g)	0	1	8.63	5.57
Vitamin C (g)	0	0	6.4	0

Use linear programming to find the number of 100-gram units of each ingredient to be used in the stir-fry, and convert to kitchen units by using Table 1.

Extended Project

Use the USDA Nutrient Database for Standard Reference to determine the calorie content and the amount of protein, fat, and carbohydrates for a recipe of your choice. You can set your own constraints on the total amounts of calories, protein, fat, and carbohydrates desired. Determine the amount of each of the ingredients that make up the recipe that satisfies your constraints. Do you think the meal would taste good if you actually made the recipe?

Sets and Probability

8

CHAPTER

We often use the relative frequency of an event from a survey to estimate unknown probabilities. For example, we can estimate the probability that a high-earning chief executive officer is in his sixties; see Example 10 in Section 8.4. Other applications of probability occur in the health and social sciences. Examples include estimating the probability a business has less than 20 employees, an adult has health insurance, or an adult works full time; see Exercises 35, 45, and 55 on page 440.

Federal officials cannot predict exactly how the number of traffic deaths is affected by the trend toward fewer drunken drivers and the increased use of seat belts. Economists cannot tell exactly how stricter federal regulations on bank loans affect the U.S. economy. The number of traffic deaths and the growth of the economy are subject to many factors that cannot be predicted precisely.

Probability theory enables us to deal with uncertainty. The basic concepts of probability are discussed in this chapter, and applications of probability are discussed in the next chapter. Sets and set operations are the basic tools for the study of probability, so we begin with them.

8.1 Sets

Think of a **set** as a well-defined collection of objects. A set of coins might include one of each type of coin now put out by the U.S. government. Another set might be made up of all the students in your English class. By contrast, a collection of young adults does not constitute a set unless the designation "young adult" is clearly defined. For example, this set might be defined as those aged 18–29.

In mathematics, sets are often made up of numbers. The set consisting of the numbers 3, 4, and 5 is written as

$$\{3, 4, 5\},$$

where **set braces, { }**, are used to enclose the numbers belonging to the set. The numbers 3, 4, and 5 are called the **elements,** or **members,** of this set. To show that 4 is an element of the set {3, 4, 5}, we use the symbol ∈ and write

$$4 \in \{3, 4, 5\},$$

read, "4 is an element of the set containing 3, 4, and 5."

Also, $5 \in \{3, 4, 5\}$. Place a slash through the symbol ∈ to show that 8 is *not* an element of this set:

$$8 \notin \{3, 4, 5\}.$$

This statement is read, "8 is not an element of the set {3, 4, 5}."

Sets are often named with capital letters, so that if

$$B = \{5, 6, 7\},$$

✓**Checkpoint 1**

Indicate whether each statement is *true* or *false*.

(a) $9 \in \{8, 4, -3, -9, 6\}$.

(b) $4 \notin \{3, 9, 7\}$.

(c) If $M = \{0, 1, 2, 3, 4\}$, then $0 \in M$.

Answers to Checkpoint exercises are found at the end of the section.

then, for example, $6 \in B$ and $10 \notin B$. ✓₁

Sometimes a set has no elements. Some examples are the set of female presidents of the United States in the period 1788–2012, the set of counting numbers less than 1, and the set of men more than 10 feet tall. A set with no elements is called the **empty set.** The symbol ∅ is used to represent the empty set.

⊘ CAUTION Be careful to distinguish between the symbols 0, ∅, and {0}. The symbol 0 represents a *number*; ∅ represents a *set* with no elements; and {0} represents a *set* with one element, the number 0. Do not confuse the empty set symbol ∅ with the zero symbol ∅ on a computer screen or printout.

Two sets are **equal** if they contain exactly the same elements. The sets {5, 6, 7}, {7, 6, 5}, and {6, 5, 7} all contain exactly the same elements and are equal. In symbols,

$$\{5, 6, 7\} = \{7, 6, 5\} = \{6, 5, 7\}.$$

This means that the ordering of the elements in a set is unimportant. Sets that do not contain exactly the same elements are *not* equal. For example, the sets {5, 6, 7} and {5, 6, 7, 8} do not contain exactly the same elements and are not equal. We show this by writing

$$\{5, 6, 7\} \neq \{5, 6, 7, 8\}.$$

Sometimes we describe a set by a common property of its elements rather than by a list of its elements. This common property can be expressed with **set-builder notation;** for example,

$$\{x \mid x \text{ has property } P\}$$

(read, "the set of all elements x such that x has property P") represents the set of all elements x having some property P.

✓**Checkpoint 2**

List the elements in the given sets.

(a) $\{x \mid x$ is a counting number more than 5 and less than 8}

(b) $\{x \mid x$ is an integer and $-3 < x \leq 1\}$

Example 1   List the elements belonging to each of the given sets.

(a) $\{x \mid x$ is a natural number less than 5}

Solution   The natural numbers less than 5 make up the set {1, 2, 3, 4}.

(b) $\{x \mid x$ is a state that borders Florida}

Solution   The states that border Florida make up the set {Alabama, Georgia}. ✓₂

The **universal set** in a particular discussion is a set that contains all of the objects being discussed. In primary school arithmetic, for example, the set of whole numbers might be the universal set, whereas in a college calculus class the universal set might be the set of all real numbers. When it is necessary to consider the universal set being used, it will be clearly specified or easily understood from the context of the problem.

Sometimes, every element of one set also belongs to another set. For example, if

$$A = \{3, 4, 5, 6\}$$

and

$$B = \{2, 3, 4, 5, 6, 7, 8\},$$

then every element of A is also an element of B. This is an example of the following definition.

A set A is a **subset** of a set B (written $A \subseteq B$) provided that every element of A is also an element of B.

Example 2 For each case, decide whether $M \subseteq N$.

(a) M is the set of all businesses making a profit in the last calendar year. N is the set of all businesses.

Solution Each business making a profit is also a business, so $M \subseteq N$.

(b) M is the set of all first-year students at a college at the end of the academic year, and N is the set of all 18-year-old students at the college at the end of the academic year.

Solution At the beginning and end of the academic year, some first-year students are older than 18, so there are elements in M that are not in N. Thus, M is not a subset of N, written $M \not\subseteq N$.

Every set A is a subset of itself, because the statement "every element of A is also an element of A" is always true. It is also true that the empty set is a subset of every set.[*]

For any set A,

$$\varnothing \subseteq A \qquad \text{and} \qquad A \subseteq A.$$

A set A is said to be a **proper subset** of a set B (written $A \subset B$) if every element of A is an element of B, but B contains at least one element that is not a member of A.

Example 3 Decide whether $E \subset F$.

(a) $E = \{2, 4, 6, 8\}$ and $F = \{1, 2, 3, 4, 5, 6, 7, 8, 9, 10\}$.

Solution Since each element of E is an element of F and F contains several elements not in E, $E \subset F$.

---

[*]This fact is not intuitively obvious to most people. If you wish, you can think of it as a convention that we agree to adopt in order to simplify the statements of several results later.

(b) *E* is the set of registered voters in Texas. *F* is the set of adults aged 18 years or older.

Solution To register to vote, one must be at least 18 years old. Not all adults at least 18 years old, however, are registered. Thus, every element of *E* is contained in *F* and *F* contains elements not in *E*. Therefore, $E \subset F$.

(c) *E* is the set of diet soda drinks. *F* is the set of diet soda drinks sweetened with Nutrasweet®.

Solution Some diet soda drinks are sweetened with the sugar substitute Splenda®. In this case, *E* is not a proper subset of *F* (written $E \not\subset F$), nor is it a subset of *F* at all ($E \nsubseteq F$). ✓₃

✓ **Checkpoint 3**

Indicate whether each statement is *true* or *false*.

(a) $\{10, 20, 30\} \subseteq \{20, 30, 40, 50\}$.

(b) $\{x \mid x \text{ is a minivan}\} \subseteq \{x \mid x \text{ is a motor vehicle}\}$.

(c) $\{a, e, i, o, u\} \subset \{a, e, i, o, u, y\}$.

(d) $\{x \mid x \text{ is a U.S. state that begins with the letter "A"}\} \subset \{$Alabama, Alaska, Arizona, Arkansas$\}$.

✓ **Checkpoint 4**

List all subsets of $\{w, x, y, z\}$.

Example 4 List all possible subsets for each of the given sets.

(a) $\{7, 8\}$

Solution A good way to find the subsets of $\{7, 8\}$ is to use a **tree diagram**—a systematic way of listing all the subsets of a given set. The tree diagram in Figure 8.1(a) shows there are four subsets of $\{7, 8\}$:

$$\varnothing, \quad \{7\}, \quad \{8\}, \quad \text{and} \quad \{7, 8\}.$$

(b) $\{a, b, c\}$

Solution The tree diagram in Figure 8.1(b) shows that there are 8 subsets of $\{a, b, c\}$:

$$\varnothing, \quad \{a\}, \quad \{b\}, \quad \{c\}, \quad \{a, b\}, \quad \{a, c\}, \quad \{b, c\}, \quad \text{and} \quad \{a, b, c\}. ✓₄$$

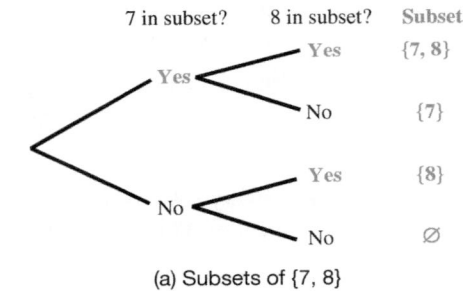

(a) Subsets of {7, 8}

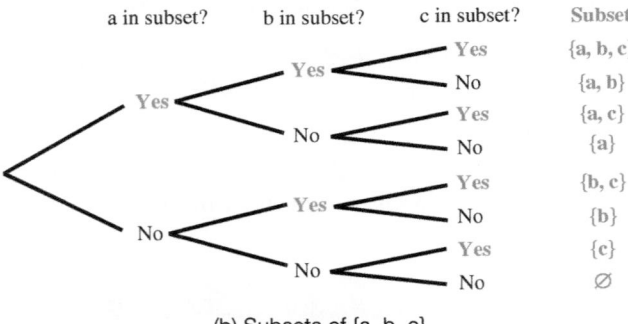

(b) Subsets of {a, b, c}

Figure 8.1

By using the fact that there are two possibilities for each element (either it is in the subset or it is not), we have found that a set with 2 elements has 4 ($=2^2$) subsets and a set with 3 elements has 8 ($=2^3$) subsets. Similar arguments work for any finite set and lead to the following conclusion.

✓ **Checkpoint 5**

Find the number of subsets for each of the given sets.

(a) $\{x \mid x$ is a season of the year$\}$

(b) $\{-6, -5, -4, -3, -2, -1, 0\}$

(c) $\{6\}$

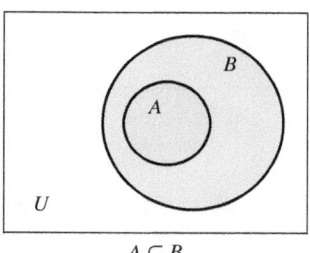

$A \subseteq B$

Figure 8.2

✓ **Checkpoint 6**

Refer to sets A, B, C, and U in the diagram.

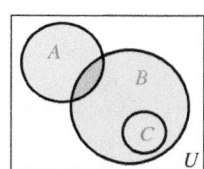

(a) Is $A \subseteq B$?

(b) Is $C \subseteq B$?

(c) Is $C \subseteq U$?

(d) Is $\varnothing \subseteq A$?

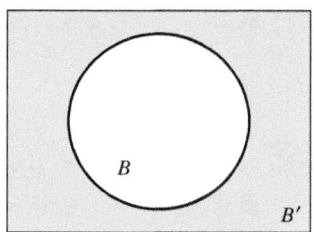

B'

Figure 8.3

✓ **Checkpoint 7**

Let $U = \{a, b, c, d, e, f, g\}$, with $K = \{c, d, f, g\}$ and $R = \{a, c, d, e, g\}$. Find

(a) K';

(b) R'.

> A set of n distinct elements has 2^n subsets.

Example 5   Find the number of subsets for each of the given sets.

(a) $\{$blue, brown, hazel, green$\}$

Solution Since this set has 4 elements, it has $2^4 = 16$ subsets.

(b) $\{x \mid x$ is a month of the year$\}$

Solution This set has 12 elements and therefore has $2^{12} = 4096$ subsets.

(c) $\varnothing$

Solution Since the empty set has 0 elements, it has $2^0 = 1$ subset, $\varnothing$ itself.

Venn diagrams are sometimes used to illustrate relationships among sets. The Venn diagram in Figure 8.2 shows a set A that is a subset of a set B, because A is entirely in B. (The areas of the regions are not meant to be proportional to the sizes of the corresponding sets.) The rectangle represents the universal set U. ✓6

Some sets have infinitely many elements. We often use the notation "$\ldots$" to indicate such sets. One example of an infinite set is the set of natural numbers, $\{1, 2, 3, 4, \ldots\}$. Another infinite set is the set of integers, $\{\ldots, -3, -2, -1, 0, 1, 2, 3, \ldots\}$.

Operations on Sets

Given a set A and a universal set U, the set of all elements of U that do *not* belong to A is called the **complement** of set A. For example, if A is the set of all the female students in your class and U is the set of all students in the class, then the complement of A would be the set of all male students in the class. The complement of set A is written A' (read "A-prime"). The Venn diagram in Figure 8.3 shows a set B. Its complement, B', is shown in color.

Some textbooks use $\overline{A}$ to denote the complement of A. This notation conveys the same meaning as A'.

Example 6   Let $U = \{1, 2, 3, 4, 5, 6, 7\}$, $A = \{1, 3, 5, 7\}$, and $B = \{3, 4, 6\}$. Find the given sets.

(a) A'

Solution Set A' contains the elements of U that are not in A:

$$A' = \{2, 4, 6\}.$$

(b) B'

Solution $B' = \{1, 2, 5, 7\}$.

(c) $\varnothing'$ and U'

Solution $\varnothing' = U$ and $U' = \varnothing$.

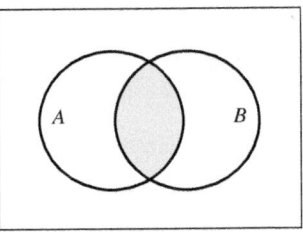

$A \cap B$

Figure 8.4

Given two sets A and B, the set of all elements belonging to *both* set A and set B is called the **intersection** of the two sets, written $A \cap B$. For example, the elements that belong to both $A = \{1, 2, 4, 5, 7\}$ and $B = \{2, 4, 5, 7, 9, 11\}$ are 2, 4, 5, and 7, so

$$A \text{ and } B = A \cap B$$
$$= \{1, 2, 4, 5, 7\} \cap \{2, 4, 5, 7, 9, 11\}$$
$$= \{2, 4, 5, 7\}.$$

The Venn diagram in Figure 8.4 shows two sets A and B, with their intersection, $A \cap B$, shown in color.

Example 7   Find the given sets.

(a) $\{9, 15, 25, 36\} \cap \{15, 20, 25, 30, 35\}$

Solution $\{15, 25\}$. The elements 15 and 25 are the only ones belonging to both sets.

(b) $\{x | x \text{ is a teenager}\} \cap \{x | x \text{ is a senior citizen}\}$

Solution $\varnothing$ since no teenager is a senior citizen.

✓**Checkpoint 8**

Find $\{1, 2, 3, 4\} \cap \{3, 5, 7, 9\}$.

Two sets that have no elements in common are called **disjoint sets.** For example, there are no elements common to both $\{50, 51, 54\}$ and $\{52, 53, 55, 56\}$, so these two sets are disjoint, and

$$\{50, 51, 54\} \cap \{52, 53, 55, 56\} = \varnothing.$$

The result of this example can be generalized as follows.

For any sets A and B,

if A and B are disjoint sets, then $A \cap B = \varnothing$.

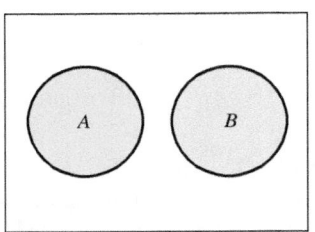

A and *B* are disjoint sets.

Figure 8.5

Figure 8.5 is a Venn diagram of disjoint sets.

The set of all elements belonging to set A or to set B, or to both sets, is called the **union** of the two sets, written $A \cup B$. For example, for sets $A = \{1, 3, 5\}$ and $B = \{3, 5, 7, 9\}$,

$$A \text{ or } B = A \cup B$$
$$= \{1, 3, 5\} \cup \{3, 5, 7, 9\}$$
$$= \{1, 3, 5, 7, 9\}.$$

The Venn diagram in Figure 8.6 shows two sets A and B, with their union, $A \cup B$, shown in color.

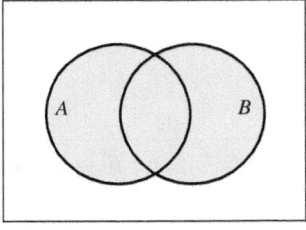

$A \cup B$

Figure 8.6

Example 8   Find the given sets.

(a) $\{1, 2, 5, 9, 14\} \cup \{1, 3, 4, 8\}$.

Solution   Begin by listing the elements of the first set, $\{1, 2, 5, 9, 14\}$. Then include any elements from the second set *that are not already listed.* Doing this gives

$$\{1, 2, 5, 9, 14\} \cup \{1, 3, 4, 8\} = \{1, 2, 3, 4, 5, 8, 9, 14\}.$$

✓**Checkpoint 9**

Find $\{a, b, c\} \cup \{a, c, e\}$.

(b) $\{\text{terriers, spaniels, chows, dalmatians}\} \cup \{\text{spaniels, collies, bulldogs}\}$

Solution $\{\text{terriers, spaniels, chows, dalmatians, collies, bulldogs}\}$.

Finding the complement of a set, the intersection of two sets, or the union of two sets is an example of a *set operation*.

Operations on Sets

Let A and B be any sets, with U signifying the universal set. Then

the **complement** of A, written A', is

$$A' = \{x \mid x \notin A \text{ and } x \in U\};$$

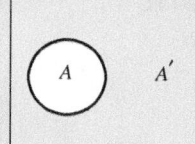

the **intersection** of A and B is

$$A \cap B = \{x \mid x \in A \textbf{ and } x \in B\};$$

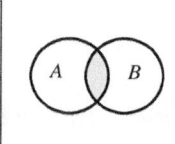

the **union** of A and B is

$$A \cup B = \{x \mid x \in A \textbf{ or } x \in B \textbf{ or both}\}.$$

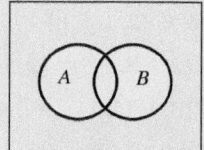

CAUTION As shown in the preceding definitions, an element is in the intersection of sets A and B if it is in *both* A and B at the same time, but an element is in the union of sets A and B if it is in *either* set A or set B, *or* in both sets A and B.

Example 9 **Business** The following table gives the 52-week high and low prices, the last price, and the change in price from the day before for six stocks on a recent day.

Stock	High	Low	Last	Change
First Solar	47.78	11.43	43.43	−4.26
Ford	14.30	8.82	14.19	+.10
IBM	215.90	181.85	203.63	+.85
JP Morgan Chase	51.00	30.83	49.14	+.96
Netflix	224.30	52.81	206.25	−4.44
Procter & Gamble	82.54	59.07	77.94	.19

Let the universal set U consist of the six stocks listed in the table. Let A contain all stocks with a high price greater than $50, B all stocks with a last price between $25 and $80, and C all stocks with a negative value for the change. Find the results of the given set operations. (Data from: www.morningstar.com on May 7, 2013.)

(a) B'

Solution Set B consists of First Solar, JP Morgan Chase, and Procter & Gamble. Set B' contains all the listed stocks that are not in set B, so

$$B' = \{\text{Ford, IBM, Netflix}\}.$$

(b) $A \cap C$

Solution   Set A consists of IBM, JP Morgan Chase, Netflix, and Procter & Gamble, and set C consists of First Solar and Netflix. Hence the stock in both A and C is

$$A \cap C = \{\text{Netflix}\}.$$

✓ **Checkpoint 10**

In Example 9, find the given set of stocks.

(a) $B \cap C$

(b) $B \cup C$

(c) $A \cup B$

Solution $A \cup B = \{$First Solar, IBM, JP Morgan Chase, Netflix, and Procter & Gamble$\}$ ✓10

8.1 Exercises

Write true or false for each statement. (See Example 1.)

1. $3 \in \{2, 5, 7, 9, 10\}$

2. $6 \in \{-2, 6, 9, 5\}$

3. $9 \notin \{2, 1, 5, 8\}$

4. $3 \notin \{7, 6, 5, 4\}$

5. $\{2, 5, 8, 9\} = \{2, 5, 9, 8\}$

6. $\{3, 7, 12, 14\} = \{3, 7, 12, 14, 0\}$

7. $\{$all whole numbers greater than 7 and less than 10$\} = \{8, 9\}$

8. $\{$all counting numbers not greater than 3$\} = \{0, 1, 2\}$

9. $\{x | x$ is an odd integer, $6 \le x \le 18\} = \{7, 9, 11, 15, 17\}$

10. $\{x | x$ is a vowel$\} = \{a, e, i, o, u\}$

11. The elements of a set may be sets themselves, as in $\{1, \{1, 3\}, \{2\}, 4\}$. Explain why the set $\{\emptyset\}$ is not the same set as $\{0\}$.

12. What is set-builder notation? Give an example.

Let $A = \{-3, 0, 3\}$, $B = \{-2, -1, 0, 1, 2\}$, $C = \{-3, -1\}$, $D = \{0\}$, $E = \{-2\}$, and $U = \{-3, -2, -1, 0, 1, 2, 3\}$. Insert $\subseteq$ or $\nsubseteq$ to make the given statements true. (See Example 2.)

13. A_____U

14. E_____A

15. A_____E

16. B_____C

17. $\emptyset$_____A

18. $\{0, 2\}$_____D

19. D_____B

20. A_____C

Find the number of subsets of the given set. (See Example 5.)

21. $\{A, B, C\}$

22. $\{$red, yellow, blue, black, white$\}$

23. $\{x | x$ is an integer strictly between 0 and 8$\}$

24. $\{x | x$ is a whole number less than 4$\}$

Find the complement of each set. (See Example 6.)

25. The set in Exercise 23 if U is the set of all integers.

26. The set in Exercise 24 if U is the set of all whole numbers.

27. Describe the intersection and union of sets. How do they differ?

Insert $\cap$ or $\cup$ to make each statement true. (See Examples 7 and 8.)

28. $\{5, 7, 9, 19\}$_____$\{7, 9, 11, 15\} = \{7, 9\}$

29. $\{8, 11, 15\}$_____$\{8, 11, 19, 20\} = \{8, 11\}$

30. $\{2, 1, 7\}$_____$\{1, 5, 9\} = \{1\}$

31. $\{6, 12, 14, 16\}$_____$\{6, 14, 19\} = \{6, 14\}$

32. $\{3, 5, 9, 10\}$_____$\emptyset = \emptyset$

33. $\{3, 5, 9, 10\}$_____$\emptyset = \{3, 5, 9, 10\}$

34. $\{1, 2, 4\}$_____$\{1, 2, 4\} = \{1, 2, 4\}$

35. $\{1, 2, 4\}$_____$\{1, 2\} = \{1, 2, 4\}$

36. Is it possible for two nonempty sets to have the same intersection and union? If so, give an example.

Let $U = \{a, b, c, d, e, f, 1, 2, 3, 4, 5, 6\}$, $X = \{a, b, c, 1, 2, 3\}$, $Y = \{b, d, f, 1, 3, 5\}$, and $Z = \{b, d, 2, 3, 5\}$.

List the members of each of the given sets, using set braces. (See Examples 6–8.)

37. $X \cap Y$

38. $X \cup Y$

39. X'

40. Y'

41. $X' \cap Y'$

42. $X' \cap Z$

43. $X \cup (Y \cap Z)$

44. $Y \cap (X \cup Z)$

Let $U = \{$all students in this school$\}$, $M = \{$all students taking this course$\}$, $N = \{$all students taking accounting$\}$, and $P = \{$all students taking philosophy$\}$.

Describe each of the following sets in words.

45. M'

46. $M \cup N$

47. $N \cap P$

48. $N' \cap P'$

49. Refer to the sets listed in the directions for Exercises 13–20. Which pairs of sets are disjoint?

50. Refer to the sets listed in the directions for Exercises 37–44. Which pairs of sets are disjoint?

Refer to Example 9 in the text. Describe each of the sets in Exercises 51–54 in words; then list the elements of each set.

51. A'　　　　　　　　52. $B \cup C$

53. $A' \cap B'$　　　　　　54. $B' \cup C$

Business *A stock broker classifies her clients by sex, marital status, and employment status. Let the universal set be the set of all clients, M be the set of male clients, S be the set of single clients, and E be the set of employed clients. Describe the following sets in words.*

55. $M \cap E$　　　　　　　56. $M' \cap S$

57. $M' \cup S'$　　　　　　58. $E' \cup S'$

Business *The U.S. advertising volume (in millions of dollars) collected by certain types of national media in the years 2009 and 2010 is shown in the following table. (Data from: ProQuest Statistical Abstract of the United States: 2013.)*

Medium	2009	2010
Television	33,723	36,210
Magazines	15,554	15,623
Digital/Online	5549	7144
Network/Satellite Radio	1100	1145
National Newspapers	873	887

List the elements of each set.

59. The set of all media that collected more than $10,000 million in both 2009 and 2010.

60. The set of all media that collected less than $6000 million in 2009 or 2010.

61. The set of all media that had revenues fall from 2009 to 2010.

62. The set of all media that rose in revenue and had at least $5000 million in revenue in both years.

Business *The top six basic cable television providers in the year 2012 are listed in the following table. Use this information for Exercises 63–70.*

Rank	Cable Provider	Basic Cable Subscribers
1	Comcast	21,995,000
2	Direct TV	20,080,000
3	Dish Network	14,056,000
4	Time Warner	12,218,000
5	Verizon	4,726,000
6	Cox	4,540,280

List the elements of the following sets. (Data from: www.ncta. com.)

63. F, the set of cable providers with more than 5 million subscribers.

64. G, the set of cable providers with between 10 million and 20 million subscribers.

65. H, the set of cable providers with less than 20 million subscribers.

66. I, the set of cable providers with more than 13 million subscribers.

67. $F \cup G$　　　　　　　68. $H \cap F$

69. I'　　　　　　　　　70. $I' \cap H$

Business *The following table gives the amount of several farm products (in millions of metric tons) exported from the United States in the years 2000 and 2011. (Data from: U.S. Department of Agriculture.)*

Product	2000	2011
Wheat	28.9	28.6
Corn	49.3	39.4
Soybeans	27.1	36.7
Rice	2.6	3.2
Cotton	6.7	11.7

List the elements of the following sets.

71. The set of farm products where exports increased from 2000 to 2011.

72. The set of farm products that had more than 20 million metric tons of exports in both 2000 and 2011.

73. The set of farm products that had less than 40 million metric tons of exports in either 2000 or 2011.

74. The set of farm products that had an increase of 4 million metric tons or more from 2000 to 2011.

✓ Checkpoint Answers

1. (a) False　　(b) True　　(c) True

2. (a) $\{6, 7\}$　　(b) $\{-2, -1, 0, 1\}$

3. (a) False　　(b) True　　(c) True　　(d) False

4. $\varnothing, \{w\}, \{x\}, \{y\}, \{z\}, \{w, x\}, \{w, y\}, \{w, z\}, \{x, y\}, \{x, z\}, \{y, z\},$ $\{w, x, y\}, \{w, x, z\}, \{w, y, z\}, \{x, y, z\}, \{w, x, y, z\}$

5. (a) 16　　(b) 128　　(c) 2

6. (a) No　　(b) Yes　　(c) Yes　　(d) Yes

7. (a) $\{a, b, e\}$　　(b) $\{b, f\}$

8. $\{3\}$

9. $\{a, b, c, e\}$

10. (a) $\{$First Solar$\}$
    (b) $\{$First Solar, JP Morgan Chase, Netflix, Procter & Gamble$\}$

8.2 Applications of Venn Diagrams and Contingency Tables

We used Venn diagrams in the previous section to illustrate set union and intersection. The rectangular region in a Venn diagram represents the universal set U. Including only a single set A inside the universal set, as in Figure 8.7, divides U into two nonoverlapping regions. Region 1 represents A', those elements outside set A, while region 2 represents those elements belonging to set A. (The numbering of these regions is arbitrary.)

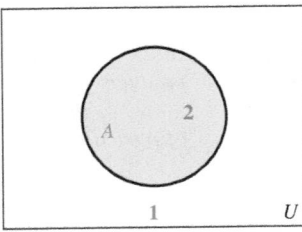

One set leads to 2 regions.
(Numbering is arbitrary.)

Figure 8.7

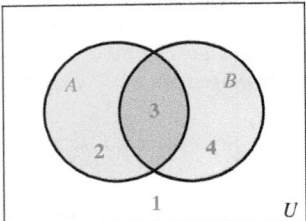

Two sets lead to 4 regions.
(Numbering is arbitrary.)

Figure 8.8

The Venn diagram of Figure 8.8 shows two sets inside U. These two sets divide the universal set into four nonoverlapping regions. As labeled in Figure 8.8, region 1 includes those elements outside both set A and set B. Region 2 includes those elements belonging to A and not to B. Region 3 includes those elements belonging to both A and B. Which elements belong to region 4? (Again, the numbering is arbitrary.)

Example 1 Draw a Venn diagram similar to Figure 8.8, and shade the regions representing the given sets.

(a) $A' \cap B$

Solution Set A' contains all the elements outside set A. As labeled in Figure 8.8, A' is represented by regions 1 and 4. Set B is represented by the elements in regions 3 and 4. The intersection of sets A' and B, the set $A' \cap B$, is given by the region common to regions 1 and 4 and regions 3 and 4. The result, region 4, is shaded in Figure 8.9.

(b) $A' \cup B'$

Solution Again, set A' is represented by regions 1 and 4 and set B' by regions 1 and 2. To find $A' \cup B'$, identify the region that represents the set of all elements in A', B', or both. The result, which is shaded in Figure 8.10, includes regions 1, 2, and 4. ✓

 Checkpoint 1

Draw Venn diagrams for the given set operations.

(a) $A \cup B'$

(b) $A' \cap B'$

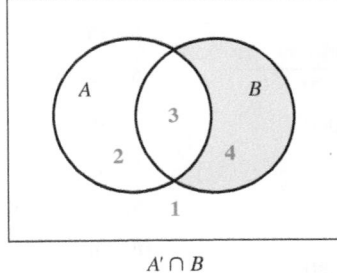

$A' \cap B$

Figure 8.9

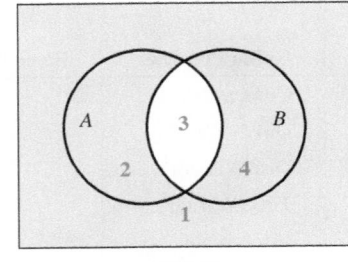

$A' \cup B'$

Figure 8.10

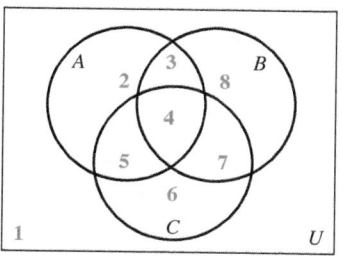

Three sets lead to 8 regions.

Figure 8.11

✓ **Checkpoint 2**

Draw Venn diagrams for the given set operations.

(a) $(B' \cap A) \cup C$

(b) $(A \cup B)' \cap C$

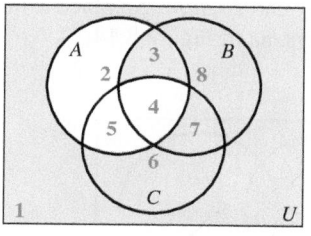

$A' \cup (B \cap C')$

Figure 8.12

Venn diagrams also can be drawn with three sets inside U. These three sets divide the universal set into eight nonoverlapping regions that can be numbered (arbitrarily) as in Figure 8.11.

| **Example 2** | Shade $A' \cup (B \cap C')$ in a Venn diagram. |

Solution First find $B \cap C'$. Set B is represented by regions 3, 4, 7, and 8, and set C' by regions 1, 2, 3, and 8. The overlap of these regions, regions 3 and 8, represents the set $B \cap C'$. Set A' is represented by regions 1, 6, 7, and 8. The union of regions 3 and 8 and regions 1, 6, 7, and 8 contains regions 1, 3, 6, 7, and 8, which are shaded in Figure 8.12. ✓2

Venn diagrams can be used to solve problems that result from surveying groups of people.

| **Example 3** | **Business** A market researcher collecting data on 100 household finds that |

81 have cable television (CT);

65 have high-speed Internet (HSI);

56 have both.

The researcher wants to answer the following questions:

(a) How many households do not have high-speed Internet?

(b) How many households have neither cable television nor high-speed Internet?

(c) How many have cable television, but not high-speed Internet?

Solution A Venn diagram like the one in Figure 8.13 will help sort out the information. In Figure 8.13(a), we place the number 56 in the region common to both cable television and high-speed Internet, because 56 households have both. Of the 81 with cable television, $81 - 56 = 25$ do not have high-speed Internet, so in Figure 8.13(b) we place 25 in the region for cable television, but not high-speed Internet. Similarly, $65 - 56 = 9$ households have high-speed Internet, but not cable television, so we place 9 in that region. Finally, the diagram shows that $100 - 9 - 56 - 25 = 10$ have neither high-speed Internet nor cable television. Now we can answer the questions.

✓ **Checkpoint 3**

(a) Place numbers in the regions on a Venn diagram if the data on the 100 households in Example 3 showed

78 with cable television;

52 with high-speed Internet;

48 with both.

(b) How many have high-speed Internet, but not cable television?

(a)

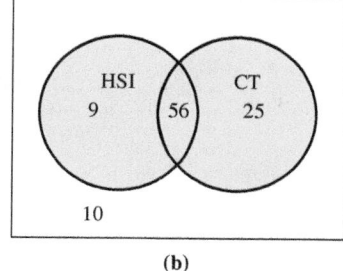

(b)

Figure 8.13

(a) $10 + 25 = 35$ do not have high-speed Internet.

(b) 10 have neither.

(c) 25 have cable television, but not high-speed Internet.

Example 4 **Social Science** A group of 60 first-year business students at a large university was surveyed, with the following results:

19 of the students read *Business Week*;

18 read the *Wall Street Journal*;

50 read *Fortune*;

13 read *Business Week* and the *Journal*;

11 read the *Journal* and *Fortune*;

13 read *Business Week* and *Fortune*;

9 read all three magazines.

Use the preceding data to answer the following questions:

(a) How many students read none of the publications?

(b) How many read only *Fortune*?

(c) How many read *Business Week* and the *Journal*, but not *Fortune*?

Solution Once again, use a Venn diagram to represent the data. Since 9 students read all three publications, begin by placing 9 in the area in Figure 8.14(a) that belongs to all three regions.

Of the 13 students who read *Business Week* and *Fortune*, 9 also read the *Journal*. Therefore, only $13 - 9 = 4$ students read just *Business Week* and *Fortune*. So place a 4 in the region common only to *Business Week* and *Fortune* readers, as in Figure 8.14(b).

Figure 8.14(a)

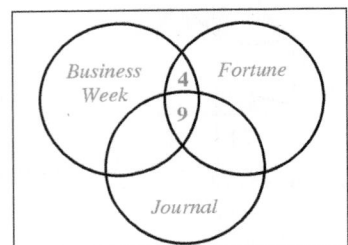

Figure 8.14(b)

In the same way, place a 4 in the region of Figure 8.14(c) common only to *Business Week* and the *Journal* readers, and 2 in the region common only to *Fortune* and the *Journal* readers.

The data shows that 19 students read *Business Week*. However, $4 + 9 + 4 = 17$ readers have already been placed in the *Business Week* region. The balance of this region in Figure 8.14(d) will contain only $19 - 17 = 2$ students. These 2 students read *Business Week* only—not *Fortune* and not the *Journal*.

Figure 8.14(c)

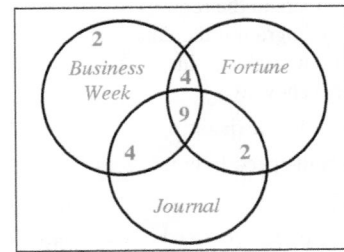

Figure 8.14(d)

In the same way, 3 students read only the *Journal* and 35 read only *Fortune*, as shown in Figure 8.14(e).

A total of $2 + 4 + 3 + 4 + 9 + 2 + 35 = 59$ students are placed in the various regions of Figure 8.14(e). Since 60 students were surveyed, $60 - 59 = 1$ student reads none of the three publications, and so 1 is placed outside the other regions in Figure 8.14(f).

Figure 8.14(e)

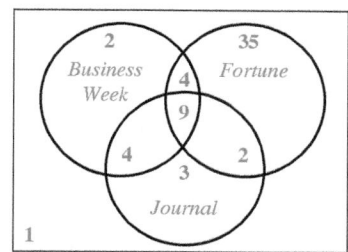

Figure 8.14(f)

Figure 8.14(f) can now be used to answer the questions asked at the beginning of this example:

(a) Only 1 student reads none of the publications.

(b) There are 35 students who read only *Fortune*.

(c) The overlap of the regions representing *Business Week* and the *Journal* shows that 4 students read *Business Week* and the *Journal*, but not *Fortune*. ✓₄

✓ **Checkpoint 4**

In Example 4, how many students read exactly,

(a) 1 of the publications?

(b) 2 of the publications?

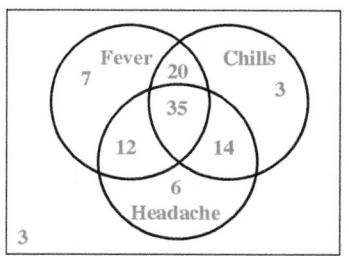

Figure 8.15

✓ **Checkpoint 5**

In Example 5, suppose 75 patients reported a fever and only 2 thought they had the flu, but did not report fever, chills, or headache. Then how many

(a) reported only a fever?

(b) reported a fever or chills?

(c) reported a fever, chills, or headache?

Example 5 **Health** Mark McCloney, M.D., saw 100 patients exhibiting flu symptoms such as fever, chills, and headache. Dr. McCloney reported the following information on patients exhibiting symptoms:

Of the 100 patients,

74 reported a fever;

72 reported chills;

67 reported a headache;

55 reported both a fever and chills;

47 reported both a fever and a headache;

49 reported both chills and a headache;

35 reported all three;

3 thought they had the flu, but did not report fever, chills, or headache.

Create a Venn diagram to represent this data. It should show the number of people in each region.

Solution Begin with the 35 patients who reported all three symptoms. This leaves $55 - 35 = 20$ who reported fever and chills, but not headache; $47 - 35 = 12$ who reported fever and headache, but not chills; and $49 - 35 = 14$ who reported chills and headache, but not fever. With this information, we have $74 - (35 + 20 + 12) = 7$ who reported fever alone; $72 - (35 + 20 + 14) = 3$ with chills alone; and $67 - (35 + 12 + 14) = 6$ with headache alone. The remaining 3 patients who thought they had the flu, but did not report fever, chills, or headache are denoted outside the 3 circles. See Figure 8.15. ✓₅

NOTE In all the preceding examples, we started in the innermost region with the intersection of the categories. This is usually the best way to begin solving problems of this type.

We use the symbol $n(A)$ to denote the *number* of elements in A. For instance, if $A = \{w, x, y, z\}$, then $n(A) = 4$. Next, we prove the following useful fact.

Addition Rule for Counting

$$n(A \cup B) = n(A) + n(B) - n(A \cap B).$$

For example, if $A = \{r, s, t, u, v\}$ and $B = \{r, t, w\}$, then $A \cap B = \{r, t\}$, so that $n(A) = 5$, $n(B) = 3$, and $n(A \cap B) = 2$. By the formula in the box, $n(A \cup B) = 5 + 3 - 2 = 6$, which is certainly true, since $A \cup B = \{r, s, t, u, v, w\}$.

Here is a proof of the statement in the box: Let x be the number of elements in A that are not in B, y be the number of elements in $A \cap B$, and z be the number of elements in B that are not in A, as indicated in Figure 8.16. That diagram shows that $n(A \cup B) = x + y + z$. It also shows that $n(A) = x + y$ and $n(B) = y + z$, so that

$$n(A) + n(B) - n(A \cap B) = (x + y) + (z + y) - y$$
$$= x + y + z$$
$$= n(A \cup B).$$

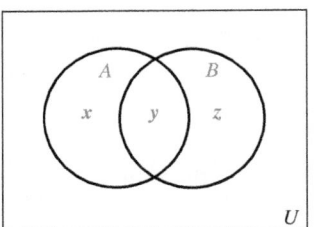

Figure 8.16

Example 6   **Social Science**   A group of 10 students meets to plan a school function. All are majoring in accounting or economics or both. Five of the students are economics majors, and 7 are majors in accounting. How many major in both subjects?

Solution   Let A represent the set of economics majors and B represent the set of accounting majors. Use the union rule, with $n(A) = 5$, $n(B) = 7$, and $n(A \cup B) = 10$. We must find $n(A \cap B)$:

$$n(A \cup B) = n(A) + n(B) - n(A \cap B)$$
$$10 = 5 + 7 - n(A \cap B).$$

So,

$$n(A \cap B) = 5 + 7 - 10 = 2. \quad \boxed{\checkmark_6}$$

✓ **Checkpoint 6**

If $n(A) = 10$, $n(B) = 7$, and $n(A \cap B) = 3$, find $n(A \cup B)$.

In addition to Venn diagrams, we can use a contingency table, which is sometimes called a cross tabulation, to summarize counts from several different groups. A contingency table is a table in a matrix format that gives the frequency distribution of several variables. With such tables, we can compute the number of elements in sets of interest, the intersection of two sets, and the union of two sets.

Example 7   **Economics**   The following contingency table gives the number (in thousands) of males (denoted with M) and females (denoted with F) who were working full-time (denoted A), working part-time (denoted B), or not working (denoted C) in the year 2010. (Data from: U.S. Census Bureau.)

	A Worked Full-time	*B* Worked Part-time	*C* Did Not Work
M Males	56,414	24,659	35,729
F Females	42,834	29,232	51,047

Find the number of people in the given sets.

(a) A

Solution   The set A consists of males and females who worked full-time. From the table, we see that there were 56,414 thousand males and 42,834 thousand females, which yields 99,248 thousand people who worked full-time in the year 2010.

(b) $F \cap A$

Solution   The set $F \cap A$ consists of all the people who are female *and* who worked full-time. We see that there are 42,834 thousand females who worked full-time.

(c) $M \cup C$

Solution   The set $M \cup C$ consists of people who are male or who did not work. Using the addition rule for counting, we have

$$n(M \cup C) = n(M) + n(C) - n(M \cap C).$$

From the table, we have $n(M) = 56{,}414 + 24{,}659 + 35{,}729 = 116{,}802$ thousand males. Also from the table we have $n(C) = 35{,}729 + 51{,}047 = 86{,}776$ thousand people who did not work. We also have that $n(M \cap C)$, the number who are male and who did work, is 35,729 thousand. Thus,

$$n(M \cup C) = n(M) + n(C) - n(M \cap C)$$
$$= 116{,}802 + 86{,}776 - 35{,}729$$
$$= 167{,}849 \text{ thousand people.}$$

✓ **Checkpoint 7**

Refer to Example 7 and find the number of people in the following sets.

(a) $A \cup B$

(b) $F \cup B$

(d) $(B \cup C) \cap F$

Solution   Begin with the set $B \cup C$, which contains all those who worked part-time or not at all. Of this set, take only those who were females for a total of $29{,}232 + 51{,}047 = 80{,}279$ thousand.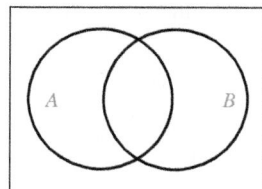

8.2 Exercises

Sketch a Venn diagram like the one shown, and use shading to show each of the given sets. (See Example 1.)

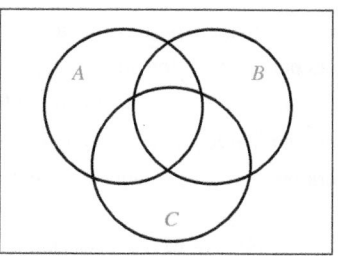

1. $A \cap B'$

2. $A \cup B'$

3. $B' \cup A'$

4. $A' \cap B'$

5. $B' \cup (A \cap B')$

6. $(A \cap B) \cup A'$

7. U'

8. $\varnothing'$

9. Three sets divide the universal set into at most _____ regions.

10. What does the notation $n(A)$ represent?

Sketch a Venn diagram like the one shown, and use shading to show each of the given sets. (See Example 2.)

11. $(A \cap C') \cup B$

12. $A \cap (B \cup C')$

13. $A' \cap (B \cap C)$

14. $(A' \cap B') \cap C$

15. $(A \cap B') \cup C$

16. $(A \cap B') \cap C$

Use Venn diagrams to answer the given questions. (See Examples 2 and 4.)

17. Health   In 2010, the percentage of assisted living residents who had both high blood pressure and dementia was 24%, the percentage with only high blood pressure was 33%, and the percentage with neither condition was 25%. What percentage of assisted living residents had only dementia? (Data from: National Center for Health Statistics.)

18. Health In 2010, the percentage of assisted living residents who had both heart disease and depression was 9%, the percentage with only heart disease was 25%, and the percentage with neither condition was 48%. What percentage of assisted living residents had only depression? (Data from: National Center for Health Statistics.)

19. Business The human resources director for a commercial real estate company received the following numbers of applications from people with the given information:

66 with sales experience;

40 with a college degree;

23 with a real estate license;

26 with sales experience and a college degree;

16 with sales experience and a real estate license;

15 with a college degree and a real estate license;

11 with sales experience, a college degree, and a real estate license;

22 with neither sales experience, a college degree, nor a real estate license.

(a) How many applicants were there?

(b) How many applicants did not have sales experience?

(c) How many had sales experience and a college degree, but not a real estate license?

(d) How many had only a real estate license?

20. Business A pet store keeps track of the purchases of customers over a four-hour period. The store manager classifies purchases as containing a dog product, a cat product, a fish product, or a product for a different kind of pet. She found that:

83 customers purchased a dog product;

101 customers purchased a cat product;

22 customers purchased a fish product;

31 customers purchased a dog and a cat product;

8 customers purchased a dog and a fish product;

10 customers purchased a cat and a fish product;

6 customers purchased a dog, a cat, and a fish product;

34 customers purchased a product for a pet other than a dog, cat, or fish.

(a) How many purchases were for a dog product only?

(b) How many purchases were for a cat product only?

(c) How many purchases were for a dog or fish product?

(d) How many purchases were there in total?

21. Natural Science A marine biologist surveys people who fish on Lake Erie and caught at least one fish to determine whether they had caught a walleye, a smallmouth bass, or a yellow perch in the last year. He finds:

124 caught at least one walleye;

133 caught at least one smallmouth bass;

146 caught at least one yellow perch;

75 caught at least one walleye and at least one smallmouth bass;

67 caught at least one walleye and at least one yellow perch;

79 caught at least one smallmouth bass and at least one yellow perch;

45 caught all three.

(a) Find the total number of people surveyed.

(b) How many caught at least one walleye or at least one smallmouth bass?

(c) How many caught only walleye?

22. Health Human blood can contain either no antigens, the A antigen, the B antigen, or both the A and B antigens. A third antigen, called the Rh antigen, is important in human reproduction and, like the A and B antigens, may or may not be present in an individual. Blood is called type A positive if the individual has the A and Rh antigens, but not the B antigen. A person having only the A and B antigens is said to have type AB-negative blood. A person having only the Rh antigen has type O-positive blood. Other blood types are defined in a similar manner. Identify the blood type of the individuals in regions (a)–(g) of the Venn diagram.

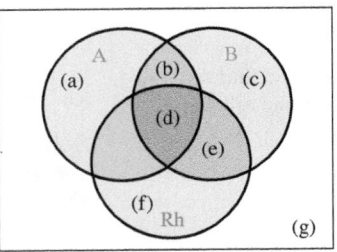

23. Natural Science Use the diagram from Exercise 22. In a certain hospital, the following data was recorded:

25 patients had the A antigen;

17 had the A and B antigens;

27 had the B antigen;

22 had the B and Rh antigens;

30 had the Rh antigen;

12 had none of the antigens;

16 had the A and Rh antigens;

15 had all three antigens.

How many patients

(a) were represented?

(b) had exactly one antigen?

(c) had exactly two antigens?

(d) had O-positive blood?

(e) had AB-positive blood?

(f) had B-negative blood?

(g) had O-negative blood?

(h) had A-positive blood?

24. Business In reviewing the portfolios of 365 of its clients, a mutual funds company categorized whether the clients were invested in international stock funds, domestic stock funds, or bond funds. It found that,

125 were invested in domestic stocks, international stocks, and bond funds;

145 were invested in domestic stocks and bond funds;

300 were invested in domestic stocks;

200 were invested in international and domestic stocks;

18 were invested in international stocks and bond funds, but not domestic stocks;

35 were invested in bonds, but not in international or domestic stocks;

87 were invested in international stocks, but not in bond funds.

(a) How many were invested in international stocks?

(b) How many were invested in bonds, but not international stocks?

(c) How many were not invested in bonds?

(d) How many were invested in international or domestic stocks?

For Exercises 25–28, use the given contingency tables. (See Example 6.)

25. Business The contingency table lists the cross tabulation of the number of business partnerships by industry and whether the partnership reported net income or net loss for the year 2009. (Data from: U.S. Internal Revenue Service.)

Industry	Partnerships with Net Income (A)	Partnerships with Net Loss (B)
Construction (C)	90,000	92,000
Wholesale Trade (W)	23,000	22,000
Finance and Insurance (F)	209,000	104,000

Using the letters given in the table, find the number of partnerships in each set.

(a) $B \cup C$ (b) F'

(c) $C \cap B$ (d) $(C \cup W) \cap A$

26. Social Science The contingency table lists the cross tabulation of whether adults feel their life is exciting, routine, or dull for males and females among the adults chosen for the 2012 General Social Survey. (Data from: www3.norc.org/gss+website.)

Life Classification	Males (M)	Females (F)
Exciting (E)	316	356
Routine (R)	234	328
Dull (D)	28	34

Using the letters given in the table, find the number of respondents in each set.

(a) $E \cap F$ (b) $R \cup M$

(c) D' (d) $(R \cup D) \cap M$

Education *In Exercises 27 and 28, the given contingency table gives the number (in thousands) of U.S. households classified by educational attainment (high school graduate or less denoted with A, some college with no degree denoted B, an associate's degree denoted with C, and a bachelor's degree or higher denoted with D) and household income ($0–$34,999 denoted with E, $35,000–$49,999 denoted with F, $50,000–$74,999 denoted G, and $75,000 and over denoted H).*

	Educational Attainment	E $0–$34,999	F $35,000–$49,999	G $50,000–$74,999	H $75,000 and Over	Total
A	High School Graduate or Less	23,682	7040	7350	7801	45,873
B	Some College, No Degree	7196	3149	4054	5824	20,223
C	Associate's Degree	3149	1614	2241	3951	10,955
D	Bachelor's Degree or Higher	5767	3707	6509	19,513	35,496
	Total	39,794	15,510	20,154	37,089	112,547

Find the number of households in the given sets. (Data from: U.S. Census Bureau.)

27. (a) $A \cap E$ (b) $A \cup H$ (c) $B \cap H'$ (d) $(A \cup B) \cap G$

28. (a) $C \cup D$ (b) $C \cap H$ (c) $D \cap E'$ (d) $(G \cup H) \cap C$

29. Restate the union rule in words.

Use Venn diagrams to answer the given questions. (See Example 5.)

30. If $n(A) = 5, n(B) = 8$, and $n(A \cap B) = 4$, what is $n(A \cup B)$?

31. If $n(A) = 12, n(B) = 27$, and $n(A \cup B) = 30$, what is $n(A \cap B)$?

32. Suppose $n(B) = 7, n(A \cap B) = 3$, and $n(A \cup B) = 20$. What is $n(A)$?

33. Suppose $n(A \cap B) = 5$, $n(A \cup B) = 35$, and $n(A) = 13$. What is $n(B)$?

Draw a Venn diagram and use the given information to fill in the number of elements for each region.

34. $n(U) = 48$, $n(A) = 26$, $n(A \cap B) = 12$, $n(B') = 30$

35. $n(A) = 28$, $n(B) = 12$, $n(A \cup B) = 30$, $n(A') = 19$

36. $n(A \cup B) = 17$, $n(A \cap B) = 3$, $n(A) = 8$, $n(A' \cup B') = 21$

37. $n(A') = 28$, $n(B) = 25$, $n(A' \cup B') = 45$, $n(A \cap B) = 12$

38. $n(A) = 28$, $n(B) = 34$, $n(C) = 25$, $n(A \cap B) = 14$, $n(B \cap C) = 15$, $n(A \cap C) = 11$, $n(A \cap B \cap C) = 9$, $n(U) = 59$

39. $n(A) = 54$, $n(A \cap B) = 22$, $n(A \cup B) = 85$, $n(A \cap B \cap C) = 4$, $n(A \cap C) = 15$, $n(B \cap C) = 16$, $n(C) = 44$, $n(B') = 63$

In Exercises 40–43, show that the statements are true by drawing Venn diagrams and shading the regions representing the sets on each side of the equals signs.*

40. $(A \cup B)' = A' \cap B'$ **41.** $(A \cap B)' = A' \cup B'$

42. $A \cap (B \cup C) = (A \cap B) \cup (A \cap C)$

43. $A \cup (B \cap C) = (A \cup B) \cap (A \cup C)$

44. Explain in words the statement about sets in question 40.

45. Explain in words the statement about sets in question 41.

46. Explain in words the statement about sets in question 42.

47. Explain in words the statement about sets in question 43.

---

*The statements in Exercises 40 and 41 are known as De Morgan's laws. They are named for the English mathematician Augustus De Morgan (1806–1871).

✓**Checkpoint Answers**

1. (a)

$A \cup B'$

(b)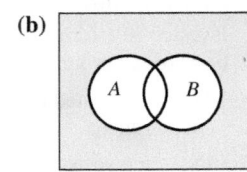

$A' \cap B'$

2. (a)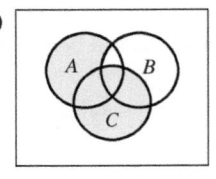

$(B' \cap A) \cup C$

(b)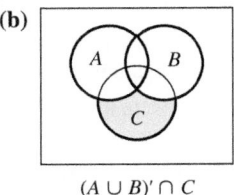

$(A \cup B)' \cap C$

3. (a)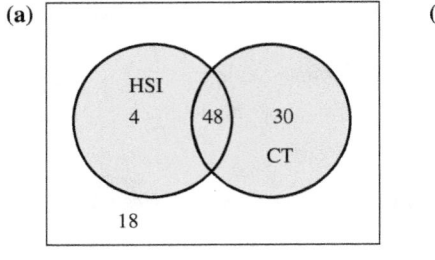

(b) 4

4. (a) 40   **(b)** 10

5. (a) 8   **(b)** 92   **(c)** 98

6. 14

7. (a) 153,139 thousand
   (b) 147,772 thousand

8.3 Introduction to Probability

If you go to a pizzeria and order two large pizzas at $14.99 each, you can easily find the *exact* price of your purchase: $29.98. For the manager at the pizzeria, however, it is impossible to predict the *exact* number of pizzas to be purchased daily. The number of pizzas purchased during a day is *random*: The quantity cannot be predicted exactly. A great many problems that come up in applications of mathematics involve random phenomena— phenomena for which exact prediction is impossible. The best that we can do is determine the *probability* of the possible outcomes.

Random Experiments and Sample Spaces

A **random experiment** (sometimes called a random phenomenon) has outcomes that we cannot predict, but that nonetheless have a regular distribution in a large number of repetitions. We call a repetition from a random experiment a **trial**. The possible results of each trial are called **outcomes**. For instance, when we flip a coin, the outcomes are heads and tails. We do not know whether a particular flip will yield heads or tails, but we do know that if we flip the coin a large a number of times, about half the flips will be heads and half will be tails. Each flip of the coin is a trial. The **sample space** (denoted by S) for a random experiment is the set of all possible outcomes. For the coin flipping, the sample space is

$$S = \{\text{heads, tails}\}.$$

Example 1   Give the sample space for each random experiment.

(a) Use the spinner in Figure 8.17.

Figure 8.17

Solution   The 7 outcomes are 1, 2, 3, . . . 7, so the sample space is

$$\{1, 2, 3, 4, 5, 6, 7\}.$$

(b) For the purposes of a public opinion poll, respondents are classified as young, middle aged, or senior and as male or female.

Solution   A sample space for this poll could be written as a set of ordered pairs:

{(young, male), (young, female), (middle aged, male),

(middle aged, female), (senior, male), (senior, female)}.

(c) An experiment consists of studying the numbers of boys and girls in families with exactly 3 children. Let *b* represent *boy* and *g* represent *girl*.

Solution   For this experiment, drawing a tree diagram can be helpful. First, we draw two starting branches to the left to indicate that the first child can be either a boy or a girl. From each of those outcomes, we draw two branches to indicate that the second child can be either a boy or girl. Last, we draw two branches from each of those outcomes to indicate that after the second child, the third child can be either a boy or a girl. The result is the tree in Figure 8.18.

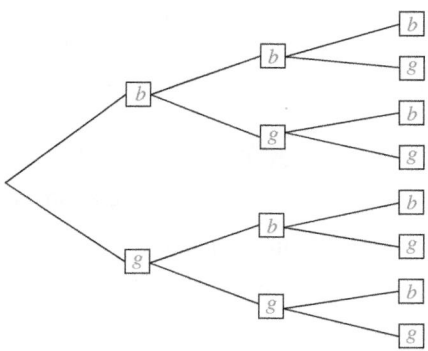

Figure 8.18

We can now easily list the members of the sample space S. We follow the eight paths of the branches to yield

$$S = \{bbb, bbg, bgb, bgg, gbb, gbg, ggb, ggg\}. \quad \boxed{\checkmark}_1$$

Events

An **event** is an outcome, or a set of outcomes, of a random experiment. Thus, an event is a subset of the sample space. For example, if the sample space for tossing a coin is $S = \{h, t\}$, then one event is $E = \{h\}$, which represents the outcome "heads."

✓**Checkpoint 1**

Draw a tree diagram for the random experiment of flipping a coin two times, and determine the sample space.

An ordinary die is a cube whose six different faces show the following numbers of dots: 1, 2, 3, 4, 5, and 6. If the die is fair (not "loaded" to favor certain faces over others), then any one of the faces is equally likely to come up when the die is rolled. The sample space for the experiment of rolling a single fair die is $S = \{1, 2, 3, 4, 5, 6\}$. Some possible events are as follows:

The die shows an even number: $E_1 = \{2, 4, 6\}$.

The die shows a 1: $E_2 = \{1\}$.

The die shows a number less than 5: $E_3 = \{1, 2, 3, 4\}$.

The die shows a multiple of 3: $E_4 = \{3, 6\}$.

Example 2 For the sample space S in Example 1(c) on the previous page, write the given events in set notation.

(a) Event H: The family has exactly two girls.

Solution Families with three children can have exactly two girls with either bgg, gbg, or ggb, so that event H is

$$H = \{bgg, gbg, ggb\}.$$

(b) Event K: The three children are the same sex.

Solution Two outcomes satisfy this condition: all boys and all girls, or

$$K = \{bbb, ggg\}.$$

(c) Event J: The family has three girls.

Solution Only ggg satisfies this condition, so

$$J = \{ggg\}. ✓_2$$

If an event E equals the sample space S, then E is a **certain event.** If event $E = \varnothing$, then E is an **impossible event.**

Example 3 Suppose a fair die is rolled. Then the sample space is $\{1, 2, 3, 4, 5, 6\}$. Find the requested events.

(a) The event "the die shows a 4."

Solution $\{4\}$.

(b) The event "the number showing is less than 10."

Solution The event is the entire sample space $\{1, 2, 3, 4, 5, 6\}$. This event is a certain event; if a die is rolled, the number showing (either 1, 2, 3, 4, 5, or 6) must be less than 10.

(c) The event "the die shows a 7."

Solution The empty set, $\varnothing$; this is an impossible event.

Since events are sets, we can use set operations to find unions, intersections, and complements of events. Here is a summary of the set operations for events.

✓ **Checkpoint 2**

Suppose a die is tossed. Write the given events in set notation.

(a) The number showing is less than 3.

(b) The number showing is 5.

(c) The number showing is 8.

✓ **Checkpoint 3**

Which of the events listed in Checkpoint 2 is

(a) certain?

(b) impossible?

Set Operations for Events

Let E and F be events for a sample space S. Then

$E \cap F$ occurs when both E **and** F occur;

$E \cup F$ occurs when E **or** F **or both** occur;

E' occurs when E does **not** occur.

Example 4 A study of college students grouped the students into various categories that can be interpreted as events when a student is selected at random. Consider the following events:

E: The student is under 20 years old;

F: The student is male;

G: The student is a business major.

Describe each of the following events in words.

(a) E'

Solution E' is the event that the student is 20 years old or older.

(b) $F' \cap G$

Solution $F' \cap G$ is the event that the student is not male and the student is a business major—that is, the student is a female business major.

(c) $E' \cup G$

Solution $E' \cup G$ is the event that the student is 20 or over or is a business major. Note that this event includes all students 20 or over, regardless of major. ✓₄

Two events that cannot both occur at the same time, such as getting both a head and a tail on the same toss of a coin, are called **disjoint events.** (Disjoint events are sometimes referred to as *mutually exclusive events.*)

Disjoint Events

Events E and F are disjoint events if $E \cap F = \varnothing$.

For any event E, E and E' are disjoint events.

Example 5 Let $S = \{1, 2, 3, 4, 5, 6\}$, the sample space for tossing a die. Let $E = \{4, 5, 6\}$, and let $G = \{1, 2\}$. Are E and G disjoint events?

Solution Yes, because they have no outcomes in common; $E \cap G = \varnothing$. See Figure 8.19. ✓₅

✓Checkpoint 4

Write the set notation for the given events for the experiment of rolling a fair die if $E = \{1, 3\}$ and $F = \{2, 3, 4, 5\}$.

(a) $E \cap F$

(b) $E \cup F$

(c) E'

✓Checkpoint 5

In Example 5, let $F = \{2, 4, 6\}$, $K = \{1, 3, 5\}$, and G remain the same. Are the given events disjoint?

(a) F and K

(b) F and G

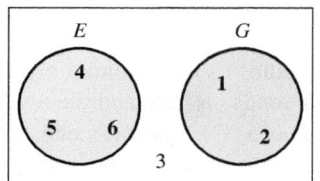

Figure 8.19

Probability

For sample spaces with *equally likely* outcomes, the probability of an event is defined as follows.

Basic Probability Principle

Let S be a sample space of equally likely outcomes, and let event E be a subset of S. Then the **probability that event E occurs** is

$$P(E) = \frac{n(E)}{n(S)}.$$

By this definition, the **probability of an event** is a number that indicates the relative likelihood of the event.

⊙ CAUTION The basic probability principle applies only when the outcomes are equally likely.

Example 6   Suppose a single fair die is rolled, with the sample space $S = \{1, 2, 3, 4, 5, 6\}$. Give the probability of each of the following events.

(a) E: The die shows an even number.

Solution   Here, $E = \{2, 4, 6\}$, a set with three elements. Because S contains six elements,

$$P(E) = \frac{3}{6} = \frac{1}{2}.$$

(b) F: The die shows a number less than 10.

Solution   Event F is a certain event, with

$$F = \{1, 2, 3, 4, 5, 6\},$$

so that

$$P(F) = \frac{6}{6} = 1.$$

(c) G: The die shows an 8.

Solution   This event is impossible, so

$$P(G) = \frac{0}{6} = 0. \quad \boxed{\checkmark_6}$$

✓**Checkpoint 6**

A fair die is rolled. Find the probability of rolling

(a) an odd number;

(b) 2, 4, 5, or 6;

(c) a number greater than 5;

(d) the number 7.

A standard deck of 52 cards has four suits—hearts (♥), clubs (♣), diamonds (♦), and spades (♠)—with 13 cards in each suit. The hearts and diamonds are red, and the spades and clubs are black. Each suit has an ace (A), a king (K), a queen (Q), a jack (J), and cards numbered from 2 to 10. The jack, queen, and king are called face cards and for many purposes can be thought of as having values 11, 12, and 13, respectively. The ace can be thought of as the low card (value 1) or the high card (value 14). See Figure 8.20. We will refer to this standard deck of cards often in our discussion of probability.

Figure 8.20

<hr>

Example 7   If a single card is drawn at random from a standard, well-shuffled, 52-card deck, find the probability of each of the given events.

(a) Drawing an ace

Solution   There are 4 aces in the deck. The event "drawing an ace" is

$$\{\text{heart ace, diamond ace, club ace, spade ace}\}.$$

Therefore,

$$P(\text{ace}) = \frac{4}{52} = \frac{1}{13}.$$

(b) Drawing a face card

Solution   Since there are 12 face cards,

$$P(\text{face card}) = \frac{12}{52} = \frac{3}{13}.$$

(c) Drawing a spade

Solution   The deck contains 13 spades, so

$$P(\text{spade}) = \frac{13}{52} = \frac{1}{4}.$$

(d) Drawing a spade or a heart

Solution   Besides the 13 spades, the deck contains 13 hearts, so

$$P(\text{spade or heart}) = \frac{26}{52} = \frac{1}{2}. \quad ✓_7$$

<hr>

✓ Checkpoint 7

A single playing card is drawn at random from an ordinary 52-card deck. Find the probability of drawing

(a) a queen;

(b) a diamond;

(c) a red card.

In the preceding examples, the probability of each event was a number between 0 and 1, inclusive. The same thing is true in general. Any event E is a subset of the sample space S, so $0 \leq n(E) \leq n(S)$. Since $P(E) = n(E)/n(S)$, it follows that $0 \leq P(E) \leq 1$.

For any event E,

$$0 \leq P(E) \leq 1.$$

In many real-life problems, the events in the sample space are not all equally likely. When this is the case, we can estimate probabilities by determining the long-run proportion that an outcome of interest will occur given many repetitions under identical, and independent, circumstances. We do this often when we perform a statistical study. The long-run proportion is called the **relative frequency probability.** Estimates based on relative frequency probability are sometimes called *empirical probabilities.* Independence in this context refers to the idea that what occurs in one run has no effect on the outcome of a subsequent run.

For example, imagine that we want to determine the probability that a newly manufactured porcelain sink contains a defect. We examine the first sink before it is shipped and see that it has no defects. So we estimate the probability of a defect as 0 because the relative frequency of defects is 0 out of 1 trial. The second sink, however, has a defect. Now our number of defects is 1 out of two trials, so our relative frequency is 1 out of 2, which is .5. The table shows the results for these two sinks and eight additional sinks.

Sink Number	1	2	3	4	5	6	7	8	9	10
Defect Y/N	N	Y	N	N	N	Y	Y	N	N	N
Relative Frequency	0/1 = 0	1/2 = .5	1/3 ≈ .333	1/4 = .25	1/5 = .2	2/6 ≈ .333	3/7 ≈ .429	3/8 = .375	3/9 ≈ .333	3/10 = .3

Notice that the relative frequency fluctuates a great deal. To get a better estimate of the probability of a defect, we need to examine the *long-run* proportion of defects. When the same conditions are repeated a large number of times, the relative frequency will stabilize to the long-run frequency. Figure 8.21 shows how the relative frequency stabilizes to some degree after 50 trials and Figure 8.22 shows the relative frequency after 1000 trials. We can see in Figure 8.22 that the long-run proportion of defects is close to .25.

Figure 8.21   Figure 8.22

📄 **NOTE**   Independence here pertains to the assumption that one sink having, or not having, a defect has no influence on whether another sink has a defect or not. We will investigate independence in greater depth in Section 8.5.

Thus, when we examine many trials of a given phenomenon of interest we can obtain a long-run estimate of the probability of interest. The next example shows one approach to finding such relative frequency probabilities.

Example 8   **Social Science**   The General Social Survey picks U.S. residents at random and asks them a great many questions. One of the questions they asked respondents in 2012 was "Do you feel your standard of living is much better, somewhat better, about the same, somewhat worse or much worse than your parents?" The table categorizes the responses.

Response	Frequency
Much Better	413
Somewhat Better	368
About the Same	296
Somewhat Worse	162
Much Worse	69

(a) Estimate the probability a U.S. resident feels his or her standard of living is much better than that of his or her parents.

Solution Let us define the set A to be the event that a resident feels his or her standard of living is much better. To find the relative frequency probability, we first need to find the total number of respondents. This is $413 + 368 + 296 + 162 + 69 = 1308$. We then divide the frequency in the much better category (in this case 413) by 1308 to obtain

$$P(A) = \frac{413}{1308} \approx .3157.$$

We use this relative frequency as our estimate of the long-run frequency and say that the estimated probability that a U.S. resident feels his or her standard of living is much better is approximately .3157.

(b) Estimate the probability of the event B that a U.S. resident feels that his or her standard of living is somewhat worse or worse.

Solution Here, we add together the number of respondents in the categories of somewhat worse and worse ($162 + 69 = 231$) to obtain

$$P(B) = \frac{162 + 69}{1308} = \frac{231}{1308} \approx .1766. \; \blacksquare_8$$

✓ Checkpoint 8

From the data given in Example 8, estimate the probability that a U.S. resident believes his or her standard of living is much better, somewhat better, or about the same as that of his or her parents.

After conducting a study such as the General Social Survey where respondents are chosen at random, we can assume independence because one person's response should have no relation to another person's response. We also use the term "estimated probability" or just "probability" rather than "relative frequency probability."

A table of frequencies, as in Example 8, sets up a probability distribution; that is, for each possible outcome of an experiment, a number, called the probability of that outcome, is assigned. This assignment may be done in any reasonable way (on a relative frequency basis, as in Example 8, or by theoretical reasoning, as in Example 6), provided that it satisfies the following conditions.

Properties of Probability

Let S be a sample space consisting of n distinct outcomes $s_1, s_2, \ldots, s_n$. An acceptable probability assignment consists of assigning to each outcome s_i a number p_i (the probability of s_i) according to the following rules:

1. The probability of each outcome is a number between 0 and 1:

$$0 \le p_1 \le 1, \quad 0 \le p_2 \le 1, \ldots, \quad 0 \le p_n \le 1.$$

2. The sum of the probabilities of all possible outcomes is 1:

$$p_1 + p_2 + p_3 + \cdots + p_n = 1.$$

8.3 Exercises

1. What is meant by a "fair" coin or die?

2. What is the sample space for a random experiment?

Write sample spaces for the random experiments in Exercises 3–9. (See Example 1.)

3. A month of the year is chosen for a wedding.

4. A day in April is selected for a bicycle race.

5. A student is asked how many points she earned on a recent 80-point test.

6. A person is asked the number of hours (to the nearest hour) he watched television yesterday.

7. The management of an oil company must decide whether to go ahead with a new oil shale plant or to cancel it.

8. A coin is tossed and a die is rolled.

9. The quarter of the year in which a company's profits were highest.

10. Define an event.

11. Define disjoint events in your own words.

Decide whether the events are disjoint. (See Example 5.)

12. Owning an SUV and owning a Hummer

13. Wearing a hat and wearing glasses

14. Being married and being under 30 years old

15. Being a doctor and being under 5 years old

16. Being male and being a nurse

17. Being female and being a pilot

For the random experiments in Exercises 18–20, write out an equally likely sample space, and then write the indicated events in set notation. (See Examples 2 and 3.)

18. A marble is drawn at random from a bowl containing 3 yellow, 4 white, and 8 blue marbles.

   (a) A yellow marble is drawn.

   (b) A blue marble is drawn.

   (c) A white marble is drawn.

   (d) A black marble is drawn.

19. Six people live in a dorm suite. Two are to be selected to go to the campus café to pick up a pizza. Of course, no one wants to go, so the six names (Connie, Kate, Lindsey, Jackie, Taisa, and Nicole) are placed in a hat. After the hat is shaken, two names are selected.

   (a) Taisa is selected.

   (b) The two names selected have the same number of letters.

20. An unprepared student takes a three-question true-or-false quiz in which he flips a coin to guess the answers. If the coin is heads, he guesses true, and if the coin is tails, he guesses false.

   (a) The student guesses true twice and guesses false once.

   (b) The student guesses all false.

   (c) The student guesses true once and guesses false twice.

In Exercises 21–23, write out the sample space and assume each outcome is equally likely. Then give the probability of the requested outcomes. (See Examples 7 and 8.)

21. In deciding what color and style to paint a room, Greg has narrowed his choices to three colors—forest sage, evergreen whisper, and opaque emerald—and two styles—rag painting and colorwash.

   (a) Greg picks a combination with colorwash.

   (b) Greg picks a combination with opaque emerald or rag painting.

22. Tami goes shopping and sees three kinds of shoes: flats, 2″ heels, and 3″ heels. They come in two shades of beige (light and dark) and black.

   (a) The shoe selected has a heel and is black.

   (b) The shoe selected has no heel and is beige.

   (c) The shoe selected has a heel and is beige.

23. Doug Hall is shopping for a new patio umbrella. There is a 10-foot and a 12-foot model, and each is available in beige, forest green, and rust.

   (a) Doug buys a 12-foot forest green umbrella.

   (b) Doug buys a 10-foot umbrella.

   (c) Doug buys a rust-colored umbrella.

24. Kathy Little is deciding between four brands of cell phones: Samsung, Motorola, Nokia, and Sony. Each of these phones comes with the option of insurance or no insurance.

   (a) Kathy picks a phone with insurance.

   (b) Kathy picks a phone that begins with the letter "S" and no insurance.

A single fair die is rolled. Find the probabilities of the given events. (See Example 6.)

25. Getting a number less than 4

26. Getting a number greater than 4

27. Getting a 2 or a 5

28. Getting a multiple of 3

David Klein wants to adopt a puppy from an animal shelter. At the shelter, he finds eight puppies that he likes: a male and female puppy from each of the four breeds of beagle, boxer, collie, and Labrador. The puppies are each so cute that Dave cannot make up his mind, so he decides to pick the dog randomly.

29. Write the sample space for the outcomes, assuming each outcome is equally likely.

Find the probability that Dave chooses the given puppy.

30. A male boxer   **31.** A male puppy

32. A collie   **33.** A female Labrador

34. A beagle or a boxer   **35.** Anything except a Labrador

36. Anything except a male beagle or male boxer.

Business *The following table gives the number of fatal work injuries categorized by cause from 2010. (Data from: U.S. Bureau of Labor Statistics.)*

Cause	Number of Fatalities
Transportation accidents	1857
Assaults and violent acts	832
Contacts with objects and equipment	738
Falls	646
Exposure to harmful substances or environments	414
Fires and explosions	191
Other	12

Find the probability that a randomly chosen work fatality had the given cause. (See Example 8.)

37. A fall   **38.** Fires and explosions

39. **Social Science** Respondents to the 2012 General Social Survey (GSS) indicated the following categorizations pertaining to attendance at religious services: (Data from: www3.norc.org/gss+website.)

Attendance	Number of Respondents
Never	496
Less than once a year	111
Once a year	264
Several times a year	191
Once a month	133
2–3 times a month	168
Nearly every week	83
Every week	380
More than once a week	140
Don't know/no answer	8
Total	1974

Find the probability that a randomly chosen person in the United States attends religious services

(a) several times a year;

(b) 2–3 times a month;

(c) nearly every week or more frequently.

40. **Social Science** Respondents to the 2012 General Social Survey (GSS) indicated whether they strongly agreed, agreed, disagreed, or strongly disagreed with the question, "It is better for men to work and for women to tend to the home." The responses are categorized in the following table. (Data from: www3.norc.org/gss+website.)

Response	Number of Respondents
Strongly Agree	87
Agree	313
Disagree	636
Strongly Disagree	249

Find the probability that a person in the United States

(a) strongly agreed or agreed with the statement;

(b) strongly disagreed with the statement;

(c) did not strongly agree with the statement.

41. **Health** For a medical experiment, people are classified as to whether they smoke, have a family history of heart disease, or are overweight. Define events E, F, and G as follows:

E: person smokes;

F: person has a family history of heart disease;

G: person is overweight.

Describe each of the following events in words.

(a) G'

(b) $F \cap G$

(c) $E \cup G'$

42. **Health** Refer to Exercise 41. Describe each of the events that follow in words.

(a) $E \cup F$

(b) $E' \cap F$

(c) $F' \cup G'$

43. **Health** The National Health and Nutrition Examination Study (NHANES) is conducted every several years by the U.S. Centers for Disease Control and Prevention. The following table gives the results from the 2010 survey of U.S. residents. The table shows the counts of women between the ages of 21 and 79 for various height (in inches) categories. (Data from: www.cdc.gov/nchs/.)

Height (Inches)	Count of Females
Less than 60	354
60–62.99	924
63–65.99	1058
66–68.99	421
69–71.99	65
72–74.99	3
75 or more	1

Find the probability that a female U.S. resident is

(a) six feet tall or taller;

(b) less than 63 inches tall;

(c) between 63 and 68.99 inches tall.

44. **Health** The same study as in Exercise 43 generates the following table for males age 21 to 79.

Height (Inches)	Count of Males
Less than 60	7
60–62.99	60
63–65.99	439
66–68.99	890
69–71.99	872
72–74.99	337
75 or more	59

Find the probability that a male U.S. resident is

(a) under 66 inches tall;

(b) more than 69 inches tall;

(c) between 66 and 74.99 inches tall.

An experiment is conducted for which the sample space is $S = \{s_1, s_2, s_3, s_4, s_5\}$. *Which of the probability assignments in Exercises 45–50 is possible for this experiment? If an assignment is not possible, tell why.*

45.

Outcomes	s_1	s_2	s_3	s_4	s_5
Probabilities	.09	.32	.21	.25	.13

46.

Outcomes	s_1	s_2	s_3	s_4	s_5
Probabilities	.92	.03	0	.02	.03

47.

Outcomes	s_1	s_2	s_3	s_4	s_5
Probabilities	1/3	1/4	1/6	1/8	1/10

48.

Outcomes	s_1	s_2	s_3	s_4	s_5
Probabilities	1/5	1/3	1/4	1/5	1/10

49.

Outcomes	s_1	s_2	s_3	s_4	s_5
Probabilities	.64	−.08	.30	.12	.02

50.

Outcomes	s_1	s_2	s_3	s_4	s_5
Probabilities	.05	.35	.5	.2	−.3

✓**Checkpoint Answers**

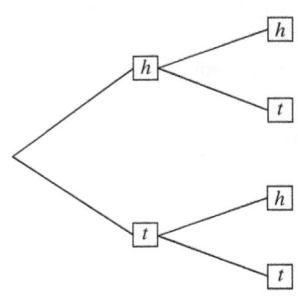

1. $\{hh, ht, th, tt\}$

2. (a) $\{1, 2\}$ (b) $\{5\}$ (c) $\varnothing$

3. (a) None   (b) Part (c)

4. (a) $\{3\}$ (b) $\{1, 2, 3, 4, 5\}$ (c) $\{2, 4, 5, 6\}$

5. (a) Yes   (b) No

6. (a) 1/2   (b) 2/3   (c) 1/6   (d) 0

7. (a) 1/13   (b) 1/4   (c) 1/2

8. About .8234

8.4 Basic Concepts of Probability

We determine the probability of more complex events in this section.

To find the probability of the union of two sets E and F in a sample space S, we use the union rule for counting given in Section 8.2:

$$n(E \cup F) = n(E) + n(F) - n(E \cap F).$$

Dividing both sides by $n(S)$ yields

$$\frac{n(E \cup F)}{n(S)} = \frac{n(E)}{n(S)} + \frac{n(F)}{n(S)} - \frac{n(E \cap F)}{n(S)}$$

$$P(E \cup F) = P(E) + P(F) - P(E \cap F).$$

This discussion is summarized in the next rule.

Addition Rule for Probability

For any events E and F from a sample space S,

$$P(E \cup F) = P(E) + P(F) - P(E \cap F).$$

In words, we have

$$P(E \text{ or } F) = P(E) + P(F) - P(E \text{ and } F).$$

(Although the addition rule applies to any events E and F from any sample space, the derivation we have given is valid only for sample spaces with equally likely simple events.)

Example 1   When playing American roulette, the croupier (attendant) spins a marble that lands in one of the 38 slots in a revolving turntable. The slots are numbered 1 to 36, with two additional slots labeled 0 and 00 that are painted green. Half the remaining slots are colored red, and half are black. (See Figure 8.23.)

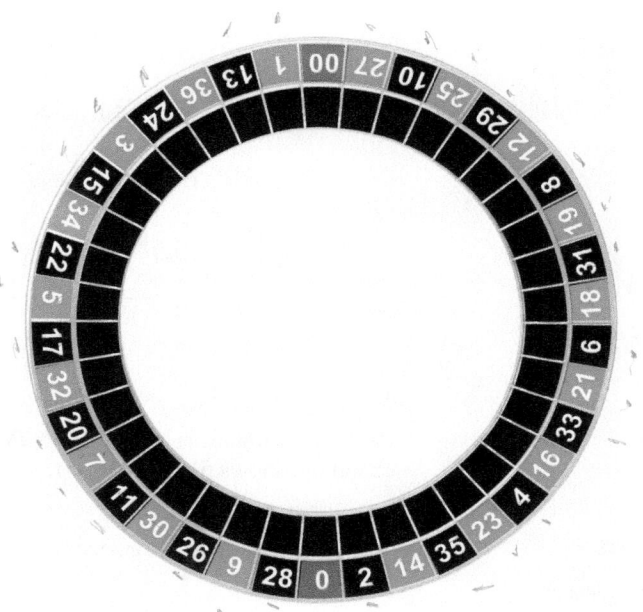

Figure 8.23

In roulette, the slots labeled 0 or 00 are not considered as even or odd. Find the probability that the marble will land in a red or even number.

Solution   Let R represent the event of the marble landing in a red slot and E the event of the marble landing in an even-numbered slot. There are 18 slots that are colored red, so $P(R) = 18/38$. There are also 18 even numbers between 1 and 36, so $P(E) = 18/38$. In order to use the addition rule, we also need to know the number of slots that are red and even numbered. Looking at Figure 8.23, we can see there are 8 such slots, which implies that $P(R \cap E) = 8/38$. Using the addition rule, we find the probability that the marble will land in a slot that is red or even numbered is

$$P(R \cup E) = P(R) + P(E) - P(R \cap E)$$
$$= \frac{18}{38} + \frac{18}{38} - \frac{8}{38} = \frac{28}{38} = \frac{14}{19}.$$

✓ **Checkpoint 1**

If an American roulette wheel is spun, find the probability of the marble landing in a black slot or a slot (excluding 0 and 00) whose number is divisible by 3.

Example 2   Suppose two fair dice (plural of *die*) are rolled. Find each of the given probabilities.

(a)   The first die shows a 2 or the sum of the results is 6 or 7.

Solution   The sample space for the throw of two dice is shown in Figure 8.24, on the following page, where 1-1 represents the event "the first die shows a 1 and the second die shows a 1," 1-2 represents the event "the first die shows a 1 and the second die shows a 2," and so on. Let A represent the event "the first die shows a 2" and B represent the event "the sum of the results is 6 or 7." These events are indicated in color in Figure 8.24. From the diagram, event A has 6 elements, B has 11 elements, and the sample space has 36 elements. Thus,

$$P(A) = \frac{6}{36}, \quad P(B) = \frac{11}{36}, \quad \text{and} \quad P(A \cap B) = \frac{2}{36}.$$

By the addition rule,

$$P(A \cup B) = P(A) + P(B) - P(A \cap B),$$

$$P(A \cup B) = \frac{6}{36} + \frac{11}{36} - \frac{2}{36} = \frac{15}{36} = \frac{5}{12}.$$

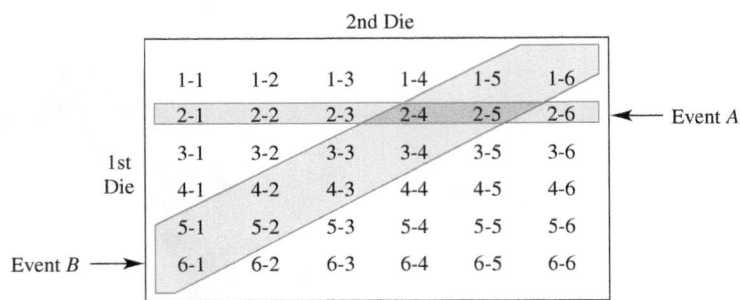

Figure 8.24

(b) The sum is 11 or the second die shows a 5.

Solution $P(\text{sum is } 11) = 2/36$, $P(\text{second die shows } 5) = 6/36$, and $P(\text{sum is } 11$ and second die shows $5) = 1/36$, so

$$P(\text{sum is } 11 \text{ or second die shows } 5) = \frac{2}{36} + \frac{6}{36} - \frac{1}{36} = \frac{7}{36}. \checkmark_2$$

✓ Checkpoint 2

In the random experiment of Example 2, find the given probabilities.

(a) The sum is 5 or the second die shows a 3.

(b) Both dice show the same number, or the sum is at least 11.

If events E and F are disjoint, then $E \cap F = \varnothing$ by definition; hence, $P(E \cap F) = 0$. Applying the addition rule yields the useful fact that follows.

Addition Rule for Disjoint Events

For disjoint events E and F,

$$P(E \cup F) = P(E) + P(F).$$

Example 3   Assume that the probability of a couple having a baby boy is the same as the probability of the couple having a baby girl. If the couple has 3 children, find the probability that at least 2 of them are girls.

Solution   The event of having at least 2 girls is the union of the disjoint events $E = $ "the family has exactly 2 girls" and $F = $ "the family has exactly 3 girls." Using the equally likely sample space

$$\{ggg, ggb, gbg, bgg, gbb, bgb, bbg, bbb\},$$

where b represents a boy and g represents a girl, we see that $P(2 \text{ girls}) = 3/8$ and $P(3 \text{ girls}) = 1/8$. Therefore,

$$P(\text{at least 2 girls}) = P(2 \text{ girls}) + P(3 \text{ girls})$$

✓ Checkpoint 3

In Example 3, find the probability of having no more than 2 girls.

$$= \frac{3}{8} + \frac{1}{8} = \frac{1}{2}. \checkmark_3$$

By definition of E', for any event E from a sample space S,

$$E \cup E' = S \quad \text{and} \quad E \cap E' = \emptyset.$$

Because $E \cap E' = \emptyset$, events E and E' are disjoint, so that

$$P(E \cup E') = P(E) + P(E').$$

However, $E \cup E' = S$, the sample space, and $P(S) = 1$. Thus,

$$P(E \cup E') = P(E) + P(E') = 1.$$

Rearranging these terms gives the following useful rule.

Complement Rule

For any event E,

$$P(E') = 1 - P(E) \quad \text{and} \quad P(E) = 1 - P(E').$$

Example 4   If a fair die is rolled, what is the probability that any number but 5 will come up?

Solution   If E is the event that 5 comes up, then E' is the event that any number but 5 comes up. $P(E) = 1/6$, so we have $P(E') = 1 - 1/6 = 5/6$. ✓4

✓ **Checkpoint 4**

(a) Let $P(K) = 2/3$. Find $P(K')$.

(b) If $P(X') = 3/4$, find $P(X)$.

Example 5   If two fair dice are rolled, find the probability that the sum of the numbers showing is greater than 3.

Solution   To calculate this probability directly, we must find each of the probabilities that the sum is 4, 5, 6, 7, 8, 9, 10, 11, and 12 and then add them. It is much simpler to first find the probability of the complement, the event that the sum is less than or equal to 3:

$$P(\text{sum} \leq 3) = P(\text{sum is } 2) + P(\text{sum is } 3)$$

$$= \frac{1}{36} + \frac{2}{36} = \frac{3}{36} = \frac{1}{12}.$$

Now use the fact that $P(E) = 1 - P(E')$ to get

$$P(\text{sum} > 3) = 1 - P(\text{sum} \leq 3) = 1 - \frac{1}{12} = \frac{11}{12}. \quad \boxed{✓5}$$

✓ **Checkpoint 5**

In Example 5, find the probability that the sum of the numbers rolled is at least 5.

Odds

Sometimes probability statements are given in terms of **odds**: a comparison of $P(E)$ with $P(E')$. For example, suppose $P(E) = \frac{4}{5}$. Then $P(E') = 1 - \frac{4}{5} = \frac{1}{5}$. These probabilities predict that E will occur 4 out of 5 times and E' will occur 1 out of 5 times. Then we say that the **odds in favor** of E are 4 to 1, or 4:1.

Odds

The **odds in favor** of an event E are defined as the ratio of $P(E)$ to $P(E')$, or

$$\frac{P(E)}{P(E')}, \qquad P(E') \neq 0.$$

Example 6 Suppose the weather forecaster says that the probability of rain tomorrow is $1/3$. Find the odds in favor of rain tomorrow.

Solution Let E be the event "rain tomorrow." Then E' is the event "no rain tomorrow." Since $P(E) = 1/3$, $P(E') = 2/3$. By the definition of odds, the odds in favor of rain are

$$\frac{1/3}{2/3} = \frac{1}{2}, \qquad \text{written 1 to 2 or 1:2.}$$

On the other hand, the odds that it will *not* rain, or the odds *against* rain, are

$$\frac{2/3}{1/3} = \frac{2}{1}, \qquad \text{written 2 to 1.}$$

If the odds in favor of an event are, say, 3 to 5, then the probability of the event is $3/8$, while the probability of the complement of the event is $5/8$. (Odds of 3 to 5 indicate 3 outcomes in favor of the event out of a total of 8 outcomes.) The above example suggests the following generalization:

If the odds favoring event E are m to n, then

$$P(E) = \frac{m}{m + n} \qquad \text{and} \qquad P(E') = \frac{n}{m + n}.$$

Example 7 Often, weather forecasters give probability in terms of percentage. Suppose the weather forecaster says that there is a 40% chance that it will snow tomorrow. Find the odds of snow tomorrow.

Solution In this case, we can let E be the event "snow tomorrow." Then E' is the event "no snow tomorrow." Now, we have $P(E) = .4 = 4/10$ and $P(E') = .6 = 6/10$. By the definition of odds in favor, the odds in favor of snow are

$$\frac{4/10}{6/10} = \frac{4}{6} = \frac{2}{3}, \qquad \text{written 2 to 3 or 2:3.}$$

It is important to put the final fraction into lowest terms in order to communicate the odds. ✔6

Example 8 The odds that a particular bid will be the low bid are 4 to 5.

(a) Find the probability that the bid will be the low bid.

Solution Odds of 4 to 5 show 4 favorable chances out of $4 + 5 = 9$ chances altogether, so

$$P(\text{bid will be low bid}) = \frac{4}{4 + 5} = \frac{4}{9}.$$

(b) Find the odds against that bid being the low bid.

Solution There is a $5/9$ chance that the bid will not be the low bid, so the odds against a low bid are

$$\frac{P(\text{bid will not be low})}{P(\text{bid will be low})} = \frac{5/9}{4/9} = \frac{5}{4},$$

or 5:4. ✔7

✓ **Checkpoint 6**

In Example 7, suppose $P(E) = 9/10$. Find the odds

(a) in favor of E;

(b) against E.

Suppose the chance of snow is 80%. Find the odds

(c) in favor of snow;

(d) against snow.

✓ **Checkpoint 7**

If the odds in favor of event E are 1 to 5, find

(a) $P(E)$;

(b) $P(E')$.

Applications

Example 9 **Social Science** Let A represent that the driver in a fatal crash was age 24 or younger and let B represent that the driver had a blood alcohol content (BAC) of .08% or higher. From data on fatal crashes in the year 2010 from the U.S. National Highway Traffic Safety Administration, we have the following probabilities.

$$P(A) = .2077, \quad P(B) = .2180, \quad P(A \cap B) = .0536.$$

(a) Find the probability that the driver was 25 or older and had a BAC level below .08%.

Solution Place the given information on a Venn diagram, starting with .0536 in the intersection of the regions A and B. (See Figure 8.25.) As stated earlier, event A has probability .2077. Since .0536 has already been placed inside the intersection of A and B,

$$.2077 - .0536 = .1541$$

goes inside region A, but outside the intersection of A and B. In the same way,

$$.2180 - .0536 = .1644$$

goes inside region B, but outside the overlap.

Since being age 25 or older is the complement of event A and having a BAC below .08% is the complement of event B, we need to find $P(A' \cap B')$. From the Venn diagram in Figure 8.25, the labeled regions have a total probability of

$$.1541 + .0536 + .1644 = .3721.$$

Since the entire region of the Venn diagram must have probability 1, the region outside A and B, namely $A' \cap B'$, has the probability

$$1 - .3721 = .6279.$$

The probability that a driver of a fatal crash is 25 or older and has a BAC below .08% is .6279.

(b) Find the probability that a driver in a fatal crash is 25 or older or has a BAC below .08%.

Solution The corresponding region for $A' \cup B'$ from Figure 8.25 has probability

$$.6279 + .1541 + .1644 = .9464. \quad ☑_8$$

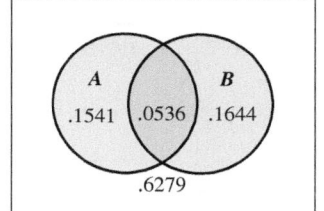

Figure 8.25

✓ **Checkpoint 8**

Using the data from Example 9, find the probability that a driver in a fatal crash

(a) has a BAC below .08%;

(b) is age 25 or older and has a BAC of .08% or higher.

Example 10 **Business** Data from the 2012 *Forbes* magazine survey of the 100 highest paid chief executive officers (CEOs) is cross classified by age (in years) and annual compensation (in millions of dollars). Let E be the event the CEO earns less than $25 million and F be the event the CEO's age is in the 60s.

		Annual Compensation (Millions of Dollars)			
		Less than 25	25–34.99	35 or more	Total
Age (Years)	Under 60	28	12	12	52
	60s	31	7	7	45
	70 or older	1	1	1	3
	Total	60	20	20	100

(a) Find $P(E)$.

Solution We need to find the total number where the pay is less than $25 million down the different age groups (see shaded column below).

		Annual Compensation (Millions of Dollars)			
		Less than 25	25–34.99	35 or more	Total
Age (Years)	Under 60	28	12	12	52
	60s	31	7	7	45
	70 or older	1	1	1	3
	Total	60	20	20	100

Thus we have $28 + 31 + 1 = 60$ is the total number who earned less than $25 million dollars and

$$P(E) = 60/100 = .60.$$

(b) Find $P(E \cap F)$

Solution We look to find the number that satisfies both conditions. We see there are 31 responses in the column for less than 25 and the row for age in the 60s (see area shaded in bright blue below).

		Annual Compensation (Millions of Dollars)			
		Less than 25	25–34.99	35 or more	Total
Age (Years)	Under 60	28	12	12	52
	60s	31	7	7	45
	70 or older	1	1	1	3
	Total	60	20	20	100

Thus,

$$P(E \cap F) = 31/100 = .31.$$

✓ **Checkpoint 9**

Let G be the event the CEO earns $35 million or more and H be the event the CEO's age is under 60. Find the following.

(a) $P(G)$

(b) $P(G \cap H)$

(c) $P(G \cup H)$

(c) Find $P(E \cup F)$.

Solution We can use the Additive Rule for Probability to find $P(E \cup F)$. We know from part (a) that $P(E) = .60$. In a similar manner to part (a), we can find $P(F)$. There are $31 + 7 + 7 = 45$ CEOs whose age is in the 60s, so $P(F) = 45/100 = .45$. With the answer to (b), using the Additive Rule yields

$$P(E \cup F) = P(E) + P(F) - P(E \cap F) = .60 + .45 - .31 = .74. \quad ✓_9$$

8.4 Exercises

Assume a single spin of the roulette wheel is made. Find the probability for the given events. (See Example 1.)

1. The marble lands in a green or black slot.

2. The marble lands in a green or even slot.

3. The marble lands in an odd or black slot.

Also with a single spin of the roulette wheel, find the probability of winning with the given bets.

4. The marble will land in a slot numbered 13–18.

5. The marble will land in slots 0, 00, 1, 2, or 3.

6. The marble will land in a slot that is a positive multiple of 3.

7. The marble will land in a slot numbered 25–36.

Two dice are rolled. Find the probabilities of rolling the given sums. (See Examples 2, 4, and 5.)

8. (a) 2   (b) 4   (c) 5   (d) 6

9. (a) 8   (b) 9   (c) 10   (d) 13

10. (a) 9 or more

(b) Less than 7

(c) Between 5 and 8 (exclusive)

11. (a) Not more than 5

(b) Not less than 8

(c) Between 3 and 7 (exclusive)

Tami goes shopping and sees three kinds of shoes: flats, 2″ heels, and 3″ heels. The shoes come in two shades of beige (light and dark) and black. If each option has an equal chance of being selected, find the probabilities of the given events.

12. The shoes Tami buys have a heel.

13. The shoes Tami buys are black.

14. The shoes Tami buys have a 2″ heel and are beige.

Ms. Elliott invites 10 relatives to a party: her mother, 3 aunts, 2 uncles, 2 sisters, 1 male cousin, and 1 female cousin. If the chances of any one guest arriving first are equally likely, find the probabilities that the given guests will arrive first.

15. (a) A sister or an aunt

(b) A sister or a cousin

(c) A sister or her mother

16. (a) An aunt or a cousin

(b) A male or an uncle

(c) A female or a cousin

Use Venn diagrams to work Exercises 17–21. (See Example 9.)

17. Suppose $P(E) = .30, P(F) = .51$, and $P(E \cap F) = .19$. Find each of the given probabilities.

(a) $P(E \cup F)$

(b) $P(E' \cap F)$

(c) $P(E \cap F')$

(d) $P(E' \cup F')$

18. Let $P(Z) = .40, P(Y) = .30$, and $P(Z \cup Y) = .58$. Find each of the given probabilities.

(a) $P(Z' \cap Y')$

(b) $P(Z' \cup Y')$

(c) $P(Z' \cup Y)$

(d) $P(Z \cap Y')$

19. Economics According to data from the 2011 American Community Survey, the probability that a U.S. resident earns $75,000 or more a year (event *A*) is .325. The probability that a U.S. resident lives in an owner-occupied home (event *B*) is .646. The probability that a U.S. resident earns $75,000 or more and lives in an owner-occupied home is .272. Find the probability of the given events. (Data from: factfinder2.census. gov.)

(a) $A \cup B$

(b) $A' \cap B$

(c) $A' \cap B'$

(d) $A' \cup B'$

20. Economics According to data from the 2011 American Community Survey, the probability that a U.S. resident earns less than $20,000 a year (event *C*) is .192. The probability that a U.S. resident lives in a rented home (event *D*) is .354. The probability that a U.S. resident earns less than $20,000 and lives in a rented home is .119. Find the probability of the given events. (Data from: factfinder2.census.gov.)

(a) $C \cup D$

(b) $C \cap D'$

(c) $C' \cap D'$

(d) $C' \cup D'$

21. Social Science According to the 2012 General Social Survey, the probability that a U.S. resident is currently married is .457 and the probability that a U.S. resident describes himself or herself as very happy is .302. The probability of being married and being very happy is .191. Find the probability of the described events. (Data from: www3.norc.org/gss+website.)

(a) Not being very happy and being married

(b) Not being married and not being very happy

(c) Not being married or not being very happy

22. Social Science According to the 2012 General Social Survey, the probability that a U.S. resident has a great deal of confidence in medicine is .389 and the probability that a U.S. resident has a great deal of confidence in major companies is .166. The probability of having a great deal of confidence in both medicine and major companies is .111. Find the probability of the described events. (Data from: www3.norc.org/gss+website.)

(a) Not having a great deal of confidence in medicine and having a great deal of confidence in major companies.

(b) Having a great deal of confidence in medicine or not having a great deal of confidence in major companies.

(c) Not having a great deal of confidence in medicine and not having a great deal of confidence in major companies.

A single fair die is rolled. Find the odds in favor of getting the results in Exercises 23–26. (See Examples 6 and 7.)

23. 2

24. 2, 3, 4

25. 2, 3, 5, or 6

26. Some number greater than 5

27. A marble is drawn from a box containing 3 yellow, 4 white, and 8 blue marbles. Find the odds in favor of drawing the given marbles.

(a) A yellow marble

(b) A blue marble

(c) A white marble

28. Find the odds of *not* drawing a white marble in Exercise 27.

29. Two dice are rolled. Find the odds of rolling a 7 or an 11.

30. Define what is meant by odds.

Education *For Exercises 31–34, find the odds of the event occurring from the given probability that a bachelor's degree recipient in 2011 majored in the given discipline. (Data from: Digest of Educational Statistics.)*

31. Business; probability 21/100.

32. Biological or biomedical sciences; probability 1/20.

33. Education; probability 6/100.

34. Health professions; probability 2/25.

Business *For Exercises 35–38, convert the given odds to the probability of the event. (Data from: The ProQuest Statistical Abstract of the United States: 2013.)*

35. The odds that a business in 2009 had less than 20 employees are 43:7.

36. The odds that a business in 2009 had 500 or more employees are 1:499.

37. The odds that a corporation that filed a tax return in 2009 was in the field of manufacturing are 6:19.

38. The odds that a corporation that filed a tax return in 2009 was in the field of wholesale retail and trade are 3:7.

✒ *One way to solve a probability problem is to repeat the experiment many times, keeping track of the results. Then the probability can be approximated by using the basic definition of the probability of an event E, which is $P(E) = n(E)/n(S)$, where E occurs $n(E)$ times out of $n(S)$ trials of an experiment. This is called the Monte Carlo method of finding probabilities. If physically repeating the experiment is too tedious, it may be simulated with the use of a random-number generator, available on most computers and scientific or graphing calculators. To simulate a coin toss or the roll of a die on a graphing calculator, change the setting to fixed decimal mode with 0 digits displayed. To simulate multiple tosses of a coin, press RAND (or RANDOM or RND#) in the PROB submenu of the MATH (or OPTN) menu, and then press ENTER repeatedly. Interpret 0 as a head and 1 as a tail. To simulate multiple rolls of a die, press RAND × 6 + .5, and then press ENTER repeatedly.*

39. Suppose two dice are rolled. Use the Monte Carlo method with at least 50 repetitions to approximate the given probabilities. Compare them with the results of Exercise 10.

   (a) P(the sum is 9 or more)

   (b) P(the sum is less than 7)

40. Suppose two dice are rolled. Use the Monte Carlo method with at least 50 repetitions to approximate the given probabilities. Compare them with the results of Exercise 11.

   (a) P(the sum is not more than 5)

   (b) P(the sum is not less than 8)

41. Suppose three dice are rolled. Use the Monte Carlo method with at least 100 repetitions to approximate the given probabilities.

   (a) P(the sum is 5 or less)

   (b) P(neither a 1 nor a 6 is rolled)

42. Suppose a coin is tossed 5 times. Use the Monte Carlo method with at least 50 repetitions to approximate the given probabilities.

   (a) P(exactly 4 heads)

   (b) P(2 heads and 3 tails)

Health *For Exercises 43–48, use the following table that is based on numbers from the 2011 American Community Survey. The table represents 2023 randomly chosen U.S. residents age 25 years or older in regard to educational attainment and health insurance status.*

Educational Attainment	Has Health Insurance	Does Not Have Health Insurance
Less than High School Graduate	192	87
High School Graduate (or GED)	459	113
Some College or an Associate's Degree	498	90
Bachelor's Degree or Higher	544	40

Find the probability of the described events. (Data from: fact-finder2.census.gov.)

43. Having health insurance.

44. Not having health insurance.

45. Being a high school graduate and having health insurance.

46. Having a bachelor's degree or not having health insurance.

47. Not having a bachelor's degree or not having health insurance.

48. Not being a high school graduate or having health insurance.

Business *For Exercises 49–54, use the table in Example 10 that cross classifies the age and salary of the top 100 earning CEOs from 2012 according to Forbes Magazine. Find the described probabilities regarding the CEO. (Data from: www.forbes.com.)*

49. Is under age 60 and earns \$35 million or more.

50. Is under age 60 or earns \$35 million or more.

51. Is not under age 60 and earns between \$25 and \$34.99 million.

52. Is not under age 60 and earns less than \$35 million.

53. Is age 60 or older or earns \$35 million or more.

54. Is not in his or her 60s and earns less than 25 million.

Business *Data from the 2012 General Social Survey can allow us to estimate how much part-time and full-time employees work per week. Use the following table to find the probabilities of the events in Exercises 55–58. (Data from: www3.norc.org/gss+website.)*

Labor Force Status	\multicolumn{7}{c}{Hours Worked in the last Week}
	0–19	20–29	30–39	40–49	50–59	60 or more	Total
Working Full-Time	155	31	99	468	127	141	1021
Working Part-Time	171	54	60	32	5	9	331
Total	326	85	159	500	132	150	1352

55. Working full-time

56. Working part-time and 0–19 hours

57. Working full-time and 40–49 hours

58. Working part-time or working less than 30 hours

59. **Natural Science** Color blindness is an inherited characteristic that is more common in males than in females. If M represents male and C represents red–green color blindness, we use the relative frequencies of the incidences of males and red–green color blindness as probabilities to get

$$P(C) = .039, \quad P(M \cap C) = .035, \quad \text{and} \quad P(M \cup C) = .495.^{*}$$

---

[*]The probabilities of a person being male or female are from *The World Almanac and Book of Facts*, 2002. The probabilities of a male and female being color blind are from *Parsons' Diseases of the Eye* (18th ed.), by Stephen J. H. Miller (Churchill Livingston, 1990), p. 269. This reference gives a range of 3 to 4% for the probability of gross color blindness in men; we used the midpoint of that range.

Find the given probabilities.

(a) $P(C')$ (b) $P(M)$
(c) $P(M')$ (d) $P(M' \cap C')$
(e) $P(C \cap M')$ (f) $P(C \cup M')$

60. Natural Science Gregor Mendel, an Austrian monk, was the first to use probability in the study of genetics. In an effort to understand the mechanism of characteristic transmittal from one generation to the next in plants, he counted the number of occurrences of various characteristics. Mendel found that the flower color in certain pea plants obeyed this scheme:

Pure red crossed with pure white produces red.

From its parents, the red offspring received genes for both red (*R*) and white (*W*), but in this case red is *dominant* and white *recessive*, so the offspring exhibits the color red. However, the offspring still carries both genes, and when two such offspring are crossed, several things can happen in the third generation. The following table, called a *Punnett square*, shows the equally likely outcomes:

		Second Parent	
		R	**W**
First Parent	**R**	*RR*	*RW*
	W	*WR*	*WW*

Use the fact that red is dominant over white to find each of the given probabilities. Assume that there are an equal number of red and white genes in the population.

(a) *P*(a flower is red)   (b) *P*(a flower is white)

✓ Checkpoint Answers

1. 13/19
2. (a) 1/4   (b) 2/9
3. 7/8
4. (a) 1/3   (b) 1/4
5. 5/6
6. (a) 9 to 1   (b) 1 to 9
   (c) 4 to 1   (d) 1 to 4
7. (a) 1/6   (b) 5/6
8. (a) .782   (b) .1644
9. (a) .20   (b) .12
   (c) .60

8.5 Conditional Probability and Independent Events

Did you ever wonder what salary the president of your college or university earns per year? The *Chronicle of Higher Education* conducted surveys in 2010 and 2011 to examine that question. The table examines whether the president earned $400,000 or more in total compensation for public and private universities and colleges. (Data from: www.chronicle.com.)

	Earned Less Than $400,000	Earned $400,000 or More	Total
Public University	102	97	199
Private University or College	249	270	519
Total	351	367	718

Let *A* be the event "earned less than $400,000" and let *B* be the event "public university president." We can find $P(A)$, $P(A')$, $P(B)$, and $P(B')$. For example, the table shows that a total of 351 presidents earned less than $400,000, so $P(A) = \dfrac{351}{718} \approx .4889$.

Suppose we want to know the probability that a public university president earns less than $400,000. From the table, there were a total of 199 total public university presidents, of which 102 earned less than $400,000. Thus,

$$P(\text{public university president earns less than } \$400{,}000) = \frac{102}{199} \approx .5126.$$

This probability (.5126) is a different number from the probability of making less than $400,000 or more (.4889) because *we have additional information* (the president is the president of a public university) *that has reduced the sample space.* In other words, we

✓ Checkpoint 1

Use the data in the table to find
(a) $P(B)$;
(b) $P(A')$;
(c) $P(B')$.

found the probability of earning less than \$400,000, *A*, given the additional information that the president is a public university president, *B*. This is called the *conditional probability* of event *A*, given that event *B* has occurred, written $P(A|B)$, which is often read as "the probability of *A* given *B*."

In the preceding example,

$$P(A|B) = \frac{102}{199} \approx .5126.$$

If we divide the numerator and denominator by 718 (the size of the sample space), this can be written as

$$P(A|B) = \frac{\dfrac{102}{718}}{\dfrac{199}{718}} = \frac{P(A \cap B)}{P(B)},$$

where $P(A \cap B)$ represents, as usual, the probability that both *A* and *B* will occur.

To generalize this result, assume that *E* and *F* are two events for a particular experiment. Assume also that the sample space *S* for the experiment has *n* possible equally likely outcomes. Suppose event *F* has *m* elements and $E \cap F$ has *k* elements ($k \leq m$). Then, using the fundamental principle of probability yields

$$P(F) = \frac{m}{n} \quad \text{and} \quad P(E \cap F) = \frac{k}{n}.$$

We now want to find $P(E|F)$: the probability that *E* occurs, given that *F* has occurred. Since we assume that *F* has occurred, we reduce the sample space to *F*; that is, we look only at the *m* elements inside *F*. (See Figure 8.26.) Of these *m* elements, there are *k* elements for which *E* also occurs, because $E \cap F$ has *k* elements. This yields

$$P(E|F) = \frac{k}{m}.$$

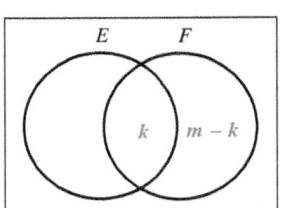

Event *F* has a total of *m* elements.

Figure 8.26

Divide numerator and denominator by *n* to get

$$P(E|F) = \frac{k/n}{m/n} = \frac{P(E \cap F)}{P(F)}.$$

The last result motivates the following definition of conditional probability. The **conditional probability** of an event *E*, given event *F*, written $P(E|F)$, is

$$P(E|F) = \frac{P(E \cap F)}{P(F)} = \frac{P(E \text{ and } F)}{P(F)}, \quad P(F) \neq 0.$$

This definition tells us that, for equally likely outcomes, conditional probability is found by *reducing the sample space to event F* and then finding the number of outcomes in *F* that are also in event *E*. Thus,

$$P(E|F) = \frac{n(E \cap F)}{n(F)}.$$

Although the definition of conditional probability was motivated by an example with equally likely outcomes, it is valid in all cases. For an intuitive explanation, think of the formula as giving the probability that both *E* and *F* occur, compared with the entire probability of *F* occuring.

Example 1   Business   Use the information at the beginning of this section from the table on the salary of public and private university and college presidents to find the following probabilities.

✓ Checkpoint 2

The table shows the results of the 2012 General Social Survey regarding happiness for married and never married respondents.

	Very Happy	Partially Happy or Not Happy	Total
Married	375	522	897
Never Married	109	416	525
Total	484	938	1422

Let M represent married respondents and V represent very happy respondents. Find each of the given probabilities.

(a) $P(V|M)$

(b) $P(V|M')$

(c) $P(M|V)$

(d) $P(M'|V')$

(e) State the probability of part (d) in words.

Figure 8.27

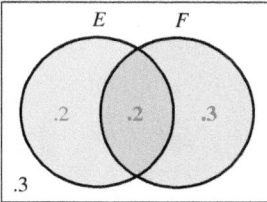

Figure 8.28

✓ Checkpoint 3

Find $P(F|E)$ if $P(E) = .3$, $P(F) = .4$, and $P(E \cup F) = .6$.

(a) $P(A|B')$

Solution In words, $P(A|B')$ is the probability of earning less than \$400,000, given that the president is not a public university president (which means he or she is a private university or college president).

$$P(A|B') = \frac{n(A \cap B')}{n(B')} = \frac{249}{519} \approx .4798.$$

(b) $P(B|A)$

Solution $P(B|A)$ represents the probability that the president is a public university president, given that he or she makes less than \$400,000. Reduce the sample space to A. Then find $n(A \cap B)$ and $n(A)$.

$$P(B|A) = \frac{n(A \cap B)}{n(A)} = \frac{102}{351} \approx .2906.$$

(c) $P(B'|A')$

Solution Here, we want the probability that the president is a private university or college president, given that he or she earns \$400,000 or more.

$$P(B'|A') = \frac{n(B' \cap A')}{n(A')} = \frac{270}{367} \approx .7357. \quad ✓2$$

Venn diagrams can be used to illustrate problems in conditional probability. A Venn diagram for Example 1, in which the probabilities are used to indicate the number in the set defined by each region, is shown in Figure 8.27. In the diagram, $P(B|A)$ is found by *reducing the sample space to just set A.* Then $P(B|A)$ is the ratio of the number in that part of set B which is also in A to the number in set A, or $.1421/(.1421 + .3468) = .1421/.4889 \approx .2907$. [This differs slightly from (b) because of rounding.]

Example 2 Given $P(E) = .4$, $P(F) = .5$, and $P(E \cup F) = .7$, find $P(E|F)$.

Solution Find $P(E \cap F)$ first. Then use a Venn diagram to find $P(E|F)$. By the addition rule,

$$P(E \cup F) = P(E) + P(F) - P(E \cap F)$$
$$.7 = .4 + .5 - P(E \cap F)$$
$$P(E \cap F) = .2.$$

Now use the probabilities to indicate the number in each region of the Venn diagram in Figure 8.28. $P(E|F)$ is the ratio of the probability of that part of E which is in F to the probability of F, or

$$P(E|F) = \frac{P(E \cap F)}{P(F)} = \frac{.2}{.5} = \frac{2}{5} = .4. \quad ✓3$$

Example 3 Two fair coins were tossed, and it is known that at least one was a head. Find the probability that both were heads.

Solution The sample space has four equally likely outcomes: $S = \{hh, ht, th, tt.\}$ Define two events

$$E_1 = \text{at least 1 head} = \{hh, ht, th\}$$

and

$$E_2 = 2 \text{ heads} = \{hh\}.$$

Because there are four equally likely outcomes, $P(E_1) = 3/4$. Also, $P(E_1 \cap E_2) = 1/4$. We want the probability that both were heads, given that at least one was a head; that is, we want to find $P(E_2|E_1)$. Because of the condition that at least one coin was a head, the reduced sample space is

$$\{hh, ht, th\}.$$

Since only one outcome in this reduced sample space is two heads,

$$P(E_2|E_1) = \frac{1}{3}.$$

Alternatively, use the definition given earlier:

$$P(E_2|E_1) = \frac{P(E_2 \cap E_1)}{P(E_1)} = \frac{1/4}{3/4} = \frac{1}{3}. \quad \boxed{4}$$

✓ **Checkpoint 4**

In Example 3, find the probability that exactly one coin showed a head, given that at least one was a head.

It is important not to confuse $P(A|B)$ with $P(B|A)$. For example, in a criminal trial, a prosecutor may point out to the jury that the probability of the defendant's DNA profile matching that of a sample taken at the scene of the crime, given that the defendant is innocent, is very small. What the jury must decide, however, is the probability that the defendant is innocent, given that the defendant's DNA profile matches the sample. Confusing the two is an error sometimes called "the prosecutor's fallacy," and the 1990 conviction of a rape suspect in England was overturned by a panel of judges who ordered a retrial, because the fallacy made the original trial unfair.[*] This mistake is often called "confusion of the inverse."

In the next section, we will see how to compute $P(A|B)$ when we know $P(B|A)$.

Product Rule

If $P(E) \neq 0$ and $P(F) \neq 0$, then the definition of conditional probability shows that

$$P(E|F) = \frac{P(E \cap F)}{P(F)} \quad \text{and} \quad P(F|E) = \frac{P(F \cap E)}{P(E)}.$$

Using the fact that $P(E \cap F) = P(F \cap E)$, and solving each of these equations for $P(E \cap F)$, we obtain the following rule.

Product Rule of Probability

If E and F are events, then $P(E \cap F)$ may be found by either of these formulas:

$$P(E \cap F) = P(F) \cdot P(E|F) \quad \text{or} \quad P(E \cap F) = P(E) \cdot P(F|E).$$

The **product rule** gives a method for finding the probability that events E and F both occur. Here is a simple way to remember the ordering of E and F in the probability rule:

$$P(E \cap F) = P(F) \cdot P(E|F) \quad \text{or} \quad P(E \cap F) = P(E) \cdot P(F|E).$$

Example 4 **Business** According to data from the U.S. Census Bureau, we can estimate the probability that a business is female owned as .282. We can also estimate the probability that a female-owned business has one to four employees as .504. What is the probability that a business is female owned *and* has one to four employees?

---

[*]David Pringle, "Who's the DNA Fingerprinting Pointing At?," *New Scientist*, January 29, 1994, pp. 51–52.

Solution Let F represent the event of "having a female-owned business" and E represent the event of "having one to four employees." We want to find $P(F \cap E)$. By the product rule,

$$P(F \cap E) = P(F)P(E \mid F).$$

From the given information, $P(F) = .282$, and the probability that a female-owned business has one to four employees is $P(E \mid F) = .504$. Thus,

$$P(F \cap E) = .282(.504) \approx .142.$$ ✔5

✓ **Checkpoint 5**

In a litter of puppies, 3 were female and 4 were male. Half the males were black. Find the probability that a puppy chosen at random from the litter would be a black male.

In Section 8.1, we used a tree diagram to find the number of subsets of a given set. By including the probabilities for each branch of a tree diagram, we convert it to a **probability tree**. The following examples show how a probability tree is used with the product rule to find the probability of a sequences of events.

Example 5 A company needs to hire a new director of advertising. It has decided to try to hire either person A or person B, both of whom are assistant advertising directors for its major competitor. To decide between A and B, the company does research on the campaigns managed by A or B (none are managed by both) and finds that A is in charge of twice as many advertising campaigns as B. Also, A's campaigns have yielded satisfactory results three out of four times, while B's campaigns have yielded satisfactory results only two out of five times. Suppose one of the competitor's advertising campaigns (managed by A or B) is selected randomly.

We can represent this situation schematically as follows: Let A denote the event "Person A does the job" and B the event "Person B does the job." Let S be the event "satisfactory results" and U the event "unsatisfactory results." Then the given information can be summarized in the probability tree in Figure 8.29. Since A does twice as many jobs as B, $P(A) = 2/3$ and $P(B) = 1/3$, as noted on the first-stage branches of the tree. When A does a job, the probability of satisfactory results is $3/4$ and of unsatisfactory results $1/4$, as noted on the second-stage branches. Similarly, the probabilities when B does the job are noted on the remaining second-stage branches. The composite branches labeled 1–4 represent the four disjoint possibilities for the running and outcome of the campaign.

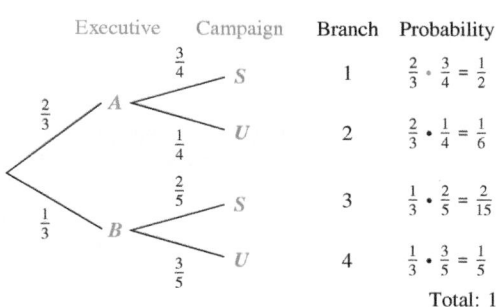

Figure 8.29

(a) Find the probability that A is in charge of a campaign that produces satisfactory results.

Solution We are asked to find $P(A \cap S)$. We know that when A does the job, the probability of success is $3/4$; that is, $P(S \mid A) = 3/4$. Hence, by the product rule,

$$P(A \cap S) = P(A) \cdot P(S \mid A) = \frac{2}{3} \cdot \frac{3}{4} = \frac{1}{2}.$$

The event $(A \cap S)$ is represented by branch 1 of the tree, and as we have just seen, its probability is the product of the probabilities that make up that branch.

(b) Find the probability that B runs a campaign that produces satisfactory results.

Solution We must find $P(B \cap S)$. This event is represented by branch 3 of the tree, and as before, its probability is the product of the probabilities of the pieces of that branch:

$$P(B \cap S) = P(B) \cdot P(S|B) = \frac{1}{3} \cdot \frac{2}{5} = \frac{2}{15}.$$

(c) What is the probability that the selected campaign is satisfactory?

Solution The event S is the union of the disjoint events $A \cap S$ and $B \cap S$, which are represented by branches 1 and 3 of the tree diagram. By the addition rule,

$$P(S) = P(A \cap S) + P(B \cap S) = \frac{1}{2} + \frac{2}{15} = \frac{19}{30}.$$

Thus, the probability of an event that appears on several branches is the sum of the probabilities of each of these branches.

(d) What is the probability that the selected campaign is unsatisfactory?

Solution $P(U)$ can be read from branches 2 and 4 of the tree:

$$P(U) = \frac{1}{6} + \frac{1}{5} = \frac{11}{30}.$$

Alternatively, because U is the complement of S,

$$P(U) = 1 - P(S) = 1 - \frac{19}{30} = \frac{11}{30}.$$

(e) Find the probability that either A runs the campaign or the results are satisfactory (or possibly both).

Solution Event A combines branches 1 and 2, while event S combines branches 1 and 3, so use branches 1, 2, and 3:

$$P(A \cup S) = \frac{1}{2} + \frac{1}{6} + \frac{2}{15} = \frac{4}{5}. \quad ✓_6$$

✓**Checkpoint 6**

Find each of the given probabilities for the scenario in Example 5.

(a) $P(U|A)$

(b) $P(U|B)$

Example 6 Suppose 6 potential jurors remain in a jury pool and 2 are to be selected to sit on the jury for the trial. The races of the 6 potential jurors are 1 Hispanic, 3 Caucasian, and 2 African-American. If we select one juror at a time, find the probability that one Caucasian and one African-American are drawn.

Solution A probability tree showing the various possible outcomes is given in Figure 8.30 on the next page. In this diagram, C represents the event "selecting a Caucasian juror" and A represents "selecting an African-American juror." On the first draw, $P(C$ on the 1st$) = 3/6 = 1/2$ because three of the six jurors are Caucasian. On the second draw, $P(A$ on the 2nd $| C$ on the 1st$) = 2/5$. One Caucasian juror has been removed, leaving 5, of which 2 are African-American.

We want to find the probability of selecting exactly one Caucasian and exactly one African-American. Two events satisfy this condition: selecting a Caucasian first and then selecting an African-American (branch 2 of the tree) and drawing an African-American juror first and then selecting a Caucasian juror (branch 4). For branch 2,

$$P(C \text{ on 1st}) \cdot P(A \text{ on 2nd} | C \text{ on 1st}) = \frac{1}{2} \cdot \frac{2}{5} = \frac{1}{5}. \quad ✓_7$$

✓**Checkpoint 7**

In Example 6, find the probability of selecting an African-American juror and then a Caucasian juror.

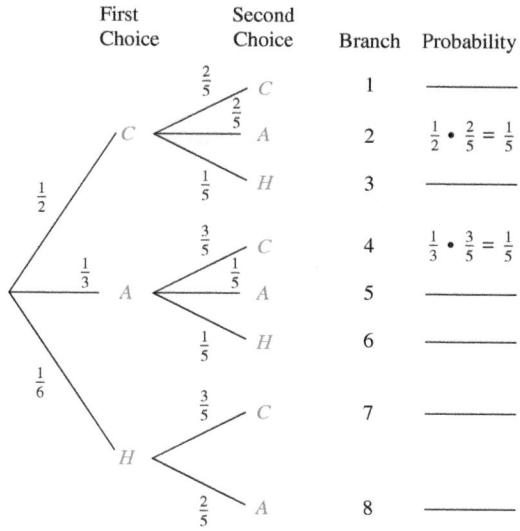

Figure 8.30

For branch 4, on which the African-American juror is selected first,

$$P(A \text{ first}) \cdot P(C \text{ second}|A \text{ first}) = \frac{1}{3} \cdot \frac{3}{5} = \frac{1}{5}.$$

Since these two events are disjoint, the final probability is the sum of the two probabilities.

$$P(\text{one } C \text{ and one } A) = P(C \text{ on 1st}) \cdot P(A \text{ on 2nd}|C \text{ on 1st})$$
$$+ P(A \text{ on 1st}) \cdot P(C \text{ on 2nd}|A \text{ on 1st}) = \frac{2}{5}. \quad \boxed{8}$$

✓ **Checkpoint 8**

In Example 6, find the probability of selecting a Caucasian juror and then a Hispanic juror.

The product rule is often used in dealing with *stochastic processes*, which are mathematical models that evolve over time in a probabilistic manner. For example, selecting different jurors is such a process, because the probabilities change with each successive selection. (Particular stochastic processes are studied further in Section 9.5.)

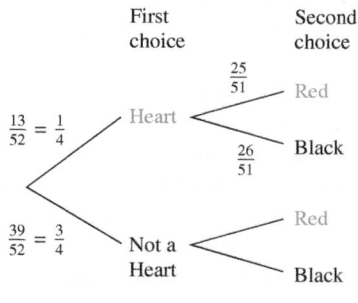

Figure 8.31

✓ **Checkpoint 9**

Find the probability of drawing a heart on the first draw and a black card on the second if two cards are drawn without replacement.

Example 7   Two cards are drawn without replacement from an ordinary deck (52 cards). Find the probability that the first card is a heart and the second card is red.

Solution   Start with the probability tree of Figure 8.31. (You may wish to refer to the deck of cards shown on page 427.) On the first draw, since there are 13 hearts in the 52 cards, the probability of drawing a heart first is $13/52 = 1/4$. On the second draw, since a (red) heart has been drawn already, there are 25 red cards in the remaining 51 cards. Thus, the probability of drawing a red card on the second draw, given that the first is a heart, is $25/51$. By the product rule of probability,

$$P(\text{heart on 1st and red on 2nd})$$
$$= P(\text{heart on 1st}) \cdot P(\text{red on 2nd}|\text{heart on 1st})$$
$$= \frac{1}{4} \cdot \frac{25}{51} = \frac{25}{204} \approx .123. \quad \boxed{9}$$

Example 8   Three cards are drawn, without replacement, from an ordinary deck. Find the probability that exactly 2 of the cards are red.

Solution Here, we need a probability tree with three stages, as shown in Figure 8.32. The three branches indicated with arrows produce exactly 2 red cards from the draws. Multiply the probabilities along each of these branches and then add:

$$P(\text{exactly 2 red cards}) = \frac{26}{52} \cdot \frac{25}{51} \cdot \frac{26}{50} + \frac{26}{52} \cdot \frac{26}{51} \cdot \frac{25}{50} + \frac{26}{52} \cdot \frac{26}{51} \cdot \frac{25}{50}$$

$$= \frac{50,700}{132,600} = \frac{13}{34} \approx .382. \quad \checkmark_{10}$$

✓ **Checkpoint 10**

Use the tree in Example 8 to find the probability that exactly one of the cards is red.

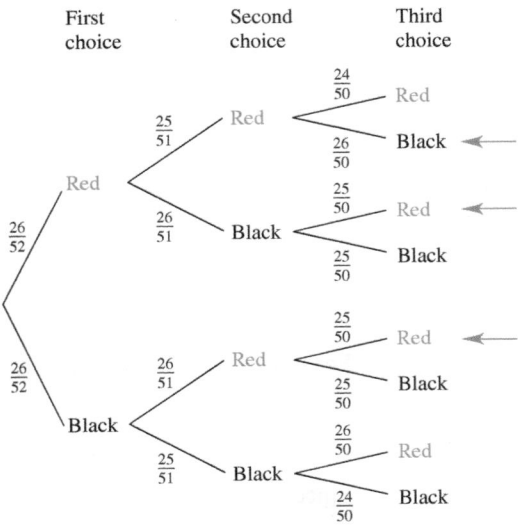

Figure 8.32

Independent Events

Suppose in Example 7 that we draw the two cards *with* replacement rather than without replacement. (That is, we put the first card back, shuffle the deck, and then draw the second card.) If the first card is a heart, then the probability of drawing a red card on the second draw is 26/52, rather than 25/51, because there are still 52 cards in the deck, 26 of them red. In this case, $P(\text{red second} \mid \text{heart first})$ is the same as $P(\text{red second})$. The value of the second card is not affected by the value of the first card. We say that the event that the second card is red is *independent* of the event that the first card is a heart, since knowledge of the first card does not influence what happens to the second card. On the other hand, when we draw *without* replacement, the events that the first card is a heart and the second is red are *dependent* events. The fact that the first card is a heart means that there is one fewer red card in the deck, influencing the probability that the second card is red.

As another example, consider tossing a fair coin twice. If the first toss shows heads, the probability that the next toss is heads is still 1/2. Coin tosses are independent events, since the outcome of one toss does not influence the outcome of the next toss. Similarly, rolls of a fair die are independent events. On the other hand, the events "the milk is old" and "the milk is sour" are dependent events: If the milk is old, there is an increased chance that it is sour. Also, in the example at the beginning of this section, the events A (the president earned less than $400,000) and B (the president was the head of a public university) are dependent events, because information about the institution type affects the probability of salary level. That is, $P(A \mid B)$ is different from $P(A)$.

If events E and F are independent, then the knowledge that E has occurred gives no (probability) information about the occurrence or nonoccurrence of event F. That is, $P(F)$ is exactly the same as $P(F \mid E)$, or

$$P(F \mid E) = P(F).$$

This, in fact, is the formal definition of independent events.

> *E* and *F* are **independent events** if
> $$P(F|E) = P(F) \quad \text{or} \quad P(E|F) = P(E).$$

If the events are not independent, they are **dependent events.**

When *E* and *F* are independent events, $P(F|E) = P(F)$, and the product rule becomes

$$P(E \cap F) = P(E) \cdot P(F|E) = P(E) \cdot P(F).$$

Conversely, if this equation holds, it follows that $P(F) = P(F|E)$. Consequently, we have the useful rule that follows.

> ## Product Rule for Independent Events
>
> *E* and *F* are independent events if and only if
> $$P(E \cap F) = P(E) \cdot P(F).$$

Example 9   **Business**   A USB flash drive requires a two-step manufacturing process. The first step involves the circuit board, and let us assume that 98% of the circuit board assemblies are satisfactory. The second step involves the plastic casing. Assume that 96.5% of the casings are satisfactory. Assume the manufacturing process of the circuit boards has no relationship with the manufacturing of the plastic casings, and find the probability that both components are satisfactory.

Solution   Since the manufacturing processes of the two components have no relationship, we can assume that event *A* (the circuit board is satisfactory) and event *B* (the plastic casing is satisfactory) are two independent events. Thus, the probability that both components are satisfactory is

$$P(A \cap B) = P(A) \cdot P(B) = (.98)(.965) = .9457. \quad \checkmark_{11}$$

✓ **Checkpoint 11**

Find the probability of getting 4 successive heads on 4 tosses of a fair coin.

🚫 **CAUTION** It is common to confuse the ideas of *disjoint* events and *independent* events. Events *E* and *F* are disjoint if $E \cap F = \varnothing$. For example, if a family has exactly one child, the only possible outcomes are $B = \{\text{boy}\}$ and $G = \{\text{girl}\}$. The events *B* and *G* are disjoint and $P(B) = P(G) = .5$. However, the events are *not* independent, since $P(G|B) = 0$ (if a family with only one child has a boy, the probability that it has a girl is then 0). Since $P(G|B) \neq P(G)$, the events are not independent. Of all the families with exactly *two* children, the events $G_1 = \{\text{first child is a girl}\}$ and $G_2 = \{\text{second child is a girl}\}$ are independent, because $P(G_2|G_1)$ equals $P(G_2)$. However, G_1 and G_2 are not disjoint, since $G_1 \cap G_2 = \{\text{both children are girls}\} \neq \varnothing$.

To show that two events *E* and *F* are independent, we can show that $P(F|E) = P(F)$, that $P(E|F) = P(E)$, or that $P(E \cap F) = P(E) \cdot P(F)$. Another way is to observe that knowledge of one outcome does not influence the probability of the other outcome, as we did for coin tosses.

📄 **NOTE** In some cases, it may not be apparent from the physical description of the problem whether two events are independent or not. For example, it is not obvious whether the event that a baseball player gets a hit tomorrow is independent of the event that he got a hit today. In such cases, it is necessary to use the definition and calculate whether $P(F|E) = P(F)$, or, equivalently, whether $P(E \cap F) = P(E) \cdot P(F)$.

Example 10 **Business** Among partnerships and corporations that file tax returns in the United States, the probability that the enterprise consists of a firm dedicated to real estate, rentals, or leasing is .241. The probability that the firm is a partnership is .352. The probability that a firm is dedicated to real estate, rentals, or leasing or is a partnership is .424. Are the events of a firm being dedicated to real estate, rentals, or leasing and a firm being a partnership independent?

Solution Let E represent the event the firm is dedicated to real estate, rentals, or leasing and let F represent the event the firm is a partnership. We must determine whether

$$P(E|F) = P(E) \quad \text{or} \quad P(F|E) = P(F).$$

We know that $P(E) = .241$, $P(F) = .352$, and $P(E \cup F) = .424$. By the addition rule, we know that

$$P(E) + P(F) - P(E \cap F) = P(E \cup F)$$
$$.241 + .352 - P(E \cap F) = .424$$
$$.593 - P(E \cap F) = .424$$
$$P(E \cap F) = .169.$$

Therefore,

$$P(E|F) = \frac{P(E \cap F)}{P(F)} = \frac{.169}{.352} \approx .480 \neq .241 = P(E).$$

Also,

$$P(F|E) = \frac{P(E \cap F)}{P(E)} = \frac{.169}{.241} \approx .701 \neq .352 = P(F).$$

Since $P(E|F) \neq P(E)$ and $P(F|E) \neq P(F)$ these two events are not independent.

✓ **Checkpoint 12**

The probability of living in Texas is .08, the probability of speaking English at home is .83, and the probability of living in Texas or speaking English at home is .854. Are the events "speaking English at home" and "living in Texas" independent?

📄 **NOTE** Although we showed that $P(E|F) \neq P(E)$ and $P(F|E) \neq P(F)$ in Example 10, only one of these results is needed to establish independence.

8.5 Exercises

If a single fair die is rolled, find the probability of rolling the given events. (See Examples 1 and 2.)

1. 3, given that the number rolled was odd

2. 5, given that the number rolled was even

3. An odd number, given that the number rolled was 3

If two fair dice are rolled (recall the 36-outcome sample space), find the probability of rolling the given events.

4. A sum of 8, given that the sum was greater than 7

5. A sum of 6, given that the roll was a "double" (two identical numbers)

6. A double, given that the sum was 9

If two cards are drawn without replacement from an ordinary deck, find the probabilities of the given event. (See Example 7.)

7. The second is a heart, given that the first is a heart

8. The second is black, given that the first is a spade

9. A jack and a 10 are drawn.

10. An ace and a 4 are drawn.

11. In your own words, explain how to find the conditional probability $P(E|F)$.

12. Your friend asks you to explain how the product rule for independent events differs from the product rule for dependent events. How would you respond?

13. Another friend asks you to explain how to tell whether two events are dependent or independent. How would you reply? (Use your own words.)

14. A student reasons that the probability in Example 3 of both coins being heads is just the probability that the other coin is a head—that is, $1/2$. Explain why this reasoning is wrong.

Decide whether the two events listed are independent.

15. S is the event that it is snowing and L is the event that the instructor is late for class.

16. R is the event that four semesters of theology are required to graduate from a certain college and A is the event that the college is a religiously affiliated school.

17. R is the event that it rains in the Amazon jungle and H is the event that an instructor in New York City writes a difficult exam.

18. T is the event that Tom Cruise's next movie grosses over $200 million and R is the event that the Republicans have a majority in Congress in the year 2020.

19. In a two-child family, if we assume that the probabilities of a child being male and a child being female are each .5, are the events "the children are the same sex" and "at most one child is male" independent? Are they independent for a three-child family?

20. Let A and B be independent events with $P(A) = \dfrac{1}{4}$ and $P(B) = \dfrac{1}{5}$. Find $P(A \cap B)$ and $P(A \cup B)$.

Business *According to data from the U.S. Internal Revenue Service, the probability that a firm has less than $25,000 in revenue if it is a partnership is .551. If the firm is a corporation, the probability of reporting less than $25,000 in revenue is .258. The probability that a firm is a partnership is .352 and the probability that a firm is a corporation is .648. Find the following probabilities.*

21. A firm with less than $25,000 in revenue is a partnership.

22. A firm has less than $25,000 in revenue.

23. **Business** According to the Bureau of Labor Statistics, for 2011, 48.5% of the civilian population 16 years or older was male, 34% was not in the labor force, and 70.1% was male or not in the labor force. Find the probability of not being in the labor force, given that the person is male.

24. **Business** Using the information from Exercise 23 and the fact that 21.6% of the population is female and not in the labor force, find the probability of not being in the labor force, given that the person is female.

Economics *For Exercises 25–28, use the following table that is based on numbers from the 2011 American Community Survey. The table represents 2023 randomly chosen U.S. residents age 25 years or older in regard to educational attainment and health insurance status.*

Educational Attainment	Has Health Insurance	Does Not Have Health Insurance
Less than High School Graduate	192	87
High School Graduate (or GED)	459	113
Some College or an Associate's Degree	498	90
Bachelor's Degree or Higher	544	40

Find the probability of the described events. (Data from: factfinder2. census.gov.)

25. Having health insurance given that the person is not a high school graduate

26. Having health insurance given that the person has a bachelor's degree or higher

27. Being a high school graduate given that the person does not have health insurance

28. Having some college or an associate's degree given that the person does have health insurance

Business *The 2012 General Social Survey asked respondents about their confidence in banks and financial institutions as well as their confidence in major corporations. Each question allowed three responses: "a great deal, only some, or hardly any." The table below summarizes the responses.*

Confidence in Banks and Financial Institutions	Confidence in Major Corporations			
	A Great Deal	Only Some	Hardly Any	Total
A Great Deal	69	59	14	142
Only Some	123	465	74	662
Hardly Any	23	288	183	494
Total	215	812	271	1298

Find the probability of the described events. (Data from: www3. norc.org/gss+website.)

29. A respondent has a great deal of confidence in banks and financial institutions given that he or she has hardly any confidence in major corporations.

30. A respondent has hardly any confidence in banks and financial institutions given that he or she has hardly any confidence in major corporations.

31. A respondent has a great deal of confidence in major corporations given that he or she has only some confidence in banks and financial institutions.

32. A respondent has hardly any confidence in major corporations given that he or she has hardly any confidence in banks and financial institutions.

Natural Science *The following table shows frequencies for red–green color blindness, where M represents that a person is male and C represents that a person is color blind.*

	M	M'	Totals
C	.042	.007	.049
C'	.485	.466	.951
Totals	.527	.473	1.000

Use the table to find the given probabilities.

33. $P(M)$ **34.** $P(C)$

35. $P(M \cap C)$ **36.** $P(M \cup C)$

37. $P(M|C)$ **38.** $P(M'|C)$

39. Are the events C and M dependent? Recall that two events E and F are dependent if $P(E|F) \neq P(E)$. (See Example 10.)

40. Are the events M' and C dependent?

Natural Science *A scientist wishes to determine whether there is any dependence between color blindness (C) and deafness (D). Use the probabilities in the table to answer Exercises 41 and 42.*

	D	D'	Total
C	.0004	.0796	.0800
C'	.0046	.9154	.9200
Total	.0050	.9950	1.0000

41. Find $P(C)$, $P(D)$, $P(C \cap D)$, and $P(C|D)$. Does $P(C) = P(C|D)$? What does that result imply regarding independence of C and D?

42. Find $P(D')$, $P(C)$, $P(D' \cap C)$, and $P(D'|C)$. Does $P(D') = P(D'|C)$? What does that result imply regarding independence of D' and C?

Social Science *The Motor Vehicle Department in a certain state has found that the probability of a person passing the test for a driver's license on the first try is .75. The probability that an individual who fails on the first test will pass on the second try is .80, and the probability that an individual who fails the first and second tests will pass the third time is .70. Find the probability of the given event.*

43. A person fails both the first and second tests

44. A person will fail three times in a row

Business *The numbers of domestic and international flights for American, Delta, and United Airlines for the year 2012 are given in the following table.*

Airline	Domestic	International	Total
American	517,971	120,976	638,947
Delta	729,997	96,611	826,608
United	527,769	135,211	662,980
Total	1,775,737	352,798	2,128,535

Find the probability of the described event. (Data from: www. transtats.bts.gov.)

45. An American flight was domestic

46. A United flight was international

47. A domestic flight was Delta

48. An international flight was United

Business *The 2012 General Social Survey determined annual household income and whether the respondent found work stressful. The household income variable is categorized below and the responses regarding stress at work were always, often, sometimes, hardly ever, and never. The results appear in the table.*

Income			

Income	Always	Often	Some-times	Hardly Ever	Never	Totals
$50,000 or less	66	128	238	97	35	564
$50,001– $100,000	30	113	145	42	14	344
More than $100,000	16	54	57	10	5	142
Total	112	295	440	149	54	1050

Table heading: **Stress at Work**

Find the probability of the described events. (Data from: www3. norc.org/gss+website.)

49. Given that the respondent earns $50,000 or less, what is the probability of never having stress?

50. Given that the respondent earns $50,000 or less, what is the probability of always having stress?

51. Given that the respondent earns more than $100,000, what is the probability of never having stress?

52. Given that the respondent earns more than $100,000, what is the probability of sometimes having stress?

53. Given that the respondent sometimes has stress, what is the probability of earning $50,000 or less?

54. Given that the respondent always has stress, what is the probability that the respondent earns between $50,001–$100,000?

Suppose the probability that the first record by a singing group will be a hit is .32. If the first record is a hit, so are all the group's subsequent records. If the first record is not a hit, the probability of the group's second record and all subsequent ones being hits is .16. If the first two records are not hits, the probability that the third is a hit is .08. The probability that a record is a hit continues to decrease by half with each successive nonhit record. Find the probability of the given event.

55. The group will have at least one hit in its first four records.

56. The group will have a hit in its first six records if the first three are not hits.

Work the given problems on independent events. (See Examples 9 and 10.)

57. **Business** Corporations such as banks, where a computer is essential to day-to-day operations, often have a second, backup computer in case of failure by the main computer. Suppose that there is a .003 chance that the main computer will fail in a given period and a .005 chance that the backup computer will fail while the main computer is being repaired. Suppose these failures represent independent events, and find the fraction of the time the corporation can assume that it will have computer service. How realistic is our assumption of independence?

58. **Business** According to data from the U.S. Department of Transportation, Delta Airlines was on time approximately

87% of the time in 2012. Use this information, and assume that the event that a given flight takes place on time is independent of the event that another flight is on time to answer the following questions

(a) Elisabeta Gueyara plans to visit her company's branch offices; her journey requires 3 separate flights on Delta Airlines. What is the probability that all of these flights will be on time?

(b) How reasonable do you believe it is to suppose the independence of being on time from flight to flight?

59. Natural Science The probability that a key component of a space rocket will fail is .03.

(a) How many such components must be used as backups to ensure that the probability that at least one of the components will work is .999999?

(b) Is it reasonable to assume independence here?

60. Natural Science A medical experiment showed that the probability that a new medicine is effective is .75, the probability that a patient will have a certain side effect is .4, and the probability that both events will occur is .3. Decide whether these events are dependent or independent.

61. Social Science A teacher has found that the probability that a student studies for a test is .6, the probability that a student gets a good grade on a test is .7, and the probability that both events occur is .52. Are these events independent?

62. Refer to Exercises 49–54. Are the events of having an income of greater than $100,000 and never having stress at work independent?

✓**Checkpoint Answers**

1. (a) About .2772   **(b)** About .5111   **(c)** About .7228

2. (a) About .4181   **(b)** About .2076   **(c)** About .7748
   (d) About .4435
   (e) The probability of never being married, given that the person is partially or not happy

3. $1/3$ **4.** $2/3$ **5.** $2/7$

6. (a) $1/4$ **(b)** $3/5$

7. $1/5$ **8.** $1/10$ **9.** $13/102 \approx .1275$

10. $13/34 \approx .382$ **11.** $1/16$ **12.** No

8.6 Bayes' Formula

Suppose the probability that a person gets lung cancer, given that the person smokes a pack or more of cigarettes daily, is known. For a research project, it might be necessary to know the probability that a person smokes a pack or more of cigarettes daily, given that the person has lung cancer. More generally, if $P(E|F)$ is known for two events E and F, can $P(F|E)$ be found? The answer is yes, we can find $P(F|E)$ by using the formula to be developed in this section. To develop this formula, we can use a probability tree to find $P(F|E)$. Since $P(E|F)$ is known, the first outcome is either F or F'. Then, for each of these outcomes, either E or E' occurs, as shown in Figure 8.33.

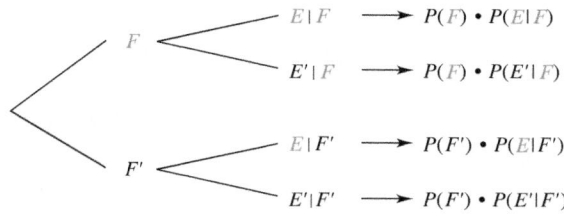

Figure 8.33

The four cases have the probabilities shown on the right. By the definition of conditional probability and the product rule,

$$P(E) = P(F \cap E) + P(F' \cap E),$$

$$P(F \cap E) = P(F) \cdot P(E|F), \quad \text{and} \quad P(F' \cap E) = P(F') \cdot P(E|F').$$

By substitution,

$$P(E) = P(F) \cdot P(E|F) + P(F') \cdot P(E|F')$$

and

$$P(F|E) = \frac{P(F \cap E)}{P(E)} = \frac{P(F) \cdot P(E|F)}{P(F) \cdot P(E|F) + P(F') \cdot P(E|F')}.$$

We have proved a special case of Bayes' formula, which is generalized later in this section. ☑₁

✓ **Checkpoint 1**

Use the special case of Bayes' formula to find $P(F|E)$ if $P(F) = .2$, $P(E|F) = .1$, and $P(E|F') = .3$. [*Hint:* $P(F') = 1 - P(F)$.]

Bayes' Formula (Special Case)

$$P(F|E) = \frac{P(F) \cdot P(E|F)}{P(F) \cdot P(E|F) + P(F') \cdot P(E|F')}.$$

Example 1   **Business**   For a fixed length of time, the probability of worker error on a certain production line is .1, the probability that an accident will occur when there is a worker error is .3, and the probability that an accident will occur when there is no worker error is .2. Find the probability of a worker error if there is an accident.

Solution   Let E represent the event of an accident, and let F represent the event of a worker error. From the given information,

$$P(F) = .1, \quad P(F') = 1 - .1 = .9 \quad P(E|F) = .3, \quad \text{and} \quad P(E|F') = .2.$$

These probabilities are shown on the probability tree in Figure 8.34.

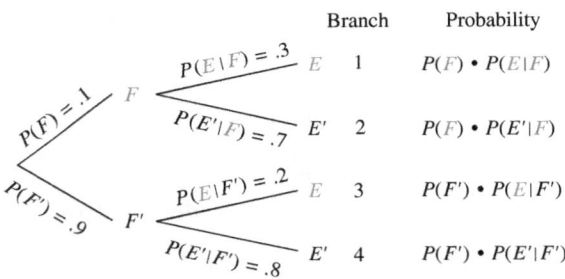

Figure 8.34

Applying Bayes' formula, we find that

$$P(F|E) = \frac{P(F) \cdot P(E|F)}{P(F) \cdot P(E|F) + P(F') \cdot P(E|F')}$$

$$= \frac{(.1)(.3)}{(.1)(.3) + (.9)(.2)} \approx .143. \; ☑₂$$

✓ **Checkpoint 2**

In Example 1, find $P(F'|E)$.

If we rewrite the special case of Bayes' formula, replacing F by F_1 and F' by F_2, then it says:

$$P(F_1|E) = \frac{P(F_1) \cdot P(E|F_1)}{P(F_1) \cdot P(E|F_1) + P(F_2) \cdot P(E|F_2)}.$$

Since $F_1 = F$ and $F_2 = F'$ we see that F_1 and F_2 are disjoint and that their union is the entire sample space. The generalization of Bayes' formula to more than two possibilities follows this same pattern.

Bayes' Formula

Suppose $F_1, F_2, \ldots, F_n$ are pairwise disjoint events (meaning that any two of them are disjoint) whose union is the sample space. Then for an event E and for each i with $1 \leq i \leq n$,

$$P(F_i|E) = \frac{P(F_i) \cdot P(E|F_i)}{P(F_1) \cdot P(E|F_1) + \cdots + P(F_n) \cdot P(E|F_n)}.$$

This result is known as Bayes' formula, after the Reverend Thomas Bayes (1702–61), whose paper on probability was published in 1764 after his death.

The statement of Bayes' formula can be daunting. It may be easier to remember the formula by thinking of the probability tree that produced it. Go through the following steps.

Using Bayes' Formula

Step 1 Start a probability tree with branches representing events $F_1, F_2, \ldots, F_n$. Label each branch with its corresponding probability.

Step 2 From the end of each of these branches, draw a branch for event E. Label this branch with the probability of getting to it, or $P(E|F_i)$.

Step 3 There are now n different paths that result in event E. Next to each path, put its probability: the product of the probabilities that the first branch occurs, $P(F_i)$, and that the second branch occurs, $P(E|F_i)$: that is, $P(F_i) \cdot P(E|F_i)$.

Step 4 $P(F_i|E)$ is found by dividing the probability of the branch for F_i by the sum of the probabilities of all the branches producing event E.

Example 2 illustrates this process.

Example 2   **Social Science**   The 2012 General Social Survey of women who are age 18 or older indicated that 87% of married women have one or more children, 48% of never married women have one or more children, and 89% of women who are divorced, separated, or widowed have one or more children. The survey also indicated that 45% of women age 18 or older were currently married, 24% had never been married, and 31% were divorced, separated, or widowed (labeled "other"). Find the probability that a woman who has one or more children is married.

Solution   Let E represent the event "having one or more children," with F_1 representing "married women," F_2 representing "never married women," and F_3 "other." Then

$$P(F_1) = .45; \quad P(E|F_1) = .87;$$
$$P(F_2) = .24; \quad P(E|F_2) = .48;$$
$$P(F_3) = .31; \quad P(E|F_3) = .89.$$

We need to find $P(F_1|E)$, the probability that a woman is married, given that she has one or more children. First, draw a probability tree using the given information, as in Figure 8.35 on the next page. The steps leading to event E are shown.

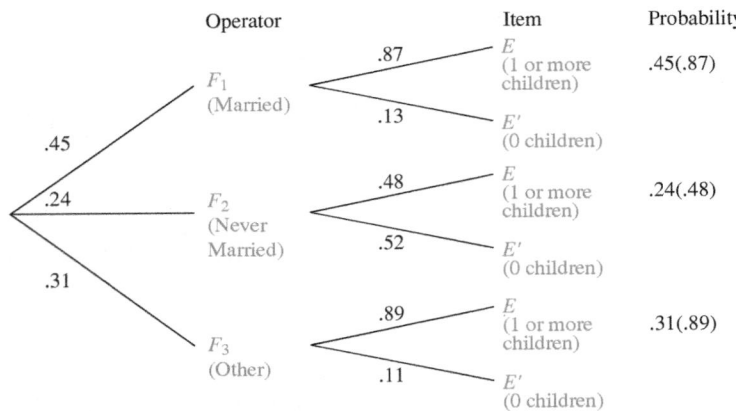

Figure 8.35

Find $P(F_1|E)$, using the top branch of the tree shown in Figure 8.35, by dividing the probability of this branch by the sum of the probabilities of all the branches leading to E:

$$P(F_1|E) = \frac{.45(.87)}{.45(.87) + .24(.48) + .31(.89)} = \frac{.3915}{.7826} \approx .500. \quad \checkmark_3$$

✓ **Checkpoint 3**

In Example 2, find

(a) $P(F_2|E)$;

(b) $P(F_3|E)$.

Example 3 **Business** A manufacturer buys items from six different suppliers. The fraction of the total number of items obtained from each supplier, along with the probability that an item purchased from that supplier is defective, is shown in the following table:

Supplier	Fraction of Total Supplied	Probability of Being Defective
1	.05	.04
2	.12	.02
3	.16	.07
4	.23	.01
5	.35	.03
6	.09	.05

Find the probability that a defective item came from supplier 5.

Solution Let F_1 be the event that an item came from supplier 1, with F_2, F_3, F_4, F_5, and F_6 defined in a similar manner. Let E be the event that an item is defective. We want to find $P(F_5|E)$. By Bayes' formula,

$$P(F_5|E) = \frac{(.35)(.03)}{(.05)(.04) + (.12)(.02) + (.16)(.07) + (.23)(.01) + (.35)(.03) + (.09)(.05)}$$

$$= \frac{.0105}{.0329} \approx .319.$$

✓ **Checkpoint 4**

In Example 3, find the probability that the defective item came from

(a) supplier 3;

(b) supplier 6.

There is about a 32% chance that a defective item came from supplier 5. Even though supplier 5 has only 3% defectives, his probability of being "guilty" is relatively high, about 32%, because of the large fraction of items he supplies. ✓₄

8.6 Exercises

For two events M and N, $P(M) = .4$, $P(N|M) = .3$, and $P(N|M') = .4$. Find each of the given probabilities. (See Example 1.)

1. $P(M|N)$

2. $P(M'|N)$

For disjoint events R_1, R_2, and R_3, $P(R_1) = .05$, $P(R_2) = .6$, and $P(R_3) = .35$. In addition, $P(Q|R_1) = .40$, $P(Q|R_2) = .30$, and $P(Q|R_3) = .60$. Find each of the given probabilities. (See Examples 2 and 3.)

3. $P(R_1|Q)$

4. $P(R_2|Q)$

5. $P(R_3|Q)$

6. $P(R_1'|Q)$

Suppose three jars have the following contents: 2 black balls and 1 white ball in the first; 1 black ball and 2 white balls in the second; 1 black ball and 1 white ball in the third. If the probability of selecting one of the three jars is 1/2, 1/3, and 1/6, respectively, find the probability that if a white ball is drawn, it came from the given jar.

7. The second jar

8. The third jar

Business *According to Forbes' list of the top 100 earning Chief Executive Officers (CEOs) of 2012, the probability of being under 60 years old was .52. The probability of earning $35 million or more for those under age 60 was .2308. The probability of earning $35 million or more for those age 60 or older was .1667. Find the following probabilities.*

9. A CEO who was earning $35 million or more was under age 60

10. A CEO who was earning less than $35 million was age 60 or older

Economics *Data from the Bureau of Labor Statistics indicates that for the year 2012, 40.8% of the labor force had a high school diploma or fewer years of education, 27.7% had some college or an associate's degree, and 31.5% had a bachelor's degree or more education. Of those with a high school diploma or fewer years of education, 17.0% earned $75,000 or more annually. Of those with some college or an associate's degree, 31.4% earned $75,000 or more, and of those with a bachelor's degree or more education, 55.0% earned $75,000 or more. Find the following probabilities that a randomly chosen labor force participant has the given characteristics.*

11. Some college or an associate's degree, given that he or she earns $75,000 or more annually

12. A bachelor's degree or more education, given that he or she earns $75,000 or more annually

13. A high school diploma or less education, given that he or she earns *less* than $75,000 annually

14. A bachelor's degree or more education, given that he or she earns *less* than $75,000 annually

Business *In 2011, the probability that the president of a 4-year college or university earned $400,000 or more in total compensation was .5111. The probability that a college or university president who earned $400,000 or more presided over a public*

institution was .2643. The probability that a college or university president who earned less than $400,000 presided over a public institution was .2906. Find the probability that a president had the given characteristics.

15. Earned $400,000 or more given at a public institution.

16. Earned less than $400,000 given at a private institution.

Social Science *Using data from the U.S. Census Bureau and the 2012 General Social Survey, the probability of being male in the United States was .493. The probability that a male considered himself "Very Happy" was .291, "Pretty Happy" was .569, and "Not Too Happy" was .139. The probability that a female considered herself "Very Happy" was .311, "Pretty Happy" was .547, and "Not Too Happy" was .142. Find the probability that a person selected at random had the given characterstics.*

17. Male, given that he is "Not Too Happy"

18. Female, given that she is "Very Happy"

19. Business The following information pertains to three shipping terminals operated by Krag Corp. (Data from: Uniform CPA Examination, November 1989.)

Terminal	Percentage of Cargo Handled	Percent Error
Land	50	2
Air	40	4
Sea	10	14

Krag's internal auditor randomly selects one set of shipping documents and ascertains that the set selected contains an error. Which of the following gives the probability that the error occurred in the Land Terminal?

(a) .02

(b) .10

(c) .25

(d) .50

20. Health The probability that a person with certain symptoms has hepatitis is .8. The blood test used to confirm this diagnosis gives positive results for 90% of people with the disease and 5% of those without the disease. What is the probability that an individual who has the symptoms and who reacts positively to the test actually has hepatitis?

Health *In a test for toxemia, a disease that affects pregnant women, a woman lies on her left side and then rolls over on her back. The test is considered positive if there is a 20-mm rise in her blood pressure within 1 minute. The results have produced the following probabilities, where T represents having toxemia at some time during the pregnancy and N represents a negative test:*

$$P(T'|N) = .90 \quad and \quad P(T|N') = .75.$$

Assume that $P(N') = .11$, and find each of the given probabilities.

21. $P(N|T)$

22. $P(N'|T)$

Business *In April 2013, the total sales from General Motors, Ford, or Chrysler was 606,334 cars or light trucks. The probability* *that the vehicle sold was made by General Motors was .392, by Ford .350, and by Chrysler .258. Additionally, the probability that a General Motors vehicle sold was a car was .395, a Ford vehicle sold was a car was .370, and a Chrysler vehicle sold was a car was .332.*

23. Given the vehicle sold was a car, find the probability it was made by General Motors.

24. Given the vehicle sold was a car, find the probability it was made by Chrysler.

25. Given the vehicle sold was a light truck, find the probability it was made by Ford.

26. Given the vehicle sold was a light truck, find the probability it was made by General Motors.

Business *At the close of the markets on May 17, 2013, there were 5905 companies listed with the New York Stock Exchange (NYSE) and NASDAQ. For the day May 17, 2013, based on data from the Wall Street Journal, the probabilities of advancing, declining, and unchanged company stocks appears below for the two exchanges.*

Exchange	Percentage of Companies Listed	Probability of Stock Advancing	Probability of Stock Declining	Probability the Stocks Remains Unchanged
NYSE	54.7%	.692	.267	.041
NASDAQ	45.3%	.657	.297	.046

Find the probability of each of the following events.

27. An advancing stock was listed on the NYSE

28. A declining stock was listed on the NASDAQ

29. An unchanged stock was listed on the NYSE

30. An advancing stock was listed on the NASDAQ

Social Science *The table gives proportions of people over age 15 in the U.S. population, and proportions of people that live alone, in a recent year. Use this table for Exercises 31–34. (Data from: U.S. Census Bureau.)*

Age	Proportion in Population Age 15 or Higher	Proportion Living Alone
15–24	.173	.034
25–34	.170	.100
35–44	.163	.089
45–64	.332	.152
65 and higher	.161	.289

31. Find the probability that a randomly selected person age 15 or older who lives alone is between the ages of 45 and 64.

32. Find the probability that a randomly selected person age 15 or older who lives alone is age 65 or older.

33. Find the probability of not living alone for a person age 15 or higher.

34. Find the probability of not living alone for a person age 15–24.

✓ Checkpoint Answers

1. $1/13 \approx .077$

2. $6/7 \approx .857$

3. (a) About .147   (b) About .353

4. (a) About .340   (b) About .137

CHAPTER 8 Summary and Review

Key Terms and Symbols

{ }	set braces
$\in$	is an element of
$\notin$	is not an element of
$\varnothing$	empty set
$\subseteq$	is a subset of
$\not\subseteq$	is not a subset of
$\subset$	is a proper subset of
A'	complement of set A
$\cap$	set intersection
$\cup$	set union
$P(E)$	probability of event E
$P(F\|E)$	probability of event F, given that event E has occurred

8.1 set, element (member), empty set, set-builder notation, universal set, subset, set operations, tree diagram, Venn diagram, complement, intersection, disjoint sets, union

8.2 addition rule for counting

8.3 experiment, trial, outcome, sample space, event, certain event, impossible event, disjoint events, basic probability principle, relative frequency probability, probability distribution

8.4 addition rule for probability, complement rule, odds

8.5 conditional probability, product rule of probability, probability tree, independent events, dependent events

8.6 Bayes' formula

Chapter 8 Key Concepts

Sets

Set A is a **subset** of set B if every element of A is also an element of B. A set of n elements has 2^n subsets.

Let A and B be any sets with universal set U.

The **complement** of A is $A' = \{x | x \notin A \text{ and } x \in U\}$.
The **intersection** of A and B is $A \cap B = \{x | x \in A \text{ and } x \in B\}$.
The **union** of A and B is $A \cup B = \{x | x \in A \text{ or } x \in B \text{ or both}\}$.
$n(A \cup B) = n(A) + n(B) - n(A \cap B)$, where $n(X)$ is the number of elements in set X.

Basic Probability Principle

Let S be a sample space of equally likely outcomes, and let event E be a subset of S. Then the probability that event E occurs is

$$P(E) = \frac{n(E)}{n(S)}.$$

Addition Rule

For any events E and F from a sample space S,

$$P(E \cup F) = P(E) + P(F) - P(E \cap F).$$

For disjoint events E and F,

$$P(E \cup F) = P(E) + P(F).$$

Complement Rule

$P(E) = 1 - P(E')$ and $P(E') = 1 - P(E)$.

Odds

The odds in favor of event E are $\dfrac{P(E)}{P(E')}$, $P(E') \neq 0$.

Properties of Probability

1. For any event E in sample space S, $0 \leq P(E) \leq 1$.

2. The sum of the probabilities of all possible distinct outcomes is 1.

Conditional Probability

The conditional probability of event E, given that event F has occurred, is

$$P(E | F) = \frac{P(E \cap F)}{P(F)}, \quad \text{where} \quad P(F) \neq 0.$$

For equally likely outcomes, conditional probability is found by reducing the sample space to event F; then

$$P(E | F) = \frac{n(E \cap F)}{n(F)}.$$

Product Rule of Probability

If E and F are events, then $P(E \cap F)$ may be found by either of these formulas:

$$P(E \cap F) = P(F) \cdot P(E | F) \quad \text{or} \quad P(E \cap F) = P(E) \cdot P(F | E).$$

Product Rule for Independent Events

E and F are independent events if and only if

$$P(E \cap F) = P(E)P(F).$$

Bayes' Formula

$$P(F_i | E) = \frac{P(F_i) \cdot P(E | F_i)}{P(F_1) \cdot P(E | F_1) + P(F_2) \cdot P(E | F_2) + \cdots + P(F_n) \cdot P(E | F_n)}.$$

Chapter 8 Review Exercises

Write true or false for each of the given statements.

1. $9 \in \{8, 4, -3, -9, 6\}$

2. $4 \in \{3, 9, 7\}$

3. $2 \notin \{0, 1, 2, 3, 4\}$

4. $0 \notin \{0, 1, 2, 3, 4\}$

5. $\{3, 4, 5\} \subseteq \{2, 3, 4, 5, 6\}$

6. $\{1, 2, 5, 8\} \subseteq \{1, 2, 5, 10, 11\}$

7. $\{1, 5, 9\} \subset \{1, 5, 6, 9, 10\}$

8. $0 \subseteq \varnothing$

List the elements in the given sets.

9. $\{x | x \text{ is a national holiday}\}$

10. $\{x | x \text{ is an integer}, -3 \leq x < 1\}$

11. {all counting numbers less than 5}

12. {$x | x$ is a leap year between 1989 and 2006}

Let U = {Vitamins A, B_1, B_2, B_3, B_6, B_{12}, C, D, E}, M = {Vitamins A, C, D, E}, and N = {Vitamins A, B_1, B_2, C, E}. Find the given sets.

13. M' **14.** N'

15. $M \cap N$ **16.** $M \cup N$

17. $M \cup N'$ **18.** $M' \cap N$

Consider these sets:

U = {Students taking Intermediate Accounting};
A = {Females};
B = {Finance majors};
C = {Students older than 22};
D = {Students with a GPA > 3.5}.

Describe each of the following in words.

19. $A \cap C$ **20.** $B \cap D$

21. $A \cup D$ **22.** $A' \cap D$

23. $B' \cap C'$

Draw a Venn diagram and shade the given set in it.

24. $B \cup A'$ **25.** $A' \cap B$

26. $A' \cap (B' \cap C)$

Business *As of May 2013, the 50 highest grossing movies as measured by domestic box office receipts could be categorized as follows. (Data from: www.the-movie-times.com.)*

27 were action movies;
34 were rated PG-13;
38 were made in the year 2000 or more recently;
22 were action and rated PG-13;
23 were action and made in the year 2000 or more recently;
28 were rated PG-13 and made in the year 2000 or more recently;
21 were action, rated PG-13, and made in the year 2000 or more recently.

27. How many movies were action movies but not rated PG-13?

28. How many movies were action or rated PG-13?

29. How many movies were made in the year 2000 or more recently or rated PG-13?

30. How many movies were not action, not rated PG-13, and made prior to the year 2000?

Write sample spaces for the given scenarios.

31. A die is rolled and the number of dots showing is noted.

32. A color is selected from the set {red, blue, green}, and then a number is chosen from the set {10, 20, 30}.

Business *A student purchases a digital music player and installs 10 songs on the device to see how it works. The genres of the songs are rock (3 songs), pop (4 songs), and alternative (3 songs). She listens to the first two songs on shuffle mode.*

33. Write the sample space for the genre if shuffle mode picks songs at random. (*Note:* Shuffle mode is allowed to play the same song twice in a row.)

34. Are the outcomes in the sample space for Exercise 33 equally likely?

Business *A customer wants to purchase a computer and printer. She has narrowed her selection among 2 Dell models, 1 Gateway model, and 2 HP models for the computer and 2 Epson models and 3 HP models for the printer.*

35. Write the sample space for the brands among which she can choose for the computer and printer.

36. Are the outcomes in the sample space for Exercise 35 equally likely?

Business *A company sells computers and copiers. Let E be the event "a customer buys a computer," and let F be the event "a customer buys a copier." In Exercises 37 and 38, write each of the given scenarios, using $\cap$, $\cup$, or ' as necessary.*

37. A customer buys neither a computer nor a copier.

38. A customer buys at least one computer or copier.

39. A student gives the answer to a probability problem as 6/5. Explain why this answer must be incorrect.

40. Describe what is meant by disjoint sets, and give an example.

41. Describe what is meant by mutually exclusive events, and give an example.

42. How are disjoint sets and mutually exclusive events related?

Finance *The Standard and Poor's 500 index had the following allocations, as of December 31, 2008. (Data from: www. standardandpoors.com.)*

Sector	Percent
Consumer Discretionary	11.87
Consumer Staples	10.84
Energy	10.58
Financials	16.46
Health Care	12.63
Industrials	10.01
Information Technology	17.93
Materials	3.38
Telecommunication Services	2.93
Utilities	3.39

Find the probability that a company chosen at random from the S&P 500 was from the given sectors.

43. Consumer Discretionary or Consumer Staples

44. Information Technology or Telecommunication Services

Finance *The sector weightings for the investments in the American Century Growth Fund as of May 13, 2013 are presented in the following table. (Data from: www.americancentury. com.)*

Sector	Percent
Information Technology	28.33
Consumer Discretionary	16.04
Consumer Staples	13.79
Health Care	13.50
Industrials	13.43
Energy	4.99
Financials	4.55
Materials	3.57
Utilities	.35

Find the probability that an investment selected at random from this fund is

45. Materials or Utilities   **46.** Not in Health Care

Education *According to data from the U.S. National Center for Education Statistics, the number (in thousands) of degree awardees for the year 2011 can be summarized in the following table.*

Degree	Number (in thousands)
Associate's	895
Bachelor's	1781
Master's	730
Doctoral	77
First-professional	103

Find the probability that a graduate selected at random has the described degree.

47. Not Associate's   **48.** Bachelor's or Master's

Finance *The following table gives the number of institutions insured by the Federal Deposit Insurance Corporation (FDIC) cross-classified by asset size and institution type, as of June 30, 2012. (Data from: www2.fdic.gov/sod.)*

Asset Size	Commercial Banks	Saving Institutions	Total
Less than $25 million	319	48	367
$25 million–$49.99 million	732	99	831
$50 million–$99.99 million	1419	176	1595
$100 million–$299.99 million	2276	343	2619
$300 million–$499.99 million	613	133	746
$500 million–$999.99 million	434	122	556
$1 billion or greater	429	102	531
Total	6222	1023	7245

If a FDIC-insured institution is chosen at random, find the probability that the institution has the following characteristics.

49. $1 billion or greater in assets

50. $25 million–$49.99 million in assets and is a savings institution

51. $300 million–$499.99 million in assets and is a commercial bank

52. Less than $25 million in assets or is a savings institution

53. $1 billion or greater in assets or is a commercial bank

54. $500 million–$999.99 million in assets, given that it is a savings institution

55. $500 million–$999.99 million in assets, given that it is a commercial bank

56. Given that an institution has $1 billion or greater in assets, what is the probability that it is a savings institution?

57. Given that an institution has less than $25 million in assets, what is the probability that it is a commercial bank?

58. Given that the institution is a commercial bank, what is the probability that it has less than $25 million in assets?

Health *The partial table shows the four possible (equally likely) combinations when both parents are carriers of the sickle-cell anemia trait. Each carrier parent has normal cells (N) and trait cells (T).*

		2nd Parent	
		N_2	T_2
1st Parent	N_1		N_1T_2
	T_1		

59. Complete the table.

60. If the disease occurs only when two trait cells combine, find the probability that a child born to these parents will have sickle-cell anemia.

61. Find the probability that the child will carry the trait, but not have the disease, if a normal cell combines with a trait cell.

62. Find the probability that the child neither is a carrier nor has the disease.

Find the probabilities for the given sums when two fair dice are rolled.

63. 8   **64.** No more than 4

65. At least 9   **66.** Odd and greater than 8

67. 2, given that the sum is less than 4

68. 7, given that at least one die shows a 4

Suppose $P(E) = .62$, $P(F) = .45$, and $P(E \cap F) = .28$. Find each of the given probabilities.

69. $P(E \cup F)$ **70.** $P(E \cap F')$

71. $P(E' \cup F)$ **72.** $P(E' \cap F')$

For the events E and F, P(E) = .2, P(E|F) = .3, and P(F) = .4. Find each of the given probabilities.

73. $P(E'|F)$ **74.** $P(E|F')$

75. Define independent events, and give an example of one.

76. Are independent events always disjoint? Are they ever disjoint? Give examples.

77. **Social Science** As reported by the National Highway Traffic Safety Administration (NHSTA), in 2011, the state of Washington had the highest rate of seat belt compliance; the odds that a driver was using a seat belt were 39:1.

   (a) What is the probability that a driver in Washington in 2011 was *not* using a seat belt?

   (b) The probability of wearing a seat belt in the state of Maryland was .942. What are the odds of wearing a seat belt in Maryland?

78. **Social Science** The report cited in Exercise 77 stated that Massachusetts had the lowest rates of seat belt compliance.

   (a) The probability of a randomly selected driver in Massachusetts using a seat belt was .732. What are the odds that a driver was using a seat belt?

   (b) In North Dakota, the odds of wearing a seatbelt were 373:127. What is the probability of wearing a seat belt in North Dakota?

Business *Of the appliance repair shops listed in the phone book, 80% are competent and 20% are not. A competent shop can repair an appliance correctly 95% of the time; an incompetent shop can repair an appliance correctly 60% of the time. Suppose an appliance was repaired correctly. Find the probability that it was repaired by the given type of shop.*

79. A competent shop

80. An incompetent shop

Suppose an appliance was repaired incorrectly. Find the probability that it was repaired by the given type of shop.

81. A competent shop

82. An incompetent shop

Business *A manufacturer buys items from four different suppliers. The fraction of the total number of items that is obtained from each supplier, along with the probability that an item purchased from that supplier is defective, is shown in the following table:*

Supplier	Fraction of Total Supplied	Probability of Defective
1	.17	.04
2	.39	.02
3	.35	.07
4	.09	.03

83. Find the probability that a defective item came from supplier 4.

84. Find the probability that a defective item came from supplier 2.

Social Science *The following tables list the number of passengers who were on the Titanic and the number of passengers who survived, according to class of ticket:*[*]

	CHILDREN		WOMEN	
	On	Survived	On	Survived
First Class	6	6	144	140
Second Class	24	24	165	76
Third Class	79	27	93	80
Total	109	57	402	296

	MEN		TOTALS	
	On	Survived	On	Survived
First Class	175	57	325	203
Second Class	168	14	357	114
Third Class	462	75	634	182
Total	805	146	1316	499

Use this information to determine the given probabilities. (Round answers to three decimal places.)

85. What is the probability that a randomly selected passenger was in second class?

86. What is the overall probability of surviving?

87. What is the probability of a first-class passenger surviving?

88. What is the probability of a child who was in third class surviving?

89. Given that a survivor is from first class, what is the probability that she was a woman?

90. Given that a male has survived, what is the probability that he was in third class?

91. Are the events "third-class survival" and "male survival" independent events? What does this imply?

92. Are the events "first-class survival" and "child survival" independent events? What does this imply?

Social Science *According to data from the 2012 American Community Survey, among workers that did not work at home, the proportion that were men was 52.8%. The following table shows the percentage of males and females whose commuting times fit the various categories. (Data from: factfinder2.census.gov.)*

Travel Time to Work	Males	Females
Less than 15 minutes	25.9%	29.9%
15–29 minutes	35.4%	37.5%
30–44 minutes	21.0%	19.2%
45–59 minutes	8.2%	6.8%
60 or more minutes	9.6%	6.6%

---

[*]Sandra L. Takis, "Titanic: A Statistical Exploration," *Mathematics Teacher* 92, no. 8, (November 1999): pp. 660–664. Reprinted with permission. ©1999 by the National Council of Teachers of Mathematics. All rights reserved.

93. What is the probability that a worker commuted less than 15 minutes?

94. What is the probability that a worker commuted 60 or more minutes?

95. What is the probability that a worker is female and commutes between 30 and 44 minutes?

96. What is the probability that a worker is male and commutes between 45 and 59 minutes?

97. Given that the worker commutes 60 or more minutes, what is the probability that the worker is male?

98. Given that the worker commutes 30 to 44 minutes, what is the probability that the worker is female?

99. Given that the worker commutes 29 minutes or less, what is the probability that the worker is female?

100. Given that the worker commutes 45 minutes or more, what is the probability that the worker is male?

Case Study 8 Medical Diagnosis

When patients undergo medical testing, a positive test result for a disease or condition can be emotionally devastating. In many cases, however, testing positive does not necessarily imply that the patient actually has the disease. Bayes' formula can be very helpful in determining the probability of actually having the disease when a patient tests positive.

Let us label the event of having the disease as D and not having the disease as D'. We will denote testing positive for the disease as T and testing negative as T'. Suppose a medical test is calibrated on patients so that we know that among patients with the disease, the test is positive 99.95% of the time. (This quantity is often called the **sensitivity** of the test.) Among patients known not to have the disease, 99.90% of the time the test gave a negative result. (This quantity is often called the **specificity** of the test.) In summary, we have

Sensitivity $= P(T|D) = .9995$ and Specificity $= P(T'|D') = .9990.$

Using the complement rule, we find that the probability the test will give a negative result when a patient has the disease is

$$P(T'|D) = 1 - P(T|D) = 1 - .9995 = .0005.$$

Similarly, for those patients without the disease, the probability of testing positive is .0010, calculated by

$$P(T|D') = 1 - P(T'|D') = 1 - .9990 = .0010.$$

These results do not yet answer the question of interest: If a patient tests positive for the disease, what is the probability the patient actually has the disease? Using our notation, we want to know $P(D|T)$. There are two steps to finding this probability. The first is that we need an estimate of the prevalence of the disease in the general population. Let us assume that one person in a thousand has the disease. We can then calculate that

$$P(D) = \frac{1}{1000} = .001 \quad \text{and} \quad P(D') = 1 - .001 \doteq .999.$$

With this information, and the previous results from testing, we can now use Bayes' formula to find $P(D|T)$:

$$P(D|T) = \frac{P(D)P(T|D)}{P(D)P(T|D) + P(D')P(T|D')}.$$

Using $P(D) = .001, P(D') = .999$, the sensitivity $P(T|D) = .9995$ and the complement to the specificity $P(T|D') = .0010$, we have

$$P(D|T) = \frac{(.001)(.9995)}{(.001)(.9995) + (.999)(.0010)} = \frac{.0009995}{.0019985} \approx .5001.$$

Hence, the probability the patient actually has the disease after testing positive for the disease is only about .5. This is approximately the same probability as guessing "heads" when flipping a coin. It seems paradoxical that a test which has such high sensitivity (in this case, .9995) and specificity (in this case, .999) could lead to a probability of merely .5 that a person who tests positive for the disease actually has the disease. This is why it is imperative to have confirmatory tests run after testing positive.

The other factor in the calculation is the prevalence of the disease among the general population. In our example, we used $P(D) = .001$. Often, it is very difficult to know how prevalent a disease is among the general population. If the disease is more prevalent, such as 1 in 100, or $P(D) = .01$, we find the probability of a patient's having the disease, given that the patient tests positive, as

$$P(D|T) = \frac{(.01)(.9995)}{(.01)(.9995) + (.99)(.0010)} = \frac{.009995}{.010985} \approx .9099.$$

So when the disease has higher prevalence, then the probability of having the disease after testing positive is also higher. If the disease has a lower prevalence (as in the case of our first example), then the probability of having the disease after testing positive could be much lower than one might otherwise think.

Exercises

1. Suppose the specificity of a test is 0.999. Find $P(T|D')$.

2. If the sensitivity of a test for a disease is .99 and the prevalence of the disease is .005, use your answer to Exercise 1 to find the probability of a patient's having the disease, given that the patient tested positive, or $P(D|T)$.

3. Recalculate your answer to Exercise 2 using a prevalence of disease of .0005.

Extended Project

For a disease or ailment of interest, find in the medical literature the prevalence of the disease or ailment among the general population, the specificity of a particular test to detect the disease or ailment, and the sensitivity of the same test. Then find the probability that a patient actually has the disease, given that the patient tested positive with the particular test. Did your results surprise you? Why or why not?

Counting, Probability Distributions, and Further Topics in Probability

9 CHAPTER

Probability has applications to quality control in manufacturing and to decision making in business. It plays a role in testing new medications, in evaluating DNA evidence in criminal trials, and in a host of other situations. See Exercises 41–43 on pages 473–474. Sophisticated counting techniques are often necessary for determining the probabilities used in these applications. See Exercises 29–30 on page 498.

Probability distributions enable us to compute the "average value" or "expected outcome" when an experiment or process is repeated a number of times. These distributions are introduced in Section 9.1 and used in Sections 9.4 and 9.6. The other focus of this chapter is the development of effective ways to count the possible outcomes of an experiment without actually listing them all (which can be *very* tedious when large numbers are involved). These counting techniques are introduced in Section 9.2 and are used to find probabilities throughout the rest of the chapter.

9.1 Probability Distributions and Expected Value

Probability distributions were introduced briefly in Section 8.4. Now we take a more complete look at them. In this section, we shall see that the *expected value* of a probability distribution is a type of average. A probability distribution depends on the idea of a *random variable*, so we begin with that.

Random Variables

One of the questions asked in the 2010 National Health and Nutrition Examination Study (NHANES) had to do with respondents' daily hours of TV or video use. The answer to that question, which we will label x, is one of the numbers 0 through 6 (corresponding to the numbers of hours of use). Since the value of x is random, x is called a random variable.

> ### Random Variable
>
> A **random variable** is a function that assigns a real number to each outcome of an experiment.

The following table gives each possible outcome of the study question on TV and video use together with the probability $P(x)$ of each outcome x. (Data from: www.cdc.gov/nchs/nhanes.htm.)

x	0	1	2	3	4	5	6
$P(x)$	.13	.24	.33	.14	.07	.07	.02

A table that lists all the outcomes with the corresponding probabilities is called a **probability distribution.** The sum of the probabilities in a probability distribution must always equal 1. (The sum in some distributions may vary slightly from 1 because of rounding.)

Instead of writing the probability distribution as a table, we could write the same information as a set of ordered pairs:

$$\{(0, .13), (1, .24), (2, .33), (3, .14), (4, .07), (5, .07), (6, .02)\}.$$

There is just one probability for each value of the random variable.

The information in a probability distribution is often displayed graphically as a special kind of bar graph called a **histogram.** The bars of a histogram all have the same width, usually 1 unit. The heights of the bars are determined by the probabilities. A histogram for the data in the probability distribution presented above is given in Figure 9.1. A histogram shows important characteristics of a distribution that may not be readily apparent in tabular form, such as the relative sizes of the probabilities and any symmetry in the distribution.

Figure 9.1

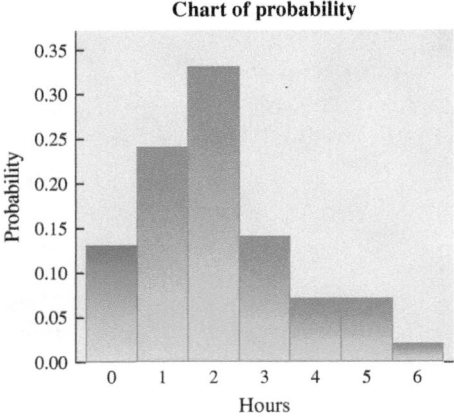

Figure 9.2

The area of the bar above $x = 0$ in Figure 9.1 is the product of 1 and .13, or $1 \cdot .13 = .13$. Since each bar has a width of 1, its area is equal to the probability that corresponds to its x-value. The probability that a particular value will occur is thus given by the area of the appropriate bar of the graph. For example, the probability that one or more hours are spent watching TV or a video is the sum of the areas for $x = 1$, $x = 2$, $x = 3$, $x = 4$, $x = 5$, and $x = 6$. This area, shown in red in Figure 9.2 on the previous page, corresponds to .87 of the total area, since

$$P(x \geq 1) = P(x = 1) + P(x = 2) + P(x = 3) + P(x = 4)$$
$$+ P(x = 5) + P(x = 6)$$
$$= .24 + .33 + .14 + .07 + .07 + .02$$
$$= .87.$$

Example 1

(a) Give the probability distribution for the number of heads showing when two coins are tossed.

Solution Let x represent the random variable "number of heads." Then x can take on the value 0, 1, or 2. Now find the probability of each outcome. When two coins are tossed, the sample space is {TT, TH, HT, HH}. So the probability of getting one head is $2/4 = 1/2$. Similar analysis of the other cases produces this table.

x	0	1	2
$P(x)$	1/4	1/2	1/4

(b) Draw a histogram for the distribution in the table. Find the probability that at least one coin comes up heads.

Solution The histogram is shown in Figure 9.3. The portion in red represents

$$P(x \geq 1) = P(x = 1) + P(x = 2)$$
$$= \frac{3}{4}. \quad \checkmark 1$$

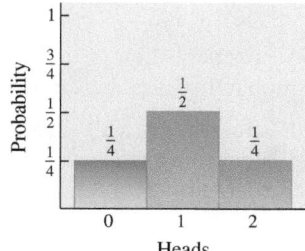

Figure 9.3

✓ Checkpoint 1

(a) Give the probability distribution for the number of heads showing when three coins are tossed.

(b) Draw a histogram for the distribution in part (a). Find the probability that no more than one coin comes up heads.

Answers to Checkpoint exercises are found at the end of the section.

TECHNOLOGY TIP Virtually all graphing calculators can produce histograms. The procedures differ on various calculators, but you usually are required to enter the outcomes in one list and the corresponding frequencies in a second list. For specific details, check your instruction manual under "statistics graphs" or "statistical plotting." To get the histogram in Figure 9.3 with a TI-84+ calculator, we entered the outcomes 0, 1, and 2 in the first list and entered the probabilities .25, .5, and .25 in a second list. Two versions of the histogram are shown in Figure 9.4. They differ slightly because different viewing windows were used. With some calculators, the probabilities must be entered as integers, so make the entries in the second list 1, 2, and 1 (corresponding to 1/4, 2/4, and 1/4, respectively), and use a window with $0 \leq y \leq 4$.

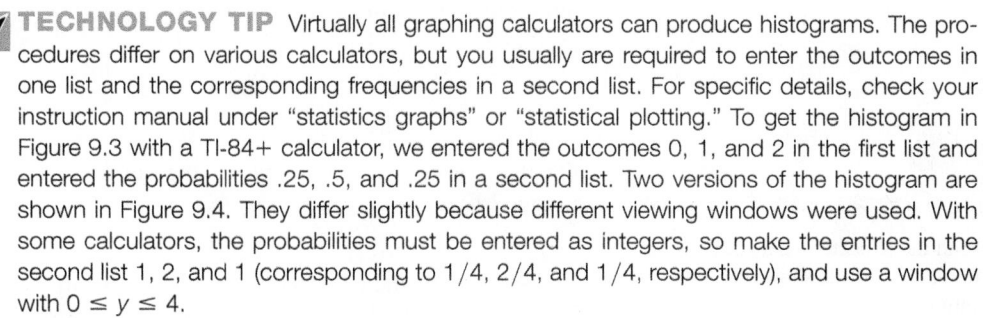

Figure 9.4

Expected Value

In working with probability distributions, it is useful to have a concept of the typical or average value that the random variable takes on. In Example 1, for instance, it seems reasonable that, on the average, one head shows when two coins are tossed. This does not tell what will happen the next time we toss two coins; we may get two heads, or we may get none. If we tossed two coins many times, however, we would expect that, in the long run, we would average about one head for each toss of two coins.

A way to solve such problems in general is to imagine flipping two coins 4 times. Based on the probability distribution in Example 1, we would expect that 1 of the 4 times we would get 0 heads, 2 of the 4 times we would get 1 head, and 1 of the 4 times we would get 2 heads. The total number of heads we would get, then, is

$$0 \cdot 1 + 1 \cdot 2 + 2 \cdot 1 = 4.$$

The expected number of heads per toss is found by dividing the total number of heads by the total number of tosses:

$$\frac{0 \cdot 1 + 1 \cdot 2 + 2 \cdot 1}{4} = 0 \cdot \frac{1}{4} + 1 \cdot \frac{1}{2} + 2 \cdot \frac{1}{4} = 1.$$

Notice that the expected number of heads turns out to be the sum of the three values of the random variable x, multiplied by their corresponding probabilities. We can use this idea to define the *expected value* of a random variable as follows.

Expected Value

Suppose that the random variable x can take on the n values $x_1, x_2, x_3, \ldots, x_n$. Suppose also that the probabilities that these values occur are, respectively, $p_1, p_2, p_3, \ldots, p_n$. Then the **expected value** of the random variable is

$$E(x) = x_1 p_1 + x_2 p_2 + x_3 p_3 + \cdots + x_n p_n.$$

Example 2 **Social Science** In the example with the TV and video usage on page 466, find the expected number of hours per day of viewing.

Solution Multiply each outcome in the table on page 466 by its probability, and sum the products:

$$E(x) = 0 \cdot .13 + 1 \cdot .24 + 2 \cdot .33 + 3 \cdot .14 + 4 \cdot .07 + 5 \cdot .07 + 6 \cdot .02$$
$$= 2.07.$$

On the average, a respondent of the survey will indicate 2.07 hours of TV or video usage. ✔2

✓ **Checkpoint 2**

Find the expected value of the number of heads showing when four coins are tossed.

Physically, the expected value of a probability distribution represents a balance point. If we think of the histogram in Figure 9.1 as a series of weights with magnitudes represented by the heights of the bars, then the system would balance if supported at the point corresponding to the expected value.

Example 3 **Business** Suppose a local symphony decides to raise money by raffling off a microwave oven worth $400, a dinner for two worth $80, and two books worth $20 each. A total of 2000 tickets are sold at $1 each. Find the expected value of winning for a person who buys one ticket in the raffle.

Solution Here, the random variable represents the possible amounts of net winnings, where net winnings = amount won − cost of ticket. For example, the net winnings of the person winning the oven are $400 (amount won) − $1 (cost of ticket) = $399, and the net winnings for each losing ticket are $0 − $1 = −$1.

The net winnings of the various prizes, as well as their respective probabilities, are shown in the table below. The probability of winning $19 is 2/2000, because there are 2 prizes worth $20. (We have not reduced the fractions in order to keep all the denominators equal.) Because there are 4 winning tickets, there are 1996 losing tickets, so the probability of winning −$1 is 1996/2000.

x	$399	$79	$19	−$1
$P(x)$	1/2000	1/2000	2/2000	1996/2000

The expected winnings for a person buying one ticket are

$$399\left(\frac{1}{2000}\right) + 79\left(\frac{1}{2000}\right) + 19\left(\frac{2}{2000}\right) + (-1)\left(\frac{1996}{2000}\right) = -\frac{1480}{2000}$$
$$= -.74.$$

On average, a person buying one ticket in the raffle will lose $.74, or 74¢.

It is not possible to lose 74¢ in this raffle: Either you lose $1, or you win a prize worth $400, $80, or $20, minus the $1 you paid to play. But if you bought tickets in many such raffles over a long time, you would lose 74¢ per ticket, on average. It is important to note that the expected value of a random variable may be a number that can never occur in any one trial of the experiment.

✓ Checkpoint 3

Suppose you buy 1 of 10,000 tickets at $1 each in a lottery where the prize is $5,000. What are your expected net winnings? What does this answer mean?

📄 **NOTE** An alternative way to compute expected value in this and other such examples is to calculate the expected amount won and then subtract the cost of the ticket afterward. The amount won is either $400 (with probability 1/2000), $80 (with probability 1/2000), $20 (with probability 2/2000), or $0 (with probability 1996/2000). The expected winnings for a person buying one ticket are then

$$400\left(\frac{1}{2000}\right) + 80\left(\frac{1}{2000}\right) + 20\left(\frac{2}{2000}\right) + 0\left(\frac{1996}{2000}\right) - 1 = -\frac{1480}{2000}$$
$$= -.74.$$

Example 4   Each day, Lynette and Tanisha toss a coin to see who buys coffee (at $1.75 a cup). One tosses, while the other calls the outcome. If the person who calls the outcome is correct, the other buys the coffee; otherwise the caller pays. Find Lynette's expected winnings.

Solution   Assume that an honest coin is used, that Tanisha tosses the coin, and that Lynette calls the outcome. The possible results and corresponding probabilities are shown in the following table:

	Possible Results			
Result of Toss	Heads	Heads	Tails	Tails
Call	Heads	Tails	Heads	Tails
Caller Wins?	Yes	No	No	Yes
Probability	1/4	1/4	1/4	1/4

Lynette wins a $1.75 cup of coffee whenever the results and calls match, and she loses $1.75 when there is no match. Her expected winnings are

$$1.75\left(\frac{1}{4}\right) + (-1.75)\left(\frac{1}{4}\right) + (-1.75)\left(\frac{1}{4}\right) + 1.75\left(\frac{1}{4}\right) = 0.$$

✓ Checkpoint 4

Find Tanisha's expected winnings.

On the average, over the long run, Lynette breaks even.

A game with an expected value of 0 (such as the one in Example 4) is called a **fair game.** Casinos do not offer fair games. If they did, they would win (on the average) $0 and have a hard time paying their employees! Casino games have expected winnings for the house that vary from 1.5 cents per dollar to 60 cents per dollar. The next example examines the popular game of roulette.

Example 5 **Business** As we saw in Chapter 8, an American roulette wheel has 38 slots. Two of the slots are marked 0 and 00 and are colored green. The remaining slots are numbered 1–36 and are colored red and black (18 slots are red and 18 slots are black). One simple wager is to bet $1 on the color red. If the marble lands in a red slot, the player gets his or her dollar back, plus $1 of winnings. Find the expected winnings for a $1 bet on red.

Solution For this bet, there are only two possible outcomes: winning or losing. The random variable has outcomes $+1$ if the marble lands in a red slot and -1 if it does not. We need to find the probability for these two outcomes. Since there are 38 total slots, 18 of which are colored red, the probability of winning a dollar is $18/38$. The player will lose if the marble lands in any of the remaining 20 slots, so the probability of losing the dollar is $20/38$. Thus, the probability distribution is

x	-1	$+1$
$P(x)$	$\dfrac{20}{38}$	$\dfrac{18}{38}$

The expected winnings are

$$E(x) = -1\left(\frac{20}{38}\right) + 1\left(\frac{18}{38}\right) = -\frac{2}{38} \approx -.053.$$

The winnings on a dollar bet for red average out to losing about a nickel on every spin of the roulette wheel. In other words, a casino earns, on average, 5.3 cents on every dollar bet on red. ✓5

Exercises 17–20 at the end of the section ask you to find the expected winnings for other bets on games of chance. The idea of expected value can be very useful in decision making, as shown by the next example.

Example 6 **Finance** Suppose that, at age 50, you receive a letter from Mutual of Mauritania Insurance Company. According to the letter, you must tell the company immediately which of the following two options you will choose: Take $50,000 at age 60 (if you are alive, and $0 otherwise), or take $65,000 at age 70 (again, if you are alive, and $0 otherwise). Based *only* on the idea of expected value, which should you choose?

Solution Life insurance companies have constructed elaborate tables showing the probability of a person living a given number of years into the future. From a recent such table, the probability of living from age 50 to age 60 is .88, while the probability of living from age 50 to 70 is .64. The expected values of the two options are as follows.

First Option: $(50,000)(.88) + (0)(.12) = 44,000;$
Second Option: $(65,000)(.64) + (0)(.36) = 41,600.$

Strictly on the basis of expected value, choose the first option. ✓6

✓ **Checkpoint 5**

A gambling game requires a $5 bet. If the player wins, she gets $1000, but if she loses, she loses her $5. The probability of winning is .001. What are the expected winnings of this game?

✓ **Checkpoint 6**

After college, a person is offered two jobs. With job *A*, after five years, there is a 50% chance of making $60,000 per year and a 50% chance of making $45,000. With job *B*, after five years, there is a 30% chance of making $80,000 per year and a 70% chance of making $35,000. Based strictly on expected value, which job should be taken?

Example 7 Social Science The table gives the probability distribution for the number of children of respondents to the 2012 General Social Survey, for those with 7 or fewer children. (Data from: www.norc.org/gss+website.)

x	0	1	2	3	4	5	6	7
$P(x)$	.275	.141	.292	.155	.086	.028	.017	.006

Find the expected value for the number of children.

Solution Using the formula for the expected value, we have

$$E(x) = 0(.275) + 1(.141) + 2(.292) + 3(.155)$$
$$+ 4(.086) + 5(.028) + 6(.017) + 7(.006)$$
$$= 1.818.$$

For those respondents with 7 or fewer children, the number of children, on average, is 1.818.

9.1 Exercises

For each of the experiments described, let x determine a random variable and use your knowledge of probability to prepare a probability distribution. (Hint: Use a tree diagram.)

1. Four children are born, and the number of boys is noted. (Assume an equal chance of a boy or a girl for each birth.)

2. Two dice are rolled, and the total number of dots is recorded.

3. Three cards are drawn from a deck. The number of Queens are counted.

4. Two names are drawn from a hat, signifying who should go pick up pizza. Three of the names are on the swim team and two are not. The number of swimmers selected is counted.

Draw a histogram for each of the given exercises, and shade the region that gives the indicated probability. (See Example 1.)

5. Exercise 1; $P(x \le 2)$

6. Exercise 2; $P(x \ge 11)$

7. Exercise 3; $P(\text{at least one queen})$

8. Exercise 4; $P(\text{fewer than two swimmers})$

Find the expected value for each random variable. (See Example 2.)

9.
x	1	3	5	7
$P(x)$	.1	.5	.2	.2

10.
y	0	15	30	40
$P(y)$	.15	.20	.40	.25

11.
z	0	2	4	8	16
$P(z)$	.21	.24	.21	.17	.17

12.
x	5	10	15	20	25
$P(x)$	.40	.30	.15	.10	.05

Find the expected values for the random variables x whose probability functions are graphed.

13.

14.

15.

16.

Find the expected winnings for the games of chance described in Exercises 17–20. (See Example 5.)

17. In one form of roulette, you bet $1 on "even." If one of the 18 positive even numbers comes up, you get your dollar back, plus another one. If one of the 20 other numbers (18 odd, 0, and 00) comes up, you lose your dollar.

18. Repeat Exercise 17 if there are only 19 noneven numbers (no 00).

19. *Numbers* is a game in which you bet $1 on any three-digit number from 000 to 999. If your number comes up, you get $500.

20. In one form of the game Keno, the house has a pot containing 80 balls, each marked with a different number from 1 to 80. You buy a ticket for $1 and mark one of the 80 numbers on it. The house then selects 20 numbers at random. If your number is among the 20, you get $3.20 (for a net winning of $2.20).

21. Business An online gambling site offers a first prize of $50,000 and two second prizes of $10,000 each for registered users when they place a bet. A random bet will be selected over a 24-hour period. Two million bets are received in the contest. Find the expected winnings if you can place one registered bet of $1 in the given period.

22. Business An online gambling site offers a lottery with a first prize of $25,000, a second prize of $10,000, and a third prize of $5000. It takes $5 to enter and a winner is selected at random. What are the expected winnings if 20,000 people enter the lottery?

Business *A contest at a fast-food restaurant offered the following cash prizes and probabilities of winning when one buys a large order of French fries for $1.89:*

Prize	Probability
$100,000	1/8,504,860
$50,000	1/302,500
$10,000	1/282,735
$1000	1/153,560
$100	1/104,560
$25	1/9,540

23. Find the expected winnings if the player buys one large order of French fries.

24. Find the expected winnings if the player buys 25 large orders of French fries in multiple visits.

25. Finance According to the Federal Deposit Insurance Corporation (FDIC), 28.3% of all U.S. households conduct some or all of their financial transactions outside of the mainstream banking system. Such people are sometimes called the "unbanked." If we select four households at random, and let x denote the number of unbanked households, the probability distribution of x is:

x	0	1	2	3	4
$P(x)$	.2643	.4173	.2470	.0650	.0064

Find the expected value for the number of unbanked households.

26. Finance Approximately 54% of U.S. residents own individual stocks, stock mutual funds, or stocks in a retirement fund. If we select five U.S. residents at random and let x denote the number who own stocks, the probability distribution of x is:

x	0	1	2	3	4	5
$P(x)$	.0206	.1209	.2838	.3332	.1956	.0459

Find the expected value for the number of U.S. residents who own stocks. (Data from: www.gallup.com.)

For Exercises 27–30, determine whether the probability distributions are valid or not. If not, explain why.

27.

x	5	10	15	20	25	30	35
$P(x)$	.01	.09	.25	.45	.05	.20	−.05

28.

x	−2	−1	0	1	2	3	4
$P(x)$	.05	.10	.75	.02	.03	.04	.01

29.

x	1	3	5	7	9	11
$P(x)$	.01	.02	.03	.04	.05	.85

30.

x	−10	−5	0	5	10
$P(x)$	.50	.10	−.20	.30	.30

For Exercises 31–35, fill in the missing value(s) to make a valid probability distribution.

31.

x	5	10	15	20	25	30
P(x)	.01	.09	.25	.45	.05	

32.

x	−3	−2	−1	0	1	2	3
P(x)		.15	.15	.15	.15	.15	.15

33.

x	10	20	30	40
P(x)	.20		.25	.30

34.

x	−50	−40	−30	−20	−10	0	10
P(x)	.05	.25	.10	.10	.05		

35.

x	1	2	3	6	12	24	48
P(x)	.10	.10	.20	.25	.05		

36. Business During the month of July, a home improvement store sold a great many air-conditioning units, but some were returned. The following table shows the probability distribution for the daily number of returns of air-conditioning units sold in July:

x	0	1	2	3	4	5
P(x)	.55	.31	.08	.04	.01	.01

Find the expected number of returns per day.

37. Finance An insurance company has written 100 policies of $15,000, 250 of $10,000, and 500 of $5000 for people age 20. If experience shows that the probability that a person will die in the next year at age 20 is .0007, how much can the company expect to pay out during the year after the policies were written?

38. Business A market researcher came upon a recent survey by the Pew Research Center that found that 47% of U.S. teenagers owned a smartphone. If six teens are selected at random, the probability distribution for x, the number of teens with smartphones, is as follows.

x	0	1	2	3	4	5	6
P(x)	.0222	.1179	.2615	.3091	.2056	.0729	.0108

Find the expected number of teens with smartphones.

39. Business In April 2013, Toyota captured 13.7% of U.S. new auto sales. If 3 new cars are selected at random, the probability distribution for x, the number of new Toyota vehicles, is given in the following table.

x	0	1	2	3
P(x)	.6427	.3061	.0486	.0026

Find the expected number of Toyota new vehicles. (Data from: www.wsj.com.)

40. Business About 65.4 percent of Americans own homes. If 5 Americans are selected at random, the probability distribution for x, the number of Americans who own homes, is given in the following table.

x	0	1	2	3	4	5
P(x)	.0050	.0469	.1772	.3349	.3165	.1196

Find the expected number of Americans who own homes. (Data from: U.S. Census Bureau.)

41. Business Levi Strauss and Company uses expected value to help its salespeople rate their accounts.[*] For each account, a salesperson estimates potential additional volume and the probability of getting it. The product of these figures gives the expected value of the potential, which is added to the existing volume. The totals are then classified as A, B, or C as follows: $40,000 or below, class C; above $40,000, up to and including $55,000, class B; above $55,000, class A. Complete the chart.

Account Number	Existing Volume	Potential Additional Volume	Probability of Additional Volume	Expected Value of Potential	Existing Volume + Expected Value of Potential	Class
1	$15,000	$10,000	.25	$2,500	$17,500	C
2	40,000	0	—	—	40,000	C
3	20,000	10,000	.20			
4	50,000	10,000	.10			
5	5,000	50,000	.50			
6	0	100,000	.60			
7	30,000	20,000	.80			

42. According to Len Pasquarelli, in the first 10 games of the 2004 professional football season in the United States, two-point conversions were successful 51.2% of the time.[†] We can compare this rate with the historical success rate of extra-point kicks of 94%.[‡]

---

[*]This example was supplied by James McDonald, Levi Strauss and Company, San Francisco.

[†]Len Pasquarelli, "Teams More Successful Going for Two," November 18, 2004, www.espn.com.

[‡]David Leonhardt, "In Football, 6 + 2 Often Equals 6," *New York Times*, January 16, 2000, p. 4-2.

(a) Calculate the expected value of each strategy.

(b) Over the long run, which strategy will maximize the number of points scored?

(c) From this information, should a team always use only one strategy? Explain.

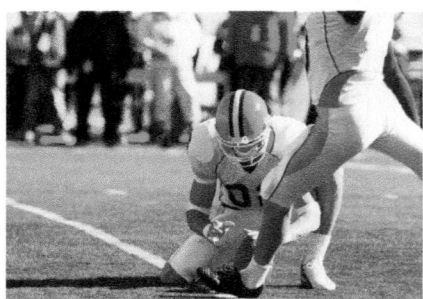

43. Health Two antibiotics are used to treat common infections. Researchers wish to compare the two antibiotics—Drug A and Drug B—for their cost effectiveness. Drug A is inexpensive, safe, and effective. Drug B is also safe. However, it is considerably more expensive and is generally more effective. Use the given tree diagram (in which costs are estimated as the total cost of the medication, a visit to a medical office, and hours of lost work) to complete the following tasks:

(a) Find the expected cost of using each antibiotic to treat a middle-ear infection.

(b) To minimize the total expected cost, which antibiotic should be chosen?

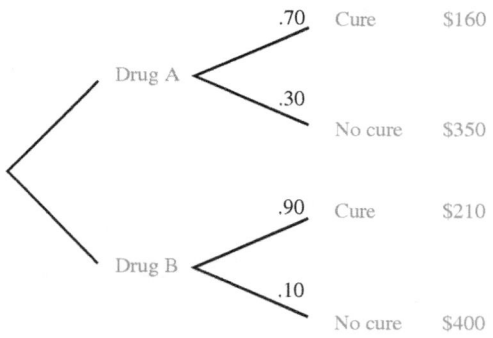

44. Physical Science One of the few methods that can be used in an attempt to cut the severity of a hurricane is to *seed* the storm. In this process, silver iodide crystals are dropped into the storm in order to decrease the wind speed. Unfortunately, silver iodide crystals sometimes cause the storm to *increase* its speed. Wind speeds may also increase or decrease even with no seeding. Use the given tree diagram to complete the following tasks.

(a) Find the expected amount of damage under each of the options, "seed" and "do not seed."

(b) To minimize total expected damage, which option should be chosen?

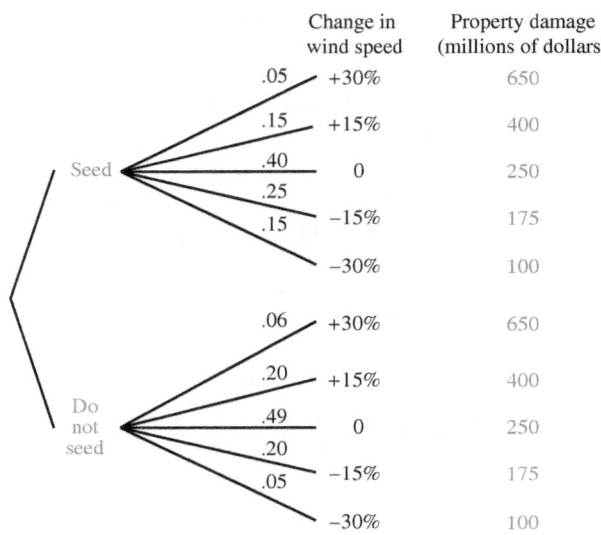

45. In the 2008 Wimbledon Championships, Roger Federer and Rafeal Nadal played in the finals. The prize money for the winner was £750,000 (British pounds sterling), and the prize money for the runner-up was £350,000. Find the expected winnings for Rafeal Nadal if

(a) we assume both players had an equal chance of winning;

(b) we use the players' prior head-to-head match record, whereby Nadal had a .67 probability of winning.

46. Bryan Miller has two cats and a dog. Each pet has a 35% probability of climbing into the chair in which Bryan is sitting, independently of how many pets are already in the chair with Bryan.

(a) Find the probability distribution for the number of pets in the chair with Bryan. (*Hint:* List the sample space.)

(b) Use the probability distribution in part (a) to find the expected number of pets in the chair with Bryan.

✓**Checkpoint Answers**

1. (a)

x	$P(x)$
0	1/8
1	3/8
2	3/8
3	1/8

(b) $1/2$

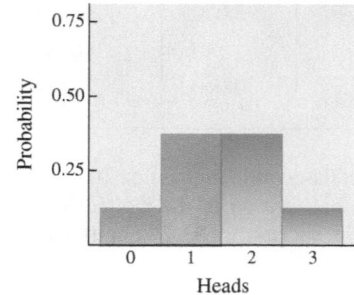

2. 2

3. −$.50. On the average, you lose $.50 per ticket purchased.

4. 0

5. −$4

6. Job *A* has an expected salary of $52,500, and job *B* has an expected salary of $48,500. Take job *A*.

9.2 The Multiplication Principle, Permutations, and Combinations

Figure 9.5

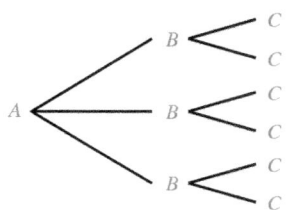

Figure 9.6

We begin with a simple example. If there are three roads from town *A* to town *B* and two roads from town *B* to town *C*, in how many ways can someone travel from *A* to *C* by way of *B*? We can solve this simple problem with the help of Figure 9.5, which lists all the possible ways to go from *A* to *C*.

The possible ways to go from *A* through *B* to *C* are a1, a2, b1, b2, c1, and c2. So there are 6 possible ways. Note that 6 is the product of $3 \cdot 2$, 3 is the number of ways to go from *A* to *B*, and 2 is the number of ways to go from *B* to *C*.

Another way to solve this problem is to use a tree diagram, as shown in Figure 9.6. This diagram shows that, for each of the 3 roads from *A*, there are 2 different routes leading from *B* to *C*, making $3 \cdot 2 = 6$ different ways.

This example is an illustration of the *multiplication principle*.

Multiplication Principle

Suppose *n* choices must be made, with

$$m_1 \text{ ways to make choice 1,}$$
$$m_2 \text{ ways to make choice 2,}$$
$$\vdots$$
$$m_n \text{ ways to make choice } n.$$

Then there are

$$m_1 \cdot m_2 \cdot \cdots \cdot m_n$$

different ways to make the entire sequence of choices.

Example 1   Suppose Angela has 9 skirts, 8 blouses, and 13 different pairs of shoes. If she is willing to wear any combination, how many different skirt–blouse–shoe choices does she have?

Solution   By the multiplication principle, there are 9 skirt choices, 8 blouse choices, and 13 shoe choices, for a total of $9 \cdot 8 \cdot 13 = 936$ skirt–blouse–shoe outfits.

Example 2   **Business**   In May 2013, there were 731 sink faucets, 543 bath vanities, and 607 medicine cabinets available to order at the Home Depot® Web site. How many different ways could you buy one sink faucet, bath vanity, and medicine cabinet?

Solution   A tree (or other diagram) would be far too complicated to use here, but the multiplication principle easily answers the question. There are

$$731 \cdot 543 \cdot 607 = 240,938,331$$

ways.

> **Example 3**   A combination lock can be set to open to any 3-letter sequence.
>
> **(a)** How many sequences are possible?
>
> **Solution**   Since there are 26 letters of the alphabet, there are 26 choices for each of the 3 letters, and, by the multiplication principle, $26 \cdot 26 \cdot 26 = 17{,}576$ different sequences.
>
> **(b)** How many sequences are possible if no letter is repeated?
>
> **Solution**   There are 26 choices for the first letter. It cannot be used again, so there are 25 choices for the second letter and then 24 choices for the third letter. Consequently, the number of such sequences is $26 \cdot 25 \cdot 24 = 15{,}600.$ ✓₁

✓ **Checkpoint 1**

(a) In how many ways can 6 business tycoons line up their golf carts at the country club?

(b) How many ways can 4 pupils be seated in a row with 4 seats?

Factorial Notation

The use of the multiplication principle often leads to products such as $5 \cdot 4 \cdot 3 \cdot 2 \cdot 1$, the product of all the natural numbers from 5 down to 1. If n is a natural number, the symbol $n!$ (read "n *factorial*") denotes the product of all the natural numbers from n down to 1. The factorial is an algebraic shorthand. For example, instead of writing $5 \cdot 4 \cdot 3 \cdot 2 \cdot 1$, we simply write $5!$. If $n = 1$, this formula is understood to give $1! = 1$.

> ### *n*-Factorial
>
> For any natural number n,
>
> $$n! = n(n - 1)(n - 2) \cdots (3)(2)(1).$$
>
> By definition, $0! = 1$.

Note that $6! = 6 \cdot 5 \cdot 4 \cdot 3 \cdot 2 \cdot 1 = 6 \cdot (5 \cdot 4 \cdot 3 \cdot 2 \cdot 1) = 6 \cdot 5!$. Similarly, the definition of $n!$ shows that

$$n! = n \cdot (n - 1)!.$$

One reason that $0!$ is defined to be 1 is to make the preceding formula valid when $n = 1$, for when $n = 1$, we have $1! = 1$ and $1 \cdot (1 - 1)! = 1 \cdot 0! = 1 \cdot 1 = 1$, so $n! = n \cdot (n - 1)!$. ✓₂

✓ **Checkpoint 2**

Evaluate:

(a) $4!$

(b) $6!$

(c) $1!$

(d) $6!/4!$

Almost all calculators have an $n!$ key. A calculator with a 10-digit display and scientific-notation capability will usually give the exact value of $n!$ for $n \leq 13$ and approximate values of $n!$ for $14 \leq n \leq 69$. The value of $70!$ is approximately $1.198 \cdot 10^{100}$, which is too large for most calculators. So how would you simplify $\dfrac{100!}{98!}$? Depending on the type of calculator, there may be an overflow problem. The next two examples show how to avoid this problem.

📈 **TECHNOLOGY TIP**
The factorial key on a graphing calculator is usually located in the PRB or PROB submenu of the MATH or OPTN menu.

> **Example 4**   Evaluate
>
> $$\frac{100!}{98!}.$$
>
> **Solution**   We use the fact that $n! = n \cdot (n - 1)!$ several times:
>
> $$\frac{100!}{98!} = \frac{100 \cdot 99!}{98!} = \frac{100 \cdot 99 \cdot 98!}{98!} = 100 \cdot 99 = 9900.$$

Example 5   Evaluate

$$\frac{5!}{2!\,3!}.$$

Solution $\dfrac{5!}{2!\,3!} = \dfrac{5 \cdot 4!}{2!\,3!} = \dfrac{5 \cdot 4 \cdot 3!}{2!\,3!} = \dfrac{5 \cdot 4}{2 \cdot 1} = 10.$

Example 6   Morse code uses a sequence of dots and dashes to represent letters and words. How many sequences are possible with at most 3 symbols?

Solution   "At most 3" means "1 or 2 or 3." Each symbol may be either a dot or a dash. Thus, the following numbers of sequences are possible in each case:

Number of Symbols	Number of Sequences
1	2
2	$2 \cdot 2 = 4$
3	$2 \cdot 2 \cdot 2 = 8$

Altogether, $2 + 4 + 8 = 14$ different sequences of at most 3 symbols are possible. Because there are 26 letters in the alphabet, some letters must be represented by sequences of 4 symbols in Morse code. ☑3

✓ **Checkpoint 3**

How many Morse code sequences are possible with at most 4 symbols?

Permutations

A **permutation** of a set of elements is an ordering of the elements. For instance, there are six permutations (orderings) of the letters A, B, and C, namely,

$$ABC, ACB, BAC, BCA, CAB, \text{ and } CBA,$$

as you can easily verify. As this listing shows, order counts when determining the number of permutations of a set of elements. By saying "order counts," we mean that the event ABC is indeed distinct from CBA or any other ordering of the three letters. We can use the multiplication principle to determine the number of possible permutations of any set.

Example 7   How many batting orders are possible for a 9-person baseball team?

Solution   There are 9 possible choices for the first batter, 8 possible choices for the second batter, 7 for the third batter, and so on, down to the eighth batter (2 possible choices) and the ninth batter (1 possibility). So the total number of batting orders is

$$9 \cdot 8 \cdot 7 \cdot 6 \cdot 5 \cdot 4 \cdot 3 \cdot 2 \cdot 1 = 362{,}880.$$

In other words, the number of permutations of a 9-person set is 9!.

The argument in Example 7 applies to any set, leading to the conclusion that follows.

The number of permutations of an n element set is $n!$.

Sometimes we want to order only some of the elements in a set, rather than all of them.

Checkpoint 4

How many ways can a merchant with limited space display 4 fabric samples side by side from her collection of 8?

Example 8 A teacher has 5 books and wants to display 3 of them side by side on her desk. How many arrangements of 3 books are possible?

Solution The teacher has 5 ways to fill the first space, 4 ways to fill the second space, and 3 ways to fill the third space. Because she wants only 3 books on the desk, there are only 3 spaces to fill, giving $5 \cdot 4 \cdot 3 = 60$ possible arrangements. ✔4

In Example 8, we say that the possible arrangements are *the permutations of 5 things taken 3 at a time*, and we denote the number of such permutations by $_5P_3$. In other words, $_5P_3 = 60$. More generally, an ordering of r elements from a set of n elements is called a **permutation of n things taken r at a time**, and the number of such permutations is denoted $_nP_r$.[*] To see how to compute this number, look at the answer in Example 8, which can be expressed like this:

$$_5P_3 = 5 \cdot 4 \cdot 3 = 5 \cdot 4 \cdot 3 \cdot \frac{2 \cdot 1}{2 \cdot 1} = \frac{5 \cdot 4 \cdot 3 \cdot 2 \cdot 1}{2 \cdot 1} = \frac{5!}{2!} = \frac{5!}{(5-3)!}.$$

A similar analysis in the general case leads to this useful fact:

Permutations

If $_nP_r$ (where $r \leq n$) is the number of permutations of n elements taken r at a time, then

$$_nP_r = \frac{n!}{(n-r)!}.$$

TECHNOLOGY TIP The permutation function on a graphing calculator is in the same menu as the factorial key. For large values of n and r, the calculator display for $_nP_r$ may be an approximation.

To find $_nP_r$, we can either use the preceding rule or apply the multiplication principle directly, as the next example shows.

Figure 9.7

Example 9 Early in 2012, 7 candidates sought the Republican nomination for president at the Iowa caucus. In a poll, how many ways could voters rank their first, second, and third choices?

Solution This is the same as finding the number of permutations of 7 elements taken 3 at a time. Since there are 3 choices to be made, the multiplication principle gives $_7P_3 = 7 \cdot 6 \cdot 5 = 210$. Alternatively, by the formula for $_nP_r$,

$$_7P_3 = \frac{7!}{(7-3)!} = \frac{7!}{4!} = \frac{7 \cdot 6 \cdot 5 \cdot 4 \cdot 3 \cdot 2 \cdot 1}{4 \cdot 3 \cdot 2 \cdot 1} = 7 \cdot 6 \cdot 5 = 210.$$

Figure 9.7 shows this result on a TI-84+ graphing calculator. ✔5

Checkpoint 5

Find the number of permutations of

(a) 5 things taken 2 at a time;

(b) 9 things taken 3 at a time.

Find each of the following:

(c) $_3P_1$;

(d) $_7P_3$;

(e) $_{12}P_2$.

Example 10 In a college admissions forum, 5 female and 4 male sophomore panelists discuss their college experiences with high school seniors.

(a) In how many ways can the panelists be seated in a row of 9 chairs?

---
[*]Another notation that is sometimes used is $P(n, r)$.

Solution   Find $_9P_9$, the total number of ways to seat 9 panelists in 9 chairs:

$$_9P_9 = \frac{9!}{(9-9)!} = \frac{9!}{0!} = \frac{9!}{1} = 9 \cdot 8 \cdot 7 \cdot 6 \cdot 5 \cdot 4 \cdot 3 \cdot 2 \cdot 1 = 362{,}880.$$

So, there are 362,880 ways to seat the 9 panelists.

(b) In how many ways can the panelists be seated if the males and females are to be alternated?

Solution   Use the multiplication principle. In order to alternate males and females, a female must be seated in the first chair (since there are 5 females and only 4 males), any of the males next, and so on. Thus, there are 5 ways to fill the first seat, 4 ways to fill the second seat, 4 ways to fill the third seat (with any of the 4 remaining females), and so on, or

$$5 \cdot 4 \cdot 4 \cdot 3 \cdot 3 \cdot 2 \cdot 2 \cdot 1 \cdot 1 = 2880.$$

So, there are 2880 ways to seat the panelists.

(c) In how many ways can the panelists be seated if the males must sit together and the females sit together?

Solution   Use the multiplication principle. We first must decide how to arrange the two groups (males and females). There are 2! ways of doing this. Next, there are 5! ways of arranging the females and 4! ways of arranging the men, for a total of

$$2! \, 5! \, 4! = 2 \cdot 120 \cdot 24 = 5760$$

ways.

✓**Checkpoint 6**

A collection of 3 paintings by one artist and 2 by another is to be displayed. In how many ways can the paintings be shown

(a) in a row?

(b) if the works of the artists are to be alternated?

(c) if one painting by each artist is displayed?

Combinations

In Example 8, we found that there are 60 ways a teacher can arrange 3 of 5 different books on a desk. That is, there are 60 permutations of 5 things taken 3 at a time. Suppose now that the teacher does not wish to arrange the books on her desk, but rather wishes to choose, at random, any 3 of the 5 books to give to a book sale to raise money for her school. In how many ways can she do this?

At first glance, we might say 60 again, but that is incorrect. The number 60 counts all possible *arrangements* of 3 books chosen from 5. However, the following arrangements, for example, would all lead to the same set of 3 books being given to the book sale:

mystery–biography–textbook	biography–textbook–mystery
mystery–textbook–biography	textbook–biography–mystery
biography–mystery–textbook	textbook–mystery–biography

The foregoing list shows 6 different *arrangements* of 3 books, but only one *subset* of 3 books. A subset of items selected *without regard to order* is called a **combination**. The number of combinations of 5 things taken 3 at a time is written $_5C_3$. Since they are subsets, combinations are *not ordered*.

To evaluate $_5C_3$, start with the $5 \cdot 4 \cdot 3$ *permutations* of 5 things taken 3 at a time. Combinations are unordered; therefore, we find the number of combinations by dividing the number of permutations by the number of ways each group of 3 can be ordered—that is, by 3!:

$$_5C_3 = \frac{5 \cdot 4 \cdot 3}{3!} = \frac{5 \cdot 4 \cdot 3}{3 \cdot 2 \cdot 1} = 10.$$

There are 10 ways that the teacher can choose 3 books at random for the book sale.

Generalizing this discussion gives the formula for the number of combinations of n elements taken r at a time, written $_nC_r$.* In general, a set of r elements can be ordered in $r!$ ways, so we divide $_nP_r$ by $r!$ to get $_nC_r$:

$$_nC_r = \frac{_nP_r}{r!}$$

$$= _nP_r \frac{1}{r!}$$

$$= \frac{n!}{(n-r)!} \cdot \frac{1}{r!} \quad \text{Definition of } _nP_r$$

$$= \frac{n!}{(n-r)!\, r!}.$$

This last form is the most useful for setting up the calculation. ✔7

✓ **Checkpoint 7**

Evaluate $\dfrac{_nP_r}{r!}$ for the given values.

(a) $n = 6, r = 2$

(b) $n = 8, r = 4$

(c) $n = 7, r = 0$

Combinations

The number of combinations of n elements taken r at a time, where $r \leq n$, is

$$_nC_r = \frac{n!}{(n-r)!r!}.$$

Example 11 From a group of 10 students, a committee is to be chosen to meet with the dean. How many different 3-person committees are possible?

Solution A committee is not ordered, so we compute

$$_{10}C_3 = \frac{10!}{(10-3)!\,3!} = \frac{10!}{7!\,3!} = \frac{10 \cdot 9 \cdot 8 \cdot 7!}{7!\,3!} = \frac{10 \cdot 9 \cdot 8}{3 \cdot 2 \cdot 1} = 120.$$

✈ **TECHNOLOGY TIP** The key for obtaining $_nC_r$ on a graphing calculator is located in the same menu as the key for obtaining $_nP_r$.

```
40 nCr 12
            5586853480
```

Figure 9.8

✓ **Checkpoint 8**

Use $\dfrac{n!}{(n-r)!\, r!}$ to evaluate $_nC_r$.

(a) $_6C_2$

(b) $_8C_4$

(c) $_7C_0$

Compare your answers with the answers to Checkpoint 7.

Example 12 In how many ways can a 12-person jury be chosen from a pool of 40 people?

Solution Since the order in which the jurors are chosen does not matter, we use combinations. The number of combinations of 40 things taken 12 at a time is

$$_{40}C_{12} = \frac{40!}{(40-12)!\,12!} = \frac{40!}{28!\,12!}.$$

Using a calculator to compute this number (Figure 9.8), we see that there are 5,586,853,480 possible ways to choose a jury. ✔8

Example 13 Three managers are to be selected from a group of 30 to work on a special project.

(a) In how many different ways can the managers be selected?

---

*Another notation that is sometimes used in place of $_nC_r$ is $\binom{n}{r}$.

Solution   Here, we wish to know the number of 3-element combinations that can be formed from a set of 30 elements. (We want combinations, not permutations, since order within the group of 3 does not matter.) So, we calculate

$$_{30}C_3 = \frac{30!}{27!\,3!} = 4060.$$

There are 4060 ways to select the project group.

(b) In how many ways can the group of 3 be selected if a certain manager must work on the project?

Solution   Since 1 manager has already been selected for the project, the problem is reduced to selecting 2 more from the remaining 29 managers:

$$_{29}C_2 = \frac{29!}{27!\,2!} = 406.$$

In this case, the project group can be selected in 406 ways.

(c) In how many ways can a nonempty group of at most 3 managers be selected from these 30 managers?

Solution   The group is to be nonempty; therefore, "at most 3" means "1 or 2 or 3." Find the number of ways for each case:

Case	Number of Ways
1	$_{30}C_1 = \dfrac{30!}{29!\,1!} = \dfrac{30 \cdot 29!}{29!\,1!} = 30$
2	$_{30}C_2 = \dfrac{30!}{28!\,2!} = \dfrac{30 \cdot 29 \cdot 28!}{28! \cdot 2 \cdot 1} = 435$
3	$_{30}C_3 = \dfrac{30!}{27!\,3!} = \dfrac{30 \cdot 29 \cdot 28 \cdot 27!}{27! \cdot 3 \cdot 2 \cdot 1} = 4060$

The total number of ways to select at most 3 managers will be the sum

$$30 + 435 + 4060 = 4525.$$

✓ **Checkpoint 9**

Five orchids from a collection of 20 are to be selected for a flower show.

(a) In how many ways can this be done?

(b) In how many different ways can the group of 5 be selected if 2 particular orchids must be included?

(c) In how many ways can at least 1 and at most 5 orchids be selected? (*Hint:* Use a calculator.)

Choosing a Method

The formulas for permutations and combinations given in this section will be very useful in solving probability problems in later sections. Any difficulty in using these formulas usually comes from being unable to differentiate among them. Both permutations and combinations give the number of ways to choose r objects from a set of n objects. The differences between permutations and combinations are outlined in the following summary.

Permutations	**Combinations**
Different orderings or arrangements of the r objects are different permutations.	Each choice or subset of r objects gives 1 combination. Order within the r objects does not matter.
$$_nP_r = \frac{n!}{(n-r)!}$$	$$_nC_r = \frac{n!}{(n-r)!\,r!}$$
Clue words: arrangement, schedule, order	Clue words: group, committee, set, sample
Order matters!	Order does not matter!

In the examples that follow, concentrate on recognizing which of the formulas should be applied.

Example 14 For each of the given problems, tell whether permutations or combinations should be used to solve the problem.

(a) How many 4-digit numbers are possible if no digits are repeated?

Solution Since changing the order of the 4 digits results in a different number, we use permutations.

(b) A sample of 3 lightbulbs is randomly selected from a batch of 15 bulbs. How many different samples are possible?

Solution The order in which the 3 lightbulbs are selected is not important. The sample is unchanged if the bulbs are rearranged, so combinations should be used.

(c) In a basketball conference with 8 teams, how many games must be played so that each team plays every other team exactly once?

Solution The selection of 2 teams for a game is an *unordered* subset of 2 from the set of 8 teams. Use combinations again.

(d) In how many ways can 4 patients be assigned to 6 hospital rooms so that each patient has a private room?

Solution The room assignments are an *ordered* selection of 4 rooms from the 6 rooms. Exchanging the rooms of any 2 patients within a selection of 4 rooms gives a different assignment, so permutations should be used. ✓10

✓**Checkpoint 10**

Solve the problems in Example 14.

Example 15 A manager must select 4 employees for promotion. Twelve employees are eligible.

(a) In how many ways can the 4 employees be chosen?

Solution Because there is no reason to consider the order in which the 4 are selected, we use combinations:

$$_{12}C_4 = \frac{12!}{4!\,8!} = 495.$$

(b) In how many ways can 4 employees be chosen (from 12) to be placed in 4 different jobs?

Solution In this case, once a group of 4 is selected, its members can be assigned in many different ways (or arrangements) to the 4 jobs. Therefore, this problem requires permutations:

$$_{12}P_4 = \frac{12!}{8!} = 11,880.$$ ✓11

✓**Checkpoint 11**

A postal worker has special-delivery mail for 7 customers.

(a) In how many ways can he arrange his schedule to deliver to all 7?

(b) In how many ways can he schedule deliveries if he can deliver to only 4 of the 7?

Example 16 **Business** Powerball is a lottery game played in 43 states (plus the District of Columbia and the U.S. Virgin Islands). For a $2 ticket, a player selects five different numbers from 1 to 59 and one powerball number from 1 to 35 (which may be the same as one of the first five chosen). A match of all six numbers wins the jackpot. How many different selections are possible?

Figure 9.9

✓**Checkpoint 12**

Under earlier Powerball rules, you had to choose five different numbers from 1 to 53 and then choose one powerball number from 1 to 42. Under those rules, how many different selections were possible?

Solution   The order in which the first five numbers are chosen does not matter. So we use combinations to find the number of combinations of 59 things taken 5 at a time—that is, $_{59}C_5$. There are 35 ways to choose one powerball number from 1 to 35. So, by the multiplication principle, the number of different selections is

$$_{59}C_5 \cdot 35 = \frac{59!}{(59-5)!\,5!} \cdot 35 = \frac{59! \cdot 35}{54!\,5!} = 175{,}223{,}510,$$

as shown in two ways on a graphing calculator in Figure 9.9. ✓₁₂

Example 17   A male student going on spring break at Daytona Beach has 8 tank tops and 12 pairs of shorts. He decides he will need 5 tank tops and 6 pairs of shorts for the trip. How many ways can he choose the tank tops and the shorts?

Solution   We can break this problem into two parts: finding the number of ways to choose the tank tops, and finding the number of ways to choose the shorts. For the tank tops, the order is not important, so we use combinations to obtain

$$_{8}C_5 = \frac{8!}{3!\,5!} = 56.$$

Likewise, order is not important for the shorts, so we use combinations to obtain

$$_{12}C_6 = \frac{12!}{6!\,6!} = 924.$$

We now know there are 56 ways to choose the tank tops and 924 ways to choose the shorts. The total number of ways to choose the tank tops and shorts can be found using the multiplication principle to obtain $56 \cdot 924 = 51{,}744.$ ✓₁₃

✓**Checkpoint 13**

Lacy wants to pack 4 of her 10 blouses and 2 of her 4 pairs of jeans for her trip to Europe. How many ways can she choose the blouses and jeans?

As Examples 16 and 17 show, often both combinations and the multiplication principle must be used in the same problem.

Example 18   To illustrate the differences between permutations and combinations in another way, suppose 2 cans of soup are to be selected from 4 cans on a shelf: noodle (N), bean (B), mushroom (M), and tomato (T). As shown in Figure 9.10(a), there are 12 ways to select 2 cans from the 4 cans if the order matters (if noodle first and bean second is considered different from bean and then noodle, for example). However, if order is unimportant, then there are 6 ways to choose 2 cans of soup from the 4, as illustrated in Figure 9.10(b).

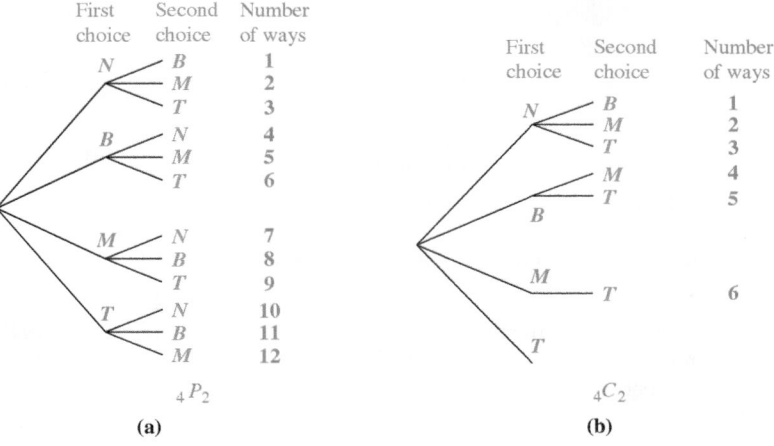

Figure 9.10

⊙ **CAUTION**   It should be stressed that not all counting problems lend themselves to either permutations or combinations.

9.2 Exercises

Evaluate the given factorials, permutations, and combinations.

1. $_4P_2$
2. $3!$
3. $_8C_5$
4. $7!$
5. $_8P_1$
6. $_7C_2$
7. $4!$
8. $_4P_4$
9. $_9C_6$
10. $_8C_2$
11. $_{13}P_3$
12. $_9P_5$

Use a calculator to find values for Exercises 13–20.

13. $_{25}P_5$
14. $_{40}P_5$
15. $_{14}P_5$
16. $_{17}P_8$
17. $_{18}C_5$
18. $_{32}C_9$
19. $_{28}C_{14}$
20. $_{35}C_{30}$

21. Some students find it puzzling that $0! = 1$, and they think that $0!$ should equal 0. If this were true, what would be the value of $_4P_4$ according to the permutations formula?

22. If you already knew the value of $8!$, how could you find the value of $9!$ quickly?

Use the multiplication principle to solve the given problems. (See Examples 1–6.)

23. **Social Science** An ancient Chinese philosophical work known as the *I Ching (Book of Changes)* is often used as an oracle from which people can seek and obtain advice. The philosophy describes the duality of the universe in terms of two primary forces: *yin* (passive, dark, receptive) and *yang* (active, light, creative). See the accompanying figure. The yin energy is represented by a broken line (– –) and the yang by a solid line (—). These lines are written on top of one another in groups of three, known as *trigrams*. For example, the trigram ☱ is called *Tui*, the Joyous, and has the image of a lake.

yin   yang

(a) How many trigrams are there altogether?

(b) The trigrams are grouped together, one on top of the other, in pairs known as hexagrams. Each hexagram represents one aspect of the *I Ching* philosophy. How many hexagrams are there?

24. **Business** How many different heating–cooling units are possible if a home owner has 3 choices for the efficiency rating of the furnace, 3 options for the fan speed, and 6 options for the air condenser?

25. **Business** An auto manufacturer produces 6 models, each available in 8 different colors, with 4 different upholstery fabrics and 3 interior colors. How many varieties of the auto are available?

26. **Business** How many different 4-letter radio station call letters can be made

(a) if the first letter must be K or W and no letter may be repeated?

(b) if repeats are allowed (but the first letter still must be K or W)?

(c) How many of the 4-letter call letters (starting with K or W) with no repeats end in R?

27. **Social Science** A Social Security number has 9 digits. How many Social Security numbers are possible? The U.S. population in 2012 was approximately 314 million. Was it possible for every U.S. resident to have a unique Social Security number? (Assume no restrictions.)

28. **Social Science** The United States Postal Service currently uses 5-digit zip codes in most areas. How many zip codes are possible if there are no restrictions on the digits used? How many would be possible if the first number could not be 0?

29. **Social Science** The Postal Service is encouraging the use of 9-digit zip codes in some areas, adding 4 digits after the usual 5-digit code. How many such zip codes are possible with no restrictions?

30. **Social Science** For many years, the state of California used 3 letters followed by 3 digits on its automobile license plates.

(a) How many different license plates are possible with this arrangement?

(b) When the state ran out of new numbers, the order was reversed to 3 digits followed by 3 letters. How many new license plate numbers were then possible?

(c) Several years ago, the numbers described in part (b) were also used up. The state then issued plates with 1 letter followed by 3 digits and then 3 letters. How many new license plate numbers will this arrangement provide?

31. **Business** A recent trip to the drug store revealed 12 different kinds of Pantene® shampoo and 10 different kinds of Pantene® conditioner. How many ways can Sherri buy 1 Pantene® shampoo and 1 Pantene® conditioner?

32. **Business** A pharmaceutical salesperson has 6 doctors' offices to call on.

(a) In how many ways can she arrange her schedule if she calls on all 6 offices?

(b) In how many ways can she arrange her schedule if she decides to call on 4 of the 6 offices?

Social Science *The United States is rapidly running out of telephone numbers. In large cities, telephone companies have introduced new area codes as numbers are used up.*

33. **(a)** Until recently, all area codes had a 0 or a 1 as the middle digit and the first digit could not be 0 or 1. How many area codes were possible with this arrangement? How many telephone numbers does the current 7-digit sequence permit per area code? (The 3-digit sequence that follows the area code cannot start with 0 or 1. Assume that there are no other restrictions.)

(b) The actual number of area codes under the previous system was 152. Explain the discrepancy between this number and your answer to part (a).

34. The shortage of area codes under the previous system was avoided by removing the restriction on the second digit. How many area codes are available under this new system?

35. A problem with the plan in Exercise 34 was that the second digit in the area code had been used to tell phone company equipment that a long-distance call was being made. To avoid changing all equipment, an alternative plan proposed a 4-digit area code and restricted the first and second digits as before. How many area codes would this plan have provided?

36. Still another solution to the area-code problem is to increase the local dialing sequence to 8 digits instead of 7. How many additional numbers would this plan create? (Assume the same restrictions.)

37. Define permutation in your own words.

Use permutations to solve each of the given problems. (See Examples 7–10.)

38. A baseball team has 15 players. How many 9-player batting orders are possible?

39. Tim is a huge fan of the latest album by country-music singer Kenny Chesney. If Tim has time to listen to only 5 of the 12 songs on the album, how many ways can he listen to the 5 songs?

40. Business From a cooler with 8 cans of different kinds of soda, 3 are selected for 3 people. In how many ways can this be done?

41. The Greek alphabet has 24 letters. How many ways can one name a fraternity using 3 Greek letters (with no repeats)?

42. Finance A customer speaks to his financial advisor about investment products. The advisor has 9 products available, but knows he will only have time to speak about 4. How many different ways can he give the details on 4 different investment products to the customer?

43. The student activity club at the college has 32 members. In how many different ways can the club select a president, a vice president, a treasurer, and a secretary?

44. A student can take only one class a semester, and she needs to take 4 more electives in any order. If there are 20 courses from which she can choose, how many ways can she take her 4 electives?

45. In a club with 17 members, how many ways can the club elect a president and a treasurer?

Use combinations to solve each of the given problems. (See Examples 11–13.)

46. Business Four items are to be randomly selected from the first 25 items on an assembly line in order to determine the defect rate. How many different samples of 4 items can be chosen?

47. Social Science A group of 4 students is to be selected from a group of 10 students to take part in a class in cell biology.

(a) In how many ways can this be done?

(b) In how many ways can the group that will *not* take part be chosen?

48. Natural Science From a group of 15 smokers and 21 non-smokers, a researcher wants to randomly select 7 smokers and 6 nonsmokers for a study. In how many ways can the study group be selected?

49. The college football team has 11 seniors. The team needs to elect a group of 4 senior co-captains. How many different 4-person groups of co-captains are possible?

50. The drama department holds auditions for a play with a cast of 5 roles. If 33 students audition, how many casts of 5 people are possible?

51. Explain the difference between a permutation and a combination.

52. Padlocks with digit dials are often referred to as "combination locks." According to the mathematical definition of combination, is this an accurate description? Explain.

Exercises 53–70 are mixed problems that may require permutations, combinations, or the multiplication principle. (See Examples 14–18.)

53. Use a tree diagram to find the number of ways 2 letters can be chosen from the set $\{P, Q, R\}$ if order is important and

(a) if repetition is allowed;

(b) if no repeats are allowed.

(c) Find the number of combinations of 3 elements taken 2 at a time. Does this answer differ from that in part (a) or (b)?

54. Repeat Exercise 53, using the set $\{P, Q, R, S\}$ and 4 in place of 3 in part (c).

55. Social Science The U.S. Senate Foreign Relations Committee in 2013 had 10 Democrats and 8 Republicans. A delegation of 5 people is to be selected to visit Iraq.

(a) How many delegations are possible?

(b) How many delegations would have all Republicans?

(c) How many delegations would have 3 Democrats and 2 Republicans?

(d) How many delegations would have at least one Democrat?

56. Natural Science In an experiment on plant hardiness, a researcher gathers 6 wheat plants, 5 barley plants, and 3 rye plants. She wishes to select 4 plants at random.

(a) In how many ways can this be done?

(b) In how many ways can this be done if exactly 2 wheat plants must be included?

57. Business According to the Baskin-Robbins® Web site, there are 21 "classic flavors" of ice cream.

(a) How many different double-scoop cones can be made if order does not matter (for example, putting chocolate on top of vanilla is equivalent to putting vanilla on top of chocolate)?

(b) How many different triple-scoop cones can be made if order does matter?

58. Finance A financial advisor offers 8 mutual funds in the high-risk category, 7 in the moderate-risk category, and 10 in the low-risk category. An investor decides to invest in 3 high-risk funds, 4 moderate-risk funds, and 3 low-risk funds. How many ways can the investor do this?

59. A lottery game requires that you pick 6 different numbers from 1 to 99. If you pick all 6 winning numbers, you win $4 million.

  (a) How many ways are there to choose 6 numbers if order is not important?

  (b) How many ways are there to choose 6 numbers if order matters?

60. In Exercise 59, if you pick 5 of the 6 numbers correctly, you win $5,000. In how many ways can you pick exactly 5 of the 6 winning numbers without regard to order?

61. The game of Set* consists of a special deck of cards. Each card has on it either one, two, or three shapes. The shapes on each card are all the same color, either green, purple, or red. The shapes on each card are the same style, either solid, shaded, or outline. There are three possible shapes—squiggle, diamond, and oval—and only one type of shape appears on a card. The deck consists of all possible combinations of shape, color, style, and number. How many cards are in a deck?

62. Health Over the course of the previous nursing shift, 16 new patients were admitted onto a hospital ward. If a nurse begins her shift by caring for 6 of the new patients, how many possible ways could the 6 patients be selected from the 16 new arrivals?

63. Natural Science A biologist is attempting to classify 52,000 species of insects by assigning 3 initials to each species. Is it possible to classify all the species in this way? If not, how many initials should be used?

64. One play in a state lottery consists of choosing 6 numbers from 1 to 44. If your 6 numbers are drawn (in any order), you win the jackpot.

  (a) How many possible ways are there to draw the 6 numbers?

  (b) If you get 2 plays for a dollar, how much would it cost to guarantee that one of your choices would be drawn?

  (c) Assuming that you work alone and can fill out a betting ticket (for 2 plays) every second, and assuming that the lotto drawing will take place 3 days from now, can you place enough bets to guarantee that 1 of your choices will be drawn?

65. A cooler contains 5 cans of Pepsi®, 1 can of Diet Coke®, and 3 cans of 7UP®; you pick 3 cans at random. How many samples are possible in which the soda cans picked are

  (a) only Pepsi;

  (b) only Diet Coke;

  (c) only 7UP;

  (d) 2 Pepsi, 1 Diet Coke;

  (e) 2 Pepsi, 1 7UP;

  (f) 2 7UP, 1 Pepsi;

  (g) 2 Diet Coke, 1 7UP?

66. A class has 9 male students and 8 female students. How many ways can the class select a committee of four people to petition the teacher not to make the final exam cumulative if the committee has to have 2 males and 2 females?

67. Health A hospital wants to test the viability of a new medication for attention deficit disorder. It has 35 adults volunteer for the study, but can only enroll 20 in the study. How many ways can it choose the 20 volunteers to enroll in the study?

68. Suppose a pizza shop offers 4 choices of cheese and 9 toppings. If the order of the cheeses and toppings does not matter, how many different pizza selections are possible when choosing two cheeses and 2 toppings?

69. In the game of bingo, each card has 5 columns. Column 1 has spaces for 5 numbers, chosen from 1 to 15. Column 2 similarly has 5 numbers, chosen from 16 to 30. Column 3 has a free space in the middle, plus 4 numbers chosen from 31 to 45. The 5 numbers in columns 4 and 5 are chosen from 46 to 60 and from 61 to 75, respectively. The numbers in each card can be in any order. How many different bingo cards are there?

70. A television commercial for Little Caesars® pizza announced that, with the purchase of two pizzas, one could receive free any combination of up to five toppings on each pizza. The commercial shows a young child waiting in line at one of the company's stores who calculates that there are 1,048,576 possibilities for the toppings on the two pizzas. Verify the child's calculation. Use the fact that Little Caesars has 11 toppings to choose from. Assume that the order of the two pizzas matters; that is, if the first pizza has combination 1 and the second pizza has combination 2, that arrangement is different from combination 2 on the first pizza and combination 1 on the second.[†]

If the n objects in a permutations problem are not all distinguishable—that is, if there are n_1 of type 1, n_2 of type 2, and so on, for r different types—then the number of distinguishable permutations is

$$\frac{n!}{n_1! \, n_2! \cdots n_r!}.$$

Example   *In how many ways can you arrange the letters in the word Mississippi?*

  This word contains 1 m, 4 i's, 4 s's, and 2 p's. To use the formula, let $n = 11$, $n_1 = 1$, $n_2 = 4$, $n_3 = 4$, and $n_4 = 2$ to get

$$\frac{11!}{1! \, 4! \, 4! \, 2!} = 34,650$$

arrangements. The letters in a word with 11 different letters can be arranged in $11! = 39,916,800$ ways.

71. Find the number of distinguishable permutations of the letters in each of the given words.

  (a) martini

  (b) nunnery

  (c) grinding

72. A printer has 5 W's, 4 X's, 3 Y's, and 2 Z's. How many different "words" are possible that use all these letters? (A "word" does not have to have any meaning here.)

*SET is a registered trademark of Cannei, LLC.

[†]Joseph F. Heiser, "Pascal and Gauss meet Little Caesars," *Mathematics Teacher*, 87 (September 1994): 389. In a letter to *Mathematics Teacher*, Heiser argued that the two combinations should be counted as the same, so the child has actually overcounted. In that case, there would be 524,288 possibilities.

73. Shirley is a shelf stocker at the local grocery store. She has 4 varieties of Stouffer's® frozen dinners, 3 varieties of Lean Cuisine® frozen dinners, and 5 varieties of Weight Watchers® frozen dinners. In how many distinguishable ways can she stock the shelves if

(a) the dinners can be arranged in any order?

(b) dinners from the same company are considered alike and have to be shelved together?

(c) dinners from the same company are considered alike, but do not have to be shelved together?

74. A child has a set of different-shaped plastic objects. There are 2 pyramids, 5 cubes, and 6 spheres. In how many ways can she arrange them in a row

(a) if they are all different colors?

(b) if the same shapes must be grouped?

(c) In how many distinguishable ways can they be arranged in a row if objects of the same shape are also the same color, but need not be grouped?

✓**Checkpoint Answers**

1. (a) 720   (b) 24

2. (a) 24   (b) 720   (c) 1   (d) 30

3. 30

4. $8 \cdot 7 \cdot 6 \cdot 5 = 1680$

5. (a) 20   (b) 504   (c) 3   (d) 210   (e) 132

6. (a) 120   (b) 12   (c) 6

7. (a) 15   (b) 70   (c) 1

8. (a) 15   (b) 70   (c) 1

9. (a) 15,504   (b) 816   (c) 21,699

10. (a) 5040   (b) 455   (c) 28   (d) 360

11. (a) 5040   (b) 840

12. 120,526,770   13. 1260

9.3   Applications of Counting

Many of the probability problems involving *dependent* events that were solved with probability trees in Chapter 8 can also be solved by using counting principles—that is, permutations and combinations. Permutations and combinations are especially helpful when the number of choices is large. The use of counting rules to solve probability problems depends on the basic probability principle introduced in Section 8.3 and repeated here.

If event E is a subset of sample space S with equally likely outcomes then the probability that event E occurs, written $P(E)$, is

$$P(E) = \frac{n(E)}{n(S)}.$$

Example 1   From a potential jury pool with 1 Hispanic, 3 Caucasian, and 2 African-American members, 2 jurors are selected one at a time without replacement. Find the probability that 1 Caucasian and 1 African-American are selected.

Solution   In Example 6 of Section 8.5, it was necessary to consider the order in which the jurors were selected. With combinations, it is not necessary: Simply count the number of ways in which 1 Caucasian and 1 African-American juror can be selected. The Caucasian can be selected in $_3C_1$ ways, and the African-American juror can be selected in $_2C_1$ ways. By the multiplication principle, both results can occur in

$$_3C_1 \cdot {_2C_1} = 3 \cdot 2 = 6 \text{ ways,}$$

giving the numerator of the probability fraction. For the denominator, 2 jurors are selected from a total of 6 candidates. This can occur in $_6C_2 = 15$ ways. The required probability is

$$P(1 \text{ Caucasian and 1 African American}) = \frac{_3C_1 \cdot {_2C_1}}{_6C_2} = \frac{3 \cdot 2}{15} = \frac{6}{15} = \frac{2}{5} = .40.$$

This result agrees with the answer found earlier.

Example 2   From a baseball team of 15 players, 4 are to be selected to present a list of grievances to the coach.

(a) In how many ways can this be done?

Solution   Four players from a group of 15 can be selected in $_{15}C_4$ ways. (Use combinations, since the order in which the group of 4 is selected is unimportant.) So,

$$_{15}C_4 = \frac{15!}{4!\ 11!} = \frac{15(14)(13)(12)}{4(3)(2)(1)} = 1365.$$

There are 1365 ways to choose 4 players from 15.

(b) One of the players is Michael Branson. Find the probability that Branson will be among the 4 selected.

Solution   The probability that Branson will be selected is the number of ways the chosen group includes him, divided by the total number of ways the group of 4 can be chosen. If Branson must be one of the 4 selected, the problem reduces to finding the number of ways the additional 3 players can be chosen. There are 3 chosen from 14 players; this can be done in

$$_{14}C_3 = \frac{14!}{3!\ 11!} = 364$$

ways. The number of ways 4 players can be selected from 15 is

$$n = {}_{15}C_4 = 1365.$$

The probability that Branson will be one of the 4 chosen is

$$P(\text{Branson is chosen}) = \frac{364}{1365} \approx .267.$$

(c) Find the probability that Branson will not be selected.

Solution   The probability that he will not be chosen is $1 - .267 = .733.$ ✓₁

Checkpoint 1

The ski club has 8 women and 7 men. What is the probability that if the club elects 3 officers at random, all 3 of them will be women?

Example 3   **Business** A manufacturing company performs a quality-control analysis on the ceramic tile it produces. It produces the tile in batches of 24 pieces. In the quality-control analysis, the company tests 3 pieces of tile per batch. Suppose a batch of 24 tiles has 4 defective tiles.

(a) What is the probability that exactly 1 of the 3 tested tiles is defective?

Solution   Let $P(1 \text{ defective})$ represent the probability of there being exactly 1 defective tile among the 3 tested tiles. To find this probability, we need to know how many ways we can select 3 tiles for testing. Since order does not matter, there are $_{24}C_3$ ways to choose 3 tiles:

$$_{24}C_3 = \frac{24!}{21!\ 3!} = \frac{24 \cdot 23 \cdot 22}{3 \cdot 2 \cdot 1} = 2024.$$

There are $_4C_1$ ways of choosing 1 defective tile from the 4 in the batch. If we choose 1 defective tile, we must then choose 2 good tiles among the 20 good tiles in the batch. We can do this in $_{20}C_2$ ways. By the multiplication principle, there are

$$_4C_1 \cdot {}_{20}C_2 = \frac{4!}{3!1!} \cdot \frac{20!}{18!\ 2!} = 4 \cdot 190 = 760$$

ways to choose exactly 1 defective tile.
Thus,

$$P(1 \text{ defective}) = \frac{760}{2024} \approx .3755.$$

(b) If at least one of the tiles in a batch is defective, the company will not ship the batch. What is the probability that the batch is not shipped?

Solution The batch will not be shipped if 1, 2, or 3 of the tiles sampled are defective. We already found the probability of there being exactly 1 defective tile in part (a). We now need to find $P(2 \text{ defective})$ and $P(3 \text{ defective})$. To find $P(2 \text{ defective})$, we need to count the number of ways to choose 2 from the 4 defective tiles in the batch and choose 1 from the 20 good tiles in the batch:

$$_4C_2 \cdot {}_{20}C_1 = \frac{4!}{2!\,2!} \cdot \frac{20!}{19!\,1!} = 6 \cdot 20 = 120.$$

To find $P(3 \text{ defective})$, we need to count the number of ways to choose 3 from the 4 defective tiles in the batch and choose 0 from the 20 good tiles in the batch:

$$_4C_3 \cdot {}_{20}C_0 = \frac{4!}{1!\,3!} \cdot \frac{20!}{20!\,0!} = 4 \cdot 1 = 4.$$

We now have

$$P(2 \text{ defective}) = \frac{120}{2024} \approx .0593 \text{ and } P(3 \text{ defective}) = \frac{4}{2024} \approx .0020.$$

Thus, the probability of rejecting the batch because 1, 2, or 3 tiles are defective is

$$P(1 \text{ defective}) + P(2 \text{ defective}) + P(3 \text{ defective}) \approx .3755 + .0593 + .0020$$
$$= .4368.$$

(c) Use the complement rule to find the probability the batch will be rejected.

Solution We reject the batch if at least 1 of the sampled tiles is defective. The opposite of at least 1 tile being defective is that none are defective. We can find the probability that none of the 3 sampled tiles is defective by choosing 0 from the 4 defective tiles and choosing 3 from the 20 good tiles:

$$_4C_0 \cdot {}_{20}C_3 = 1 \cdot 1140 = 1140.$$

Therefore, the probability that none of the sampled tiles is defective is

$$P(0 \text{ defective}) = \frac{1140}{2024} \approx .5632.$$

Using the complement rule, we have

$$P(\text{at least 1 defective}) \approx 1 - .5632 = .4368,$$

the same answer as in part (b). Using the complement rule can often save time when multiple probabilities need to be calculated for problems involving "at least 1." ✓ 2

✓ Checkpoint 2

A batch of 15 granite slabs is mined, and 4 have defects. If the manager spot-checks 3 slabs at random, what is the probability that at least 1 slab is defective?

Example 4   In a common form of 5-card draw poker, a hand of 5 cards is dealt to each player from a deck of 52 cards. (For a review of a standard deck, see Figure 8.20 in Section 8.3.) There is a total of

$$_{52}C_5 = \frac{52!}{5!\,47!} = 2{,}598{,}960$$

such hands possible. Find the probability of being dealt each of the given hands.

(a) Heart-flush hand (5 hearts)

Solution There are 13 hearts in a deck; there are

$$_{13}C_5 = \frac{13!}{5!\,8!} = \frac{13(12)(11)(10)(9)}{5(4)(3)(2)(1)} = 1287$$

different hands containing only hearts. The probability of a heart flush is

$$P(\text{heart flush}) = \frac{1287}{2{,}598{,}960} \approx .000495.$$

(b) A flush of any suit (5 cards, all from 1 suit)

Solution   There are 4 suits to a deck, so

$$P(\text{flush}) = 4 \cdot P(\text{heart flush}) = 4(.000495) \approx .00198.$$

(c) A full house of aces and eights (3 aces and 2 eights)

Solution   There are $_4C_3$ ways to choose 3 aces from among the 4 in the deck and $_4C_2$ ways to choose 2 eights, so

$$P(3 \text{ aces}, 2 \text{ eights}) = \frac{_4C_3 \cdot {_4C_2}}{_{52}C_5} \approx .00000923.$$

(d) Any full house (3 cards of one value, 2 of another)

Solution   There are 13 values in a deck, so there are 13 choices for the first value mentioned, leaving 12 choices for the second value. (Order *is* important here, since a full house of aces and eights, for example, is not the same as a full house of eights and aces.)

$$P(\text{full house}) = \frac{13 \cdot {_4C_3} \cdot 12 \cdot {_4C_2}}{_{52}C_5} \approx .00144.$$

✓ **Checkpoint 3**

Find the probability of being dealt a poker hand (5 cards) with 4 kings.

Example 5   A cooler contains 8 different kinds of soda, among which 3 cans are Pepsi®, Coke®, and Sprite®. What is the probability, when picking at random, of selecting the 3 cans in the particular order listed in the previous sentence?

Solution   Use permutations to find the number of arrangements in the sample, because order matters:

$$n = {_8P_3} = 8(7)(6) = 336.$$

Since each can is different, there is only 1 way to choose Pepsi, Coke, and Sprite in that order, so the probability is

$$\frac{1}{336} = .0030.$$

✓ **Checkpoint 4**

Martha, Leonard, Calvin, and Sheila will be handling the officer duties of president, vice president, treasurer, and secretary.

(a) If the offices are assigned randomly, what is the probability that Calvin is the president?

(b) If the offices are assigned randomly, what is the probability that Sheila is president, Martha is vice president, Calvin is treasurer, and Leonard is secretary?

Example 6   Suppose a group of 5 people is in a room. Find the probability that at least 2 of the people have the same birthday.

Solution   "Same birthday" refers to the month and the day, not necessarily the same year. Also, ignore leap years, and assume that each day in the year is equally likely as a birthday. First find the probability that *no 2 people* among 5 people have the same birthday. There are 365 different birthdays possible for the first of the 5 people, 364 for the second (so that the people have different birthdays), 363 for the third, and so on. The number of ways the 5 people can have different birthdays is thus the number of permutations of 365 things (days) taken 5 at a time, or

$$_{365}P_5 = 365 \cdot 364 \cdot 363 \cdot 362 \cdot 361.$$

The number of ways that the 5 people can have the same or different birthdays is

$$365 \cdot 365 \cdot 365 \cdot 365 \cdot 365 = (365)^5.$$

Finally, the *probability* that none of the 5 people have the same birthday is

$$\frac{_{365}P_5}{(365)^5} = \frac{365 \cdot 364 \cdot 363 \cdot 362 \cdot 361}{365 \cdot 365 \cdot 365 \cdot 365 \cdot 365} \approx .973.$$

The probability that at least 2 of the 5 people *do* have the same birthday is $1 - .973 = .027$.

Example 6 can be extended for more than 5 people. In general, the probability that no 2 people among n people have the same birthday is

$$\frac{_{365}P_n}{(365)^n}.$$

The probability that at least 2 of the n people *do* have the same birthday is

$$1 - \frac{_{365}P_n}{(365)^n}. \quad \boxed{5}$$

✓ Checkpoint 5

Evaluate $1 - \frac{_{365}P_n}{(365)^n}$ for

(a) $n = 3$;

(b) $n = 6$.

The following table shows this probability for various values of n:

Number of People, n	Probability That at Least 2 Have the Same Birthday
5	.027
10	.117
15	.253
20	.411
22	.476
23	**.507**
25	.569
30	.706
35	.814
40	.891
50	.970

✓ Checkpoint 6

Set up (but do not calculate) the probability that at least 2 of the 9 members of the Supreme Court have the same birthday.

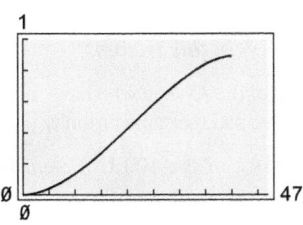

Figure 9.11

The probability that 2 people among 23 have the same birthday is .507, a little more than half. Many people are surprised at this result; somehow it seems that a larger number of people should be required. ✓6

Using a graphing calculator, we can graph the probability formula in the previous example as a function of n, but the graphing calculator must be set to evaluate the function at integer points. Figure 9.11 was produced on a TI-84+ by letting $Y_1 = 1 - (365 \text{ nPr } X)/365^X$ on the interval $0 \le x \le 47$. (This domain ensures integer values for x.) Notice that the graph does not extend past $x = 39$. This is because $P(365, n)$ and 365^n are too large for the calculator when $n \ge 40$.

9.3 Exercises

Business *Suppose in Example 3 that the number of defective tiles in a batch of 24 is 5 rather than 4. If 3 tiles are sampled at random, the management would like to know the probability that*

1. exactly 1 of the sampled tiles is defective;

2. the batch is rejected (that is, at least 1 sampled tile is defective).

Business *A shipment of 8 computers contains 3 with defects. Find the probability that a sample of the given size, drawn from the 8, will not contain a defective computer. (See Example 3.)*

3. 1

4. 2

5. 3

6. 5

A radio station runs a promotion at an auto show with a money box with 10 $100 tickets, 12 $50 tickets, and 20 $25 tickets. The box contains an additional 200 "dummy" tickets with no value. Three tickets are randomly drawn. Find the given probabilities. (See Examples 1 and 2.)

7. All $100 tickets

8. All $50 tickets

9. Exactly two $25 tickets and no other money winners

10. One ticket of each money amount

11. No tickets with money

12. At least one money ticket

Two cards are drawn at random from an ordinary deck of 52 cards. (See Example 4.)

13. How many 2-card hands are possible?

Find the probability that the 2-card hand in Exercise 13 contains the given cards.

14. 2 kings

15. No deuces (2's)

16. 2 face cards

17. Different suits

18. At least 1 black card

19. No more than 1 diamond

20. Discuss the relative merits of using probability trees versus combinations to solve probability problems. When would each approach be most appropriate?

21. Several examples in this section used the rule $P(E') = 1 - P(E)$. Explain the advantage (especially in Example 6) of using this rule.

Natural Science *A shipment contains 8 igneous, 7 sedimentary, and 7 metamorphic rocks. If we select 5 rocks at random, find the probability that*

22. all 5 are igneous;

23. exactly 3 are sedimentary;

24. only 1 is metamorphic.

25. In Exercise 59 in Section 9.2, we found the number of ways to pick 6 different numbers from 1 to 99 in a state lottery.

(a) Assuming that order is unimportant, what is the probability of picking all 6 numbers correctly to win the big prize?

(b) What is the probability if order matters?

26. In Exercise 25 (a), what is the probability of picking exactly 5 of the 6 numbers correctly?

27. Example 16 in Section 9.2 shows that the probability of winning the Powerball lottery is 1/175,223,510. If Juanita and Michelle each play Powerball on one particular evening, what is the probability that both will select the winning numbers if they make their selections independently of each other?

28. **Business** A cell phone manufacturer randomly selects 5 phones from every batch of 50 produced. If at least one of the phones is found to be defective, then each phone in the batch is tested individually. Find the probability that the entire batch will need testing if the batch contains

(a) 8 defective phones;

(b) 2 defective phones.

29. **Social Science** Of the 15 members of President Barack Obama's first Cabinet, 4 were women. Suppose the president randomly selected 4 advisors from the cabinet for a meeting. Find the probability that the group of 4 would be composed as follows:

(a) 3 woman and 1 man;

(b) All men;

(c) At least one woman.

30. **Business** A car dealership has 8 red, 9 silver, and 5 black cars on the lot. Ten cars are randomly chosen to be displayed in front of the dealership. Find the probability that

(a) 4 are red and the rest are silver;

(b) 5 are red and 5 are black;

(c) exactly 8 are red.

31. **Health** Twenty subjects volunteer for a study of a new cold medicine. Ten of the volunteers are ages 20–39, 8 are ages 40–59, and 2 are age 60 or older. If we select 7 volunteers at random, find the probability that

(a) all the volunteers selected are ages 20–39;

(b) 5 of the volunteers are ages 20–39 and 2 are age 60 or older;

(c) exactly 3 of the volunteers are ages 40–59.

For Exercises 32–34, refer to Example 6 in this section.

32. Set up the probability that at least 2 of the 43 men who have served as president of the United States have had the same birthday.[*]

33. Set up the probability that at least 2 of the 100 U.S. senators have the same birthday.

34. Set up the probability that at least 2 of the 50 U.S. governors have the same birthday.

One version of the New York State lottery game Quick Draw has players selecting 4 numbers at random from the numbers 1–80. The state picks 20 winning numbers. If the player's 4 numbers are selected by the state, the player wins $55. (Data from: www.nylottery.org.)

35. What is the probability of winning?

36. If the state picks 3 of the player's numbers, the player wins $5. What is the probability of winning $5?

---

[*]In fact, James Polk and Warren Harding were both born on November 2. Although Barack Obama is the 44th president, the 22nd and 24th presidents were the same man: Grover Cleveland.

37. What is the probability of having none of your 4 numbers selected by the state?

38. During the 1988 college football season, the Big Eight Conference ended the season in a "perfect progression," as shown in the following table:[*]

Won	Lost	Team
7	0	Nebraska (NU)
6	1	Oklahoma (OU)
5	2	Oklahoma State (OSU)
4	3	Colorado (CU)
3	4	Iowa State (ISU)
2	5	Missouri (MU)
1	6	Kansas (KU)
0	7	Kansas State (KSU)

Someone wondered what the probability of such an outcome might be.

(a) Assuming no ties and assuming that each team had an equally likely probability of winning each game, find the probability of the perfect progression shown in the table.

(b) Under the same assumptions, find a general expression for the probability of a perfect progression in an n-team league.

---
[*]From Richard Madsen, "On the Probability of a Perfect Progression." *American Statistics* 45, no. 3 (August 1991): 214. Reprinted with permission from the American Statistician. Copyright 1991 by the American Statistical Association. All rights reserved.

39. Use a computer or a graphing calculator and the Monte Carlo method with $n = 50$ to estimate the probabilities of the given hands at poker. (See the directions for Exercises 39–43 on page 440.) Assume that aces are either high or low. Since each hand has 5 cards, you will need $50 \cdot 5 = 250$ random numbers to "look at" 50 hands. Compare these experimental results with the theoretical results.

(a) A pair of aces

(b) Any two cards of the same value

(c) Three of a kind

40. Use a computer or a graphing calculator and the Monte Carlo method with $n = 20$ to estimate the probabilities of the given 13-card bridge hands. Since each hand has 13 cards, you will need $20 \cdot 13 = 260$ random numbers to "look at" 20 hands.

(a) No aces

(b) 2 kings and 2 aces

(c) No cards of one particular suit—that is, only 3 suits represented

✓**Checkpoint Answers**

1. .123   **2.** About .637   **3.** .00001847

4. **(a)** 1/4   **(b)** 1/24

5. **(a)** .008   **(b)** .040

6. $1 - {}_{365}P_9/365^9$

9.4 Binomial Probability

In Section 9.1, we learned about probability distributions where we listed each outcome and its associated probability. After learning in Sections 9.2 and 9.3 how to count the number of possible outcomes, we are now ready to understand a special probability distribution known as the *binomial distribution*. This distribution occurs when the same experiment is repeated many times and each repetition is independent of previous ones. One outcome is designated a success and any other outcome is considered a failure. For example, you might want to find the probability of rolling 8 twos in 12 rolls of a die (rolling two is a success; rolling anything else is a failure). The individual trials (rolling the die once) are called **Bernoulli trials**, or **Bernoulli processes**, after the Swiss mathematician Jakob Bernoulli (1654–1705).

If the probability of a success in a single trial is p, then the probability of failure is $1 - p$ (by the complement rule). When Bernoulli trials are repeated a fixed number of times, and each trial's outcome is independent of the other trials' outcomes, the resulting distribution of outcomes is called a **binomial distribution**, or a **binomial experiment**. A binomial experiment must satisfy the following conditions.

> **Binomial Experiment**
>
> **1.** The same experiment is repeated a fixed number of times.
> **2.** There are only two possible outcomes: success and failure.
> **3.** The probability of success for each trial is constant.
> **4.** The repeated trials are independent.

The basic characteristics of binomial experiments are illustrated by a recent poll of small businesses (250 employees or fewer) conducted by the National Federation of Independent Businesses. The poll found that 36% of small businesses pay for the health insurance of all or almost all full-time employees. (Data from: www.nfib.com.) We use Y to denote the event that a small business does this, and N to denote the event that it does not. If we sample 5 small businesses at random and use .36 as the probability for Y, we will generate a binomial experiment, since all of the requirements are satisfied:

The sampling is repeated a fixed number of times (5);

there are only two outcomes of interest (Y or N);

the probability of success is constant ($p = .36$);

"at random" guarantees that the trials are independent.

To calculate the probability that all 5 randomly chosen businesses pay for health insurance, we use the product rule for independent events (Section 8.5) and $P(Y) = .36$ to obtain

$$P(YYYYY) = P(Y) \cdot P(Y) \cdot P(Y) \cdot P(Y) \cdot P(Y) = (.36)^5 \approx .006.$$

Determining the probability that 4 out of 5 businesses chose to pay for health insurance is slightly more complicated. The business that does not pay could be the first, second, third, fourth, or fifth business surveyed. So we have the following possible outcomes:

$$N\,Y\,Y\,Y\,Y$$
$$Y\,N\,Y\,Y\,Y$$
$$Y\,Y\,N\,Y\,Y$$
$$Y\,Y\,Y\,N\,Y$$
$$Y\,Y\,Y\,Y\,N$$

So the total number of ways in which 4 successes (and 1 failure) can occur is 5, which is the number $_5C_4$. The probability of each of these 5 outcomes is

$$P(Y) \cdot P(Y) \cdot P(Y) \cdot P(Y) \cdot P(N) = (.36)^4(1 - .36)^1 = (.36)^4(.64).$$

Since the 5 outcomes where there are 4 Ys and one N represent disjoint events, we multiply by $_5C_4 = 5$:

$$P(4\ Y\text{s out of 5 trials}) = {_5C_4}(.36)^4(.64)^{5-4} = 5(.36)^4(.64)^1 \approx .054.$$

The probability of obtaining exactly 3 Ys and 2 Ns can be computed in a similar way. The probability of any one way of achieving 3 Ys and 2 Ns will be

$$(.36)^3(.64)^2.$$

Again, the desired outcome can occur in more than one way. Using combinations, we find that the number of ways in which 3 Ys and 2 Ns can occur is $_5C_3 = 10$. So, we have

 Checkpoint 1

Find the probability of obtaining

(a) exactly 2 businesses that pay for health insurance;

(b) exactly 1 business that pays for health insurance;

(c) exactly no business that pays for health insurance.

$$P(3\ Y\text{s out of 5 trials}) = {_5C_3}(.36)^3(.64)^{5-3} = 10(.36)^3(.64)^2 \approx .191.$$

With the probabilities just generated and the answers to Checkpoint 1, we can write the probability distribution for the number of small businesses that pay for health insurance for all or almost all their full-time employees when 5 businesses are selected at random:

x	0	1	2	3	4	5
$P(x)$	.107	.302	.340	.191	.054	.006

When the outcomes and their associated probabilities are written in this form, it is very easy to calculate answers to questions such as, What is the probability that 3 or more businesses pay for the health insurance of their full-time employees? We see from the table that

$$P(3\ \text{or more } Y\text{s}) = .191 + .054 + .006 = .251.$$

On the *TI-84+* calculator, use "binompdf(n,p,x)" in the DISTR menu to compute the probability of exactly x successes in n trials (where p is the probability of success in a single trial). Use "binomcdf(n,p,x)" to compute the probability of at most x successes in n trials. Figure 9.12 shows the probability of exactly 3 successes in 5 trials and the probability of at most 3 successes in 5 trials, with the probability of success set at .36 for each case.

```
binompdf(5,.36,3)
            .19110297�
binomcdf(5,.36,3)
            .94�20567�4
```

Figure 9.12

Similarly, the probability of one or fewer businesses paying for health insurance is

$$P(1 \text{ or fewer } Ys) = .302 + .107 = .409.$$

The example illustrates the following fact.

Binomial Probability

If p is the probability of success in a single trial of a binomial experiment, the probability of x successes and $n - x$ failures in n independent repeated trials of the experiment is

$$_nC_x p^x (1 - p)^{n-x}.$$

Example 1   **Business** According to a 2012 study conducted by the Society for Human Resource Management, 81% of U.S. employees reported overall job satisfaction. Suppose a random sample of 6 employees is chosen. Find the probability of the given scenarios. (Data from: www.shrm.org.)

(a) Exactly 4 of the 6 employees have overall job satisfaction.

Solution   We can think of the 6 employees as independent trials, and a success occurs if a worker has overall job satisfaction. This is a binomial experiment with $p = .81, n = 6$, and $x = 4$. By the binomial probability rule,

$$\begin{aligned}
P(\text{exactly } 4) &= {}_6C_4 (.81)^4 (1 - .81)^{6-4} \\
&= 15(.81)^4 (.19)^2 \\
&\approx .233.
\end{aligned}$$

(b) All 6 employees have overall job satisfaction.

Solution   Let $x = 6$. Then we have

$$\begin{aligned}
P(\text{exactly } 6) &= {}_6C_6 (.81)^6 (1 - .81)^{6-6} \\
&= 1(.81)^6 (.19)^0 \\
&\approx .282. \quad ✔_2
\end{aligned}$$

✔ **Checkpoint 2**

According to the study in Example 1, 72% of employees were satisfied with how their work contributed to their organization's business goals. If 4 employees are selected at random, find the probability that exactly the given number were satisfied with how their work contributed to their organization's business goals:

(a) 1 of the 4;

(b) 3 of the 4.

Example 2   Suppose a family has 3 children.

(a) Find the probability distribution for the number of girls.

Solution   Let $x =$ the number of girls in three births. According to the binomial probability rule, the probability of exactly one girl being born is

$$P(x = 1) = {}_3C_1 \left(\frac{1}{2}\right)^1 \left(\frac{1}{2}\right)^2 = 3\left(\frac{1}{2}\right)^3 = \frac{3}{8}.$$

The other probabilities in this distribution are found similarly, as shown in the following table:

x	0	1	2	3
$P(x)$	${}_3C_0 \left(\frac{1}{2}\right)^0 \left(\frac{1}{2}\right)^3 = \frac{1}{8}$	${}_3C_1 \left(\frac{1}{2}\right)^1 \left(\frac{1}{2}\right)^2 = \frac{3}{8}$	${}_3C_2 \left(\frac{1}{2}\right)^2 \left(\frac{1}{2}\right)^1 = \frac{3}{8}$	${}_3C_3 \left(\frac{1}{2}\right)^3 \left(\frac{1}{2}\right)^0 = \frac{1}{8}$

(b) Find the expected number of girls in a 3-child family.

Solution For a binomial distribution, we can use the following method (which is presented here with a "plausibility argument," but not a full proof): Because 50% of births are girls, it is reasonable to expect that 50% of a sample of children will be girls. Since 50% of 3 is $3(.50) = 1.5$, we conclude that the expected number of girls is 1.5. ✓3

✓**Checkpoint 3**

Find the probability of getting 2 fours in 8 tosses of a die.

The expected value in Example 2(b) was the product of the number of births and the probability of a single birth being a girl—that is, the product of the number of trials and the probability of success in a single trial. The same conclusion holds in the general case.

> ### Expected Value for a Binomial Distribution
>
> When an experiment meets the four conditions of a binomial experiment with n fixed trials and constant probability of success p, the expected value is
>
> $$E(x) = np.$$

Example 3 **Business** According to real estate data provider CoreLogic, as presented in the *Los Angeles Times* on March 13, 2013, approximately 21.5% of U.S. households with a mortgage owed more on their mortgage than the value of the home (commonly known as being underwater). If we select 15 U.S. households with a mortgage at random, find the following probabilities.

(a) The probability that exactly 5 of the households had a mortgage that was underwater.

Solution The experiment is repeated 15 times, with having an underwater mortgage being considered a success. The probability of success is .215. Since the selection is done at random, the trials are considered independent. Thus, we have a binomial experiment, and

$$P(x = 5) = {}_{15}C_5(.215)^5(.785)^{10} \approx .123.$$

(b) The probability that at most 3 households had a mortgage that was underwater.

Solution "At most 3" means 0, 1, 2, or 3 successes. We must find the probability for each case and then use the addition rule for disjoint events:

$$P(x = 0) = {}_{15}C_0(.215)^0(.785)^{15} \approx .026;$$
$$P(x = 1) = {}_{15}C_1(.215)^1(.785)^{14} \approx .109;$$
$$P(x = 2) = {}_{15}C_2(.215)^2(.785)^{13} \approx .209;$$
$$P(x = 3) = {}_{15}C_3(.215)^3(.785)^{12} \approx .248.$$

Thus,

$$P(\text{at most } 3) = .026 + .109 + .209 + .248 = .592.$$

(c) The expected number of households with mortgages that are underwater.

Solution Because this is a binomial experiment, we can use the formula $E(x) = np = 15(.215) = 3.225$. In repeated samples of 15 households, the average number of households with underwater mortgages is 3.225. ✓4

✓**Checkpoint 4**

In the article described in Example 3, the *Los Angeles Times* reported that 24% of households with mortgages in Los Angeles were underwater. If 10 households with mortgages are selected at random, find the probability that

(a) exactly 2 are underwater;

(b) at most 2 are underwater.

(c) What is the expected number of households that are underwater?

Example 4 **Business** According to the Small Business Administration, 1/3 (about .333) of new businesses fail within two years. If 10 new businesses are selected at random, what is the probability that at least one business will fail within two years?

Solution We can treat this problem as a binomial experiment with $n = 10, p = .333$, and x representing the number of business that fail within two years. "At least 1 of 10" means 1 or 2 or 3, etc., up to all 10. It is simpler here to find the probability that none of the 10 selected business failed [namely: $P(x = 0)$] and then find the probability that at least one of the businesses failed by calculating $1 - P(x = 0)$. The calculations are:

$$P(x = 0) = {}_{10}C_0(.333)^0(.667)^{10} \approx .017;$$
$$P(x \geq 1) = 1 - P(x = 0) \approx 1 - .017 = .983.$$

✓ **Checkpoint 5**

In Example 4, find the probability that

(a) at least 2 businesses fail within 2 years;

(b) at most 4 of the businesses fail within 2 years.

(c) What is the expected value?

Example 5 If each member of a 9-person jury acts independently of the other members and makes the correct determination of guilt or innocence with probability .65, find the probability that the majority of the jurors will reach a correct verdict.*

Solution Since the jurors in this particular situation act independently, we can treat the problem as a binomial experiment. Thus, the probability that the majority of the jurors will reach the correct verdict is given by

$$P(\text{at least } 5) = {}_9C_5(.65)^5(.35)^4 + {}_9C_6(.65)^6(.35)^3 + {}_9C_7(.65)^7(.35)^2$$
$$+ {}_9C_8(.65)^8(.35)^1 + {}_9C_9(.65)^9$$
$$\approx .2194 + .2716 + .2162 + .1004 + .0207$$
$$= .8283.$$

 TECHNOLOGY TIP Some spreadsheets provide binomial probabilities. In Microsoft Excel, for example, the command "=BINOMDIST (5, 9, .65, 0)" gives .21939, which is the probability for $x = 5$ in Example 5. Alternatively, the command "= BINOMDIST (4, 9, .65, 1)" gives .17172 as the probability that 4 or fewer jurors will make the correct decision. Subtract .17172 from 1 to get .82828 as the probability that the majority of the jurors will make the correct decision. This value agrees with the value found in Example 5.

*Bernard Grofman, "A Preliminary Model of Jury Decision Making as a Function of Jury Size, Effective Jury Decision Rule, and Mean Juror Judgmental Competence," *Frontiers in Economics* (1979), pp. 98–110.

9.4 Exercises

In Exercises 1–39, see Examples 1–5.

Business *According to a report from the U.S. Department of Commerce, approximately 70% of U.S. households subscribed to broadband Internet services in the year 2010. Find the probabilities that the given number of households selected at random from 10 households have broadband Internet.*

1. Exactly 6   **2.** Exactly 5

3. None   **4.** All

5. At least 1   **6.** At most 4

Business *The report cited for Exercises 1–6 reported that the state of Utah had the highest rate of broadband Internet subscriptions with 80% of households. Find the probabilities that the given number of households selected at random from 8 households in Utah have broadband Internet.*

7. Exactly 2   **8.** Exactly 1

9. None   **10.** All

11. At least 1   **12.** At most 2

A coin is tossed 5 times. Find the probability of getting

13. all heads;   **14.** exactly 3 heads;

15. no more than 3 heads;   **16.** at least 3 heads.

17. How do you identify a probability problem that involves a binomial experiment?

18. Why do combinations occur in the binomial probability formula?

Business *According to the U.S. Bureau of Labor Statistics, 48% of employed U.S. college graduates are in jobs that require less than a 4-year college education. For Exercises 19–21, find the probability for the described number of graduates in jobs that require less than a 4-year college education if 15 employed college graduates were selected at random.*

19. exactly 3;

20. none;

21. at most 2.

22. If 200 employed college graduates were selected at random, what would be the expected number of graduates in jobs that require less than a 4-year college education?

Business *In a poll conducted by Gallup in early 2013, 54% of small-businesses owners indicated that health care costs are hurting the operating environment of their business "a lot." If 9 small-business owners were selected at random, find the probability that the given number of business owners feel that health care costs were hurting the operating environment a lot.*

23. all 9 businesses;   **24.** all but 1 business;

25. at most 3 businesses;   **26.** exactly 5 businesses.

27. If 500 small-business owners were selected at random, what is the expected number that indicate that health care costs were harming the operating environment of their business a lot?

28. In Exercise 27, what would the number be if 1250 small-business owners were selected?

Natural Science *The probability that a birth will result in twins is .027. Assuming independence (perhaps not a valid assumption), what are the probabilities that, out of 100 births in a hospital, there will be the given numbers of sets of twins? (Data from: The World Almanac and Book of Facts, 2001.)*

29. Exactly 2 sets of twins   **30.** At most 2 sets of twins

Social Science *According to the Web site Answers.com, 10–13% of Americans are left handed. Assume that the percentage is 11%. If we select 9 people at random, find the probability that the number who are left handed is*

31. exactly 2;   **32.** at least 2;

33. none;   **34.** at most 3.

35. In a class of 35 students, how many left-handed students should the instructor expect?

Business *The 2012 General Social Survey indicated that 11% of U.S. residents have a great deal of confidence in banks and financial institutions. If 16 U.S. residents were chosen at random, find the probability that the number given had a great deal of confidence in banks and financial institutions. (Data from: www3.norc.org/gss+website.)*

36. exactly 2;

37. at most 3;

38. at least 4.

39. If we select 300 U.S. residents at random, what is the expected number who have a great deal of confidence in banks and financial institutions?

40. If we select 800 U.S. residents at random, what is the expected number who have a great deal of confidence in banks and financial institutions?

Business *In the state of Texas, pickup trucks account for 23% of the state's registered vehicles. If 100 registered vehicles are selected at random, determine the following. (Data from: www.wsj.com.)*

41. What is the probability that 20 or less of the selected vehicles are pickup trucks?

42. What is the probability that 30 or more of the selected vehicles are pickup trucks?

43. What is the expected number of pickup trucks?

44. If 1000 registered vehicles are selected at random, what is the expected number of pickup trucks?

✓**Checkpoint Answers**

1. (a) About .340 **(b)** About .302 **(c)** About .107

2. (a) About .063 **(b)** About .418

3. About .2605

4. (a) About .288 **(b)** About .556 **(c)** 2.4

5. (a) About .896 **(b)** About .786 **(c)** 3.33

9.5 Markov Chains

In Section 8.5, we touched on **stochastic processes**—mathematical models that evolve over time in a probabilistic manner. In the current section, we study a special kind of stochastic process called a **Markov chain**, in which the outcome of an experiment depends only on the outcome of the previous experiment. In other words, the next state of the system depends only on the present state, not on preceding states. Such experiments are common enough in applications to make their study worthwhile. Markov chains are named after the Russian mathematician A. A. Markov (1856–1922), who started the theory of stochastic processes. To see how Markov chains work, we look at an example.

> **Example 1**   **Business** A small town has only two dry cleaners: Johnson and NorthClean. Johnson's manager hopes to increase the firm's market share by an extensive advertising campaign. After the campaign, a market research firm finds that there is a probability of .8 that a Johnson customer will bring his next batch of dirty items to Johnson and a .35 chance that a NorthClean customer will switch to Johnson for his next batch. Assume that the probability that a customer comes to a given cleaner depends only on where the last load of clothes was taken. If there is a .8 chance that a Johnson customer will return to Johnson, then there must be a $1 - .8 = .2$ chance that the customer will switch to NorthClean. In the same way, there is a $1 - .35 = .65$ chance that a NorthClean customer will return to NorthClean. If an individual bringing a load to Johnson is said to be in state 1 and an individual bringing a load to NorthClean is said to be in state 2, then these probabilities of change from one cleaner to the other are as shown in the following table:

		Second Load	
	State	1	2
First Load	1	.8	.2
	2	.35	.65

> The information from the table can be written in other forms. Figure 9.13 is a **transition diagram** that shows the two states and the probabilities of going from one to another.

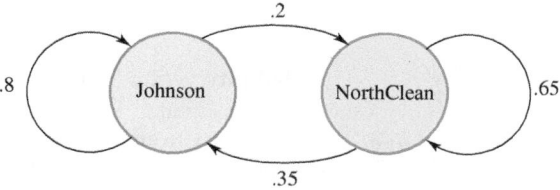

Figure 9.13

> In a **transition matrix**, the states are indicated at the side and top, as follows:

$$\begin{array}{cc} & \text{Second Load} \\ & \begin{array}{cc} \text{Johnson} & \text{NorthClean} \end{array} \\ \begin{array}{l} \text{First Load}\quad \text{Johnson} \\ \phantom{\text{First Load}}\quad \text{NorthClean} \end{array} & \begin{bmatrix} .8 & .2 \\ .35 & .65 \end{bmatrix} \end{array}$$

> A **transition matrix** has the following features:
>
> 1. It is square, since all possible states must be used both as rows and as columns.
> 2. All entries are between 0 and 1, inclusive, because all entries represent probabilities.
> 3. The sum of the entries in any row must be 1, because the numbers in the row give the probability of changing from the state at the left to one of the states indicated across the top.

✓**Checkpoint 1**

You are given the transition matrix

$$\begin{array}{cc} & \text{State} \\ & \begin{array}{cc} 1 & 2 \end{array} \\ \text{State}\ \begin{array}{c} 1 \\ 2 \end{array} & \begin{bmatrix} .3 & .7 \\ .1 & .9 \end{bmatrix}. \end{array}$$

(a) What is the probability of changing from state 1 to state 2?

(b) What does the number .1 represent?

(c) Draw a transition diagram for this information.

> **Example 2**   **Business** Suppose that when the new promotional campaign began, Johnson had 40% of the market and NorthClean had 60%. Use the probability tree in Figure 9.14 to find how these proportions would change after another week of advertising.

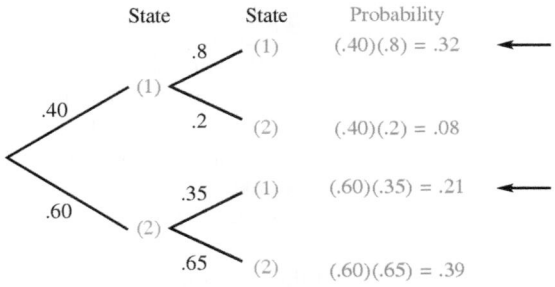

State 1: taking cleaning to Johnson
State 2: taking cleaning to NorthClean

Figure 9.14

Solution   Add the numbers indicated with arrows to find the proportion of people taking their cleaning to Johnson after one week:

$$.32 + .21 = .53$$

Similarly, the proportion taking their cleaning to NorthClean is

$$.08 + .39 = .47.$$

The initial distribution of 40% and 60% becomes 53% and 47%, respectively, after 1 week.

These distributions can be written as the *probability vectors*

$$[.40 \quad .60] \quad \text{and} \quad [.53 \quad .47].$$

A **probability vector** is a one-row matrix, with nonnegative entries, in which the sum of the entries is equal to 1.

The results from the probability tree of Figure 9.14 are exactly the same as the result of multiplying the initial probability vector by the transition matrix (multiplication of matrices was discussed in Section 6.4):

$$[.4 \quad .6]\begin{bmatrix} .8 & .2 \\ .35 & .65 \end{bmatrix} = [.53 \quad .47].$$

If v denotes the original probability vector $[.4 \quad .6]$ and P denotes the transition matrix, then the market share vector after one week is $vP = [.53 \quad .47]$. To find the market share vector after two weeks, multiply the vector $vP = [.53 \quad .47]$ by P; this amounts to finding vP^2.

Checkpoint 2 shows that after 2 weeks, the market share vector is $vP^2 = [.59 \quad .41]$. To get the market share vector after three weeks, multiply this vector by P; that is, find vP^3. Do not use the rounded answer from Checkpoint 2.

Continuing this process gives each cleaner's share of the market after additional weeks:

✔**Checkpoint 2**

Find the product

$$[.53 \ .47]\begin{bmatrix} .8 & .2 \\ .35 & .65 \end{bmatrix}.$$

✔**Checkpoint 3**

Find each cleaner's market share after three weeks.

Weeks after Start	Johnson	NorthClean	
0	.4	.6	v
1	.53	.47	vP^1
2	.59	.41	vP^2
3	.61	.39	vP^3
4	.63	.37	vP^4
12	.64	.36	vP^{12}
13	.64	.36	vP^{13}

The results seem to approach the probability vector $[.64 \quad .36]$.

What happens if the initial probability vector is different from [.4 .6]? Suppose [.75 .25] is used; then the same powers of the transition matrix as before give the following results:

Week after Start	Johnson	NorthClean	
0	.75	.25	v
1	.69	.31	vP^1
2	.66	.34	vP^2
3	.65	.35	vP^3
4	.64	.36	vP^4
5	.64	.36	vP^5
6	.64	.36	vP^6

The results again seem to be approaching the numbers in the probability vector [.64 .36], the same numbers approached with the initial probability vector [.4 .6]. In either case, the long-range trend is for a market share of about 64% for Johnson and 36% for NorthClean. The example suggests that this long-range trend does not depend on the initial distribution of market shares. This means that if the initial market share for Johnson was less than 64%, the advertising campaign has paid off in terms of a greater long-range market share. If the initial share was more than 64%, the campaign did not pay off.

Regular Transition Matrices

One of the many applications of Markov chains is in finding long-range predictions. It is not possible to make long-range predictions with all transition matrices, but for a large set of transition matrices, long-range predictions *are* possible. Such predictions are always possible with **regular transition matrices.** A transition matrix is **regular** if some power of the matrix contains all positive entries. A Markov chain is a **regular Markov chain** if its transition matrix is regular.

Example 3 Decide whether the given transition matrices are regular.

(a) $A = \begin{bmatrix} .3 & .1 & .6 \\ 0 & .2 & .8 \\ .3 & .7 & 0 \end{bmatrix}$.

Solution Square A:

$$A^2 = \begin{bmatrix} .27 & .47 & .26 \\ .24 & .60 & .16 \\ .09 & .17 & .74 \end{bmatrix}.$$

Since all entries in A^2 are positive, matrix A is regular.

(b) $B = \begin{bmatrix} .3 & 0 & .7 \\ 0 & 1 & 0 \\ 0 & 0 & 1 \end{bmatrix}$.

Solution Find various powers of B:

$$B^2 = \begin{bmatrix} .09 & 0 & .91 \\ 0 & 1 & 0 \\ 0 & 0 & 1 \end{bmatrix}; \quad B^3 = \begin{bmatrix} .027 & 0 & .973 \\ 0 & 1 & 0 \\ 0 & 0 & 1 \end{bmatrix}; \quad B^4 = \begin{bmatrix} .0081 & 0 & .9919 \\ 0 & 1 & 0 \\ 0 & 0 & 1 \end{bmatrix}.$$

✓ **Checkpoint 4**

Decide whether the given transition matrices are regular.

(a) $\begin{bmatrix} 0 & 1 \\ 1 & 0 \end{bmatrix}$

(b) $\begin{bmatrix} .45 & .55 \\ 1 & 0 \end{bmatrix}$

Notice that all of the powers of B shown here have zeros in the same locations. Thus, further powers of B will still give the same zero entries, so that no power of matrix B contains all positive entries. For this reason, B is not regular. ✓ 4

📄 **NOTE** If a transition matrix P has some zero entries, and P^2 does as well, you may wonder how far you must compute P^n to be certain that the matrix is not regular. The answer is that if zeros occur in identical places in both P^n and P^{n+1} for any n, then they will appear in those places for all higher powers of P, so P is not regular.

Suppose that v is any probability vector. It can be shown that, for a regular Markov chain with a transition matrix P, there exists a single vector V that does not depend on v, such that $v \cdot P^n$ gets closer and closer to V as n gets larger and larger.

Equilibrium Vector of a Markov Chain

If a Markov chain with transition matrix P is regular, then there is a unique vector V such that, for any probability vector v and for large values of n,

$$v \cdot P^n \approx V.$$

Vector V is called the equilibrium vector, or the fixed vector, of the Markov chain.

In the example with Johnson Cleaners, the equilibrium vector V is approximately [.64 .36]. Vector V can be determined by finding P^n for larger and larger values of n and then looking for a vector that the product $v \cdot P^n$ approaches. Such a strategy can be very tedious, however, and is prone to error. To find a better way, start with the fact that, for a large value of n,

$$v \cdot P^n \approx V,$$

as mentioned in the preceding box. We can multiply both sides of this result by P, $v \cdot P^n \cdot P \approx V \cdot P$, so that

$$v \cdot P^n \cdot P = v \cdot P^{n+1} \approx VP.$$

Since $v \cdot P^n \approx V$ for large values of n, it is also true that $v \cdot P^{n+1} \approx V$ for large values of n. (The product $v \cdot P^n$ approaches V, so that $v \cdot P^{n+1}$ must also approach V.) Thus, $v \cdot P^{n+1} \approx V$ and $v \cdot P^{n+1} \approx VP$, which suggests that

$$VP = V.$$

If a Markov chain with transition matrix P is regular, then the equilibrium vector V satisfies

$$VP = V.$$

The equilibrium vector V can be found by solving a system of linear equations, as shown in the remaining examples.

Example 4   Find the long-range trend for the Markov chain in Examples 1 and 2, with transition matrix

$$P = \begin{bmatrix} .8 & .2 \\ .35 & .65 \end{bmatrix}.$$

Solution This matrix is regular, since all entries are positive. Let P represent this transition matrix and let V be the probability vector $[v_1 \quad v_2]$. We want to find V such that

$$VP = V,$$

or

$$[v_1 \quad v_2] \begin{bmatrix} .8 & .2 \\ .35 & .65 \end{bmatrix} = [v_1 \quad v_2].$$

Multiply on the left to get

$$[.8v_1 + .35v_2 \quad .2v_1 + .65v_2] = [v_1 \quad v_2].$$

Set corresponding entries from the two matrices equal to obtain

$$.8v_1 + .35v_2 = v_1; \quad .2v_1 + .65v_2 = v_2.$$

Simplify each of these equations:

$$-.2v_1 + .35v_2 = 0; \quad .2v_1 - .35v_2 = 0.$$

These last two equations are really the same. (The equations in the system obtained from $VP = V$ are always dependent.) To find the values of v_1 and v_2, recall that $V = [v_1 \quad v_2]$ is a probability vector, so that

$$v_1 + v_2 = 1.$$

Find v_1 and v_2 by solving the system

$$-.2v_1 + .35v_2 = 0$$
$$v_1 + v_2 = 1.$$

We can rewrite the second equation as $v_1 = 1 - v_2$. Now substitute for v_1 in the first equation:

$$-.2(1 - v_2) + .35v_2 = 0.$$

Solving for v_2 yields

$$-.2 + .2v_2 + .35v_2 = 0$$
$$-.2 + .55v_2 = 0$$
$$.55v_2 = .2$$
$$v_2 \approx .364.$$

Since $v_2 \approx .364$ and $v_1 = 1 - v_2$, it follows that $v_1 \approx 1 - .364 = .636$, and the equilibrium vector is $[.636 \quad .364] \approx [.64 \quad .36]$.

Example 5 **Business** The probability that a complex assembly line works correctly depends on whether the line worked correctly the last time it was used. The various probabilities are as given in the following transition matrix:

	Works Properly Now	Does Not
Worked Properly Before	.79	.21
Did Not	.68	.32

Find the long-range probability that the assembly line will work properly.

Solution Begin by finding the equilibrium vector $[v_1 \quad v_2]$, where

$$[v_1 \quad v_2] \begin{bmatrix} .79 & .21 \\ .68 & .32 \end{bmatrix} = [v_1 \quad v_2].$$

Multiplying on the left and setting corresponding entries equal gives the equations

$$.79v_1 + .68v_2 = v_1 \quad \text{and} \quad .21v_1 + .32v_2 = v_2,$$

or

$$-.21v_1 + .68v_2 = 0 \quad \text{and} \quad .21v_1 - .68v_2 = 0.$$

Substitute $v_1 = 1 - v_2$ in the first of these equations to get

$$-.21(1 - v_2) + .68v_2 = 0$$
$$-.21 + .21v_2 + .68v_2 = 0$$
$$-.21 + .89v_2 = 0$$
$$.89v_2 = .21$$
$$v_2 = \frac{.21}{.89} = \frac{21}{89},$$

and $v_1 = 1 - \dfrac{21}{89} = \dfrac{68}{89}$. The equilibrium vector is $[68/89 \quad 21/89]$. In the long run, the

✓ **Checkpoint 5**

company can expect the assembly line to run properly $\dfrac{68}{89} \approx 76\%$ of the time. ✓₅

In Example 5, suppose the company modifies the line so that the transition matrix becomes

$$\begin{bmatrix} .85 & .15 \\ .75 & .25 \end{bmatrix}.$$

Find the long-range probability that the assembly line will work properly.

Example 6   **Business**   Data from the *Wall Street Journal* web site showed that the probability that a vehicle purchased in the United States in April 2013 was from General Motors (*GM*) was .185, from Ford (*F*) was .165, from Chrysler (*C*) was .122, and from other car manufacturers (*O*) was .528. The following transition matrix indicates market share changes from year to year.

$$\begin{array}{c c} & \begin{array}{cccc} GM & F & C & O \end{array} \\ \begin{array}{c} GM \\ F \\ C \\ O \end{array} & \begin{bmatrix} .85 & .04 & .05 & .06 \\ .02 & .91 & .03 & .04 \\ .01 & .01 & .95 & .03 \\ .03 & .02 & .06 & .89 \end{bmatrix} \end{array}$$

(a) Find the probability that a vehicle purchased in the next year was from Ford.

Solution   To find the market share for each company in the next year we multiply the current market share vector $[.185 \quad .165 \quad .122 \quad .528]$ by the transition matrix. We obtain

$$[.185 \quad .165 \quad .122 \quad .528]\begin{bmatrix} .85 & .04 & .05 & .06 \\ .02 & .91 & .03 & .04 \\ .01 & .01 & .95 & .03 \\ .03 & .02 & .06 & .89 \end{bmatrix}$$

$$= [.17761 \quad .16933 \quad .16178 \quad .49128].$$

The second entry (.16933) indicates that the probability that the vehicle purchased in the next year was from Ford is .16933.

(b) If the trend continues, find the long-term probability that when a new vehicle is purchased, it is from Ford.

Solution   We need to find the equilibrium vector $[v_1 \quad v_2 \quad v_3 \quad v_4]$ where

$$[v_1 \quad v_2 \quad v_3 \quad v_4]\begin{bmatrix} .85 & .04 & .05 & .06 \\ .02 & .91 & .03 & .04 \\ .01 & .01 & .95 & .03 \\ .03 & .02 & .06 & .89 \end{bmatrix} = [v_1 \quad v_2 \quad v_3 \quad v_4].$$

Multiplying on the left side and setting corresponding entries equal gives the equations:

$$.85v_1 + .02v_2 + .01v_3 + .03v_4 = v_1$$
$$.04v_1 + .91v_2 + .01v_3 + .02v_4 = v_2$$
$$.05v_1 + .03v_2 + .95v_3 + .06v_4 = v_3$$
$$.06v_1 + .04v_2 + .03v_3 + .89v_4 = v_4.$$

Simplifying these equations yields:

$$-.15v_1 + .02v_2 + .01v_3 + .03v_4 = 0$$
$$.04v_1 - .09v_2 + .01v_3 + .02v_4 = 0$$
$$.05v_1 + .03v_2 - .05v_3 + .06v_4 = 0$$
$$.06v_1 + .04v_2 + .03v_3 - .11v_4 = 0.$$

Since V is a probability vector, the entries have to add up to 1, so we have

$$v_1 + v_2 + v_3 + v_4 = 1.$$

This gives five equations and four unknown values:

$$v_1 + v_2 + v_3 + v_4 = 1$$
$$-.15v_1 + .02v_2 + .01v_3 + .03v_4 = 0$$
$$.04v_1 - .09v_2 + .01v_3 + .02v_4 = 0$$
$$.05v_1 + .03v_2 - .05v_3 + .06v_4 = 0$$
$$.06v_1 + .04v_2 + .03v_3 - .11v_4 = 0.$$

The system can be solved with the Gauss-Jordan method set forth in Section 6.2. Start with the augmented matrix

$$\begin{bmatrix} 1 & 1 & 1 & 1 & 1 \\ -.15 & .02 & .01 & .03 & 0 \\ .04 & -.09 & .01 & .02 & 0 \\ .05 & .03 & -.05 & .06 & 0 \\ .06 & .04 & .03 & -.11 & 0 \end{bmatrix}.$$

The solution of this system is

$$V \approx [.103 \quad .156 \quad .494 \quad .248].$$

The second entry (.156) tells us the long-term probability that a purchased vehicle is from Ford. ✓ 6

✓ Checkpoint 6

Find the equilibrium vector for the transition matrix

$$P = \begin{bmatrix} .3 & .7 \\ .5 & .5 \end{bmatrix}.$$

In Example 4, we found that $[.64 \quad .36]$ was the equilibrium vector for the regular transition matrix

$$P = \begin{bmatrix} .8 & .2 \\ .35 & .65 \end{bmatrix}.$$

Observe what happens when you take powers of the matrix P (the displayed entries have been rounded for easy reading, but the full decimals were used in the calculations):

$$P^2 = \begin{bmatrix} .71 & .29 \\ .51 & .49 \end{bmatrix}; \quad P^3 = \begin{bmatrix} .67 & .33 \\ .58 & .42 \end{bmatrix}; \quad P^4 = \begin{bmatrix} .65 & .35 \\ .61 & .39 \end{bmatrix};$$

$$P^5 = \begin{bmatrix} .64 & .36 \\ .62 & .38 \end{bmatrix}; \quad P^6 = \begin{bmatrix} .64 & .36 \\ .63 & .37 \end{bmatrix}; \quad P^{10} = \begin{bmatrix} .64 & .36 \\ .64 & .36 \end{bmatrix}.$$

As these results suggest, higher and higher powers of the transition matrix P approach a matrix having all identical rows—rows that have as entries the entries of the equilibrium vector V.

If you have the technology to compute matrix powers easily (such as a graphing calculator), you can approximate the equilibrium vector by taking higher and higher powers of the transition matrix until all its rows are identical. Figure 9.15 shows part of this process for the transition matrix

$$B = \begin{bmatrix} .79 & .21 \\ .68 & .32 \end{bmatrix}$$

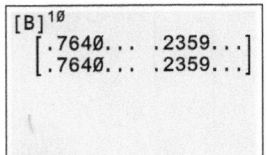

Figure 9.15

Figure 9.15 indicates that the equilibrium vector is approximately [.764   .236], which is what was found algebraically in Example 5.

The results of this section can be summarized as follows.

Properties of Regular Markov Chains

Suppose a regular Markov chain has a transition matrix P.

1. As n gets larger and larger, the product $v \cdot P^n$ approaches a unique vector V for any initial probability vector v. Vector V is called the *equilibrium vector*, or *fixed vector*.

2. Vector V has the property that $VP = V$.

3. To find V, solve a system of equations obtained from the matrix equation $VP = V$ and from the fact that the sum of the entries of V is 1.

4. The powers P^n come closer and closer to a matrix whose rows are made up of the entries of the equilibrium vector V.

9.5 Exercises

Decide which of the given vectors could be a probability vector.

1. $\begin{bmatrix} \frac{1}{4} & \frac{3}{4} \end{bmatrix}$

2. $\begin{bmatrix} \frac{11}{16} & \frac{5}{16} \end{bmatrix}$

3. $[0 \quad 1]$

4. $[.3 \quad .3 \quad .3]$

5. $[.3 \quad -.1 \quad .6]$

6. $\begin{bmatrix} \frac{2}{5} & \frac{3}{10} & .3 \end{bmatrix}$

Decide which of the given matrices could be a transition matrix. Sketch a transition diagram for any transition matrices.

7. $\begin{bmatrix} .7 & .2 \\ .5 & .5 \end{bmatrix}$

8. $\begin{bmatrix} \frac{1}{4} & \frac{3}{4} \\ 0 & 1 \end{bmatrix}$

9. $\begin{bmatrix} \frac{4}{9} & \frac{1}{3} \\ \frac{1}{5} & \frac{7}{10} \end{bmatrix}$

10. $\begin{bmatrix} 0 & 1 & 0 \\ .3 & .3 & .3 \\ 1 & 0 & 0 \end{bmatrix}$

11. $\begin{bmatrix} \frac{1}{2} & \frac{1}{4} & 1 \\ \frac{2}{3} & 0 & \frac{1}{3} \\ \frac{1}{3} & 1 & 0 \end{bmatrix}$

12. $\begin{bmatrix} .2 & .3 & .5 \\ 0 & 0 & 1 \\ .1 & .9 & 0 \end{bmatrix}$

In Exercises 13–15, write any transition diagrams as transition matrices.

13.

14.

15.

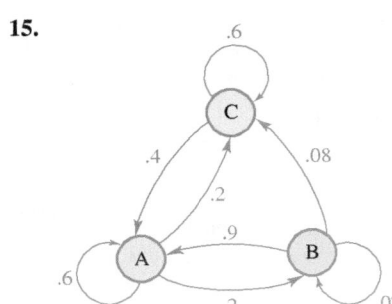

$$\mathbf{30.}\begin{bmatrix} .1 & .2 & .2 & .3 & .2 \\ .2 & .1 & .1 & .2 & .4 \\ .2 & .1 & .4 & .2 & .1 \\ .3 & .1 & .1 & .2 & .3 \\ .1 & .3 & .1 & .1 & .4 \end{bmatrix}\qquad \mathbf{31.}\begin{bmatrix} .3 & .2 & .3 & .1 & .1 \\ .4 & .2 & .1 & .2 & .1 \\ .1 & .3 & .2 & .2 & .2 \\ .2 & .1 & .3 & .2 & .2 \\ .1 & .1 & .4 & .2 & .2 \end{bmatrix}$$

Decide whether the given transition matrices are regular. (See Example 3.)

16. $\begin{bmatrix} 1 & 0 \\ .25 & .75 \end{bmatrix}$ **17.** $\begin{bmatrix} .2 & .8 \\ .9 & .1 \end{bmatrix}$

18. $\begin{bmatrix} .3 & .5 & .2 \\ 1 & 0 & 0 \\ .5 & .1 & .4 \end{bmatrix}$ **19.** $\begin{bmatrix} 0 & 1 & 0 \\ .3 & .3 & .4 \\ 1 & 0 & 0 \end{bmatrix}$

20. $\begin{bmatrix} .25 & .40 & .30 & .05 \\ .18 & .23 & .59 & 0 \\ 0 & .15 & .36 & .49 \\ .28 & .32 & .24 & .16 \end{bmatrix}$ **21.** $\begin{bmatrix} .23 & .41 & 0 & .36 \\ 0 & .27 & .21 & .52 \\ 0 & 0 & 1 & 0 \\ .48 & 0 & .39 & .13 \end{bmatrix}$

Find the equilibrium vector for each of the given transition matrices. (See Examples 4 and 5.)

22. $\begin{bmatrix} .3 & .7 \\ .4 & .6 \end{bmatrix}$ **23.** $\begin{bmatrix} .55 & .45 \\ .19 & .81 \end{bmatrix}$

24. $\begin{bmatrix} \frac{5}{8} & \frac{3}{8} \\ \frac{7}{9} & \frac{2}{9} \end{bmatrix}$ **25.** $\begin{bmatrix} \frac{2}{3} & \frac{1}{3} \\ \frac{1}{8} & \frac{7}{8} \end{bmatrix}$

26. $\begin{bmatrix} .25 & .35 & .4 \\ .1 & .3 & .6 \\ .55 & .4 & .05 \end{bmatrix}$ **27.** $\begin{bmatrix} .16 & .28 & .56 \\ .43 & .12 & .45 \\ .86 & .05 & .09 \end{bmatrix}$

28. $\begin{bmatrix} .15 & .15 & .70 \\ .42 & .38 & .20 \\ .16 & .28 & .56 \end{bmatrix}$ **29.** $\begin{bmatrix} .44 & .31 & .25 \\ .80 & .11 & .09 \\ .26 & .31 & .43 \end{bmatrix}$

For each of the given transition matrices, use a graphing calculator or computer to find the first five powers of the matrix. Then find the probability that state 2 changes to state 4 after 5 repetitions of the experiment.

32. Health In a recent year, the percentage of patients at a doctor's office who received a flu shot was 26%. A campaign by the doctors and nurses was designed to increase the percentage of patients who obtain a flu shot. The doctors and nurses believed there was an 85% chance that someone who received a shot in year 1 would obtain a shot in year 2. They also believed that there was a 40% chance that a person who did not receive a shot in year 1 would receive a shot in year 2.

(a) Give the transition matrix for this situation.

(b) Find the percentages of patients in year 2 who received, and did not receive, a flu shot.

(c) Find the long-range trend for the Markov chain representing receipt of flu shots at the doctor's office.

33. Social Science Six months prior to an election, a poll found that only 35% of state voters planned to vote for a casino gambling initiative. After a media blitz emphasizing the new jobs that are created as a result of casinos, a new poll found that among those who did not favor it previously, 30% now favored the initiative. Among those who favored the initiative initially, 90% still favored it.

(a) Give the transition matrix for this situation.

(b) Find the percentage who favored the gambling initiative after the media blitz.

(c) Find the long-term percentage who favor the initiative if the trends and media blitz continue.

34. Business The probability that a complex assembly line works correctly depends on whether the line worked correctly the last time it was used. There is a .91 chance that the line will work correctly if it worked correctly the time before and a .68 chance that it will work correctly if it did *not* work correctly the time before. Set up a transition matrix with this information, and find the long-run probability that the line will work correctly. (See Example 5.)

35. Business Suppose something unplanned occurred to the assembly line of Exercise 34, so that the transition matrix becomes

	Works	Doesn't Work
Works	.81	.19
Doesn't Works	.77	.23

Find the new long-run probability that the line will work properly.

36. Natural Science In Exercise 60 of Section 8.4 (p. 441), we discussed the effect on flower color of cross-pollinating pea plants. As shown there, since the gene for red is dominant and the gene for white is recessive, 75% of the pea plants have red flowers and 25% have white flowers, because plants with 1 red and 1 white gene appear red. If a red-flowered plant is crossed with a red-flowered plant known to have 1 red and 1 white gene, then 75% of the offspring will be red and 25% will be white. Crossing a red-flowered plant that has 1 red and 1 white gene with a white-flowered plant produces 50% red-flowered offspring and 50% white-flowered offspring.

(a) Write a transition matrix using this information.

(b) Write a probability vector for the initial distribution of colors.

(c) Find the distribution of colors after 4 generations.

(d) Find the long-range distribution of colors.

37. Natural Science   Snapdragons with 1 red gene and 1 white gene produce pink-flowered offspring. If a red snapdragon is crossed with a pink snapdragon, the probabilities that the offspring will be red, pink, or white are $1/2$, $1/2$, and 0, respectively. If 2 pink snapdragons are crossed, the probabilities of red, pink, or white offspring are $1/4$, $1/2$, and $1/4$, respectively. For a cross between a white and a pink snapdragon, the corresponding probabilities are 0, $1/2$, and $1/2$. Set up a transition matrix and find the long-range prediction for the fraction of red, pink, and white snapdragons.

38. Natural Science   Markov chains can be utilized in research into earthquakes. Researchers in Italy give the following example of a transition table in which the rows are magnitudes of an earthquake and the columns are magnitudes of the next earthquake in the sequence.[*]

	2.5	2.6	2.7	2.8
2.5	3/7	1/7	2/7	1/7
2.6	1/2	0	1/4	1/4
2.7	1/3	1/3	0	1/3
2.8	1/4	1/2	0	1/4

Thus, the probability of a 2.5-magnitude earthquake being followed by a 2.8-magnitude earthquake is $1/7$. If these trends were to persist, find the long-range trend for the probabilities of each magnitude for the subsequent earthquake.

39. Social Science   An urban center finds that 60% of the population own a home (O), 39.5% are renters (R), and .5% are homeless (H). The study also finds the following transition probabilities per year.

$$
\begin{array}{c}
 \\
O \\
R \\
H
\end{array}
\begin{array}{ccc}
O & R & H \\
\left[\begin{array}{ccc}
.90 & .10 & 0 \\
.09 & .909 & .001 \\
0 & .34 & .66
\end{array}\right]
\end{array}
$$

(a) Find the probability that residents own, rent, and are homeless after one year.

(b) Find the long-range probabilities for the three categories.

40. Business   An insurance company classifies its drivers into three groups: G_0 (no accidents), G_1 (one accident), and G_2 (more than one accident). The probability that a driver in G_0 will stay in G_0 after 1 year is .85, that he will become a G_1 is .10, and that he will become a G_2 is .05. A driver in G_1 cannot move to G_0. (This insurance company has a long memory!) There is a .80 probability that a G_1 driver will stay in G_1 and a

.20 probability that he will become a G_2. A driver in G_2 must stay in G_2.

(a) Write a transition matrix using this information.

Suppose that the company accepts 50,000 new policy-holders, all of whom are in group G_0. Find the number in each group

(b) after 1 year;   **(c)** after 2 years;

(d) after 3 years;   **(e)** after 4 years.

(f) Find the equilibrium vector here. Interpret your result.

41. Business   The difficulty with the mathematical model of Exercise 40 is that no "grace period" is provided; there should be a certain probability of moving from G_1 or G_2 back to G_0 (say, after 4 years with no accidents). A new system with this feature might produce the following transition matrix:

$$
\left[\begin{array}{ccc}
.85 & .10 & .05 \\
.15 & .75 & .10 \\
.10 & .30 & .60
\end{array}\right].
$$

Suppose that when this new policy is adopted, the company has 50,000 policyholders in group G_0. Find the number in each group

(a) after 1 year;

(b) after 2 years;

(c) after 3 years.

(d) Find the equilibrium vector here. Interpret your result.

42. Business   Suppose research on three major cell phone companies revealed the following transition matrix for the probability that a person with one cell phone carrier switches to another.

		Will Switch to	
	Company A	Company B	Company C
Now has Company A	.91	.07	.02
Company B	.03	.87	.10
Company C	.14	.04	.82

The current share of the market is [.26, .36, .38] for Companies A, B, and C, respectively. Find the share of the market held by each company after

(a) 1 year;   **(b)** 2 years;   **(c)** 3 years.

(d) What is the long-range prediction?

43. Business   Using data similar to those in Example 6, the probability that a new vehicle purchased was from Toyota (T) was .137, American Honda Motor Corporation (H) was .102, and all other manufacturers (O) was .761. Use the transition matrix below for market share changes from year to year.

$$
\begin{array}{c}
 \\
T \\
H \\
O
\end{array}
\begin{array}{ccc}
T & H & O \\
\left[\begin{array}{ccc}
.95 & .02 & .03 \\
.04 & .92 & .04 \\
.09 & .07 & .84
\end{array}\right]
\end{array}
$$

(a) Find the probability that a new vehicle purchased in the next year was from Toyota.

(b) Find the long-term probability that a new vehicle purchase was from Honda.

---

[*]Michele Lovallo, Vincenzo Lapenna, and Luciano Telesca, "Transition matrix analysis of earthquake magnitude sequences," *Chaos, Solitons, and Fractals* 24 (2005): 33–43.

44. Social Science At one liberal arts college, students are classified as humanities majors, science majors, or undecided. There is a 23% chance that a humanities major will change to a science major from one year to the next and a 40% chance that a humanities major will change to undecided. A science major will change to humanities with probability .12 and to undecided with probability .38. An undecided student will switch to humanities or science with probabilities of .45 and .28, respectively. Find the long-range prediction for the fraction of students in each of these three majors.

45. Business In a queuing chain, we assume that people are queuing up to be served by, say, a bank teller. For simplicity, let us assume that once two people are in line, no one else can enter the line. Let us further assume that one person is served every minute, as long as someone is in line. Assume further that, in any minute, there is a probability of .4 that no one enters the line, a probability of .3 that exactly one person enters the line, and a probability of .3 that exactly two people enter the line, assuming that there is room. If there is not enough room for two people, then the probability that one person enters the line is .5. Let the state be given by the number of people in line.

(a) Give the transition matrix for the number of people in line:

$$\begin{array}{c} \\ 0 \\ 1 \\ 2 \end{array}\begin{array}{c} \begin{array}{ccc} 0 & 1 & 2 \end{array} \\ \left[\begin{array}{ccc} ? & ? & ? \\ ? & ? & ? \\ ? & ? & ? \end{array}\right]. \end{array}$$

(b) Find the transition matrix for a 2-minute period.

(c) Use your result from part (b) to find the probability that a queue with no one in line has two people in line 2 minutes later.

Use a graphing calculator or computer for Exercises 46 and 47.

46. Business A company with a new training program classified each employee in one of four states: s_1, never in the program; s_2,

currently in the program; s_3, discharged; s_4, completed the program. The transition matrix for this company is as follows.

$$\begin{array}{c} \\ s_1 \\ s_2 \\ s_3 \\ s_4 \end{array}\begin{array}{c} \begin{array}{cccc} s_1 & s_2 & s_3 & s_4 \end{array} \\ \left[\begin{array}{cccc} .4 & .2 & .05 & .35 \\ 0 & .45 & .05 & .5 \\ 0 & 0 & 1 & 0 \\ 0 & 0 & 0 & 1 \end{array}\right]. \end{array}$$

(a) What percentage of employees who had never been in the program (state s_1) completed the program (state s_4) after the program had been offered five times?

(b) If the initial percentage of employees in each state was [.5 .5 0 0], find the corresponding percentages after the program had been offered four times.

47. Business Find the long-range prediction for the percentage of employees in each state for the company training program in Exercise 46.

✓ **Checkpoint Answers**

1. (a) .7

(b) The probability of changing from state 2 to state 1

(c)

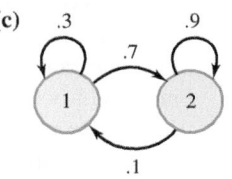

2. [.59 .41] (rounded)

3. [.61 .39] (rounded)

4. (a) No **(b)** Yes

5. $5/6 \approx 83\%$

6. [5/12 7/12]

9.6 Decision Making

John F. Kennedy once remarked that he had assumed that, as president, it would be difficult to choose between distinct, opposite alternatives when a decision needed to be made. Actually, he found that such decisions were easy to make; the hard decisions came when he was faced with choices that were not as clear cut. Most decisions fall into this last category—decisions that must be made under conditions of uncertainty. In Section 9.1, we saw how to use expected values to help make a decision. Those ideas are extended in this section, where we consider decision making in the face of uncertainty. We begin with an example.

Example 1 **Business** Freezing temperatures are endangering the orange crop in central California. A farmer can protect his crop by burning smudge pots; the heat from the pots keeps the oranges from freezing. However, burning the pots is expensive, costing $20,000. The farmer knows that if he burns smudge pots, he will be able to sell his crop for a net profit (after the costs of the pots are deducted) of $50,000, provided that the freeze does develop and wipes out other orange crops in California. If he does nothing, he will either lose the $10,000 he has already invested in the crop if it does freeze or make a profit of $46,000 if it does not freeze. (If it does not freeze, there will be a large supply of oranges, and thus his profit will be lower than if there were a small supply.) What should the farmer do?

Solution   He should begin by carefully defining the problem. First, he must decide on the **states of nature**—the possible alternatives over which he has no control. Here, there are two: freezing temperatures and no freezing temperatures. Next, the farmer should list the things he can control—his actions or **strategies.** He has two possible strategies: to use smudge pots or not. The consequences of each action under each state of nature, called **payoffs,** are summarized in a **payoff matrix,** as follows, where the payoffs in this case are the profits for each possible combination of events:

$$
\begin{array}{cc}
 & \begin{array}{cc} \textit{States of Nature} \\ \text{Freeze} \quad \text{No Freeze} \end{array} \\
\textit{Strategies of Farmer} \quad \begin{array}{c} \text{Use Smudge Pots} \\ \text{Do Not Use Pots} \end{array} & \begin{bmatrix} \$50{,}000 & \$26{,}000 \\ -\$10{,}000 & \$46{,}000 \end{bmatrix}
\end{array}
$$

To get the $26,000 entry in the payoff matrix, use the profit if there is no freeze, namely, $46,000, and subtract the $20,000 cost of using the pots. ✔1

Once the farmer makes the payoff matrix, what then? The farmer might be an optimist (some might call him a gambler); in this case, he might assume that the best will happen and go for the biggest number of the matrix ($50,000). For that profit, he must adopt the strategy "use smudge pots."

On the other hand, if the farmer is a pessimist, he would want to minimize the worst thing that could happen. If he uses smudge pots, the worst thing that could happen to him would be a profit of $26,000, which will result if there is no freeze. If he does not use smudge pots, he might face a loss of $10,000. To minimize the worst, he once again should adopt the strategy "use smudge pots."

Suppose the farmer decides that he is neither an optimist nor a pessimist, but would like further information before choosing a strategy. For example, he might call the weather forecaster and ask for the probability of a freeze. Suppose the forecaster says that this probability is only .2. What should the farmer do? He should recall the discussion of expected value and work out the expected profit for each of his two possible strategies. If the probability of a freeze is .2, then the probability that there is no freeze is .8. This information leads to the following expected values:

If smudge pots are used: $50{,}000(.2) + 26{,}000(.8) = 30{,}800;$
If no smudge pots are used: $-10{,}000(.2) + 46{,}000(.8) = 34{,}800.$

Here, the maximum expected profit, $34,800, is obtained if smudge pots are not used. ✔2

As the example shows, the farmer's beliefs about the probabilities of a freeze affect his choice of strategies.

✓ Checkpoint 1

Explain how each of the given payoffs in the matrix were obtained.

(a)   −$10,000

(b) $50,000

✓ Checkpoint 2

What should the farmer do if the probability of a freeze is .6? What is his expected profit?

Example 2   **Business**   An owner of several greeting-card stores must decide in July about the type of displays to emphasize for Sweetest Day in October. He has three possible choices: emphasize chocolates, emphasize collectible gifts, or emphasize gifts that can be engraved. His success is dependent on the state of the economy in October. If the economy is strong, he will do well with the collectible gifts, while in a weak economy, the chocolates do very well. In a mixed economy, the gifts that can be engraved will do well. He first prepares a payoff matrix for all three possibilities, where the numbers in the matrix represent his profits in thousands of dollars:

$$
\begin{array}{c}
 & \text{States of Nature} \\
 & \begin{array}{ccc} \text{Weak} & \text{Mixed} & \text{Strong} \\ \text{Economy} & & \text{Economy} \end{array}
\end{array}
$$

$$
\textit{Strategies} \quad
\begin{array}{c}
\text{Chocolates} \\
\text{Collectibles} \\
\text{Engraved}
\end{array}
\left[
\begin{array}{ccc}
85 & 30 & 75 \\
45 & 45 & 110 \\
60 & 95 & 85
\end{array}
\right].
$$

(a) What would an optimist do?

Solution If the owner is an optimist, he should aim for the biggest number on the matrix, 110 (representing $110,000 in profit). His strategy in this case would be to display collectibles.

(b) How would a pessimist react?

Solution A pessimist wants to find the best of the worst things that can happen. If he displays collectibles, the worst that can happen is a profit of $45,000. For displaying engravable items, the worst is a profit of $60,000, and for displaying chocolates, the worst is a profit of $30,000. His strategy here is to use the engravable items.

(c) Suppose the owner reads in a business magazine that leading experts believe that there is a 50% chance of a weak economy in October, a 20% chance of a mixed economy, and a 30% chance of a strong economy. How might he use this information?

Solution The owner can now find his expected profit for each possible strategy.

$$
\begin{array}{ll}
\text{Chocolates} & 85(.5) + 30(.20) + 75(.30) = 71; \\
\text{Collectibles} & 45(.5) + 45(.20) + 110(.30) = 64.5; \\
\text{Engraved} & 60(.5) + 95(.20) + 85(.30) = 74.5.
\end{array}
$$

Here, the best strategy is to display gifts that can be engraved; the expected profit is 74.5, or $74,500. ✔3

✔ **Checkpoint 3**

Suppose the owner reads another article, which gives the following predictions: a 35% chance of a weak economy, a 25% chance of an in-between economy, and a 40% chance of a strong economy. What is the best strategy now? What is the expected profit?

9.6 Exercises

1. Business A developer has $100,000 to invest in land. He has a choice of two parcels (at the same price): one on the highway and one on the coast. With both parcels, his ultimate profit depends on whether he faces light opposition from environmental groups or heavy opposition. He estimates that the payoff matrix is as follows (the numbers represent his profit):

$$
\begin{array}{c}
 & \textit{Opposition} \\
 & \begin{array}{cc} \text{Light} & \text{Heavy} \end{array}
\end{array}
$$

$$
\begin{array}{c}
\text{Highway} \\
\text{Coast}
\end{array}
\left[
\begin{array}{cc}
\$70{,}000 & \$30{,}000 \\
\$150{,}000 & -\$40{,}000
\end{array}
\right].
$$

What should the developer do if he is

(a) an optimist?

(b) a pessimist?

(c) Suppose the probability of heavy opposition is .8. What is his best strategy? What is the expected profit?

(d) What is the best strategy if the probability of heavy opposition is only .4?

2. Business Mount Union College has sold out all tickets for a jazz concert to be held in the stadium. If it rains, the show will have to be moved to the gym, which has a much smaller seating capacity. The dean must decide in advance whether to set up the seats and the stage in the gym, in the stadium, or in both, just in case. The following payoff matrix shows the net profit in each case:

$$
\begin{array}{c}
 & \text{States of Nature} \\
 & \begin{array}{cc} \text{Rain} & \text{No Rain} \end{array}
\end{array}
$$

$$
\textit{Strategies} \quad
\begin{array}{c}
\text{Set up in Stadium} \\
\text{Set up in Gym} \\
\text{Set up in Both}
\end{array}
\left[
\begin{array}{cc}
-\$1550 & \$1500 \\
\$1000 & \$1000 \\
\$750 & \$1400
\end{array}
\right].
$$

What strategy should the dean choose if she is

(a) an optimist?

(b) a pessimist?

(c) If the weather forecaster predicts rain with a probability of .6, what strategy should she choose to maximize the expected profit? What is the maximum expected profit?

3. Business An analyst must decide what fraction of the automobile tires produced at a particular manufacturing plant are defective. She has already decided that there are three possibilities for the fraction of defective items: .02, .09, and .16. She may recommend two courses of action: upgrade the equipment at the plant or make no upgrades. The following payoff matrix represents the *costs* to the company in each case, in hundreds of dollars:

$$\begin{array}{c} & \textit{Defectives} \\ & \begin{array}{ccc} .02 & .09 & .16 \end{array} \\ \textit{Strategies} \begin{array}{c} \text{Upgrade} \\ \text{No Upgrade} \end{array} & \left[\begin{array}{ccc} 130 & 130 & 130 \\ 28 & 180 & 450 \end{array} \right]. \end{array}$$

What strategy should the analyst recommend if she is

(a) an optimist?

(b) a pessimist?

(c) Suppose the analyst is able to estimate probabilities for the three states of nature as follows:

Fraction of Defectives	Probability
.02	.70
.09	.20
.16	.10

Which strategy should she recommend? Find the expected cost to the company if that strategy is chosen.

4. Business The research department of the Allied Manufacturing Company has developed a new process that it believes will result in an improved product. Management must decide whether to go ahead and market the new product or not. The new product may be better than the old one, or it may not be better. If the new product is better and the company decides to market it, sales should increase by $50,000. If it is not better and the old product is replaced with the new product on the market, the company will lose $25,000 to competitors. If management decides not to market the new product, the company will lose $40,000 if it is better and will lose research costs of $10,000 if it is not.

(a) Prepare a payoff matrix.

(b) If management believes that the probability that the new product is better is .4, find the expected profits under each strategy and determine the best action.

5. Business A businessman is planning to ship a used machine to his plant in Nigeria. He would like to use it there for the next 4 years. He must decide whether to overhaul the machine before sending it. The cost of overhaul is $2600. If the machine fails when it is in operation in Nigeria, it will cost him $6000 in lost production and repairs. He estimates that the probability that it will fail is .3 if he does not overhaul it and .1 if he does overhaul it. Neglect the possibility that the machine might fail more than once in the 4 years.

(a) Prepare a payoff matrix.

(b) What should the businessman do to minimize his expected costs?

6. Business A contractor prepares to bid on a job. If all goes well, his bid should be $25,000, which will cover his costs plus his usual profit margin of $4000. However, if a threatened labor strike actually occurs, his bid should be $35,000 to give him the same profit. If there is a strike and he bids $25,000, he will lose $5500. If his bid is too high, he may lose the job entirely, while if it is too low, he may lose money.

(a) Prepare a payoff matrix.

(b) If the contractor believes that the probability of a strike is .6, how much should he bid?

7. Business An artist travels to craft fairs all summer long. She must book her booth at a June craft show six months in advance and decide if she wishes to rent a tent for an extra $500 in case it rains on the day of the show. If it does not rain, she believes she will earn $3000 at the show. If it rains, she believes she will earn only $2000, provided she has a tent. If she does not have a tent and it does rain, she will have to pack up and go home and will thus earn $0. Weather records over the last 10 years indicate that there is a .4 probability of rain in June.

(a) Prepare a profit matrix.

(b) What should the artist do to maximize her expected revenue?

8. Business An investor has $50,000 to invest in stocks. She has two possible strategies: buy conservative blue-chip stocks or buy highly speculative stocks. There are two states of nature: the market goes up and the market goes down. The following payoff matrix shows the net amounts she will have under the various circumstances.

$$\begin{array}{c} & \begin{array}{cc} \text{Market Up} & \text{Market Down} \end{array} \\ \begin{array}{c} \text{Buy Blue Chip} \\ \text{Buy Speculative} \end{array} & \left[\begin{array}{cc} \$60{,}000 & \$46{,}000 \\ \$80{,}000 & \$32{,}000 \end{array} \right]. \end{array}$$

What should the investor do if she is

(a) an optimist?

(b) a pessimist?

(c) Suppose there is a .6 probability of the market going up. What is the best strategy? What is the expected profit?

(d) What is the best strategy if the probability of a market rise is .2?

Sometimes the numbers (or payoffs) in a payoff matrix do not represent money (profits or costs, for example). Instead, they may represent utility. A utility is a number that measures the satisfaction (or lack of it) that results from a certain action. Utility numbers must be assigned by each individual, depending on how he or she feels about a situation. For example, one person might assign a utility of +20 for a week's vacation in San Francisco, with −6 being assigned if the vacation were moved to Sacramento. Work the problems that follow in the same way as the preceding ones.

9. Social Science A politician must plan her reelection strategy. She can emphasize jobs or she can emphasize the environment. The voters can be concerned about jobs or about the environment. Following is a payoff matrix showing the utility of each possible outcome.

$$\begin{array}{c} & \textit{Voters} \\ & \begin{array}{cc} \text{Jobs} & \text{Environment} \end{array} \\ \textit{Candidate} \begin{array}{c} \text{Jobs} \\ \text{Environment} \end{array} & \left[\begin{array}{cc} +40 & -10 \\ -12 & +30 \end{array} \right] \end{array}$$

The political analysts feel that there is a .35 chance that the voters will emphasize jobs. What strategy should the candidate adopt? What is its expected utility?

10. In an accounting class, the instructor permits the students to bring a calculator or a reference book (but not both) to an examination. The examination itself can emphasize either numbers or definitions. In trying to decide which aid to take to an examination, a student first decides on the utilities shown in the following payoff matrix:

$$
\begin{array}{cc}
 & \textit{Exam Emphasizes} \\
 & \text{Numbers} \quad \text{Definition}
\end{array}
$$

$$
\textit{Student Chooses} \quad
\begin{array}{c}
\text{Calculator} \\
\text{Book}
\end{array}
\left[
\begin{array}{cc}
+50 & 0 \\
+15 & +35
\end{array}
\right]
$$

(a) What strategy should the student choose if the probability that the examination will emphasize numbers is .6? What is the expected utility in this case?

(b) Suppose the probability that the examination emphasizes numbers is .4. What strategy should the student choose?

✓**Checkpoint Answers**

1. (a) If the crop freezes and smudge pots are not used, the farmer's profit is −$10,000 for labor costs.

(b) If the crop freezes and smudge pots are used, the farmer makes a profit of $50,000.

2. Use smudge pots; $40,400

3. Engravable; $78,750

CHAPTER 9 Summary and Review

Key Terms and Symbols

9.1 random variable
probability distribution
histogram
expected value
fair game

9.2 n! (n factorial)
multiplication principle

permutations
combinations

9.4 Bernoulli trials (processes)
binomial experiment
binomial probability

9.5 stochastic processes
Markov chain

state
transition diagram
transition matrix
probability vector
regular transition
   matrix
regular Markov chain

equilibrium vector
   (fixed vector)

9.6 states of nature
strategies
payoffs
payoff matrix

Chapter 9 Key Concepts

Expected Value For a random variable x with values $x_1, x_2, \ldots, x_n$ and probabilities $p_1, p_2, \ldots, p_n$, the expected value is

$$E(x) = x_1 p_1 + x_2 p_2 + \cdots + x_n p_n.$$

Multiplication Principle If there are m_1 ways to make a first choice, m_2 ways to make a second choice, and so on, then there are $m_1 m_2 \cdots m_n$ different ways to make the entire sequence of choices.

Permutations The number of **permutations** of n elements taken r at a time is $_nP_r = \dfrac{n!}{(n-r)!}$.

Combinations The number of **combinations** of n elements taken r at a time is

$$_nC_r = \frac{n!}{(n-r)!r!}.$$

Binomial Experiments Binomial Experiments have the following characteristics: (1) The same experiment is repeated a finite number of times; (2) there are only *two* outcomes, labeled success and failure; (3) the probability of success is the same for each trial; and (4) the trials are independent. If the probability of success in a single trial is p, the probability of x successes in n trials is
$$_nC_x p^x(1-p)^{n-x}.$$

Markov Chains A **transition matrix** must be square, with all entries between 0 and 1 inclusive, and the sum of the entries in any row must be 1. A Markov chain is *regular* if some power of its transition matrix P contains all positive entries. The long-range probabilities for a regular Markov chain are given by the **equilibrium**, or **fixed**, **vector** V, where, for any initial probability vector v, the products vP^n approach V as n gets larger and $VP = V$. To find V, solve the system of equations formed by $VP = V$ and the fact that the sum of the entries of V is 1.

Decision Making A **payoff matrix**, which includes all available strategies and states of nature, is used in decision making to define the problem and the possible solutions. The expected value of each strategy can help to determine the best course of action.

Chapter 9 Review Exercises

In Exercises 1–4, (a) sketch the histogram of the given probability distribution, and (b) find the expected value.

1.

x	0	1	2	3
$P(x)$	.22	.54	.16	.08

2.

x	−3	−2	−1	0	1	2	3
$P(x)$	.15	.20	.25	.18	.12	.06	.04

3.

x	−10	0	10
$P(x)$	$\dfrac{1}{3}$	$\dfrac{1}{3}$	$\dfrac{1}{3}$

4.

x	0	2	4	6
$P(x)$	.35	.15	.2	.3

5. Business The probability distribution of the number of mortgages held on a household is given below. Find the expected number of mortgages. (Data from: www.census.gov/housing/ahs.)

x	1	2	3	4
$P(x)$	.84513	.15221	.00251	.00014

6. Social Science The probability distribution of the number of bedrooms in a given household is presented below. Find the expected number of bedrooms. (Data from: www.census.gov/housing/ahs.)

x	0	1	2	3	4	5	6	7	8
$P(x)$	.0115	.1324	.2671	.3819	.1655	.0355	.0053	.0006	.0001

In Exercises 7 and 8, (a) give the probability distribution, and (b) find the expected value.

7. Business A grocery store has 10 bouquets of flowers for sale, 3 of which are rose displays. Two bouquets are selected at random, and the number of rose bouquets is noted.

8. Social Science In a class of 10 students, 3 did not do their homework. The professor selects 3 members of the class to present solutions to homework problems on the board and records how many of those selected did not do their homework.

Solve the given problems.

9. Suppose someone offers to pay you $100 if you draw 3 cards from a standard deck of 52 cards and all the cards are hearts. What should you pay for the chance to win if it is a fair game?

10. You pay $2 to play a game of "Over/Under," in which you will roll two dice and note the sum of the results. You can bet that the sum will be less than 7 (under), exactly 7, or greater than 7 (over). If you bet "under" and you win, you get your $2 back, plus $2 more. If you bet 7 and you win, you get your $2 back, plus $4, and if you bet "over" and win, you get your $2 back, plus $2 more. What are the expected winnings for each type of bet?

11. Business In April 2013, Apple's estimated share of the personal computer market was 5%. If we select 3 new computer purchases at random and define x to be the number of computers that are Apple, the probability distribution is as given below. Find the expected value for x. (Data from: www.cnn.com.)

x	0	1	2	3
$P(x)$	.8574	.1354	.0071	.0001

12. Social Science According to data from the American Housing Survey, approximately 20% of U.S. residents do not have a vehicle available at the residence for personal use. If we select 5 people at random and define x to be the number that do not have access to a vehicle, the following probability distribution is given. Find the expected value for x. (Data from: www.census.gov/housing/ahs.)

x	0	1	2	3	4	5
$P(x)$	0.3277	0.4096	0.2048	0.0512	0.0064	0.0003

13. In how many ways can 8 different taxis line up at the airport?

14. How many variations are possible for gold, silver, and bronze medalists in the 50-meter swimming race if there are 8 finalists?

15. In how many ways can a sample of 3 computer monitors be taken from a batch of 12 identical monitors?

16. If 4 of the 12 monitors in Exercise 15 are broken, in how many ways can the sample of 3 include the following?

   (a) 1 broken monitor;

   (b) no broken monitors;

   (c) at least 1 broken monitor.

17. In how many ways can 6 students from a class of 30 be arranged in the first row of seats? (There are 6 seats in the first row.)

18. In how many ways can the six students in Exercise 17 be arranged in a row if a certain student must be first?

19. In how many ways can the 6 students in Exercise 17 be arranged if half the students are science majors and the other half are business majors and if

   (a) like majors must be together?

   (b) science and business majors are alternated?

20. Explain under what circumstances a permutation should be used in a probability problem and under what circumstances a combination should be used.

21. Discuss under what circumstances the binomial probability formula should be used in a probability problem.

Suppose 2 cards are drawn without replacement from an ordinary deck of 52 cards. Find the probabilities of the given results.

22. Both cards are black.

23. Both cards are hearts.

24. Exactly 1 is a face card.

25. At most 1 is an ace.

An ice cream stand contains 4 custard flavors, 6 ice cream flavors, and 2 frozen yogurt selections. Three customers come to the window. If each customer's selection is random, find the probability that the selections include

26. all ice cream;

27. all custard;

28. at least one frozen yogurt;

29. one custard, one ice cream, and one frozen yogurt;

30. at most one ice cream.

In Exercises 31 and 32, we study the connection between sets (from Chapter 8) and combinations.

31. Given a set with n elements,

(a) what is the number of subsets of size 0? of size 1? of size 2? of size n?

(b) Using your answer from part (a) give an expression for the total number of subsets of a set with n elements.

32. Using your answers from Exercise 31 and the results from Chapter 8

(a) explain why the following equation must be true:

$$_nC_0 + {}_nC_1 + {}_nC_2 + \ldots + {}_nC_n = 2^n.$$

(b) verify the equation in part (a) for $n = 4$ and $n = 5$.

Business *According to the Wall Street Journal, the drug company Actavis obtains 75% of its revenue from the sales of generic drugs.*

33. Suppose 7 Actavis drug sales are selected at random. Find the probability distribution for x, the number of Actavis generic drug sales. Find the expected number of drug sales that are from generic drugs.

34. Suppose 10 Actavis drug sales are selected at random. Find the probability distribution for x, the number of Actavis generic drug sales. Find the expected number of generic drug sales. (*Hint:* Carry your calculations to six decimal places.)

35. Finance As of May 2013, the Vanguard Capital Value Fund had 14.5% of its assets invested in energy stocks. If 6 stocks are selected at random from the fund, find the probability that the given numbers of stocks are energy stocks.

(a) None of the stocks

(b) At least 2 of the stocks

(c) At most 4 of the stocks

36. Business As of May 2013, 22% of the Janus Health Global Life Sciences Fund (a high-growth investment mutual fund) was invested in foreign stocks. If 4 stocks from the fund are picked at random, find the probability that the given numbers of stocks are foreign stocks.

(a) All 4 stocks

(b) At least 1 stock

(c) At most 2 stocks

37. Business In 2013, the percentage of banking institutions insured by the Federal Deposit Insurance Corporation (FDIC)

with total assets of $100 million or more was 61.4%. Suppose that we select 5 insured banking institutions at random. (Data from: www2.fdic.gov/sod.)

(a) Give the probability distribution for x, the number of banking institutions with $100 million or more in assets.

(b) Give the expected value for the number of banking institutions with $100 million or more in assets.

Decide whether each matrix is a regular transition matrix.

38. $\begin{bmatrix} 0 & 1 \\ .77 & .23 \end{bmatrix}$ **39.** $\begin{bmatrix} -.2 & .4 \\ .3 & .7 \end{bmatrix}$

40. $\begin{bmatrix} .21 & .15 & .64 \\ .50 & .12 & .38 \\ 1 & 0 & 0 \end{bmatrix}$ **41.** $\begin{bmatrix} .22 & 0 & .78 \\ .40 & .33 & .27 \\ 0 & .61 & .39 \end{bmatrix}$

42. Business Using e-mail for professional correspondence has become a major component of a worker's day. A study classified e-mail use into 3 categories for an office day: no use, light use (1–60 minutes), and heavy use (more than 60 minutes). Researchers observed a pool of 100 office workers over a month and developed the following transition matrix of probabilities from day to day:

		Current Day		
		No Use	Light Use	Heavy Use
	No use	.35	.15	.50
Previous Day	Light Use	.30	.35	.35
	Heavy Use	.15	.30	.55

Suppose the initial distribution for the three categories is [.2, .4, .4]. Find the distribution after

(a) 1 day;

(b) 2 days.

(c) What is the long-range prediction for the distribution of e-mail use?

43. Business An analyst at a major brokerage firm that invests in Europe, North America, and Asia has examined the investment records for a particular international stock mutual fund over several years. The analyst constructed the following transition matrix for the probability of switching the location of an equity from year to year:

		Current Year		
		Europe	North America	Asia
	Europe	.80	.14	.06
Previous Year	North America	.04	.85	.11
	Asia	.03	.13	.84

If the initial investment vector is 15% in Europe, 60% in North America, and 25% in Asia,

(a) find the percentages in Europe, North America, and Asia after 1 year;

(b) find the percentages in Europe, North America, and Asia after 3 years;

(c) find the long-range percentages in Europe, North America, and Asia.

44. Social Science A candidate for city council can come out in favor of a new factory, be opposed to it, or waffle on the issue. The change in votes for the candidate depends on what her opponent does, with payoffs as shown in the following matrix:

$$\begin{array}{c} & & \textit{Opponent} \\ & & \text{Favors} \quad \text{Waffles} \quad \text{Opposes} \\ \textit{Candidate} & \begin{array}{l} \text{Favors} \\ \text{Waffles} \\ \text{Opposes} \end{array} & \left[\begin{array}{ccc} 0 & -1000 & -4000 \\ 1000 & 0 & -500 \\ 5000 & 2000 & 0 \end{array}\right]. \end{array}$$

(a) What should the candidate do if she is an optimist?

(b) What should she do if she is a pessimist?

(c) Suppose the candidate's campaign manager feels that there is a 40% chance that the opponent will favor the plant and a 35% chance that he will waffle. What strategy should the candidate adopt? What is the expected change in the number of votes?

(d) The opponent conducts a new poll that shows strong opposition to the new factory. This changes the probability that he will favor the factory to 0 and the probability that he will waffle to .7. What strategy should our candidate adopt? What is the expected change in the number of votes now?

45. Social Science When teaching, an instructor can adopt a strategy using either active learning or lecturing to help students learn best. A class often reacts very differently to these two strategies. A class can prefer lecturing or active learning. A department chair constructs the following payoff matrix of the average point gain (out of 500 possible points) on the final exam after studying many classes that use active learning and many that use lecturing and polling students as to their preference:

$$\begin{array}{c} & & \textit{Students in class prefer} \\ & & \text{Lecture} \quad \text{Active Learning} \\ \begin{array}{l} \textit{Instructor} \\ \textit{uses} \end{array} & \begin{array}{l} \text{Lecture} \\ \text{Active Learning} \end{array} & \left[\begin{array}{cc} 50 & -80 \\ -30 & 100 \end{array}\right]. \end{array}$$

(a) If the department chair uses the preceding information to decide how to teach her own classes, what should she do if she is an optimist?

(b) What about if she is a pessimist?

(c) If the polling data shows that there is a 75% chance that a class will prefer the lecture format, what strategy should she adopt? What is the expected payoff?

(d) If the chair finds out that her next class has had more experience with active learning, so that there is now a 60% chance that the class will prefer active learning, what strategy should she adopt? What is the expected payoff?

Exercises 46 and 47 are taken from actuarial examinations given by the Society of Actuaries.

46. Business A company is considering the introduction of a new product that is believed to have probability .5 of being successful and probability .5 of being unsuccessful. Successful products pass quality control 80% of the time. Unsuccessful products pass quality control 25% of the time. If the product is successful, the net profit to the company will be $40 million; if unsuccessful, the net loss will be $15 million. Determine the expected net profit if the product passes quality control.

(a) $23 million
(b) $24 million
(c) $25 million
(d) $26 million
(e) $27 million

47. Business A merchant buys boxes of fruit from a grower and sells them. Each box of fruit is either Good or Bad. A Good box contains 80% excellent fruit and will earn $200 profit on the retail market. A Bad box contains 30% excellent fruit and will produce a loss of $1000. The a priori probability of receiving a Good box of fruit is .9. Before the merchant decides to put the box on the market, he can sample one piece of fruit to test whether it is excellent. Based on that sample, he has the option of rejecting the box without paying for it. Determine the expected value of the right to sample. (*Hint:* If the merchant samples the fruit, what are the probabilities of accepting a Good box, accepting a Bad box, and not accepting the box? What are these probabilities if he does not sample the fruit?)

(a) 0
(b) $16
(c) $34
(d) $72
(e) $80

48. Business An issue of *Mathematics Teacher* included "Overbooking Airline Flights," an article by Joe Dan Austin. In this article, Austin developed a model for the expected income for an airline flight. With appropriate assumptions, the probability that exactly x of n people with reservations show up at the airport to buy a ticket is given by the binomial probability formula. Assume the following: Six reservations have been accepted for 3 seats, $p = .6$ is the probability that a person with a reservation will show up, a ticket costs $100, and the airline must pay $100 to anyone with a reservation who does not get a ticket. Complete the following table:

Number Who Show Up (x)	0	1	2	3	4	5	6
Airline's Income							
$P(x)$							

(a) Use the table to find $E(I)$, the expected income from the 3 seats.

(b) Find $E(I)$ for $n = 3, n = 4$, and $n = 5$. Compare these answers with $E(I)$ for $n = 6$. For these values of n, how many reservations should the airline book for the 3 seats in order to maximize the expected revenue?

*Problems No. 46 and 47: Business from Course 130 Examination, Operations Research. Copyright © Society of Actuaries. Reproduced by permission of Society of Actuaries.

Case Study 9 Quick Draw® from the New York State Lottery

At bars and restaurants in the state of New York, patrons can play an electronic lottery game called Quick Draw.* A similar game is available in many other states. There are 10 ways for a patron to play this game. Prior to the draw, a person may bet $1 on games called 10-spot, 9-spot, 8-spot, 7-spot, 6-spot, 5-spot, 4-spot, 3-spot, 2-spot, and 1-spot. Depending on the game, the player will choose numbers from 1 to 80. For the 10-spot game, the player chooses 10 numbers; for a 9-spot game, the player chooses 9 numbers; etc. Every four minutes, the State of New York chooses 20 numbers at random from the numbers 1 to 80. For example, if a player chose the 6-spot game, he or she will have picked 6 numbers. If 3, 4, 5, or 6 of the numbers the player picked are also numbers the state picked randomly, then the player will win money. Each game has different ways to win, with differing payoff amounts. Notice with the 10-spot, 9-spot, 8-spot, and 7-spot, a player can win by matching 0 numbers correctly. The accompanying tables show the payoffs for the different games. Notice that a player does not have to match all the numbers he or she picked in order to win.

10-spot Game

Numbers Matched	Winnings per $1 Played
10	$100,000
9	$5000
8	$300
7	$45
6	$10
5	$2
0	$5

9-spot Game

Numbers Matched	Winnings per $1 Played
9	$30,000
8	$3000
7	$125
6	$20
5	$5
0	$2

8-spot Game

Numbers Matched	Winnings per $1 Played
8	$10,000
7	$550
6	$75
5	$6
0	$2

7-spot Game

Numbers Matched	Winnings per $1 Played
7	$5000
6	$100
5	$20
4	$2
0	$1

6-spot Game

Numbers Matched	Winnings per $1 Played
6	$1000
5	$55
4	$6
3	$1

5-spot Game

Numbers Matched	Winnings per $1 Played
5	$300
4	$20
3	$2

4-spot Game

Numbers Matched	Winnings per $1 Played
4	$55
3	$5
2	$1

3-spot Game

Numbers Matched	Winnings per $1 Played
3	$23
2	$2

2-spot Game

Numbers Matched	Winnings per $1 Played
2	$10

1-spot Game

Numbers Matched	Winnings per $1 Played
1	$2

With our knowledge of counting, it is possible for us to calculate the probability of winning for these different games.

Example 1 Find the probability distribution for the number of matches for the 6-spot game.

Solution Let us define x to be the number of matches when playing 6-spot. The outcomes of x are then 0, 1, 2, . . . , 6. To find the probabilities of these matches, we need to do a little thinking. First, we need to know how many ways a player can pick 6 numbers from the selection of 1 to 80. Since the order in which the player picks the numbers does not matter, the number of ways to pick 6 numbers is

$$_{80}C_6 = \frac{80!}{74!\,6!} = 300,500,200.$$

To find the probability of the outcomes of 0 to 6, we can think of the 80 choices broken into groups: 20 winning numbers the state picked and 60 losing numbers the state did not pick. If x, the number of matches, is 0, then the player picked 0 numbers from the 20 winning numbers and 6 from the 60 losing numbers. Using the multiplication principle, we find that this quantity is

$$_{20}C_0 \cdot {}_{60}C_6 = \left(\frac{20!}{20!\,0!}\right)\left(\frac{60!}{54!\,6!}\right) = (1)(50,063,860) = 50,063,860.$$

---

*More information on Quick Draw can be found at www.nylottery.org; click on "Daily Games."

Therefore,

$$P(x = 0) = \frac{{}_{20}C_0 \cdot {}_{60}C_6}{{}_{80}C_6} = \frac{50,063,860}{300,500,200} \approx .16660.$$

Similarly for $x = 1, 2, \ldots, 6$, and completing the probability distribution table, we have

x	$P(x)$
0	$\dfrac{{}_{20}C_0 \cdot {}_{60}C_6}{{}_{80}C_6} \approx .16660$
1	$\dfrac{{}_{20}C_1 \cdot {}_{60}C_5}{{}_{80}C_6} \approx .36349$
2	$\dfrac{{}_{20}C_2 \cdot {}_{60}C_4}{{}_{80}C_6} \approx .30832$
3	$\dfrac{{}_{20}C_3 \cdot {}_{60}C_3}{{}_{80}C_6} \approx .12982$
4	$\dfrac{{}_{20}C_4 \cdot {}_{60}C_2}{{}_{80}C_6} \approx .02854$
5	$\dfrac{{}_{20}C_5 \cdot {}_{60}C_1}{{}_{80}C_6} \approx .00310$
6	$\dfrac{{}_{20}C_6 \cdot {}_{60}C_0}{{}_{80}C_6} \approx .00013$

Example 2 Find the expected winnings for a $1 bet on the 6-spot game.

Solution To find the expected winnings, we take the winnings for each number of matches and subtract our $1 initial payment fee. Thus, we have the following:

x	Net Winnings	$P(x)$
0	−$1	.16660
1	−$1	.36349
2	−$1	.30832
3	$0	.12982
4	$5	.02854
5	$54	.00310
6	$999	.00013

The expected winnings are

$$\begin{aligned}E(\text{winnings}) &= (-1)\cdot.16660 + (-1)\cdot.36349 \\ &\quad + (-1)\cdot.30832 + 0\cdot.12982 + 5(.02854) \\ &\quad + 54(.00310) + 999(.00013) \\ &= -.39844.\end{aligned}$$

Thus, for every $1 bet on the 6-spot game, a player would lose about 40 cents. Put another way, the state gets about 40 cents, on average, from every $1 bet on 6-spot.

Exercises

1. If New York State initiates a promotion where players earn "double payoffs" for the 6-spot game (that is, if a player matched 3 numbers, she would win $2; if she matched 4 numbers, she would win $12; etc.), find the expected winnings.

2. Would it be in the state's interest to offer such a promotion? Why or why not?

3. Find the probability distribution for the 4-spot game.

4. Find the expected winnings for the 4-spot game.

5. If the state offers double payoffs for the 4-spot game, what are the expected winnings?

Extended Projects

1. In Ohio, a game similar to Quick Draw is KENO. Investigate the rules, bets, and payoffs of this game. Determine in what ways it is similar to Quick Draw and in what way it differs. Examine the expected value if any of the games were to offer double payoffs. Are any of the expected values with double payoffs positive?

2. Investigate whether your own state or a state near you has a game similar to Quick Draw. Determine if the rules, bets, and payoffs of this game are similar to Quick Draw. Determine in what ways the game in your state is similar to Quick Draw and in what way it differs. Examine the consequences on the expected value if the games were to offer double payoffs.

Introduction to Statistics

10

Statistics has applications to almost every aspect of modern life. The digital age is creating a wealth of data that needs to be summarized, visualized, and analyzed, from the earnings of major-league baseball teams to movies' box-office receipts and the sales for the soft-drink industry. See Exercises 25 and 26 on pages 534 and 535, and Exercises 51–56 on page 556.

Statistics is the science that deals with the collection and summarization of data. Methods of statistical analysis make it possible to draw conclusions about a population on the basis of data from a sample of the population. Statistical models have become increasingly useful in manufacturing, government, agriculture, medicine, and the social sciences and in all types of research. An Indianapolis race-car team, for example, is using statistics to improve its performance by gathering data on each run around the track. The team samples data 300 times a second and uses computers to process the data. In this chapter, we give a brief introduction to some of the key topics from statistical methodology.

10.1 Frequency Distributions

Researchers often wish to learn characteristics or traits of a specific **population** of individuals, objects, or units. The traits of interest are called **variables,** and it is these that we measure or label. Often, however, a population of interest is very large or constantly changing, so measuring each unit is impossible. Thus, researchers are forced to collect data on a subset of the population of interest, called a **sample.**

Sampling is a complex topic, but the universal aim of all sampling methods is to obtain a sample that "represents" the population of interest. One common way of obtaining a representative sample is to perform simple random sampling, in which every unit of the population has an equal chance to be selected to be in the sample. Suppose we wanted to study the height of students enrolled in a class. To obtain a random sample, we could place slips of paper containing the names of everyone in class in a hat, mix the papers, and draw 10 names blindly. We would then record the height (the variable of interest) for each student selected.

A simple random sample can be difficult to obtain in real life. For example, suppose you want to take a random sample of voters in your congressional district to see which candidate they prefer in the next election. If you do a telephone survey, you have a representative sample of people who are at home to answer the telephone, but those who are rarely home to answer the phone, those who have an unlisted number or only a cell phone, those who cannot afford a telephone, and those who refuse to answer telephone surveys are underrepresented. Such people may have an opinion different from those of the people you interview.

A famous example of an inaccurate poll was made by the *Literary Digest* in 1936. Its survey indicated that Alfred Landon would win the presidential election; in fact, Franklin Roosevelt won with 62% of the popular vote. The *Digest*'s major error was mailing its surveys to a sample of those listed in telephone directories. During the Depression, many poor people did not have telephones, and the poor voted overwhelmingly for Roosevelt. Modern pollsters use sophisticated techniques to ensure that their sample is as representative as possible.

Once a sample has been collected and all data of interest are recorded, the data must be organized so that conclusions may be more easily drawn. With numeric responses, one method of organization is to group the data into intervals, usually of equal size.

Example 1   **Education**   The following list gives the 2011–2012 annual tuition (in thousands of dollars) for a random sample of 40 community colleges. (Data from: www.collegeboard.org.)

3.8	1.1	2.5	3.5	4.0	3.8	3.9	4.2	3.1	3.9
5.0	1.1	2.0	3.4	3.5	1.1	2.3	4.8	1.1	3.1
3.5	5.1	3.3	3.2	2.1	5.3	2.6	2.3	2.5	3.6
4.9	3.0	2.4	3.6	3.1	3.7	5.1	3.5	2.0	4.4

Identify the population and the variable, group the data into intervals, and find the frequency of each interval.

Solution   The population is all community colleges. The variable of interest is the tuition (in thousands of dollars). The lowest value is 1.1 (corresponding to $1100) and the highest value is 5.3 (corresponding to $5300). One convenient way to group the intervals is in intervals of size .5, starting with 1.0–1.4 and ending with 5.0–5.4. This grouping provides an interval for each value in the list and results in 9 equally sized intervals of a convenient size. Too many intervals of smaller size would not simplify the data enough, while too few intervals of larger size would conceal information that the data might provide.

The first step in summarizing the data is to tally the number of schools in each interval. Then total the tallies in each interval, as in the following table:

Tuition Amount (in thousands of dollars)	Tally	Frequency
1.0–1.4	IIII	4
1.5–1.9		0
2.0–2.4	IIII I	6
2.5–2.9	III	3
3.0–3.4	IIII II	7
3.5–3.9	IIII IIII I	11
4.0–4.4	III	3
4.5–4.9	II	2
5.0–5.4	IIII	4

✓ **Checkpoint 1**

An accounting firm selected 24 complex tax returns prepared by a certain tax preparer. The data on the number of errors per return were as follows:

8	12	0	6	10	8	0	14
8	12	14	16	4	14	7	11
9	12	7	15	11	21	22	19

Prepare a grouped frequency distribution for these data. Use intervals 0–4, 5–9, and so on.

Answers to Checkpoint exercises are found at the end of the section.

This table is an example of a **grouped frequency distribution.**

The frequency distribution in Example 1 shows information about the data that might not have been noticed before. For example, the interval with the largest number of colleges is 3.5–3.9. However, some information has been lost; for example, we no longer know exactly how many colleges charged 3.9 ($3900) for tuition.

Picturing Data

The information in a grouped frequency distribution can be displayed graphically with a **histogram,** which is similar to a bar graph. In a histogram, the number of observations in each interval determines the height of each bar, and the size of each interval determines the width of each bar. If equally sized intervals are used, all the bars have the same width.

A **frequency polygon** is another form of graph that illustrates a grouped frequency distribution. The polygon is formed by joining consecutive midpoints of the tops of the histogram bars with straight-line segments. Sometimes the midpoints of the first and last bars are joined to endpoints on the horizontal axis where the next midpoint would appear. (See Figure 10.1.)

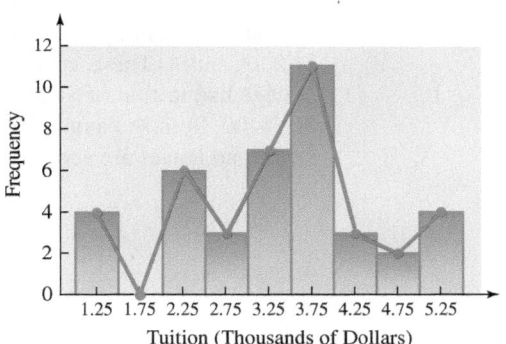

Figure 10.1

Example 2   **Education**   A grouped frequency distribution of community college tuition was found in Example 1. Draw a histogram and a frequency polygon for this distribution.

Solution   First, draw a histogram, shown in blue in Figure 10.1. To get a frequency polygon, connect consecutive midpoints of the tops of the bars. The frequency polygon is shown in red. ✔2

✓ **Checkpoint 2**

Make a histogram and a frequency polygon for the distribution found in Checkpoint 1.

↗ **TECHNOLOGY TIP**   As noted in Section 9.1, most graphing calculators can display histograms. Many will also display frequency polygons (which are usually labeled LINE or xyLINE in calculator menus). When dealing with grouped frequency distributions, however, certain adjustments must be made on a calculator:

1. *The histogram's bar width affects the shape of the graph.* If you use a bar width of .4 in Example 1, the calculator may produce a histogram with gaps in it. To avoid this, use the interval $1.0 \leq x < 1.5$ in place of $1.1 \leq x \leq 1.4$, and similarly for other intervals, and make .5 the bar width.

2. *A calculator list of outcomes must consist of single numbers, not intervals.* The table in Example 1, for instance, cannot be entered as shown. To convert the first column of the table for calculator use, choose the midpoint number in each interval—1.25 for the first interval, 1.75 for the second interval, 2.25 for the third interval, etc. Then use 1.25, 1.75, 2.25, . . . , 5.25 as the list of outcomes to be entered into the calculator. The frequency list (the last column of the table) remains the same.

Figure 10.2

Following this procedure, we obtain the calculator-generated histogram and frequency polygon in Figure 10.2 for the data from Example 1. Note that the width of each histogram bar is .5. Some calculators cannot display both the histogram and the frequency polygon on the same screen, as is done here.

Stem-and-leaf plots allow us to organize the data into a distribution without the disadvantage of losing the original information. In a **stem-and-leaf plot,** we separate the digits in each data point into two parts consisting of the first one or two digits (the stem) and the remaining digit (the leaf). We also provide a key to show the reader the units of the data that were recorded.

Example 3 **Education** Construct a stem-and-leaf plot for the data in Example 1.

Solution Since the data is made up of two-digit numbers, we use the first digit for the stems: 1, 2, 3, 4, and 5 (which in this case represents thousands of dollars). The second digit provides the leaves (which here represents hundreds of dollars). For example, if we look at the seventh row of the stem-and-leaf plot, we have a stem value of 4 and leaf values of 0, 2, and 4. These values correspond to entries of 4.0, 4.2, and 4.4, meaning that one college had tuition of $4000, another had tuition of $4200, and a third college had tuition of $4400. In this example, each row corresponds to an interval in the frequency table. The stems and leaves are separated by a vertical line.

Stem	Leaves
1	1111
1	
2	001334
2	556
3	0111234
3	55556678899
4	024
4	89
5	0113

Units: 5|3 = $5300

If we turn the page on its side, the distribution looks like a histogram, but a stem-and-leaf plot still retains each of the original data values. We used each stem digit twice (except the last one), because, as with a histogram, using too few intervals conceals useful information about the shape of the distribution. ✓₃

✓ Checkpoint 3

Make a stem-and-leaf plot for the data in Example 1, using one stem each for 1, 2, 3, 4, and 5.

NOTE In this example we have split the leaves into two groups: those with leaf values of 0–4 and 5–9. We leave a row empty if there are no data values. For example, since there were no schools in Example 1 with tuition between $1500 and $1900, that row is left blank. We do not put a zero, however, as that would imply that a school had tuition of $1000. Not all stem-and-leaf plots split the leaves with two rows per stem, but it can help the reader discern the values more easily. Often there is only a single row per stem, but another common approach is to use five rows per stem where leaves of 0–1, 2–3, 4–5, 6–7, and 8–9 are grouped together.

Example 4 **Health** List the original data for the following stem-and-leaf plot of resting pulses taken on the first day of class for 36 students:

Stem	Leaves
4	8
5	278
6	034455688888
7	02222478
8	2269
9	00002289

Units: 9|0 = 90 beats per minute

The first stem and its leaf correspond to the data point 48 beats per minute. Similarly, the rest of the data are 52, 57, 58, 60, 63, 64, 64, 65, 65, 66, 68, 68, 68, 68, 68, 70, 72, 72, 72, 72, 74, 77, 78, 82, 82, 86, 89, 90, 90, 90, 90, 92, 92, 98, and 99 beats per minute. ✓ 4

✓**Checkpoint 4**

List the original data for the following heights (inches) of students:

Stem	Leaves
5	9
6	00012233334444
6	55567777799
7	0111134
7	558

Units: 7|5 = 75 inches

Assessing the Shape of a Distribution

Histograms and stem-and-leaf plots are very useful in assessing what is called the **shape** of the distribution. One common shape of data is seen in Figure 10.3(a). When all the bars of a histogram are approximately the same height, we say the data has a **uniform** shape. In Figure 10.3(b), we see a histogram that is said to be bell shaped, or **normal.** We use the "normal" label when the frequency peaks in the middle and tapers off equally on each side. When the data do not taper off equally on each side, we say the data are **skewed.** If the data taper off further to the left, we say the data are **left skewed** (Figure 10.3(c)). When the data taper off further to the right, we say the data are **right skewed** (Figure 10.3(d)). (Notice that with skewed data, we say "left skewed" or "right skewed" to refer to the tail, and not the peak of the data.)

(a)

(b)

(c)

(d)

Figure 10.3

> **Example 5** **Health** Characterize the shapes of the given distributions for 1000 adult males. (Data from: www.cdc.gov/nchs/nhanes.htm.)
>
> **(a)** Height (inches); see Figure 10.4.
>
>
>
> **Figure 10.4**
>
> **Solution** The shape is **normal** because the shape peaks in the middle and tapers equally on each side.
>
> **(b)** Body mass index (kg/m^2); see Figure 10.5.
>
>
>
> **Figure 10.5**
>
> **Solution** The shape is **right skewed** because the tail is to the right. ✓₅
>
> It is important to note that most data are *not* normal, as we will see in the upcoming exercises and the next section. Using the label "normal" is a bit of a misnomer, because many important distributions, such as income, house prices, and infant birth weights, are skewed. It is also important to know that not all distributions have an easy-to-classify shape. This is especially true when samples are small.

✓ **Checkpoint 5**

Characterize the shape of the distribution from the following stem-and-leaf plot of ages (years):

Stem	Leaves
1	88888
2	22334
2	5579
3	333344
3	59
4	3344
4	667779
5	34
5	5679
6	1
6	
7	13
7	678

Units: 7|8 = 78 years

10.1 Exercises

Finance *The data for Exercises 1–4 consist of a random sample of 40 companies that were part of the S&P 500 and information was current as of May 24, 2013. For each variable, (a) group the data as indicated; (b) prepare a frequency distribution with columns for intervals and frequencies; (c) construct a histogram. (See Examples 1 and 2.) (Data from: compiled by author from www.morningstar.com.)*

1. The variable is volume of shares traded (in millions). Use 9 intervals, starting with 0–.9, 1.0–1.9, etc.

2. The variable is forward P/E (forward price to earnings ratio calculated as market price per share divided by the expected earnings per share). Use 9 intervals, starting with 0–9.9, 10.0–19.9, etc.

13.1	21.9	11.3	13.0	9.3	14.3	33.4	9.6	14.3	14.1
26.0	18.4	7.1	12.3	13.8	51.1	20.7	21.6	13.7	14.2
14.0	8.8	20.4	8.8	73.9	16.1	13.7	16.5	12.3	13.7
12.6	9.6	13.4	20.4	6.3	81.0	7.2	30.0	9.7	14.1

3. The variable is earnings per share. Use 6 intervals, starting with −5.00 to −.01, 0 to 4.99, etc.

3.72	1.12	1.43	23.48	8.48	1.3	0.87	13.32	5.47	2.67
1.22	1.64	0.65	4.57	2.55	0.98	0.89	−0.24	2.94	0.35
2.54	3.44	3.04	4.99	0.29	2.81	1.58	6.06	3.15	2.67
3.48	1.58	5.66	3.16	3.75	−0.41	6.58	2.52	5.06	0.97

4. The variable is P/B (price to book ratio calculated as the market price of the stock divided by the quantity total assets minus liabilities). Use 7 intervals, starting with −15.0 to −10.1, −10.0 to −5.1, etc.

2.6	3.4	1.2	−9.7	3.1	1.4	−0.7	1.7	3.5	3.9
3.3	8.4	0.3	2.1	4.2	2.1	12.5	2.9	1.8	1.2
−14.1	1.1	5.7	1.3	15.8	1.8	1.9	4.7	1.6	2.2
1.9	1.5	3.3	5.3	1.2	1.9	1.7	5.4	2.3	1.0

Economics *The data for Exercises 5–8 consist of random samples of 30 households from the 2011 American Housing Survey. Construct a frequency distribution and a histogram for each data set.*

5. Annual household income (in thousands of dollars).

75	83	16	181	79	8	153	64	1	25
80	10	11	12	13	15	114	39	1	16
65	74	15	62	61	197	36	37	70	95

6. Square feet (in hundreds) of the housing unit.

15	9	14	14	8	30	14	9	17	18
10	23	11	9	25	14	7	8	15	19
30	12	20	10	27	7	19	15	21	34

7. Amount (in dollars) of monthly electric bill.

104	85	34	38	60	36	224	82	37	134
115	112	72	53	71	167	133	151	54	30
108	147	315	140	109	218	159	156	104	51

8. Amount (in dollars) of annual water and sewage bill.

1137	78	510	1200	414	45	425	420	520	990
515	600	360	400	493	70	1890	800	396	1226
1320	800	1200	480	540	600	360	600	360	600

Construct a frequency distribution and a histogram for the data in Exercises 9 and 10.

9. Business The ages (in years) of the 30 highest-earning chief executive officers in 2012, according to *Forbes*.

53	72	55	67	59	57	55	59	61	60
59	56	63	58	58	52	61	65	61	50
65	59	58	66	57	64	58	59	66	56

10. Business The number of hours worked in a week for 30 workers selected at random from the 2012 General Social Survey. (Data from: www3.norc.org/gss+website.)

30	45	16	20	70	40	48	40	50	50
40	60	21	5	45	35	44	40	20	53
45	28	45	72	20	48	15	40	15	30

For Exercises 11–20, construct a stem-and-leaf plot for the data in the indicated exercise. (See Examples 3 and 4.)

11. Exercise 1

12. Exercise 2 (round to nearest whole number)

13. Exercise 5 (round to the nearest ten)

14. Exercise 6

15. Exercise 7 (round to the nearest ten)

16. Exercise 8 (round to the nearest hundred)

17. Exercise 9

18. Exercise 10

19. Social Science The following data give the percentage of residents with a high school education or more for the 50 states in the year 2010. (Data from: U.S. Census Bureau.)

83	87	81	90	91
81	91	87	88	91
90	89	92	86	87
89	82	90	89	90
88	82	85	88	83
86	90	92	84	90
84	86	88	84	92
90	89	83	90	82
88	89	85	84	91
87	92	85	81	86

20. Social Science The following data give the percentage of residents with a bachelor's degree or more for the 50 states in the year 2010. (Data from: U.S. Census Bureau.)

22	30	39	25	26
28	24	25	33	23
26	31	32	27	26
20	23	20	28	29
30	25	26	25	34
36	30	29	23	34
36	21	29	29	31
28	21	22	27	18
26	27	33	30	24
27	36	35	25	22

Describe the shape of each of the given histograms. (See Example 5.)

21.

22.

23.

24.

25. Economics The following histogram shows the percentage of residential properties in negative equity or near negative equity for 43 states for which data were available in July 2012. (Data from: www.corelogic.com.)

Percent in Negative Equity or Near Negative Equity

(a) Describe the shape of the distribution.

(b) How many states had their percentage between 10% and 14.9%?

(c) How many states had their percentage above 30%?

26. Business The number of FDIC insured savings institutions (as opposed to commercial banks) in each state (with DC and Guam) is presented in the histogram below. (Data from: www2. fdic.gov.)

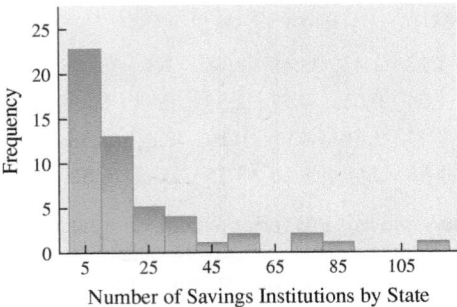

Number of Savings Institutions by State

(a) Describe the shape of the histogram.

(b) How many states have fewer than 10 savings institutions?

(c) How many states have more than 60 savings institutions?

27. Business The stem-and-leaf plot below summarizes the total deposits (in hundreds of millions of dollars) for the savings institutions in the state of Maryland in 2012. (Data from: www2.fdic.gov.)

Stem	Leaves
0	122344
0	5667899
1	0123344
1	777
2	
2	5788
3	12
3	
4	3
4	78
5	
5	
6	4
6	5

Units: $6|5 = \$65$ hundred million ($6.5 billion)

(a) Describe the shape of the distribution.

(b) How many savings institutions had total deposits below $100 million?

(c) How many savings institutions had total deposits above $400 million?

28. **Business** The percentage of mortgage loan applications that were denied in the year 2010 is summarized by state in the following stem-and-leaf plot. (Data from: www.ffiec.gov.)

Stem	Leaves
1	4
1	6667777
1	88888899999
2	0001
2	2233333
2	444455
2	667777
2	8889
3	000
3	2

Units: 3|2 = 32%

(a) Describe the shape of the distribution.

(b) How many states have a denial percentage higher than 25%?

(c) How many states have a denial percentage below 20%?

29. **Business** For the 20 states that produce a large number of broiler chickens, the following stem-and-leaf plot gives the production in billions of pounds for the year 2011. (Data from: U.S. Department of Agriculture.)

Stem	Leaves
0	223449
1	03455567
2	
3	6
4	6
5	679
6	
7	4

Units: 7|4 = 7.4 billion pounds

(a) Describe the shape of the distribution.

(b) How many states had production below 1 billion pounds?

(c) How many states had production above 2 billion pounds?

30. The grade distribution for scores on a final exam is shown in the following stem-and-leaf plot:

Stem	Leaves
2	7
3	
3	
4	01
4	899
5	4
5	5
6	122
6	58
7	00124
7	9
8	0044
8	5679
9	00223334
9	5788

Units: 9|8 = 98%

(a) What is the shape of the grade distribution?

(b) How many students earned 90% or better?

(c) How many students earned less than 60%?

✓ Checkpoint Answers

1.

Interval	Frequency
0–4	3
5–9	7
10–14	9
15–19	3
20–24	2
	Total: 24

2.

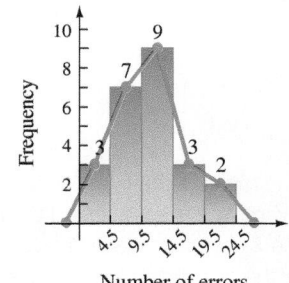

3.

Stem	Leaves
1	1111
2	001334556
3	0111234555556678899
4	02489
5	0113

Units: 5|3 = $5300

4. 59, 60, 60, 60, 61, 62, 62, 63, 63, 63, 63, 64, 64, 64, 64, 65, 65, 65, 66, 67, 67, 67, 67, 67, 69, 69, 70, 71, 71, 71, 71, 73, 74, 75, 75, 78

5. Right skewed

10.2 Measures of Center

Often, we want to summarize data numerically with a measure that represents a "typical" outcome. There are several ways to do this, and we generally call such a summary a "measure of center." In this section, we learn about the three most common measures of center: the mean, median, and mode.

Mean

The three most important measures of center are the mean, the median, and the mode. The most used of these is the mean, which is similar to the expected value of a probability distribution. The **arithmetic mean** (or just the "mean") of a set of numbers is the sum of the numbers, divided by the total number of numbers. We write the sum of n numbers $x_1, x_2, x_3, \ldots, x_n$ in a compact way with **summation notation,** also called **sigma notation.** With the Greek letter Σ (sigma), the sum

$$x_1 + x_2 + x_3 + \cdots + x_n$$

is written

$$x_1 + x_2 + x_3 + \cdots + x_n = \sum_{i=1}^{n} x_i.$$

In statistics, $\sum_{i=1}^{n} x_i$ is often abbreviated as just Σx. The symbol $\bar{x}$ (read "x-bar") is used to represent the mean of a sample.

Mean

The mean of the n numbers $x_1, x_2, x_3, \ldots, x_n$ is

$$\bar{x} = \frac{x_1 + x_2 + \cdots + x_n}{n} = \frac{\Sigma x}{n}.$$

 TECHNOLOGY TIP Computing the mean is greatly simplified by the statistical capabilities of most scientific and graphing calculators. Calculators vary considerably in how data are entered, so read your instruction manual to learn how to enter lists of data and the corresponding frequencies. On scientific calculators with statistical capabilities, there are keys for finding most of the measures of center discussed in this section. On graphing calculators, most or all of these measures can be obtained with a single keystroke. (Look for a *one-variable statistics* option, which is often labeled 1-VAR, in the STAT menu or its CALC submenu.)

 TECHNOLOGY TIP
The mean of the five numbers in Example 1 is easily found by using the $\bar{x}$ key on a scientific calculator or the one-variable statistics key on a graphing calculator. A graphing calculator will also display additional information, which will be discussed in the next section.

 Checkpoint 1

Find the mean dollar amount of the following purchases of eight students selected at random at the campus bookstore during the first week of classes:

$250.56	$567.32
$45.29	$321.56
$120.22	$561.04
$321.07	$226.90

Example 1 **Business** Corporate profits (in billions of dollars) for the years 2008–2012 are given in the following table:

Year	2008	2009	2010	2011	2012
Profits	1248	1362	1800	1943	1951

Find the mean amount of corporate profits for the 5 years. (Data from: U.S. Bureau of Economic Analysis.)

Solution Let $x_1 = 1248, x_2 = 1362, x_3 = 1800, x_4 = 1943$, and $x_5 = 1951$. Here, $n = 5$ since there are 5 numbers in the list. Thus,

$$\bar{x} = \frac{1248 + 1362 + 1800 + 1943 + 1951}{5} = 1660.8$$

The mean amount of corporate profits in the 5-year period was $1,660,800,000,000.

The mean of data that have been arranged into a frequency distribution is found in a similar way. For example, suppose the following quiz score data are collected:

Value	Frequency
84	2
87	4
88	7
93	4
99	3
	Total: 20

The value 84 appears twice, 87 four times, and so on. To find the mean, first add 84 two times, 87 four times, and so on; or get the same result faster by multiplying 84 by 2, 87 by 4, and so on, and then adding the results. Dividing the sum by 20, the total of the frequencies, gives the mean:

$$\bar{x} = \frac{(84 \cdot 2) + (87 \cdot 4) + (88 \cdot 7) + (93 \cdot 4) + (99 \cdot 3)}{20}$$

$$= \frac{168 + 348 + 616 + 372 + 297}{20}$$

$$= \frac{1801}{20}$$

$$\bar{x} = 90.05.$$

Verify that your calculator gives the same result.

Example 2 Social Science An instructor of a finite-mathematics class at a small liberal-arts college collects data on the age of her students. The data are recorded in the following frequency distribution:

Age	Frequency	Age × Frequency
18	12	18 · 12 = 216
19	9	19 · 9 = 171
20	5	20 · 5 = 100
21	2	21 · 2 = 42
22	2	22 · 2 = 44
	Total: 30	Total: 573

Find the mean age.

Solution The age 18 appears 12 times, 19 nine times, and so on. To find the mean, first multiply 18 by 12, 19 by 9, and so on, to get the column "Age × Frequency," which has been added to the frequency distribution. Adding the products from this column gives a total of 573. The total from the frequency column is 30. The mean age is

$$\bar{x} = \frac{573}{30} = 19.1.$$

The mean of grouped data is found in a similar way. For grouped data, intervals are used, rather than single values. To calculate the mean, it is assumed that all of the values in a given interval are located at the midpoint of the interval. The letter x is used to represent the midpoints, and f represents the frequencies, as shown in the next example.

✓ Checkpoint 2

Find $\bar{x}$ for the following frequency distribution for the variable of years of schooling for a sample of construction workers.

Years	Frequency
7	2
9	3
11	6
13	4
15	4
16	1

Example 3 **Business** The grouped frequency distribution for annual tuition (in thousands of dollars) for the 40 community colleges described in Example 1 of Section 10.1 is as follows:

Tuition Amount (in thousands of dollars)	Midpoint, x	Frequency, f	Product, xf
1.0–1.4	1.2	4	4.8
1.5–1.9	1.7	0	0
2.0–2.4	2.2	6	13.2
2.5–2.9	2.7	3	8.1
3.0–3.4	3.2	7	22.4
3.5–3.9	3.7	11	40.7
4.0–4.4	4.2	3	12.6
4.5–4.9	4.7	2	9.4
5.0–5.4	5.2	4	20.8
		Total: 40	Total: 132

✓ **Checkpoint 3**

Find the mean of the following grouped frequency distribution for the number of classes completed thus far in the college careers of a random sample of 52 students:

Classes	Frequency
0–5	6
6–10	10
11–20	12
21–30	15
31–40	9

Find the mean from the grouped frequency distribution.

Solution A column for the midpoint of each interval has been added. The numbers in this column are found by adding the endpoints of each interval and dividing by 2. For the interval 1.0–1.4, the midpoint is $(1.0 + 1.4)/2 = 1.2$. The numbers in the product column on the right are found by multiplying each frequency by its corresponding midpoint. Finally, we divide the total of the product column by the total of the frequency column to get

$$\bar{x} = \frac{132}{40} = 3.3.$$

It is important to know that information is always lost when the data are grouped. It is more accurate to use the original data, rather than the grouped frequency, when calculating the mean, but the original data might not be available. Furthermore, the mean based upon the grouped data is typically not too different from the mean based upon the original data, and there may be situations in which the extra accuracy is not worth the effort. ✓₃

NOTE If we had used different intervals in Example 3, the mean would have come out to be a slightly different number. This is demonstrated in Checkpoint 4. ✓₄

✓ **Checkpoint 4**

Find the mean for the college tuition data using the following intervals for the grouped frequency distribution:

Tuition Amount	Frequency
1.0–1.9	4
2.0–2.9	9
3.0–3.9	18
4.0–4.9	5
5.0–5.9	4

The formula for the mean of a grouped frequency distribution is as follows.

Mean of a Grouped Distribution

The mean of a distribution in which x represents the midpoints, f denotes the frequencies, and $n = \Sigma f$ is

$$\bar{x} = \frac{\Sigma(xf)}{n}.$$

The mean of a random sample is a random variable, and for this reason it is sometimes called the **sample mean.** The sample mean is a random variable because it assigns a number to the experiment of taking a random sample. If a different random sample were taken, the mean would probably have a different value, with some values being more probable than others. For example, if another set of 40 community colleges were selected in Example 3, the mean tuition amount might have been 3.4.

We saw in Section 9.1 how to calculate the expected value of a random variable when we know its probability distribution. The expected value is sometimes called the **population mean,** denoted by the Greek letter μ. In other words,

$$E(x) = \mu.$$

Furthermore, it can be shown that the expected value of $\bar{x}$ is also equal to μ; that is,

$$E(\bar{x}) = \mu.$$

For instance, consider again the 40 community colleges in Example 3. We found that $\bar{x} = 3.3$, but the value of μ, the average for all tuition amounts, is unknown. If a good estimate of μ were needed, the best guess (based on these data) is 3.3.

Median

Asked by a reporter to give the average height of the players on his team, a Little League coach lined up his 15 players by increasing height. He picked out the player in the middle and pronounced this player to be of average height. This kind of average, called the **median,** is defined as the middle entry in a set of data arranged in either increasing or decreasing order. If the number of entries is even, the median is defined to be the mean of the two middle entries. The following table shows how to find the median for the two sets of data {8, 7, 4, 3, 1} and {2, 3, 4, 7, 9, 12} after each set has been arranged in increasing order.

Odd Number of Entries	Even Number of Entries
1	2
3	3
Median = 4	4
7	7 $\left.\right\}$ Median $= \dfrac{4 + 7}{2} = 5.5$
8	9
	12

NOTE As shown in the table, when the number of entries is even, the median is not always equal to one of the data entries.

Example 4   Find the median number of hours worked per week

(a) for a sample of 7 male students whose work hours were

$$0, 7, 10, 20, 22, 25, 30.$$

Solution   The median is the middle number, in this case 20 hours per week. (Note that the numbers are already arranged in numerical order.) In this list, three numbers are smaller than 20 and three are larger.

(b) for a sample of 11 female students whose work hours were

$$20, 0, 20, 30, 35, 30, 20, 23, 16, 38, 25.$$

Solution   First, arrange the numbers in numerical order, from smallest to largest, or vice versa:

$$0, 16, 20, 20, 20, 23, 25, 30, 30, 35, 38.$$

The middle number can now be determined; the median is 23 hours per week.

(c) for a sample of 10 students of either gender whose work hours were

$$25, 18, 25, 20, 16, 12, 10, 0, 35, 32.$$

Solution Write the numbers in numerical order:

$$0, 10, 12, 16, 18, 20, 25, 25, 32, 35.$$

There are 10 numbers here; the median is the mean of the two middle numbers, or

$$\text{median} = \frac{18 + 20}{2} = 19.$$

The median is 19 hours per week.

 CAUTION Remember, the data must be arranged in numerical order before you locate the median. ✓5

> ### ✓ Checkpoint 5
>
> Find the median for the given heights in inches.
>
> **(a)** 60, 72, 64, 75, 72, 65, 68, 70
>
> **(b)** 73, 58, 77, 66, 69, 69, 66, 68, 67

Both the mean and the median of a sample are examples of a **statistic,** which is simply a number that gives summary information about a sample. In some situations, the median gives a truer representative or typical element of the data than the mean does. For example, suppose that in an office there are 10 salespersons, 4 secretaries, the sales manager, and Ms. Daly, who owns the business. Their annual salaries are as follows: support staff, $30,000 each; salespersons, $50,000 each; manager, $70,000; and owner, $400,000. The mean salary is

$$\bar{x} = \frac{(30,000)4 + (50,000)10 + 70,000 + 400,000}{16} = \$68,125.$$

> ### ⤢ TECHNOLOGY TIP
>
> Many graphing calculators (including most TI- and Casio models) display the median when doing one-variable statistics. You may have to scroll down to a second screen to find it.

However, since 14 people earn less than $68,125 and only 2 earn more, the mean does not seem very representative. The median salary is found by ranking the salaries by size: $30,000, $30,000, $30,000, $30,000, $50,000, $50,000, . . . , $400,000. There are 16 salaries (an even number) in the list, so the mean of the 8th and 9th entries will give the value of the median. The 8th and 9th entries are both $50,000, so the median is $50,000. In this example, the median is more representative of the distribution than the mean is.

When the data include extreme values (such as $400,000 in the preceding example), the mean may not provide an accurate picture of a typical value. So the median is often a better measure of center than the mean for data with extreme values, such as income levels and house prices. In general, the median is a better measure of center whenever we see right-skewed or left-skewed distributions.

Mode

Sue's scores on 10 class quizzes include one 7, two 8's, six 9's, and one 10. She claims that her average grade on quizzes is 9, because most of her scores are 9's. This kind of "average," found by selecting the most frequent entry, is called the **mode.**

> ### ✓ Checkpoint 6
>
> Find the mode for each of the given data sets.
>
> **(a)** Highway miles per gallon of an automobile: 25, 28, 32, 19, 15, 25, 30, 25
>
> **(b)** Price paid for last haircut or styling: $11, $35, $35, $10, $0, $12, $0, $35, $38, $42, $0, $25
>
> **(c)** Class enrollment in six sections of calculus: 30, 35, 26, 28, 29, 19

Example 5 Find the mode for the given data sets.

(a) Ages of retirement: 55, 60, 63, 63, 70, 55, 60, 65, 68, 65, 65, 71, 65, 65

Solution The number 65 occurs more often than any other, so it is the mode. It is sometimes convenient, but not necessary, to place the numbers in numerical order when looking for the mode.

(b) Total cholesterol score: 180, 200, 220, 260, 220, 205, 255, 240, 190, 300, 240

Solution Both 220 and 240 occur twice. This list has *two* modes, so it is bimodal.

(c) Prices of new cars: $25,789, $43,231, $33,456, $19,432, $22,971, $29,876

Solution No number occurs more than once. This list has no mode. ✓6

The mode has the advantages of being easily found and not being influenced by data that are extreme values. It is often used in samples where the data to be "averaged" are not numerical. A major disadvantage of the mode is that there may be more than one, in case of ties, or there may be no mode at all when all entries occur with the same frequency.

The mean is the most commonly used measure of center. Its advantages are that it is easy to compute, it takes all the data into consideration, and it is reliable—that is, repeated samples are likely to give similar means. A disadvantage of the mean is that it is influenced by extreme values, as illustrated in the salary example.

The median can be easy to compute and is influenced very little by extremes. A disadvantage of the median is the need to rank the data in order; this can be tedious when the number of items is large.

Example 6 **Business** A sample of 10 working adults was asked "How many hours did you work last week?" Their responses appear below. (Data from: www.norc.org/gss+website.)

$$40, 35, 43, 40, 30, 40, 45, 40, 55, 20.$$

Find the mean, median, and mode of the data.

Solution The mean number of hours worked is

$$\bar{x} = \frac{40 + 35 + 43 + 40 + 30 + 40 + 45 + 40 + 55 + 20}{10} = 38.8 \text{ hours.}$$

After the numbers are arranged in order from smallest to largest, the middle number, or median, is 40 hours.

The number 40 occurs more often than any other, so it is the mode.

✓**Checkpoint 7**

Following is a list of the number of movies seen at a theater in the last three months by nine students selected at random:

$$1, 0, 2, 5, 2, 0 , 0, 1, 4$$

(a) Find the mean.

(b) Find the median.

(c) Find the mode.

10.2 Exercises

Find the mean for each data set. Round to the nearest tenth. (See Example 1.)

1. **Business** Secretarial salaries (U.S. dollars):

   $21,900, $22,850, $24,930, $29,710, $28,340, $40,000.

2. **Business** Starting teaching salaries (U.S. dollars):

   $38,400, $39,720, $28,458, $29,679, $33,679.

3. **Physical Science** Earthquakes on the Richter scale:

   3.5, 4.2, 5.8, 6.3, 7.1, 2.8, 3.7, 4.2, 4.2, 5.7.

4. **Health** Body temperatures of self-classified "healthy" students (degrees Fahrenheit):

   96.8, 94.1, 99.2, 97.4, 98.4, 99.9, 98.7, 98.6.

5. **Health** Lengths of foot (inches) for adult men:

   9.2, 10.4, 13.5, 8.7, 9.7.

Find the mean for each distribution. Round to the nearest tenth. (See Examples 2 and 3.)

6. **Education** Scores on a quiz, on a scale from 0 to 10:

Value	Frequency
7	4
8	6
9	7
10	11

7. **Education** Age (years) of students in an introductory accounting class:

Value	Frequency
19	3
20	5
21	25
22	8
23	2
24	1
28	1

8. Social Science Commuting distance (miles) for students at a university:

Value	Frequency
0	15
1	12
2	8
5	6
10	5
17	2
20	1
25	1

9. Business Estimated miles per gallon of automobiles:

Value	Frequency
9	5
11	10
15	12
17	9
20	6
28	1

10–14. *Find the median of the data in Exercises 1–5. (See Example 4.)*

Find the mode or modes for each of the given lists of numbers. (See Example 5.)

15. Health Ages (years) of children in a day-care facility:

1, 2, 2, 1, 2, 2, 1, 1, 2, 2, 3, 4, 2, 3, 4, 2, 3, 2, 3.

16. Health Ages (years) in the intensive care unit at a local hospital:

68, 64, 23, 68, 70, 72, 72, 68.

17. Education Heights (inches) of students in a statistics class:

62, 65, 71, 74, 71, 76, 71, 63, 59, 65, 65, 64, 72, 71, 77, 63, 65.

18. Health Minutes of pain relief from acetaminophen after childbirth:

60, 240, 270, 180, 240, 210, 240, 300, 330, 360, 240, 120.

19. Education Grade point averages for 5 students:

3.2, 2.7, 1.9, 3.7, 3.9.

20. When is the median the most appropriate measure of center?

21. When would the mode be an appropriate measure of center?

Finance *The data for Exercises 22–23 come from a random sample of 40 companies that were part of the S&P 500 and the information was current as of May 24, 2013. For grouped data, the modal class is the interval containing the most data values. Give the mean and modal class for each of the given collections of grouped data. (See Example 3. Data from: www.morningstar.com.)*

22. The variable is volume of shares traded (in millions).

Interval	Frequency
0–.9	11
1.0–1.9	15
2.0–2.9	3
3.0–3.9	4
4.0–4.9	2
5.0–5.9	4
6.0–6.9	0
7.0–7.9	0
8.0–8.9	1

23. The variable is forward P/E (forward price to earnings ratio calculated as market price per share divided by the expected earnings per share).

Interval	Frequency
0–9.9	9
10.0–19.9	20
20.0–29.9	6
30.0–39.9	2
40.0–49.9	0
50.0–59.9	1
60.0–69.9	0
70.0–79.9	1
80.0–89.9	1

24. To predict the outcome of the next congressional election, you take a survey of your friends. Is this a random sample of the voters in your congressional district? Explain why or why not.

Work each problem. (See Example 6.)

25. Business The following table gives the value (in millions of dollars) of the 10 most valued baseball teams, as estimated by *Forbes* in 2012.

Rank	Team	Value
1	New York Yankees	2300
2	Los Angeles Dodgers	1615
3	Boston Red Sox	1312
4	Chicago Cubs	1000
5	Philadelphia Phillies	893
6	New York Mets	811
7	San Francisco Giants	786
8	Texas Rangers	764
9	Los Angeles Angels of Anaheim	718
10	St. Louis Cardinals	716

Find the following statistics for these data:

(a) mean;

(b) median.

26. Business The following table gives the value (in millions of dollars) of the 10 most valued National Football League teams, as estimated by *Forbes* in 2012.

Rank	Team	Value
1	Dallas Cowboys	2100
2	New England Patriots	1635
3	Washington Redskins	1600
4	New York Giants	1468
5	Houston Texans	1305
6	New York Jets	1284
7	Philadelphia Eagles	1260
8	Chicago Bears	1190
9	San Francisco 49ers	1175
10	Green Bay Packers	1161

Find the following statistics for these data:

(a) mean;

(b) median.

27. Business The 12 movies that have earned the most revenue (in millions of dollars) from U.S. domestic box-office receipts are given in the table. (Data from: www.boxofficemojo.com.)

Rank	Title	U.S. Box-Office Receipts
1	Avatar	761
2	Titanic	659
3	Marvel's The Avengers	623
4	The Dark Knight	535
5	Star Wars	475
6	Star Wars: Episode—The Phantom Menace	461
7	The Dark Knight Rises	448
8	Shrek 2	441
9	E.T.: The Extra-Terrestrial	435
10	Pirates of the Caribbean: Dead Man's Chest	423
11	The Lion King	423
12	Toy Story 3	415

(a) Find the mean value in dollars for this group of movies.

(b) Find the median value in dollars for this group of movies.

28. Natural Science The number of recognized blood types varies by species, as indicated in the following table.[*]

[*]*The Handy Science Answer Book*, Carnegie Library of Pittsburgh, Pennsylvania, p. 264.

Animal	Number of Blood Types
Pig	16
Cow	12
Chicken	11
Horse	9
Human	8
Sheep	7
Dog	7
Rhesus Monkey	6
Mink	5
Rabbit	5
Mouse	4
Rat	4
Cat	2

Find the mean, median, and mode of this data.

29. Business The revenue (in millions of dollars) for the Starbucks Corporation for the years 2003–2012 is given in the table. (Data from: www.morningstar.com.)

Year	Revenue
2003	4075.5
2004	5294.3
2005	6369.3
2006	7786.9
2007	9411.5
2008	10,383.0
2009	9775.0
2010	10,707.0
2011	11,700.0
2012	13,300.0

(a) Calculate the mean and median for these data.

(b) What year's revenue is closest to the mean?

Natural Science *The table gives the average monthly high and low temperatures, in degrees Fahrenheit, for Raleigh, North Carolina, over the course of a year. (Data from: www.weather.com.)*

Month	High	Low
January	49	30
February	53	32
March	61	40
April	71	48
May	78	57
June	84	65
July	88	69
August	86	68
September	80	62
October	70	49
November	61	42
December	52	33

Find the mean and median for each of the given subgroups.

30. The high temperatures **31.** The low temperatures

For Exercises 32–33 determine the shape of the distribution from the histogram and then decide whether the mean or median is a better measure of center. If the mean is the better measure, calculate the value. If the median is the better measure, give the midpoint of the interval that contains it.

32. Education The percentage of United States residents with a high school diploma or higher for the 50 states in the year 2010 are given below. (Data from: U.S. Census Bureau.)

Interval	Frequency
80–81.9	3
82–83.9	6
84–85.9	7
86–87.9	8
88–89.9	10
90–91.9	12
92–93.9	4

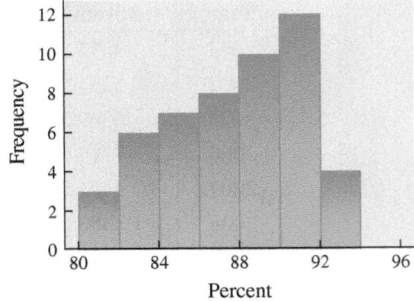

33. Economics The following frequency distribution and histogram represent the amount (in dollars) of the annual water and sewage bill. (Data from: U.S. Housing Survey.)

Interval	Frequency
0–249	3
250–499	10
500–749	8
750–999	3
1000–1249	4
1250–1499	1
1500–1749	0
1750–1999	1

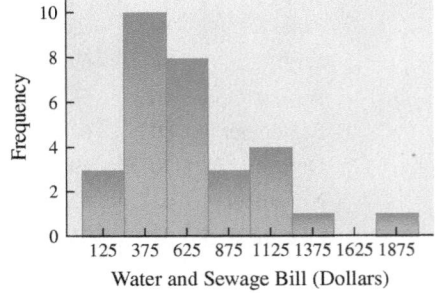

34. Business The stem-and-leaf plot below summarizes the total deposits (in hundreds of millions of dollars) for the savings institutions in the state of Maryland in 2012. (Data from: www2.fdic.gov.)

Stem	Leaves
0	122344
0	5667899
1	0123344
1	777
2	
2	5788
3	12
3	
4	3
4	78
5	
5	
6	4
6	5

Units: 6|5 = $65 hundred million

(a) Describe the shape of the distribution.

(b) Find the median.

35. Business The percentage of mortgage loan applications that were denied in the year 2010 is summarized by state in the following stem-and-leaf plot. (Data from: www.ffiec.gov.)

Stem	Leaves
1	4
1	6667777
1	88888899999
2	0001
2	2233333
2	444455
2	667777
2	8889
3	000
3	2

Units: 3|2 = 32%

(a) Describe the shape of the distribution.

(b) Find the median percentage.

✓ **Checkpoint Answers**

1. $301.75   **2.** $\bar{x} = 11.75$ **3.** 18.90   **4.** 3.35

5. (a) 69 inches   **(b)** 68 inches

6. (a) 25 miles per gallon   **(b)** $0 and $35

(c) No mode

7. (a) About 1.7   **(b)** 1   **(c)** 0

10.3 Measures of Variation

The mean, median, and mode are measures of center for a list of numbers, but tell nothing about the *spread* of the numbers in the list. For example, look at the following data sets of number of times per week three people ate meals at restaurants over the course of five weeks:

Jill:	3	5	6	3	3
Miguel:	4	4	4	4	4
Sharille:	10	1	0	0	9

Each of these three data sets has a mean of 4, but the amount of dispersion or variation within the lists is different. This difference may reflect different dining patterns over time. Thus, in addition to a measure of center, another kind of measure is needed that describes how much the numbers vary.

The largest number of restaurant meals for Jill is 6, while the smallest is 3, a difference of 3. For Miguel, the difference is 0; for Sharille, it is 10. The difference between the largest and smallest number in a sample is called the **range,** one example of a measure of variation. The range is 3 for Jill, 0 for Miguel, and 10 for Sharille. The range has the advantage of being very easy to compute and gives a rough estimate of the variation among the data in the sample. However, it depends only on the two extremes and tells nothing about how the other data are distributed between the extremes.

✈ TECHNOLOGY TIP
Many graphing calculators show the largest and smallest numbers in a list when displaying one-variable statistics, usually on the second screen of the display.

✓ Checkpoint 1

Find the range for this sample of the number of miles from students' homes to college: 15, 378, 5, 210, 125.

Example 1 **Business** Find the range for each given data set for a small sample of people.

(a) Price paid for last haircut (with tip): 10, 0, 15, 30, 20, 18, 50, 120, 75, 95, 0, 5

Solution The highest number here is 120; the lowest is 0. The range is the difference of these numbers, or

$$120 - 0 = 120.$$

(b) Amount spent for last vehicle servicing: 30, 19, 125, 150, 430, 50, 225

Solution Range $= 430 - 19 = 411$. ✓₁

To find another useful measure of variation, we begin by finding the **deviations from the mean**—the differences found by subtracting the mean from each number in a distribution.

Example 2 Find the deviations from the mean for the following sample of ages.

$$32, \quad 41, \quad 47, \quad 53, \quad 57.$$

Solution Adding these numbers and dividing by 5 gives a mean of 46 years. To find the deviations from the mean, subtract 46 from each number in the sample. For example, the first deviation from the mean is $32 - 46 = -14$; the last is $57 - 46 = 11$ years. All of the deviations are listed in the following table.

Age	Deviation from Mean
32	−14
41	−5
47	1
53	7
57	11

✓ Checkpoint 2

Find the deviations from the mean for the following sample of number of miles traveled by various people to a vacation location:

135, 60, 50, 425, 380.

To check your work, find the sum of the deviations. It should always equal 0. (The answer is always 0 because the positive and negative deviations cancel each other out.) ✓₂

To find a measure of variation, we might be tempted to use the mean of the deviations. However, as just mentioned, this number is always 0, no matter how widely the data are dispersed. To avoid the problem of the positive and negative deviations averaging to 0, we could take absolute values and find $\sum |x - \bar{x}|$ and then divide it by n to get the *mean absolute deviation*. However, statisticians generally prefer to square each deviation to get nonnegative numbers and then take the square root of the mean of the squared variations in order to preserve the units of the original data (such as inches, pounds). (Using squares instead of absolute values allows us to take advantage of some algebraic properties that make other important statistical methods much easier.) The squared deviations for the data in Example 2 are shown in the following table:

Number	Deviation from Mean	Square of Deviation
32	-14	196
41	-5	25
47	1	1
53	7	49
57	11	121

In this case, the mean of the squared deviations is

$$\frac{196 + 25 + 1 + 49 + 121}{5} = \frac{392}{5} = 78.4.$$

This number is called the **population variance,** because the sum was divided by $n = 5$, the number of items in the original list.

Since the deviations from the mean must add up to 0, if we know any 4 of the 5 deviations, the 5th can be determined. That is, only $n - 1$ of the deviations are free to vary, so we really have only $n - 1$ independent pieces of information, or *degrees of freedom*. Using $n - 1$ as the divisor in the formula for the mean gives

$$\frac{196 + 25 + 1 + 49 + 121}{5 - 1} = \frac{392}{4} = 98.$$

This number, 98, is called the **sample variance** of the distribution and is denoted s^2, because it is found by averaging a list of squares. In this case, the population and sample variances differ by quite a bit. But when n is relatively large, as is the case in real-life applications, the difference between them is rather small.

Sample Variance

The variance of a sample of n numbers $x_1, x_2, x_3, \ldots, x_n$, with mean $\bar{x}$, is

$$s^2 = \frac{\sum (x - \bar{x})^2}{n - 1}.$$

When computing the sample variance by hand, it is often convenient to use the following shortcut formula, which can be derived algebraically from the definition in the preceding box:

$$s^2 = \frac{\sum x^2 - n\bar{x}^2}{n - 1}.$$

To find the sample variance, we square the deviations from the mean, so the variance is in squared units. To return to the same units as the data, we use the *square root* of the variance, called the **sample standard deviation,** denoted s.

Sample Standard Deviation

The standard deviation of a sample of n numbers $x_1, x_2, x_3, \ldots, x_n$, with mean $\bar{x}$, is

$$s = \sqrt{\frac{\Sigma(x - \bar{x})^2}{n - 1}}.$$

📄 **NOTE** The **population standard deviation** is

$$\sigma = \sqrt{\frac{\Sigma(x - \mu)^2}{n}},$$

where n is the population size.

🖊 **TECHNOLOGY TIP** When a graphing calculator computes one-variable statistics for a list of data, it usually displays the following information (not necessarily in this order, and sometimes on two screens) and possibly other information as well:

Information	Notation
Number of data entries	n or $N\Sigma$
Mean	$\bar{x}$ or mean Σ
Sum of all data entries	Σx or TOT Σ
Sum of the squares of all data entries	Σx^2
Sample standard deviation	Sx or sx or $x\sigma_{n-1}$ or SSDEV
Population standard deviation	σx or $x\sigma_n$ or PSDEV
Largest/smallest data entries	maxX/minX or MAXΣ/MINΣ
Median	Med or MEDIAN

📄 **NOTE** In the rest of this section, we shall deal exclusively with the sample variance and the sample standard deviation. So whenever standard deviation is mentioned, it means "sample standard deviation," not population standard deviation.

As its name indicates, the standard deviation is the most commonly used measure of variation. The standard deviation is a measure of the variation from the mean. The size of the standard deviation indicates how spread out the data are from the mean.

Time	Square of the Time
2	4
8	64
3	9
2	4
6	36
11	121
31	961
9	81
72	1280

Example 3   **Social Science**   Find the standard deviation for the following sample of the lengths (in minutes) of eight consecutive cell phone conversations by one person:

$$2, \quad 8, \quad 3, \quad 2, \quad 6, \quad 11, \quad 31, \quad 9.$$

Work by hand, using the shortcut variance formula on page 538.

Solution   Arrange the work in columns, as shown in the table in the margin. Now use the first column to find the mean:

$$\bar{x} = \frac{\Sigma x}{8} = \frac{72}{8} = 9 \text{ minutes.}$$

The total of the second column gives $\sum x^2 = 1280$. The variance is

$$s^2 = \frac{\sum x^2 - n\bar{x}^2}{n-1}$$

$$= \frac{1280 - 8(9)^2}{8-1}$$

$$\approx 90.3$$

and the standard deviation is

$$s \approx \sqrt{90.3} \approx 9.5 \text{ minutes.} \quad \blacksquare_3$$

 Checkpoint 3

Find the standard deviation for a sample of the number of miles traveled by various people to a vacation location:

135, 60, 50, 425, 380.

TECHNOLOGY TIP The screens in Figure 10.6 show two ways to find variance and standard deviation on a TI-84+ calculator: with the LIST menu and with the STAT menu. The data points are first entered in a list—here, L_5. See your instruction book for details.

  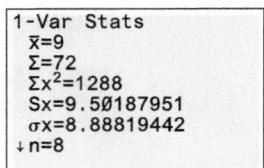

Figure 10.6

In a spreadsheet, enter the data in cells A1 through A8. Then, in cell A9, type "=VAR(A1:A8)" and press Enter. The standard deviation can be calculated either by taking the square root of cell A9 or by typing "=STDEV (A1:A8)" in cell A10 and pressing Enter.

CAUTION We must be careful to divide by $n - 1$, not n, when calculating the standard deviation of a sample. Many calculators are equipped with statistical keys that compute the variance and standard deviation. Some of these calculators use $n - 1$, and others use n for these computations; some may have keys for both. Check your calculator's instruction book before using a statistical calculator for the exercises.

One way to interpret the standard deviation uses the fact that, for many populations, most of the data are within three standard deviations of the mean. (See Section 10.4.) This implies that, in Example 3, most of the population data from which this sample is taken are between

$$\bar{x} - 3s = 9 - 3(9.5) = -19.5$$

and

$$\bar{x} + 3s = 9 + 3(9.5) = 37.5.$$

For Example 3, the preceding calculations imply that most phone conversations are less than 37.5 minutes long. This approach of determining whether sample observations are beyond 3 standard deviations of the mean is often employed in conducting quality control in many industries.

For data in a grouped frequency distribution, a slightly different formula for the standard deviation is used.

Standard Deviation for a Grouped Distribution

The standard deviation for a sample distribution with mean $\bar{x}$, where x is an interval midpoint with frequency f and $n = \sum f$, is

$$s = \sqrt{\frac{\sum f x^2 - n\bar{x}^2}{n-1}}.$$

The formula indicates that the product fx^2 is to be found for each interval. Then all the products are summed, n times the square of the mean is subtracted, and the difference is divided by one less than the total frequency—that is, by $n - 1$. The square root of this result is s, the standard deviation. The standard deviation found by this formula may (and probably will) differ somewhat from the standard deviation found from the original data.

> ⊘ **CAUTION** In calculating the standard deviation for either a grouped or an ungrouped distribution, using a rounded value for the mean or variance may produce an inaccurate value.

Tuition Amount (in thousands of dollars)	Frequency
1.0–1.4	4
1.5–1.9	0
2.0–2.4	6
2.5–2.9	3
3.0–3.4	7
3.5–3.9	11
4.0–4.4	3
4.5–4.9	2
5.0–5.4	4

Example 4   **Business**   The following frequency distribution gives the 2011–2012 annual tuition (in thousands of dollars) for a random sample of 40 community colleges. (Data from: www.collegeboard.org.)

Find the sample standard deviation s for these data.

Solution   We first need to find the mean $\bar{x}$ for these grouped data. We find the midpoint of each interval and label it x. We multiply the frequency by the midpoint x to obtain fx:

Tuition Amount (in thousands of dollars)	Frequency f	Midpoint x	fx
1.0–1.4	4	1.2	4.8
1.5–1.9	0	1.7	0
2.0–2.4	6	2.2	13.2
2.5–2.9	3	2.7	8.1
3.0–3.4	7	3.2	22.4
3.5–3.9	11	3.7	40.7
4.0–4.4	3	4.2	12.6
4.5–4.9	2	4.7	9.4
5.0–5.4	4	5.2	20.8
	Total = 40		Total = 132

Therefore,

$$\bar{x} = \frac{132}{40} = 3.3.$$

Now that we have the mean value, we can modify our table to include columns for x^2 and fx^2. We obtain the following results:

Tuition Amount (in thousands of dollars)	Frequency f	Midpoint x	fx	x^2	fx^2
1.0–1.4	4	1.2	4.8	1.44	5.76
1.5–1.9	0	1.7	0	2.89	0
2.0–2.4	6	2.2	13.2	4.84	29.04
2.5–2.9	3	2.7	8.1	7.29	21.87
3.0–3.4	7	3.2	22.4	10.24	71.68
3.5–3.9	11	3.7	40.7	13.69	150.59
4.0–4.4	3	4.2	12.6	17.64	52.92
4.5–4.9	2	4.7	9.4	22.09	44.18
5.0–5.4	4	5.2	20.8	27.04	108.16
	Total = 40				Total = 484.2

We now use the formula for the standard deviation with $n = 40$ to find s:

$$s = \sqrt{\frac{\sum fx^2 - n\bar{x}^2}{n - 1}}$$

$$= \sqrt{\frac{484.2 - 40(3.3)^2}{40 - 1}}$$

$$\approx 1.1. \quad \boxed{4}$$

 Checkpoint 4

Find the standard deviation for the following grouped frequency distribution of the number of classes completed thus far in the college careers of a random sample of 52 students:

Classes	Frequency
0–5	6
6–10	10
11–20	12
21–30	15
31–40	9

Another way to interpret the standard deviation is to think of it as an *approximation* of the average deviation from the mean. In Example 4, the mean tuition was $3300 and the standard deviation was $1100. One way to think of what the value $1100 represents is as the approximate average deviation from $3300 for the 40 community colleges in the sample. Some colleges charge tuition close to $3300 and some charge tuition further from $3300, but the approximate average deviation from $3300 is $1100.

NOTE A calculator is almost a necessity for finding a standard deviation. With a nongraphing calculator, a good procedure to follow is first to calculate $\bar{x}$. Then, for each x, square that number, and multiply the result by the appropriate frequency. If your calculator has a key that accumulates a sum, use it to accumulate the total in the last column of the table. With a graphing calculator, simply enter the midpoints and the frequencies, and then ask for the one-variable statistics.

10.3 Exercises

1. How are the variance and the standard deviation related?

2. Why can't we use the sum of the deviations from the mean as a measure of dispersion of a distribution?

Finance *Use the following table for Exercises 3–10, which lists expenditures (in billions of dollars with the exception of Parks and Recreation, which is in millions of dollars) for a random sample of seven states. Find the range and standard deviation among the seven states for each category of government expenditure. (See Examples 1–3.) (Data from: U.S. Census Bureau.)*

Type of Expenditure	GA	IL	LA	MI	NH	OH	PA
Education	24.9	34.8	12.0	29.1	3.6	32.8	35.1
Public Welfare	9.7	17.8	6.4	12.9	2.0	18.4	24.5
Hospitals	5.1	2.6	4.6	3.5	0.1	4.0	3.0
Health	2.0	3.1	0.9	3.8	0.1	3.9	3.8
Highways	3.4	8.2	2.9	3.7	0.7	4.8	8.6
Police Protection	2.2	4.6	1.4	2.4	0.3	3.3	3.1
Fire Protection	1.0	2.3	0.6	2.3	0.2	1.8	0.7
Parks and Recreation	964	2552	709	725	107	1226	1194

(Table header spanning GA–PA: State)

3. Education

4. Public Welfare

5. Hospitals

6. Health

7. Highways

8. Police Protection

9. Fire Protection

10. Parks and Recreation

Education *Find the standard deviation for the grouped data in Exercises 11 and 12. (See Example 4.)*

11. Number of credits for a sample of college students:

College Credits	Frequency
0–24	4
25–49	3
50–74	6
75–99	3
100–124	5
125–149	9

12. Scores on a calculus exam:

Scores	Frequency
30–39	1
40–49	6
50–59	13
60–69	22
70–79	17
80–89	13
90–99	8

Finance *The data for Exercises 13–14 come from a random sample of 40 companies that were part of the S&P 500 and information was current as of May 24, 2013. (Hint: Do not round the mean when calculating the standard deviation.) (Data from: www. morningstar.com.)*

13. Closing stock price (dollars).

37.76	56.94	54.99	156.83
46.04	80.58	17.35	51.33
28.26	55.81	49.79	45.20
415.81	10.35	30.65	79.60
86.21	51.62	73.83	24.87
34.41	47.16	61.58	95.04
15.34	74.04	228.74	180.45
125.45	29.19	57.31	40.06
125.12	13.07	45.22	53.75
62.30	104.80	129.19	27.49

Find the mean and standard deviation of the closing stock price.

14. Market capitalization (billions of dollars).

58.9	12.1	14.3	19.4
8.2	85.1	11.2	8.8
3.1	5.1	9.7	87.4
15	3.5	11.8	142.9
56.7	6.1	12.8	21.8
7.6	19.4	13.7	7
4.1	7.9	14.4	14.7
243.2	3.1	22.4	19.4
13.2	7.2	7.2	10.2
40.9	8.8	39.3	5.1

Find the mean and standard deviation of the market capitalization.

An application of standard deviation is given by Chebyshev's theorem. (P. L. Chebyshev was a Russian mathematician who lived from 1821 to 1894.) This theorem, which applies to any distribution of numerical data, states,

For any distribution of numerical data, at least $1 - 1/k^2$ of the numbers lie within k standard deviations of the mean.

Example *For any distribution, at least*

$$1 - \frac{1}{3^2} = 1 - \frac{1}{9} = \frac{8}{9}$$

of the numbers lie within 3 standard deviations of the mean. Find the fraction of all the numbers of a data set lying within the given numbers of standard deviations from the mean.

15. 2   **16.** 4   **17.** 1.5

In a certain distribution of numbers, the mean is 50, with a standard deviation of 6. Use Chebyshev's theorem to tell what percent of the numbers are

18. between 32 and 68;

19. between 26 and 74;

20. less than 38 or more than 62;

21. less than 32 or more than 68;

22. less than 26 or more than 74.

Business *For Exercises 23–28 use the following table, which gives the total amounts of sales (in millions of dollars) for aerobic, basketball, cross-training, and walking shoes in the United States for the years 2005–2011. (Hint: Use a mean value calculated to at least 4 decimal places when calculating the standard deviation.) (Data from: ProQuest Statistical Abstract of the United States: 2013.)*

Year	Aerobic	Basketball	Cross-training	Walking
2005	261	878	1437	3673
2006	262	964	1516	4091
2007	280	892	1584	4197
2008	260	718	1626	4204
2009	223	741	2071	4416
2010	249	721	2121	4256
2011	252	729	2143	4299

Find the mean and standard deviation for the type of shoe listed.

23. Aerobic shoes

24. Basketball shoes

25. Cross-training shoes

26. Walking shoes

27. Which type of shoe shows greater variation: aerobic or cross-training?

28. Which type of shoe shows greater variation: basketball or walking?

For Exercises 29–32, see Example 4.

29. Economics A sample of 40 households from the American Housing Survey generates the following frequency table of household income (in thousands). Find the standard deviation.

Interval	Frequency
0–29	12
30–59	3
60–89	10
90–119	2
120–149	0
150–179	1
180–209	2

30. Business The number of hours worked in a week for 30 workers selected at random from the 2012 General Social Survey appears in the following frequency table. Find the standard deviation. (Data from: www3.norc.org/gss+website.)

Interval	Frequency
0–9	1
10–19	3
20–29	5
30–39	3
40–49	12
50–59	3
60–69	1
70–79	2

31. Natural Science   The number of recognized blood types of various animal species is given in the following table:

Animal	Number of Blood Types
Pig	16
Cow	12
Chicken	11
Horse	9
Human	8
Sheep	7
Dog	7
Rhesus Monkey	6
Mink	5
Rabbit	5
Mouse	4
Rat	4
Cat	2

In Exercise 28 of the previous section, the mean was found to be 7.38.

(a) Find the variance and the standard deviation of this data.

(b) How many of these animals have blood types that are within 1 standard deviation of the mean?

32. Business   The Quaker Oats Company conducted a survey to determine whether a proposed premium, to be included with purchases of the firm's cereal, was appealing enough to generate new sales.[*] Four cities were used as test markets, where the cereal was distributed with the premium, and four cities were used as control markets, where the cereal was distributed without the premium. The eight cities were chosen on the basis of their similarity in terms of population, per-capita income, and total cereal purchase volume. The results were as follows:

		Percent Change in Average Market Shares per Month
Test Cities	1	+18
	2	+15
	3	+7
	4	+10
Control Cities	1	+1
	2	−8
	3	−5
	4	0

(a) Find the mean of the change in market share for the four test cities.

(b) Find the mean of the change in market share for the four control cities.

(c) Find the standard deviation of the change in market share for the test cities.

(d) Find the standard deviation of the change in market share for the control cities.

(e) Find the difference between the mean of part (a) and the mean of part (b). This represents the estimate of the percent change in sales due to the premium.

(f) The two standard deviations from part (c) and part (d) were used to calculate an "error" of ± 7.95 for the estimate in part (e). With this amount of error, what is the smallest and largest estimate of the increase in sales? (*Hint:* Use the answer to part (e).)

On the basis of the results of this exercise, the company decided to mass-produce the premium and distribute it nationally.

33. Business   The following table gives 10 samples of three measurements made during a production run:

SAMPLE NUMBER									
1	**2**	**3**	**4**	**5**	**6**	**7**	**8**	**9**	**10**
2	3	−2	−3	−1	3	0	−1	2	0
−2	−1	0	1	2	2	1	2	3	0
1	4	1	2	4	2	2	3	2	2

(a) Find the mean $\bar{x}$ for each sample of three measurements.

(b) Find the standard deviation s for each sample of three measurements.

(c) Find the mean $\bar{\bar{x}}$ of the sample means.

(d) Find the mean $\bar{s}$ of the sample standard deviations.

(e) The upper and lower control limits of the sample means here are $\bar{\bar{x}} \pm 1.954\bar{s}$. Find these limits. If any of the measurements are outside these limits, the process is out of control. Decide whether this production process is out of control.

34. Discuss what the standard deviation tells us about a distribution.

Social Science   *Shown in the following table are the reading scores of a second-grade class given individualized instruction*

---

[*]This example was supplied by Jeffery S. Berman, senior analyst, Marketing Information, Quaker Oats Company.

and the reading scores of a second-grade class given traditional instruction in the same school:

Scores	Individualized Instruction	Traditional Instruction
50–59	2	5
60–69	4	8
70–79	7	8
80–89	9	7
90–99	8	6

35. Find the mean and standard deviation for the individualized-instruction scores.

36. Find the mean and standard deviation for the traditional-instruction scores.

37. Discuss a possible interpretation of the differences in the means and the standard deviations in Exercises 35 and 36.

✓ Checkpoint Answers

1. 373

2. Mean is 210; deviations are $-75, -150, -160, 215,$ and 170.

3. 179.5 miles

4. 10.91 classes

10.4 Normal Distributions and Boxplots

Suppose a bank is interested in improving its services to customers. The manager decides to begin by finding the amount of time tellers spend on each transaction, rounded to the nearest minute. The times for 75 different transactions are recorded, with the results shown in the following table, where the frequencies listed in the second column are divided by 75 to find the empirical probabilities:

Time	Frequency	Probability
1	3	$3/75 = .04$
2	5	$5/75 \approx .07$
3	9	$9/75 = .12$
4	12	$12/75 = .16$
5	15	$15/75 = .20$
6	11	$11/75 \approx .15$
7	10	$10/75 \approx .13$
8	6	$6/75 = .08$
9	3	$3/75 = .04$
10	1	$1/75 \approx .01$

Figure 10.7(a), on the following page, shows a histogram and frequency polygon for the data. The heights of the bars are the empirical probabilities, rather than the frequencies. The transaction times are given to the nearest minute. Theoretically, at least, they could have been timed to the nearest tenth of a minute, or hundredth of a minute, or even more precisely. In each case, a histogram and frequency polygon could be drawn. If the times are measured with smaller and smaller units, there are more bars in the histogram and the frequency polygon begins to look more and more like the curve in Figure 10.7(b) instead of a polygon. Actually, it is possible for the transaction times to take on any real-number value greater than 0. A distribution in which the outcomes can take on any real-number value within some interval is a **continuous distribution.** The graph of a continuous distribution is a curve.

The distribution of heights (in inches) of college women is another example of a continuous distribution, since these heights include infinitely many possible measurements,

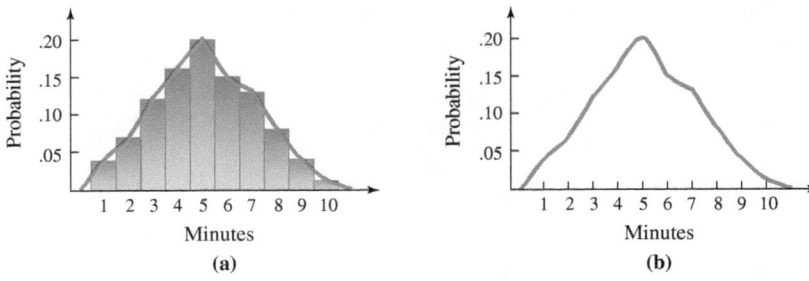

Figure 10.7

such as 53, 58.5, 66.3, 72.666, and so on. Figure 10.8 shows the continuous distribution of heights of college women. Here, the most frequent heights occur near the center of the interval displayed.

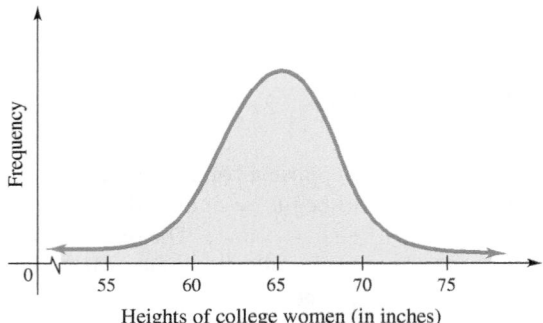

Figure 10.8

Normal Distributions

As discussed on page 523, we say that data are normal (or normally distributed) when their graph is well approximated by a bell-shaped curve. (See Figure 10.9.) We call the graphs of such distributions **normal curves.** Examples of distributions that are approximately normal are the heights of college women and cholesterol levels in adults. We use the Greek letters μ (mu) to denote the mean and σ (sigma) to denote the standard deviation of a normal distribution.

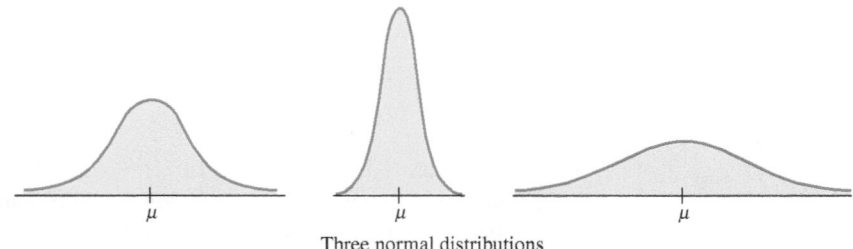

Three normal distributions

Figure 10.9

There are many normal distributions, depending on μ and σ. Some of the corresponding normal curves are tall and thin, and others short and wide, as shown in Figure 10.9. But every normal curve has the following properties:

1. Its peak occurs directly above the mean μ.
2. The curve is symmetric about the vertical line through the mean. (That is, if you fold the graph along this line, the left half of the graph will fit exactly on the right half.)

3. The curve never touches the x-axis—it extends indefinitely in both directions.

4. The area under the curve (and above the horizontal axis) is 1. (As can be shown with calculus, this is a consequence of the fact that the sum of the probabilities in any distribution is 1.)

A normal distribution is completely determined by its mean μ and standard deviation σ.* A small standard deviation leads to a tall, narrow curve like the one in the center of Figure 10.9, because most of the data are close to the mean. A large standard deviation means the data are very spread out, producing a flat, wide curve like the one on the right in Figure 10.9.

Since the area under a normal curve is 1, parts of this area can be used to determine certain probabilities. For instance, Figure 10.10(a) is the probability distribution of the annual rainfall in a certain region. The probability that the annual rainfall will be between 25 and 35 inches is the area under the curve from 25 to 35. The general case, shown in Figure 10.10(b), can be stated as follows.

> The area of the shaded region under the normal curve from a to b is the probability that an observed data value will be between a and b.

(a)

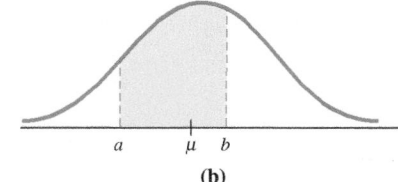
(b)

Figure 10.10

To use normal curves effectively, we must be able to calculate areas under portions of them. These calculations have already been done for the normal curve with mean $\mu = 0$ and standard deviation $\sigma = 1$ (which is called the **standard normal curve**) and are available in Table 2 at the back of the book. Examples 1 and 2 demonstrate how to use Table 2 to find such areas. Later, we shall see how the standard normal curve may be used to find areas under any normal curve.

The horizontal axis of the standard normal curve is usually labeled z. Since the standard deviation of the standard normal curve is 1, the numbers along the horizontal axis (the z-values) measure the number of standard deviations above or below the mean $z = 0$.

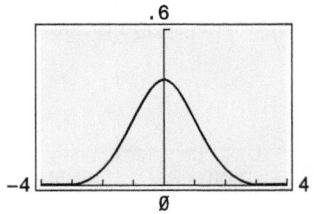

Figure 10.11

⬛ **TECHNOLOGY TIP** Some graphing calculators (such as the TI-84+ and most Casios) have the ability to graph a normal distribution, given its mean and standard deviation, and to find areas under the curve between two x-values. For an area under the curve, some calculators will give the corresponding z-value. For details, see your instruction book. (Look for "distribution" or "probability distribution.") A calculator-generated graph of the standard normal curve is shown in Figure 10.11.

---

*As shown in more advanced courses, its graph is the graph of the function

$$f(x) = \frac{1}{\sigma\sqrt{2\pi}}e^{-(x-\mu)^2/(2\sigma^2)},$$

where $e \approx 2.71828$ is the real number introduced in Section 4.1.

Example 1   Find the given areas under the standard normal curve.

(a)   The area between $z = 0$ and $z = 1$, the shaded region in Figure 10.12

Solution   Find the entry 1 in the z-column of Table 2. The entry next to it in the A-column is .3413, which means that the area between $z = 0$ and $z = 1$ is .3413. Since the total area under the curve is 1, the shaded area in Figure 10.12 is 34.13% of the total area under the normal curve.

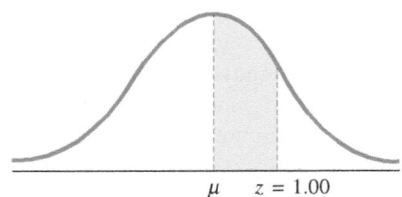

μ $z = 1.00$

Figure 10.12

Checkpoint 1

Find the percent of the area between the mean and

(a) $z = 1.51$;

(b) $z = -2.04$.

(c)   Find the percent of the area in the shaded region.

(b)   The area between $z = -2.43$ and $z = 0$

Solution   Table 2 lists only positive values of z. But the normal curve is symmetric around the mean $z = 0$, so the area between $z = 0$ and $z = -2.43$ is the same as the area between $z = 0$ and $z = 2.43$. Find 2.43 in the z-column of Table 2. The entry next to it in the A-column shows that the area is .4925. Hence, the shaded area in Figure 10.13 is 49.25% of the total area under the curve. ✓1 ✓2

μ $z = .72$

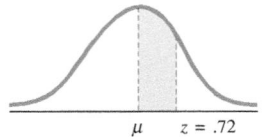

Checkpoint 2

If your calculator can graph probability distributions and find areas, use it to find the areas requested in Example 1.

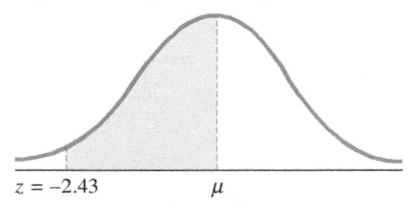

$z = -2.43$ μ

Figure 10.13

Scrolled

```
normalcdf(-2.43,0,0,1)
        .4924505896
normalcdf(-1E99,-2.43,0,1)
        .007549411
```

Figure 10.14

TECHNOLOGY TIP   Because of their convenience and accuracy, graphing calculators and computers have made normal-curve tables less important. Figure 10.14 shows how part (b) of Example 1 can be done on a TI-84+ calculator using a command from the DISTR menu. The second result in the calculator screen gives the area between $-\infty$ and $z = -2.43$; the entry $-1\text{E}99$ represents $-1 \cdot 10^{99}$, which is used to approximate $-\infty$.

Many statistical software packages are widely used today. All of these packages are set up in a way that is similar to a spreadsheet, and they all can be used to generate normal curve values. In addition, most spreadsheets can perform a wide range of statistical calculations.

Example 2   Use technology or Table 2 to find the percent of the total area for the given areas under the standard normal curve.

(a)   The area between .88 standard deviations *below* the mean and 2.35 standard deviations *above* the mean (that is, between $z = -.88$ and $z = 2.35$)

Solution   First, draw a sketch showing the desired area, as in Figure 10.15. From Table 2, the area between the mean and .88 standard deviations below the mean is .3106. Also, the area from the mean to 2.35 standard deviations above the mean is .4906. As the figure shows, the total desired area can be found by *adding* these numbers:

$$\begin{array}{r} .3106 \\ +.4906 \\ \hline .8012. \end{array}$$

The shaded area in Figure 10.15 represents 80.12% of the total area under the normal curve.

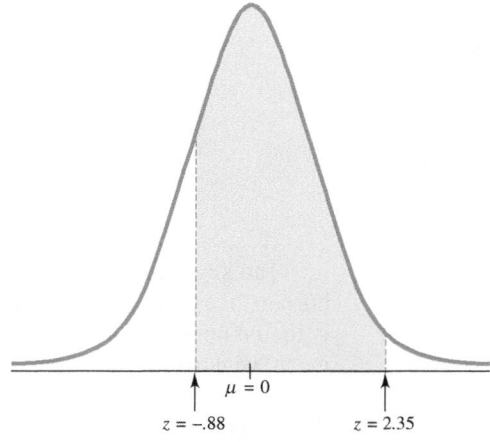

Figure 10.15

(b) The area between .58 standard deviations above the mean and 1.94 standard deviations above the mean

Solution Figure 10.16 shows the desired area. The area between the mean and .58 standard deviations above the mean is .2190. The area between the mean and 1.94 standard deviations above the mean is .4738. As the figure shows, the desired area is found by *subtracting* one area from the other:

$$\begin{array}{r} .4738 \\ -.2190 \\ \hline .2548. \end{array}$$

The shaded area of Figure 10.16 represents 25.48% of the total area under the normal curve.

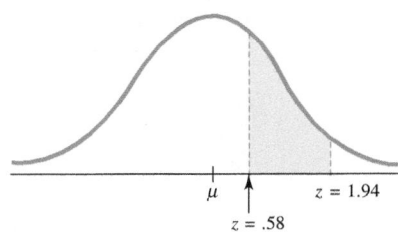

Figure 10.16

(c) The area to the right of 2.09 standard deviations above the mean

Solution The total area under a normal curve is 1. Thus, the total area to the right of the mean is 1/2, or .5000. From Table 2, the area from the mean to 2.09 standard deviations

✓**Checkpoint 3**

Find the given standard normal-curve areas as percentages of the total area.

(a) Between .31 standard deviations below the mean and 1.01 standard deviations above the mean

-.31 μ 1.01

(b) Between .38 standard deviations and 1.98 standard deviations below the mean

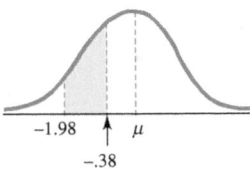

-1.98 ↑ μ
      -.38

(c) To the right of 1.49 standard deviations above the mean

μ   1.49

(d) What percent of the area is within 1 standard deviation of the mean? within 2 standard deviations of the mean? within 3 standard deviations of the mean? What can you conclude from the last answer?

✓**Checkpoint 4**

Find each z-score, using the information in Example 3.

(a) x = 36

(b) x = 55

above the mean is .4817. The area to the right of 2.09 standard deviations is found by subtracting .4817 from .5000:

$$\begin{array}{r} .5000 \\ -.4817 \\ \hline .0183. \end{array}$$

A total of 1.83% of the total area is to the right of 2.09 standard deviations above the mean. Figure 10.17 (which is not to scale) shows the desired area. ✓ 3

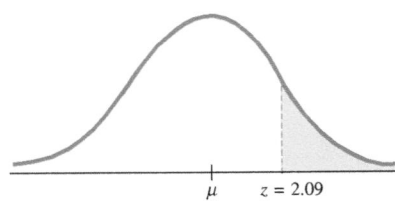

μ   z = 2.09

Figure 10.17

The key to finding areas under *any* normal curve is to express each number x on the horizontal axis in terms of standard deviations above or below the mean. The **z-score** for x is the number of standard deviations that x lies from the mean (positive if x is above the mean, negative if x is below the mean).

Example 3 If a normal distribution has mean 60 and standard deviation 5, find the given z-scores.

(a) The z-score for x = 65

Solution Since 65 is 5 units above 60 and the standard deviation is 5, 65 is 1 standard deviation above the mean. So its z-score is 1.

(b) The z-score for x = 52.5

Solution The z-score is −1.5, because 52.5 is 7.5 units below the mean (since 52.5 − 60 = −7.5) and 7.5 is 1.5 standard deviations (since 7.5/5 = 1.5). ✓ 4

In Example 3(b) we found the z-score by taking the difference between 52.5 and the mean and dividing this difference by the standard deviation. The same procedure works in the general case.

Z-Score

If a normal distribution has mean μ and standard deviation σ, then the z-score for the number x is

$$z = \frac{x - \mu}{\sigma}.$$

The importance of z-scores is the following fact, whose proof is omitted.

Area under a Normal Curve

The area under a normal curve between x = a and x = b is the same as the area under the standard normal curve between the z-score for a and the z-score for b.

Therefore, by converting to z-scores and using a graphing calculator or Table 2 for the standard normal curve, we can find areas under any normal curve. Since these areas are probabilities (as explained earlier), we can now handle a variety of applications.

Graphing calculators, computer programs, and CAS programs (such as DERIVE) can be used to find areas under the normal curve and, hence, probabilities. The equation of the standard normal curve, with $\mu = 0$ and $\sigma = 1$, is

$$f(x) = (1/\sqrt{2\pi})e^{-x^2/2}.$$

A good approximation of the area under this curve (and above $y = 0$) can be found by using the x-interval $[-4, 4]$. However, calculus is needed to find such areas.

Example 4   **Business**   Dixie Office Supplies finds that its sales force drives an average of 1200 miles per month per person, with a standard deviation of 150 miles. Assume that the number of miles driven by a salesperson is closely approximated by a normal distribution.

(a) Find the probability that a salesperson drives between 1200 and 1600 miles per month.

Solution   Here, $\mu = 1200$ and $\sigma = 150$, and we must find the area under the normal distribution curve between $x = 1200$ and $x = 1600$. We begin by finding the z-score for $x = 1200$:

$$z = \frac{x - \mu}{\sigma} = \frac{1200 - 1200}{150} = \frac{0}{150} = 0.$$

The z-score for $x = 1600$ is

$$z = \frac{x - \mu}{\sigma} = \frac{1600 - 1200}{150} = \frac{400}{150} = 2.67.^{*}$$

So the area under the curve from $x = 1200$ to $x = 1600$ is the same as the area under the standard normal curve from $z = 0$ to $z = 2.67$, as indicated in Figure 10.18. A graphing calculator or Table 2 shows that this area is .4962. Therefore, the probability that a salesperson drives between 1200 and 1600 miles per month is .4962.

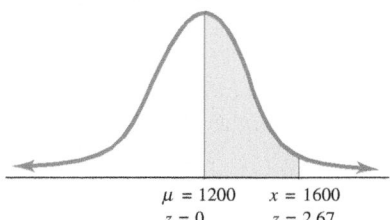

$\mu = 1200$ $x = 1600$
$z = 0$ $z = 2.67$

Figure 10.18

(b) Find the probability that a salesperson drives between 1000 and 1500 miles per month.

Solution   As shown in Figure 10.19, z-scores for both $x = 1000$ and $x = 1500$ are needed.

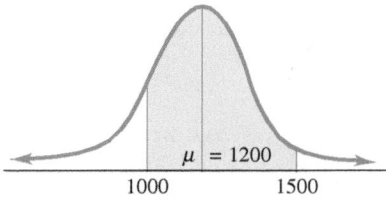

$\mu = 1200$
1000   1500

Figure 10.19

---

*All z-scores here are rounded to two decimal places.

For $x = 1000$,   For $x = 1500$,

$$z = \frac{1000 - 1200}{150}$$ $$z = \frac{1500 - 1200}{150}$$

$$= \frac{-200}{150}$$ $$= \frac{300}{150}$$

$$= -1.33.$$ $$= 2.00.$$

From Table 2, $z = 1.33$ leads to an area of .4082, while $z = 2.00$ corresponds to .4773. A total of $.4082 + .4773 = .8855$, or 88.55%, of all drivers travel between 1000 and 1500 miles per month. From this calculation, the probability that a driver travels between 1000 and 1500 miles per month is .8855. ✓5

✓**Checkpoint 5**

With the data from Example 4, find the probability that a salesperson drives between 1000 and 1450 miles per month.

Example 5   **Health**   With data from the 2009–2010 National Health and Nutritional Examination Survey (NHANES), we can use 186 (mg/dL) as an estimate of the mean total cholesterol level for all Americans and 41 (mg/dL) as an estimate of the standard deviation. Assuming total cholesterol levels to be normally distributed, what is the probability that an American chosen at random has a cholesterol level higher than 250? If 200 Americans are chosen at random, how many can we expect to have total cholesterol higher than 250? (Data from: www.cdc.gov/nchs/nhanes.htm.)

Solution   Here, $\mu = 186$ and $\sigma = 41$. The probability that a randomly chosen American has cholesterol higher than 250 is the area under the normal curve to the right of $x = 250$. The z-score for $x = 250$ is

$$z = \frac{x - \mu}{\sigma} = \frac{250 - 186}{41} = \frac{64}{41} = 1.56.$$

From Table 2, we see that the area to the right of 1.56 is $.5 - .4406 = .0594$, which is 5.94% of the total area under the curve. Therefore, the probability of a randomly chosen American having cholesterol higher than 250 is .0594.

With 5.94% of Americans having total cholesterol higher than 250, selecting 200 Americans at random yields

$$5.94\% \text{ of } 200 = .0594 \cdot 200 = 11.88.$$

Approximately 12 of these Americans can be expected to have a total cholesterol level higher than 250. ✓6

✓**Checkpoint 6**

Using the mean and standard deviation from Example 5, find the probability that an adult selected at random has a cholesterol level below 150.

📄 **NOTE**   Notice in Example 5 that $P(z \geq 1.56) = P(z > 1.56.)$. The area under the curve is the same whether we include the endpoint or not. Notice also that $P(z = 1.56) = 0$, because no area is included.

⊘ **CAUTION**   When calculating the normal probability, it is wise to draw a normal curve with the mean and the z-scores every time. This practice will avoid confusion as to whether you should add or subtract probabilities.

As mentioned earlier, z-scores are standard deviations, so $z = 1$ corresponds to 1 standard deviation above the mean, and so on. As found in Checkpoint 3(d) of this section, 68.26% of the area under a normal curve lies within 1 standard deviation of the mean. Also, 95.46% lies within 2 standard deviations of the mean, and 99.74% lies within 3 standard deviations of the mean. These results, summarized in Figure 10.20, can be used to get quick estimates when you work with normal curves.

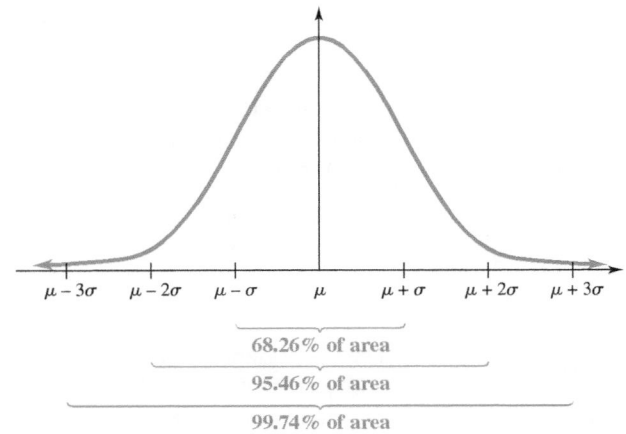

Figure 10.20

Boxplots

The normal curve is useful because you can easily read various characteristics of the data from the picture. Boxplots are another graphical means of presenting key characteristics of a data set. The idea is to arrange the data in increasing order and choose three numbers $Q_1, Q_2,$ and Q_3 that divide it into four equal parts, as indicated schematically in the following diagram:

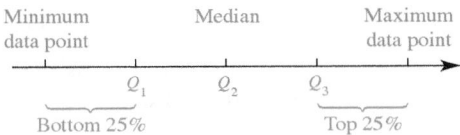

The number Q_1 is called the **first quartile,** the median Q_2 is called the **second quartile,** and Q_3 is called the **third quartile.** The minimum, $Q_1, Q_2, Q_3,$ and the maximum are often called the **five-number summary,** and they are used to construct a boxplot, as illustrated in Examples 6 and 7.

> **Example 6** The following table gives the revenue (in billions of dollars) for Home Depot and Lowe's home improvement corporations for the given years. Construct a boxplot for the Home Depot revenue data. (Data from: www.morningstar.com.)

Year	2004	2005	2006	2007	2008	2009	2010	2011	2012	2013
Home Depot	64.8	73.1	81.5	90.8	77.3	71.3	66.2	68.0	70.4	74.8
Lowe's	30.8	36.5	43.2	46.9	48.3	48.2	47.2	48.8	50.2	50.5

Solution First, we have to order the revenues from low to high:

$$64.8, 66.2, 68.0, 70.4, 71.3, 73.1, 74.8, 77.3, 81.5, 90.8,$$

The minimum revenue is 64.8, and the maximum revenue is 90.8. Since there is an even number of data points, the median revenue Q_2 is 72.2 (halfway between the two center entries). To find Q_1, which separates the lower 25% of the data from the rest, we first calculate

$$25\% \text{ of } n \text{ (rounded up to the nearest integer),}$$

where n is the number of data points. Here, $n = 10$, and so $.25(10) = 2.5$, which rounds up to 3. Now count to the *third* revenue (in order) to get $Q_1 = 68.0$.

Similarly, since Q_3 separates the lower 75% of the data from the rest, we calculate

75% of n (rounded up to the nearest integer).

When $n = 10$, we have $.75(10) = 7.5$, which rounds up to 8. Count to the *eighth* observation (in order), getting $Q_3 = 77.3$.

The five key numbers for constructing the boxplot are as follows:

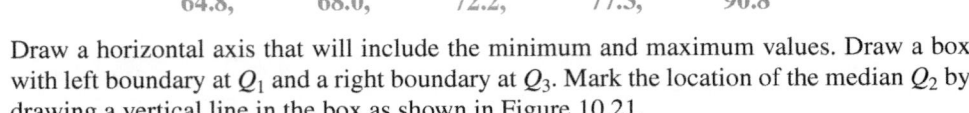

Minimum, Q_1, Q_2, Q_3,   Maximum

64.8,   68.0,   72.2,   77.3,   90.8

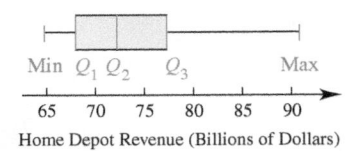

Min Q_1 Q_2 Q_3 Max

65   70   75   80   85   90
Home Depot Revenue (Billions of Dollars)

Figure 10.21

Draw a horizontal axis that will include the minimum and maximum values. Draw a box with left boundary at Q_1 and a right boundary at Q_3. Mark the location of the median Q_2 by drawing a vertical line in the box as shown in Figure 10.21.

Boxplots are useful in showing the location of the middle 50% of the data. This is the region of the box between Q_1 and Q_3. Boxplots are also quite useful in comparing two distributions that are measured on the same scale, as we will see in Example 7.

Example 7   **Business**   Construct a boxplot for the Lowe's revenue data in Example 6 with the Home Depot revenue boxplot on the same graph.

Solution   The Lowe's data first need to be sorted low to high:

30.8, 36.5, 43.2, 46.9, 47.2, 48.2, 48.3, 48.8, 50.2, 50.5.

The minimum is 30.8, the maximum is 50.5, and the median $Q_2 = 47.7$. Again, $n = 10$, and so

25% of $n = .25(10) = 2.5$, which rounds up to 3,

so that $Q_1 = 43.2$ (the *third* revenue). Similarly,

75% of $n = .75(10) = 7.5$, which rounds up to 8,

so that $Q_3 = 48.8$ (the *eighth* revenue).

We can now use the minimum, Q_1, Q_2, and Q_3, and the maximum to place the boxplot of Lowe's data below the Home Depot boxplot, as shown in Figure 10.22.

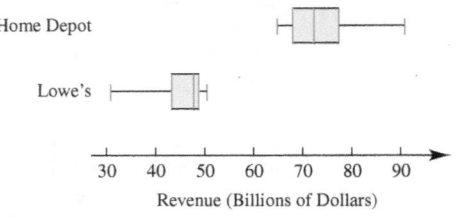

Home Depot

Lowe's

30   40   50   60   70   80   90
Revenue (Billions of Dollars)

Figure 10.22

When we compare the revenue distributions in this way, we see how much more revenue Home Depot generated in the studied years than Lowe's. Because the box for Home Depot is wider, and the distance from the minimum to the maximum is also wider for Home Depot, we can also say that there is a greater degree of variability for Home Depot.

✓**Checkpoint 7**

Create a boxplot for the weights (in kilograms) for eight first-year students:

88, 79, 67, 69, 58, 53, 89, 57.

➤ **TECHNOLOGY TIP** Many graphing calculators can graph boxpots for single-variable data. The procedure is similar to plotting data with the STAT PLOT menu.

10.4 Exercises

1. The peak in a normal curve occurs directly above _____.

2. The total area under a normal curve (above the horizontal axis) is _____.

3. How are z-scores found for normal distributions with $\mu \neq 0$ or $\sigma \neq 1$?

4. How is the standard normal curve used to find probabilities for normal distributions?

Find the percentage of the area under a normal curve between the mean and the given number of standard deviations from the mean. (See Example 1.)

5. 1.75

6. .26

7. −.43

8. −2.4

Find the percentage of the total area under the standard normal curve between the given z-scores. (See Examples 1 and 2.)

9. $z = 1.41$ and $z = 2.83$ 10. $z = .64$ and $z = 2.11$

11. $z = -2.48$ and $z = -.05$

12. $z = -1.63$ and $z = -1.08$

13. $z = -3.05$ and $z = 1.36$

14. $z = -2.91$ and $z = -.51$

Find a z-score satisfying each of the given conditions. (Hint: Use Table 2 backward or a graphing calculator.)

15. 5% of the total area is to the right of z.

16. 1% of the total area is to the left of z.

17. 15% of the total area is to the left of z.

18. 25% of the total area is to the right of z.

19. For any normal distribution, what is the value of $P(x \leq \mu)$? of $P(x \geq \mu)$?

20. Using Chebyshev's theorem and the normal distribution, compare the probability that a number will lie within 2 standard deviations of the mean of a probability distribution. (See Exercises 15–22 of Section 10.3.) Explain what you observe.

21. Repeat Exercise 20, using 3 standard deviations.

Assume the distributions in Exercises 22–30 are all normal. (See Example 4.)

22. **Business** According to the label, a regular can of Campbell's™ soup holds an average of 305 grams, with a standard deviation of 4.2 grams. What is the probability that a can will be sold that holds more than 306 grams?

23. **Business** A jar of Adams Old Fashioned Peanut Butter contains 453 grams, with a standard deviation of 10.1 grams. Find the probability that one of these jars contains less than 450 grams.

24. **Business** A General Electric soft-white three-way lightbulb has an average life of 1200 hours, with a standard deviation of 50 hours. Find the probability that the life of one of these bulbs will be between 1150 and 1300 hours.

25. **Business** A 100-watt lightbulb has an average brightness of 1640 lumens, with a standard deviation of 62 lumens. What is the probability that a 100-watt bulb will have a brightness between 1600 and 1700 lumens?

26. **Social Science** The scores on a standardized test in a suburban high school have a mean of 80, with a standard deviation of 12. What is the probability that a student will have a score less than 60?

27. **Health** Using the data from the same study as in Example 5, we find that the average HDL cholesterol level is 52.6 mg/dL, with a standard deviation of 15.5 mg/dL. Find the probability that an individual will have an HDL cholesterol level greater than 60 mg/dL.

28. **Business** The production of cars per day at an assembly plant has mean 120.5 and standard deviation 6.2. Find the probability that fewer than 100 cars are produced on a random day.

29. **Business** Starting salaries for accounting majors have mean $53,300, with standard deviation $3,200. What is the probability an individual will start at a salary above $56,000?

30. **Social Science** The driving distance to work for residents of a certain community has mean 21 miles and standard deviation 3.6 miles. What is the probability that an individual drives between 10 and 20 miles to work?

Business *Scores on the Graduate Management Association Test (GMAT) are approximately normally distributed. The mean score for 2007–2008 is 540, with a standard deviation of 100. For the following exercises, find the probability that a GMAT test taker selected at random earns a score in the given range, using the normal distribution as a model. (Data from: www.gmac.com.)*

31. Between 540 and 700

32. Between 300 and 540

33. Between 300 and 700

34. Less than 400

35. Greater than 750

36. Between 600 and 700

37. Between 300 and 400

Social Science *New studies by Federal Highway Administration traffic engineers suggest that speed limits on many thoroughfares are set arbitrarily and often are artificially low. According to traffic engineers, the ideal limit should be the "85th-percentile speed," the speed at or below which 85% of the traffic moves. Assuming that speeds are normally distributed, find the 85th-percentile speed for roads with the given conditions.*

38. The mean speed is 55 mph, with a standard deviation of 10 mph.

39. The mean speed is 40 mph, with a standard deviation of 5 mph.

Education *One professor uses the following system for assigning letter grades in a course:*

Grade	Total Points
A	Greater than $\mu + \frac{3}{2}\sigma$
B	$\mu + \frac{1}{2}\sigma$ to $\mu + \frac{3}{2}\sigma$
C	$\mu - \frac{1}{2}\sigma$ to $\mu + \frac{1}{2}\sigma$
D	$\mu - \frac{3}{2}\sigma$ to $\mu - \frac{1}{2}\sigma$
F	Below $\mu - \frac{3}{2}\sigma$

What percentage of the students receive the given grades?

40. A   **41.** B   **42.** C

43. Do you think the system in Exercises 40–42 would be more likely to be fair in a large first-year class in psychology or in a graduate seminar of five students? Why?

Health *In nutrition, the recommended daily allowance of vitamins is a number set by the government as a guide to an individual's daily vitamin intake. Actually, vitamin needs vary drastically from person to person, but the needs are very closely approximated by a normal curve. To calculate the recommended daily allowance, the government first finds the average need for vitamins among people in the population and then the standard deviation. The recommended daily allowance is defined as the mean plus 2.5 times the standard deviation.*

44. What percentage of the population will receive adequate amounts of vitamins under this plan?

Find the recommended daily allowance for the following vitamins.

45. Mean = 550 units, standard deviation = 46 units

46. Mean = 1700 units, standard deviation = 120 units

47. Mean = 155 units, standard deviation = 14 units

48. Mean = 1080 units, standard deviation = 86 units

Education *The mean performance score of a large group of fifth-grade students on a math achievement test is 88. The scores are known to be normally distributed. What percentage of the students had scores as follows?*

49. More than 1 standard deviation above the mean

50. More than 2 standard deviations above the mean

Business *The table gives the annual revenue for Pepsi Co. and Coca-Cola Co. (in billions of U.S. dollars) for a 10-year period. (Data from: www.morningstar.com.) (See Examples 6 and 7.)*

Year	Pepsi	Coca-Cola
2003	27.0	21.0
2004	29.3	22.0
2005	32.6	23.1
2006	35.1	24.1
2007	39.5	28.9
2008	43.3	31.9
2009	43.2	31.0
2010	57.8	35.1
2011	66.6	46.5
2012	65.5	48.0

51. What is the five-number summary for Pepsi?

52. What is the five-number summary for Coca-Cola?

53. Construct a boxplot for Pepsi.

54. Construct a boxplot for Coca-Cola.

55. Graph the boxplots for Pepsi and Coca-Cola on the same scale. Are the distributions similar?

56. Which company has the higher median of sales over the 10-year period?

Finance *Use the following table for Exercises 57–60. The table contains data from a random sample of 12 states and lists expenditures (in billions of dollars) by category spent by states and local communities. (Data from: U.S. Census Bureau.)*

State	Education	Public Welfare
AL	13.2	6.0
AR	13.4	8.5
CO	13.2	4.2
GA	25.0	9.7
IA	9.3	4.6
MI	29.1	12.9
MO	14.2	7.4
NC	23.7	11.2
NJ	31.8	14.0
OH	32.8	18.4
WA	18.4	14.0
WV	5.3	3.0

57. What is the five-number summary for the expenditures on education?

58. What is the five-number summary for the expenditures on public welfare?

59. Construct a boxplot for the expenditures on education.

60. Construct a boxplot for the expenditures on public welfare.

Finance *For Exercises 61–62, use the boxplots below from data similar to Exercises 57–60 for state and local community expenditures on hospitals and highways.*

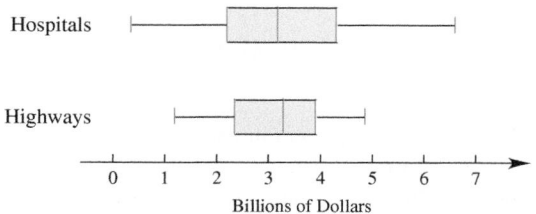

61. Estimate Q_1, Q_2, and Q_3 for hospital and highway spending.

62. Is there greater variability in hospital spending or highway spending? How do you know?

Finance *For Exercises 63–64, use the boxplots below constructed from data similar to those in Exercises 57–60 for state and local community expenditures on police and fire protection.*

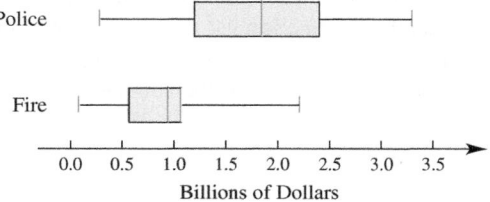

63. Is there greater variability in spending on police or fire protection? How do you know?

64. Estimate Q_1, Q_2, and Q_3 for police and fire protection spending.

✓**Checkpoint Answers**

1. (a) 43.45%   (b) 47.93%   (c) 26.42%

2. (a) 34.13%   (b) 49.25%

3. (a) 46.55%   (b) 32.82%   (c) 6.81%
    (d) 68.26%, 95.46%, 99.74%;
    almost all the data lie within 3 standard deviations of the mean.

4. (a) −4.8   (b) −1

5. .8607

6. .1894

7.

10.5 Normal Approximation to the Binomial Distribution

As we saw in Section 9.4, many practical experiments have only two possible outcomes, sometimes referred to as success or failure. Such experiments are called Bernoulli trials or Bernoulli processes. Examples of Bernoulli trials include flipping a coin (with heads being a success, for instance, and tails a failure) and testing a computer chip coming off the assembly line to see whether it is defective. A binomial experiment consists of repeated independent Bernoulli trials, such as flipping a coin 10 times or taking a random sample of 20 computer chips from the assembly line. In Section 9.4, we found the probability distribution for several binomial experiments, such as sampling five people with bachelor's degrees in education and counting how many are women. The probability distribution for a binomial experiment is known as a **binomial distribution.**

As another example, it is reported that 44% of registered vehicles in the United States are vans, pickup trucks, or sport utility vehicles (SUVs). (Data from: *The Statistical Abstract of the United States*: 2012.) Suppose an auto insurance agent wants to verify this statistic and records the type of vehicle for 10 randomly selected drivers. The agent finds that 3 out of 10, or 30%, are vans, pickups, or SUVs. How likely is this result if the figure for all vehicles is truly 44%? We can answer that question with the binomial probability formula

$$_nC_x \cdot p^x(1 - p)^{n-x},$$

where n is the sample size (10 in this case); x is the number of vans, pickups, or SUVs (3 in this case); and p is the probability that a vehicle is a van, pickup, or SUV (.44 in this case). We obtain

$$P(x = 3) = {}_{10}C_3 \cdot (.44)^3(1 - .44)^7$$
$$\approx 120(.085184)(.017271)$$
$$\approx .1765.$$

The probability is approximately 18%, so this result is not unusual.

Suppose that the insurance agent takes a larger random sample, say, of 100 drivers. What is the probability that 30 or fewer vehicles are vans, pickups, or SUVs if the 44% figure is accurate? Calculating $P(x = 0) + P(x = 1) + \cdots + P(x = 30)$ is a formidable task. One solution is provided by graphing calculators or computers. There is, however, a low-tech method that has the advantage of connecting two different distributions: the normal and the binomial. The normal distribution is continuous, since the random variable can be any real number. The binomial distribution is *discrete*, because the random variable can take only integer values between 0 and n. Nevertheless, the normal distribution can be used to give a good approximation to binomial probability. We call this approximation the **normal approximation.**

In order to use the normal approximation, we first need to know the mean and standard deviation of the binomial distribution. Recall from Section 9.4 that, for the binomial distribution, $E(x) = np$. In Section 10.2, we referred to $E(x)$ as μ, and that notation will be used here. It is shown in more advanced courses in statistics that the standard deviation of the binomial distribution is given by $\sigma = \sqrt{np(1 - p)}$.

Mean and Standard Deviation for the Binomial Distribution

For the binomial distribution, the mean and standard deviation are respectively given by

$$\mu = np \quad \text{and} \quad \sigma = \sqrt{np(1 - p)},$$

where n is the number of trials and p is the probability of success on a single trial. ☑₁

✔️ **Checkpoint 1**

Find μ and σ for a binomial distribution having $n = 120$ and $p = 1/6$.

Example 1 Suppose a fair coin is flipped 15 times.

(a) Find the mean and standard deviation for the number of heads.

Solution With $n = 15$ and $p = 1/2$, the mean is

$$\mu = np = 15\left(\frac{1}{2}\right) = 7.5.$$

The standard deviation is

$$\sigma = \sqrt{np(1 - p)} = \sqrt{15\left(\frac{1}{2}\right)\left(1 - \frac{1}{2}\right)}$$
$$= \sqrt{15\left(\frac{1}{2}\right)\left(\frac{1}{2}\right)} = \sqrt{3.75} \approx 1.94.$$

We expect, on average, to get 7.5 heads out of 15 tosses. Most of the time, the number of heads will be within three standard deviations of the mean, or between $7.5 - 3(1.94) = 1.68$ and $7.5 + 3(1.94) = 13.32$.

(b) Find the probability distribution for the number of heads, and draw a histogram of the probabilities.

Solution   The probability distribution is found by putting $n = 15$ and $p = 1/2$ into the formula for binomial probability. For example, the probability of getting 9 heads is given by

$$P(x = 9) = {}_{15}C_9\left(\frac{1}{2}\right)^9\left(1 - \frac{1}{2}\right)^6 \approx .15274.$$

Probabilities for the other values of x between 0 and 15, as well as a histogram of the probabilities, are shown in Figure 10.23.

x	$P(x)$
0	.00003
1	.00046
2	.00320
3	.01389
4	.04166
5	.09164
6	.15274
7	.19638
8	.19638
9	.15274
10	.09164
11	.04166
12	.01389
13	.00320
14	.00046
15	.00003

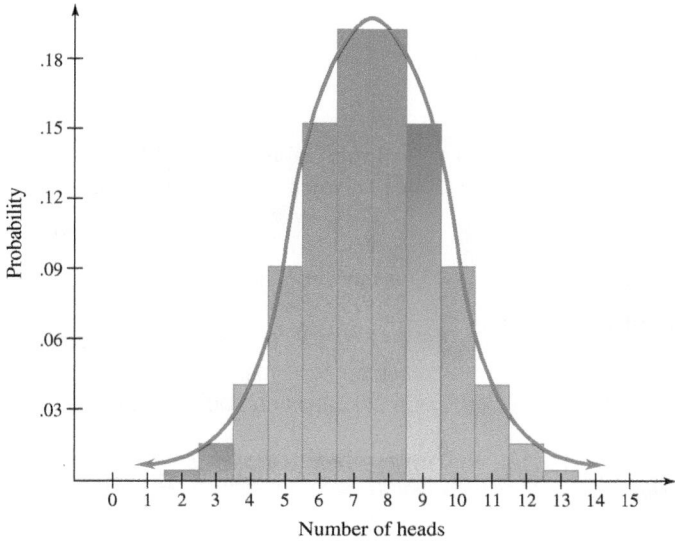

Figure 10.23

In Figure 10.23, we have superimposed the normal curve with $\mu = 7.5$ and $\sigma = 1.94$ over the histogram of the distribution. Notice how well the normal distribution fits the binomial distribution. This approximation was first discovered in 1718 by Abraham De Moivre (1667–1754) for the case $p = 1/2$. The result was generalized by the French mathematician Pierre-Simon Laplace (1749–1827) in a book published in 1812. As n becomes larger and larger, a histogram for the binomial distribution looks more and more like a normal curve. Figures 10.24(a) and (b), show histograms of the binomial distribution with $p = .3$, using $n = 8$ and $n = 50$, respectively.

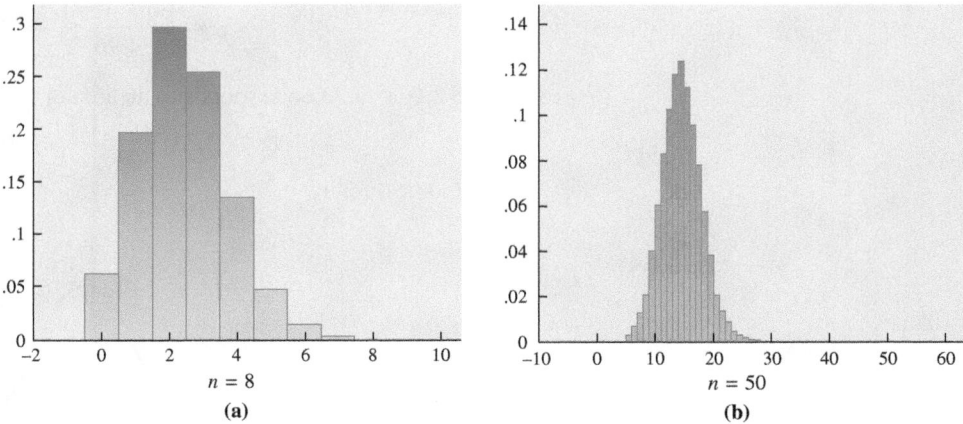

Figure 10.24

The probability of getting exactly 9 heads in the 15 tosses, or .15274, is the same as the area of the blue bar in Figure 10.23. As the graph suggests, the blue area is approximately equal to the area under the normal curve from $x = 8.5$ to $x = 9.5$. The normal curve is higher than the top of the bar in the left half, but lower in the right half.

To find the area under the normal curve from $x = 8.5$. to $x = 9.5$, first find z-scores, as in the previous section. Use the mean and the standard deviation for the distribution, which we have already calculated, to get z-scores for $x = 8.5$ and $x = 9.5$:

$$\text{For } x = 8.5, \qquad\qquad \text{For } x = 9.5,$$

$$z = \frac{8.5 - 7.5}{1.94} \qquad\qquad z = \frac{9.5 - 7.5}{1.94}$$

$$= \frac{1.00}{1.94} \qquad\qquad = \frac{2.00}{1.94}$$

$$z \approx .52. \qquad\qquad z \approx 1.03.$$

From Table 2, $z = .52$ gives an area of .1985, and $z = 1.03$ gives .3485. The difference between these two numbers is the desired result:

$$.3485 - .1985 = .1500.$$

This answer is not far from the more accurate answer of .15274 found earlier. ✔2

> **CAUTION** The normal-curve approximation to a binomial distribution is quite accurate, *provided that n is large and p is not close to 0 or 1.* As a rule of thumb, the normal-curve approximation can be used as long as both np and $n(1 - p)$ are at least 5.

 Checkpoint 2

Use the normal distribution to find the probability of getting exactly the given number of heads in 15 tosses of a coin.

(a) 7

(b) 10

Example 2   **Business**   Consider the previously discussed sample of 100 vehicles selected at random, where 44% of the registered vehicles are vans, pickups, or SUVs.

(a) Use the normal distribution to approximate the probability that at least 61 vehicles are vans, pickups, or SUVs.

Solution   First, find the mean and the standard deviation, using $n = 100$ and $p = .44$:

$$\mu = 100(.44) \qquad\qquad \sigma = \sqrt{100(.44)(1 - .44)}$$

$$= 44. \qquad\qquad\qquad = \sqrt{100(.44)(.56)}$$

$$\qquad\qquad\qquad\qquad \approx 4.96.$$

As the graph in Figure 10.25 shows, we need to find the area to the right of $x = 60.5$ (since we want 61 or more vehicles to be vans, pickups, or SUVs). The z-score corresponding to $x = 60.5$ is

$$z = \frac{60.5 - 44}{4.96} \approx 3.33.$$

From Table 2, $z = 3.33$ corresponds to an area of .4996, so

$$P(z > 3.33) = .5 - .4996 = .0004.$$

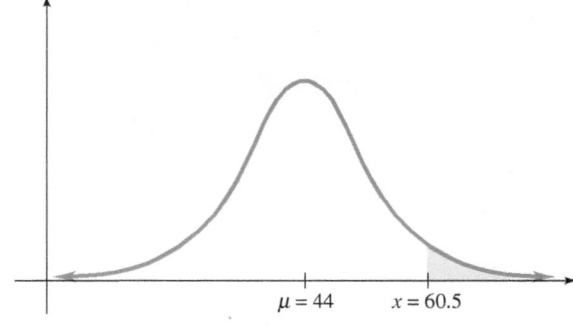

Figure 10.25

This is an extremely low probability. If an insurance agent obtained 61 vehicles that were vans, pickups, or SUVs in a sample of 100, she would suspect that either her sample is not truly random or the 44% figure is too low.

(b) Calculate the probability of finding between 51 and 58 vehicles that were vans, pickups, or SUVs in a random sample of 100.

Solution As Figure 10.26 shows, we need to find the area between $x = 50.5$, and $x = 58.5$:

$$\text{If } x = 50.5, \text{ then } z = \frac{50.5 - 44}{4.96} \approx .1.31.$$

$$\text{If } x = 58.5, \text{ then } z = \frac{58.5 - 44}{4.96} \approx 2.92.$$

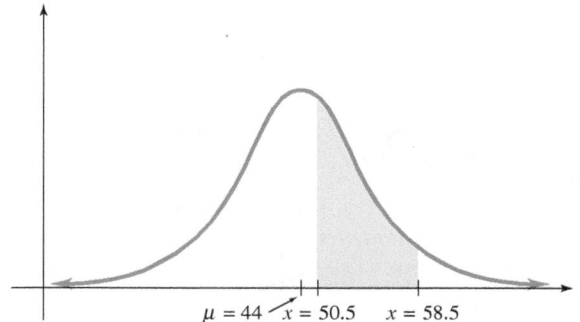

$\mu = 44$ $x = 50.5$ $x = 58.5$

Figure 10.26

Use Table 2 to find that $z = 1.31$ corresponds to an area of .4049 and $z = 2.92$ yields .4983. The final answer is the difference of these numbers:

$$P(1.31 \le z \le 2.92) = .4983 - .4049 = .0934.$$

The probability of finding between 51 and 58 vehicles that are vans, pickups, or SUVs is approximately .0934. ✓₃

✓ Checkpoint 3

In April 2013, Michigan had an unemployment rate of 8.4%. Find the approximate probability that in a random sample of 200 adults from Michigan during that month, the given numbers of people would be unemployed. (Data from: U.S. Bureau of Labor Statistics.)

(a) Exactly 12

(b) 15 or fewer

(c) More than 10

10.5 Exercises

1. What must be known to find the mean and standard deviation of a binomial distribution?

2. What is the rule of thumb for using the normal distribution to approximate a binomial distribution?

Suppose 16 coins are tossed. Find the probability of getting each of the given results by using (a) the binomial probability formula and (b) the normal-curve approximation. (See Examples 1 and 2.)

3. Exactly 8 heads

4. Exactly 9 heads

5. More than 13 tails

6. Fewer than 6 tails

For the remaining exercises in this section, use the normal-curve approximation to the binomial distribution.

Suppose 1000 coins are tossed. Find the probability of getting each of the given results.

7. Exactly 500 heads

8. Exactly 510 heads

9. 475 or more heads

10. Fewer than 460 tails

A die is tossed 120 times. Find the probability of getting each of the given results. (See Example 2.)

11. Exactly twenty 5's

12. Exactly twenty-four 4's

13. More than seventeen 3's

14. Fewer than twenty-one 6's

15. A reader asked Mr. Statistics (a feature in *Fortune* magazine) about the game of 26 once played in the bars of Chicago.[*] In

---

[*]Daniel Seligman and Patty De Llosa, "Ask Mr. Statistics," *Fortune*, May 1, 1995, p. 141.

this game, the player chooses a number between 1 and 6 and then rolls a cup full of 10 dice 13 times. Out of the 130 numbers rolled, if the number chosen appears at least 26 times, the player wins. Calculate the probability of winning.

For Exercises 16–24, see Example 2.

16. Natural Science For certain bird species, with appropriate assumptions, the number of nests escaping predation has a binomial distribution.[*] Suppose the probability of success (that is, a nest's escaping predation) is .3. Find the probability that at least half of 26 nests escape predation.

17. Natural Science Let us assume, under certain appropriate assumptions, that the probability of a young animal eating x units of food is binomially distributed, with n equal to the maximum number of food units the animal can acquire and p equal to the probability per time unit that an animal eats a unit of food. Suppose $n = 120$ and $p = .6$.

(a) Find the probability that an animal consumes 80 units of food.

(b) Suppose the animal must consume at least 70 units of food to survive. What is the probability that this happens?

Finance *For Exercises 18–22, the data are from the report from the National Center for Education Statistics titled "The Condition of Education" (nces.ed.gov/programs/coe/).*

18. In 2009–2010, 82% of entering freshman at 4-year colleges and universities received some kind of financial aid. Suppose 50 entering freshman are selected at random.

(a) Find the probability that at least 35 received financial aid.

(b) Find the probability that at most 45 received financial aid.

19. In the fall of 2010, 86% of first-time, full-time students received loans at for-profit colleges and universities. If a random sample of 500 students is selected, find the probability that at least 440 students received loans.

20. In the fall of 2010, 63% of first-time, full-time students received loans at private nonprofit colleges and universities. If a random sample of 500 students is selected, find the probability that at least 325 students received loans.

21. In the fall of 2010, 24% of first-time, full-time students received loans at public 2-year colleges. If a random sample of 500 students is selected, find the probability that at most 140 students received loans.

22. In the fall of 2010, 50% of first-time, full-time students received loans at public 4-year colleges or universities. If a random sample of 500 students is selected, find the probability that at most 275 students received loans.

23. Natural Science A flu vaccine has a probability of 80% of preventing a person who is inoculated from getting the flu. A county health office inoculates 134 people. Find the probabilities of the given results.

(a) Exactly 12 of the people inoculated get the flu.

(b) No more than 12 of the people inoculated get the flu.

(c) None of the people inoculated get the flu.

24. Natural Science The probability that a male will be color blind is .042. Find the probabilities that, in a group of 53 men, the given conditions will be true.

(a) Exactly 6 are color blind.

(b) No more than 6 are color blind.

(c) At least 1 is color blind.

Business *In the first quarter of 2013, Verizon held approximately 37% of the U.S. wireless market, while AT&T held 28%. Use this information for Exercises 25–30 and assume that 1000 wireless phone customers are selected at random. (Data from: Kantar Worldpanel ComTech USA's consumer panel, www.kantarworldpanel.com.)*

25. What is the expected number of Verizon customers?

26. What is the expected number of AT&T customers?

27. What is the probability that at least 400 will be Verizon customers?

28. What is the probability that at least 300 will be AT&T customers?

29. What is the probability that at most 325 will be Verizon customers?

30. What is the probability that at most 250 will be AT&T customers?

31. Natural Science The blood types B– and AB– are the rarest of the eight human blood types, representing 1.5% and .6% of the population, respectively. (Data from: National Center for Statistics and Analysis.)

(a) If the blood types of a random sample of 1000 blood donors are recorded, what is the probability that 10 or more of the samples are AB–?

(b) If the blood types of a random sample of 1000 blood donors are recorded, what is the probability that 20 to 40, inclusive, of the samples are B–?

(c) If a particular city had a blood drive in which 500 people gave blood and 3% of the donations were B–, would we have reason to believe that this town has a higher-than-normal number of donors who are B–? (*Hint:* Calculate the probability of 15 or more donors being B– for a random sample of 500, and then consider the probability obtained.)

32. In the 1989 U.S. Open, four golfers each made a hole in one on the same par-3 hole on the same day. *Sports Illustrated* writer R. Reilly stated the probability of getting a hole in one for a given golf pro on a given par-3 hole to be $1/3709$.[†]

(a) For a specific par-3 hole, use the binomial distribution to find the probability that 4 or more of the 156 golf pros in the tournament field shoot a hole in one.[‡]

(b) For a specific par-3 hole, use the normal approximation to the binomial distribution to find the probability that 4 or more of the 156 golf pros in the tournament field shoot a

---

[*]From G. deJong, *American Naturalist*, vol 110.

[†]R. Reilly, "King of the Hill," *Sports Illustrated*, June 1989, pp. 20–25.
[‡]Bonnie Litwiller and David Duncan, "The Probability of a Hole in One," *School Science and Mathematics* 91, no. 1 (January 1991): 30.

hole in one. Why must we be very cautious when using this approximation for this application?

(c) If the probability of a hole in one remains constant and is 1/3709 for any par-3 hole, find the probability that, in 20,000 attempts by golf pros, there will be 4 or more holes in one. Discuss whether this assumption is reasonable.

 Checkpoint Answers

1. $\mu = 20$; $\sigma = 4.08$

2. **(a)** .1985   **(b)** .0909

3. **(a)** .0472   **(b)** .3707   **(c)** .9463

CHAPTER 10 Summary and Review

Key Terms and Symbols

10.1 random sample
grouped frequency
   distribution
histogram
frequency polygon
stem-and-leaf-plot
uniform distribution
right-skewed distribution
left-skewed distribution
normal distribution

10.2 Σ, summation (sigma)
   notation
$\bar{x}$, sample mean
μ, population mean
(arithmetic) mean
median
statistic
mode

10.3 s^2, sample variance
s, sample standard deviation

σ, population standard
   deviation
range
deviations from the mean
variance
standard deviation

10.4 μ, mean of a normal
   distribution
σ, standard deviation of a
   normal distribution

continuous distribution
normal curves
standard normal curve
z-score
boxplot
quartile
five-number summary

10.5 binomial distribution

Chapter 10 Key Concepts

Frequency Distributions

To organize the data from a sample, we use a **grouped frequency distribution**—a set of intervals with their corresponding frequencies. The same information can be displayed with a **histogram**—a type of bar graph with a bar for each interval. The height of each bar is equal to the frequency of the corresponding interval. A **stem-and-leaf plot** presents the individual data in a similar form, so it can be viewed as a bar graph as well. Another way to display this information is with a **frequency polygon**, which is formed by connecting the midpoints of consecutive bars of the histogram with straight-line segments.

Measures of Center

The **mean** $\bar{x}$ of a frequency distribution is the expected value.

For n numbers $x_1, x_2, \ldots, x_n$,
$$\bar{x} = \frac{\Sigma x}{n}.$$

For a grouped distribution,
$$\bar{x} = \frac{\Sigma(xf)}{n}.$$

The **median** is the middle entry (or mean of the two middle entries) in a set of data arranged in either increasing or decreasing order.

The **mode** is the most frequent entry in a set of numbers.

Measures of Variability

The **range** of a distribution is the difference between the largest and smallest numbers in the distribution.

The **sample standard deviation** s is the square root of the sample **variance**.

For n numbers,
$$s = \sqrt{\frac{\Sigma x^2 - n\bar{x}^2}{n-1}}.$$

For a grouped distribution,
$$s = \sqrt{\frac{\Sigma fx^2 - n\bar{x}^2}{n-1}}.$$

The Normal Distribution

A **normal distribution** is a continuous distribution with the following properties: The highest frequency is at the mean; the graph is symmetric about a vertical line through the mean; the total area under the curve, above the x-axis, is 1. If a normal distribution has mean μ and standard deviation σ, then the z-score for the number x is $z = \dfrac{x - \mu}{\sigma}$. The **area under a normal curve** between $x = a$ and $x = b$ gives the probability that an observed data value will be between a and b.

Boxplots

A **boxplot** organizes a list of data using the minimum and maximum values, the median, and the first and third quartiles to give a visual overview of the distribution.

Normal Approximation to the Binomial Distribution

The **binomial distribution** is a distribution with the following properties: For n independent repeated trials, in which the probability of success in a single trial is p, the probability of x successes is $_nC_x p^x(1-p)^{n-x}$. The mean is $\mu = np$, and the standard deviation is

$$\sigma = \sqrt{np(1-p)}.$$

For a large number of trials, the normal distribution can be used to approximate binomial probabilities.

Chapter 10 Review Exercises

Business   *For Exercises 1 and 2, (a) write a frequency distribution; (b) draw a histogram. The data come from a random sample of 40 companies from the S&P 500. (Data from: www.morningstar.com.)*

1. The variable is 2012 revenue (in billions of dollars).

39.9	9.7	9.2	33.3
1.4	10.0	4.0	57.7
5.0	4.4	28.6	10.4
8.1	4.1	3.6	2.6
65.9	1.8	3.9	12.5
3.6	2.9	19.4	11.7
6.7	1.7	15.2	18.1
8.2	10.9	4.2	2.2
24.4	4.4	16.5	16.3
1.6	10.5	9.6	5.2

2. The variable is 2012 earnings per share (dollars).

3.72	1.64	3.04	5.66
1.12	0.65	4.99	3.16
1.43	4.57	0.29	3.75
8.48	2.55	2.81	6.58
1.30	0.98	1.58	2.52
0.87	0.89	6.06	5.06
2.86	2.94	3.15	0.97
5.47	0.35	2.67	3.46
2.67	2.54	3.48	2.60
1.22	3.44	1.58	7.54

3. Draw a stem-and-leaf plot for the data in Exercise 1. (Round to the nearest units place.)

4. Draw a stem-and-leaf plot for the data in Exercise 2. (Round to the nearest tenth.)

5. Find the mean and median for the first 10 revenues of Exercise 1.

    39.9, 1.4, 5.0, 8.1, 65.9, 3.6, 6.7, 8.2, 24.4, 1.6

6. Find the mean and median for the first 10 earnings per share values of Exercise 2.

    3.72, 1.12, 1.43, 8.48, 1.30, .87, 2.86, 5.47, 2.67, 1.22

7. **Business**   The following table gives the frequency counts for 40 companies from the S&P 500 and the variable is the net earnings (in millions of dollars). Find the mean and median for these data.

Interval	Frequency	Interval	Frequency
0–499	18	3000–3499	0
500–999	11	3500–3999	0
1000–1499	2	4000–4499	0
1500–1999	2	4500–4999	0
2000–2499	2	5000–5499	1
2500–2999	2	5500–5999	2

8. **Business**   The following table gives the frequency counts for 40 companies from the S&P 500 and the variable is the market capitalization (in billions of dollars). Find the mean and median for these data.

Interval	Frequency	Interval	Frequency
0–9.9	16	50–50.9	2
10–19.9	15	60–60.9	0
20–20.9	2	70–70.9	0
30–30.9	2	80–80.9	2
40–40.9	1		

9. Discuss some reasons for organizing data into a grouped frequency distribution.

10. What do the mean, median, and mode of a distribution have in common? How do they differ? Describe each in a sentence or two.

Find the median and the mode (or modes) for each of the given data sets.

11. **Business**   Hours worked for 10 adults. (Data from: www3.norc.org/gss+website.)

    30, 45, 16, 20, 70, 40, 48, 40, 50, 50

12. **Social Science**   The percentage of residents with a bachelor's degree or higher for 10 states. (Data from: U.S. Census Bureau.)

    22, 28, 26, 20, 30, 36, 36, 28, 26, 27

The modal class is the interval containing the most data values. Find the modal class for the distributions of the given data sets.

13. The data in Exercise 7

14. The data in Exercise 8

For the given histograms, identify the shape of the distribution.

15.

16.

17.

18.

19. What is meant by the range of a distribution?

20. How are the variance and the standard deviation of a distribution related? What is measured by the standard deviation?

Find the range and the standard deviation for each of the given distributions.

21. The data in Exercise 11

22. The data in Exercise 12

Find the standard deviation for each of the given distributions.

23. The data summarized in the frequency table of Exercise 7

24. The data summarized in the frequency table of Exercise 8

25. Finance The annual dividend yield percentages for Target Corporation are given in the following table. Find the mean and standard deviation of the yields for the 5-year period. (Data from: www.morningstar.com.)

Year	2008	2009	2010	2011	2012
Dividend Yield %	1.74	1.36	1.40	2.15	2.23

26. Finance The market capitalization amounts (in billions of dollars) for various years for Wal Mart Inc. are given in the following table. Find the mean and standard deviation of the capitalization amounts for the 5-year period. (Data from: www.morningstar.com.)

Year	2008	2009	2010	2011	2012
Capitalization Amounts	220	203	192	205	228

27. Describe the characteristics of a normal distribution.

28. What is meant by a skewed distribution?

Find the given areas under the standard normal curve.

29. Between $z = 0$ and $z = 1.35$

30. To the left of $z = .38$

31. Between $z = -1.88$ and $z = 2.41$

32. Between $z = 1.53$ and $z = 2.82$

33. Find a z-score such that 8% of the area under the curve is to the right of z.

34. Why is the normal distribution not a good approximation of a binomial distribution that has a value of p close to 0 or 1?

Health *For Exercises 35–38, use the fact that according to data from the 2009–2010 National Health and Nutrition Examination Study (NHANES), the mean height of males between ages 21 and 80 was 68.7 inches with a standard deviation of 3.1 inches. The mean height of females (for the same age range) was 63.2 inches with a standard deviation of 2.9 inches. The distribution of height for both sexes is approximately normal. (Data from: www.cdc.gov/nchs/nhanes.htm.)*

35. Find the probability that a female is taller than 70 inches.

36. Find the probability that a male is shorter than 62 inches.

37. Find the probability that a female is shorter than 60 inches.

38. Find the probability that a male is taller than 72 inches.

Business *The table gives the number of vehicles (in thousands) sold within the United States in April 2012 and April 2013 for 12 auto manufacturers. (Data from: Wall Street Journal.)*

Auto Manufacturer	April 2012 Sales	April 2013 Sales
General Motors Corp.	214	238
Ford Motor Corp.	180	212
Chrysler LLC	141	157
Toyota Motor Sales USA	178	176
American Honda Motor Co. Inc.	122	131
Nissan North America Inc.	71	88
Hyundai Motor America	62	63
Mazda	22	20
Kia Motors America Inc.	48	48
Subaru of America Inc.	26	33
Mercedes-Benz	24	25
Volkswagen of America Inc.	38	34

39. (a) Find the mean and standard deviation of sales for the April 2012 data.

(b) Which company is closest to the mean sales for the April 2012 data?

40. (a) Find the mean and standard deviation of sales for the April 2013 data.

(b) Which company is closest to the mean sales for the April 2013 data?

41. Find the five-number summary for the April 2012 sales.

42. Find the five-number summary for the April 2013 sales.

43. Construct a boxplot for the April 2012 sales data.

44. Construct a boxplot for the April 2013 sales data.

45. **Business** Find the five-number summary and construct a boxplot for the hours worked for the following sample of 10 workers. (Data from: www3.norc.org/gss+website.)

40, 60, 21, 5, 45, 35, 44, 40, 20, 53

46. **Education** Find the five-number summary and construct a boxplot for the percentage of residents who have earned a high school diploma or higher for the following sample of 10 states. (Data from: U.S. Census Bureau.)

81, 87, 92, 90, 85, 92, 88, 83, 85, 85

Business *According to the Federal Deposit Insurance Corporation (FDIC), approximately 25% of U.S. residents conduct some or all their financial transactions outside the United States banking system. These residents are sometimes called the "unbanked." For Exercises 47–50, assume that a random sample of 750 United States residents are selected. Approximate the probability of the given events.*

47. More than 200 are unbanked.

48. Less than 150 are unbanked.

49. Less than 190 are unbanked.

50. More than 160 are unbanked.

Business *According to a study by the Pew Research Center, 78% of teenagers in 2012 had a cell phone. For Exercises 51–54 assume that 1000 teenagers are selected at random and approximate the probability of the given events.*

51. At least 800 have a cell phone.

52. At most 750 have a cell phone.

53. At most 795 have a cell phone.

54. At least 760 have a cell phone.

Case Study 10 Standard Deviation as a Measure of Risk

When investing, the idea of risk is difficult to define. Some individuals may deem an investment product to be of high risk if it loses all of its value in a short time, others may define a product as risky if it loses some portion of its value in a short time, and still others may define a product as risky if there is even a remote chance of it losing its value over a long period of time.

One way investors try to quantify risk is to examine the volatility of the return for an investment product. Volatility refers to how the return on the investment fluctuates from the average level of return. One simple measure of volatility is to calculate the standard deviation of the annual rate of return.

For example, if a fund has an annual return of 2% each and every year, then the mean is 2% and the standard deviation would be 0 (because there is no variation from the mean). This fund would have very low volatility. What is also interesting is that a fund that *lost* 2% each and every year would also have a standard deviation of 0 (because it too does

not ever vary from its mean of –2%). Nevertheless, the standard deviation can be helpful in assessing the risk and volatility related to an investment fund.

Let us examine two mutual funds—Fund A and Fund B. The following table lists the annual rate of return for these two funds.

Fund A	Fund B
3.2	9.1
6.6	-3.4
3.9	2.1
5.3	11.4
5.2	1.1
5.8	9.7

CASE STUDY 10   Standard Deviation as a Measure of Risk   **567**

If we calculate the average rate of return for both funds, we obtain 5%. We can notice, however, even by casual inspection, that there is greater variability in Fund B than in Fund A. If we use the notation s_A to denote the standard deviation of fund A and s_B to denote the standard deviation of fund B, we can use the methods of Section 10.3 to obtain the following values for the standard deviation.

$$s_A = \sqrt{\frac{(3.2-5)^2 + (6.6-5)^2 + (3.9-5)^2 + (5.3-5)^2 + (5.2-5)^2 + (5.8-5)^2}{5}} \approx 1.25$$

$$s_B = \sqrt{\frac{(9.1-5)^2 + (-3.4-5)^2 + (2.1-5)^2 + (11.4-5)^2 + (1.1-5)^2 + (9.7-5)^2}{5}} \approx 5.90$$

Our calculations confirm that there is greater variability in Fund B. Thus, Fund B is said to carry more risk.

The way that standard deviation is used in the financial products industry is to examine monthly returns. For example, the website morningstar.com explains that it uses a 36-month window of monthly returns. They then calculate the average monthly return and the standard deviation from those returns. They then report these values (the mean return and the standard deviation) corrected for an annualized return rate. This should be clear in the following example.

To calculate the standard deviation for the TIAA-CREF Equity Index Retail fund (TINRX), we examine the monthly returns for 36 months from May 2013 back to June 2010.

Month	Return	Month	Return	Month	Return
MAY 2013	2.34	MAY 2012	−6.19	MAY 2011	−1.22
APR 2013	1.56	APR 2012	−0.64	APR 2011	3.01
MAR 2013	3.92	MAR 2012	3.03	MAR 2011	0.39
FEB 2013	1.29	FEB 2012	4.14	FEB 2011	3.63
JAN 2013	5.46	JAN 2012	5.07	JAN 2011	2.16
DEC 2012	1.22	DEC 2011	0.72	DEC 2010	6.74
NOV 2012	0.73	NOV 2011	−0.21	NOV 2010	0.55
OCT 2012	−1.79	OCT 2011	11.34	OCT 2010	3.85
SEP 2012	2.57	SEP 2011	−7.72	SEP 2010	9.42
AUG 2012	2.44	AUG 2011	−5.96	AUG 2010	−4.72
JUL 2012	1.04	JUL 2011	−2.33	JUL 2010	6.94
JUN 2012	3.84	JUN 2011	−1.81	JUN 2010	−5.83

Our first step is to calculate the mean return. We find the average monthly rate of return to be 1.3606. We then calculate the standard deviation value and obtain 4.2350. To convert these values from monthly return rates to annual return rates, we multiply the mean by 12 and the standard deviation by $\sqrt{12}$. The annual return rate is $12(1.3606) = 16.3272$ and the annual standard deviation is $\sqrt{12}(4.2350) = 14.6705$. These values are often reported rounded to two decimal places (16.33 and 14.67).

Many financial websites report these values for return rates based on monthly calculations. For example, on the morningstar.com website, clicking on a link for "Ratings and Risk" will display the mean and standard deviation values under a heading of "Volatility Measures." With this information, it is easier to make direct comparisons to other funds. For the same period, the S&P 500 had a mean return of 16.87 and a standard deviation of 14.02. Thus, we see that the TIAA-CREF fund had a slightly lower average return and a slightly higher level of risk.

An additional way that investors interpret the standard deviation is that they assume future returns will follow an approximate normal distribution. We know from Section 10.4 (and, in particular, Figure 10.20) that 68% of data that is normally distributed will fall within one standard deviation of the mean. With the TIAA-CREF fund example, we then expect that the probability of a future return being within one standard deviation of the mean of 16.33% is 68%. With the standard deviation value of 14.67, our bounds on this interval are

$$(16.33 - 14.67, 16.33 + 14.67) = (1.66, 31.00).$$

Furthermore, we expect the annual return to fall within 2 standard deviations of the mean approximately 95% of the time:

$$(16.33 - 2*14.67, 16.33 + 2*14.67) = (-13.01, 45.67).$$

The standard deviation is not a perfect measure of risk. It is possible to invest in a fund with a low standard deviation and still lose money. It is, however, a useful way to compare funds in similar categories.

Exercises

For Exercises 1–10, use the following table, which gives the monthly returns for the Janus Growth and Income S Fund, the S&P 500, and the sector returns for large growth funds. (Data from: www.morningstar.com.)

Month	Janus	S&P	Large Growth	Month	Janus	S&P	Large Growth
MAY 2013	1.33	2.34	2.63	NOV 2011	−0.8	−0.22	−1.06
APR 2013	3.01	1.93	1.25	OCT 2011	14.17	10.93	11.78
MAR 2013	4.26	3.75	3.19	SEP 2011	−10.38	−7.03	−8.45
FEB 2013	1.54	1.36	0.65	AUG 2011	−7.94	−5.43	−6.67
JAN 2013	4.8	5.18	4.75	JUL 2011	−2.81	−2.03	−1.27
DEC 2012	1.8	0.91	0.52	JUN 2011	−1.21	−1.67	−1.5
NOV 2012	0.56	0.58	1.95	MAY 2011	−1.07	−1.13	−1.27
OCT 2012	−1.87	−1.85	−3.01	APR 2011	3.67	2.96	2.91
SEP 2012	1.84	2.58	2.3	MAR 2011	−0.24	0.04	0.37
AUG 2012	2.77	2.25	3.27	FEB 2011	4	3.43	3.27
JUL 2012	2.11	1.39	0.47	JAN 2011	2.38	2.37	1.83
JUN 2012	2.8	4.12	2.6	DEC 2010	4.93	6.68	5.54
MAY 2012	−7.19	−6.01	−7.37	NOV 2010	−1.18	0.01	1.08
APR 2012	−0.94	−0.63	−0.7	OCT 2010	3.65	3.8	4.62
MAR 2012	2.32	3.29	3.37	SEP 2010	9.31	8.92	10.81
FEB 2012	5.33	4.32	5.34	AUG 2010	−4.22	−4.51	−4.72
JAN 2012	6.45	4.48	6.31	JUL 2010	6.02	7.01	6.73
DEC 2011	0.43	1.02	−1.14	JUN 2010	−3.92	−5.23	−5.62

1. Find the mean monthly return for the Janus fund. Convert this value to the annual return.

2. Find the mean monthly return for the S&P 500. Convert this value to the annual return.

3. Find the mean monthly return for the Large Growth funds. Convert this value to the annual return.

4. Which fund has the highest annual rate of return?

5. Find the standard deviation of the monthly returns for the Janus fund. Convert this value to the annual return.

6. Find the standard deviation of the monthly returns for the S&P 500. Convert this value to the annual return.

7. Find the standard deviation of the monthly returns for the Large Growth funds. Convert this value to the annual return.

8. Which fund has the highest level of risk?

9. Determine the bounds for 68% of future annual returns for the Janus Fund.

10. Determine the bounds for 95% of future annual returns for the Janus Fund.

Extended Projects

1. Investigate several mutual funds of your choice. Use a financial data website and obtain the monthly returns for the funds of your choice. Calculate the mean return and the standard deviation of the monthly data and convert the values to the annual values. Determine which funds have the highest return values and which have the lowest standard deviation values.

2. Investigate other measures of risk for investment products. Compare these measures with the standard deviation discussed here.

Differential Calculus

11

CHAPTER

CHAPTER OUTLINE

How fast is the number of cell phone subscriptions growing? At what rate is the number of Internet users increasing? How are home prices changing? These questions and many others in the fields of business, finance, health, political science, psychology, sociology, and economics can be answered by using calculus. See Exercise 65 on page 630, Example 12 on page 658, and Exercise 72 on page 660.

The algebraic problems considered in earlier chapters dealt with *static* situations:

What is the revenue when *x* items are sold?

How much interest is earned in 2 years?

What is the equilibrium price?

Calculus, on the other hand, deals with *dynamic* situations:

At what rate is the economy growing?

How fast is a rocket going at any instant after liftoff?

How quickly can production be increased without adversely affecting profits?

The techniques of calculus will allow us to answer many questions like these that deal with rates of change.

The key idea underlying the development of calculus is the concept of limit, so we begin by studying limits.

11.1 Limits

We have often dealt with a problem like this: "Find the value of the function $f(x)$ when $x = a$." The underlying idea of "limit," however, is to examine what the function does *near x = a*, rather than what it does *at x = a*. If you would like to refresh your understanding of functions and functional notation, see Chapter 3.

Example 1 The function

$$f(x) = \frac{2x^2 - 3x - 2}{x - 2}$$

is not defined when $x = 2$. (Why?) What happens to the values of $f(x)$ when x is *very close* to 2?

Solution Evaluate f at several numbers that are very close to $x = 2$, as in the following table:

x	1.99	1.999	2	2.0001	2.001
$f(x)$	4.98	4.998	—	5.0002	5.002

The table suggests that

> as x gets closer and closer to 2 from either direction, the corresponding value of $f(x)$ gets closer and closer to 5.

In fact, by experimenting further, you can convince yourself that the values of $f(x)$ can be made *as close as you want* to 5 by taking values of x close enough to 2. This situation is usually described by saying "The *limit* of $f(x)$ as x approaches 2 is the number 5," which is written symbolically as

$$\lim_{x \to 2} f(x) = 5, \quad \text{or equivalently,} \quad \lim_{x \to 2} \frac{2x^2 - 3x - 2}{x - 2} = 5.$$

The graph of f shown in Figure 11.1 also shows that $\lim_{x \to 2} f(x) = 5$.

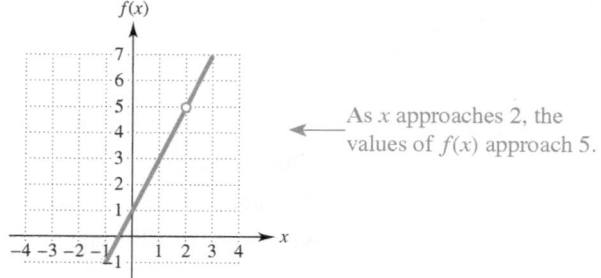

As x approaches 2, the values of $f(x)$ approach 5.

Figure 11.1

✓ **Checkpoint 1**

Use a calculator to estimate

$$\lim_{x \to 1} \frac{x^3 + x^2 - 2x}{x - 1}$$

by completing the following table:

x	$f(x)$
.9	
.99	
.999	
1.0001	
1.001	
1.01	
1.1	

Answers to Checkpoint exercises are found at the end of the section.

The informal definition of "limit" that follows is similar to the situation in Example 1, but now f is any function, and a and L are fixed real numbers (in Example 1, $a = 2$ and $L = 5$).

Limit of a Function

Let f be a function, and let a and L be real numbers. Assume that $f(x)$ is defined for all x near $x = a$. Suppose that

> as x takes values very close (but not equal) to a (on both sides of a), the corresponding values of $f(x)$ are very close (and possibly equal) to L

and that

> the values of $f(x)$ can be made as close as you want to L for all values of x that are close enough to a.

Then the number L is the **limit** of the function $f(x)$ as x approaches a, which is written

$$\lim_{x \to a} f(x) = L.$$

This definition is *informal* because the expressions "near," "very close," and "as close as you want" have not been precisely defined. In particular, the tables used in Example 1 and the next set of examples provide strong intuitive evidence, but not a proof, of what the limits must be.

Example 2   If $f(x) = x^2 + x + 1$, what is $\lim_{x \to 3} f(x)$?

Solution   Make a table showing the values of the function at numbers very close to 3:

			x approaches 3 from the left → 3 ← *x* approaches 3 from the right				
x	2.9	2.99	2.9999	3	3.0001	3.01	3.1
f(x)	12.31	12.9301	12.9993 …		13.0007 …	13.0701	13.71

$f(x)$ approaches 13 $f(x)$ approaches 13

The table suggests that as x approaches 3 from either direction, $f(x)$ gets closer and closer to 13 and, hence, that

$$\lim_{x \to 3} f(x) = 13, \qquad \text{or equivalently,} \qquad \lim_{x \to 3} (x^2 + x + 1) = 13.$$

Note that the function $f(x)$ is defined when $x = 3$ and that $f(3) = 3^2 + 3 + 1 = 13$. So in this case, the limit of $f(x)$ as x approaches 3 is $f(3)$, the value of the function at 3.

Example 3   Use a graphing calculator to find

$$\lim_{x \to 3} \frac{x - 3}{e^{x-3} - 1}.$$

Solution   There are two ways to estimate the limit.

Graphical Method   Graph $f(x) = \dfrac{x - 3}{e^{x-3} - 1}$ in a very narrow window near $x = 3$. Use the trace feature to move along the graph and observe the y-coordinates as x gets very close to 3 from either side. Figure 11.2 suggests that $\lim_{x \to 3} f(x) = 1$.

(a)

(b)

Figure 11.2

X	Y1	
2.99	1.005	
2.999	1.0005	
2.9999	1.0001	
3	ERROR	
3.0001	.99995	
3.001	.9995	
3.01	.99501	
X=3		

Figure 11.3

Numerical Method   Use the table feature to make a table of values for $f(x)$ when x is very close to 3. Figure 11.3 shows that when x is very close to 3, $f(x)$ is very close to 1. (The table displays "error" at $x = 3$ because the function is not defined when $x = 3$.) Thus, it appears that

$$\lim_{x \to 3} \frac{x - 3}{e^{x-3} - 1} = 1.$$

The function has the limit 1 as x approaches 3, even though $f(3)$ is not defined.

Example 4   Find $\lim_{x \to 4} f(x)$, where f is the function whose rule is

$$f(x) = \begin{cases} 0 & \text{if } x \text{ is an integer} \\ 1 & \text{if } x \text{ is not an integer} \end{cases}$$

and whose graph is shown in Figure 11.4.

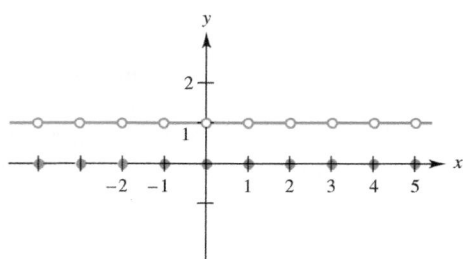

Figure 11.4

Solution   The definition of the limit as x approaches 4 involves only values of x that are close, but not equal, to 4—corresponding to the part of the graph on either side of 4, but not at 4 itself. Now, $f(x) = 1$ for all these numbers (because the numbers very near 4, such as 3.99995 and 4.00002, are not integers). Thus, for all x very close to 4, the corresponding value of $f(x)$ is 1, so $\lim_{x \to 4} f(x) = 1$. However, since 4 is an integer, $f(4) = 0$. Therefore, $\lim_{x \to 4} f(x) \neq f(4)$.

Examples 1–4 illustrate the following facts.

Limits and Function Values

If the limit of a function $f(x)$ as x approaches a exists, then there are three possibilities:

1. $f(a)$ is not defined, but $\lim_{x \to a} f(x)$ is defined.   (Examples 1 and 3)
2. $f(a)$ is defined and $\lim_{x \to a} f(x) = f(a)$.   (Example 2)
3. $f(a)$ is defined, but $\lim_{x \to a} f(x) \neq f(a)$.   (Example 4)

Finding Limits Algebraically

As we have seen, tables are very useful for estimating limits. However, it is often more efficient and accurate to find limits algebraically. We begin with two simple functions.

Consider the constant function $f(x) = 5$. To compute $\lim_{x \to a} f(x)$, you must ask "When x is very close to a, what is the value of $f(x)$?" The answer is easy because no matter what

x is, the value of $f(x)$ is *always* the number 5. As x gets closer and closer to a, the value of $f(x)$ is always 5. Hence,

$$\lim_{x \to a} f(x) = 5, \qquad \text{which is usually written} \qquad \lim_{x \to a} 5 = 5.$$

The same thing is true for *any* constant function.

Limit of a Constant Function

If d is a constant, then, for any real number a,

$$\lim_{x \to a} d = d.$$

Now consider the *identity function*, whose rule is $f(x) = x$. When x is very close to a number a, the corresponding value of $f(x)$ (namely, x itself) is very close to a. So we have the following conclusion.

Limit of the Identity Function

For every real number a,

$$\lim_{x \to a} x = a.$$

The facts in the two preceding boxes, together with the properties of limits that follow, will enable us to find a wide variety of limits.

Properties of Limits

Let $a, r, A,$ and B be real numbers, and let f and g be functions such that

$$\lim_{x \to a} f(x) = A \qquad \text{and} \qquad \lim_{x \to a} g(x) = B.$$

Then the following properties hold:

1. $\lim_{x \to a} [f(x) + g(x)] = A + B = \lim_{x \to a} f(x) + \lim_{x \to a} g(x)$ *Sum Property*
(The limit of a sum is the sum of the limits.)

2. $\lim_{x \to a} [f(x) - g(x)] = A - B = \lim_{x \to a} f(x) - \lim_{x \to a} g(x)$ *Difference Property*
(The limit of a difference is the difference of the limits.)

3. $\lim_{x \to a} [f(x) \cdot g(x)] = A \cdot B = \lim_{x \to a} f(x) \cdot \lim_{x \to a} g(x)$ *Product Property*
(The limit of a product is the product of the limits.)

4. $\lim_{x \to a} \dfrac{f(x)}{g(x)} = \dfrac{A}{B} = \dfrac{\lim_{x \to a} f(x)}{\lim_{x \to a} g(x)} \quad (B \neq 0)$ *Quotient Property*

(The limit of a quotient is the quotient of the limits, provided that the limit of the denominator is nonzero.)

5. For any real number for which A^r exists,
$$\lim_{x \to a} [f(x)]^r = A^r = [\lim_{x \to a} f(x)]^r.$$ *Power Property*
(The limit of a power is the power of the limit.)

Although we won't prove these properties (a rigorous definition of limit is needed for that), you should find most of them plausible. For instance, if the values of $f(x)$ get very close to A and the values of $g(x)$ get very close to B when x approaches a, it is reasonable to expect that the corresponding values of $f(x) + g(x)$ will get very close to $A + B$ (Property 1) and that the corresponding values of $f(x)g(x)$ will get very close to AB (Property 3).

Example 5   **Business**   The amount of revenue generated (in billions of dollars) over a 5-year period from General Electric can be approximated by the function $f(x) = -4x^2 + 20x + 150$ where $x = 0$ corresponds to the year 2005. Find $\lim\limits_{x \to 5} f(x)$. (Data from: www.morningstar.com.)

Solution $\lim\limits_{x \to 5} (-4x^2 + 20x + 150)$

$$= \lim_{x \to 5} (-4x^2) + \lim_{x \to 5} 20x + \lim_{x \to 5} 150 \qquad \text{Sum property}$$

$$= \lim_{x \to 5} (-4) \cdot \lim_{x \to 5} x^2 + \lim_{x \to 5} 20 \cdot \lim_{x \to 5} x + \lim_{x \to 5} 150 \qquad \text{Product property}$$

$$= \lim_{x \to 5} (-4) \cdot [\lim_{x \to 5} x]^2 + \lim_{x \to 5} 20 \cdot \lim_{x \to 5} x + \lim_{x \to 5} 150 \qquad \text{Power property}$$

$$= -4 \cdot 5^2 + 20 \cdot 5 + 150 = 150 \qquad \begin{array}{l}\text{Constant-function limit}\\\text{and identity-function limit}\end{array}$$

Example 5 shows that $\lim\limits_{x \to 5} f(x) = 150$, where $f(x) = -4x^2 + 20x + 150$. Note that $f(5) = -4 \cdot 5^2 + 20 \cdot 5 + 150 = 150$. In other words, the limit as x approaches 5 is the value of the function at 5:

$$\lim_{x \to 5} f(x) = f(5).$$

The same analysis used in Example 5 works with any polynomial function and leads to the following conclusion.

Polynomial Limits

If f is a polynomial function and a is a real number, then

$$\lim_{x \to a} f(x) = f(a).$$

In other words, the limit is the value of the function at $x = a$.

✓**Checkpoint 2**

If $f(x) = 2x^3 - 5x^2 + 8$, find the given limits.

(a) $\lim\limits_{x \to 2} f(x)$

(b) $\lim\limits_{x \to -3} f(x)$

This property will be used frequently. ✓₂

Example 6   Find each limit.

(a) $\lim\limits_{x \to 2} [(x^2 + 1) + (x^3 - x + 3)]$

Solution $\lim\limits_{x \to 2} [(x^2 + 1) + (x^3 - x + 3)]$

$$= \lim_{x \to 2} (x^2 + 1) + \lim_{x \to 2} (x^3 - x + 3) \qquad \text{Sum property}$$

$$= (2^2 + 1) + (2^3 - 2 + 3) = 5 + 9 = 14. \qquad \text{Polynomial limit}$$

(b) $\lim\limits_{x \to -1} (x^3 + 4x)(2x^2 - 3x)$

Solution $\lim\limits_{x \to -1} (x^3 + 4x)(2x^2 - 3x)$

$$= \lim\limits_{x \to -1} (x^3 + 4x) \cdot \lim\limits_{x \to -1} (2x^2 - 3x) \qquad \text{Product property}$$

$$= [(-1)^3 + 4(-1)] \cdot [2(-1)^2 - 3(-1)] \qquad \text{Polynomial limit}$$

$$= (-1 - 4)(2 + 3) = -25.$$

(c) $\lim\limits_{x \to -1} 5(3x^2 + 2)$

Solution $\lim\limits_{x \to -1} 5(3x^2 + 2) = \lim\limits_{x \to -1} 5 \cdot \lim\limits_{x \to -1} (3x^2 + 2) \qquad \text{Product property}$

$$= 5[3(-1)^2 + 2] \qquad \begin{array}{l}\text{Constant-function limit and} \\ \text{polynomial limit}\end{array}$$

$$= 25.$$

(d) $\lim\limits_{x \to 9} \sqrt{4x - 11}$

Solution   Begin by writing the square root in exponential form.

$$\lim\limits_{x \to 9} \sqrt{4x - 11} = \lim\limits_{x \to 9} [4x - 11]^{1/2}$$

$$= [\lim\limits_{x \to 9} (4x - 11)]^{1/2} \qquad \text{Power property}$$

$$= [4 \cdot 9 - 11]^{1/2} \qquad \text{Polynomial limit}$$

$$= [25]^{1/2} = \sqrt{25} = 5. \quad \boxed{✓_3}$$

✓ **Checkpoint 3**

Use the limit properties to find the given limits.

(a) $\lim\limits_{x \to 4} (3x - 9)$

(b) $\lim\limits_{x \to -1} (2x^2 - 4x + 1)$

(c) $\lim\limits_{x \to 2} \sqrt{3x + 3}$

When a rational function, such as $f(x) = \dfrac{x}{x + 2}$, is defined at $x = a$, it is easy to find the limit of $f(x)$ as x approaches a.

Example 7   Find

$$\lim\limits_{x \to 5} \frac{x}{x + 3}.$$

Solution $\lim\limits_{x \to 5} \dfrac{x}{x + 3} = \dfrac{\lim\limits_{x \to 5} x}{\lim\limits_{x \to 5} (x + 3)} \qquad \text{Quotient property}$

$$= \frac{5}{5 + 3} = \frac{5}{8}. \qquad \text{Polynomial limit}$$

Note that $f(5) = \dfrac{5}{5 + 3} = \dfrac{5}{8}$. So the limit of $f(x)$ as x approaches 5 is the value of the function at 5:

$$\lim\limits_{x \to 5} f(x) = f(5). \quad \boxed{✓_4}$$

✓ **Checkpoint 4**

Find the given limits.

(a) $\lim\limits_{x \to 2} \dfrac{2x - 1}{3x + 4}$

(b) $\lim\limits_{x \to -1} \dfrac{x - 2}{3x - 1}$

The argument used in Example 7 works in the general case and proves the following result.

Rational Limits

If f is a rational function and a is a real number such that $f(a)$ is defined, then

$$\lim\limits_{x \to a} f(x) = f(a).$$

In other words, the limit is the value of the function at $x = a$.

If a rational function is not defined at the number a, the preceding property cannot be used. Different techniques are needed in such cases to find the limit (if one exists), as we shall see in Examples 8 and 9.

The definition of the limit as x approaches a involves only the values of the function when x is *near* a, but not the value of the function *at* a. So two functions that agree for all values of x, except possibly at $x = a$, will necessarily have the same limit when x approaches a. Thus, we have the following fact.

Limit Theorem

If f and g are functions that have limits as x approaches a, and $f(x) = g(x)$ for all x near a, then

$$\lim_{x \to a} f(x) = \lim_{x \to a} g(x).$$

Example 8   Find

$$\lim_{x \to 2} \frac{x^2 + x - 6}{x - 2}.$$

Solution   The quotient property cannot be used here, because

$$\lim_{x \to 2} (x - 2) = 0.$$

We can, however, simplify the function by rewriting the fraction as

$$\frac{x^2 + x - 6}{x - 2} = \frac{(x + 3)(x - 2)}{x - 2}.$$

When $x \neq 2$, the quantity $x - 2$ is nonzero and may be cancelled, so that

$$\frac{x^2 + x - 6}{x - 2} = x + 3 \qquad \text{for all } x \neq 2.$$

Now the limit theorem can be used:

✓ **Checkpoint 5**

Find $\lim_{x \to 1} \dfrac{2x^2 + x - 3}{x - 1}$.

$$\lim_{x \to 2} \frac{x^2 + x - 6}{x - 2} = \lim_{x \to 2} (x + 3) = 2 + 3 = 5. \ \boxed{✓_5}$$

Example 9   Find

$$\lim_{x \to 4} \frac{\sqrt{x} - 2}{x - 4}.$$

Solution   As $x \to 4$, both the numerator and the denominator approach 0, giving the meaningless expression $0/0$. To change the form of the expression, algebra can be used to rationalize the numerator by multiplying both the numerator and the denominator by $\sqrt{x} + 2$. This gives

$$\frac{\sqrt{x} - 2}{x - 4} = \frac{\sqrt{x} - 2}{x - 4} \cdot \frac{\sqrt{x} + 2}{\sqrt{x} + 2} = \frac{\sqrt{x} \cdot \sqrt{x} + 2\sqrt{x} - 2\sqrt{x} - 4}{(x - 4)(\sqrt{x} + 2)}$$

✓ **Checkpoint 6**

Find the given limits.

(a) $\lim_{x \to 1} \dfrac{\sqrt{x} - 1}{x - 1}$

(b) $\lim_{x \to 9} \dfrac{\sqrt{x} - 3}{x - 9}$

$$= \frac{x - 4}{(x - 4)(\sqrt{x} + 2)} = \frac{1}{\sqrt{x} + 2} \qquad \text{for all } x \neq 4.$$

Now use the limit theorem and the properties of limits:

$$\lim_{x \to 4} \frac{\sqrt{x} - 2}{x - 4} = \lim_{x \to 4} \frac{1}{\sqrt{x} + 2} = \frac{1}{\sqrt{4} + 2} = \frac{1}{2 + 2} = \frac{1}{4}. \ \boxed{✓_6}$$

Existence of Limits

It is possible that $\lim\limits_{x \to a} f(x)$ may not exist; that is, there may be no number L satisfying the definition of $\lim\limits_{x \to a} f(x) = L$. This can happen in many ways, two of which are illustrated next.

Example 10 Given that

$$g(x) = \frac{x^2 + 4}{x - 2}, \text{ find } \lim_{x \to 2} g(x).$$

Solution The quotient property cannot be used, since $\lim\limits_{x \to 2} (x - 2) = 0$, and the limit theorem does not apply because $x^2 + 4$ does not factor. So we use the following table and the graph of g in Figure 11.5:

	x approaches 2 from the left $\rightarrow$				2	$\leftarrow$ x approaches 2 from the right		
x	1.8	1.9	1.99	1.999	2	2.001	2.01	2.05
$g(x)$	−36.2	−76.1	−796	−7996		8004	804	164
	$g(x)$ gets smaller and smaller					$g(x)$ gets larger and larger		

The table and the graph both show that as x approaches 2 from the left, $g(x)$ gets smaller and smaller, but as x approaches 2 from the right, $g(x)$ gets larger and larger. Since $g(x)$ does not get closer and closer to a single real number as x approaches 2 from either side,

$$\lim_{x \to 2} \frac{x^2 + 4}{x - 2} \text{ does not exist.} \quad \boxed{7}$$

Example 11 What is

$$\lim_{x \to 0} \frac{|x|}{x}?$$

Solution The function $f(x) = \dfrac{|x|}{x}$ is not defined when $x = 0$. Recall the definition of absolute value:

$$|x| = \begin{cases} x & \text{if } x \geq 0 \\ -x & \text{if } x < 0 \end{cases}.$$

Consequently, when $x > 0$,

$$f(x) = \frac{|x|}{x} = \frac{x}{x} = 1,$$

and when $x < 0$,

$$f(x) = \frac{|x|}{x} = \frac{-x}{x} = -1.$$

The graph of f is shown in Figure 11.6. As x approaches 0 from the right, x is always positive, and the corresponding value of $f(x)$ is 1. But as x approaches 0 from the left, x is always negative, and the corresponding value of $f(x)$ is −1. Thus, as x approaches 0 from *both* sides, the corresponding values of $f(x)$ do not get closer and closer to a *single* real number. Therefore, the limit does not exist.[*]

_____

[*]However, the behavior of this function near $x = 0$ can be described by *one-sided limits*, which are discussed in the next section.

Sidebar (left margin)

Figure 11.5

✓ **Checkpoint 7**

Let $f(x) = \dfrac{x^2 + 9}{x - 3}$. Find the given limits.

(a) $\lim\limits_{x \to 3} f(x)$

(b) $\lim\limits_{x \to 0} f(x)$

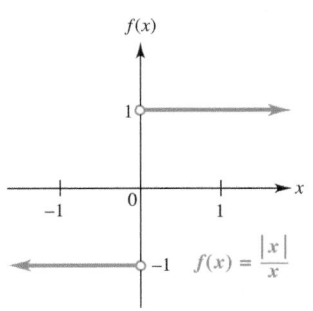

$f(x) = \dfrac{|x|}{x}$

Figure 11.6

The function f whose graph is shown in Figure 11.7 illustrates various facts about limits that were discussed earlier in this section.

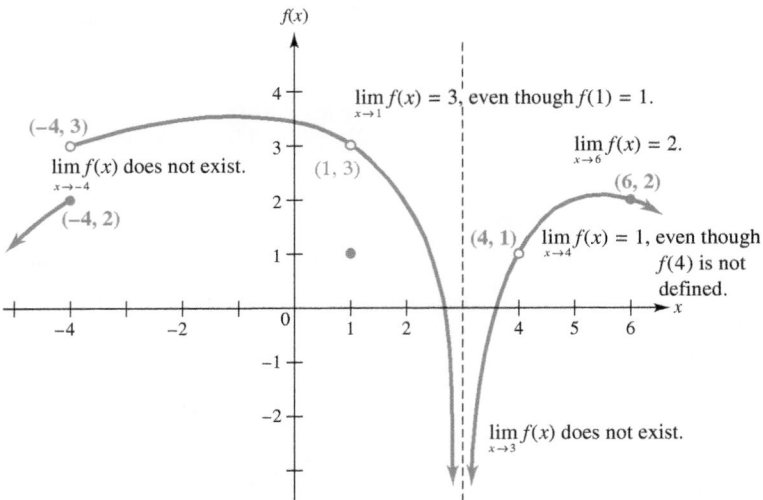

Figure 11.7

11.1 Exercises

Use the given graph to determine the value of the indicated limits. (See Examples 3, 4, 10, and 11 and Figure 11.7.)

1. (a) $\lim_{x \to 3} f(x)$ (b) $\lim_{x \to -1} f(x)$

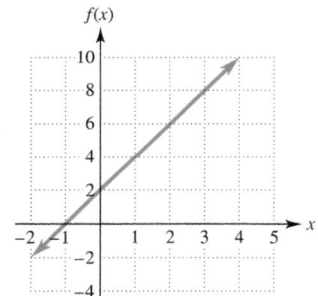

2. (a) $\lim_{x \to 3} g(x)$ (b) $\lim_{x \to 0} g(x)$

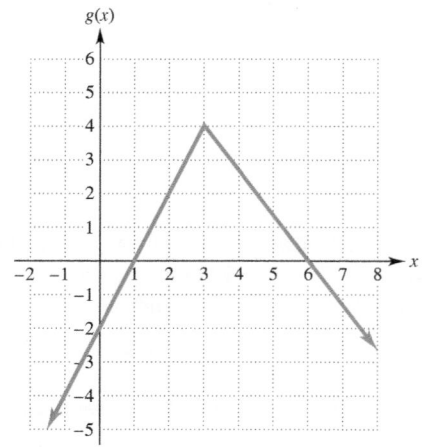

3. (a) $\lim_{x \to 0} F(x)$ (b) $\lim_{x \to 1} F(x)$

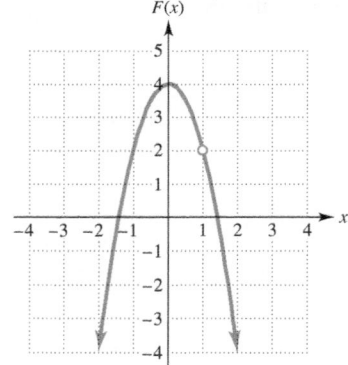

4. (a) $\lim_{x \to 1} g(x)$ (b) $\lim_{x \to 0} g(x)$

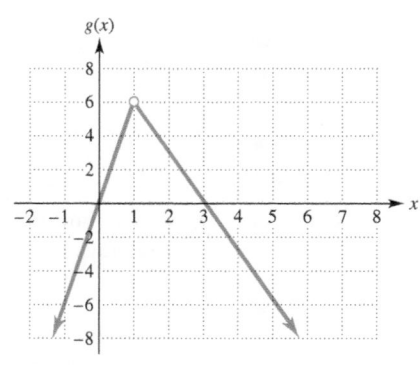

5. (a) $\lim\limits_{x\to-3} f(x)$ **(b)** $\lim\limits_{x\to2} f(x)$

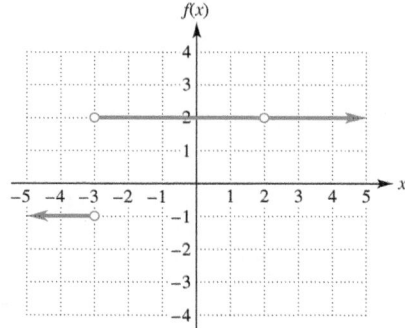

6. (a) $\lim\limits_{x\to4} f(x)$ **(b)** $\lim\limits_{x\to9} f(x)$

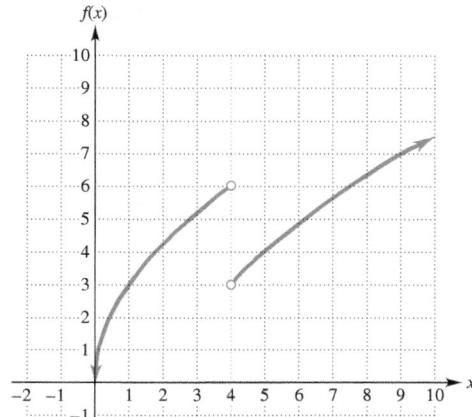

7. (a) $\lim\limits_{x\to-2} h(x)$ **(b)** $\lim\limits_{x\to0} h(x)$

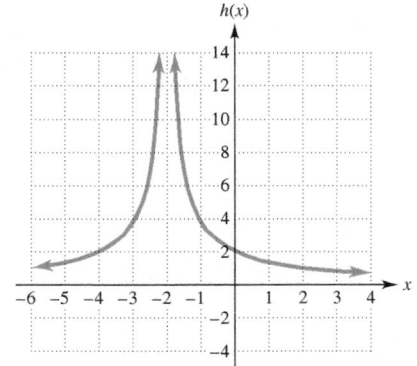

8. (a) $\lim\limits_{x\to3} f(x)$ **(b)** $\lim\limits_{x\to2} f(x)$

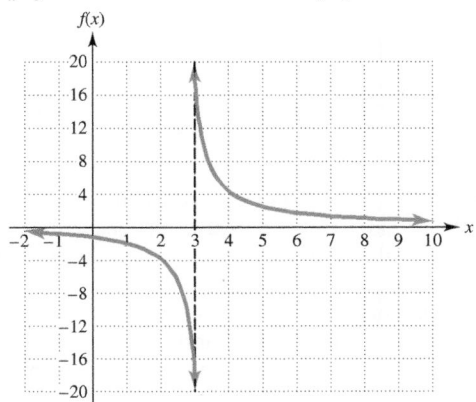

9. Explain why $\lim\limits_{x\to1} F(x)$ in Exercise 3(b) exists, but $\lim\limits_{x\to-3} f(x)$ in Exercise 5(a) does not.

10. In Exercise 4(a), why does $\lim\limits_{x\to1} g(x)$ exist even though $g(1)$ is not defined?

Use a calculator to estimate the given limits numerically. (See Examples 1–3.)

11. $\lim\limits_{x\to1} \dfrac{\ln x}{x - 1}$ **12.** $\lim\limits_{x\to5} \dfrac{\ln x - \ln 5}{x - 5}$

13. $\lim\limits_{x\to0} (x \ln|x|)$ **14.** $\lim\limits_{x\to0} \dfrac{x}{\ln|x|}$

15. $\lim\limits_{x\to0} \dfrac{e^{3x} - 1}{x}$ **16.** $\lim\limits_{x\to0} \dfrac{x}{e^x - 1}$

17. $\lim\limits_{x\to3} \dfrac{x^3 - 3x^2 - 4x + 12}{x - 3}$

18. $\lim\limits_{x\to4} \dfrac{.1x^4 - .8x^3 + 1.6x^2 + 2x - 8}{x - 4}$

19. $\lim\limits_{x\to-2} \dfrac{x^4 + 2x^3 - x^2 + 3x + 1}{x + 2}$

20. $\lim\limits_{x\to0} \dfrac{e^{2x} + e^x - 2}{e^x - 1}$

Suppose $\lim\limits_{x\to4} f(x) = 25$ and $\lim\limits_{x\to4} g(x) = 10$. Use the limit properties to find the given limits. (See Examples 6 and 7.)

21. $\lim\limits_{x\to4} [f(x) - g(x)]$ **22.** $\lim\limits_{x\to4} [g(x) \cdot f(x)]$

23. $\lim\limits_{x\to4} \dfrac{f(x)}{g(x)}$ **24.** $\lim\limits_{x\to4} [3 \cdot f(x)]$

25. $\lim\limits_{x\to4} \sqrt{f(x)}$ **26.** $\lim\limits_{x\to4} [g(x)]^3$

27. $\lim\limits_{x\to4} \dfrac{f(x) + g(x)}{2g(x)}$ **28.** $\lim\limits_{x\to4} \dfrac{5g(x) + 2}{1 - f(x)}$

29. (a) Graph the function f whose rule is

$$f(x) = \begin{cases} 3 - x & \text{if } x < -2 \\ x + 2 & \text{if } -2 \le x < 2. \\ 1 & \text{if } x \ge 2 \end{cases}$$

Use the graph in part (a) to find the following limits:

(b) $\lim\limits_{x\to-2} f(x)$;   **(c)** $\lim\limits_{x\to1} f(x)$;   **(d)** $\lim\limits_{x\to2} f(x)$.

30. (a) Graph the function g whose rule is

$$g(x) = \begin{cases} x^2 & \text{if } x < -1 \\ x + 2 & \text{if } -1 \le x < 1. \\ 3 - x & \text{if } x \ge 1 \end{cases}$$

Use the graph in part (a) to find the following limits:

(b) $\lim\limits_{x\to-1} g(x)$;   **(c)** $\lim\limits_{x\to0} g(x)$;   **(d)** $\lim\limits_{x\to1} g(x)$.

Use algebra and the properties of limits as needed to find the given limits. If the limit does not exist, say so. (See Examples 5–9.)

31. $\lim\limits_{x\to2} (3x^3 - 4x^2 - 5x + 2)$

32. $\lim\limits_{x \to -1} (2x^3 - x^2 - 6x + 1)$

33. $\lim\limits_{x \to 3} \dfrac{4x + 7}{10x + 1}$

34. $\lim\limits_{x \to -2} \dfrac{x + 6}{8x - 5}$

35. $\lim\limits_{x \to 5} \dfrac{x^2 - 25}{x - 5}$

36. $\lim\limits_{x \to -4} \dfrac{x^2 - 16}{x + 4}$

37. $\lim\limits_{x \to 4} \dfrac{x^2 - x - 12}{x - 4}$

38. $\lim\limits_{x \to 5} \dfrac{x^2 - 3x - 10}{x - 5}$

39. $\lim\limits_{x \to 2} \dfrac{x^2 - 5x + 6}{x^2 - 6x + 8}$

40. $\lim\limits_{x \to -2} \dfrac{x^2 + 3x + 2}{x^2 - x - 6}$

41. $\lim\limits_{x \to 4} \dfrac{(x + 4)^2(x - 5)}{(x - 4)(x + 4)^2}$

42. $\lim\limits_{x \to -3} \dfrac{(x + 3)(x - 3)(x + 4)}{(x + 8)(x + 3)(x - 4)}$

43. $\lim\limits_{x \to 3} \sqrt{x^2 - 3}$

44. $\lim\limits_{x \to 3} \sqrt{x^2 - 7}$

45. $\lim\limits_{x \to 4} \dfrac{-6}{(x - 4)^2}$

46. $\lim\limits_{x \to -2} \dfrac{3x}{(x + 2)^3}$

47. $\lim\limits_{x \to 0} \dfrac{[1/(x + 3)] - 1/3}{x}$

48. $\lim\limits_{x \to 0} \dfrac{[-1/(x + 2)] + 1/2}{x}$

49. $\lim\limits_{x \to 25} \dfrac{\sqrt{x} - 5}{x - 25}$

50. $\lim\limits_{x \to 36} \dfrac{\sqrt{x} - 6}{x - 36}$

51. $\lim\limits_{x \to 5} \dfrac{\sqrt{x} - \sqrt{5}}{x - 5}$

52. (a) Approximate $\lim\limits_{x \to 0} (1 + x)^{1/x}$ to five decimal places. (Evaluate the function at numbers closer and closer to 0 until successive approximations agree in the first five places.)

(b) Find the decimal expansion of the number e to as many places as your calculator can manage.

(c) What do parts (a) and (b) suggest about the exact value of $\lim\limits_{x \to 0} (1 + x)^{1/x}$?

Work these exercises.

53. Business A company training program has determined that a new employee can process an average of $P(s)$ pieces of work per day after s days of on-the-job training, where

$$P(s) = \frac{105s}{s + 7}.$$

Find the given quantities.

(a) $P(1)$ **(b)** $P(13)$ **(c)** $\lim\limits_{s \to 13} P(s)$

54. Health The concentration of a drug in a patient's bloodstream h hours after it was injected is given by

$$A(h) = \frac{.3h}{h^2 + 3}.$$

Find the given quantities.

(a) $A(.5)$ **(b)** $A(1)$ **(c)** $\lim\limits_{h \to 1} A(h)$

55. Business An independent driver working for a taxicab company must pay the company \$95 per day and pay for the cost of fuel. The driver's daily cost is approximated by:

$$c(x) = 95 + .20x$$

where x is the number of miles driven. The average cost per mile, denoted by $\bar{c}(x)$, is found by dividing $c(x)$ by x. Find and interpret the given quantities.

(a) $\bar{c}(25)$ **(b)** $\bar{c}(100)$ **(c)** $\lim\limits_{x \to 250} \bar{c}(x)$

56. Natural Science The electricity consumption, $f(t)$, of a residence is shown in the accompanying figure for a 24-hour day during which the residence experienced a power outage for an instant. Find the given quantities.

(a) $f(8)$

(b) $\lim\limits_{t \to 8} f(t)$

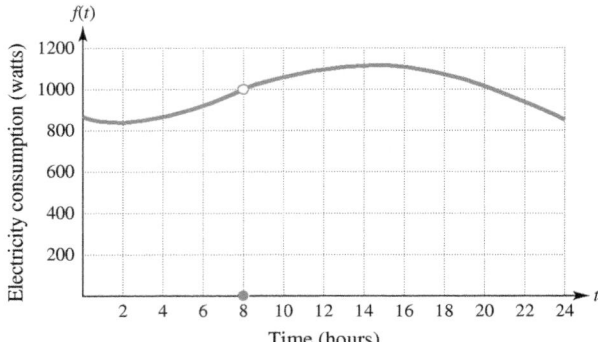

57. Business The number of employees, $f(t)$, at a major airline dropped dramatically in 2012 due to layoffs, as shown in the accompanying figure. Use the graph to find the given limits.

(a) $\lim\limits_{t \to 2010} f(t)$ **(b)** $\lim\limits_{t \to 2011} f(t)$ **(c)** $\lim\limits_{t \to 2012} f(t)$

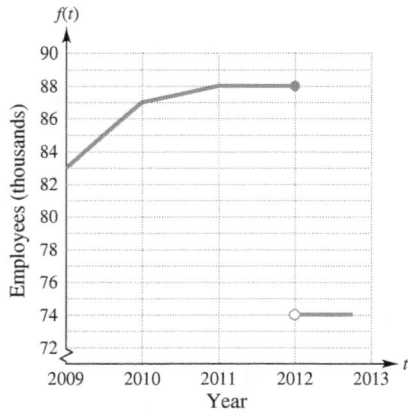

58. Economics A period of U.S. economic expansion began in June 2009, indicated by $t = 0$ in the accompanying figure. Employment figures are indexed to 100 at the start of the expansion. The blue line represents $c(t)$, the employment index during the current economic expansion; the red line represents $a(t)$, the average of the ten previous expansions; and the green line represents $m(t)$, the minimum values from the previous ten expansions. Use the figure to approximate and interpret the following quantities. (Data from: Federal Reserve Economic Research.)

(a) $\lim\limits_{t\to6} c(t) - m(t)$ (b) $\lim\limits_{t\to6} c(t) - a(t)$

(c) $\lim\limits_{t\to12} c(t) - m(t)$ (d) $\lim\limits_{t\to12} c(t) - a(t)$

(e) $\lim\limits_{t\to27} c(t) - m(t)$ (f) $\lim\limits_{t\to27} c(t) - a(t)$

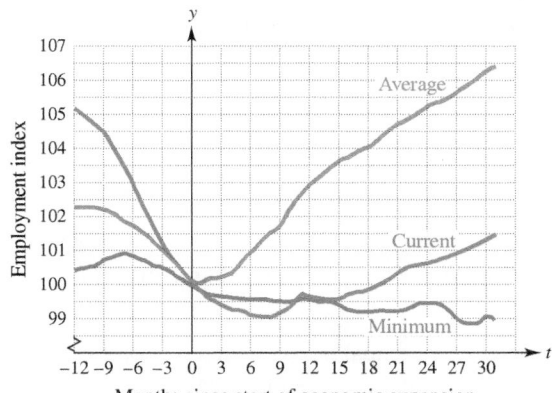

Months since start of economic expansion

59. Social Science The populations of the Midwestern and Western regions of the United States are shown in the accompanying figure, represented by $M(t)$ and $W(t)$, respectively. Approximate the given limits. (Data from: United States Census Bureau.)

(a) $\lim\limits_{t\to2000} M(t) - W(t)$

(b) $\lim\limits_{t\to2010} M(t) - W(t)$

(c) Approximately when are the populations of the two regions equal?

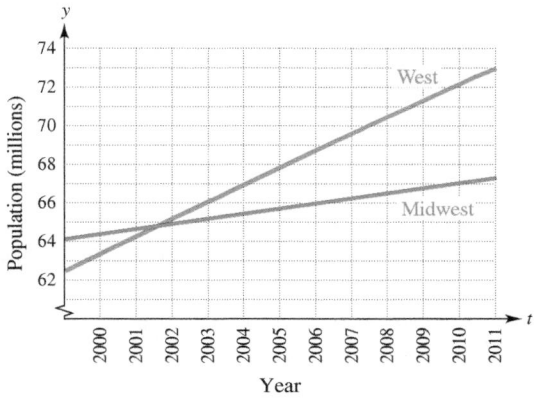

Year

✓**Checkpoint Answers**

1. 2.61; 2.9601; 2.996; 3.0004; 3.004; 3.0401; 3.41; the limit appears to be 3.

2. (a) 4   (b) −91

3. (a) 3   (b) 7   (c) 3

4. (a) $\dfrac{3}{10}$ (b) $\dfrac{3}{4}$ 5. 5

6. (a) $\dfrac{1}{2}$ (b) $\dfrac{1}{6}$

7. (a) Does not exist   (b) −3

11.2 One-Sided Limits and Limits Involving Infinity

In addition to the limits introduced in Section 11.1, which will be used frequently, there are several other kinds of limits that will appear briefly in Sections 11.9 and 13.3. We begin with one-sided limits.

One-Sided Limits

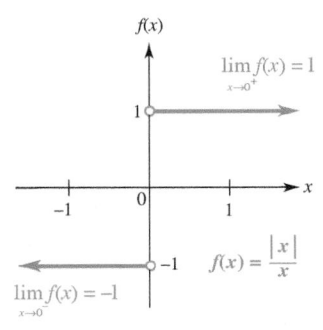

Figure 11.8

Example 11 of Section 11.1 showed that the limit as x approaches 0 of $f(x) = \dfrac{|x|}{x}$ does not exist. However, we can adapt the limit concept to describe the behavior of $f(x)$ near $x = 0$ as follows: First, look at the right half of the graph of $f(x)$ in Figure 11.8.

As x takes values very close to 0 (with $x > 0$), the corresponding values of $f(x)$ are very close (in fact, equal) to 1.

We express this fact in symbols by writing

$$\lim_{x\to0^+} f(x) = 1,$$

which is read,

The limit of $f(x)$ as x approaches 0 from the right is 1.

Now consider the left half of the graph in Figure 11.8.

As x takes values very close to 0 (with $x < 0$), the corresponding values of $f(x)$ are very close (in fact, equal) to -1.

We express this fact by writing

$$\lim_{x \to 0^-} f(x) = -1,$$

which is read,

The limit of $f(x)$ as x approaches 0 from the left is -1.

The same idea carries over to the general case.

One-Sided Limits

Let f be a function, and let a, K, and M be real numbers. Assume that $f(x)$ is defined for all x near a, with $x > a$. Suppose that

as x takes values very close (but not equal) to a (with $x > a$), the corresponding values of $f(x)$ are very close (and possibly equal) to K,

and that

the values of $f(x)$ can be made as close as you want to K for all values of x (with $x > a$) that are close enough to a.

Then the number K is the **limit of $f(x)$ as x approaches a from the right,** which is written

$$\lim_{x \to a^+} f(x) = K.$$

The statement "M is the **limit of $f(x)$ as x approaches a from the left,**" which is written

$$\lim_{x \to a^-} f(x) = M,$$

is defined in a similar fashion. (Just replace K by M and "$x > a$" by "$x < a$" in the previous definition.)

We sometimes refer to a limit of the form $\lim_{x \to a^-} f(x)$ as a **left-hand limit** and a limit of the form $\lim_{x \to a^+} f(x)$ as a **right-hand limit**. The limit $\lim_{x \to a} f(x)$, as defined in Section 11.1, is sometimes called a **two-sided limit**.

Figure 11.9

Example 1   The graph of a function f is shown in Figure 11.9. Use it to find the following quantities.

(a) $\lim_{x \to -3^-} f(x)$ **(b)** $\lim_{x \to -3^+} f(x)$ **(c)** $\lim_{x \to -3} f(x)$ **(d)** $f(-3)$

(e) For which value(s) of x is $f(x) = -3$?

(f) $\lim_{x \to 2^-} f(x)$ **(g)** $\lim_{x \to 2^+} f(x)$ **(h)** $\lim_{x \to 2} f(x)$ **(i)** $f(2)$

(j) For which value(s) of x is $f(x) = 2$?

Solution

(a) The graph shows that as x approaches –3 from the left, the corresponding values of $f(x)$ approach 2, therefore $\lim_{x \to -3^-} f(x) = 2$.

(b) As x approaches –3 from the right, the corresponding values of $f(x)$ approach 1, therefore $\lim_{x \to -3^+} f(x) = 1$.

(c) Since the left- and right-hand limits are not equal, the two-sided limit $\lim_{x \to -3} f(x)$ does not exist.

(d) When $x = -3$, the corresponding function value is $f(-3) = 2$.

(e) There are no x-values for which the value of the function is $f(x) = -3$.

In a manner similar to parts (a)–(e), the graph shows the following answers to parts (f)–(j).

(f) $\lim_{x \to 2^-} f(x) = -1$

(g) $\lim_{x \to 2^+} f(x) = -1$

(h) $\lim_{x \to 2} f(x) = -1$

(i) $f(2)$ is undefined.

(j) The x-values corresponding to when $f(x) = 2$ are $x = -3$ and $x = -2$.

✓**Checkpoint 1**

Use Figure 11.9 to find the given quantities.

(a) $\lim_{x \to 0^-} f(x)$

(b) $\lim_{x \to 0^+} f(x)$

(c) $\lim_{x \to 0} f(x)$

(d) $f(0)$

(e) For which value(s) of x is $f(x) = 0$?

In parts (a)–(c) of Example 1, the left- and right-hand limits exist, but are not equal, and the two-sided limit does not exist. In parts (f)–(h), however, all three limits exist and are equal to one another. This case is an example of the following fact.

Two-Sided Limits

Let f be a function, and let a and L be real numbers. Then

$$\lim_{x \to a} f(x) = L \quad \text{exactly when} \quad \lim_{x \to a^-} f(x) = L \quad \text{and} \quad \lim_{x \to a^+} f(x) = L.$$

In other words, f has a two-sided limit at a exactly when it has both a left-hand and right-hand limit at a and these two limits are the same.

Although its proof is omitted, the following fact will be used frequently:

All of the properties and theorems about limits in Section 11.1 are valid for left-hand limits and for right-hand limits.

Example 2 Find each of the given limits.

(a) $\lim_{x \to 2^+} \sqrt{4 - x^2}$ and $\lim_{x \to 2^-} \sqrt{4 - x^2}$

Solution Since $f(x) = \sqrt{4 - x^2}$ is not defined when $x > 2$, the right-hand limit (which requires that $x > 2$) does not exist. For the left-hand limit, write the square root in exponential form and apply the appropriate limit properties (see pages 573 and 574).

$$\lim_{x \to 2^-} \sqrt{4 - x^2} = \lim_{x \to 2^-} (4 - x^2)^{1/2} \quad \text{Exponential form}$$
$$= [\lim_{x \to 2^-} (4 - x^2)]^{1/2} \quad \text{Power property}$$
$$= 0^{1/2} = 0. \quad \text{Polynomial limit}$$

(b) $\lim\limits_{x \to 3^+} [\sqrt{x-3} + x^2 + 1]$

Solution $\lim\limits_{x \to 3^+} [\sqrt{x-3} + x^2 + 1]$

$$= \lim_{x \to 3^+} [(x-3)^{1/2} + x^2 + 1] \qquad \text{Exponential form}$$

$$= \lim_{x \to 3^+} (x-3)^{1/2} + \lim_{x \to 3^+} x^2 + \lim_{x \to 3^+} 1 \qquad \text{Sum property}$$

$$= [\lim_{x \to 3^+} (x-3)]^{1/2} + \lim_{x \to 3^+} x^2 + \lim_{x \to 3^+} 1 \qquad \text{Power property}$$

$$= 0^{1/2} + 9 + 1 = 10. \qquad \text{Polynomial limits} \;\checkmark_{2}$$

✓ **Checkpoint 2**

Find the given limits.

(a) $\lim\limits_{x \to 3^+} \sqrt{x^2 - 9}$

(b) $\lim\limits_{x \to -2^-} [\sqrt{x^2 - 4} + x^2 + 4]$

✓ **Checkpoint 3**

Use Figure 11.10 to find the given quantities.

(a) $c(2)$

(b) $\lim\limits_{x \to 2^-} c(x)$

(c) $\lim\limits_{x \to 2^+} c(x)$

(d) $\lim\limits_{x \to 2} c(x)$

Example 3 **Business** The cost, $c(x)$, of a New York City taxicab fare during nonpeak hours (assuming no standing time) where x is the distance of the trip (in miles) is $3 upon entry plus $.40 per fifth of a mile. Use the accompanying figure to verify that each of the following statements is true. (Data from: www.nyc.gov.)

(a) $c(0) = \$3$ **(b)** $c(1.2) = \$5.40$ **(c)** $\lim\limits_{x \to 1.2^-} c(x) = \$5$

(d) $\lim\limits_{x \to 1.2^+} c(x) = \$5.40$ **(e)** $\lim\limits_{x \to 1.2} c(x)$ does not exist

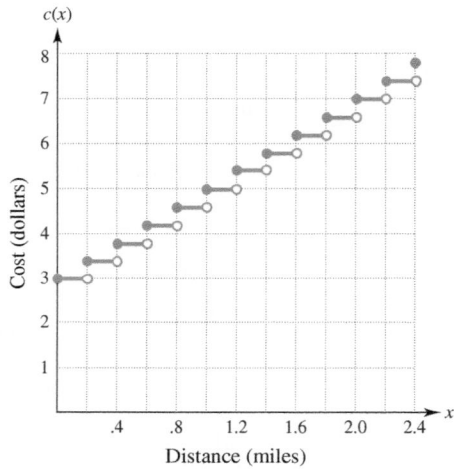

Figure 11.10

Infinite Limits

In the next part of the discussion, it is important to remember that

the symbol ∞, which is usually read "infinity," does *not* represent a real number.

Nevertheless, the word "infinity" and the symbol ∞ are often used as a convenient shorthand to describe the behavior of some functions. Consider the function f whose graph is shown in Figure 11.11 on the following page.

The graph shows that as x approaches 3 (on either side), the corresponding values of $f(x)$ get larger and larger without bound. We express this behavior by writing

$$\lim_{x \to 3} f(x) = \infty,$$

which is read, "The limit of $f(x)$ as x approaches 3 is infinity."

Similarly, as x approaches 1 (on either side), the corresponding values of $f(x)$ get more and more negative (smaller and smaller) without bound. We write

$$\lim_{x \to 1} f(x) = -\infty,$$

which is read, "The limit of $f(x)$ as x approaches 1 is negative infinity."

✓**Checkpoint 4**

Use "infinite limits" to describe the behavior of the function whose graph is given, near the specified number.

(a) $f(x) = \dfrac{3}{5-x}$ near $x = 5$

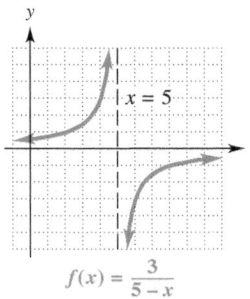

$$f(x) = \frac{3}{5-x}$$

(b) $f(x) = \dfrac{2-x}{x+3}$ near $x = -3$

$$f(x) = \frac{2-x}{x+3}$$

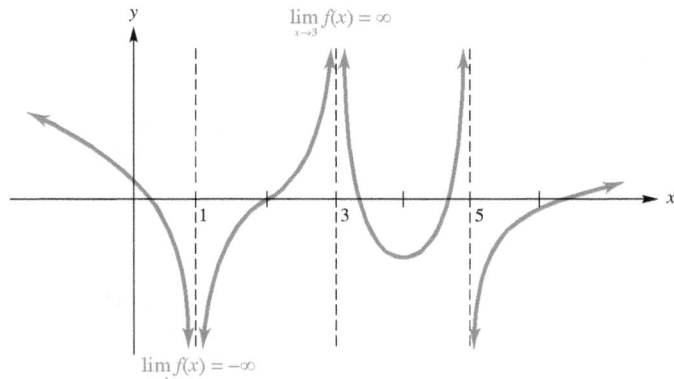

Figure 11.11

The behavior of f near $x = 5$ can be described in a similar fashion with the use of one-sided limits. When x is close to 5, the corresponding values of $f(x)$ get very large on the left side of 5 and very small on the right side of 5, so we write

$$\lim_{x\to5^-} f(x) = \infty \qquad \text{and} \qquad \lim_{x\to5^+} f(x) = -\infty$$

and say, "The limit of $f(x)$ as x approaches 5 from the left is infinity" and "The limit of $f(x)$ as x approaches 5 from the right is negative infinity."

In all the situations just described, the language of limits and the word "infinity" are useful for describing the behavior of a function that does not have a limit in the sense discussed in Section 11.1. In particular, this language provides an algebraic way to describe precisely the fact that the function in Figure 11.11 has different types of vertical asymptotes at $x = 1$, $x = 3$, and $x = 5$. ✓4

Limits at Infinity

The word "limit" has been used thus far to describe the values of a function $f(x)$ when x is near a particular number a. Now we consider the behavior of a function when x is very large or very small.

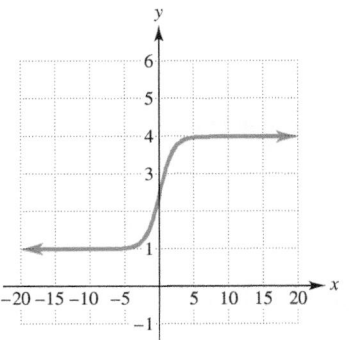

Figure 11.12

Example 4 Figure 11.12 shows the graph of

$$f(x) = \frac{3}{1+e^{-x}} + 1.$$

(a) Describe the behavior of f when x is very large.

Solution The right side of the graph appears to coincide with the horizontal line through 4. Actually, as x gets larger and larger, the corresponding values of $f(x)$ are very close (but not equal) to 4, as you can verify with a calculator or by using the trace feature of a graphing calculator (Figure 11.13 on the next page).[*] We describe this situation by writing

$$\lim_{x\to\infty} f(x) = 4,$$

which is read "The limit of $f(x)$ as x approaches infinity is 4."

(b) Describe the behavior of f when x is very small.

Solution To say that x gets very small means that it moves to the left on the axis (that is, x gets more and more negative). The graph suggests that when x is very small, the

[*]Because of round-off, a TI-84+ will say that $f(x) = 4$ when $x > 28$. Actually $f(x)$ is always less than 4. Similar remarks apply to other calculators.

$$\lim_{x \to \infty} f(x) = 4$$

As x gets larger and larger, the values of $f(x)$ approach 4.

$$\lim_{x \to -\infty} f(x) = 1$$

As x gets more and more negative, the values of $f(x)$ approach 1.

Figure 11.13   **Figure 11.14**

corresponding values of $f(x)$ are very close to 1. You can verify this with a calculator or the trace feature on a graphing calculator (Figure 11.14).[*] We describe this situation by writing

$$\lim_{x \to -\infty} f(x) = 1,$$

which is read, "The limit of $f(x)$ as x approaches negative infinity is 1." ✓5

Once again, the words "infinity" and "negative infinity" and the symbols ∞ and $-\infty$ do *not* denote numbers. They are just a convenient shorthand to express the idea that x takes very large or very small values.

A general definition of the kind of limits illustrated in Example 4 is given next. It is an informal one, as was the definition of limit in Section 11.1.

✓ **Checkpoint 5**

The graph of a function g is shown. Use the language of limits, as in Example 4, to describe the behavior of g when

(a) x is very small;

(b) x is very large.

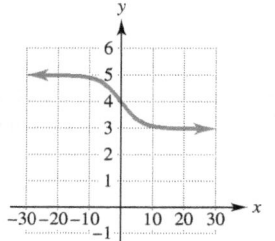

Limits at Infinity

Let f be a function that is defined for all large positive values of x, and let L be a real number. Suppose that

> as x takes larger and larger positive values, increasing without bound, the corresponding values of $f(x)$ are very close (and possibly equal) to L

and that

> the values of $f(x)$ can be made arbitrarily close (as close as you want) to L by taking large enough values of x.

Then we say that

the limit of $f(x)$ as x approaches infinity is L,

which is written

$$\lim_{x \to \infty} f(x) = L.$$

Similarly, if f is defined for all small negative values of x and M is a real number, then the statement

$$\lim_{x \to -\infty} f(x) = M,$$

which is read

the limit of $f(x)$ as x approaches negative infinity is M,

means that

> as x takes smaller and smaller negative values, decreasing without bound, the corresponding values of $f(x)$ are very close (and possibly equal) to M

and

> the values of $f(x)$ can be made arbitrarily close (as close as you want) to M by taking small enough values of x.

---

[*]Because of round-off, a TI-84+ will say that $f(x) = 1$ when $x < -28$. In fact, $f(x)$ is always more than 1. Similar remarks apply to other calculators.

Example 5   Find the given limits.

(a) $\displaystyle\lim_{x\to\infty}\frac{1}{x}$.

Solution   Make a table of values when x is very large:

x gets larger and larger				
x	50	100	1000	10,000
$1/x$	.02	.01	.001	.0001

$\dfrac{1}{x}$ approaches 0

The table shows that $1/x$ gets very close to 0 as x takes larger and larger values, which suggests that $\displaystyle\lim_{x\to\infty}\frac{1}{x}=0$. You can reach the same conclusion by examining the right side of the graph of $f(x)=1/x$ in Figure 11.15.

(b) $\displaystyle\lim_{x\to-\infty}\frac{1}{x}$

Solution   Make a table of values when x is very small:

x gets smaller and smaller				
x	-50	-100	-1000	$-10,000$
$1/x$	$-.02$	$-.01$	$-.001$	$-.0001$

$\dfrac{1}{x}$ approaches 0

The table shows that $1/x$ gets very close to 0 as x takes smaller and smaller values, which suggests that $\displaystyle\lim_{x\to-\infty}\frac{1}{x}=0$. The left side of the graph of $f(x)=1/x$ in Figure 11.15 shows this result graphically.

If the graph of a function approaches a horizontal line very closely when x is very large or very small, we say that this line is a **horizontal asymptote** of the graph. In Example 5, we see that the horizontal line $y=0$ (the x-axis) is a horizontal asymptote for the graph of $f(x)=\dfrac{1}{x}$.

Limits at infinity have many of the properties of ordinary limits. Consider, for instance, the constant function $f(x)=6$. As x gets larger and larger (or smaller and smaller), the corresponding value of $f(x)$ is *always* 6. Hence, $\displaystyle\lim_{x\to\infty}f(x)=6$ and $\displaystyle\lim_{x\to-\infty}f(x)=6$. Similarly, for any constant d,

$$\lim_{x\to\infty}d=d\qquad\text{and}\qquad\lim_{x\to-\infty}d=d.$$

Finally, we note the following:

All of the properties of limits in Section 11.1 (page 573) are valid for limits at infinity.

Example 6   Find

$$\lim_{x\to\infty}\frac{4x^2+3x}{5x^2-x+2}.$$

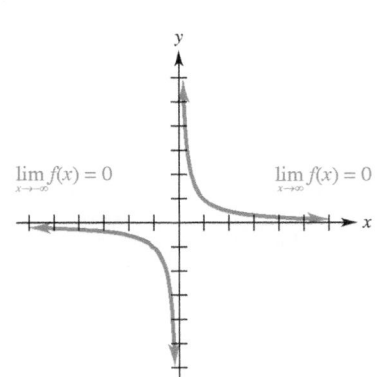

$\displaystyle\lim_{x\to-\infty}f(x)=0$ $\displaystyle\lim_{x\to+\infty}f(x)=0$

Figure 11.15

Solution Begin by writing the function in a different form. First divide both numerator and denominator by x^2 (which is the highest power of x appearing in either the numerator or denominator).* Then simplify and rewrite the result as follows:

$$\frac{4x^2 + 3x}{5x^2 - x + 2} = \frac{\dfrac{4x^2 + 3x}{x^2}}{\dfrac{5x^2 - x + 2}{x^2}} = \frac{\dfrac{4x^2}{x^2} + \dfrac{3x}{x^2}}{\dfrac{5x^2}{x^2} - \dfrac{x}{x^2} + \dfrac{2}{x^2}} = \frac{4 + \dfrac{3}{x}}{5 - \dfrac{1}{x} + \dfrac{2}{x^2}}$$

$$= \frac{4 + 3 \cdot \dfrac{1}{x}}{5 - \dfrac{1}{x} + 2 \cdot \dfrac{1}{x} \cdot \dfrac{1}{x}}.$$

Now use the limit properties and Example 5 to compute the limit:

$$\lim_{x \to \infty} \frac{4x^2 + 3x}{5x^2 - x + 2} = \lim_{x \to \infty} \frac{4 + 3 \cdot \dfrac{1}{x}}{5 - \dfrac{1}{x} + 2 \cdot \dfrac{1}{x} \cdot \dfrac{1}{x}} \qquad \text{Preceding equation}$$

$$= \frac{\displaystyle\lim_{x \to \infty} \left[4 + 3 \cdot \dfrac{1}{x} \right]}{\displaystyle\lim_{x \to \infty} \left[5 - \dfrac{1}{x} + 2 \cdot \dfrac{1}{x} \cdot \dfrac{1}{x} \right]} \qquad \text{Quotient property}$$

$$= \frac{\displaystyle\lim_{x \to \infty} 4 + \lim_{x \to \infty} \left(3 \cdot \dfrac{1}{x} \right)}{\displaystyle\lim_{x \to \infty} 5 - \lim_{x \to \infty} \dfrac{1}{x} + \lim_{x \to \infty} \left(2 \cdot \dfrac{1}{x} \cdot \dfrac{1}{x} \right)} \qquad \text{Sum and difference properties}$$

$$= \frac{\displaystyle\lim_{x \to \infty} 4 + \lim_{x \to \infty} 3 \cdot \lim_{x \to \infty} \dfrac{1}{x}}{\displaystyle\lim_{x \to \infty} 5 - \lim_{x \to \infty} \dfrac{1}{x} + \lim_{x \to \infty} 2 \cdot \lim_{x \to \infty} \dfrac{1}{x} \cdot \lim_{x \to \infty} \dfrac{1}{x}} \qquad \text{Product property}$$

$$= \frac{4 + 3 \cdot 0}{5 - 0 + 2 \cdot 0 \cdot 0} = \frac{4}{5}. \qquad \begin{array}{l}\text{Constant-function limits}\\ \text{and Example 5}\end{array}$$

Example 7 Find

$$\lim_{x \to -\infty} \frac{2x^2}{3 - x^3}.$$

Solution Divide both numerator and denominator by x^3, the highest power of x appearing in either one.* Then simplify and rewrite:

$$\frac{2x^2}{3 - x^3} = \frac{\dfrac{2x^2}{x^3}}{\dfrac{3 - x^3}{x^3}} = \frac{\dfrac{2x^2}{x^3}}{\dfrac{3}{x^3} - \dfrac{x^3}{x^3}} = \frac{\dfrac{2}{x}}{\dfrac{3}{x^3} - 1} = \frac{2 \cdot \dfrac{1}{x}}{3 \cdot \dfrac{1}{x} \cdot \dfrac{1}{x} \cdot \dfrac{1}{x} - 1}.$$

---

*In Examples 6 and 7, we are interested only in nonzero values of x, and dividing both numerator and denominator by a nonzero quantity will not change the value of the function.

Now proceed as in Example 6:

$$\lim_{x \to -\infty} \frac{2x^2}{3 - x^3} = \lim_{x \to -\infty} \frac{2 \cdot \dfrac{1}{x}}{3 \cdot \dfrac{1}{x} \cdot \dfrac{1}{x} \cdot \dfrac{1}{x} - 1}$$ Preceding equation

$$= \frac{\lim\limits_{x \to -\infty} \left[2 \cdot \dfrac{1}{x} \right]}{\lim\limits_{x \to -\infty} \left[3 \cdot \dfrac{1}{x} \cdot \dfrac{1}{x} \cdot \dfrac{1}{x} - 1 \right]}$$ Quotient property

$$= \frac{\lim\limits_{x \to -\infty} \left[2 \cdot \dfrac{1}{x} \right]}{\lim\limits_{x \to -\infty} \left[3 \cdot \dfrac{1}{x} \cdot \dfrac{1}{x} \cdot \dfrac{1}{x} \right] - \lim\limits_{x \to -\infty} 1}$$ Difference property

$$= \frac{\lim\limits_{x \to -\infty} 2 \cdot \lim\limits_{x \to -\infty} \dfrac{1}{x}}{\lim\limits_{x \to -\infty} 3 \cdot \lim\limits_{x \to -\infty} \dfrac{1}{x} \cdot \lim\limits_{x \to -\infty} \dfrac{1}{x} \cdot \lim\limits_{x \to -\infty} \dfrac{1}{x} - \lim\limits_{x \to -\infty} 1}$$ Product property

$$= \frac{2 \cdot 0}{3 \cdot 0 \cdot 0 \cdot 0 - 1} = \frac{0}{-1} = 0.$$ Constant-function limits and Example 5 ✓₆

✓ **Checkpoint 6**

Find the given limits.

(a) $\displaystyle\lim_{x \to -\infty} \frac{5x^3}{2x^3 - x + 4}$

(b) $\displaystyle\lim_{x \to \infty} \frac{10x^3 - 9x}{28 + 11x^4}$

The technique in Examples 6 and 7 carries over to any rational function $f(x) = g(x)/h(x)$, where the degree of $g(x)$ is less than or equal to the degree of $h(x)$. These limits provide a mathematical justification for the treatment of horizontal asymptotes in Section 3.7.

11.2 Exercises

The graph of the function f is shown. Use it to compute the given limits. (See Example 1.)

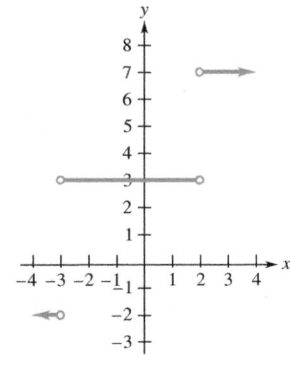

The graph of the function f is shown. Use it to compute the given limits. (See Example 1.)

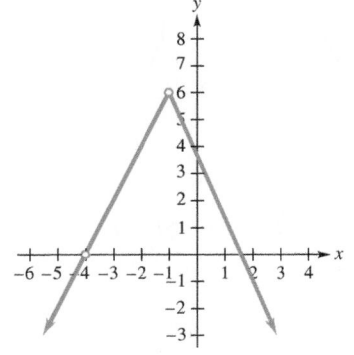

1. $\displaystyle\lim_{x \to 2} f(x)$ 2. $\displaystyle\lim_{x \to 2^+} f(x)$

3. $\displaystyle\lim_{x \to -3} f(x)$ 4. $\displaystyle\lim_{x \to -3^+} f(x)$

5. $\displaystyle\lim_{x \to -1^-} f(x)$ 6. $\displaystyle\lim_{x \to -1^+} f(x)$

7. $\displaystyle\lim_{x \to -4^-} f(x)$ 8. $\displaystyle\lim_{x \to -4^+} f(x)$

In Exercises 9–12, use the graph of the function f to determine the given limits. (See Example 1 and Figure 11.11.)

(a) $\lim_{x \to -2^-} f(x)$

(b) $\lim_{x \to 0^+} f(x)$

(c) $\lim_{x \to 3^-} f(x)$

(d) $\lim_{x \to 3^+} f(x)$

9.

10.

11.

12.

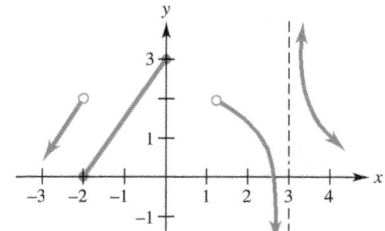

Find the given limits. (See Example 2.)

13. $\lim_{x \to 2^+} \sqrt{x^2 - 4}$

14. $\lim_{x \to 3^-} \sqrt{9 - x^2}$

15. $\lim_{x \to 0^+} \sqrt{x} + x + 1$

16. $\lim_{x \to 1^+} \sqrt{x - 1} + 1$

17. $\lim_{x \to -2^+} (x^3 - x^2 - x + 1)$

18. $\lim_{x \to -2^-} (2x^3 + 3x^2 + 5x + 2)$

19. $\lim_{x \to -5^+} \dfrac{\sqrt{x + 5} + 5}{x^2 - 5}$

20. $\lim_{x \to 1^+} \dfrac{x^3 - 2}{\sqrt{x^3 - 1} + 2}$

21. Graph the function f whose rule is

$$f(x) = \begin{cases} 3 - x & \text{if } x < -2 \\ x + 2 & \text{if } -2 \le x < 2 \\ 1 & \text{if } x = 2 \\ 4 - x & \text{if } x > 2 \end{cases}$$

Use the graph to evaluate the given limits.

(a) $\lim_{x \to -2^-} f(x)$ (b) $\lim_{x \to -2^+} f(x)$ (c) $\lim_{x \to -2} f(x)$

22. Let f be the function in Exercise 21. Evaluate the given limits.

(a) $\lim_{x \to 2^-} f(x)$ (b) $\lim_{x \to 2^+} f(x)$ (c) $\lim_{x \to 2} f(x)$

23. For the function f whose graph is shown, find

(a) $\lim_{x \to 2} f(x)$;   (b) $\lim_{x \to -2^+} f(x)$;   (c) $\lim_{x \to -2^-} f(x)$.

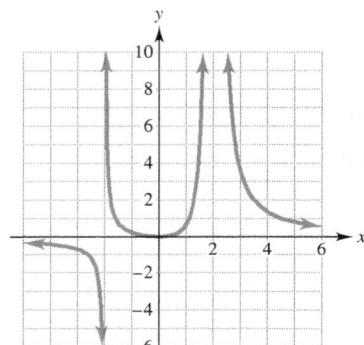

24. For the function g whose graph is shown, find

(a) $\lim_{x \to 3} g(x)$;   (b) $\lim_{x \to -2^+} g(x)$;   (c) $\lim_{x \to -2^-} g(x)$.

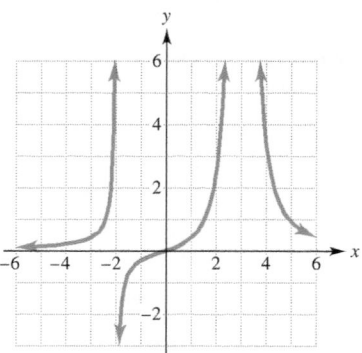

Use a calculator to estimate the given limits.

25. $\lim_{x \to 4} \dfrac{-6}{(x - 4)^2}$

26. $\lim_{x \to -2} \dfrac{2x}{(x + 2)^2}$

27. $\lim_{x \to -3^+} \dfrac{2 - x}{x + 3}$

28. $\lim_{x \to -1^+} \dfrac{2}{1 + x}$

Use the given graph of the function f to find $\lim\limits_{x \to \infty} f(x)$ and $\lim\limits_{x \to -\infty} f(x)$. (See Example 4.)

29.

30.

31.

32.

33.

34.

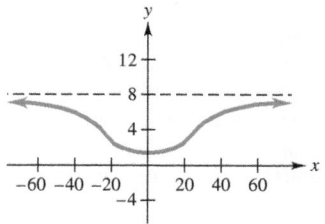

Use a calculator to estimate the limits given numerically. (See Example 5.)

35. $\lim\limits_{x \to \infty} [\sqrt{x^2 + 1} - (x + 1)]$

36. $\lim\limits_{x \to -\infty} [\sqrt{x^2 + x + 1} + x]$

37. $\lim\limits_{x \to -\infty} \dfrac{x^{2/3} - x^{4/3}}{x^3}$

38. $\lim\limits_{x \to \infty} \dfrac{x^{5/4} + x}{2x - x^{5/4}}$

39. $\lim\limits_{x \to -\infty} e^{1/x}$

40. $\lim\limits_{x \to \infty} \dfrac{e^{1/x}}{x}$

41. $\lim\limits_{x \to \infty} \dfrac{\ln x}{x}$

42. $\lim\limits_{x \to \infty} \dfrac{5}{1 + (1.1)^{-x/20}}$

Use the properties of limits to find the given limits. (See Examples 6 and 7.)

43. $\lim\limits_{x \to \infty} \dfrac{10x^2 - 5x + 8}{3x^2 + 8x - 29}$

44. $\lim\limits_{x \to \infty} \dfrac{44x^2 - 12x + 82}{11x^2 - 35x - 37}$

45. $\lim\limits_{x \to -\infty} \dfrac{5x + 9x^2 - 17}{21x + 5x^3 + 12x^2}$

46. $\lim\limits_{x \to -\infty} \dfrac{11x + 21}{7 + 67x - x^2}$

47. $\lim\limits_{x \to -\infty} \dfrac{8x^5 + 7x^4 - 10x^3}{25 - 4x^5}$

48. $\lim\limits_{x \to \infty} \dfrac{7x^4 + 3x^3 - 12x^2 + x - 76}{x^4 - 33x^3 - 17x^2 + 6}$

49. $\lim\limits_{x \to -\infty} \dfrac{(4x - 1)(x + 2)}{5x^2 - 3x + 1}$

50. $\lim\limits_{x \to \infty} \dfrac{(3x - 1)(4x + 3)}{6x^2 - x + 7}$

51. $\lim\limits_{x \to \infty} \left(\dfrac{1}{4x^2} \right)$

52. $\lim\limits_{x \to -\infty} (7x^2 + 2)^{-2}$

53. $\lim\limits_{x \to -\infty} \left(\dfrac{18x}{x - 9} - \dfrac{3x}{x + 4} \right)$

54. $\lim\limits_{x \to \infty} \left(\dfrac{2x}{x^2 + 2} + \dfrac{17x}{x^3 - 11} \right)$

Use the definition of absolute value to find the given limits.

55. $\lim\limits_{x \to \infty} \dfrac{x}{|x|}$

56. $\lim\limits_{x \to -\infty} \dfrac{x}{|x|}$

57. $\lim\limits_{x \to -\infty} \dfrac{x}{|x| + 1}$

58. Use the change-of-base formula for logarithms (in Section 4.3) to show that $\lim\limits_{x \to \infty} \dfrac{\ln x}{\log x} = \ln 10$.

Work these exercises.

59. **Business** A metropolitan waterworks normally charges a flat monthly rate of $20 for up to 4000 gallons of water consumption and a rate of $5 per thousand gallons of water for consumption in excess of 4000 gallons. To encourage conservation during a severe drought, the waterworks imposed an excessive use surcharge and an additional rate increase for residential customers who consumed more than 10,000 gallons of water in a month. Use the accompanying graph, which shows the monthly cost, $c(x)$, of consuming x gallons of water to find the given quantities.

(a) $\lim_{x \to 4^-} c(x)$ (b) $\lim_{x \to 4^+} c(x)$ (c) $\lim_{x \to 4} c(x)$

(d) $\lim_{x \to 10^-} c(x)$ (e) $\lim_{x \to 10^+} c(x)$ (f) $\lim_{x \to 10} c(x)$

(g) What rate does the waterworks charge for consumption in excess of 10,000 gallons?

(h) What is the amount of the surcharge for customers who consume more than 10,000 gallons of water?

60. **Finance** The opening price of a stock typically differs somewhat from the closing price the previous day. The accompanying graph shows the stock price for Verizon Communications, $f(t)$, over two trading days where $t = 0$ corresponds to the opening of trading on February 16, 2012. Each trading day lasts 6.5 hours, beginning at 9:30 a.m. and concluding at 4:00 p.m. Eastern time. Since t represents the time (in hours) that the market has been open for trading, $t = 13$ represents the close of trading on February 17, 2012. Approximate and interpret the given limits. (Data from: www.morningstar.com.)

(a) $\lim_{t \to 6.5^-} f(t)$ (b) $\lim_{t \to 6.5^+} f(t)$ (c) $\lim_{t \to 6.5} f(t)$

61. **Business** According to the Virginia Department of Social Services, an individual daycare provider in Virginia may care for up to eight children (ages two to four). If a daycare provider

hires an additional worker, it increases capacity but also incurs additional expense. The accompanying graph approximates the monthly profit, $p(x)$, from providing care for x children. Find the given quantities.

(a) $\lim_{x \to 8^-} p(x)$ (b) $\lim_{x \to 8^+} p(x)$ (c) $\lim_{x \to 8} p(x)$

(d) How many children must be cared for to break even (zero profit)?

(e) How many children must be cared for to make hiring a second provider beneficial?

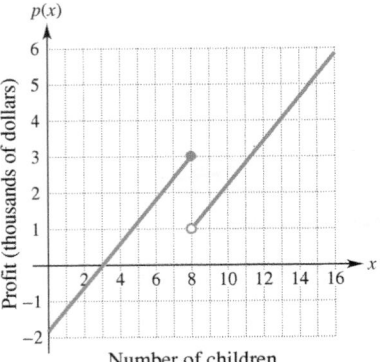

62. **Business** The cost of a first-class stamp increased slowly between 1919 and 1968 and has increased more rapidly since 1968. The cost (in cents) can be approximated by

$$c(x) = \begin{cases} .08x + .56 & \text{if } 19 \le x \le 68 \\ .89x - 54.52 & \text{if } x > 68 \end{cases},$$

where $x = 0$ corresponds to the year 1900. Find the given limits. (Data from: United States Postal Service.)

(a) $\lim_{x \to 68^-} c(x)$ (b) $\lim_{x \to 68^+} c(x)$ (c) $\lim_{x \to 68} c(x)$

63. **Business** An aquarium parking garage charges $3 for up to and including one hour and $2 for each additional hour (or fraction of an hour), up to a daily maximum of $15. Let $c(t)$ represent the daily cost of parking, where t is the number of hours parked. Find the given quantities.

(a) $c(1.5)$ (b) $c(2)$ (c) $c(2.5)$

(d) $c(3)$ (e) $c(8)$ (f) $\lim_{t \to 1.5} c(t)$

(g) $\lim_{t \to 2^-} c(t)$ (h) $\lim_{t \to 2^+} c(t)$ (i) $\lim_{t \to 2} c(t)$

(j) $\lim_{t \to 8} c(t)$

64. **Natural Science** If you travel from Birmingham, Alabama to Atlanta, Georgia at an average speed of r miles per hour, the time (in hours) it takes to complete the trip is given by $T(r) = \dfrac{150}{r}$. Find and interpret the given limits.

(a) $\lim_{r \to 75} T(r)$ (b) $\lim_{r \to \infty} T(r)$ (c) $\lim_{r \to 0^+} T(r)$

65. **Business** The cost of printing a certain paperback book using a publish-on-demand service is $c(x) = 6000 + 5x$, where x is the number of books printed. The average cost per book, denoted by $\bar{c}(x)$, is found by dividing $c(x)$ by x. Find and interpret the given quantities.

(a) $\bar{c}(100)$ (b) $\bar{c}(1000)$ (c) $\lim_{x \to \infty} \bar{c}(x)$

66. Health The concentration of a drug in a patient's blood-stream h hours after it was injected is given by

$$A(h) = \frac{.17h}{h^2 + 2}.$$

Find and interpret $\lim_{h \to \infty} A(h)$.

67. Natural Science Researchers have developed a mathematical model that can be used to estimate the number of teeth, $N(t)$, at time t (days of incubation) for *Alligator mississippiensis*[*]:

$$N(t) = 71.8e^{-8.96e^{-.0685t}}.$$

(a) Find $N(65)$, the number of teeth of an alligator that hatched after 65 days.

(b) Find $\lim_{t \to \infty} N(t)$, and use this value as an estimate of the number of teeth of a newborn alligator. Does this estimate differ significantly from the estimate of part (a)?

---

[*]Kulesa, P., G. Cruywagen, et al. "On a Model Mechanism for the Spatial Patterning of Teeth Primordia in the Alligator," *Journal of Theoretical Biology*, Vol. 180, 1996, pp. 287–296.

✓ **Checkpoint Answers**

1. (a) 4   **(b)** 1
(c) Does not exist   **(d)** 3
(e) $x = 1$ and $x = 3$

2. (a) 0   **(b)** 8

3. (a) \$7.00   **(b)** \$6.60   **(c)** \$7.00
(d) Does not exist

4. (a) $\lim_{x \to 5^-} \frac{3}{5-x} = \infty$ and $\lim_{x \to 5^+} \frac{3}{5-x} = -\infty$
(b) $\lim_{x \to -3^-} \frac{2-x}{x+3} = -\infty$ and $\lim_{x \to -3^+} \frac{2-x}{x+3} = \infty$

5. (a) $\lim_{x \to -\infty} g(x) = 5$ **(b)** $\lim_{x \to \infty} g(x) = 3$

6. (a) $\frac{5}{2}$ **(b)** 0

11.3 Rates of Change

One of the main applications of calculus is determining how one variable changes in relation to another. A person in business wants to know how profit changes with respect to changes in advertising, while a person in medicine wants to know how a patient's reaction to a drug changes with respect to changes in the dose.

We begin the discussion with a familiar situation. A driver makes the 168-mile trip from Cleveland to Columbus, Ohio, in 3 hours. The following table shows how far the driver has traveled from Cleveland at various times:

Time (in hours)	0	.5	1	1.5	2	2.5	3
Distance (in miles)	0	22	52	86	118	148	168

If f is the function whose rule is

$$f(x) = \text{distance from Cleveland at time } x,$$

then the table shows, for example, that $f(2) = 118$ and $f(3) = 168$. So the distance traveled from time $x = 2$ to $x = 3$ is $168 - 118$—that is, $f(3) - f(2)$. In a similar fashion, we obtain the other entries in the following chart:

Time Interval	Distance Traveled
$x = 2$ to $x = 3$	$f(3) - f(2) = 168 - 118 = 50$ miles
$x = 1$ to $x = 3$	$f(3) - f(1) = 168 - 52 = 116$ miles
$x = 0$ to $x = 2.5$	$f(2.5) - f(0) = 148 - 0 = 148$ miles
$x = .5$ to $x = 1$	$f(1) - f(.5) = 52 - 22 = 30$ miles
$x = a$ to $x = b$	$f(b) - f(a)$ miles

The last line of the chart shows how to find the distance traveled in any time interval $(0 \le a < b \le 3)$.

Since distance = average speed × time,

$$\text{average speed} = \frac{\text{distance traveled}}{\text{time interval}}.$$

In the preceding chart, you can compute the length of each time interval by taking the difference between the two times. For example, from $x = 1$ to $x = 3$ is a time interval of length $3 - 1 = 2$ hours; hence, the average speed over this interval is $116/2 = 58$ mph. Similarly, we have the following information:

Time Interval	Average Speed $= \dfrac{\text{Distance Traveled}}{\text{Time Interval}}$
$x = 2$ to $x = 3$	$\dfrac{f(3) - f(2)}{3 - 2} = \dfrac{168 - 118}{3 - 2} = \dfrac{50}{1} = 50$ mph
$x = 1$ to $x = 3$	$\dfrac{f(3) - f(1)}{3 - 1} = \dfrac{168 - 52}{3 - 1} = \dfrac{116}{2} = 58$ mph
$x = 0$ to $x = 2.5$	$\dfrac{f(2.5) - f(0)}{2.5 - 0} = \dfrac{148 - 0}{2.5 - 0} = \dfrac{148}{2.5} = 59.2$ mph
$x = .5$ to $x = 1$	$\dfrac{f(1) - f(.5)}{1 - .5} = \dfrac{52 - 22}{1 - .5} = \dfrac{30}{.5} = 60$ mph
$x = a$ to $x = b$	$\dfrac{f(b) - f(a)}{b - a}$ mph

The last line of the chart shows how to compute the average speed over any time interval $(0 \le a < b \le 3)$. ✓₁

Now, speed (miles per hour) is simply the *rate of change* of distance with respect to time, and what was done for the distance function f in the preceding discussion can be done with any function.

✓ **Checkpoint 1**

Find the average speed
(a) from $t = 1.5$ to $t = 2$;
(b) from $t = s$ to $t = r$.

Quantity	Meaning for the Distance Function	Meaning for an Arbitrary Function f
$b - a$	Time interval = change in time from $x = a$ to $x = b$	Change in x from $x = a$ to $x = b$
$f(b) - f(a)$	Distance traveled = corresponding change in distance as time changes from a to b	Corresponding change in $f(x)$ as x changes from a to b
$\dfrac{f(b) - f(a)}{b - a}$	**Average speed** = average rate of change of distance with respect to time as time changes from a to b	**Average rate of change** of $f(x)$ with respect to x as x changes from a to b (where $a < b$)

Example 1   If $f(x) = x^2 + 4x + 5$, find the average rate of change of $f(x)$ with respect to x as x changes from -2 to 3.

Solution   This is the situation described in the last line of the preceding chart, with $a = -2$ and $b = 3$. The average rate of change is

$$\frac{f(3) - f(-2)}{3 - (-2)} = \frac{(3)^2 + 4(3) + 5 - [(-2)^2 + 4(-2) + 5]}{3 - (-2)} = \frac{26 - 1}{5}$$

$$= \frac{25}{5} = 5. \quad ✓₂$$

✓ **Checkpoint 2**

Find the average rate of change of $f(x)$ in Example 1 when x changes from
(a) 0 to 4;
(b) 2 to 7.

Example 2   **Finance**   Suppose $D(t)$ is the value of the Dow Jones Industrial Average (DJIA) at time t. Figure 11.16 on the following page shows the values of $D(t)$ for the end of the given year over a twelve-year period. (Data from: www.morningstar.com.)

Approximate the average rate of change of the DJIA with respect to time over the given intervals.

Year	DJIA
2000	10,787
2001	10,022
2002	8342
2003	10,454
2004	10,783
2005	10,718
2006	12,463
2007	13,265
2008	8776
2009	10,428
2010	11,578
2011	12,218

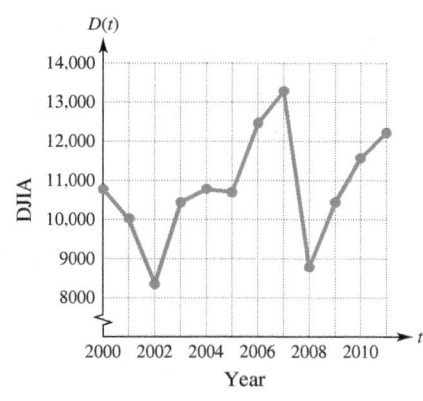

Figure 11.16

(a) From the end of 2007 to the end of 2008

Solution The table says that the DJIA stood at 13,265 at the end of 2007 and 8776 at the end of 2008; that is $D(2007) = 13,265$ and $D(2008) = 8776$. The average rate of change over this period is

$$\frac{D(2008) - D(2007)}{2008 - 2007} = \frac{8776 - 13,265}{2008 - 2007} = \frac{-4489}{1} = -4489.$$

The negative number implies that the DJIA was decreasing at an average rate of 4489 index points per year.

(b) From the end of 2008 to the end of 2011

Solution The table shows that $D(2011) = 12,218$, and we saw earlier that $D(2008) = 8776$. The average rate of change is

$$\frac{D(2011) - D(2008)}{2011 - 2008} = \frac{12,218 - 8776}{2011 - 2008} = \frac{3442}{3} \approx 1147.3.$$

Thus the Dow was increasing at an average rate of 1147.3 index points per year during this period. ✓₃

Example 2 also illustrates the geometric interpretation of the average rate of change. In part (b), for instance,

$$\text{average rate of change from 2008 to 2011} = \frac{D(2011) - D(2008)}{2011 - 2008} = \frac{12,218 - 8776}{2011 - 2008} \approx 1147.3 \frac{\text{index points}}{\text{year}}.$$

This last number is precisely the *slope* of the line from (2008, 8776) to (2011, 12,218) on the graph of D, as shown in red in Figure 11.17. The same thing is true in general.

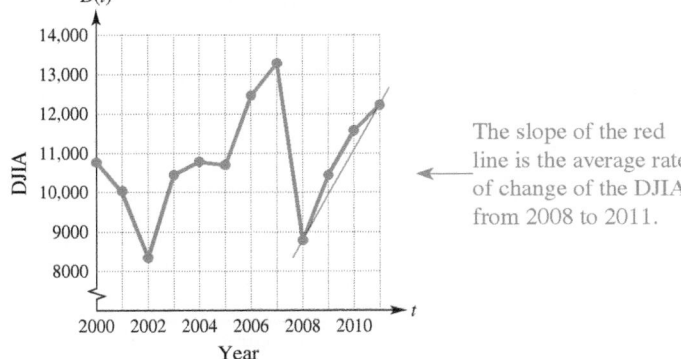

The slope of the red line is the average rate of change of the DJIA from 2008 to 2011.

Figure 11.17

✓ **Checkpoint 3**

Use Figure 11.16 (and the corresponding table of values) to find the average rate of change of the DJIA with respect to time over the given interval.

(a) From the end of 2005 to the end of 2011

(b) From the end of 2006 to the end of 2011

Geometric Meaning of Average Rate of Change

If f is a function, then the average rate of change of $f(x)$ with respect to x, as x changes from a to b, namely,

$$\frac{f(b) - f(a)}{b - a},$$

is the slope of the line joining the points $(a, f(a))$ and $(b, f(b))$ on the graph of f. Examples are shown in Figure 11.18.

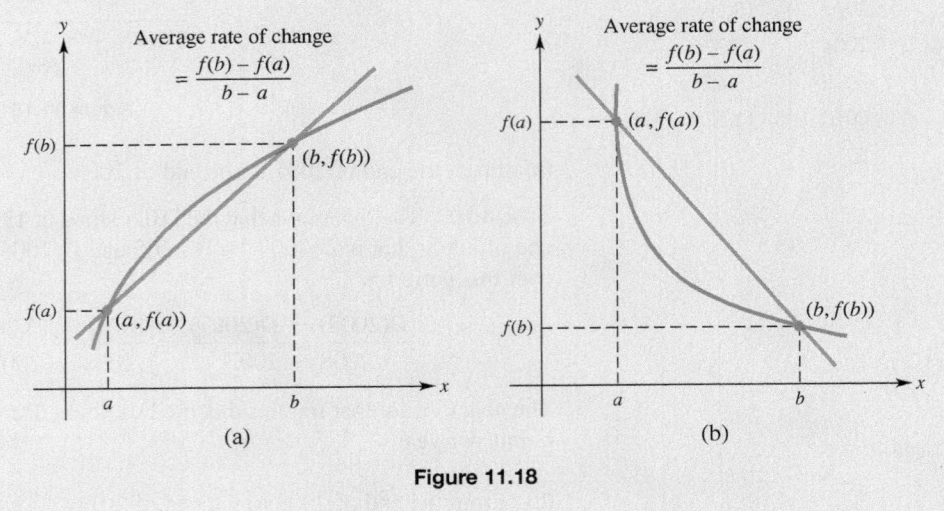

(a)   (b)

Figure 11.18

Instantaneous Rate of Change

Suppose a car is stopped at a traffic light. When the light turns green, the car begins to move along a straight road. Assume that the distance traveled by the car is given by the function

$$s(t) = 2t^2 \quad (0 \le t \le 30),$$

where time t is measured in seconds and the distance $s(t)$ at time t is measured in feet. We know how to find the *average* speed of the car over any time interval, so we now turn to a different problem: determining the *exact* speed of the car at a particular instant—say, $t = 10$.[*]

The intuitive idea is that the exact speed at $t = 10$ is very close to the average speed over a very short time interval near $t = 10$. If we take shorter and shorter time intervals near $t = 10$, the average speeds over these intervals should get closer and closer to the exact speed at $t = 10$. In other words,

the exact speed at $t = 10$ is the limit of the average speeds over shorter and shorter time intervals near $t = 10$.

The following chart illustrates this idea:

Intervals	Average Speed
$t = 10$ to $t = 10.1$	$\dfrac{s(10.1) - s(10)}{10.1 - 10} = \dfrac{204.02 - 200}{.1} = 40.2$ ft/sec
$t = 10$ to $t = 10.01$	$\dfrac{s(10.01) - s(10)}{10.01 - 10} = \dfrac{200.4002 - 200}{.01} = 40.02$ ft/sec
$t = 10$ to $t = 10.001$	$\dfrac{s(10.001) - s(10)}{10.001 - 10} = \dfrac{200.040002 - 200}{.001} = 40.002$ ft/sec

[*]As distance is measured in feet and time in seconds here, speed is measured in feet per second. It may help to know that 15 mph is equivalent to 22 ft/sec and 60 mph to 88 ft/sec.

The chart suggests that the exact speed at $t = 10$ is 40 ft/sec. We can confirm this intuition by computing the average speed from $t = 10$ to $t = 10 + h$, where h is any very small nonzero number. (The chart does this for $h = .1$, $h = .01$, and $h = .001$.) The average speed from $t = 10$ to $t = 10 + h$ is

$$\frac{s(10 + h) - s(10)}{(10 + h) - 10} = \frac{s(10 + h) - s(10)}{h}$$

$$= \frac{2(10 + h)^2 - 2 \cdot 10^2}{h}$$

$$= \frac{2(100 + 20h + h^2) - 200}{h}$$

$$= \frac{200 + 40h + 2h^2 - 200}{h}$$

$$= \frac{40h + 2h^2}{h} = \frac{h(40 + 2h)}{h} \qquad (h \neq 0)$$

$$= 40 + 2h.$$

Saying that the time interval from 10 to $10 + h$ gets shorter and shorter is equivalent to saying that h gets closer and closer to 0. Hence, the exact speed at $t = 10$ is the limit, as h approaches 0, of the average speeds over the intervals from $t = 10$ to $t = 10 + h$; that is,

$$\lim_{h \to 0} \frac{s(10 + h) - s(10)}{h} = \lim_{h \to 0} (40 + 2h)$$

$$= 40 \text{ ft/sec.}$$

In the preceding example, the car moved in one direction along a straight line. Now suppose that an object is moving back and forth along a number line, with its position at time t given by the function $s(t)$. The **velocity** of the object is the rate of motion in the direction in which it is moving. **Speed** is the absolute value of velocity. For example, a velocity of -30 ft/sec indicates a speed of 30 ft/sec in the negative direction, while a velocity of 40 ft/sec indicates a speed of 40 ft/sec in the positive direction.

Hereafter, we deal with **average velocity** and **instantaneous velocity** instead of average speed and exact speed, respectively. When the term "velocity" is used alone, it means instantaneous velocity.

Let a be a fixed number. By replacing 10 by a in the preceding discussion, we see that the average velocity of the object from time $t = a$ to time $t = a + h$ is the quotient

$$\frac{s(a + h) - s(a)}{(a + h) - a} = \frac{s(a + h) - s(a)}{h}.$$

The instantaneous velocity at time a is the limit of this quotient as h approaches 0.

Velocity

If an object moves along a straight line, with position $s(t)$ at time t, then the **velocity** of the object at $t = a$ is

$$\lim_{h \to 0} \frac{s(a + h) - s(a)}{h},$$

provided that this limit exists.

Example 3   **Natural Science**   The distance, in feet, of an object from a starting point is given by $s(t) = 2t^2 - 5t + 40$, where t is time in seconds.

(a) Find the average velocity of the object from 2 seconds to 4 seconds.

Solution   The average velocity is

$$\frac{s(4) - s(2)}{4 - 2} = \frac{52 - 38}{2} = \frac{14}{2} = 7$$

feet per second.

(b) Find the instantaneous velocity at 4 seconds.

Solution   For $t = 4$, the instantaneous velocity is

$$\lim_{h \to 0} \frac{s(4 + h) - s(4)}{h}$$

feet per second. We have

$$\begin{aligned}
s(4 + h) &= 2(4 + h)^2 - 5(4 + h) + 40 \\
&= 2(16 + 8h + h^2) - 20 - 5h + 40 \\
&= 32 + 16h + 2h^2 - 20 - 5h + 40 \\
&= 2h^2 + 11h + 52
\end{aligned}$$

and

$$s(4) = 2(4)^2 - 5(4) + 40 = 52.$$

Thus,

$$s(4 + h) - s(4) = (2h^2 + 11h + 52) - 52 = 2h^2 + 11h,$$

and the instantaneous velocity at $t = 4$ is

$$\lim_{h \to 0} \frac{2h^2 + 11h}{h} = \lim_{h \to 0} \frac{h(2h + 11)}{h}$$

$$= \lim_{h \to 0} (2h + 11) = 11 \text{ ft/sec.}$$

✓ **Checkpoint 4**

In Example 3, if $s(t) = t^2 + 3$, find

(a) the average velocity from 1 second to 5 seconds;

(b) the instantaneous velocity at 5 seconds.

Example 4   **Health**   The velocity of blood cells is of interest to physicians; a velocity slower than normal might indicate a constriction, for example. Suppose the position of a red blood cell in a capillary is given by

$$s(t) = 1.2t + 5,$$

where $s(t)$ gives the position of a cell in millimeters from some reference point and t is time in seconds. Find the velocity of this cell at time $t = a$.

Solution   We have $s(a) = 1.2a + 5$. To find $s(a + h)$, substitute $a + h$ for the variable t in $s(t) = 1.2t + 5$:

$$s(a + h) = 1.2(a + h) + 5.$$

Now use the definition of velocity:

$$\begin{aligned}
v(a) &= \lim_{h \to 0} \frac{s(a + h) - s(a)}{h} \\
&= \lim_{h \to 0} \frac{1.2(a + h) + 5 - (1.2a + 5)}{h} \\
&= \lim_{h \to 0} \frac{1.2a + 1.2h + 5 - 1.2a - 5}{h} = \lim_{h \to 0} \frac{1.2h}{h} = 1.2 \text{ mm/sec.}
\end{aligned}$$

✓ **Checkpoint 5**

Repeat Example 4 with $s(t) = .3t - 2$.

The velocity of the blood cell at $t = a$ is 1.2 millimeters per second, regardless of the value of a. In other words, the blood velocity is a constant 1.2 millimeters per second at any time.

The ideas underlying the concept of the velocity of a moving object can be extended to any function f. In place of average velocity at time t, we have the average rate of change of $f(x)$ with respect to x as x changes from one value to another. Taking limits leads to the following definition.

Instantaneous Rate of Change

The **instantaneous rate of change** for a function f when $x = a$ is

$$\lim_{h \to 0} \frac{f(a + h) - f(a)}{h},$$

provided that this limit exists.

Example 5 **Business** A company determines that the cost (in hundreds of dollars) of manufacturing x cases of computer mice is

$$C(x) = -.2x^2 + 8x + 40 \qquad (0 \le x \le 20).$$

(a) Find the average rate of change of cost for manufacturing between 5 and 10 cases.

Solution Use the formula for average rate of change. The cost to manufacture 5 cases is

$$C(5) = -.2(5^2) + 8(5) + 40 = 75,$$

or $7500. The cost to manufacture 10 cases is

$$C(10) = -.2(10^2) + 8(10) + 40 = 100,$$

or $10,000. The average rate of change of cost is

$$\frac{C(10) - C(5)}{10 - 5} = \frac{100 - 75}{5} = 5.$$

Thus, on the average, cost is increasing at the rate of $500 per case when production is increased from 5 to 10 cases.

(b) Find the instantaneous rate of change with respect to the number of cases produced when 5 cases are produced.

Solution The instantaneous rate of change when $x = 5$ is given by

$$\lim_{h \to 0} \frac{C(5 + h) - C(5)}{h}$$

$$= \lim_{h \to 0} \frac{[-.2(5 + h)^2 + 8(5 + h) + 40] - [-.2(5^2) + 8(5) + 40]}{h}$$

$$= \lim_{h \to 0} \frac{[-5 - 2h - .2h^2 + 40 + 8h + 40] - [75]}{h}$$

$$= \lim_{h \to 0} \frac{6h - .2h^2}{h} \qquad \text{Combine terms.}$$

$$= \lim_{h \to 0} (6 - .2h) \qquad \text{Divide by } h.$$

$$= 6. \qquad \text{Calculate the limit.}$$

When 5 cases are manufactured, the cost is increasing at the rate of $600 per case.

The rate of change of the cost function is called the **marginal cost.**[*] Similarly, **marginal revenue** and **marginal profit** are the rates of change of the revenue and profit functions, respectively. Part (b) of Example 5 shows that the marginal cost when 5 cases are manufactured is $600 per case.

Example 6 **Health** The total number of bachelor's degrees (in thousands) earned in the health professions in year t can be approximated by

$$f(t) = 52e^{.094t} \qquad (3 \le t \le 10),$$

where $t = 0$ corresponds to the year 2000. (Data from: *The Statistical Abstract of the United States*: 2012.)

(a) Find the rate of change of the number of health professions bachelor's degrees in 2004.

Solution Since $t = 0$ corresponds to the year 2000, we must find the instantaneous rate of change of $f(t)$ at $t = 4$. The algebraic techniques used in the preceding examples will not work with an exponential function, but the rate of change can be approximated by a graphing calculator or spreadsheet program. The average rate of change from 4 to $4 + h$ is:

$$\text{average rate of change} = \frac{f(4 + h) - f(4)}{h} = \frac{52e^{.094(4+h)} - 52e^{.094(4)}}{h}.$$

Figure 11.19

To approximate the instantaneous rate of change, we evaluate this quantity for very small values of h, as shown in Figure 11.19 (in which X is used in place of h, and Y1 is the average rate of change). The table suggests that at $t = 4$, the instantaneous rate of change can be approximated by:

$$\text{instantaneous rate of change} = \lim_{h \to 0} \frac{52e^{.094(4+h)} - 52e^{.094(4)}}{h} \approx 7.119.$$

Thus, the number of bachelor's degrees in the health professions was increasing at a rate of about 7119 degrees per year in 2004.

(b) Find the rate of change in 2009.

Solution The instantaneous rate of change of $f(t)$ when $t = 9$ is

$$\lim_{h \to 0} \frac{f(9 + h) - f(9)}{h} = \lim_{h \to 0} \frac{52e^{.094(9+h)} - 52e^{.094(9)}}{h} \approx 11.391,$$

Figure 11.20

as shown in Figure 11.20. In 2009, therefore, the number of health professions degrees was increasing at a rate of about 11,391 degrees per year.

---

[*]Marginal cost for linear cost functions was discussed in in Section 3.3.

11.3 Exercises

Find the average rate of change for the given functions. (See Example 1.)

1. $f(x) = x^2 + 2x$ between $x = 0$ and $x = 6$

2. $f(x) = -4x^2 - 6$ between $x = 1$ and $x = 7$

3. $f(x) = 2x^3 - 4x^2 + 6$ between $x = -1$ and $x = 2$

4. $f(x) = -3x^3 + 2x^2 - 4x + 2$ between $x = 0$ and $x = 2$

5. $f(x) = \sqrt{x}$ between $x = 1$ and $x = 9$

6. $f(x) = \sqrt{3x - 2}$ between $x = 2$ and $x = 6$

7. $f(x) = \dfrac{1}{x - 1}$ between $x = -2$ and $x = 0$

8. $f(x) = .4525\, e^{1.556\sqrt{x}}$ between $x = 4$ and $x = 4.5$

Work these exercises. (See Example 2.)

9. Business The accompanying graph shows the total sales, in thousands of dollars, from the distribution of *x* thousand catalogs. Find and interpret the average rate of change of sales with respect to the number of catalogs distributed for the given changes in *x*.

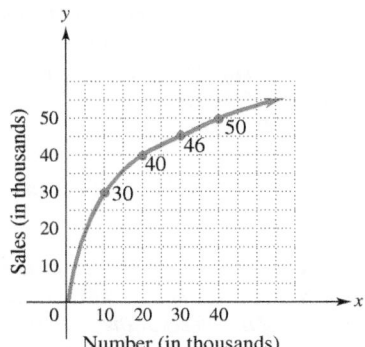

(a) 10 to 20   (b) 20 to 30   (c) 30 to 40

(d) What is happening to the average rate of change of sales as the number of catalogs distributed increases?

(e) Explain why what you have found in part (d) might happen.

10. Health The accompanying graph shows the relationship between waist circumference (in inches) and weight (in pounds) for American males (blue) and females (red). Find the average rate of change in weight for changes in waist circumference from

(a) 32 to 44 inches for males;

(b) 28 to 40 inches for females.

(c) Do we need to calculate the rate of change at any other points for males or females? Explain. (Data from: National Health and Nutrition Examination Study (NHANES) 2005–2006.)

11. Finance The accompanying graph gives the value of the S&P 500 Index for 12 months, where $x = 1$ corresponds to January, 2011. (Data from: www.morningstar.com.)

(a) Which time period has the greater average rate of change: month 2 to month 3, month 7 to month 9, or month 9 to month 10?

(b) Which time period has the greater average rate of change: month 3 to month 4, or month 9 to month 10?

(c) Which time period has the greater average rate of change in absolute value: month 4 to month 7, or month 7 to month 9?

12. Business The accompanying figure shows the number of Facebook users from its launch in 2004 until 2012. (Data from: Facebook.)

(a) Approximately when did Facebook reach 350 million users?

(b) Approximately how many Facebook users were there at the start of 2011?

(c) Which time period has the largest rate of change: [2004, 2009] or [2009, 2012] or [2004, 2012]?

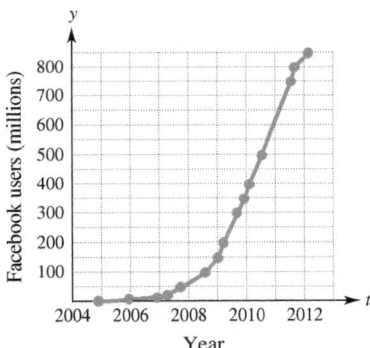

13. Business The accompanying graph shows the revenue (in billions of dollars) generated by the automaker BMW from 2001 to 2010. Find and interpret the approximate average rate of change in the revenue for each period. (Data from: www.morningstar.com.)

(a) 2004 to 2007   (b) 2007 to 2009   (c) 2004 to 2009

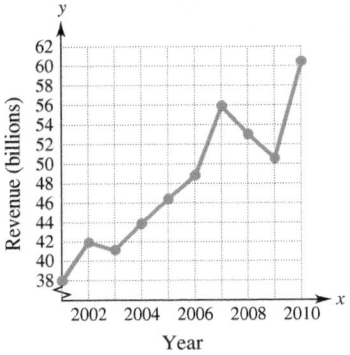

14. Social Science The accompanying graph shows projected enrollment (in millions) in high school, $h(t)$, and college, $c(t)$, in the United States from 2011 to 2020. (Data from: *The Statistical Abstract of the United States*: 2012.)

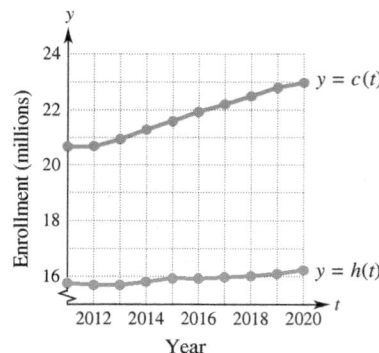

Year

(a) Find the projected average rate of change in college enrollment over the period 2016 to 2020.

(b) Find the projected average rate of change in high school enrollment over the period 2015 to 2016.

15. Business The accompanying figure shows the number of full-time employees of Apple, Inc. (in millions) as a function of the revenue generated by Apple, Inc. (in billions). Find and interpret the average rate of change of employees with respect to revenue for the following changes in revenue. (Data from: www.mergentonline.com.)

(a) $5 billion to $32 billion

(b) $32 billion to $108 billion

(c) $5 billion to $108 billion

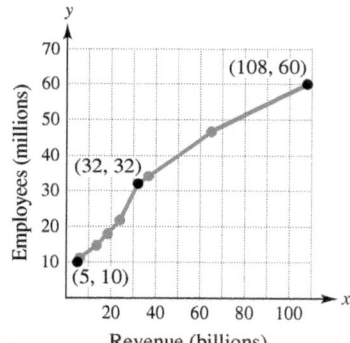

Revenue (billions)

16. Business The accompanying figure shows the number of privately owned housing units started (in thousands) in the United States. Find and interpret the average rate of change for each period. (Data from: *The Statistical Abstract of the United States*: 2012.)

(a) 2002 to 2006   (b) 2006 to 2008   (c) 2000 to 2010

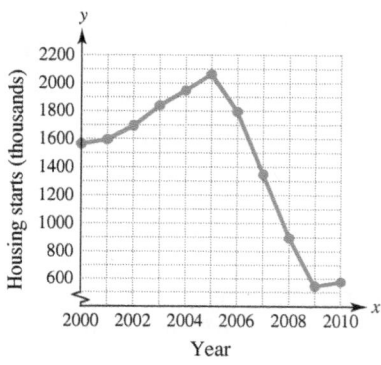

Year

17. Explain the difference between the average rate of change of $y = f(x)$ as x changes from a to b and the instantaneous rate of change of y at $x = a$.

18. If the instantaneous rate of change of $f(x)$ with respect to x is positive when $x = 1$, is f increasing or decreasing there?

Exercises 19–21 deal with a car moving along a straight road, as discussed on pages 596–597. At time t seconds, the distance of the car (in feet) from the starting point is $s(t) = 2.2t^2$. Find the instantaneous velocity of the car at

19. $t = 5$ **20.** $t = 20$

21. What was the average velocity of the car during the first 30 seconds?

An object moves along a straight line; its distance (in feet) from a fixed point at time t seconds is $s(t) = t^2 + 4t + 3$. Find the instantaneous velocity of the object at the given times. (See Example 3.)

22. $t = 6$ **23.** $t = 1$ **24.** $t = 10$

25. Physical Science A car is moving along a straight test track. The position (in feet) of the car, $s(t)$, at various times t is measured, with the following results:

t (seconds)	0	2	4	6	8	10
$s(t)$ (feet)	0	10	14	20	30	36

Find and interpret the average velocities for the following changes in t:

(a) 0 to 2 seconds;   (b) 2 to 4 seconds;

(c) 4 to 6 seconds;   (d) 6 to 8 seconds.

(e) Estimate the instantaneous velocity at 4 seconds

    (i) by using the formula for estimating the instantaneous rate (with $h = 2$) and

    (ii) by averaging the answers for the average velocity in the 2 seconds before and the 2 seconds afterwards (that is, the answers to parts (b) and (c)).

(f) Estimate the instantaneous velocity at 6 seconds, using the two methods in part (e).

In Exercises 26–30, find (a) $f(a + h)$; (b) $\dfrac{f(a + h) - f(a)}{h}$; (c) the instantaneous rate of change of f when $a = 5$. (See Examples 3–5.)

26. $f(x) = x^2 + x$ **27.** $f(x) = x^2 - x - 1$

28. $f(x) = x^2 + 2x + 2$ **29.** $f(x) = x^3$

30. $f(x) = x^3 - x$

Solve Exercises 31–34 by algebraic methods. (See Examples 3–5.)

31. Business The revenue (in thousands of dollars) from producing x units of an item is

$$R(x) = 10x - .002x^2.$$

(a) Find the average rate of change of revenue when production is increased from 1000 to 1001 units.

(b) Find the marginal revenue when 1000 units are produced.

(c) Find the additional revenue if production is increased from 1000 to 1001 units.

(d) Compare your answers for parts (a) and (c). What do you find?

32. Business Suppose customers in a hardware store are willing to buy $N(p)$ boxes of nails at p dollars per box, as given by

$$N(p) = 80 - 5p^2 \quad (1 \le p \le 4).$$

(a) Find the average rate of change of demand for a change in price from \$2 to \$3.

(b) Find the instantaneous rate of change of demand when the price is \$2.

(c) Find the instantaneous rate of change of demand when the price is \$3.

(d) As the price is increased from \$2 to \$3, how is demand changing? Is the change to be expected?

33. Health Epidemiologists in College Station, Texas, estimate that t days after the flu begins to spread in town, the percentage of the population infected by the flu is approximated by

$$p(t) = t^2 + t \quad (0 \le t \le 5).$$

(a) Find the average rate of change of p with respect to t over the interval from 1 to 4 days.

(b) Find the instantaneous rate of change of p with respect to t at $t = 3$.

34. Health The maximum recommended heart rate (in beats per minute) is given by $h(x) = 220 - x$ where x represents the age of the individual. (Data from: American Heart Association.)

(a) Find and interpret the average rate of change of $h(x)$ with respect to x for $18 \le x \le 28$ years.

(b) Find and interpret the instantaneous rate of change of $h(x)$ with respect to x at $x = 23$ years.

(c) Explain why your answers in parts (a) and (b) are the same in this case.

Use technology to work Exercises 35–38. (See Example 6.)

35. Social Science The number of bachelor's degrees (in thousands) earned in the social sciences and history in year x can be approximated by $f(x) = 24 \ln x + 117$, where $x = 3$ corresponds to the year 2003. Estimate the rate at which the number of social science and history degrees was changing in the given year. (Data from: *The Statistical Abstract of the United States*: 2012.)

(a) 2004   **(b)** 2012

36. Business The amount of revenue (in billions of dollars) generated by the bookstore industry in year x can be approximated by $f(x) = -.1x^2 + 1.22x + 3.47$, where $x = 0$ corresponds to the year 2000. Estimate the rate at which revenue was changing in the given year. (Data from: *The Statistical Abstract of the United States*: 2012.)

(a) 2006   **(b)** 2011

37. Health The metabolic rate of a person who has just eaten a meal tends to go up and then, after some time has passed, returns to a resting metabolic rate. This phenomenon is known as the *thermic effect of food*. Researchers have indicated that the thermic effect of food (in kJ/hr) for a particular person is

$$F(t) = -10.28 + 175.9te^{-t/1.3},$$

where t is the number of hours that have elapsed since eating a meal.*

(a) Graph the given function in a window with $0 \le x \le 6$ and $-20 \le y \le 100$.

(b) Find the average rate of change of the thermic effect of food during the first hour after eating.

(c) Use a graphing calculator to find the instantaneous rate of change of the thermic effect of food exactly 1 hour after eating.

(d) Use a graphing calculator to estimate when the function stops increasing and begins to decrease.

38. Health The mesiodistal crown length (as shown in the accompanying diagram) of deciduous mandibular first molars in fetuses is related to the postconception age of the tooth as

$$L(t) = -.01t^2 + .788t - 7.048,$$

where $L(t)$ is the crown length, in millimeters, of the molar t weeks after conception.†

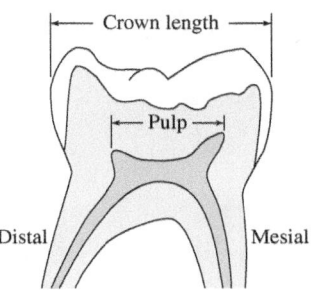

(a) Find the average rate of growth in mesiodistal crown length during weeks 22 through 28.

(b) Find the instantaneous rate of growth in mesiodistal crown length when the tooth is exactly 22 weeks of age.

(c) Graph the given function in a window with $0 \le x \le 50$ and $0 \le y \le 9$.

(d) Does a function that increases and then begins to decrease make sense for this particular application? What do you suppose is happening during the first 11 weeks? Does this function accurately model crown length during those weeks?

✓ Checkpoint Answers

1. (a) 64 mph   **(b)** $\dfrac{f(r) - f(s)}{r - s}$ mph

2. (a) 8   **(b)** 13

3. (a) Changing at the average rate of 250 index points per year

    (b) Changing at the average rate of -49 index points per year

4. (a) 6 ft per second   **(b)** 10 ft per second

5. The velocity is .3 millimeter per second.

*Reed, G. and J. Hill, "Measuring the Thermic Effect of Food," *American Journal of Clinical Nutrition*, Vol. 63, 1996, pp. 164–169.)

†Harris, E. F., J. D. Hicks, and B. D. Barcroft, "Tissue Contributions to Sex and Race: Differences in Tooth Crown Size of Deciduous Molars," *American Journal of Physical Anthropology*, Vol. 115, 2001, pp. 223–237.

11.4 Tangent Lines and Derivatives

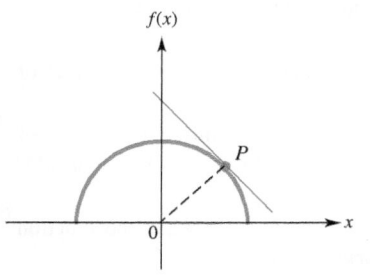

f(x)

Figure 11.21

We now develop a geometric interpretation of the rates of change considered in the previous section. In geometry, a tangent line to a circle at a point P is defined to be the line through P that is perpendicular to the radius OP, as in Figure 11.21 (which shows only the top half of the circle). If you think of this circle as a road on which you are driving at night, then the tangent line indicates the direction of the light beam from your headlights as you pass through the point P. This analogy suggests a way of extending the idea of a tangent line to any curve: the tangent line to the curve at a point P indicates the "direction" of the curve as it passes through P. Using this intuitive idea of direction, we see, for example, that the lines through P_1 and P_3 in Figure 11.22 appear to be tangent lines, whereas the lines through P_2 and P_4 do not.

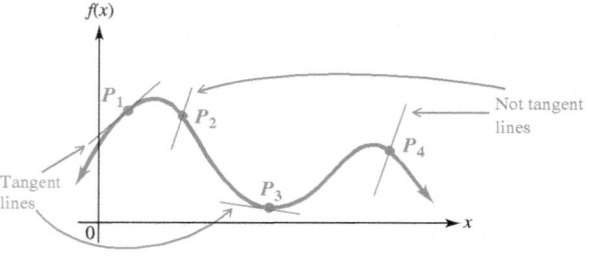

Figure 11.22

We can use these ideas to develop a precise definition of the tangent line to the graph of a function f at the point R. As shown in Figure 11.23, choose a second point S on the graph and draw the line through R and S; this line is called a **secant line.** You can think of this secant line as a rough approximation of the tangent line.

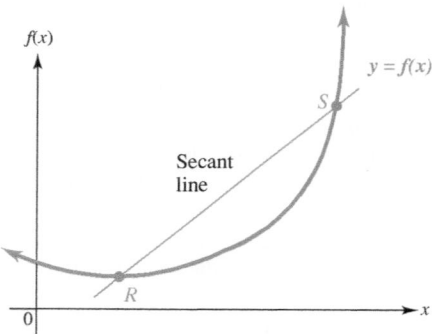

Figure 11.23

Now suppose that the point S slides down the curve closer to R. Figure 11.24 on the next page shows successive positions S_2, S_3, and S_4 of the point S. The closer S gets to R, the better the secant line RS approximates our intuitive idea of the tangent line at R.

In particular, the closer S gets to R, the closer the slope of the secant line gets to the slope of the tangent line. Informally, we say that

the slope of tangent line at R = the limit of the slope of secant line RS as
S gets closer and closer to R.

In order to make this statement more precise, suppose the first coordinate of R is a. Then the first coordinate of S can be written as $a + h$ for some number h. (In Figure 11.24, h is the distance on the x-axis between the two first coordinates.) Thus, R has coordinates

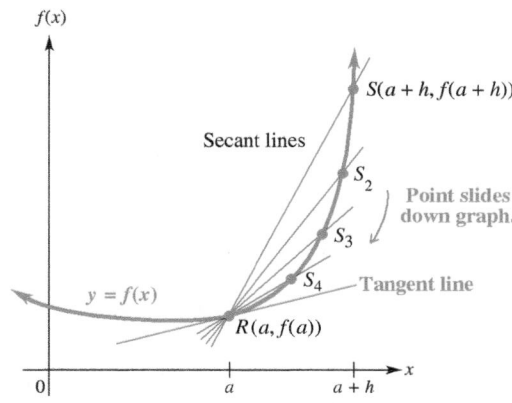

Figure 11.24

$(a, f(a))$ and S has coordinates $(a + h, f(a + h))$, as shown in Figure 11.24. Consequently, the slope of the secant line RS is

$$\frac{f(a + h) - f(a)}{(a + h) - a} = \frac{f(a + h) - f(a)}{h}.$$

Now, as S moves closer to R, their first coordinates move closer to each other, that is, h gets smaller and smaller. Hence,

$$\text{slope of tangent line at } R = \text{limit of slope of secant line } RS$$
$$\text{as } S \text{ gets closer and closer to } R$$
$$= \text{limit of } \frac{f(a + h) - f(a)}{h}$$
$$\text{as } h \text{ gets closer and closer to } 0$$
$$= \lim_{h \to 0} \frac{f(a + h) - f(a)}{h}.$$

This intuitive development suggests the following formal definition.

Tangent Line

The **tangent line** to the graph of $y = f(x)$ at the point $(a, f(a))$ is the line through this point having slope

$$\lim_{h \to 0} \frac{f(a + h) - f(a)}{h},$$

provided that this limit exists. If this limit does not exist, then there is no tangent line at the point.

The slope of the tangent line at a point is also called the **slope of the curve** at that point. Since the slope of a line indicates its direction (see the table on page 78), the slope of the tangent line at a point indicates the direction of the curve at that point. For a review of slope and equations of lines, see Section 2.2.

Example 1 Consider the graph of $y = x^2 + 2$.

(a) Find the slope of the tangent line to the graph when $x = -1$.

Solution Use the preceding definition with $f(x) = x^2 + 2$ and $a = -1$. The slope of the tangent line is calculated as follows:

$$\text{Slope of tangent} = \lim_{h \to 0} \frac{f(a + h) - f(a)}{h}$$

$$= \lim_{h \to 0} \frac{[(-1 + h)^2 + 2] - [(-1)^2 + 2]}{h}$$

$$= \lim_{h \to 0} \frac{[1 - 2h + h^2 + 2] - [1 + 2]}{h}$$

$$= \lim_{h \to 0} \frac{-2h + h^2}{h} = \lim_{h \to 0} (-2 + h) = -2.$$

So the slope of the tangent line is -2.

(b) Find the equation of the tangent line.

Solution When $x = -1$, then $y = (-1)^2 + 2 = 3$. So the tangent line passes through the point $(-1, 3)$ and has slope -2. Its equation can be found with the point–slope form of the equation of a line (see Chapter 2):

$y - y_1 = m(x - x_1)$	Point-slope form
$y - 3 = -2[x - (-1)]$	Substitute.
$y - 3 = -2(x + 1)$	Simplify.
$y - 3 = -2x - 2$	Distributive property
$y = -2x + 1.$	Solve for y.

Figure 11.25 shows a graph of $f(x) = x^2 + 2$ along with a graph of the tangent line at $x = -1$.

 Checkpoint 1

Let $f(x) = x^2 + 2$.
Find the equation of the tangent line to the graph at the point where $x = 1$.

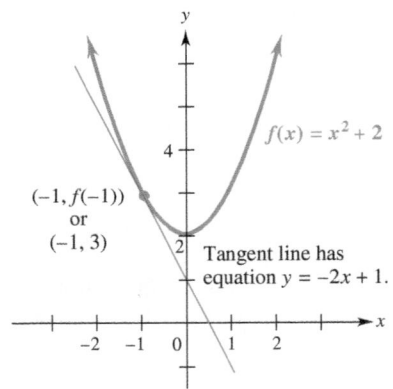

$f(x) = x^2 + 2$

$(-1, f(-1))$
or
$(-1, 3)$

Tangent line has
equation $y = -2x + 1$.

Figure 11.25

TECHNOLOGY TIP When finding the equation of a tangent line algebraically, you can confirm your answer with a graphing calculator by graphing both the function and the tangent line on the same screen to see if the tangent line appears to be correct.

Once a function has been graphed, many graphing calculators can draw the tangent line at any specified point. Most also display the slope of the tangent line, and some actually display its equation. Look for TANGENT or TANLN in the MATH, DRAW, or SKETCH menu.

 Checkpoint 2

Use a graphing calculator to confirm your answer to Checkpoint 1 by graphing $f(x) = x^2 + 2$ and the tangent line at the point where $x = 1$ on the same screen.

In Figure 11.25, the tangent line $y = -2x + 1$ appears to coincide with the graph of $f(x) = x^2 + 2$ near the point $(-1, 3)$. This becomes more obvious when both $f(x)$ and the tangent line are graphed in a very small window on a graphing calculator (Figure 11.26). The graph and the tangent line now appear virtually identical near $(-1, 3)$. The table of values in Figure 11.27 (in which Y_1 is $f(x)$ and Y_2 the tangent line) confirms the fact that the tangent line is a good approximation of the function when x is very close to -1.

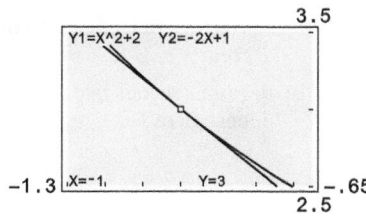

X	Y1	Y2
-1.1	3.21	3.2
-1.05	3.1025	3.1
-1.02	3.0404	3.04
-1	3	3
-.97	2.9409	2.94
-.94	2.8836	2.88
-.9	2.81	2.8

X=-.9

Figure 11.26   **Figure 11.27**

The same thing is true in the general case.

Tangent Line

If it exists, the tangent line to the graph of a function f at $x = a$ is a good approximation of the function f near $x = a$.

Suppose the graph of a function f is a straight line. The fact in the preceding box suggests that the tangent line to f at any point should be the graph of f itself (because it is certainly the best possible linear approximation of f). The next example shows that this is indeed the case.

Example 2   Let a be any real number. Find the equation of the tangent line to the graph of $f(x) = 7x + 3$ at the point where $x = a$.

Solution   According to the definition, the slope of the tangent line is

$$\lim_{h \to 0} \frac{f(a + h) - f(a)}{h} = \lim_{h \to 0} \frac{[7(a + h) + 3] - [7a + 3]}{h}$$

$$= \lim_{h \to 0} \frac{[7a + 7h + 3] - 7a - 3}{h}$$

$$= \lim_{h \to 0} \frac{7h}{h} = \lim_{h \to 0} 7 = 7.$$

Hence, the equation of the tangent line at the point $(a, f(a))$ is

$$y - y_1 = m(x - x_1)$$
$$y - f(a) = 7(x - a)$$
$$y = 7x - 7a + \overbrace{f(a)}$$
$$y = 7x - 7a + 7a + 3$$
$$y = 7x + 3.$$

Thus, the tangent line *is* the graph of $f(x) = 7x + 3$.

Secant lines and tangent lines (or, more precisely, their slopes) are the geometric analogues of the average and instantaneous rates of change studied in the previous section, as summarized in the following chart:

Quantity	Algebraic Interpretation	Geometric Interpretation
$\dfrac{f(a + h) - f(a)}{h}$	Average rate of change of f from $x = a$ to $x = a + h$	Slope of the secant line through $(a, f(a))$ and $(a + h, f(a + h))$
$\lim\limits_{h \to 0} \dfrac{f(a + h) - f(a)}{h}$	Instantaneous rate of change of f at $x = a$	Slope of the tangent line to the graph of f at $(a, f(a))$

The Derivative

If $y = f(x)$ is a function and a is a number in its domain, then we shall use the symbol $f'(a)$ to denote the special limit

$$\lim_{h \to 0} \frac{f(a + h) - f(a)}{h},$$

provided that it exists. In other words, to each number a, we can assign the number $f'(a)$ obtained by calculating the preceding limit. This process defines an important new function.

Derivative

The **derivative** of the function f is the function denoted f' whose value at the number x is defined to be the number

$$f'(x) = \lim_{h \to 0} \frac{f(x + h) - f(x)}{h},$$

provided that this limit exists.

The derivative function f' has as its domain all the points at which the specified limit exists, and the value of the derivative function at the number x is the number $f'(x)$. Using x instead of a here is similar to the way that $g(x) = 2x$ denotes the function that assigns to each number a the number $2a$.

If $y = f(x)$ is a function, then its derivative is denoted either by f' or by y'. If x is a number in the domain of $y = f(x)$ such that $y' = f'(x)$ is defined, then the function f is said to be **differentiable** at x. The process that produces the function f' from the function f is called **differentiation.**

The derivative function may be interpreted in many ways, two of which were already discussed:

1. The derivative function f' gives the *instantaneous rate of change* of $y = f(x)$ with respect to x. This instantaneous rate of change can be interpreted as marginal cost, marginal revenue, or marginal profit (if the original function represents cost, revenue, or profit, respectively) or as velocity (if the original function represents displacement along a line). From now on, we will use "rate of change" to mean "instantaneous rate of change."

2. The derivative function f' gives the *slope* of the graph of f at any point. If the derivative is evaluated at $x = a$, then $f'(a)$ is the slope of the tangent line to the curve at the point $(a, f(a))$.

Example 3   Use the graph of the function $f(x)$ in Figure 11.28 to answer the given questions.

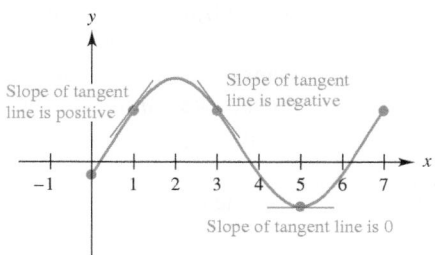

Figure 11.28

(a) Is $f'(3)$ positive or negative?

Solution   We know that $f'(3)$ is the slope of the tangent line to the graph at the point where $x = 3$. Figure 11.28 shows that this tangent line slants downward from left to right, meaning that its slope is negative. Hence, $f'(3) < 0$.

(b) Which is larger, $f'(1)$ or $f'(5)$?

Solution   Figure 11.28 shows that the tangent line to the graph at the point where $x = 1$ slants upward from left to right, meaning that its slope, $f'(1)$, is a positive number. The tangent line at the point where $x = 5$ is horizontal, so that it has slope 0. (That is, $f'(5) = 0$). Therefore, $f'(1) > f'(5)$.

(c) For what values of x is $f'(x)$ positive?

Solution   On the graph, find the points where the tangent line has positive slope (slants upward from left to right). At each such point, $f'(x) > 0$. Figure 11.28 shows that this occurs when $0 < x < 2$ and when $5 < x < 7$. ✔3

✔**Checkpoint 3**

The graph of a function g is shown. Determine whether the given numbers are positive, negative, or zero.

(a) $g'(0)$

(b) $g'(-1)$

(c) $g'(3)$

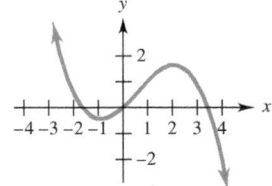

Example 4   **Natural Science**   A student brings a cold soft drink to a 50-minute math class but is too busy during class to drink it. If $C(t)$ represents the temperature of the soft drink (in degrees Fahrenheit) t minutes after the start of class, interpret the meaning of the following statements, including units.

(a) Interpret $C(0) = 38$.

Solution   Since $C(t)$ represents the temperature of the drink at time t, $C(0) = 38$ means that the temperature of the drink was 38°F at the start of class.

(b) Interpret $C(50) - C(0) = 30$.

Solution   Since $C(b) - C(a)$ represents the change in temperature from time $t = a$ to time $t = b$ minutes, $C(50) - C(0) = 30$ means that the drink warmed up by 30°F between the start and end of class.

(c) Interpret $\dfrac{C(50) - C(0)}{50 - 0} = .6$.

Solution   Since $\dfrac{C(b) - C(a)}{b - a}$ represents the average rate of change of $C(t)$ from time $t = a$ to time $t = b$ minutes, $\dfrac{C(50) - C(0)}{50 - 0} = .6$ means that the drink warmed up at an average rate of .6°F per minute during class.

(d) Interpret $C'(0) = 1.5$.

Solution Since $C'(t)$ represents the instantaneous rate of change of the temperature of the drink with respect to time, $C'(0) = 1.5$ means that, at the start of the class, the temperature is changing at an instantaneous rate of 1.5°F per minute. Since the average rate of change over a very small time interval is a good *approximation* of the instantaneous rate of change, we can think of $C'(0) = 1.5$ as saying that, at the start of class, the drink will warm up by *approximately* 1.5°F in the next minute. ✔️4

The rule of a derivative function can be found by using the definition of the derivative and the following four-step procedure.

✔ **Checkpoint 4**

For the function $C(t)$ in Example 4, interpret the following, including units.

(a) $C(50) = 68$

(b) $C(50) - C(25) = 7.6$

(c) $\dfrac{C(50) - C(25)}{50 - 25} = .3$

(d) $C'(50) = .2$

Finding $f'(x)$ from the Definition of the Derivative

Step 1 Find $f(x + h)$.

Step 2 Find $f(x + h) - f(x)$.

Step 3 Divide by h to get $\dfrac{f(x + h) - f(x)}{h}$.

Step 4 Treat x as a constant and let $h \to 0$.

$$f'(x) = \lim_{h \to 0} \frac{f(x + h) - f(x)}{h} \text{ if this limit exists.}$$

Example 5 Let $f(x) = x^3 - 4x$.

(a) Find the derivative $f'(x)$.

Solution By definition,

$$f'(x) = \lim_{h \to 0} \frac{f(x + h) - f(x)}{h}.$$

Step 1 Find $f(x + h)$.
Replace x with $x + h$ in the rule of $f(x)$:

$$f(x) = x^3 - 4x$$
$$f(x + h) = (x + h)^3 - 4(x + h)$$
$$= (x^3 + 3x^2h + 3xh^2 + h^3) - 4(x + h)$$
$$= x^3 + 3x^2h + 3xh^2 + h^3 - 4x - 4h.$$

Step 2 Find $f(x + h) - f(x)$.
Since $f(x) = x^3 - 4x$,

$$f(x + h) - f(x) = (x^3 + 3x^2h + 3xh^2 + h^3 - 4x - 4h) - (x^3 - 4x)$$
$$= x^3 + 3x^2h + 3xh^2 + h^3 - 4x - 4h - x^3 + 4x$$
$$= 3x^2h + 3xh^2 + h^3 - 4h.$$

Step 3 Form and simplify the quotient $\dfrac{f(x + h) - f(x)}{h}$:

$$\frac{f(x + h) - f(x)}{h} = \frac{3x^2h + 3xh^2 + h^3 - 4h}{h}$$
$$= \frac{h(3x^2 + 3xh + h^2 - 4)}{h}$$
$$= 3x^2 + 3xh + h^2 - 4.$$

Step 4   Find the limit as h approaches 0 of the result in Step 3, treating x as a constant:

$$f'(x) = \lim_{h \to 0} \frac{f(x+h) - f(x)}{h} = \lim_{h \to 0} (3x^2 + 3xh + h^2 - 4)$$

$$= 3x^2 - 4.$$

Therefore, the derivative of $f(x) = x^3 - 4x$ is $f'(x) = 3x^2 - 4$.

(b) Calculate and interpret $f'(1)$.

Solution   The procedure in part (a) works for *every* x and $f'(x) = 3x^2 - 4$. Hence, when $x = 1$,

$$f'(1) = 3 \cdot 1^2 - 4 = -1.$$

The number -1 is the slope of the tangent line to the graph of $f(x) = x^3 - 4x$ at the point where $x = 1$ (that is, at $(1, f(1)) = (1, -3)$).

(c) Find the equation of the tangent line to the graph of $f(x) = x^3 - 4x$ at the point where $x = 1$.

Solution   By part (b), the point on the graph where $x = 1$ is $(1, -3)$, and the slope of the tangent line is $f'(1) = -1$. Therefore, the equation is

$$y - (-3) = (-1)(x - 1) \qquad \text{Point–slope form}$$

$$y = -x - 2. \qquad \text{Slope–intercept form}$$

Both $f(x)$ and the tangent line are shown in Figure 11.29. ✓ 5

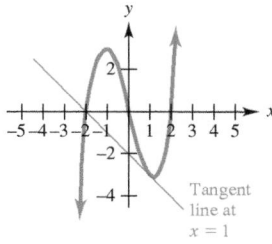

Figure 11.29

✓ **Checkpoint 5**

Let $f(x) = -5x^2 + 4$. Find the given expressions.

(a) $f(x + h)$

(b) $f(x + h) - f(x)$

(c) $\dfrac{f(x + h) - f(x)}{h}$

(d) $f'(x)$

(e) $f'(3)$

(f) $f'(0)$

⊘ **CAUTION**

1. In Example 5(a), note that $f(x + h) \neq f(x) + h$ because, by Step 1,

$$f(x + h) = x^3 + 3x^2 h + 3xh^2 + h^3 - 4x - 4h,$$

but

$$f(x) + h = (x^3 - 4x) + h = x^3 - 4x + h.$$

2. In Example 5(b), do not confuse $f(1)$ and $f'(1)$. $f(1)$ is the value of the original function $f(x) = x^3 - 4x$ at $x = 1$, namely, -3, whereas $f'(1)$ is the value of the derivative function $f'(x) = 3x^2 - 4$ at $x = 1$, namely, -1.

Example 6   Let $f(x) = 1/x$. Find $f'(x)$.

Solution

Step 1 $f(x + h) = \dfrac{1}{x + h}$.

Step 2 $f(x + h) - f(x) = \dfrac{1}{x + h} - \dfrac{1}{x}$

$$= \frac{x - (x + h)}{x(x + h)} \qquad \text{Find a common denominator.}$$

$$= \frac{x - x - h}{x(x + h)} \qquad \text{Simplify the numerator.}$$

$$= \frac{-h}{x(x + h)}.$$

Step 3 $\dfrac{f(x + h) - f(x)}{h} = \dfrac{\dfrac{-h}{x(x + h)}}{h}$

$= \dfrac{-h}{x(x + h)} \cdot \dfrac{1}{h}$ Invert and multiply.

$= \dfrac{-1}{x(x + h)}.$

Step 4 $f'(x) = \lim\limits_{h \to 0} \dfrac{f(x + h) - f(x)}{h} = \lim\limits_{h \to 0} \dfrac{-1}{x(x + h)}$

$= \dfrac{-1}{x(x + 0)} = \dfrac{-1}{x(x)} = \dfrac{-1}{x^2}.$ ✓6

✓**Checkpoint 6**

Let $f(x) = -5/x$. Find the given expressions.

(a) $f(x + h)$

(b) $f(x + h) - f(x)$

(c) $\dfrac{f(x + h) - f(x)}{h}$

(d) $f'(x)$

(e) $f'(-1)$

Example 7   Let $g(x) = \sqrt{x}$. Find $g'(x)$.

Solution

Step 1 $g(x + h) = \sqrt{x + h}.$

Step 2 $g(x + h) - g(x) = \sqrt{x + h} - \sqrt{x}.$

Step 3 $\dfrac{g(x + h) - g(x)}{h} = \dfrac{\sqrt{x + h} - \sqrt{x}}{h}.$

At this point, in order to be able to divide by h, multiply both numerator and denominator by $\sqrt{x + h} + \sqrt{x}$, that is, rationalize the *numerator*:

$\dfrac{g(x + h) - g(x)}{h} = \dfrac{\sqrt{x + h} - \sqrt{x}}{h} \cdot \dfrac{\sqrt{x + h} + \sqrt{x}}{\sqrt{x + h} + \sqrt{x}}$

$= \dfrac{(\sqrt{x + h})^2 - (\sqrt{x})^2}{h(\sqrt{x + h} + \sqrt{x})}$

$= \dfrac{x + h - x}{h(\sqrt{x + h} + \sqrt{x})} = \dfrac{1}{\sqrt{x + h} + \sqrt{x}}.$

Step 4 $g'(x) = \lim\limits_{h \to 0} \dfrac{1}{\sqrt{x + h} + \sqrt{x}} = \dfrac{1}{\sqrt{x} + \sqrt{x}} = \dfrac{1}{2\sqrt{x}}.$

Example 8   **Business**   A sales representative for a textbook-publishing company frequently makes a 4-hour drive from her home in a large city to a university in another city. Let $s(t)$ represent her position t hours into the trip (where position is measured in miles on the highway, with position 0 corresponding to her home). Then $s(t)$ is given by

$$s(t) = -5t^3 + 30t^2.$$

(a) How far from home will she be after 1 hour? after $1\frac{1}{2}$ hours?

Solution   Her distance from home after 1 hour is

$$s(1) = -5(1)^3 + 30(1)^2 = 25,$$

or 25 miles. After $1\frac{1}{2}$ (or $\frac{3}{2}$) hours, it is

$$s\left(\frac{3}{2}\right) = -5\left(\frac{3}{2}\right)^3 + 30\left(\frac{3}{2}\right)^2 = \frac{405}{8} = 50.625,$$

or 50.625 miles.

Therefore, there is no derivative at 0. However, the derivative of $f(x) = |x|$ *does* exist for all values of x other than 0.

Since a vertical line has an undefined slope, the derivative cannot exist at any point where the tangent line is vertical, as at x_5 in Figure 11.31. This figure summarizes various ways that a derivative can fail to exist.

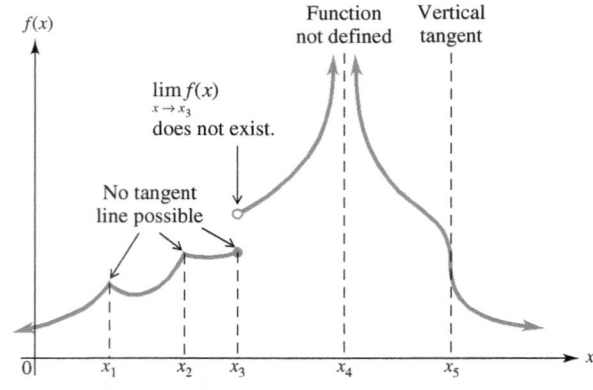

Figure 11.31

⭐ Derivatives and Technology

Many computer programs (such as Mathematica and Maple) and a few graphing calculators (such as the TI-89) can find symbolic formulas for the derivatives of most functions. Although other graphing calculators cannot find the rule of a derivative function, most of them can approximate the numerical value of the derivative function at any number where it is defined by using the **numerical derivative** feature. (See Exercise 50 at the end of this section for an explanation of computational technique used by the numerical derivative feature.)

⭐ **Example 9**   **Social Science** A psychology experiment found that the number of facts $N(t)$ remembered t days after the facts were memorized was given by

$$N(t) = \frac{10.003}{1 + .0003e^{.8t}}.$$

Use a graphing calculator to find an approximate value of $N'(10)$ and interpret the answer.

Solution   The numerical derivative feature is labeled nDeriv, or d/dx, or nDer and is usually in the MATH or CALC menu or one of its submenus. Most calculators require that we use x as the independent variable instead of t, so we will write the function as $N(x) = \frac{10.003}{1 + .0003e^{.8x}}$. Check your instruction manual for the correct syntax, but on many graphing calculators, entering either

$$\text{nDeriv}(10.003/(1 + .0003e^{.8x}), x, 10) \quad \text{or}$$
$$\text{d/dx}(10.003/(1 + .0003e^{.8x}), x, 10)$$

produces an (approximate) value of $N'(10)$. Answers will vary slightly depending on the calculator, but you are likely to get an answer close to -1.9943694066.

The negative sign implies that the number of facts remembered is decreasing over time. One interpretation of $N'(10) \approx -2$ is that 10 days after the facts were memorized, they are being forgotten at a rate of about 2 facts per day. In other words, 10 days after the facts were memorized, approximately 2 facts will be forgotten during the next day. ✓8

✓ **Checkpoint 8**

If $f(x) = x^{2/3} - 8x^3 + 4^x$, use a graphing calculator to find the (approximate) value of

(a) $f'(2)$;

(b) $f'(3.2)$.

TECHNOLOGY TIP On many graphing calculators, if you have the function $f(x)$ stored in the function memory as, say, Y_1, you can use Y_1 with the nDeriv key instead of typing in the rule of $f(x)$.

Example 10 **Finance** If \$15,000 is deposited in a money market account that pays 1.2% per year compounded monthly, then the amount in the account after n months is

$$A(n) = 15{,}000\left(1 + \frac{.012}{12}\right)^n = 15{,}000(1.001)^n.$$

Use a graphing calculator to find an approximate value of $A'(120)$ and interpret the answer.

Solution Using the numerical derivative feature on a typical graphing calculator gives an approximate value of $A'(120) = 16.90$. This means that at time $t = 120$ months, the instantaneous rate of change of the account balance with respect to time is 16.90 dollars per month. We can also describe this by saying that 10 years (120 months) after making the deposit, the balance on the account will increase by *approximately* \$16.90 in the next month. Note that the *actual* change in the balance over the next one month is given by:

$$A(121) - A(120) = 15{,}000(1.001)^{121} - 15{,}000(1.001)^{120} = \$16.91. \quad \text{✓}_9$$

✓ **Checkpoint 9**

For the account in Example 10, suppose that one year has passed since the initial deposit. Use a derivative to approximate how much the balance will change in the next month.

⊙ CAUTION Because of the approximation methods used, the nDeriv key may display an answer at numbers where the derivative is not defined. For instance, we saw earlier that the derivative of $f(x) = |x|$ is not defined when $x = 0$, but the nDeriv key on most calculators produces 1 or 0 or -1 as $f'(0)$.

11.4 Exercises

Find $f'(x)$ for each function. Then find $f'(2)$, $f'(0)$, and $f'(-3)$. (See Examples 5–7.)

1. $f(x) = 8x + 6$
2. $f(x) = 9 - 2x$
3. $f(x) = -4x^2 + 11x$
4. $f(x) = x^2 - 3x + 7$
5. $f(x) = x^3$
6. $f(x) = x^3 - 6x$
7. $f(x) = \dfrac{-2}{x}$
8. $f(x) = \dfrac{4}{x-1}$
9. $f(x) = 2\sqrt{x}$
10. $f(x) = 4\sqrt{x}$

The derivatives of each of the given functions were found in Examples 5–8. Use them to find the equation of the tangent line to the graph of the function at the given point. (See Examples 1 and 2.)

11. $g(x) = \sqrt{x}$ at $x = 9$
12. $f(x) = x^3 - 4x$ at $x = 2$
13. $f(x) = 1/x$ at $x = -2$
14. $s(t) = -5t^3 + 30t^2$ at $t = 2$

For each of the given functions, (a) find the slope of the tangent line to the graph at the given point; (b) find the equation of the tangent line. (See Examples 1 and 2.)

15. $f(x) = x^2 + 3$ at $x = 2$
16. $g(x) = 1 - 2x^2$ at $x = -1$
17. $h(x) = \dfrac{7}{x}$ at $x = 3$
18. $f(x) = \dfrac{-3}{x}$ at $x = -4$
19. $g(x) = 5\sqrt{x}$ at $x = 9$
20. $g(x) = \sqrt{x+1}$ at $x = 15$ (*Hint:* In Step 3, multiply numerator and denominator by $\sqrt{15 + h} + \sqrt{15}$.)

Use the fact that $f'(c)$ is the slope of the tangent line to the graph of $f(x)$ at $x = c$ to work these exercises. (See Example 3.)

21. In the graph on the next page of the function f, at which of the labeled x-values is
    (a) $f(x)$ the largest?
    (b) $f(x)$ the smallest?
    (c) $f'(x)$ the smallest?
    (d) $f'(x)$ the closest to 0?

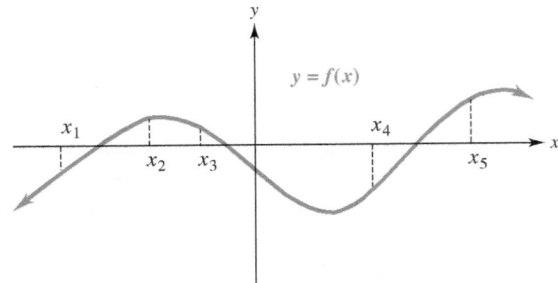

22. Sketch the graph of the *derivative* of the function g whose graph is shown. (*Hint:* Consider the slope of the tangent line at each point along the graph of g. Are there any points where there is no tangent line?)

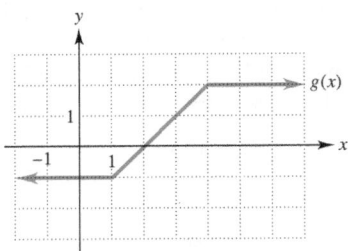

23. Sketch the graph of a function g with the property that $g'(x) > 0$ for $x < 0$ and $g'(x) < 0$ for $x > 0$. Many correct answers are possible.

24. **Physical Science** The accompanying graph shows the temperature in an oven during a self-cleaning cycle.[*] (The open circles on the graph are not points of discontinuity, but merely the times when the thermal door lock turns on and off.) The oven temperature is 100° when the cycle begins and 600° after half an hour. Let $T(x)$ be the temperature (in degrees Fahrenheit) after x hours.

(a) Find and interpret $T'(.5)$.

(b) Find and interpret $T'(2)$.

(c) Find and interpret $T'(3.5)$.

25. At what x-values does the derivative of the function graphed in Exercise 24 fail to exist?

26. **Health** The graph shows how the risk of coronary heart attack (CHA) rises as blood cholesterol increases.[†]

(a) Approximate the average rate of change of the risk of coronary heart attack as blood cholesterol goes from 100 to 300 mg/dL.

(b) Is the rate of change when blood cholesterol is 100 mg/dL higher or lower than the average rate of change in part (a)? What feature of the graph shows this?

(c) Do part (b) when blood cholesterol is 300 mg/dL.

(d) Do part (b) when blood cholesterol is 200 mg/dL.

In Exercises 27 and 28, tell which graph, (a) or (b), represents velocity and which represents distance from a starting point. (Hint: Consider where the derivative is zero, positive, or negative.)

27. (a)

(b)

28. (a)

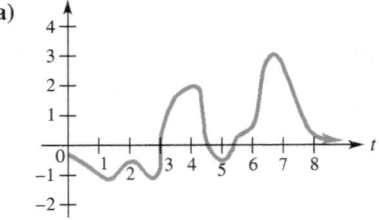

[†]John C. LaRosa, et al., "The Cholesterol Facts: A Joint Statement by the American Heart Association and the National Heart, Lung, and Blood Institute," *Circulation* 81, no. 5 (May 1990): 1722.

[*]*Whirlpool Use and Care Guide, Self-Cleaning Electric Range.*

(b)

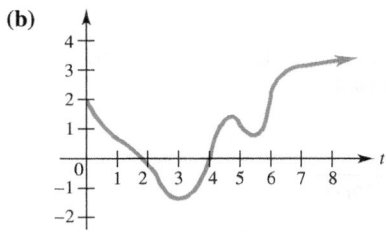

Find all points where the functions whose graphs are shown do not have derivatives. (See Figure 11.31 and the preceding discussion.)

29.

30.

31.

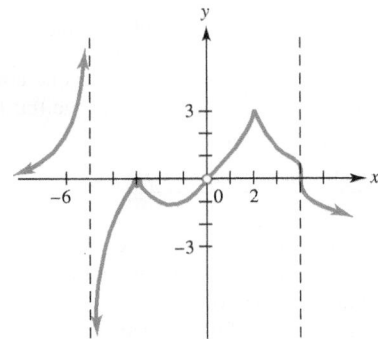

32. (a) Sketch the graph of $g(x) = \sqrt[3]{x}$ for $-1 \le x \le 1$.

(b) Explain why the derivative of $g(x)$ is not defined at $x = 0$. (*Hint:* What is the slope of the tangent line at $x = 0$?)

Work these exercises. (See Example 4.)

33. Natural Science A tourist drops a stone off the Cliffs of Moher, Ireland and it falls into the Atlantic Ocean. Let $s(t)$ represent the position of the stone (in feet above sea level) t seconds after it was dropped. Explain what the equations $s(7) = 0$ and $s'(7) = -224$ mean in practical terms.

34. Natural Science Kayakers like to paddle Slippery Rock Creek, Pennsylvania when the river is at a safe level between 1 and 4 feet high (the river level is measured at a fixed location). Let $H(t)$ represent yesterday's river level (in feet) t hours after midnight. Due to a flash flood, it happened that $H(13) = 3.5$ and $H'(13) = 3$. Explain what this means in practical terms for a kayaker.

35. Natural Science On a hiking trail up Mount LeConte, Tennessee, the trailhead has an elevation of 3830 feet and the summit has an elevation of 6953 feet (above sea level). Let $T(x)$ represent the record high temperature on the trail (in degrees Fahrenheit) at an elevation x feet above sea level.

(a) What are the units for $T'(x)$?

(b) Would you expect the sign of $T'(x)$ to be positive, negative, or zero? Why?

36. Social Science A polling firm determines that the percent of likely voters who support a certain mayoral candidate can be represented by a function $P(t)$ where t is measured in weeks since the candidate entered the race. Interpret the given equations, including units.

(a) $P'(2) = .5$ **(b)** $P'(6) = 3$

37. Finance You plan to take out a 30-year fixed-rate mortgage for $300,000. Let $P(r)$ be your monthly payment if the interest rate is r% per year, compounded monthly. Interpret the given equations, including units.

(a) $P(5) = 1,610.46$ **(b)** $P'(5) = 183.37$

38. Finance You plan to take out a 30-year fixed-rate mortgage at an interest rate of 5.25% per year, compounded monthly. Let $P(A)$ be your monthly payment if A is the initial amount of the loan. Would you expect the sign of $P'(A)$ to be positive, negative, or zero? Why?

39. Finance You plan to take out a 30-year fixed-rate mortgage and you want your monthly payment to be $1200. The amount of the loan you can afford depends on the interest rate you will have to pay. Let $A(r)$ be the amount of the money you can borrow if the interest rate is r% per year, compounded monthly. Interpret the given equations, including units.

(a) $A(5) = 223,537.94$ **(b)** $A'(5) = -25,449.21$

40. Finance A credit card statement includes information on how long it will take to pay off the card if you make only the minimum payments and how long it will take if you make larger payments. Let $M(p)$ represent the number of months it will take to pay off your credit card if you make a monthly payment of $$p$ (assuming no additional charges are made).

(a) Explain what $M(25) = 50$ means.

(b) Would you expect $M'(p)$ to be positive, negative, or zero? Why?

(c) What are the units for $M'(p)$?

(d) Explain what $M'(25) = -3$ means.

41. Natural Science In one research study, the population of a certain shellfish in an area at time t was closely approximated by the accompanying graph. Estimate and interpret the derivative at each of the marked points.

42. Health The eating behavior of a typical human during a meal can be described by

$$I(t) = 27 + 72t - 1.5t^2,$$

where t is the number of minutes since the meal began and $I(t)$ represents the amount (in grams) that the person has eaten at time t.[*]

(a) Find the rate of change of the intake of food for a person 5 minutes into a meal, and interpret it.

(b) Verify that the rate at which food is consumed is zero 24 minutes after the meal starts.

(c) Comment on the assumptions and usefulness of this function after 24 minutes. On the basis of your answer, determine a logical range for the function.

Use numerical derivatives to work these exercises. (See Examples 9 and 10.)

43. Business The amount of money (in billions of U.S. dollars) that China spends on research and development can be approximated by the function $f(t) = 26.67e^{.166t}$, where $t = 0$ corresponds to the year 2000. (Data from: National Science Foundation, *National Patterns of R&D Resources*, annual report.)

(a) Estimate the value of the derivative in the years 2000, 2006, and 2012.

(b) What does your answer in part (a) say about the rate at which research and development spending is increasing in China?

44. Business The revenue (in millions) generated by Southwest Airlines can be approximated by the function $R(x) = 1.073x^3 + 52.763x^2 + 137.72x + 5366.4$, where $x = 0$ corresponds to the year 2000. Estimate the derivative for the years 2010 and 2014. (Data from: www.morningstar.com.)

45. Social Science The number of licensed drivers in the United States (in millions) can be approximated by the function $g(x) = 180.532x^{.068}$, where $x = 4$ corresponds to the year 2004. Estimate and interpret the value of the derivative in 2014. (Data from: www.fhwa.dot.gov.)

46. Health The temperature of a patient (in degrees Fahrenheit) during a 12-hour hospital shift is modeled by $P(t) = 98.6 + 2.3te^{-.25t}$, where t is measured in hours since the start of the shift.

(a) Use a calculator to sketch $y = P(t)$, and give a general description of the graph in terms of what it means for the patient.

(b) Find and interpret $P(1)$ and $P'(1)$.

(c) Find and interpret $P(8)$ and $P'(8)$.

Use technology for Exercises 47–50.

47. (a) Graph the (numerical) derivative of

$$f(x) = .5x^5 - 2x^3 + x^2 - 3x + 2 \text{ for } -3 \le x \le 3.$$

(b) Graph $g(x) = 2.5x^4 - 6x^2 + 2x - 3$ on the same screen.

(c) How do the graphs of $f'(x)$ and $g(x)$ compare? What does this suggest that the derivative of $f(x)$ is?

48. Repeat Exercise 47 for $f(x) = (x^2 + x + 1)^{1/3}$ (with $-6 \le x \le 6$) and $g(x) = \dfrac{2x + 1}{3(x^2 + x + 1)^{2/3}}$.

49. By using a graphing calculator to compare graphs, as in Exercises 47 and 48, decide which of the given functions *could* be the derivative of $y = \dfrac{4x^2 + x}{x^2 + 1}$.

(a) $f(x) = \dfrac{2x + 1}{2x}$

(b) $g(x) = \dfrac{x^2 + x}{2x}$

(c) $h(x) = \dfrac{2x + 1}{x^2 + 1}$

(d) $k(x) = \dfrac{-x^2 + 8x + 1}{(x^2 + 1)^2}$

50. If f is a function such that $f'(x)$ is defined, then it can be proved that

$$f'(x) = \lim_{h \to 0} \frac{f(x + h) - f(x - h)}{2h}.$$

Consequently, when h is very small, say, $h = .001$,

$$f'(x) \approx \frac{f(x + h) - f(x - h)}{2h}$$
$$= \frac{f(x + .001) - f(x - .001)}{.002}.$$

(a) In Example 7, we saw that the derivative of $f(x) = \sqrt{x}$ is the function $f'(x) = \dfrac{1}{2\sqrt{x}}$. Make a table in which the first column lists $x = 1, 6, 11, 16,$ and 21; the second column lists the corresponding values of $f'(x)$; and the third column lists the corresponding values of

$$\frac{f(x + .001) - f(x - .001)}{.002}.$$

(b) How do the second and third columns of the table compare? (If you use the table feature on a graphing calculator, the entries in the table will be rounded off, so move the cursor over each entry to see it fully displayed at the bottom of the screen.) Your answer to this question may explain why most graphing calculators use the method in the third column to compute numerical derivatives.

Checkpoint Answers

1. $y = 2x + 1$

2.

3. (a) Positive   (b) Zero   (c) Negative

4. (a) At the end of class, the drink was 68°F.

---

[*]Kissileff, H. R. and J. L. Guss, "Microstructure of Eating Behaviour in Humans," *Appetite*, Vol. 36, No. 1, Feb. 2001, pp. 70–78.

(b) The drink warmed up by 7.6°F between $t = 25$ and $t = 50$ minutes.

(c) The average rate of change of the temperature of the drink between $t = 25$ and $t = 50$ minutes was .3°F/min.

(d) At the end of class, the drink will warm up by approximately .2°F in the next minute.

5. (a) $-5x^2 - 10xh - 5h^2 + 4$

(b) $-10xh - 5h^2$ **(c)** $-10x - 5h$ **(d)** $-10x$

(e) -30 **(f)** 0

6. (a) $\dfrac{-5}{x + h}$ **(b)** $\dfrac{5h}{x(x + h)}$ **(c)** $\dfrac{5}{x(x + h)}$

(d) $\dfrac{5}{x^2}$ **(e)** 5

7. $s'(t) = -15t^2 + 60t$

8. (a) -73.29 **(b)** -128.2

9. $\$15.17$

11.5 Techniques for Finding Derivatives

In the previous section, the derivative of a function was defined as a special limit. The mathematical process of finding this limit, called *differentiation*, resulted in a new function that was interpreted in several different ways. Using the definition to calculate the derivative of a function is a very involved process, even for simple functions. In this section, we develop rules that make the calculation of derivatives much easier. Keep in mind that even though the process of finding a derivative will be greatly simplified with these rules, *the interpretation of the derivative will not change.*

In addition to y' and $f'(x)$, there are several other commonly used notations for the derivative.

Notations for the Derivative

The derivative of the function $y = f(x)$ may be denoted in any of the following ways:

$$f'(x), \quad y', \quad \frac{dy}{dx}, \quad \frac{d}{dx}[f(x)], \quad D_x y, \quad \text{or} \quad D_x[f(x)].$$

The dy/dx notation for the derivative is sometimes referred to as *Leibniz notation,* named after one of the coinventors of calculus, Gottfried Wilhelm Leibniz (1646–1716). (The other was Sir Isaac Newton (1642–1727).)

For example, the derivative of $y = x^3 - 4x$, which we found in Example 5 of the last section to be $y' = 3x^2 - 4$, can also be written in the following ways:

$$\frac{dy}{dx} = 3x^2 - 4;$$

$$\frac{d}{dx}(x^3 - 4x) = 3x^2 - 4;$$

$$D_x(x^3 - 4x) = 3x^2 - 4.$$

A variable other than x may be used as the independent variable. For example, if $y = f(t)$ gives population growth as a function of time, then the derivative of y with respect to t could be written as

$$f'(t), \quad \frac{dy}{dt}, \quad \frac{d}{dt}[f(t)], \quad \text{or} \quad D_t[f(t)].$$

In this section, the definition of the derivative,

$$f'(x) = \lim_{h \to 0} \frac{f(x + h) - f(x)}{h},$$

is used to develop some rules for finding derivatives more easily than by the four-step process of the previous section. The first rule tells how to find the derivative of a constant function, such as $f(x) = 5$. Since $f(x + h)$ is also 5, $f'(x)$ is by definition

$$f'(x) = \lim_{h \to 0} \frac{f(x + h) - f(x)}{h}$$

$$= \lim_{h \to 0} \frac{5 - 5}{h} = \lim_{h \to 0} \frac{0}{h} = \lim_{h \to 0} 0 = 0.$$

The same argument works for $f(x) = k$, where k is a constant real number, establishing the following rule.

Constant Rule

If $f(x) = k$, where k is any real number, then

$$f'(x) = 0.$$

(The derivative of a constant function is 0.)

Figure 11.32

Figure 11.32 illustrates the constant rule; it shows a graph of the horizontal line $y = k$. At any point P on this line, the tangent line at P is the line itself. Since a horizontal line has a slope of 0, the slope of the tangent line is 0. This finding agrees with the constant rule: The derivative of a constant is 0.

Example 1   Find and label the derivative of the given function.

(a) $f(x) = 25$

Solution   Since 25 is a constant, we can write $f'(x) = 0$, $\dfrac{d}{dx}[f(x)] = 0$, or $D_x[f(x)] = 0$.

(b) $y = \pi$

Solution   Since π is a constant with value equal to $3.14159265 \ldots$, we have $y' = 0$, $dy/dx = 0$, or $D_x y = 0$.

(c) $y = 4^3$

Solution   Since 4^3 is the constant 64, we have $y' = 0$, $dy/dx = 0$, or $D_x y = 0$. ✓₁

Functions of the form $y = x^n$, where n is a fixed real number, are common in applications. We now find the derivative functions when $n = 2$ and $n = 3$:

$$f(x) = x^2 \qquad\qquad f(x) = x^3$$

$$f'(x) = \lim_{h \to 0} \frac{f(x + h) - f(x)}{h} \qquad f'(x) = \lim_{h \to 0} \frac{f(x + h) - f(x)}{h}$$

$$= \lim_{h \to 0} \frac{(x + h)^2 - x^2}{h} \qquad = \lim_{h \to 0} \frac{(x + h)^3 - x^3}{h}$$

$$= \lim_{h \to 0} \frac{(x^2 + 2xh + h^2) - x^2}{h} \qquad = \lim_{h \to 0} \frac{(x^3 + 3x^2h + 3xh^2 + h^3) - x^3}{h}$$

$$= \lim_{h \to 0} \frac{2xh + h^2}{h} \qquad = \lim_{h \to 0} \frac{3x^2h + 3xh^2 + h^3}{h}$$

$$f'(x) = \lim_{h \to 0} (2x + h) = 2x \qquad f'(x) = \lim_{h \to 0} (3x^2 + 3xh + h^2) = 3x^2.$$

✓ **Checkpoint 1**

Find the derivative of the given function.

(a) $y = -4$

(b) $f(x) = \pi^3$

(c) $y = 0$

Similar calculations show that

$$\frac{d}{dx}(x^4) = 4x^3 \qquad \text{and} \qquad \frac{d}{dx}(x^5) = 5x^4.$$

The pattern here (the derivative is the product of the exponent on the original function and a power of x that is one less) suggests that the derivative of $y = x^n$ is $y' = nx^{n-1}$, which is indeed the case. (See Exercise 77 at the end of this section.)

Furthermore, the pattern holds even when n is not a positive integer. For instance, in Example 6 of the last section we showed that

$$\text{if } f(x) = \frac{1}{x}, \qquad \text{then } f'(x) = -\frac{1}{x^2}.$$

This is the same result that the preceding pattern produces:

$$\text{If } f(x) = \frac{1}{x} = x^{-1}, \qquad \text{then } f'(x) = (-1)x^{-1-1} = -x^{-2} = -\frac{1}{x^2}.$$

Similarly, Example 7 in the last section showed that the derivative of $g(x) = \sqrt{x}$ is $g'(x) = \frac{1}{2\sqrt{x}}$, and the preceding pattern gives the same answer:

$$\text{If } g(x) = \sqrt{x} = x^{1/2}, \qquad \text{then } g'(x) = \frac{1}{2}x^{\frac{1}{2}-1} = \frac{1}{2}x^{-1/2} = \frac{1}{2} \cdot \frac{1}{x^{1/2}} = \frac{1}{2\sqrt{x}}.$$

Consequently, the following statement should be plausible.

Power Rule

If $f(x) = x^n$ for any number n, then

$$f'(x) = nx^{n-1}.$$

(The derivative of $f(x) = x^n$ is found by multiplying the exponent n on the original function by a power of x that is one less.)

Example 2   For each of the given functions, find the derivative.

(a) $y = x^8$

Solution   The exponent for x is $n = 8$. Using the power rule, we multiply by 8 and decrease the power on x by 1 to obtain $y' = 8x^7$.

(b) $y = x$

Solution   The exponent for x is $n = 1$. Using the power rule, we multiply by 1 and decrease the power on x by 1 to obtain $y' = 1x^0$. Recall that $x^0 = 1$ if $x \neq 0$. So we have $y' = 1$.

(c) $y = t^{3/2}$

Solution   The exponent for t is $n = \frac{3}{2}$. Using the power rule, we multiply by $\frac{3}{2}$ and decrease the power on t by 1 to obtain $D_t(y) = \frac{3}{2}t^{3/2-1} = \frac{3}{2}t^{1/2}$.

(d) $y = \sqrt[3]{x}$

Solution First we rewrite $y = \sqrt[3]{x}$ as $y = x^{\frac{1}{3}}$. Using the power rule, we multiply by $\frac{1}{3}$ and decrease the power on x by 1 to obtain

$$\frac{dy}{dx} = \frac{1}{3}x^{1/3-1} = \frac{1}{3}x^{-2/3} = \frac{1}{3x^{2/3}} = \frac{1}{3\sqrt[3]{x^2}}.$$

(e) $y = \dfrac{1}{x^3}$

Solution Rewrite $y = \dfrac{1}{x^3}$ as $y = x^{-3}$. Using the power rule, we multiply by -3 and decrease the power on x by 1 to obtain $\dfrac{dy}{dx} = -3x^{-4} = -\dfrac{3}{x^4}.$ ✓ 2

✓ **Checkpoint 2**

(a) If $y = x^4$, find y'.
(b) If $y = x^{17}$, find y'.
(c) If $y = x^{-2}$, find dy/dx.
(d) If $y = t^{-5}$, find dy/dt.
(e) If $y = t^{5/4}$, find y'.

The next rule shows how to find the derivative of the product of a constant and a function.

Constant Times a Function

Let k be a real number. If $g'(x)$ exists, then the derivative of $f(x) = k \cdot g(x)$ is

$$f'(x) = k \cdot g'(x).$$

(The derivative of a constant times a function is the constant times the derivative of the function.)

Example 3

(a) If $y = 8x^4$, find y'.

Solution Since the derivative of $g(x) = x^4$ is $g'(x) = 4x^3$ and $y = 8x^4 = 8g(x)$,

$$y' = 8g'(x) = 8(4x^3) = 32x^3.$$

(b) If $y = -\dfrac{3}{4}t^{12}$, find dy/dt.

Solution $\dfrac{dy}{dt} = -\dfrac{3}{4}\left[\dfrac{dy}{dt}(t^{12})\right] = -\dfrac{3}{4}(12t^{11}) = -9t^{11}.$

(c) Find $D_x(15x)$.

Solution $D_x(15x) = 15 \cdot D_x(x) = 15(1) = 15.$

(d) If $y = 6/x^2$, find y'.

Solution Replace $\dfrac{6}{x^2}$ by $6 \cdot \dfrac{1}{x^2}$, or $6x^{-2}$. Then

$$y' = 6(-2x^{-3}) = -12x^{-3} = -\frac{12}{x^3}.$$

(e) Find $D_x(10x^{3/2})$, and use a graphing calculator to confirm your answer numerically and graphically.

Solution $D_x(10x^{3/2}) = 10\left(\dfrac{3}{2}x^{1/2}\right) = 15x^{1/2}$.

To confirm this result numerically, make a table of values for $y_1 = 15x^{1/2}$ and $y_2 =$ the numerical derivative of $10x^{3/2}$; check your instruction manual for the correct syntax for y_2, which is probably one of the following:

$$\text{nDeriv}(10x^{3/2}, x), \quad \text{Nderiv}(10x^{3/2}, x, x),$$
$$\text{d/dx}(10x^{3/2}), \quad \text{or} \quad \text{d/dx}(10x^{3/2}, x).$$

Figure 11.33(a) indicates that the corresponding values are identical to three decimal places. To confirm this result graphically, graph y_1 and y_2 on the same screen and verify that the graphs appear to be the same. (See Figure 11.33(b)).

✔ 3

✔ **Checkpoint 3**

Find the derivative of the given function.

(a) $y = 12x^3$

(b) $f(t) = 30t^7$

(c) $y = -35t$

(d) $y = 5\sqrt{x}$

(e) $y = -10/t$

X	Y1	Y2
5	33.541	33.541
6	36.742	36.742
7	39.686	39.686
8	42.426	42.426
9	45	45
10	47.434	47.434
11	49.749	49.749

X=11

(a)

(b)

Figure 11.33

Confirming your calculations numerically or graphically, as in part (e) of Example 3, is a good way to detect algebraic errors. If you compute the rule of the derivative $f'(x)$, but its graph differs from the graph of the numerical derivative of $f(x)$, then you have made a mistake. If the two graphs appear to be identical, then you are *probably* correct. (The fact that two graphs appear identical on a calculator screen does not *prove* that they really are identical.)

The final rule in this section is for the derivative of a function that is a sum or difference of functions.

Sum-or-Difference Rule

If $f(x) = u(x) + v(x)$, and if $u'(x)$ and $v'(x)$ exist, then

$$f'(x) = u'(x) + v'(x).$$

If $f(x) = u(x) - v(x)$, and if $u'(x)$ and $v'(x)$ exist, then

$$f'(x) = u'(x) - v'(x).$$

(The derivative of a sum or difference of two functions is the sum or difference of the derivatives of the functions.)

For a proof of this rule, see Exercise 78 at the end of this section. This rule also works for sums and differences with more than two terms.

Example 4 Find the derivatives of the given functions.

(a) $y = 6x^3 + 15x^2$

Solution Let $u(x) = 6x^3$ and $v(x) = 15x^2$. Then

$$y = u(x) + v(x) \quad \text{and}$$
$$y' = u'(x) + v'(x)$$
$$= 6(3x^2) + 15(2x) = 18x^2 + 30x.$$

(b) $p(t) = 8t^4 - 6\sqrt{t} + \dfrac{5}{t}$

Solution   Rewrite $p(t)$ as $p(t) = 8t^4 - 6t^{1/2} + 5t^{-1}$; then $p'(t) = 32t^3 - 3t^{-1/2} - 5t^{-2}$, which also may be written as $p'(t) = 32t^3 - \dfrac{3}{\sqrt{t}} - \dfrac{5}{t^2}$.

(c) $f(x) = 5\sqrt[3]{x^2} + 4x^{-2} + 7$

Solution   Rewrite $f(x)$ as $f(x) = 5x^{2/3} + 4x^{-2} + 7$. Then

$$D_x[f(x)] = \frac{10}{3}(x^{-1/3}) - 8x^{-3},$$

or

$$D_x[f(x)] = \frac{10}{3\sqrt[3]{x}} - \frac{8}{x^3}.$$

The rules developed in this section make it possible to find the derivative of a function more directly than with the definition of the derivative, so that applications of the derivative can be dealt with more effectively. The examples that follow illustrate some business applications.

Marginal Analysis

In business and economics, the rates of change of such variables as cost, revenue, and profit are important considerations. Economists use the word *marginal* to refer to rates of change: for example, *marginal cost* refers to the rate of change of cost with respect to the number of items produced. Since the derivative of a function gives the rate of change of the function, a marginal cost (or revenue, or profit) function is found by taking the derivative of the cost (or revenue, or profit) function. Roughly speaking, the marginal cost at some level of production x is the cost of producing the $(x + 1)$st item, as we now show. (Similar statements could be made for revenue or profit.)

Look at Figure 11.34, where $C(x)$ represents the cost of producing x units of some item. Then the cost of producing $x + 1$ units is $C(x + 1)$. The cost of the $(x + 1)$st unit is, therefore, $C(x + 1) - C(x)$. This quantity is shown on the graph in Figure 11.34.

Now, if C is the cost function, then the marginal cost C' represents the slope of the tangent line at any point $(x, C(x))$. The graph in Figure 11.35 shows the cost function C and the tangent line at point $P = (x, C(x))$. We know that the slope of the tangent line at P is $C'(x)$ and that the slope can be computed using the triangle PQR in Figure 11.35:

$$C'(x) = \text{slope} = \frac{QR}{PR} = \frac{QR}{1} = QR.$$

So the length of the line segment QR is the number $C'(x)$.

Figure 11.34

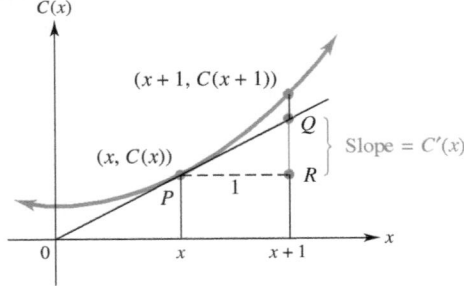

Figure 11.35

Superimposing the graphs from Figures 11.34 and 11.35, as in Figure 11.36, shows that $C'(x)$ is indeed very close to $C(x + 1) - C(x)$. Therefore, we have the conclusion in the following box.

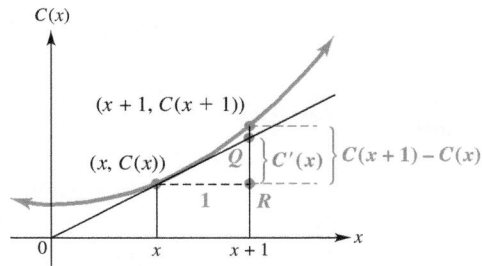

Figure 11.36

Marginal Cost

If $C(x)$ is the cost function, then the marginal cost (rate of change of cost) is given by the derivative $C'(x)$:

$$C'(x) \approx \text{cost of making one more item after } x \text{ items have been made.}$$

The marginal revenue $R'(x)$ and marginal profit $P'(x)$ are interpreted similarly.

Example 5   **Business**   A land developer has purchased 115 acres in the Blue Ridge Mountains to subdivide and sell as one-acre lots for mountain homes. Construction of gravel roads to access the lots is more expensive at higher elevations on the property. The cost of access roads (in thousands of dollars) for x lots can be approximated by

$$C(x) = 150 + 9x + .5x^{1.6} \qquad (0 \le x \le 115).$$

Find and interpret the marginal cost for the given values of x.

(a) $x = 25$

Solution   To find the marginal cost, first find the derivative of the cost function:

$$C'(x) = 9 + .5(1.6x^{.6}) = 9 + .8x^{.6}.$$

When $x = 25$,

$$C'(25) = 9 + .8(25)^{.6} = 14.519.$$

After 25 access roads have been constructed, the cost of constructing one more access road will be *approximately* \$14,519.

Note that the *actual* cost of constructing one more access road is:

$$C(26) - C(25) = (150 + 9(26) + .5(26)^{1.6}) - (150 + 9(25) + .5(25)^{1.6})$$
$$\approx 14.585.$$

So the actual cost to construct one additional road is \$14,585.

(b) $x = 50$

Solution   After 50 access roads have been constructed, the cost of constructing an additional access road will be *approximately*

$$C'(50) = 9 + .8(50)^{.6} = 17.365,$$

or $17,365. Compare this result with that for part (a). The cost of accessing one additional lot is almost $3000 more after 50 lots have road access than the cost of accessing one additional lot when only 25 lots have road access. Management must be careful to keep track of marginal costs. If the marginal cost of producing an extra unit exceeds the revenue received from selling it, the company will lose money on that unit. ✓6

Demand Functions

The **demand function**, defined by $p = f(x)$, relates the number of units, x, of an item that consumers are willing to purchase at the price p. (Demand functions were also discussed in Section 3.3.) The total revenue $R(x)$ is related to the price per unit and the amount demanded (or sold) by the equation

$$R(x) = xp = x \cdot f(x).$$

Example 6   **Business**   The demand function for a certain product is given by

$$p = \frac{50,000 - x}{25,000}.$$

Find the marginal revenue when $x = 10,000$ units and p is in dollars.

Solution   From the function p, the revenue function is given by

$$R(x) = xp$$
$$= x\left(\frac{50,000 - x}{25,000}\right)$$
$$= \frac{50,000x - x^2}{25,000} = 2x - \frac{1}{25,000}x^2.$$

The marginal revenue is

$$R'(x) = 2 - \frac{2}{25,000}x.$$

When $x = 10,000$, the marginal revenue is

$$R'(10,000) = 2 - \frac{2}{25,000}(10,000) = 1.2,$$

or $1.20 per unit. Thus, the next unit sold (at sales of 10,000) will produce additional revenue of about $1.20. ✓7

In economics, the demand function is written in the form $p = f(x)$, as in Example 6. From the perspective of a consumer, it is probably more reasonable to think of the quantity demanded as a function of price. Mathematically, these two viewpoints are equivalent. In Example 6, the demand function could have been written from the consumer's viewpoint as

$$x = 50,000 - 25,000p.$$

Example 7   **Business**   Suppose that the cost function for the product in Example 6 is given by

$$C(x) = 2100 + .25x \qquad (0 \le x \le 30,000).$$

Find the marginal profit from the production of the given numbers of units.

✓ **Checkpoint 6**

A cost function is given by $C(x) = 2790 + 30x + 12\sqrt{x}$. Find the marginal cost at the given production levels.

(a) $x = 1$

(b) $x = 4$

✓ **Checkpoint 7**

Suppose the demand function for x units of an item is

$$p = 5 - \frac{x}{1000},$$

where p is the price in dollars. Find

(a) the marginal revenue;

(b) the marginal revenue at $x = 500$;

(c) the marginal revenue at $x = 1000$.

(a) 15,000

Solution From Example 6, the revenue from the sale of x units is

$$R(x) = 2x - \frac{1}{25,000}x^2.$$

Since profit P is given by $P = R - C$,

$$P(x) = R(x) - C(x)$$

$$= \left(2x - \frac{1}{25,000}x^2 \right) - (2100 + .25x)$$

$$= 2x - \frac{1}{25,000}x^2 - 2100 - .25x$$

$$= 1.75x - \frac{1}{25,000}x^2 - 2100.$$

The marginal profit from the sale of x units is

$$P'(x) = 1.75 - \frac{2}{25,000}x = 1.75 - \frac{1}{12,500}x.$$

At $x = 15,000$, the marginal profit is

$$P'(15,000) = 1.75 - \frac{1}{12,500}(15,000) = .55,$$

or $.55 per unit. This means that the next unit sold (at sales of 15,000) will produce additional profit of about 55¢.

(b) 21,875

Solution When $x = 21,875$, the marginal profit is

$$P'(21,875) = 1.75 - \frac{1}{12,500}(21,875) = 0.$$

(c) 25,000

Solution When $x = 25,000$, the marginal profit is

$$P'(25,000) = 1.75 - \frac{1}{12,500}(25,000) = -.25,$$

or $-$.25 per unit.

As shown by parts (b) and (c), if more than 21,875 units are sold, the marginal profit is negative. This indicates that increasing production beyond that level will *reduce* profit. ☑8

✓ **Checkpoint 8**

For a certain product, the cost is $C(x) = 1300 + .80x$ and the revenue is $R(x) = 6x - \dfrac{2x^2}{11,000}$ for x units.

(a) Find the profit $P(x)$.

(b) Find $P'(12,000)$.

(c) Find $P'(25,000)$.

(d) Interpret the results of parts (b) and (c).

The final example shows a medical application of the derivative as the rate of change of a function.

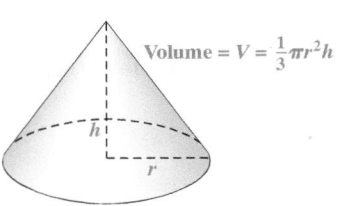
Volume = $V = \frac{1}{3}\pi r^2 h$

Figure 11.37

Example 8 **Health** A tumor has the approximate shape of a cone. (See Figure 11.37.) The radius of the tumor is fixed by the bone structure at 2 centimeters, but the tumor is growing along the height of the cone. The formula for the volume of a cone is $V = \frac{1}{3}\pi r^2 h$, where r is the radius of the base and h is the height of the cone. Find the rate of change of the volume of the tumor with respect to the height.

Solution To emphasize that the rate of change of the volume is found with respect to the height, we use the symbol dV/dh for the derivative. For this tumor, r is fixed at 2 cm. By substituting 2 for r,

$$V = \frac{1}{3}\pi r^2 h \quad \text{becomes} \quad V = \frac{1}{3}\pi \cdot 2^2 \cdot h, \quad \text{or} \quad V = \frac{4}{3}\pi h.$$

Since $4\pi/3$ is constant,

$$\frac{dV}{dh} = \frac{4\pi}{3} \approx 4.2 \text{ cu cm per cm.}$$

For each additional centimeter that the tumor grows in height, its volume will increase by approximately 4.2 cubic centimeters. ✓9

✓ Checkpoint 9

A balloon is spherical. The formula for the volume of a sphere is $V = (4/3)\pi r^3$, where r is the radius of the sphere. Find the given quantities.

(a) dV/dr

(b) The rate of change of the volume when $r = 3$ inches

11.5 Exercises

Find the derivatives of the given functions. (See Examples 1–4.)

1. $f(x) = 4x^2 - 3x + 5$

2. $g(x) = 8x^2 + 2x - 12$

3. $y = 2x^3 + 3x^2 - 6x + 2$

4. $y = 4x^3 + 24x + 4$

5. $g(x) = x^4 + 3x^3 - 8x - 7$

6. $f(x) = 6x^6 - 3x^4 + x^3 - 3x + 9$

7. $f(x) = 6x^{1.5} - 4x^5$ 8. $f(x) = -2x^{2.5} + 8x^5$

9. $y = -15x^{3/2} + 2x^{1.9} + x$ 10. $y = 18x^{1.6} - 4x^{3.1} + x^4$

11. $y = 24t^{3/2} + 4t^{1/2}$ 12. $y = -24t^{5/2} - 6t^{1/2}$

13. $y = 8\sqrt{x} + 6x^{3/4}$ 14. $y = -100\sqrt{x} - 11x^{2/3}$

15. $g(x) = 6x^{-5} - 2x^{-1}$ 16. $y = 8x^{-2} + 6x^{-1} + 1$

17. $y = 10x^{-2} + 6x^{-4} + 3x$

18. $y = 3x^{-7} + 4x^{-5} - 9x^{-4} + 21x^{-1}$

19. $f(t) = \frac{-4}{t} + \frac{8}{t^2}$ 20. $f(t) = \frac{8}{t} - \frac{5}{t^2}$

21. $y = \frac{12 - 7x + 6x^3}{x^4}$ 22. $y = \frac{102 - 6x + 17x^4}{x^6}$

23. $g(x) = 5x^{-1/2} - 7x^{1/2} + 101x$

24. $f(x) = -8x^{-1/2} - 8x^{1/2} + 12x$

25. $y = 7x^{-3/2} + 8x^{-1/2} + x^3 - 9$

26. $y = 2x^{-3/2} + 9x^{-1/2} + x^{-4} - x^2$

27. $y = \frac{19}{\sqrt[4]{x}}$ 28. $y = \frac{-5}{\sqrt[3]{x}}$

29. $y = \frac{-8t}{\sqrt[3]{t^2}}$ 30. $g(t) = \frac{10t}{\sqrt[3]{t^8}}$

Find each of the given derivatives. (See Examples 1–4.)

31. $\frac{dy}{dx}$ if $y = 8x^{-5} - 9x^{-4} + 9x^4$

32. $\frac{dy}{dx}$ if $y = -3x^{-2} - 4x^{-5} + 5x^{-7}$

33. $D_x\left(9x^{-1/2} + \frac{2}{x^{3/2}}\right)$

34. $D_x\left(\frac{8}{\sqrt[4]{x}} - \frac{3}{\sqrt{x^3}}\right)$

35. $f'(-2)$ if $f(x) = 6x^2 - 2x$

36. $f'(3)$ if $f(x) = 9x^3 - 6x^2$

37. $f'(4)$ if $f(t) = 2\sqrt{t} - \frac{3}{\sqrt{t}}$

38. $f'(8)$ if $f(t) = -5\sqrt[3]{t} + \frac{6}{\sqrt[3]{t}}$

39. If $f(x) = -\frac{(3x^2 + x)^2}{7}$, which of the following is *closest* to $f'(1)$?

(a) -12 (b) -9 (c) -6
(d) -3 (e) 0 (f) 3

40. If $g(x) = -3x^{3/2} + 4x^2 - 9x$, which of the following is *closest* to $g'(4)$?

(a) 3 (b) 6 (c) 9
(d) 12 (e) 15 (f) 18

Find the slope and the equation of the tangent line to the graph of each function at the given value of x.

41. $f(x) = x^4 - 2x^2 + 1; x = 1$

42. $g(x) = -x^5 + 4x^2 - 2x + 2; x = 2$

43. $y = 4x^{1/2} + 2x^{3/2} + 1; x = 4$

44. $y = -x^{-3} + 5x^{-1} + x; x = 2$

Work these exercises. (See Examples 5 and 7.)

45. Business The profit in dollars from the sale of x expensive watches is

$$P(x) = .03x^2 - 4x + 3x^8 - 5000.$$

Find the marginal profit for the given values of x.

(a) $x = 100$ (b) $x = 1000$

(c) $x = 5000$ (d) $x = 10,000$

46. Business The total cost to produce x handcrafted weather vanes is

$$C(x) = 100 + 12x + .1x^2 + .001x^3.$$

Find the marginal cost for the given values of x.

(a) $x = 0$ (b) $x = 10$

(c) $x = 30$ (d) $x = 50$

47. Business Often, sales of a new product grow rapidly at first and then slow down with time. This is the case with the sales represented by the function

$$S(t) = 10,000 - 10,000t^{-.2} + 100t^{.1},$$

where t represents time in years. Find the rate of change of sales for the given values of t.

(a) $t = 1$ (b) $t = 10$

48. Business The revenue equation (in billions of dollars) for corn production in the United States is approximated by

$$R(x) = .016x^2 + 1.034x + 11.338,$$

where x is in billions of bushels. (Data from: www.usda.gov.)

(a) Find the marginal-revenue function.

(b) Find the marginal revenue for the production of 10 billion bushels.

(c) Find the marginal revenue for the production of 20 billion bushels.

49. Business The revenue equation (in hundreds of millions of dollars) for barley production in the United States is approximated by

$$R(x) = .0608x^2 + 1.4284x + 2.3418,$$

where x is in hundreds of millions of bushels. (Data from: www.usda.gov.)

(a) Find the marginal-revenue function.

(b) Find the marginal revenue for the production of 500,000,000 bushels.

(c) Find the marginal revenue for the production of 700,000,000 bushels.

50. Business The total cost in dollars to produce x hundred tee shirts imprinted with a college logo can be approximated by

$$C(x) = 1500 + 1000x^{.9} \quad (0 \le x \le 50).$$

Find the marginal cost for the given production levels.

(a) 1500 shirts   (b) 2000 shirts

51. Business The revenue generated from the sale of x picnic tables is given by

$$R(x) = 20x - \frac{x^2}{500}.$$

(a) Find the marginal revenue when $x = 1000$ units.

(b) Determine the actual revenue from the sale of the 1001st item.

(c) Compare the answers to parts (a) and (b). How are they related?

52. Business The profit (in dollars) from producing x hundred kegs of beer is given by $P(x) = 1500 + 30x - 2x^2$. Find the marginal profit at the given production levels. In each case, decide whether the firm should increase production of beer.

(a) 700   (b) 650

(c) 1200   (d) 1800

53. Business The demand for a certain item is given by $D(p) = -p^2 + 5p + 1$, where p represents the price of an item in dollars.

(a) Find the rate of change of demand with respect to price.

(b) Find and interpret the rate of change of demand when the price is 12 dollars.

54. Business The profit in dollars from the sale of x hundred linear feet of custom wood molding can be approximated by

$$P(x) = 400x - 490\sqrt{x} - 600 \quad (5 \le x \le 25).$$

Find the marginal profit for the given values of x.

(a) $x = 10$ (b) $x = 15$

Work these exercises. (See Example 6.)

55. Business The annual demand equation for handcrafted violins by a certain violin maker can be approximated by $p = 24 - x$ where p is the price in thousands of dollars and x is the quantity of violins demanded. Find and interpret the marginal revenue for each of the given production levels.

(a) $x = 5$ (b) $x = 10$ (c) $x = 12$

56. Business The cost (in thousands of dollars) of making x violins described in the previous exercise can be approximated by $C(x) = 15 + 1.2x$. Find the marginal profit for each of the given production levels.

(a) $x = 5$ (b) $x = 10$ (c) $x = 12$

57. Business Assume that a demand equation is given by $x = 5000 - 100p$. Find the marginal revenue for the given production levels (values of x). (*Hint:* Solve the demand equation for p and use $R(x) = xp$.)

(a) 1000 units   (b) 2500 units

(c) 3000 units

58. Business Suppose that, for the situation in Exercise 57, the cost of producing x units is given by $C(x) = 3000 - 20x + .03x^2$. Find the marginal profit for each of the given production levels.

(a) 500 units   (b) 815 units

(c) 1000 units

Work these exercises.

59. Business An insurance company typically offers discounts for purchasing larger amounts of life insurance coverage. For a female under 30 years of age who qualifies for the lowest premiums, the annual cost (in dollars) of a life insurance policy can be approximated by

$$C(x) = 3\sqrt[4]{x^3},$$

where x is the amount of life insurance coverage (in thousands of dollars). Find and interpret the given quantities. (Data from: www.abendowment.org/insurance/life20_rate.asp.)

(a) $C(100)$ and $C'(100)$ (b) $C(1000)$ and $C'(1000)$

60. Business For a male 50 years of age who qualifies for the lowest premiums, the annual cost (in dollars) of a life insurance policy can be approximated by $C(x) = 5.60x^{.88}$, where x is the amount of life insurance coverage (in thousands of dollars). Find and interpret the given quantities. (Data from: www.abendowment.org/insurance/life20_rate.asp.)

(a) $C(100)$ and $C'(100)$ (b) $C(1000)$ and $C'(1000)$

61. Business A marketing firm is interested in the percentage of the total United States population that is age 0–17 years. This percentage can be estimated by $P(x) = 26x^{-.03}$, where $x = 0$ corresponds to the year 2000 and the estimate is valid through the year 2025. Find and interpret the given quantities. (Data from: www.childstats.gov.)

(a) $P(14)$ and $P'(14)$ (b) $P(24)$ and $P'(24)$

62. Business A marketing firm is interested in the percentage of the total United States population that is age 65 years or older. This percentage can be estimated by $P(x) = .01x^2 - .01x + 12$, where $x = 0$ corresponds to the year 2000 and the estimate is valid through the year 2025. Find and interpret the given quantities. (Data from: www.childstats.gov.)

(a) $P(14)$ and $P'(14)$ (b) $P(24)$ and $P'(24)$

63. Social Science The women's 100-meter dash was introduced to the Olympic Games in 1928. Between 1928 and 2012, the winning time (in seconds) can be approximated by $W(x) = .000178x^2 - .0404x + 13.068$, where $x = 0$ corresponds to the year 1900. (Data from: www.Olympic.org.)

(a) Would you expect the derivative of $W(x)$ to be positive, negative, or zero? Why?

(b) Find and interpret the rate of change of $W(x)$ in 1928.

(c) Find and interpret the rate of change of $W(x)$ in 2012.

64. Finance The total amount (in billions of dollars) of currency (in notes) circulating in the United States can be approximated by $M(x) = .52x^3 - 7.52x^2 + 62.37x + 559.79$ where $x = 0$ corresponds to the year 2000. Find the derivative of $M(x)$ and use it to find the rate of change of the currency in circulation in the given years. (Data from: U.S. Federal Reserve.)

(a) 2001   (b) 2011

65. Economics The Case-Shiller Composite 20 Home Price Index can be approximated by $C(x) = .114x^4 - 2.8x^3 + 19.89x^2 - 30.56x + 118.14$, where $x = 0$ corresponds to the year 2000. Find and interpret the rate of change of this home price index in the given years. (Data from: Standard & Poor's.)

(a) 2008   (b) 2011

66. Social Science According to the U.S. Census Bureau, the number of Americans (in thousands) who are expected to be over 100 years old in year x is approximated by the function $f(x) = .27x^2 + 3.52x + 51.78$, where $x = 0$ corresponds to the year 2000 and the formula is valid through 2045.

(a) Find a formula giving the rate of change in the number of Americans over 100 years old.

(b) What is the rate of change in the number of Americans expected to be over 100 years old in the year 2020?

(c) Is the number of Americans expected to be over 100 years old in 2020 increasing or decreasing?

67. Natural Science A short length of blood vessel has a cylindrical shape. The volume of a cylinder is given by $V = \pi r^2 h$. Suppose an experimental device is set up to measure the volume of blood in a blood vessel of fixed length 80 mm as the radius changes.

(a) Find dV/dr.

Suppose a drug is administered that causes the blood vessel to expand. Evaluate dV/dr for the following values of r, and interpret your answers:

(b) 4 mm;   (c) 6 mm;   (d) 8 mm.

68. Health The birth weight (in pounds) of an infant can be approximated by the function

$$g(x) = .0011x^{2.394},$$

where x represents the number of completed weeks of gestation.

(a) Find the function $g'(x)$.

(b) Evaluate $g'(32)$.

(c) Evaluate $g'(40)$.

(d) Interpret the results of parts (b) and (c).

69. Health The body mass index (BMI) is a number that can be calculated for any individual as follows: Multiply weight (in pounds) by 703 and divide by the person's height (in inches) squared. That is,

$$\text{BMI} = \frac{703w}{h^2},$$

where w is in pounds and h is in inches. The National Heart, Lung, and Blood Institute uses the BMI to determine whether a person is "overweight" ($25 \le \text{BMI} < 30$) or "obese" ($\text{BMI} \ge 30$).

(a) Calculate the BMI for a male who weighs 220 pounds and is 6'2" tall.

(b) How much weight would the person in part (a) have to lose until he reaches a BMI of 24.9 and is no longer "overweight"?

(c) For a 125-lb female, what is the rate of change of BMI with respect to height? (*Hint:* Take the derivative of the function $f(h) = \frac{703(125)}{h^2}$.)

(d) Calculate and interpret the meaning of $f'(65)$.

70. Health To increase the velocity of the air flowing through the trachea when a human coughs, the body contracts the windpipe, producing a more effective cough. Tuchinsky determined that the velocity V of the air flowing through the trachea during a cough is given by

$$V = C(R_0 - R)R^2,$$

where C is a constant based on individual body characteristics, R_0 is the radius of the windpipe before the cough, and R is the radius of the windpipe during the cough.[*]

(a) Think of V as a function of R. Multiply out the rule for V and find $\dfrac{dV}{dR}$. (*Hint: C* and R_0 are constants here; if you cannot see what to do, it may help to consider the case when $C = 2$ and $R_0 = .15$.)

(b) It can be shown that the maximum velocity of the cough occurs when $\dfrac{dV}{dR} = 0$. Find the value of R that maximizes the velocity.[†] (Remember that R must be positive.)

Physical Science *We saw earlier that the velocity of a particle moving in a straight line is given by*

$$\lim_{h \to 0} \frac{s(t + h) - s(t)}{h},$$

where s(t) gives the position of the particle at time t. This limit is the derivative of s(t), so the velocity of a particle is given by s′(t). If v(t) represents velocity at time t, then v(t) = s′(t). For each of the given position functions, find (a) v(t); (b) the velocity when t = 0, t = 5, and t = 10.

71. $s(t) = 8t^2 + 3t + 1$

72. $s(t) = 10t^2 - 5t + 6$

73. $s(t) = 2t^3 + 6t^2$

74. $s(t) = -t^3 + 3t^2 + t - 1$

75. **Physical Science** If a rock is dropped from a 144-foot-high building, its position (in feet above the ground) is given by $s(t) = -16t^2 + 144$, where t is the time in seconds since it was dropped.

(a) What is its velocity 1 second after being dropped? 2 seconds after being dropped?

(b) When will it hit the ground?

(c) What is its velocity upon impact?

76. **Physical Science** A ball is thrown vertically upward from the ground at a velocity of 64 feet per second. Its distance from the ground at t seconds is given by $s(t) = -16t^2 + 64t$.

(a) How fast is the ball moving 2 seconds after being thrown? 3 seconds after being thrown?

(b) How long after the ball is thrown does it reach its maximum height?

(c) How high will the ball go?

77. Perform each step and give reasons for your results in the following proof that the derivative of $y = x^n$ is $y' = n \cdot x^{n-1}$ (we

prove this result only for positive integer values of n, but it is valid for all values of n):

(a) Recall the binomial theorem from algebra:

$$(p + q)^n = p^n + n \cdot p^{n-1}q + \frac{n(n - 1)}{2}p^{n-2}q^2 + \cdots + q^n.$$

Evaluate $(x + h)^n$.

(b) Find the quotient $\dfrac{(x + h)^n - x^n}{h}$.

(c) Use the definition of the derivative to find y'.

78. Perform each step and give reasons for your results in the following proof that the derivative of $y = f(x) + g(x)$ is

$$y' = f'(x) + g'(x).$$

(a) Let $s(x) = f(x) + g(x)$. Show that

$$s'(x) = \lim_{h \to 0} \frac{[f(x + h) + g(x + h)] - [f(x) + g(x)]}{h}.$$

(b) Show that

$$s'(x) = \lim_{h \to 0}\left[\frac{f(x + h) - f(x)}{h} + \frac{g(x + h) - g(x)}{h}\right].$$

(c) Finally, show that $s'(x) = f'(x) + g'(x)$.

Use a graphing calculator or computer to graph each function and its derivative on the same screen. Determine the values of x where the derivative is (a) positive, (b) zero, and (c) negative. (d) What is true of the graph of the function in each case?

79. $g(x) = 6 - 4x + 3x^2 - x^3$

80. $k(x) = 2x^4 - 3x^3 + x$

✓Checkpoint Answers

1. (a) 0   (b) 0   (c) 0

2. (a) $y' = 4x^3$ (b) $y' = 17x^{16}$ (c) $dy/dx = -2/x^3$

(d) $dy/dt = -5/t^6$ (e) $y' = \dfrac{5}{4}t^{1/4}$

3. (a) $36x^2$ (b) $210t^6$ (c) -35

(d) $(5/2)x^{-1/2}$, or $5/(2\sqrt{x})$ (e) $10t^{-2}$, or $10/t^2$

4. (a) $y' = -30x^2 - 6$

(b) $y' = \dfrac{40}{7}t^{1/7} + \dfrac{5}{2}t^{-1/2}$, or $y' = \dfrac{40}{7}t^{1/7} + \dfrac{5}{2t^{1/2}}$

(c) $f'(t) = \dfrac{-1}{\sqrt{t}} - \dfrac{4}{t^2}$

5. Both graphs look like this:

6. (a) \$36 per unit   (b) \$33 per unit

---

[*]Philip Tuchinsky, "The Human Cough," *UMAP Module 211* (Lexington, MA: COMAP, Inc, 1979): 1–9.

[†]Interestingly, Tuchinsky also states that X-rays indicate that the body naturally contracts the windpipe to this radius during a cough.

7. (a) $R'(x) = 5 - \dfrac{x}{500}$

  (b) \$4   **(c)** \$3

8. (a) $P(x) = 5.2x - \dfrac{2x^2}{11,000} - 1300$

  (b) .84   **(c)** −3.89

  (d) Profit is increasing by \$.84 per unit at 12,000 units in part (b) and decreasing by \$3.89 per unit at 25,000 units in part (c).

9. (a) $4\pi r^2$

  (b) 36π cubic inches per inch

11.6 Derivatives of Products and Quotients

In the last section, we saw that the derivative of the sum of two functions can be obtained by taking the sum of the derivatives. What about products? Is the derivative of a product of two functions equal to the product of their derivatives? For example, if

$$u(x) = 2x + 4 \quad \text{and} \quad v(x) = 3x^2,$$

then the product of u and v is

$$f(x) = (2x + 4)(3x^2) = 6x^3 + 12x^2.$$

Using the rules of the last section, we have

$$u'(x) = 2, \quad v'(x) = 6x, \quad \text{and} \quad f'(x) = 18x^2 + 24x,$$

so that

$$u'(x) \cdot v'(x) = 12x \quad \text{and} \quad f'(x) = 18x^2 + 24x.$$

Obviously, these two functions are *not* the same, which shows that the derivative of the product is *not* equal to the product of the derivatives. ✔
The correct rule for finding the derivative of a product is as follows.

✔ **Checkpoint 1**

Let $u(x) = x^2$ and $v(x) = x^3$.

(a) Find $f(x) = u(x) \cdot v(x)$.

(b) Find $f'(x) = [u(x) \cdot v(x)]'$.

(c) Find $u'(x)$.

(d) Find $v'(x)$.

(e) Find $u'(x) \cdot v'(x)$.

(f) Check that
$[u(x) \cdot v(x)]' \neq u'(x) \cdot v'(x)$.

> **Product Rule**
>
> If $f(x) = u(x) \cdot v(x)$, and if both $u'(x)$ and $v'(x)$ exist, then
>
> $$f'(x) = u(x) \cdot v'(x) + v(x) \cdot u'(x).$$
>
> (The derivative of a product of two functions is the first function times the derivative of the second, plus the second function times the derivative of the first.)

To sketch the method used to prove the product rule, let

$$f(x) = u(x) \cdot v(x).$$

Then $f(x + h) = u(x + h) \cdot v(x + h)$, and, by definition,

$$f'(x) = \lim_{h \to 0} \frac{f(x + h) - f(x)}{h}$$

$$= \lim_{h \to 0} \frac{u(x + h) \cdot v(x + h) - u(x) \cdot v(x)}{h}.$$

Now subtract and add $u(x + h) \cdot v(x)$ in the numerator, giving

$$f'(x) = \lim_{h \to 0} \frac{u(x + h) \cdot v(x + h) - u(x + h) \cdot v(x) + u(x + h) \cdot v(x) - u(x) \cdot v(x)}{h}.$$

Factor $u(x + h)$ from the first two terms of the numerator, and factor $v(x)$ from the last two terms. Then use the properties of limits (Section 11.1) as follows:

$$f'(x) = \lim_{h \to 0} \frac{u(x + h)[v(x + h) - v(x)] + v(x)[u(x + h) - u(x)]}{h}$$

$$= \lim_{h \to 0} u(x + h)\left[\frac{v(x + h) - v(x)}{h}\right] + \lim_{h \to 0} v(x)\left[\frac{u(x + h) - u(x)}{h}\right]$$

$$= \lim_{h \to 0} u(x + h) \cdot \lim_{h \to 0} \frac{v(x + h) - v(x)}{h} + \lim_{h \to 0} v(x) \cdot \lim_{h \to 0} \frac{u(x + h) - u(x)}{h}. \quad (*)$$

If u' and v' both exist, then

$$\lim_{h \to 0} \frac{u(x + h) - u(x)}{h} = u'(x) \qquad \text{and} \qquad \lim_{h \to 0} \frac{v(x + h) - v(x)}{h} = v'(x).$$

The fact that u' exists can be used to prove that

$$\lim_{h \to 0} u(x + h) = u(x),$$

and since no h is involved in $v(x)$,

$$\lim_{h \to 0} v(x) = v(x).$$

Substituting these results into equation $(*)$ gives

$$f'(x) = u(x) \cdot v'(x) + v(x) \cdot u'(x),$$

the desired result.

Example 1   Let $f(x) = (2x + 4)(3x^2)$. Use the product rule to find $f'(x)$.

Solution   Here, f is given as the product of $u(x) = 2x + 4$ and $v(x) = 3x^2$. By the product rule and the fact that $u'(x) = 2$ and $v'(x) = 6x$,

$$f'(x) = u(x) \cdot v'(x) + v(x) \cdot u'(x)$$
$$= (2x + 4)(6x) + (3x^2)(2)$$
$$= 12x^2 + 24x + 6x^2 = 18x^2 + 24x.$$

This result is the same as that found at the beginning of the section. ✔2

✔ **Checkpoint 2**

Use the product rule to find the derivatives of the given functions.

(a) $f(x) = (5x^2 + 6)(3x)$

(b) $g(x) = (8x)(4x^2 + 5x)$

Example 2   Find the derivative of $y = (\sqrt{x} + 3)(x^2 - 5x)$.

Solution   Let $u(x) = \sqrt{x} + 3 = x^{1/2} + 3$ and $v(x) = x^2 - 5x$. Then

$$y' = u(x) \cdot v'(x) + v(x) \cdot u'(x)$$

$$= (x^{1/2} + 3)(2x - 5) + (x^2 - 5x)\left(\frac{1}{2}x^{-1/2}\right)$$

$$= 2x^{3/2} - 5x^{1/2} + 6x - 15 + \frac{1}{2}x^{3/2} - \frac{5}{2}x^{1/2}$$

$$= \frac{5}{2}x^{3/2} + 6x - \frac{15}{2}x^{1/2} - 15. ✔3$$

✔ **Checkpoint 3**

Find the derivatives of the given functions.

(a) $f(x) = (x^2 - 3)(\sqrt{x} + 5)$

(b) $g(x) = (\sqrt{x} + 4)(5x^2 + x)$

We could have found the derivatives in Examples 1 and 2 by multiplying out the original functions. The product rule then would not have been needed. In the next section, however, we shall see products of functions where the product rule is essential.

What about *quotients* of functions? To find the derivative of the quotient of two functions, use the next rule.

Quotient Rule

If $f(x) = \dfrac{u(x)}{v(x)}$, if all indicated derivatives exist, and if $v(x) \neq 0$, then

$$f'(x) = \frac{v(x) \cdot u'(x) - u(x) \cdot v'(x)}{[v(x)]^2}.$$

(The derivative of a quotient is the denominator times the derivative of the numerator, minus the numerator times the derivative of the denominator, all divided by the square of the denominator.)

The proof of the quotient rule is similar to that of the product rule and is omitted here.

CAUTION Just as the derivative of a product is *not* the product of the derivatives, the derivative of a quotient is *not* the quotient of the derivatives. If you are asked to take the derivative of a product or a quotient, it is essential that you recognize that the function contains a product or quotient and then use the appropriate rule.

Example 3 Find $f'(x)$ if

$$f(x) = \frac{2x - 1}{4x + 3}.$$

Solution Let $u(x) = 2x - 1$, with $u'(x) = 2$. Also, let $v(x) = 4x + 3$, with $v'(x) = 4$. Then, by the quotient rule,

$$f'(x) = \frac{v(x) \cdot u'(x) - u(x) \cdot v'(x)}{[v(x)]^2}$$

$$= \frac{(4x + 3)(2) - (2x - 1)(4)}{(4x + 3)^2}$$

$$= \frac{8x + 6 - 8x + 4}{(4x + 3)^2}$$

$$f'(x) = \frac{10}{(4x + 3)^2}.$$

✓**Checkpoint 4**

Find the derivatives of the given functions.

(a) $f(x) = \dfrac{3x + 7}{5x + 8}$

(b) $g(x) = \dfrac{2x + 11}{5x - 1}$

CAUTION In the second step of Example 3, we had the expression

$$\frac{(4x + 3)(2) - (2x - 1)(4)}{(4x + 3)^2}.$$

Students often incorrectly "cancel" the $4x + 3$ in the numerator with one factor of the denominator. Because the numerator is a *difference* of two products, however, you must multiply and combine terms *before* looking for common factors in the numerator and denominator.

Example 4 Find

$$D_x\!\left(\frac{x - 2x^2}{4x^2 + 1}\right).$$

Solution   Use the quotient rule:

$$D_x\left(\frac{x - 2x^2}{4x^2 + 1}\right) = \frac{(4x^2 + 1)D_x(x - 2x^2) - (x - 2x^2)D_x(4x^2 + 1)}{(4x^2 + 1)^2}$$

$$= \frac{(4x^2 + 1)(1 - 4x) - (x - 2x^2)(8x)}{(4x^2 + 1)^2}$$

$$= \frac{4x^2 - 16x^3 + 1 - 4x - 8x^2 + 16x^3}{(4x^2 + 1)^2}$$

$$= \frac{-4x^2 - 4x + 1}{(4x^2 + 1)^2}. \quad \boxed{\checkmark 5}$$

✓ **Checkpoint 5**

Find each derivative. Write your answer with positive exponents.

(a) $D_x\left(\dfrac{x^{-2} - 1}{x^{-1} + 2}\right)$

(b) $D_x\left(\dfrac{2 + x^{-1}}{x^3 + 1}\right)$

Example 5   Find

$$D_x\left(\frac{(3 - 4x)(5x + 1)}{7x - 9}\right).$$

Solution   This function has a product within a quotient. Instead of multiplying the factors in the numerator first (which is an option), we can use the quotient rule together with the product rule. Use the quotient rule first to get

$$D_x\left(\frac{(3 - 4x)(5x + 1)}{7x - 9}\right)$$

$$= \frac{(7x - 9)D_x[(3 - 4x)(5x + 1)] - [(3 - 4x)(5x + 1)]D_x(7x - 9)}{(7x - 9)^2}.$$

Now use the product rule to find $D_x[(3 - 4x)(5x + 1)]$ in the numerator:

$$= \frac{(7x - 9)[(3 - 4x)5 + (5x + 1)(-4)] - (3 + 11x - 20x^2)(7)}{(7x - 9)^2}$$

$$= \frac{(7x - 9)(15 - 20x - 20x - 4) - (21 + 77x - 140x^2)}{(7x - 9)^2}$$

$$= \frac{(7x - 9)(11 - 40x) - 21 - 77x + 140x^2}{(7x - 9)^2}$$

$$= \frac{-280x^2 + 437x - 99 - 21 - 77x + 140x^2}{(7x - 9)^2}$$

$$= \frac{-140x^2 + 360x - 120}{(7x - 9)^2}. \quad \boxed{\checkmark 6}$$

✓ **Checkpoint 6**

Find each derivative.

(a) $D_x\left(\dfrac{(3x - 1)(4x + 2)}{2x}\right)$

(b) $D_x\left(\dfrac{5x^2}{(2x + 1)(x - 1)}\right)$

Average Cost

Suppose $y = C(x)$ gives the total cost of manufacturing x items. As mentioned earlier, the average cost per item is found by dividing the total cost by the number of items. The rate of change of average cost, called the *marginal average cost*, is the derivative of the average cost.

Average Cost

If the total cost of manufacturing x items is given by $C(x)$, then the **average cost per item** is

$$\overline{C}(x) = \frac{C(x)}{x}.$$

The **marginal average cost** is the derivative of the average-cost function $\overline{C}'(x)$.

A company naturally would be interested in making the average cost as small as possible. We will see in the next chapter that this can be done by using the derivative of $C(x)/x$. The derivative often can be found with the quotient rule, as in the next example.

Example 6   **Business**   The total cost (in dollars) to manufacture x mobile phones is given by

$$C(x) = \frac{50x^2 + 30x + 4}{x + 2} + 80{,}000.$$

(a) Find the average cost per phone.

Solution   The average cost is given by the total cost divided by the number of items:

$$\overline{C}(x) = \frac{C(x)}{x} = \frac{1}{x}C(x) = \frac{1}{x}\left(\frac{50x^2 + 30x + 4}{x + 2} + 80{,}000\right)$$

$$= \frac{50x^2 + 30x + 4}{x^2 + 2x} + \frac{80{,}000}{x}$$

$$= \frac{50x^2 + 30x + 4}{x^2 + 2x} + 80{,}000x^{-1}.$$

(b) Find the average cost per phone for each of the following production levels:

5000;   10,000;   100,000.

Solution   Evaluate $\overline{C}(x)$ at each of the numbers, either by hand or by using technology, as in Figure 11.38. Note that the average cost per phone is $65.99 when 5000 phones are produced, and that reduces to $50.80 when 100,000 are produced.

(c) Find the marginal average cost.

Solution   The marginal average cost is the derivative of the average-cost function. Using the sum rule and the quotient rule yields

$$\overline{C}'(x) = \frac{(x^2 + 2x)(100x + 30) - (50x^2 + 30x + 4)(2x + 2)}{(x^2 + 2x)^2} + (-1)80{,}000x^{-2}$$

$$= \frac{(100x^3 + 230x^2 + 60x) - (100x^3 + 160x^2 + 68x + 8)}{(x^2 + 2x)^2} - \frac{80{,}000}{x^2}$$

$$= \frac{70x^2 - 8x - 8}{(x^2 + 2x)^2} - \frac{80{,}000}{x^2}.$$

(d) Find the marginal average cost at production levels of 500 phones and 1000 phones.

Solution   Evaluating the marginal average-cost function at $x = 500$ yields

$$\overline{C}'(500) = \frac{70(500)^2 - 8(500) - 8}{(500^2 + 2(500))^2} - \frac{80{,}000}{500^2} \approx -.32.$$

Therefore, at a production level of 500 phones, if an additional phone is produced, the *average cost per phone* is decreased by approximately 32 cents per phone.

Similarly, $\overline{C}'(1000) \approx -.08$ means that, at a production level of 1000 phones, if an additional phone is produced, the average cost per phone is decreased by approximately 8 cents per phone. ✓ 7

X	Y1
5000	65.986
10000	57.993
100000	50.799
X=	

Figure 11.38

✓ **Checkpoint 7**

A cost function is given by

$$C(x) = \frac{x^2 + 2x + 5}{x + 1} + 1000.$$

(a) Find the average cost.

(b) Find the marginal average cost.

Example 7   **Business**   The cost (in hundreds of dollars) incurred by a flower shop to produce x hundred flower arrangements for delivery on Valentine's day is given by

$$C(x) = x^2 + 3x + 18.$$

(a) Find the marginal cost at a production level of 200 flower arrangements.

Solution Since the marginal cost function is $C'(x) = 2x + 3$, the marginal cost at a production level of 200 arrangements is $C'(2) = 2(2) + 3 = 7$. At this production level, the cost of producing an *additional* hundred arrangements is approximately $700.

(b) Find the average cost at a production level of 200 flower arrangements.

Solution The average cost is

$$\overline{C}(x) = \frac{C(x)}{x} = \frac{x^2 + 3x + 18}{x} = x + 3 + \frac{18}{x}.$$

Evaluating at $x = 2$ yields $\overline{C}(2) = 2 + 3 + \frac{18}{2} = 14$. At a production level of 200 arrangements, the average cost is $1400 per hundred arrangements (or $14 per arrangement).

(c) Find the marginal average cost at production levels of 200 and 500 flower arrangements.

Solution The marginal average cost is the derivative of the average-cost function:

$$\overline{C}'(x) = \left(x + 3 + \frac{18}{x} \right)' = 1 - \frac{18}{x^2}.$$

Evaluating at $x = 2$ yields $\overline{C}'(2) = 1 - \frac{18}{2^2} = -3.5$. At this production level, if an additional hundred arrangements are produced, the average cost will be *decreased* by approximately $350 per hundred arrangements. Increasing production will lower the average cost.

Similarly, $\overline{C}'(5) = 1 - \frac{18}{5^2} = .28$. At this higher production level, if an additional hundred arrangements are produced, the average cost will be *increased* by approximately $28 per hundred arrangements. It would not make good business sense to increase production, since it would raise the average cost.

(d) Find the level of production at which the marginal average cost is zero.

Solution Set the derivative $\overline{C}'(x) = 0$ and solve for x:

$$1 - \frac{18}{x^2} = 0$$

$$\frac{x^2 - 18}{x^2} = 0 \qquad \text{Find a common denominator.}$$

$$x^2 - 18 = 0 \qquad \text{A rational function can be zero only when the numerator is zero.}$$

$$x^2 = 18$$

$$x = \pm\sqrt{18} \approx \pm 4.24.$$

You cannot make a negative number of flower arrangements, so $x = 4.24$. The production of 424 flower arrangements will yield a marginal average cost of zero dollars. ✔8

✓**Checkpoint 8**

The total cost (in hundreds of dollars) to produce x thousand items is given by

$$C(x) = 2x^2 + 15x + 50.$$

(a) Find $\overline{C}'(4)$.

(b) At a production level of 4000 items, if an additional 1000 items are produced, will the average cost per item increase or decrease?

11.6 Exercises

Use the product rule to find the derivatives of the given functions. (See Examples 1 and 2.) (Hint for Exercises 6–9: Write the quantity as a product.)

1. $y = (x^2 - 2)(3x + 2)$

2. $y = (2x^2 + 3)(3x + 5)$

3. $y = (6x^3 + 2)(5x - 3)$

4. $y = (2x^2 + 4x - 3)(5x^3 + 2x + 2)$

5. $y = (x^4 - 2x^3 + 2x)(4x^2 + x - 3)$

6. $y = (3x - 4)^2$

7. $y = (5x^2 + 12x)^2$

8. $y = (3x^2 - 8)^2$

9. $y = (4x^3 + 6x^2)^2$

Use the quotient rule to find the derivatives of the given functions. (See Examples 3 and 4.)

10. $y = \dfrac{x + 1}{2x - 1}$

11. $y = \dfrac{3x - 5}{x - 3}$

12. $f(x) = \dfrac{7x + 1}{3x + 6}$

13. $f(t) = \dfrac{t^2 - 4t}{t + 3}$

14. $y = \dfrac{4x + 11}{x^2 - 3}$

15. $g(x) = \dfrac{3x^2 + x}{2x^3 - 2}$

16. $k(x) = \dfrac{-x^2 + 6x}{4x^3 + 3}$

17. $y = \dfrac{x^2 - 4x + 2}{x + 3}$

18. $y = \dfrac{x^2 + 7x - 2}{x - 2}$

19. $r(t) = \dfrac{\sqrt{t}}{3t + 4}$

20. $y = \dfrac{5x + 8}{\sqrt{x}}$

21. $y = \dfrac{9x - 8}{\sqrt{x}}$

22. $y = \dfrac{2 - 7x}{5 - x}$

23. $y = \dfrac{59}{4x + 11}$

24. $f(t) = \dfrac{2t^2 + t}{t - 9}$

Find the derivative of each of the given functions. (See Example 5.)

25. $f(p) = \dfrac{(6p - 7)(11p - 1)}{4p + 3}$

26. $f(t) = \dfrac{(8t - 3)(2t + 5)}{t - 7}$

27. $g(x) = \dfrac{x^3 - 8}{(3x + 9)(2x - 1)}$

28. $f(x) = \dfrac{x^3 - 1}{(4x - 1)(3x + 7)}$

29. Find the error in the following work:

$$D_x\left(\frac{2x + 5}{x^2 - 1}\right) = \frac{(2x + 5)(2x) - (x^2 - 1)2}{(x^2 - 1)^2}$$

$$= \frac{4x^2 + 10x - 2x^2 + 2}{(x^2 - 1)^2}$$

$$= \frac{2x^2 + 10x + 2}{(x^2 - 1)^2}.$$

30. Find the error in the following work:

$$D_x\left(\frac{x^2 - 4}{x^3}\right) = x^3(2x) - (x^2 - 4)(3x^2)$$

$$= 2x^4 - 3x^4 + 12x^2 = -x^4 + 12x^2.$$

Find the equation of the tangent line to the graph of f(x) at the given point.

31. $f(x) = \dfrac{x}{x - 2}$ at $(3, 3)$

32. $f(x) = \dfrac{x}{x^2 + 2}$ at $(2, \frac{1}{3})$

33. $f(x) = \dfrac{(x - 1)(2x + 3)}{x - 5}$ at $(9, 42)$

34. $f(x) = \dfrac{(x + 3)^2}{x + 2}$ at $(-4, -\frac{1}{2})$

Work these exercises. (See Examples 6 and 7.)

35. **Business**   A hotdog vendor must pay a monthly fee to operate a food cart in the city park. The cost in dollars of selling x hundred hotdogs in a month can be approximated by

$$C(x) = 200 + 75x.$$

(a) Find the average-cost function.

(b) Find and interpret the average cost at sales levels of 1000 hotdogs and 5000 hotdogs.

(c) Find the marginal average-cost function.

(d) Find and interpret the marginal average cost at sales levels of 1000 hotdogs and 5000 hotdogs.

36. **Business**   For the vendor in the previous exercise, the revenue generated by selling x hundred hotdogs is $R(x) = 400x$ and so the profit function (revenue minus cost) is given by

$$P(x) = 325x - 200.$$

(a) Find and interpret the average profit at sales levels of 2000 hotdogs and 4000 hotdogs.

(b) Find and interpret the marginal average profit at sales levels of 2000 hotdogs and 4000 hotdogs.

37. **Business**   The Student Government Association is making Mother's Day gift baskets to sell at a fund-raiser. If the SGA makes a larger quantity of baskets, it can purchase materials in bulk. The total cost (in hundreds of dollars) of making x gift baskets can be approximated by

$$C(x) = \frac{10x + 1}{x + 100}.$$

(a) Find the marginal cost function and the marginal cost at $x = 20$ and $x = 40$.

(b) Find the average-cost function and the average cost at $x = 20$ and $x = 40$.

(c) Find the marginal average-cost function and the marginal average cost at $x = 20$ and $x = 40$.

38. **Business**   According to inventory records at a shoe store, the number of pairs of sandals (in hundreds) in stock can be approximated by

$$S(x) = \frac{2x + 175}{x + 10},$$

where x is the number of days since the start of the season. For the given times, find the number of pairs of sandals in stock and the rate at which sandals are being sold.

(a) The start of the season

(b) Sixty days after the start of the season

39. **Health**   During the course of an illness, a patient's temperature (in degrees Fahrenheit) x hours after the start of the illness is given by

$$T(x) = \frac{10x}{x^2 + 5} + 98.6.$$

(a) Find dT/dx.

Evaluate dT/dx at the following times, and interpret your answer:

(b) $x = 0$;   **(c)** $x = 1$;

(d) $x = 3$;   **(e)** $x = 9$.

40. Business The number of visitors (in thousands) who have entered a theme park on a typical day can be approximated by

$$V(x) = \frac{8x}{2x + 7},$$

where x is the number of hours since the park opened. At the given times, find the number of visitors who have entered the park and the rate at which visitors are entering.

(a) 2 hours after the park opens

(b) 6 hours after the park opens

Work these exercises.

41. Natural Science Murrell's formula for calculating the total amount of rest, in minutes, required after performing a particular type of work activity for 30 minutes is given by the formula

$$R(w) = 30\frac{w - 4}{w - 1.5},$$

where w is the work expended in kilocalories per min (kcal/min).[*]

(a) A value of 5 for w indicates light work, such as riding a bicycle on a flat surface at 10 miles per hour. Find $R(5)$.

(b) A value of 7 for w indicates moderate work, such as mowing grass with a push mower on level ground. Find $R(7)$.

(c) Find $R'(5)$ and $R'(7)$ and compare your answers. Explain whether these answers do or do not make sense.

42. Health When a certain drug is introduced into a muscle, the muscle responds by contracting. The amount of contraction, s, in millimeters, is related to the concentration of the drug, x, in milliliters, by

$$s(x) = \frac{x}{m + nx},$$

where m and n are constants.

(a) Find $s'(x)$.

(b) Evaluate $s'(x)$ when $x = 50$, $m = 10$, and $n = 3$.

(c) Interpret your results for part (b).

43. Business The average number of vehicles waiting in line to enter a parking lot can be modeled by the function

$$f(x) = \frac{x^2}{2(1 - x)},$$

where x is a quantity between 0 and 1 known as the traffic intensity.[†] Find the rate of change of the number of vehicles waiting

with respect to the traffic intensity for the following values of the intensity:

(a) $x = .1$ **(b)** $x = .6$.

44. Natural Science Using data collected by zoologist Reto Zach, researchers can estimate the work done by a crow to break open a whelk (a large marine snail) by the function

$$W = \left(1 + \frac{20}{H - .93}\right)H,$$

where H is the height of the whelk (in meters) when it is dropped.[‡]

(a) Find $\frac{dW}{dH}$.

(b) The amount of work is minimized when $\frac{dW}{dH} = 0$. Find the value of H that minimizes W.

(c) Interestingly, Zach observed the crows dropping the whelks from an average height of 5.23 meters. What does this imply?

45. Business Cashiers at a grocery store are required to learn codes for 80 produce items sold by the pound. The number of codes that a typical cashier has memorized after working x shifts can be approximated by

$$M(x) = \frac{80x^2}{x^2 + 75}.$$

(a) Find $M'(x)$, the rate at which the cashier is memorizing codes after x shifts.

(b) At what rate is the cashier memorizing codes after 1 shift? 3 shifts? 5 shifts? 8 shifts? 20 shifts?

(c) Interpret your results for part (b).

46. Natural Science The time it takes (in hours) to travel on the Garden State Parkway from the Delaware Memorial Bridge to the George Washington Bridge (assuming a 1-minute waiting time per toll plaza) can be approximated by

$$T(v) = \frac{117 + .3v}{v},$$

where v is the average velocity (in mph) while driving, excluding periods when stopped at toll plazas.

(a) Find and interpret $T(60)$.

(b) Find and interpret $T'(60)$.

✓**Checkpoint Answers**

1. (a) $f(x) = u(x)v(x) = x^5$ **(b)** $f'(x) = [u(x)v(x)]' = 5x^4$

(c) $u'(x) = 2x$ **(d)** $v'(x) = 3x^2$

(e) $u'(x)v'(x) = 6x^3$

(f) $5x^4 \neq 6x^3$, so the derivative of the product is not equal to the product of the derivatives

2. (a) $45x^2 + 18$ **(b)** $96x^2 + 80x$

[*]Mark Sanders and Ernest McCormick, *Human Factors in Engineering and Design*, Seventh Edition (New York: McGraw-Hill, 1993), pp. 243–246.

[†]F. Mannering and W. Kilareski, *Principles of Highway Engineering and Traffic Control*, Second Edition (John Wiley and Sons, 1997).

[‡]Brian Kellar and Heather Thompson, "Whelk-come to Mathematics," *Mathematics Teacher* 92, no. 6 (September 1999): 475–481.

3. (a) $\dfrac{5}{2}x^{3/2} + 10x - \dfrac{3}{2}x^{-1/2}$

(b) $\dfrac{25}{2}x^{3/2} + 40x + \dfrac{3}{2}x^{1/2} + 4$

4. (a) $\dfrac{-11}{(5x + 8)^2}$ (b) $\dfrac{-57}{(5x - 1)^2}$

5. (a) $\dfrac{-1 - 4x - x^2}{x^2 + 4x^3 + 4x^4}$ (b) $-\dfrac{6x^4 + 4x^3 + 1}{x^2(x^3 + 1)^2}$

6. (a) $\dfrac{6x^2 + 1}{x^2}$ (b) $\dfrac{-5x^2 - 10x}{(2x + 1)^2(x - 1)^2}$

7. (a) $\overline{C}(x) = \dfrac{x^2 + 2x + 5}{x^2 + x} + \dfrac{1000}{x}$

(b) $\overline{C}'(x) = -\dfrac{x^2 + 10x + 5}{(x^2 + x)^2} - \dfrac{1000}{x^2}$

8. (a) -1.125 (b) Decrease

11.7 The Chain Rule

Many of the most useful functions for applications are created by combining simpler functions. Viewing complex functions as combinations of simpler functions often makes them easier to understand and use.

Composition of Functions

Consider the function h whose rule is $h(x) = \sqrt{x^3}$. To compute $h(4)$, for example, you first find $4^3 = 64$ and then take the square root: $\sqrt{64} = 8$. So the rule of h may be rephrased as follows:

First apply the function $f(x) = x^3$.

Then apply the function $g(x) = \sqrt{x}$ to the preceding result.

The same idea can be expressed in functional notation like this:

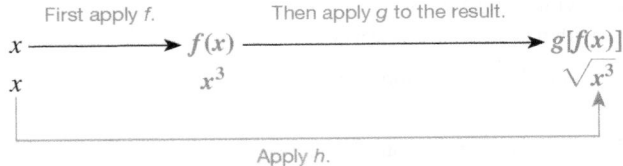

So the rule of h may be written as $h(x) = g[f(x)]$, where $f(x) = x^3$ and $g(x) = \sqrt{x}$. We can think of the functions g and f as being "composed" to create the function h. Here is a formal definition of this idea.

Composite Function

Let f and g be functions. The **composite function,** or **composition,** of g and f is the function whose values are given by $g[f(x)]$ for all x in the domain of f such that $f(x)$ is in the domain of g.

Example 1   Let $f(x) = 2x - 1$ and $g(x) = \sqrt{3x + 5}$. Find each of the following.

(a) $g[f(4)]$

Solution   Find $f(4)$ first:

$$f(4) = 2 \cdot 4 - 1 = 8 - 1 = 7.$$

Then

$$g[f(4)] = g[7] = \sqrt{3 \cdot 7 + 5} = \sqrt{26}.$$

(b) $f[g(4)]$

Solution Since $g(4) = \sqrt{3 \cdot 4 + 5} = \sqrt{17}$,

$$f[g(4)] = 2 \cdot \sqrt{17} - 1 = 2\sqrt{17} - 1.$$

(c) $f[g(-2)]$

Solution This composite function does not exist, since -2 is not in the domain of g. ✓₁

✓ **Checkpoint 1**

Let $f(x) = 3x - 2$ and $g(x) = (x - 1)^5$. Find the following.

(a) $g[f(2)]$

(b) $f[g(2)]$

Example 2 Let $f(x) = 4x + 1$ and $g(x) = 2x^2 + 5x$. Find each of the following.

(a) $g[f(x)]$

Solution Use the given functions:

$$\begin{aligned}
g[f(x)] &= g[4x + 1] \\
&= 2(4x + 1)^2 + 5(4x + 1) \\
&= 2(16x^2 + 8x + 1) + 20x + 5 \\
&= 32x^2 + 16x + 2 + 20x + 5 \\
&= 32x^2 + 36x + 7.
\end{aligned}$$

(b) $f[g(x)]$

Solution By the definition of a composite function, with f and g interchanged, we have

$$\begin{aligned}
f[g(x)] &= f[2x^2 + 5x] \\
&= 4(2x^2 + 5x) + 1 \\
&= 8x^2 + 20x + 1. \; ✓_2
\end{aligned}$$

✓ **Checkpoint 2**

Let $f(x) = \sqrt{x + 4}$ and $g(x) = x^2 + 5x + 1$. Find $f[g(x)]$ and $g[f(x)]$.

As Example 2 shows, $f[g(x)]$ usually is *not* equal to $g[f(x)]$. In fact, it is rare to find two functions f and g for which $f[g(x)] = g[f(x)]$.

It is often necessary to write a given function as the composite of two other functions, as is illustrated in the next example.

Example 3

(a) Express the function $h(x) = (x^3 + x^2 - 5)^4$ as the composite of two functions.

Solution One way to do this is to let $f(x) = x^3 + x^2 - 5$ and $g(x) = x^4$; then

$$g[f(x)] = g[x^3 + x^2 - 5] = (x^3 + x^2 - 5)^4 = h(x).$$

(b) Express the function $h(x) = \sqrt{4x^2 + 5}$ as the composite of two functions in two different ways.

✓ **Checkpoint 3**

Express the given function as a composite of two other functions.

(a) $h(x) = (7x^2 + 5)^4$

(b) $h(x) = \sqrt{15x^2 + 1}$

Solution One way is to let $f(x) = 4x^2 + 5$ and $g(x) = \sqrt{x}$, so that

$$g[f(x)] = g[4x^2 + 5] = \sqrt{4x^2 + 5} = h(x).$$

Another way is to let $k(x) = 4x^2$ and $t(x) = \sqrt{x + 5}$; then

$$t[k(x)] = t[4x^2] = \sqrt{4x^2 + 5} = h(x). \; ✓_3$$

The Chain Rule

The product and quotient rules tell how to find the derivative of fg and f/g from the derivatives of f and g. To develop a way to find the derivative of the composite function $f[g(x)]$ from the derivatives of f and g, we consider an example.

Metal expands or contracts as the temperature changes, and the temperature changes over a period of time. Think of the length y of a metal bar as a function of the temperature d, say, $y = f(d)$, and the temperature d as a function of time x, say, $d = g(x)$. Then

$$y = f(d) = f(g(x)).$$

So the composite function $f(g(x))$ gives the length y as a function of time x.

Suppose that the length of the bar is increasing at the rate of 2 mm for every degree increase in temperature and that the temperature is increasing at the rate of 4° per hour. In functional notation, this means that $f'(d) = 2$ and $g'(x) = 4$. During the course of an hour, the length of the bar will increase by $2 \cdot 4 = 8$ mm. So the rate of change of the length y with respect to time x is 8 mm/hr; that is, $y' = 8$. Consequently,

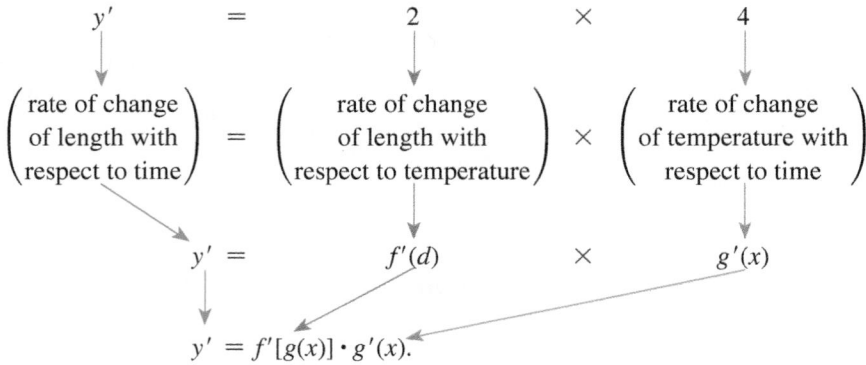

This example shows how the derivative of the composite function y is related to the derivatives of f and g. The same result holds for any composite function.

Chain Rule

If f and g are functions and $y = f[g(x)]$, then

$$y' = f'[g(x)] \cdot g'(x),$$

provided that $f'[g(x)]$ and $g'(x)$ exist.

(To find the derivative of $f[g(x)]$, find the derivative of $f(x)$, replace each x with $g(x)$, and multiply the result by the derivative of $g(x)$.)

Example 4 Use the chain rule to find $D_x\sqrt{15x^2 + 1}$.

Solution Write $\sqrt{15x^2 + 1}$ as $(15x^2 + 1)^{1/2}$. Let $f(x) = x^{1/2}$ and $g(x) = 15x^2 + 1$. Then $\sqrt{15x^2 + 1} = f[g(x)]$ and

$$D_x(15x^2 + 1)^{1/2} = f'[g(x)] \cdot g'(x).$$

Here, $f'(x) = \frac{1}{2}x^{-1/2}$, with $f'[g(x)] = \frac{1}{2}[g(x)]^{-1/2}$, and $g'(x) = 30x$ so that

$$D_x\sqrt{15x^2 + 1} = \frac{1}{2}[g(x)]^{-1/2} \cdot g'(x)$$

$$= \frac{1}{2}(15x^2 + 1)^{-1/2} \cdot (30x)$$

$$= \frac{15x}{(15x^2 + 1)^{1/2}}. \quad ✓_4$$

✓ **Checkpoint 4**

Let $y = \sqrt{2x^4 + 3}$.
Find dy/dx.

The chain rule can also be stated in the Leibniz notation for derivatives. If y is a function of u, say, $y = f(u)$, and u is a function of x, say, $u = g(x)$, then

$$f'(u) = \frac{dy}{du} \quad \text{and} \quad g'(x) = \frac{du}{dx}.$$

Now y can be considered a function of x, namely, $y = f(u) = f(g(x))$. According to the chain rule, the derivative of y is

$$\frac{dy}{dx} = f'(g(x)) \cdot g'(x) = f'(u) \cdot g'(x) = \frac{dy}{du} \cdot \frac{du}{dx}.$$

Thus, we have the following alternative version of the chain rule.

The Chain Rule (Alternative Form)

If y is a function of u, say, $y = f(u)$, and if u is a function of x, say, $u = g(x)$, then $y = f(u) = f[g(x)]$ and

$$\frac{dy}{dx} = \frac{dy}{du} \cdot \frac{du}{dx},$$

provided that dy/du and du/dx exist.

One way to remember the chain rule is to *pretend* that dy/du and du/dx are fractions, with du "canceling out."

Example 5 Find dy/dx if $y = (3x^2 - 5x)^7$.

Solution Let $y = u^7$, where $u = 3x^2 - 5x$. Then $\frac{dy}{du} = 7u^6$ and $\frac{du}{dx} = 6x - 5$.
Hence,

$$\frac{dy}{dx} = \frac{dy}{du} \cdot \frac{du}{dx}$$

$$= 7u^6 \cdot (6x - 5).$$

Replacing u with $3x^2 - 5x$ gives

✓ **Checkpoint 5**

Use the chain rule to find dy/dx if
$y = 10(2x^2 + 1)^4$.

$$\frac{dy}{dx} = 7(3x^2 - 5x)^6(6x - 5). \quad ✓_5$$

Each of the functions in Examples 4 and 5 has the form $y = u^n$, with u a function of x:

$$y = (15x^2 + 1)^{1/2} \quad \text{and} \quad y = (3x^2 - 5x)^7.$$
$$y = u^{1/2} \qquad\qquad\qquad y = u^7.$$

Their derivatives are

$$y' = \frac{1}{2}(15x^2 + 1)^{-1/2}(30x) \quad \text{and} \quad y' = 7(3x^2 - 5x)^6(6x - 5)$$

$$y' = \frac{1}{2}u^{-1/2}\,u' \qquad\qquad\qquad y' = 7u^6\,u'.$$

Thus, these functions are examples of the following special case of the chain rule.

Generalized Power Rule

Let u be a function of x, and let $y = u^n$, for any real number n. Then

$$y' = n \cdot u^{n-1} \cdot u',$$

provided that u' exists.

(The derivative of $y = u^n$ is found by decreasing the exponent on u by 1 and multiplying the result by the exponent n and by the derivative of u with respect to x.)

Example 6

(a) Use the generalized power rule to find the derivative of $y = (3 + 5x)^2$.

Solution Let $u = 3 + 5x$ and $n = 2$. Then $u' = 5$. By the generalized power rule,

$$y' = n \cdot u^{n-1} \cdot u'$$

$$
\begin{array}{cccc}
n & u & n-1 & u' \\
\downarrow & \downarrow & \downarrow & \downarrow
\end{array}
$$

$$= 2 \cdot (3 + 5x)^{2-1} \cdot \frac{d}{dx}(3 + 5x)$$

$$= 2(3 + 5x)^{2-1} \cdot 5$$

$$= 10(3 + 5x)$$

$$= 30 + 50x.$$

(b) Find y' if $y = (3 + 5x)^{-3/4}$.

Solution Use the generalized power rule with $n = -\dfrac{3}{4}$, $u = 3 + 5x$, and $u' = 5$:

$$y' = -\frac{3}{4}(3 + 5x)^{(-3/4)-1}(5)$$

$$= -\frac{15}{4}(3 + 5x)^{-7/4}. \quad \boxed{\checkmark\, 6}$$

✓ **Checkpoint 6**

Find dy/dx for the given functions.

(a) $y = (2x + 5)^6$

(b) $y = (4x^2 - 7)^3$

(c) $f(x) = \sqrt{3x^2 - x}$

(d) $g(x) = (2 - x^4)^{-3}$

Example 7 Find the derivative of the given function.

(a) $y = 2(7x^2 + 5)^4$

Solution   Let $u = 7x^2 + 5$. Then $u' = 14x$, and

$$
\begin{array}{cccc}
n & u & n-1 & u' \\
\downarrow & \downarrow & \downarrow & \downarrow
\end{array}
$$

$$y' = 2 \cdot 4(7x^2 + 5)^{4-1} \cdot \frac{d}{dx}(7x^2 + 5)$$

$$= 2 \cdot 4(7x^2 + 5)^3(14x)$$

$$= 112x(7x^2 + 5)^3.$$

(b) $y = \sqrt{9x + 2}$

Solution   Write $y = \sqrt{9x + 2}$ as $y = (9x + 2)^{1/2}$. Then

$$y' = \frac{1}{2}(9x + 2)^{-1/2}(9) = \frac{9}{2}(9x + 2)^{-1/2}.$$

The derivative also can be written as

$$y' = \frac{9}{2(9x + 2)^{1/2}} \quad \text{or} \quad y' = \frac{9}{2\sqrt{9x + 2}}. \quad \checkmark_7$$

✓ Checkpoint 7

Find dy/dx for the given functions.

(a) $y = 12(x^2 + 6)^5$

(b) $y = 8(4x^2 + 2)^{3/2}$

⊘ CAUTION

(a) A common error is to forget to multiply by $g'(x)$ when using the generalized power rule. Remember, the generalized power rule is an example of the chain rule, so the derivative must involve a "chain," or product, of derivatives.

(b) Another common mistake is to write the derivative as $n[g'(x)]^{n-1}$. Remember to leave $g(x)$ unchanged and then to multiply by $g'(x)$.

Sometimes both the generalized power rule and either the product or quotient rule are needed to find a derivative, as the next two examples show.

Example 8   Find the derivative of $y = 4x(3x + 5)^5$.

Solution   Write $4x(3x + 5)^5$ as the product

$$y = 4x \cdot (3x + 5)^5.$$

According to the product rule,

$$y' = 4x \cdot \frac{d}{dx}(3x + 5)^5 + (3x + 5)^5 \cdot \frac{d}{dx}(4x).$$

Use the generalized power rule to find the derivative of $(3x + 5)^5$;

$$\text{Derivative of } (3x+5)^5 \qquad \text{Derivative of } 4x$$

$$y' = 4x[\overbrace{5(3x + 5)^4 \cdot 3}] + (3x + 5)^5 \overbrace{(4)}$$

$$= 60x(3x + 5)^4 + 4(3x + 5)^5$$

$$= 4(3x + 5)^4[15x + (3x + 5)^1] \qquad \text{Factor out the greatest common}$$

$$= 4(3x + 5)^4(18x + 5). \quad \checkmark_8 \qquad \text{factor, } 4(3x + 5)^4.$$

✓ Checkpoint 8

Find the derivatives of the given functions.

(a) $y = 9x(x + 7)^2$

(b) $y = -3x(4x^2 + 7)^3$

Example 9   Find the derivative of

$$y = \frac{(3x + 2)^7}{x - 1}.$$

Solution Use the quotient rule and the generalized power rule:

$$\frac{dy}{dx} = \frac{(x-1)\cdot\frac{d}{dx}(3x+2)^7 - (3x+2)^7\frac{d}{dx}(x-1)}{(x-1)^2} \quad \text{Quotient rule}$$

$$= \frac{(x-1)[7(3x+2)^6\cdot 3] - (3x+2)^7(1)}{(x-1)^2} \quad \text{Generalized power rule}$$

$$= \frac{21(x-1)(3x+2)^6 - (3x+2)^7}{(x-1)^2}$$

$$= \frac{(3x+2)^6[21(x-1) - (3x+2)]}{(x-1)^2} \quad \begin{array}{l}\text{Factor out the greatest}\\\text{common factor, } (3x+2)^6.\end{array}$$

$$= \frac{(3x+2)^6[21x - 21 - 3x - 2]}{(x-1)^2} \quad \text{Simplify inside brackets.}$$

$$= \frac{(3x+2)^6(18x-23)}{(x-1)^2}. \quad \boxed{\checkmark\,9}$$

✓**Checkpoint 9**

Find the derivatives of the given functions.

(a) $y = \dfrac{(5x+2)^3}{11x}$

(b) $y = \dfrac{(x-12)^7}{6x+1}$

Applications

Some applications requiring the use of the chain rule or the generalized power rule are illustrated in the next three examples.

Example 10   **Business**   During a week-long promotion, the profit generated by an online sporting goods retailer from the sale of n official basketballs is given by

$$P(n) = \frac{45n^2}{3n+10}.$$

Sales are approximately constant at a rate of 25 basketballs per day, therefore $\dfrac{dn}{dt} = 25$. How fast is profit changing 4 days after the start of the promotion?

Solution   We want to find $\dfrac{dP}{dt}$, the rate of change of profit with respect to time. By the chain rule,

$$\frac{dP}{dt} = \frac{dP}{dn}\frac{dn}{dt}.$$

First find $\dfrac{dP}{dn}$ as follows:

$$\frac{dP}{dn} = \frac{(3n+10)(90n) - (45n^2)(3)}{(3n+10)^2} \quad \text{Quotient rule}$$

$$= \frac{270n^2 + 900n - 135n^2}{(3n+10)^2}$$

$$= \frac{135n^2 + 900n}{(3n+10)^2}.$$

With sales at 25 basketballs per day, 4 days after the start of the promotion, $n = (4\text{ days})(25\text{ basketballs/day}) = 100$ basketballs. So after 4 days,

$$\frac{dP}{dn} = \frac{135(100)^2 + 900(100)}{(3(100)+10)^2} \approx 14.9844.$$

We are given that $\dfrac{dn}{dt} = 25$, so we have

$$\frac{dP}{dt} = \frac{dP}{dn}\frac{dn}{dt} = (14.9844)(25) \approx 374.61.$$

After 4 days, profit from basketballs is increasing at a rate of $374.61 per day. ✓10

Example 11   **Business**   A generous aunt deposits $20,000 in an account to be used by her newly born niece to attend college. The account earns interest at the rate of r percent per year, compounded monthly. At the end of 18 years, the balance in the account is given by

$$A = 20,000\left(1 + \frac{r}{1200}\right)^{216}.$$

Find the rate of change of A with respect to r if $r = 1.5, 2.5,$ or 3.

Solution   First find dA/dr, using the generalized power rule:

$$\frac{dA}{dr} = (216)(20,000)\left(1 + \frac{r}{1200}\right)^{215}\left(\frac{1}{1200}\right) = 3600\left(1 + \frac{r}{1200}\right)^{215}.$$

If $r = 1.5$, we obtain

$$\frac{dA}{dr} = 3600\left(1 + \frac{1.5}{1200}\right)^{215} = 4709.19,$$

or $4709.19 per percentage point. If $r = 2.5$, we obtain

$$\frac{dA}{dr} = 3600\left(1 + \frac{2.5}{1200}\right)^{215} = 5631.55,$$

or $5631.55 per percentage point. If $r = 3$, we obtain

$$\frac{dA}{dr} = 3600\left(1 + \frac{3}{1200}\right)^{215} = 6158.07,$$

or $6158.07 per percentage point. This means that when the interest rate is 3%, an increase of 1% in the interest rate will produce an increase in the balance of approximately $6158.07. ✓11

The chain rule can be used to develop the formula for the **marginal-revenue product,** an economic concept that approximates the change in revenue when a manufacturer hires an additional employee. Start with $R = px$, where R is total revenue from the daily production of x units and p is the price per unit. The demand function is $p = f(x)$, as before. Also, x can be considered a function of the number of employees, n. Since $R = px$, and x—and therefore, p—depends on n, R can also be considered a function of n. To find an expression for dR/dn, use the product rule for derivatives on the function $R = px$ to get

$$\frac{dR}{dn} = p \cdot \frac{dx}{dn} + x \cdot \frac{dp}{dn}. \qquad (*)$$

By the chain rule,

$$\frac{dp}{dn} = \frac{dp}{dx} \cdot \frac{dx}{dn}.$$

Substituting for dp/dn in equation (∗) yields

$$\frac{dR}{dn} = p \cdot \frac{dx}{dn} + x\left(\frac{dp}{dx} \cdot \frac{dx}{dn}\right)$$

$$= \left(p + x \cdot \frac{dp}{dx}\right)\frac{dx}{dn}. \qquad \text{Factor out } \frac{dx}{dn}.$$

The expression for dR/dn gives the marginal-revenue product.

Example 12   **Business**   Find the marginal-revenue product dR/dn (in dollars per employee) when $n = 20$ if the demand function is $p = 600/\sqrt{x}$ and $x = 5n$.

Solution   As shown previously,

$$\frac{dR}{dn} = \left(p + x \cdot \frac{dp}{dx}\right)\frac{dx}{dn}.$$

Find dp/dx and dx/dn. From

$$p = \frac{600}{\sqrt{x}} = 600x^{-1/2},$$

we have the derivative

$$\frac{dp}{dx} = -300x^{-3/2}.$$

Also, from $x = 5n$, we have

$$\frac{dx}{dn} = 5.$$

Then, by substitution,

$$\frac{dR}{dn} = \left[\frac{600}{\sqrt{x}} + x(-300x^{-3/2})\right]5 = \left[\frac{600}{\sqrt{x}} - \frac{300}{\sqrt{x}}\right]5 = \frac{1500}{\sqrt{x}}.$$

If $n = 20$, then $x = 100$, and

$$\frac{dR}{dn} = \frac{1500}{\sqrt{100}}$$

$$= 150.$$

✓ **Checkpoint 12**

Find the marginal-revenue product at $n = 10$ if the demand function is $p = 1000/x^2$ and $x = 8n$. Interpret your answer.

This means that hiring an additional employee when production is at a level of 100 items will produce an increase in revenue of $150. ✓₁₂

11.7 Exercises

Let $f(x) = 2x^2 + 3x$ and $g(x) = 4x - 1$. Find each of the given values. (See Example 1.)

1. $f[g(5)]$

2. $f[g(-4)]$

3. $g[f(5)]$

4. $g[f(-4)]$

Find $f[g(x)]$ and $g[f(x)]$ for the given functions. (See Example 2.)

5. $f(x) = 8x + 12; g(x) = 2x + 3$

6. $f(x) = -6x + 9; g(x) = 5x + 7$

7. $f(x) = -x^3 + 2; g(x) = 4x + 2$

8. $f(x) = 2x; g(x) = 6x^2 - x^3 - 1$

9. $f(x) = \frac{1}{x}; g(x) = x^2$

10. $f(x) = \frac{2}{x^4}; g(x) = 2 - x$

11. $f(x) = \sqrt{x + 2}; g(x) = 8x^2 - 6x$

12. $f(x) = 9x^2 - 11x; g(x) = 2\sqrt{x + 2}$

Write each function as a composition of two functions. (There may be more than one way to do this.) (See Example 3.)

13. $y = (4x + 3)^5$

14. $y = (x^2 + 2)^{1/5}$

15. $y = \sqrt{6 + 3x^2}$

16. $y = \sqrt{x + 3} - \sqrt[3]{x + 3}$

17. $y = \dfrac{\sqrt{x + 3}}{\sqrt{x - 3}}$

18. $y = \dfrac{2x}{\sqrt{x + 5}}$

19. $y = (x^{1/2} - 3)^3 + (x^{1/2} - 3) + 5$

20. $y = (x^2 + 5x)^{1/3} - 2(x^2 + 5x)^{2/3} + 7$

Find the derivative of each of the given functions. (See Examples 4–7.)

21. $y = (7x - 12)^5$

22. $y = (13x - 3)^4$

23. $y = 7(4x + 3)^4$

24. $y = -4(3x - 2)^7$

25. $y = -4(10x^2 + 8)^5$

26. $y = -3(x^4 + 7x^2)^3$

27. $y = 11(3x + 5)^{3/2}$

28. $y = 13(4x - 2)^{2/3}$

29. $y = -7(4x^2 + 9x)^{3/2}$

30. $y = 11(5x^2 + 6x)^{3/2}$

31. $y = 8\sqrt{4x + 7}$

32. $y = -3\sqrt{7x - 1}$

33. $y = -2\sqrt{x^2 + 4x}$

34. $y = 4\sqrt{2x^2 + 3}$

Use the product or quotient rule or the generalized power rule to find the derivative of each of the given functions. (See Examples 8 and 9.)

35. $y = (x + 1)(x - 3)^2$

36. $y = (2x + 1)^3(x - 5)$

37. $y = 5(x + 3)^2(2x - 1)^5$

38. $y = -9(x + 4)^2(2x - 3)^3$

39. $y = (3x + 1)^3\sqrt{x}$

40. $y = (3x + 5)^2\sqrt{x + 1}$

41. $y = \dfrac{1}{(x - 2)^3}$

42. $y = \dfrac{-3}{(4x + 1)^2}$

43. $y = \dfrac{(2x - 7)^2}{4x - 1}$

44. $y = \dfrac{(x - 4)^2}{5x + 2}$

45. $y = \dfrac{x^2 + 5x}{(3x + 1)^3}$

46. $y = \dfrac{4x^3 - x}{(x - 3)^2}$

47. $y = (x^{1/2} + 2)(2x + 3)$

48. $y = (4 - x^{2/3})(x + 1)^{1/2}$

Consider the following table of values of the functions f and g and their derivatives at various points:

x	1	2	3	4
$f(x)$	2	4	1	3
$f'(x)$	-6	-7	-8	-9
$g(x)$	2	3	4	1
$g'(x)$	2/7	3/7	4/7	5/7

Find each of the given derivatives.

49. (a) $D_x(f[g(x)])$ at $x = 1$ (b) $D_x(f[g(x)])$ at $x = 2$

50. (a) $D_x(g[f(x)])$ at $x = 1$ (b) $D_x(g[f(x)])$ at $x = 2$

51. If $f(x) = (2x^2 + 3x + 1)^{50}$, then which of the following is closest to $f'(0)$?

(a) 1   (b) 50   (c) 100

(d) 150   (e) 200   (f) 250

52. The graphs of $f(x) = 3x + 5$ and $g(x) = 4x - 1$ are straight lines.

(a) Show that the graph of $f[g(x)]$ is also a straight line.

(b) How are the slopes of the graphs of $f(x)$ and $g(x)$ related to the slope of the graph of $f[g(x)]$?

Work these exercises. (See Examples 10 and 11.)

53. Business Suppose the demand for a certain brand of vacuum cleaner is given by

$$D(p) = \dfrac{-p^2}{100} + 500,$$

where p is the price in dollars. If the price, in terms of the cost c, is expressed as

$$p(c) = 2c - 10,$$

find the demand in terms of the cost.

54. Natural Science An oil well off the Gulf Coast is leaking, spreading oil in a circle over the surface. At any time t, in minutes, after the beginning of the leak, the radius of the circular oil slick on the surface is $r(t) = t^2$ feet. Let $A(r) = \pi r^2$ represent the area of a circle of radius r. Find and interpret $A[r(t)]$.

55. Business You are driving on a business trip to another city. Let $D(g)$ represent the distance (in miles) you can drive on g gallons of gas. Let $T(D)$ represent the time it takes (in hours) to drive a distance of D miles. Let $f(g) = T[D(g)]$.

(a) What does $f(g) = T[D(g)]$ represent?

(b) Explain what $D(4) = 120$ means in practical terms.

(c) Explain what $T'(120) = \dfrac{1}{60}$ means in practical terms.

(d) Explain what $D'(4) = 30$ means in practical terms.

(e) Find and interpret $f'(4)$.

56. Business A contractor has determined formulas for the following functions. Let $H(d)$ be the number of hours that a tile-setter will work for d dollars. Let $A(t)$ be the area (in square feet) that a tile-setter can tile in t hours. Let $f(d) = A[H(d)]$.

(a) What does $f(d) = A[H(d)]$ represent?

(b) Explain what $f'(900) = .4$ means in practical terms.

57. Business The cost of producing x bags of dog food is given by

$$C(x) = 600 + \sqrt{200 + 25x^2 - x} \qquad (0 \le x \le 5000).$$

Find the marginal-cost function.

58. Business The cost (in hundreds of dollars) of producing x smart phones is given by

$$C(x) = 900 + \sqrt{5x^2 + 4x + 1200}.$$

(a) Find the marginal-cost function.

(b) Find and interpret $C'(200)$.

59. Business The revenue function from the sale of x earbuds for portable music players is given by

$$R(x) = 15\sqrt{500x - 2x^2} \qquad (0 \le x \le 200).$$

(a) Find the marginal-revenue function.

(b) Evaluate the marginal-revenue function at $x = 40$, 80, 120, and 160.

(c) Explain the significance of the answers found in part (b).

60. Business The profit (in thousands of dollars) of producing x thousand pairs of running shoes is given by

$$P(x) = 45\sqrt[3]{x^3 + 246x + 500} - 500 \qquad (0 \le x \le 100).$$

(a) Is the company profitable or losing money when producing 2000 pairs of running shoes? 6000 pairs?

(b) Find the marginal-profit function.

61. Business A tablet computer is purchased for $500. Its value in dollars after t years can be approximated by

$$V(t) = \frac{500}{(2t + 1)^2} \qquad (0 \le t \le 4).$$

(a) Find the value of the tablet computer 2 years after purchase.

(b) At time $t = 2$ years, use a derivative to estimate how much the value will change within the next year.

62. Health The percent of patients who report being symptom-free t days after the onset of a certain illness can be approximated by

$$F(t) = 100 - \frac{200}{\sqrt{t^2 + 4}} \qquad (0 \le t \le 7).$$

Find the rate at which patients are recovering after the given number of days.

(a) 2 days   **(b)** 5 days

63. Business The demand function for tickets to the student theatrical production is given by

$$p = \sqrt{900 - 2x} \qquad (0 \le x \le 450),$$

where x is the number of tickets demanded and p is the price in dollars.

(a) Find the revenue as a function of x.

(b) Find the marginal-revenue function.

(c) Find and interpret the marginal revenue at $x = 250$.

64. Business The demand (in thousands) for a certain smart phone app as a function of the price $\$p$ is given by

$$x = 30(8 - .5p^2)^{1/2} \qquad (0 \le p \le 4).$$

(a) Find the demand when the price is $2.

(b) Find the rate of change of demand with respect to price when the price is $2.

65. Finance An amount of $15,000 is deposited in an account with an interest rate of r percent per year, compounded monthly. At the end of 8 years, the balance in the account is given by

$$A = 15{,}000\left(1 + \frac{r}{1200}\right)^{96}.$$

Find the rate of change of A with respect to r (written as a percentage) for the given interest rates.

(a) 2.5%   **(b)** 3.25%   **(c)** 4%

66. Finance An amount of $8000 is invested in a 5-year certificate of deposit with an interest rate of r percent per year, compounded quarterly. On the maturity date, the value of the certificate of deposit is given by

$$A = 8000\left(1 + \frac{r}{400}\right)^{20}.$$

(a) Would you expect the rate of change of A with respect to r to be positive, negative, or zero? Why?

(b) Find $\dfrac{dA}{dr}$.

(c) Find and interpret $\dfrac{dA}{dr}$ at an interest rate of 2%. (Use $r = 2$ not $r = .02$, since r is written as a percentage.)

67. Finance An amount of $25,000 is invested in a money market account with an interest rate of r percent per year, compounded monthly. At the end of 2 years, the balance on the account is given by

$$A = 25{,}000\left(1 + \frac{r}{1200}\right)^{24}.$$

Find and interpret the rate of change of A with respect to r (written as a percentage) for the given interest rates.

(a) 1%   **(b)** 2%   **(c)** 4%

68. Finance The price (present value) of a zero coupon bond with a face value of $5000, a maturity date of 10 years, and an interest rate of r percent compounded annually is given by

$$P = \frac{5000}{\left(1 + \dfrac{r}{100}\right)^{10}}.$$

(a) Find the price of this bond, assuming an interest rate of 4%. (Use $r = 4$ not $r = .04$, since r is written as a percentage.)

(b) Would you expect the rate of change of P with respect to r to be positive, negative, or zero? Why?

(c) Find $\dfrac{dP}{dr}$.

(d) Find and interpret $\dfrac{dP}{dr}$ at an interest rate of 4%.

Work these exercises. (See Example 12.)

69. Business Find the marginal-revenue product for a manufacturer with 10 workers if the demand function is $p = \dfrac{200 - x}{4}$ and if $x = 6n$.

70. Business Find the marginal-revenue product for a manufacturer with 5 workers if the demand function is $p = \dfrac{210}{\sqrt{x}}$ and if $x = 45n$.

Work the following exercises.

71. Business A cost function is given by $C(x) = \sqrt{6x + 5}$, where x is the number of items produced.

  (a) Find the average-cost function.

  (b) Find the marginal average-cost function.

72. Social Science The percent of the adult population of a city who have heard about a scandal in the city government t days after it occurs can be approximated by

$$F(t) = \frac{85t}{\sqrt{t^2 + 2}}.$$

  (a) What percent of the population is aware of the scandal after 1 day?

  (b) Find $F'(t)$.

  (c) Find and interpret $F'(1)$.

73. Natural Science To test an individual's use of calcium, a researcher injects a small amount of radioactive calcium into the person's bloodstream. The calcium remaining in the bloodstream is measured each day for several days. Suppose the amount of the calcium remaining in the bloodstream, in milligrams per cubic centimeter, t days after the initial injection is approximated by

$$C(t) = \frac{1}{2}(2t + 1)^{-1/2}.$$

Find the rate of change of C with respect to time for each of the given number of days.

  (a) $t = 0$ **(b)** $t = 4$

  (c) $t = 6$ **(d)** $t = 7.5$

74. Health The strength of a person's reaction to a certain drug is given by

$$R(Q) = Q\left(C - \frac{Q}{3}\right)^{1/2},$$

where Q represents the quantity of the drug given to the patient and C is a constant. The derivative $R'(Q)$ is called the *sensitivity* to the drug.

  (a) Find $R'(Q)$.

  (b) Find $R'(Q)$ if $Q = 87$ and $C = 59$.

75. Social Science Studies show that after t hours on the job, the number of items a supermarket cashier can scan per minute is given by

$$F(t) = 60 - \frac{150}{\sqrt{8 + t^2}}.$$

  (a) Find $F'(t)$, the rate at which the cashier's speed is increasing.

  (b) At what rate is the cashier's speed increasing after 5 hours? 10 hours? 20 hours? 40 hours?

  (c) Are your answers in part (b) increasing or decreasing with time? Is this reasonable? Explain.

76. Natural Science The volume and surface area of a jawbreaker candy of any radius r are given by the formulas

$$V(r) = \frac{4}{3}\pi r^3 \quad \text{and} \quad S(r) = 4\pi r^2,$$

respectively. It is estimated that the radius of a jawbreaker while in a person's mouth is

$$r(t) = 6 - \frac{3}{17}t,$$

where $r(t)$ is in mm and t is in min.[*]

  (a) What is the life expectancy of a jawbreaker?

  (b) Find $\dfrac{dV}{dt}$ and $\dfrac{dS}{dt}$ when $t = 17$, and interpret your answer.

  (c) Construct an analogous experiment using some other type of food, or verify the results of this experiment.

✓ Checkpoint Answers

1. (a) 243   **(b)** 1

2. $f[g(x)] = \sqrt{x^2 + 5x + 5}$;

  $g[f(x)] = (\sqrt{x + 4})^2 + 5\sqrt{x + 4} + 1$

    $= x + 5 + 5\sqrt{x + 4}$

3. There are several correct answers, including

  (a) $h(x) = f[g(x)]$, where $f(x) = x^4$ and $g(x) = 7x^2 + 5$;

  (b) $h(x) = f[g(x)]$, where $f(x) = \sqrt{x}$ and $g(x) = 15x^2 + 1$.

4. $\dfrac{dy}{dx} = \dfrac{4x^3}{\sqrt{2x^4 + 3}}$

5. $160x(2x^2 + 1)^3$

6. (a) $12(2x + 5)^5$ **(b)** $24x(4x^2 - 7)^2$

  (c) $\dfrac{6x - 1}{2\sqrt{3x^2 - x}}$ **(d)** $\dfrac{12x^3}{(2 - x^4)^4}$

7. (a) $120x(x^2 + 6)^4$ **(b)** $96x(4x^2 + 2)^{1/2}$

8. (a) $9(x + 7)(3x + 7)$ **(b)** $-21(4x^2 + 7)^2(4x^2 + 1)$

9. (a) $\dfrac{11(5x + 2)^2(10x - 2)}{121x^2}$ **(b)** $\dfrac{(x - 12)^6(36x + 79)}{(6x + 1)^2}$

10. \$117.55 per day

11. \$6437.32 per percentage point

12. $-\$1.25$; hiring an additional employee will produce a decrease in revenue of \$1.25.

[*]Roger Guffey, "The Life Expectancy of a Jawbreaker: An Application of the Composition of Functions," *Mathematics Teacher* 92, no. 2 (February 1999): 125–127.

11.8   Derivatives of Exponential and Logarithmic Functions

The exponential function $f(x) = e^x$ and the logarithmic function to the base e, $g(x) = \ln x$, were studied in Chapter 4. (Recall that $e \approx 2.71828$.) We are interested in exponential and logarithmic functions because they arise naturally in a variety of applications in business, economics, and the social and life sciences. In this section, we shall find the derivatives of these functions. In order to do that, we must first find a limit that will be needed in our calculations.

We claim that

$$\lim_{h \to 0} \frac{e^h - 1}{h} = 1.$$

$$y_1 = \frac{e^h - 1}{h}$$

Figure 11.39

Although a rigorous proof of this fact is beyond the scope of this book, a graphing calculator provides both graphical and numerical support, as shown in Figure 11.39.*

To find the derivative of $f(x) = e^x$, we use the definition of the derivative function,

$$f'(x) = \lim_{h \to 0} \frac{f(x + h) - f(x)}{h},$$

provided that this limit exists. (Remember that h is the variable here and x is treated as a constant.)

For $f(x) = e^x$, we see that

$$f'(x) = \lim_{h \to 0} \frac{e^{x+h} - e^x}{h}$$

$$= \lim_{h \to 0} \frac{e^x e^h - e^x}{h} \qquad \text{Product property of exponents}$$

$$= \lim_{h \to 0} \frac{e^x(e^h - 1)}{h} \qquad \text{Factor out } e^x.$$

$$= \lim_{h \to 0} e^x \cdot \lim_{h \to 0} \frac{e^h - 1}{h}, \qquad \text{Product property of limits}$$

provided that the last two limits exist. But h is the variable here and x is constant; therefore,

$$\lim_{h \to 0} e^x = e^x.$$

Combining this fact with our previous work, we see that

$$f'(x) = \lim_{h \to 0} e^x \cdot \lim_{h \to 0} \frac{e^h - 1}{h} = e^x \cdot 1 = e^x.$$

In other words, *the exponential function $f(x) = e^x$ is its own derivative.*

Example 1   Find each derivative.

(a) $y = x^3 e^x$

Solution   The product rule and the fact that $f(x) = e^x$ is its own derivative show that

$$y' = x^3 \cdot D_x(e^x) + e^x \cdot D_x(x^3)$$

$$= x^3 \cdot e^x + e^x \cdot 3x^2 = e^x(x^3 + 3x^2).$$

---

*As usual, the variable X is used in place of h on a calculator.

(b) $y = (2e^x + x)^5$

Solution   By the generalized power, sum, and constant rules,

$$y' = 5(2e^x + x)^4 \cdot D_x(2e^x + x)$$
$$= 5(2e^x + x)^4 \cdot [D_x(2e^x) + D_x(x)]$$
$$= 5(2e^x + x)^4 \cdot [2D_x(e^x) + 1]$$
$$= 5(2e^x + x)^4(2e^x + 1). \quad ✓_1$$

✓ **Checkpoint 1**

Differentiate the given expressions.

(a) $(2x^2 - 1)e^x$

(b) $(1 - e^x)^{1/2}$

Example 2   Find the derivative of $y = e^{x^2 - 3x}$.

Solution   Let $f(x) = e^x$ and $g(x) = x^2 - 3x$. Then

$$y = e^{x^2 - 3x} = e^{g(x)} = f[g(x)],$$

and $f'(x) = e^x$ and $g'(x) = 2x - 3$. By the chain rule,

$$y' = f'[g(x)] \cdot g'(x)$$
$$= e^{g(x)} \cdot (2x - 3)$$
$$= e^{x^2 - 3x} \cdot (2x - 3) = (2x - 3)e^{x^2 - 3x}.$$

The argument used in Example 2 can be used to find the derivative of $y = e^{g(x)}$ for any differentiable function g. Let $f(x) = e^x$; then $y = e^{g(x)} = f[g(x)]$. By the chain rule,

$$y' = f'[g(x)] \cdot g'(x) = e^{g(x)} \cdot g'(x) = g'(x)e^{g(x)}.$$

We summarize these results as follows.

Derivatives of e^x and $e^{g(x)}$

If $y = e^x$, then $y' = e^x$.

If $y = e^{g(x)}$, then $y' = g'(x) \cdot e^{g(x)}$.

⚠ CAUTION   Notice the difference between the derivative of a variable to a constant power, such as $D_x x^3 = 3x^2$, and the derivative of a constant to a variable power, like $D_x e^x = e^x$. Remember, $D_x e^x \neq xe^{x-1}$.

Example 3   Find derivatives of the given functions.

(a) $y = e^{7x}$

Solution   Let $g(x) = 7x$, with $g'(x) = 7$. Then

$$y' = g'(x)e^{g(x)} = 7e^{7x}.$$

(b) $y = 5e^{-3x}$

Solution   Here, let $g(x) = -3x$ and $g'(x) = -3$, so that

$$y' = 5(-3e^{-3x}) = -15e^{-3x}.$$

✓ **Checkpoint 2**

Find the derivative of the given function.

(a) $y = 4e^{11x}$

(b) $y = -5e^{(-9x+2)}$

(c) $y = e^{-x^3}$

(c) $y = 8e^{4x^3}$

Solution   Let $g(x) = 4x^3$, with $g'(x) = 12x^2$. Then

$$y' = 8(12x^2 e^{4x^3}) = 96x^2 e^{4x^3}. \quad ✓_2$$

Example 4 Let

$$y = \frac{250,000}{2 + 15e^{-4x}}.\ \text{Find } y'.$$

Solution Use the quotient rule:

$$y' = \frac{(2 + 15e^{-4x})(0) - 250,000(-60e^{-4x})}{(2 + 15e^{-4x})^2}$$

$$= \frac{15,000,000e^{-4x}}{(2 + 15e^{-4x})^2}. \checkmark_3$$

Checkpoint 3

Find the derivative of the given function.

(a) $y = \dfrac{e^x}{12 + x}$

(b) $y = \dfrac{9000}{15 + 3e^x}$

Example 5 **Natural Science** A 100-gram sample of a radioactive substance decays exponentially. The amount left after t years is given by $A(t) = 100e^{-.12t}$. Find the rate of change of the amount after 3 years.

Solution The rate of change is given by the derivative dA/dt:

$$\frac{dA}{dt} = 100(-.12e^{-.12t}) = -12e^{-.12t}.$$

After 3 years ($t = 3$), the rate of change is

$$\frac{dA}{dt} = -12e^{-.12(3)} = -12e^{-.36} \approx -8.4$$

grams per year.

Example 6 If $y = 10^x$, find y'.

Solution By one of the basic properties of logarithms (page 202), we have $10 = e^{\ln 10}$. Therefore,

$$y = 10^x = (e^{\ln 10})^x = e^{(\ln 10)x},$$

and

$$y' = \frac{d}{dx}[(\ln 10)x] \cdot e^{(\ln 10)x} \qquad \text{By the preceding box, with } g(x) = (\ln 10)x$$

$$= (\ln 10)e^{(\ln 10)x} \qquad \text{Remember that ln 10 is a constant.}$$

$$= (\ln 10)(e^{\ln 10})^x$$

$$= (\ln 10)10^x. \qquad e^{\ln 10} = 10 \quad \checkmark_4$$

Checkpoint 4

Adapt the solution of Example 6 to find the derivative of $y = 25^x$.

Derivatives of Logarithmic Functions

To find the derivative of $g(x) = \ln x$, we use the definitions and properties of natural logarithms that were developed in Section 4.3:

$$g(x) = \ln x \qquad \text{means} \qquad e^{g(x)} = x,$$

and for all $x > 0$, $y > 0$, and every real number r,

$$\ln xy = \ln x + \ln y, \qquad \ln \frac{x}{y} = \ln x - \ln y, \qquad \text{and} \qquad \ln x^r = r \ln x.$$

Note that we must have $x > 0$ and $y > 0$ because logarithms of zero and negative numbers are not defined.

Differentiating with respect to x on each side of $e^{g(x)} = x$ shows that

$$D_x(e^{g(x)}) = D_x(x)$$
$$g'(x) \cdot e^{g(x)} = 1.$$

Because $e^{g(x)} = x$, this last equation becomes

$$g'(x) \cdot x = 1$$
$$g'(x) = \frac{1}{x}$$

$$\frac{d}{dx}(\ln x) = \frac{1}{x} \qquad \text{for all } x > 0.$$

Example 7

(a) Assume that $x > 0$, and use properties of logarithms to find the derivative of $y = \ln 6x$.

Solution $\quad y' = \dfrac{d}{dx}(\ln 6x)$

$$= \frac{d}{dx}(\ln 6 + \ln x) \qquad \text{Product rule for logarithms}$$

$$= \frac{d}{dx}(\ln 6) + \frac{d}{dx}(\ln x). \qquad \text{Sum rule for derivatives}$$

Be careful here: $\ln 6$ is a *constant* ($\ln 6 \approx 1.79$), so its derivative is 0 (*not* $\frac{1}{6}$). Hence,

$$y' = \frac{d}{dx}(\ln 6) + \frac{d}{dx}(\ln x) = 0 + \frac{1}{x} = \frac{1}{x}.$$

(b) Assume that $x > 0$, and use the chain rule to find the derivative of $y = \ln 6x$.

Solution Let $f(x) = \ln x$ and $g(x) = 6x$, so that $y = \ln 6x = \ln g(x) = f(g(x))$. Then, by the chain rule,

$$y' = f'[g(x)] \cdot g'(x) = \frac{1}{g(x)} \cdot \frac{d}{dx}(6x) = \frac{1}{6x} \cdot 6 = \frac{1}{x}.$$

The argument used in Example 6(b) applies equally well in the general case. The derivative of $y = \ln g(x)$, where $g(x)$ is a function and $g(x) > 0$, can be found by letting $f(x) = \ln x$, so that $y = f[g(x)]$, and applying the chain rule:

$$y' = f'[g(x)] \cdot g'(x) = \frac{1}{g(x)} \cdot g'(x) = \frac{g'(x)}{g(x)}.$$

We summarize these results as follows.

Derivatives of ln x and ln $g(x)$

If $y = \ln x$, then $y' = \dfrac{1}{x}$ $\quad (x > 0)$.

If $y = \ln g(x)$, then $y' = \dfrac{g'(x)}{g(x)}$ $\quad (g(x) > 0)$.

Example 8 Find the derivatives of the given functions.

(a) $y = \ln(3x^2 - 4x)$

Solution Let $g(x) = 3x^2 - 4x$, so that $g'(x) = 6x - 4$. From the second formula in the preceding box,

$$y' = \frac{g'(x)}{g(x)} = \frac{6x - 4}{3x^2 - 4x}.$$

(b) $y = 3x \ln x^2$

Solution Since $3x \ln x^2$ is the product of $3x$ and $\ln x^2$, use the product rule:

$$y' = (3x)\left(\frac{d}{dx} \ln x^2\right) + (\ln x^2)\left(\frac{d}{dx}(3x)\right)$$

$$= 3x\left(\frac{2x}{x^2}\right) + (\ln x^2)(3) \qquad \text{Take derivatives.}$$

$$= 6 + 3 \ln x^2$$

$$= 6 + \ln (x^2)^3 \qquad \text{Property of logarithms}$$

$$= 6 + \ln x^6. \qquad \text{Property of exponents}$$

(c) $y = \ln[(x^2 + x + 1)(4x - 3)^5]$

Solution Here, we use the properties of logarithms before taking the derivative (the same thing could have been done in part (b) by writing $\ln x^2$ as $2 \ln x$):

$$y = \ln[(x^2 + x + 1)(4x - 3)^5]$$

$$= \ln(x^2 + x + 1) + \ln(4x - 3)^5 \qquad \text{Property of logarithms}$$

$$= \ln(x^2 + x + 1) + 5 \ln (4x - 3); \qquad \text{Property of logarithms}$$

$$y' = \frac{2x + 1}{x^2 + x + 1} + 5 \cdot \frac{4}{4x - 3} \qquad \text{Take derivatives.}$$

$$= \frac{2x + 1}{x^2 + x + 1} + \frac{20}{4x - 3}. \quad \boxed{5}$$

✓ **Checkpoint 5**

Find y' for the given functions.

(a) $y = \ln(7 + x)$

(b) $y = \ln(4x^2)$

(c) $y = \ln(8x^3 - 3x)$

(d) $y = x^2 \ln x$

The function $y = \ln(-x)$ is defined for all $x < 0$ (since $-x > 0$ when $x < 0$.) Its derivative can be found by applying the derivative rule for $\ln g(x)$ with $g(x) = -x$:

$$y' = \frac{g'(x)}{g(x)}$$

$$= \frac{-1}{-x}$$

$$= \frac{1}{x}.$$

This is the same as the derivative of $y = \ln x$, with $x > 0$. Since

$$|x| = \begin{cases} x & \text{if } x > 0 \\ -x & \text{if } x < 0 \end{cases},$$

we can combine two results into one in the manner that follows.

Derivative of ln |x|

If $y = \ln|x|$, then $y' = \dfrac{1}{x}$ $(x \neq 0)$.

Example 9 Let $y = e^x \ln|x|$. Find y'.

Solution Use the product rule:

$$y' = e^x \cdot \frac{1}{x} + \ln|x| \cdot e^x = e^x\left(\frac{1}{x} + \ln|x|\right). \quad \text{\checkmark}_6$$

✓ Checkpoint 6

Find the derivative of each function.

(a) $y = e^{x^2} \ln|x|$

(b) $y = x^2/\ln|x|$

Example 10 If $f(x) = \log x$, find $f'(x)$.

Solution By the change-of-base theorem (page 204),

$$f(x) = \log x = \frac{\ln x}{\ln 10} = \frac{1}{\ln 10} \cdot \ln x.$$

Since $1/\ln 10$ is a constant,

$$f'(x) = \frac{1}{\ln 10} \cdot \frac{d}{dx}(\ln x) = \frac{1}{\ln 10} \cdot \frac{1}{x} = \frac{1}{(\ln 10)x}.$$

Often, a population or the sales of a certain product will start growing slowly, then grow more rapidly, and then gradually level off. Such growth can frequently be approximated by a *logistic function* of the form

$$f(x) = \frac{c}{1 + ae^{kx}}$$

for appropriate constants a, c, and k. (Logistic functions were introduced in Section 4.2.)

Example 11 **Finance** If a person borrows \$120,000 on a 30-year fixed-rate mortgage at 5.7% interest per year, compounded monthly, then the required monthly payment is \$696. However, the borrower would like to pay off the loan early by making larger monthly payments. The actual number of months it will take to pay off the mortgage if a payment of p dollars is made each month is approximated by

$$f(p) = 211 \ln\left(\frac{p}{p - 570}\right) \quad (p \geq 696).$$

Find $f(710)$ and $f'(710)$ and explain what your answers mean for the borrower.

Solution Evaluating $f(p)$ at $p = 710$ yields:

$$f(710) = 211 \ln\left(\frac{710}{710 - 570}\right) = 211 \ln\left(\frac{710}{140}\right) \approx 342.6.$$

Making monthly payments of \$710 means that the borrower will pay off the loan in 343 months instead of 360 months (the payment in the final month will be somewhat smaller). Prior to taking the derivative, we may choose to use properties of logarithms to rewrite $f(p)$ as follows:

$$f(p) = 211 \ln\left(\frac{p}{p - 570}\right) = 211[\ln p - \ln(p - 570)] = 211 \ln(p) - 211 \ln(p - 570).$$

Differentiating $f(p)$ with respect to p yields

$$f'(p) = 211\left(\frac{1}{p}\right) - 211\left(\frac{1}{p - 570}\right) = \frac{211}{p} - \frac{211}{p - 570}.$$

By evaluating the derivative at $p = 710$ we find that

$$f'(710) = \frac{211}{710} - \frac{211}{710 - 570} = \frac{211}{710} - \frac{211}{140} \approx -1.2.$$

✓ Checkpoint 7

If $f(x) = 6 \ln\left(\dfrac{x}{7 - 3x}\right)$, find $f'(2)$.

This means that, when $p = $ \$710, increasing the monthly payment by 1 dollar will shorten the length of time needed to pay off the loan by approximately 1 month. $\text{\checkmark}_7$

Example 12 **Business** The number of cell phone subscriptions in the United States (in millions) in year t can be approximated by

$$f(t) = \frac{320}{1 + 34e^{-.28t}},$$

where $t = 0$ corresponds to the year 1990. Find the rate of change of cell phone subscriptions in 1990, 2004, and 2014. (Data from: www.worldbank.org.)

Solution Use the quotient rule to find the derivative of $f(t)$:

$$f'(t) = \frac{(1 + 34e^{-.28t})(0) - 320(34(-.28)e^{-.28t})}{(1 + 34e^{-.28t})^2}$$

$$= \frac{3046.4e^{-.28t}}{(1 + 34e^{-.28t})^2}.$$

The rate of change in 1990 ($t = 0$) is

$$f'(0) = \frac{3046.4e^{-.28(0)}}{(1 + 34e^{-.28(0)})^2} \approx 2.49.$$

Similarly, we compute that $f'(14) \approx 21.55$ and $f'(24) \approx 3.39$. This means that, in 1990, cell phone subscriptions were increasing at a rate of 2.49 million per year. By 2004, the rate of change had jumped dramatically to 21.55 million per year. By 2014, the rate of increase had slowed to 3.39 million per year. ✓8

✓ **Checkpoint 8**

Suppose that a fish population is given by

$$f(x) = \frac{4000}{1 + e^{.5x}},$$

where x is time in years. Find the rate of change of the population when

(a) $x = 0$

(b) $x = 3$

(c) Is the population increasing or decreasing?

11.8 Exercises

Find the derivatives of the given functions. (See Examples 1–4 and 7–9.)

1. $y = e^{5x}$

2. $y = e^{-4x}$

3. $f(x) = 5e^{2x}$

4. $f(x) = 4e^{-2x}$

5. $g(x) = -4e^{-7x}$

6. $g(x) = 6e^{x/2}$

7. $y = e^{x^2}$

8. $y = e^{-x^2}$

9. $f(x) = e^{x^3/3}$

10. $y = e^{4-x^3}$

11. $y = -3e^{3x^2+5}$

12. $y = 4e^{2x^2-4}$

13. $y = \ln(-10x^2 + 7x)$

14. $y = \ln(11 - 2x)$

15. $y = \ln\sqrt{5x + 1}$

16. $y = \ln\sqrt{x - 8}$

17. $f(x) = \ln[(5x + 9)(x^2 + 1)]$

18. $y = \ln[(4x + 1)(5x - 2)]$

19. $y = \ln\left(\frac{4 - x}{3x + 8}\right)$

20. $f(x) = \ln\left(\frac{7x - 1}{12x + 5}\right)$

21. $y = x^4 e^{-3x}$

22. $y = xe^{3x}$

23. $y = (6x^2 - 5x)e^{-3x}$

24. $y = (x - 5)^2 e^{3x}$

25. $y = \ln(8x^3 - 3x)^{1/2}$

26. $y = \ln(x^5 + 8x^2)^{3/2}$

27. $y = x \ln(9 - x^4)$

28. $y = -4x \ln(x + 12)$

29. $y = x^4 \ln|x|$

30. $y = (2x^3 - 1) \ln|x|$

31. $y = \dfrac{-5 \ln|x|}{5 - 2x}$

32. $y = \dfrac{3 \ln|x|}{3x + 4}$

33. $y = \sqrt{\ln(x - 3)}$

34. $y = [\ln(x + 1)]^4$

35. $y = \dfrac{e^x - 1}{\ln|x|}$

36. $y = \dfrac{e^x}{\ln|x|}$

37. $y = \dfrac{e^x - e^{-x}}{x}$

38. $y = \dfrac{e^x + e^{-x}}{x}$

39. $f(x) = e^{3x+2} \ln(4x - 5)$

40. $y = e^{x^3} \ln|x|$

41. $y = \dfrac{700}{7 - 10e^{.4x}}$

42. $f(x) = \dfrac{2400}{3 + 8e^{.2x}}$

43. $y = \dfrac{500}{12 + 5e^{-.5x}}$

44. $y = \dfrac{10{,}000}{9 + 4e^{-.2x}}$

45. $y = \ln(\ln|x|)$

46. $y = 5e^{e^x}$

Find the derivatives of the given functions. (See Examples 6 and 10.) The chain rule is needed in Exercises 48–52.

47. $y = 8^x$

48. $y = 8^{x^2}$

49. $y = 15^{2x}$

50. $f(x) = 2^{-x}$

51. $g(x) = \log 6x$

52. $y = \log(x^2 + 1)$

🔲 *For Exercises 53–56, find the equation of the tangent line to the graph of f at the given point.*

53. $f(x) = \dfrac{e^x}{2x + 1}$ at $(0, 1)$ **54.** $f(x) = \dfrac{x^2}{e^x}$ when $x = 1$

55. $f(x) = \ln(1 + x^2)$ at $(0, 0)$

56. $f(x) = \ln(2x^2 - 7x)$ when $x = -1$

57. If $f(x) = e^{2x}$, find $f'[\ln(1/4)]$.

58. If $g(x) = 3e \ln[\ln x]$, find $g'(e)$.

Work these exercises. (See Example 5.)

59. Business The gross national income of China (in billions of U.S. dollars) can be approximated by

$$P(t) = 1048e^{.165t},$$

where $t = 0$ corresponds to the year 2000. At what rate is Chinese gross national income changing in the given year? (Data from: www.worldbank.org.)

(a) 2010   (b) 2014

60. Business The amount of money (in billions of U.S. dollars) that China spends on research and development can be approximated by $f(t) = 26.67e^{.166t}$, where $t = 0$ corresponds to the year 2000. Find the rate of change of Chinese research and development spending in 2012. (Data from: National Science Foundation, *National Patterns of R&D Resources*, annual report.)

61. Finance Total United States reserves (in billions of dollars), including gold, can be approximated by

$$R(x) = 87e^{.166x} \qquad (4 \le x \le 10),$$

where $x = 4$ corresponds to the year 2004. Find the amount of U.S. reserves and the rate of change of U.S. reserves in 2010.(Data from: www.worldbank.org.)

62. Finance The United States experienced a recession during 2007–2009. The percent of nonperforming loans in year x can be approximated by

$$N(x) = .038e^{.537x} \qquad (5 \le x \le 9),$$

where $x = 5$ corresponds to the year 2005. Find the percentage of nonperforming loans and the rate of change of this percentage in 2009. (Data from: www.worldbank.org.)

63. Social Science The number of doctorates (in thousands) awarded in the field of science in the United States is approximated by the function

$$g(x) = 17.6e^{.043x},$$

where $x = 2$ corresponds to the year 2002. (Data from: www.nsf.gov/statistics/infbrief/nsf09307.)

(a) Find $g(10)$.   (b) Find $g'(10)$.

(c) Interpret your answers for parts (a) and (b).

64. Health The preschool mortality rate (number of deaths under age 5 per 1000 people) in Russia can be approximated by

$$M(t) = 23e^{-.068t},$$

where $t = 0$ corresponds to the year 2000. Assuming this model remains accurate, find the Russian preschool mortality rate and how this mortality rate will be changing in 2016. (Data from: www.worldbank.org.)

65. Finance The United States government debt as a percent of gross domestic product (GDP) can be approximated by

$$D(x) = 36.42e^{.081x} \qquad (6 \le x \le 12),$$

where $x = 0$ corresponds to the year 2000. Find how U.S. government debt as a percent of GDP was changing in 2011. (Data from: U.S. Bureau of the Public Debt.)

66. Business A business provides a \$50,000 life insurance policy for each of its employees. The annual cost in dollars of a policy (which depends on the age of the employee) can be approximated by $C(x) = 4.55e^{.075x}$, where x is the age of the employee in years ($18 \le x \le 65$). Find and interpret the given quantities. (Data from: Internal Revenue Code section 79, Table 01.)

(a) $C(20)$ and $C'(20)$ (b) $C(60)$ and $C'(60)$

67. Health The temperature of a certain patient (in degrees Fahrenheit) t hours after the onset of an infection can be approximated by

$$P(t) = 98.6 + te^{-.2t}.$$

Find how the patient's temperature is changing at the given times.

(a) $t = 1$ (b) $t = 12$

68. Business The number of hourly hits (in thousands) on a company's website x hours after a news story breaks can be approximated by

$$H(x) = 1 + 30xe^{-.5x}.$$

Find the rate of change of hits to this website for the given number of hours after the story breaks.

(a) 1 hour   (b) 12 hours

Work these exercises. (See Examples 11 and 12.)

69. Natural Science The population of a bed of clams in the Great South Bay off Long Island is approximated by the logistic function

$$G(t) = \frac{52{,}000}{1 + 12e^{-.52t}},$$

where t is measured in years. Find the clam population and its rate of growth after

(a) 1 year   (b) 4 years   (c) 10 years.

(d) What happens to the rate of growth over time?

70. Business The number of cell phone subscriptions per 100 people in Spain can be approximated by

$$f(t) = \frac{112}{1 + 510e^{-.6t}},$$

where $t = 0$ corresponds to the year 1990. Find the number of cell phone subscriptions per 100 people in Spain and the rate of change of this number in the given year. (Data from: www.worldbank.org.)

(a) 1990   (b) 2002   (c) 2014

71. Health The function

$$V(t) = \frac{1100}{(1 + 1023e^{-.02415t})^4},$$

where t is in months and $V(t)$ is in cubic centimeters, models the relationship between the volume of a breast tumor and the amount of time it has been growing.[*]

[*]Data from John Spratt et al., "Decelerating Growth and Human Breast Cancer," *Cancer* 71, no. 6 (1993): 2013–2019.

(a) Find the tumor volume at 240 months.

(b) Assuming that the shape of a tumor is spherical, find the radius of the tumor from part (a). (*Hint:* The volume of a sphere is given by the formula $v = \frac{4}{3}\pi r^3$.)

(c) If a tumor of volume .5 cm^3 is detected, according to the formula, how long has it been growing? What does this imply?

(d) Calculate the rate of change of tumor volume at 240 months. Interpret this rate.

72. Business   The percent of the population of the United States who are Internet users is approximated by

$$f(t) = \frac{80}{1 + 48e^{-.4t}},$$

where $t = 0$ corresponds to the year 1990. Find the percent of the population who are Internet users and the rate at which this percentage is changing in the given year. (Data from: www. worldbank.org.)

(a) 1990   **(b)** 2000   **(c)** 2015

73. Education   The number of bachelor's degrees (in thousands) earned in the social sciences and history in year x can be approximated by

$$f(x) = 24 \ln x + 117,$$

where $x = 3$ corresponds to the year 2003. Find the rate at which the number of social science and history degrees is changing in the given year. (Data from: *The Statistical Abstract of the United States*: 2012.)

(a) 2012   **(b)** 2016

74. Business   The producer price index (PPI) for net output of the construction sand and gravel mining industry can be approximated by

$$f(x) = 94 \ln(x) + 61,$$

where $x = 5$ corresponds to the year 2005. Find the rate of change of the PPI for this industry in 2014. (Data from: United States Bureau of Labor Statistics.)

Work the following exercises.

75. Business   Suppose the demand function for x thousand of a certain item is

$$p = 100 + \frac{50}{\ln x} \qquad (x > 1),$$

where p is in dollars.

(a) Find the marginal revenue.

(b) Find the revenue from the next thousand items at a demand of 8000 ($x = 8$).

76. Finance   A person owes $4000 on a credit card that charges an annual interest rate of 15.9%, compounded monthly. If the card holder makes no additional charges and makes a payment of p dollars each month, the number of months it will take to pay off the debt is given by

$$f(p) = 76 \ln\left(\frac{p}{p - 53}\right) \qquad (p > 53).$$

(a) Find and interpret $f(78)$.

(b) Would you expect $f'(p)$ to be positive or negative?

(c) Find and interpret $f'(78)$.

77. Finance   An individual deposits $250 in an account that earns 2.8% interest per year, compounded monthly. The number of months needed for the balance in the account to reach an amount of A dollars is given by

$$f(A) = 429 \ln\left(\frac{A}{250}\right).$$

(a) Find and interpret $f(300)$.

(b) Would you expect $f'(A)$ to be positive or negative?

(c) Find and interpret $f'(300)$.

78. Physical Science   The Richter scale provides a measure of the magnitude of an earthquake. One of the largest Richter numbers M ever recorded for an earthquake was 8.9, from the 1933 earthquake in Japan. The following formula shows a relationship between the amount of energy released, E, and the Richter number:

$$M = \frac{2 \ln E - 2 \ln .007}{3 \ln 10}.$$

Here, E is measured in kilowatt-hours (kWh).[*]

(a) For the 1933 earthquake in Japan, what value of E gives a Richter number $M = 8.9$?

(b) If the average household uses 247 kilowatt-hours per month, for how many months would the energy released by an earthquake of this magnitude power 10 million households?

(c) Find the rate of change of the Richter number M with respect to energy when $E = 70{,}000$ kWh.

(d) What happens to $\frac{dM}{dE}$ as E increases?

79. Social Science   A child is waiting at a street corner for a gap in traffic so that she can safely cross the street. A mathematical model for traffic shows that if the child's expected waiting time is to be at most 1 minute, then the maximum traffic flow (in cars per hour) is given by

$$f(x) = \frac{67{,}338 - 12{,}595 \ln x}{x},$$

where x is the width of the street in feet.[†] Find the maximum traffic flow and the rate of change of the maximum traffic flow with respect to street width when x is the given number.

(a) 30 feet   **(b)** 40 feet

80. Health   One measure of whether a dialysis patient has been adequately dialyzed is the urea reduction ratio (URR). It is generally agreed that a patient has been adequately dialyzed when the URR exceeds a value of .65. The value of the URR can be

---

[*]Christopher Bradley, "Media Clips," *Mathematics Teacher* 93, no. 4 (April 2000): 300–303.

[†]Edward A. Bender, *An Introduction to Mathematical Modeling*, Dover Publications, Inc., 2000.

calculated for a particular patient from the following formula by Gotch:

$$URR = 1 - e^{-.0056t+.04} - \frac{8t(1 - e^{-.0056t+.04})}{126t + 900}.$$

Here, t is measured in minutes.[*]

(a) Find the value of the URR after this patient receives dialysis for 180 minutes. Has the patient received adequate dialysis?

(b) Find the value of the URR after the patient receives dialysis for 240 minutes. Has the patient received adequate dialysis?

✗ (c) Use the numerical derivative feature on a graphing calculator to compute the instantaneous rate of change of the URR when the time on dialysis is 240 minutes. Interpret this rate.

81. **Natural Science** The age–weight relationship of female Arctic foxes caught in Svalbard, Norway, can be estimated by the function

$$M(t) = 3102e^{-e^{-.022(t-56)}},$$

where t is the age of the fox in days and $M(t)$ is the weight of the fox in grams.[†]

(a) Estimate the weight of a female fox that is 200 days old.

(b) Estimate the rate of change in weight of an Arctic fox that is 200 days old.

✗ (c) Use a graphing calculator to graph $M(t)$, and then describe the growth pattern.

✗ (d) Use the table function on a graphing calculator or a spreadsheet to develop a chart that shows the estimated weight and growth rate of female foxes for days 50, 100, 150, 200, 250, and 300.

✓ **Checkpoint Answers**

1. (a) $(2x^2 - 1)e^x + 4xe^x$ (b) $\dfrac{-e^x}{2(1 - e^x)^{1/2}}$

2. (a) $y' = 44e^{11x}$ (b) $y' = 45e^{(-9x+2)}$
   (c) $y' = -3x^2 e^{-x^3}$

3. (a) $y' = \dfrac{e^x(11 + x)}{(12 + x)^2}$ (b) $y' = \dfrac{-27,000e^x}{(15 + 3e^x)^2}$

4. $y' = (\ln 25)25^x$

5. (a) $y' = \dfrac{1}{7 + x}$ (b) $y' = \dfrac{2}{x}$

   (c) $y' = \dfrac{24x^2 - 3}{8x^3 - 3x}$ (d) $y' = x(1 + 2\ln x)$

6. (a) $y' = e^{x^2}\left(\dfrac{1}{x} + 2x\ln|x|\right)$ (b) $y' = \dfrac{2x\ln|x| - x}{(\ln|x|)^2}$

7. 21

8. (a) -500 fish per year   (b) About -298 fish per year
   (c) Decreasing

---

[*]Edward Kessler, Nathan Ritchey, et al., "Urea Reduction Ratio and Urea Kinetic Modeling: A Mathematical Analysis of Changing Dialysis Parameters," *American Journal of Nephrology* 18 (1998): 471–477.

[†]Pal Prestrud and Kjell Nilssen, "Growth, Size, and Sexual Dimorphism in Arctic Foxes," *Journal of Mammalogy* 76, no. 2 (May 1995): 522–530.

11.9 Continuity and Differentiability

Intuitively speaking, a function is **continuous** at a point if you can draw the graph of the function near that point without lifting your pencil from the paper. Conversely, a function is **discontinuous** at a point if the pencil *must* be lifted from the paper in order to draw the graph on both sides of the point.

Looking at some graphs that have points of discontinuity will clarify the idea of continuity at a point. Each of the three graphs in Figure 11.40 is continuous *except* at $x = 2$. As

(a)

(b)

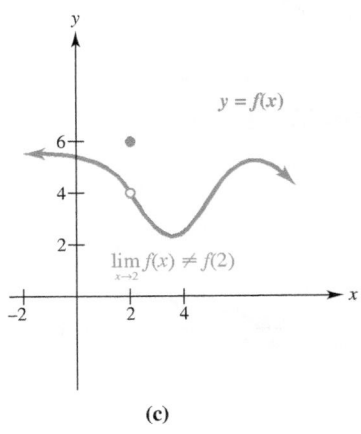
(c)

Figure 11.40

usual, an open circle indicates that the point is not part of the graph. You cannot draw these graphs without lifting your pencil at $x = 2$, at least for an instant.

However, there are different reasons why each function is discontinuous at $x = 2$:

1. In graph (a), $f(2)$ is not defined (because there is a hole in the graph).
2. In graph (b), $\lim_{x \to 2} f(x)$ does not exist (because the left-hand limit does not equal the right-hand limit—see Section 11.2).
3. In graph (c), $f(2)$ is defined and $\lim_{x \to 2} f(x)$ does exist, but $\lim_{x \to 2} f(x) \neq f(2)$ (because $\lim_{x \to 2} f(x) = 4$ whereas $f(2) = 6$).

By phrasing each of these considerations positively, we obtain the following definition.

Continuity at a Point

A function f is **continuous** at $x = c$ if

(a) $f(c)$ is defined;

(b) $\lim_{x \to c} f(x)$ exists;

(c) $\lim_{x \to c} f(x) = f(c)$.

If f is not continuous at $x = c$, it is **discontinuous** there.

The idea behind condition (c) is this: To draw the graph near $x = c$ without lifting your pencil, it must be the case that when x is very close to c, $f(x)$ must be very close to $f(c)$—otherwise, you would have to lift the pencil at $x = c$, as happens in Figure 11.40 at $x = 2$. ✓₁

✓ **Checkpoint 1**

Find any points of discontinuity for the given functions.

(a)

(b)

(c)
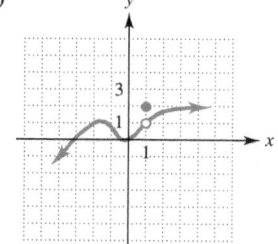

Example 1 Tell why the given functions are discontinuous at the indicated point.

(a) $f(x)$ in Figure 11.41 at $x = 3$

Solution The open circle on the graph in Figure 11.41 at the point where $x = 3$ means that $f(3)$ is not defined. Because of this, part (a) of the definition fails.

Figure 11.41

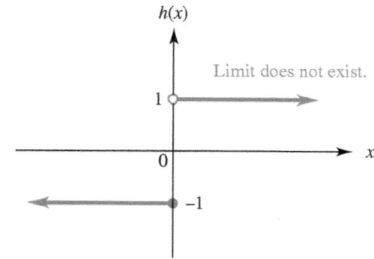

Figure 11.42

(b) $h(x)$ in Figure 11.42 at $x = 0$

Solution The graph in Figure 11.42 shows that $h(0) = -1$. Also, as x approaches 0 from the left, $h(x)$ is -1. However, as x approaches 0 from the right, $h(x)$ is 1. As mentioned in Section 11.1, for a limit to exist at a particular value of x, the values of $h(x)$ must approach a single number. Since no single number is approached by the values of $h(x)$ as x approaches 0, $\lim\limits_{x \to 0} h(x)$ does not exist, and part (b) of the definition fails.

(c) $g(x)$ at $x = 4$ in Figure 11.43

Solution In Figure 11.43, the heavy dot above 4 shows that $g(4)$ is defined. In fact, $g(4) = 1$. However, the graph also shows that

$$\lim_{x \to 4} g(x) = -2,$$

so $\lim\limits_{x \to 4} g(x) \neq g(4)$, and part (c) of the definition fails.

Figure 11.43

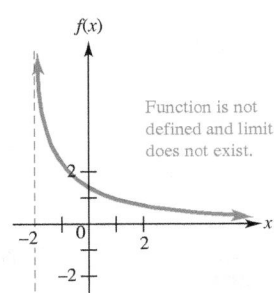

Figure 11.44

(d) $f(x)$ in Figure 11.44 at $x = -2$

Solution The function f graphed in Figure 11.44 is not defined at -2, and $\lim\limits_{x \to -2} f(x)$ does not exist. Either of these reasons is sufficient to show that f is not continuous at -2. (Function f *is* continuous at any value of x greater than -2, however.) ✓2

Continuity at Endpoints

One-sided limits (see Section 11.2) can be used to define continuity at an endpoint of a graph.[*] Consider the endpoint $(1, 0)$ of the graph of the half-circle function $f(x) = \sqrt{1 - x^2}$ in Figure 11.45. Note that f has a left-hand limit at $x = 1$. Furthermore,

$$f(1) = 0 \quad \text{and} \quad \lim_{x \to 1^-} f(x) = 0, \quad \text{so that} \quad \lim_{x \to 1^-} f(x) = f(1).$$

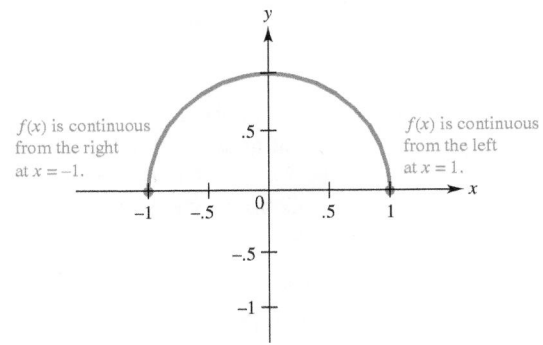

Figure 11.45

We say that $f(x)$ is *continuous from the left* at $x = 1$. A similar situation occurs with the other endpoint $(-1, 0)$: There is a right-hand limit at $x = -1$, and we have $\lim\limits_{x \to -1^+} f(x) = 0 = f(-1)$. We say that $f(x)$ is *continuous from the right* at $x = -1$.

✓ **Checkpoint 2**

Tell why the given functions are discontinuous at the indicated point.

(a)

(b)

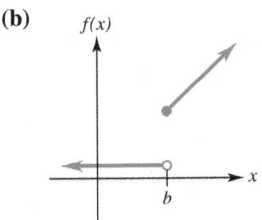

This situation is an example of the following definition.

Continuity from the Left and from the Right

A function f is **continuous from the left** at $x = c$ if

(a) $f(c)$ is defined;

(b) $\lim\limits_{x \to c^-} f(x)$ exists;

(c) $\lim\limits_{x \to c^-} f(x) = f(c)$.

Similarly, f is **continuous from the right** at $x = c$ if

(a) $f(c)$ is defined;

(b) $\lim\limits_{x \to c^+} f(x)$ exists;

(c) $\lim\limits_{x \to c^+} f(x) = f(c)$.

✓ **Checkpoint 3**

State whether the given function is continuous from the left, continuous from the right, or neither at the given value of x.

(a) $f(x)$ in Figure 11.40(b) at $x = 2$

(b) $h(x)$ in Figure 11.42 at $x = 0$

(c) $g(x)$ in Figure 11.43 at $x = 4$

Note that a function which is continuous at $x = c$ is automatically continuous from the left and from the right at $x = c$. ✔3

Continuity on an Interval

When discussing the continuity of a function, it is often helpful to use interval notation, which was introduced in Chapter 1. The following chart should help you recall how it is used.

Interval	Name	Description	Interval Notation
	Open interval	$-2 < x < 3$	$(-2, 3)$
	Closed interval	$-2 \le x \le 3$	$[-2, 3]$
	Open interval	$x < 3$	$(-\infty, 3)$
	Open interval	$x > -5$	$(-5, \infty)$

Remember, the symbol ∞ does not represent a number; ∞ is used for convenience in interval notation to indicate that the interval extends without bound in the positive direction. Also, $-\infty$ indicates no bound in the negative direction. ✔4

Continuity at a point was defined previously. Continuity on an interval is defined as follows.

✓ **Checkpoint 4**

Write each of the following in interval notation.

(a)

(b)

(c)

Continuity on Open and Closed Intervals

A function f is **continuous on the open interval** (a, b) if f is continuous at every x-value in the interval (a, b).

A function f is **continuous on the closed interval** $[a, b]$ if

1. f is continuous on the open interval (a, b);

2. f is continuous from the right at $x = a$;

3. f is continuous from the left at $x = b$.

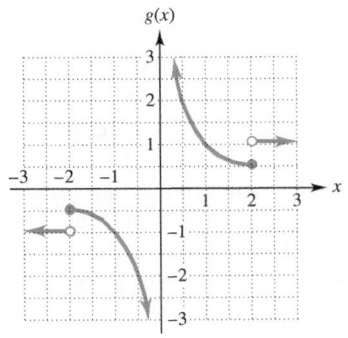

Figure 11.46

Intuitively, a function is continuous on an interval if you can draw the entire graph of f over that interval without lifting your pencil from the paper.

Example 2   Is the function of Figure 11.46 continuous on the given x-intervals?

(a) $(0, 2)$

Solution   The function g is discontinuous only at $x = -2, 0$, and 2. Hence, g is continuous at every point of the open interval $(0, 2)$, which does not include 0 or 2.

(b) $[0, 2]$

Solution   The function g is not defined at $x = 0$, so it is not continuous from the right there. Therefore, it is not continuous on the closed interval $[0, 2]$.

(c) $(1, 3)$

Solution   This interval contains a point of discontinuity at $x = 2$. So g is not continuous on the open interval $(1, 3)$.

(d) $[-2, -1]$

Solution   The function g is continuous on the open interval $(-2, -1)$, continuous from the right at $x = -2$, and continuous from the left at $x = -1$. Hence, g is continuous on the closed interval $[-2, -1]$. ✓ 5

✓ **Checkpoint 5**

Are the functions whose graphs are shown continuous on the indicated intervals?

(a) $[-4, -1]$; $[2, 5]$

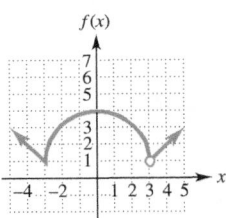

(b) $(1, 3)$; $[4, 6]$

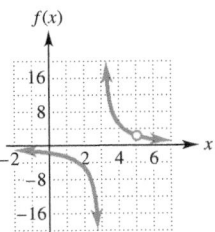

✓ **Checkpoint 6**

Suppose a smart phone data plan for heavy users charges $50 for the first 5 GB of data and then $15 for each additional 2 GB of data (or fraction thereof). If $C(x)$ is the cost (in dollars) of using x GB of data, find any points of discontinuity for C on the interval $(0, 10)$.

Example 3   **Business**   The monthly cost $C(x)$ (in dollars) of a popular smart phone data plan for the use of x gigabytes of data is $30 for the first 2 GB of data plus $10 for each additional GB of data (or fraction thereof). (Data from: Verizon Wireless, 2012 prices.)

(a) Sketch the graph of $y = C(x)$ on the interval $0 \leq x \leq 5$.

Solution   For any amount of data usage up to and including 2 GB, the charge is $30. The charge for using more than 2 GB but less than 3 GB of data is $40. Similar results lead to the graph in Figure 11.47.

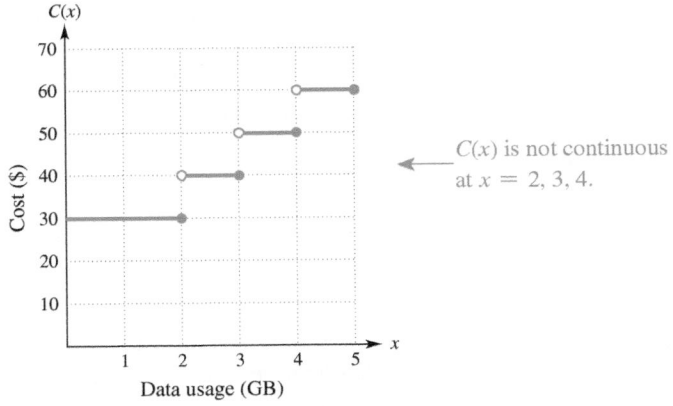

Figure 11.47

(b) Find any points of discontinuity for C on the interval $(0, 5)$.

Solution   As the graph suggests, C is discontinuous at $x = 2, 3, 4$ gigabytes. However, C is continuous from the left at each of these x-values. ✓ 6

Figure 11.48

Figure 11.49

Continuity and Technology

Because of the way a graphing calculator or computer graphs functions, the graph of a continuous function may look like disconnected, closely spaced line segments (Figure 11.48). Furthermore, calculators often have trouble accurately portraying graphs at points of discontinuity. For instance, "jump discontinuities" (such as those at $x = 2$, 3, and 4 in Figure 11.47) may appear as "stair steps," with vertical line segments connecting separate pieces of the graph (Figure 11.49). Similarly, a hole in the graph (such as the one at $x = 4$ in Figure 11.43) may not be visible on a calculator screen, depending on what viewing window is used. Nor can a calculator indicate whether an endpoint is included in the graph.

One reason these inaccuracies appear is due to the manner in which a calculator graphs: It plots points and connects them with line segments. In effect, the calculator assumes that the function is continuous unless it actually computes a function value and determines that it is undefined. In that case, it will skip a pixel and not connect points on either side of it.

The moral of this story is that a calculator or computer is only a tool. In order to use it correctly and effectively, you must understand the mathematics involved. When you do, it is usually easy to interpret screen images correctly.

Continuity and Differentiability

As shown earlier in this chapter, a function fails to have a derivative at a point where the function is not defined, where the graph of the function has a "sharp point," or where the graph has a vertical tangent line. (See Figure 11.50.)

The function graphed in Figure 11.50 is continuous on the interval (x_1, x_2) and has a derivative at each point on this interval. On the other hand, the function is also continuous on the interval $(0, x_2)$, but does *not* have a derivative at each point on the interval. (See x_1 on the graph.)

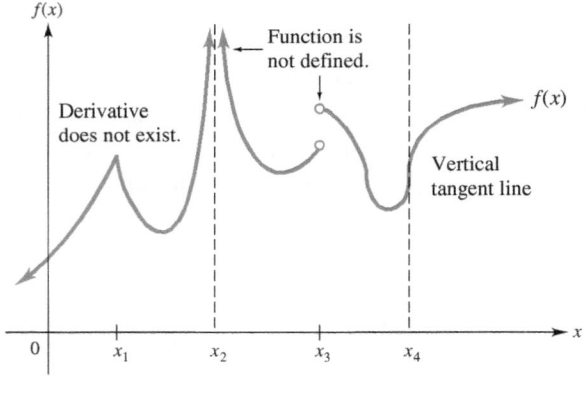

Figure 11.50

A similar situation holds in the general case.

> If the derivative of a function exists at a point, then the function is continuous at that point. However, a function may be continuous at a point and not have a derivative there.

Example 4   **Business**   The Fair Labor Standards Act requires overtime pay for covered, nonexempt employees at a rate of not less than one and one-half times an employee's regular rate of pay after 40 hours of work in a workweek. A fast food restaurant pays an entry-level employee $10 per hour for regular pay and time-and-a-half for overtime pay. Let $P(x)$ represent the employee's gross pay prior to taxes and other withholdings (in dollars) for working x hours in a week. The graph of $y = P(x)$ is shown in Figure 11.51. Find any points where P is discontinuous. Also find any points where P is not differentiable. (Data from: United States Department of Labor.)

✓ Checkpoint 7

State whether the function whose graph is shown is continuous and/ or differentiable at the given values of x.

(a) $x = 2$

(b) $x = 4$

(c) $x = 6$

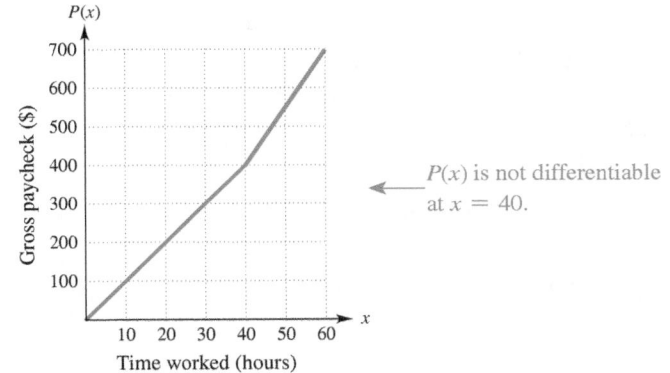

Figure 11.51

Solution The graph indicates that P is a continuous function since it can be drawn without lifting pencil from paper. However, P is not differentiable at $x = 40$ hours where the graph has a sharp corner. ✓ 7

📐 **TECHNOLOGY TIP** In some viewing windows, a calculator graph may appear to have a sharp corner when, in fact, the graph is differentiable at that point. When in doubt, try a different window to see if the corner disappears.

11.9 Exercises

Find all points of discontinuity for the functions whose graphs are shown. (See Example 1.)

1.

2.

3.

4.

5.

6.

7.

8.

Are the given functions continuous at the given values of x?

9. $f(x) = \dfrac{4}{x - 2}$; $x = 0, x = 2$

10. $g(x) = \dfrac{5}{x+5}; x = -5, x = 5$

11. $h(x) = \dfrac{1}{x(x-3)}; x = 0, x = 3, x = 5$

12. $h(x) = \dfrac{-1}{(x-2)(x+3)}; x = 0, x = 2, x = 3$

13. $g(x) = \dfrac{x+2}{x^2 - x - 2}; x = 1, x = 2, x = -2$

14. $h(x) = \dfrac{3x}{6x^2 + 15x + 6}; x = 0, x = -\dfrac{1}{2}, x = 3$

15. $g(x) = \dfrac{x^2 - 4}{x - 2}; x = 0, x = 2, x = -2$

16. $h(x) = \dfrac{x^2 - 25}{x + 5}; x = 0, x = 5, x = -5$

17. $f(x) = \begin{cases} x - 2 & \text{if } x \le 3 \\ 2 - x & \text{if } x > 3 \end{cases}; x = 2, x = 3$

18. $g(x) = \begin{cases} e^x & \text{if } x < 0 \\ x + 1 & \text{if } 0 \le x \le 3; x = 0, x = 3 \\ 2x - 3 & \text{if } x > 3 \end{cases}$

Find all x-values where the function is discontinuous.

19. $g(x) = x^2 - 5x + 12$ **20.** $f(x) = \dfrac{x^2 - 9}{x + 3}$

21. $h(x) = \dfrac{|x + 4|}{x + 4}$ **22.** $f(x) = \dfrac{7 + x}{x(x - 3)}$

23. $k(x) = e^{\sqrt{x-2}}$ **24.** $r(x) = \ln\left(\dfrac{x}{x - 3}\right)$

In Exercises 25–26, (a) graph the given function, and (b) find all values of x where the function is discontinuous.

25. $f(x) = \begin{cases} 2 & \text{if } x < 1 \\ x + 3 & \text{if } 1 \le x < 4 \\ 8 & \text{if } x \ge 4 \end{cases}$

26. $g(x) = \begin{cases} -10 & \text{if } x < -2 \\ x^2 + 4x - 6 & \text{if } -2 \le x < 2 \\ 10 & \text{if } x \ge 2 \end{cases}$

In Exercises 27 and 28, find the constant k that makes the given function continuous at x = 2.

27. $f(x) = \begin{cases} x + k & \text{if } x \le 2 \\ 5 - x & \text{if } x > 2 \end{cases}$

28. $g(x) = \begin{cases} x^k & \text{if } x \le 2 \\ 2x + 4 & \text{if } x > 2 \end{cases}$

Work these exercises. (See Examples 3 and 4.)

29. **Finance** Officials in California have raised and lowered the state sales tax in various years. The accompanying figure shows the California state sales tax for 2001–2012. Let $T(x)$ represent the sales tax rate (as a percent) in year x. Find the given quantities. (Data from: www.boe.ca.gov/sutax/taxrateshist.htm.)

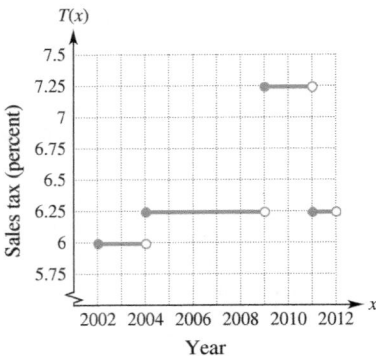

(a) $\lim\limits_{x \to 2010^-} T(x)$ **(b)** $\lim\limits_{x \to 2010^+} T(x)$

(c) $\lim\limits_{x \to 2010} T(x)$ **(d)** $\lim\limits_{x \to 2011^-} T(x)$

(e) $\lim\limits_{x \to 2011^+} T(x)$ **(f)** $\lim\limits_{x \to 2011} T(x)$

(g) Find all values on the interval (2002, 2012) where T is discontinuous.

(h) Find all values on the interval (2002, 2012) where T is not differentiable.

30. **Natural Science** Suppose a gram of ice is at a temperature of $-100°C$. The accompanying graph shows the temperature of the ice as an increasing number of calories of heat are applied. Where is this function discontinuous? Where is it differentiable?

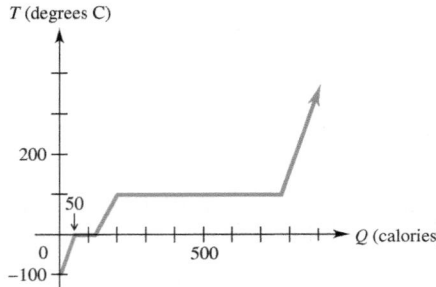

31. **Social Science** With certain skills (such as music), learning is rapid at first and then levels off. However, sudden insights may cause learning to speed up sharply. A typical graph of such learning is shown in the accompanying figure. Where is the function discontinuous? Where is it differentiable?

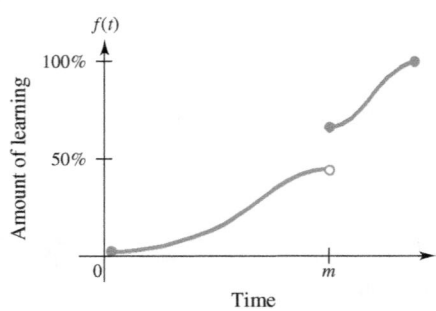

32. **Business** A pick-your-own strawberry farm charges $10 per gallon of strawberries. The cost of partial gallons is prorated except that there is a minimum charge of $10. Customers who pick more than 4 gallons receive a $10 discount off their total order. The accompanying figure shows the price (in dollars), $P(x)$, of picking x gallons of strawberries. Find the given quantities.

(a) $P(1)$

(b) $\lim\limits_{x \to 1} P(x)$

(c) $P(4)$

(d) $\lim\limits_{x \to 4} P(x)$

(e) Find all values on the interval $(0, 8)$ where P is discontinuous.

(f) Find all values on the interval $(0, 8)$ where P is not differentiable.

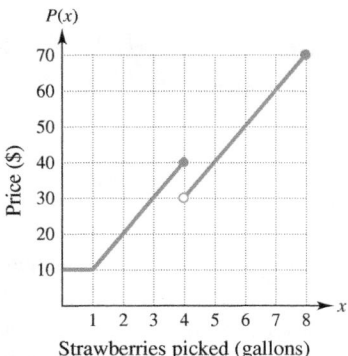

Work the following exercises.

33. Business The accompanying table shows the price (in dollars), $C(x)$, of mailing a first-class letter weighing x ounces domestically in 2012. (Data from: www.usps.gov.)

Weight Not Over . . . (oz)	Price ($)
1	0.45
2	0.65
3	0.85
3.5	1.05

(a) Sketch a graph of $y = C(x)$ on the interval $[0, 3.5]$.

(b) $\lim\limits_{x \to 1^-} C(x)$

(c) $\lim\limits_{x \to 1^+} C(x)$

(d) $\lim\limits_{x \to 1} C(x)$

(e) $\lim\limits_{x \to 2.5^-} C(x)$

(f) $\lim\limits_{x \to 2.5^+} C(x)$

(g) $\lim\limits_{x \to 2.5} C(x)$

(h) Find all values on the interval $(0, 3.5)$ where C is discontinuous.

34. Business A nut supplier offers discounts for buying in bulk. The accompanying table shows the price per pound for jumbo raw Georgia pecans (with the cost of partial pounds being prorated). Let $C(x)$ represent the cost (in dollars) of purchasing x pounds of nuts. Find the cost of buying the given amounts.

(a) ½ pound

(b) 10 pounds

(c) 11 pounds

(d) Find all values where C is discontinuous.

Pounds Purchased	Price per Pound
$0 < x \le 1$	$16.99
$1 < x \le 10$	$15.99
$10 < x \le 30$	$14.50

35. Business The state of Connecticut has established maximum charges, $C(x)$, (in dollars) for nonconsensual towing of vehicles (up to 10,000 lbs) a distance of x miles. The base charge of $88 includes mileage to the scene, preparing the vehicle, and the first 2 miles of the tow (loaded miles). In addition there is a mileage charge of $4.75 per mile (or fraction of a mile) in excess of 2 loaded miles. Find the given quantities. (Data from: www.ct.gov.)

(a) $C(1)$

(b) $\lim\limits_{x \to 1} C(x)$

(c) $C(4)$

(d) $\lim\limits_{x \to 4} C(x)$

(e) Find all values where C is discontinuous on the interval $(0, 5)$.

36. Business The cost of hourly parking at Ronald Reagan National Washington Airport is $2 per half hour (or fraction thereof) for the first two hours, and then $4 per hour (or fraction thereof) for the third through eighth hours, with a daily maximum of $36. Let $C(x)$ be the cost (in dollars) of parking for x hours. Find the left-hand, right-hand, and two-sided limits at the given x-values. (Data from: www.metwashairports.com/reagan, 2012 prices.)

(a) $x = 1.5$

(b) $x = 5$

(c) $x = 10$

(d) Find all values where C is discontinuous.

Write each of the given ranges in interval notation.

37.

38.

39.

40.

41. On which of the following intervals is the function in Exercise 6 continuous: $(-6, 0)$; $[0, 3]$; $(4, 8)$?

42. On which of the following intervals is the function in Exercise 5 continuous: $(-3, 0)$; $[0, 3]$; $[1, 3]$?

43. Health During pregnancy, a woman's weight naturally increases during the course of the event. When she delivers, her weight immediately decreases by the approximate weight of the child. Suppose that a 120-lb woman gains 27 lb during pregnancy, delivers a 7-lb baby, and then, loses the remaining weight during the next 20 weeks.

(a) Graph the weight gain and loss during the pregnancy and the 20 weeks following the birth of the baby. Assume that the pregnancy lasts 40 weeks, that delivery occurs immediately after this time interval, and that the weight gain and loss before and after birth, respectively, are linear.

(b) Is this function continuous? If not, then find the value(s) of t where the function is discontinuous.

✓**Checkpoint Answers**

1. (a) $x = -1, 1$ **(b)** $x = -2$ **(c)** $x = 1$

2. (a) $f(a)$ does not exist.   **(b)** $\lim_{x \to b} f(x)$ does not exist.

3. (a) Continuous from the right

     (b) Continuous from the left

     (c) Neither

4. (a) $(-5, 3)$ **(b)** $[4, 7]$ **(c)** $(-\infty, -1]$

5. (a) Yes; no   **(b)** Yes; no

6. $x = 5, 7, 9$ GB

7. (a) Continuous, differentiable

     (b) Continuous, not differentiable

     (c) Not continuous, not differentiable

CHAPTER 11 Summary and Review

Key Terms and Symbols

11.1 $\lim_{x \to a} f(x)$ limit of $f(x)$ as x approaches a

limit of a constant function

limit of the identity function

properties of limits

polynomial limits

limit theorem

11.2 $\lim_{x \to a^+} f(x)$ limit of $f(x)$ as x approaches a from the right

$\lim_{x \to a^-} f(x)$ limit of $f(x)$ as x approaches a from the left

$\lim_{x \to \infty} f(x)$ limit of $f(x)$ as x approaches infinity

$\lim_{x \to -\infty} f(x)$ limit of $f(x)$ as x approaches negative infinity

infinite limits

11.3 average rate of change

geometric meaning of average rate of change

velocity

instantaneous rate of change

marginal cost, revenue, profit

11.4 y', derivative of y

$f'(x)$, derivative of $f(x)$

secant line

tangent line

derivative

differentiable

11.5 $\dfrac{dy}{dx}$, derivative of $y = f(x)$

$D_x[f(x)]$, derivative of $f(x)$

$\dfrac{d}{dx}[f(x)]$, derivative of $f(x)$

derivative rules

demand function

11.6 $\overline{C}(x)$, average cost per item

product rule

quotient rule

marginal average cost

11.7 $g[f(x)]$, composite function

chain rule

generalized power rule

marginal-revenue product

11.8 derivatives of exponential functions

derivatives of logarithmic functions

11.9 continuous at a point

discontinuous

continuous from the left and from the right

interval notation

continuous on an open or closed interval

Chapter 11 Key Concepts

Limit of a Function

Let f be a function, and let a and L be real numbers. Suppose that as x takes values very close (but not equal) to a (on both sides of a), the corresponding values of $f(x)$ are very close (and possibly equal) to L and that the values of $f(x)$ can be made arbitrarily close to L for all values of x that are close enough to a. Then L is the **limit** of f as x approaches a, written $\lim_{x \to a} f(x) = L$.

One-Sided Limits

The **limit of f as x approaches a from the right**, written $\lim_{x \to a^+} f(x)$, is defined by replacing the phrase "on both sides of a" by "with $x > a$" in the definition of the limit of a function.

The **limit of f as x approaches a from the left**, written $\lim_{x \to a^-} f(x)$, is defined by replacing the phrase "on both sides of a" by "with $x < a$" in the definition of the limit of a function.

Properties of Limits

Let $a, k, A,$ and B be real numbers, and let f and g be functions such that

$$\lim_{x \to a} f(x) = A \quad \text{and} \quad \lim_{x \to a} g(x) = B.$$

Then

1. $\lim_{x \to a} k = k$ (for any constant k);

2. $\lim_{x \to a} x = a$ (for any real number a);

3. $\lim_{x \to a} [f(x) \pm g(x)] = A \pm B = \lim_{x \to a} f(x) \pm \lim_{x \to a} g(x)$;

4. $\lim_{x \to a} [f(x) \cdot g(x)] = A \cdot B = \lim_{x \to a} f(x) \cdot \lim_{x \to a} g(x)$;

5. $\quad \lim\limits_{x \to a} \dfrac{f(x)}{g(x)} = \dfrac{A}{B} = \dfrac{\lim\limits_{x \to a} f(x)}{\lim\limits_{x \to a} g(x)} \qquad (B \neq 0);$

6. for any real number r for which A^r exists,

$$\lim_{x \to a} [f(x)]^r = A^r = [\lim_{x \to a} f(x)]^r.$$

Polynomial Limits

If f is a polynomial function, then $\lim\limits_{x \to a} f(x) = f(a)$.

Limit Theorem

If f and g are functions that have limits as x approaches a, and $f(x) = g(x)$ for all $x \neq a$, then $\lim\limits_{x \to a} f(x) = \lim\limits_{x \to a} g(x)$.

Limits at Infinity

Let f be a function that is defined for all large values of x, and let L be a real number.

Suppose that as x takes larger and larger values, increasing without bound, the corresponding values of $f(x)$ are very close (and possibly equal) to L, and suppose that the values of $f(x)$ can be made arbitrarily close to L by taking large enough values of x. Then L is the **limit of f as x approaches infinity**, written $\lim\limits_{x \to \infty} f(x) = L$.

Let f be a function that is defined for all small negative values of x, and let M be a real number. Suppose that as x takes smaller and smaller negative values, decreasing without bound, the corresponding values of $f(x)$ are very close (and possibly equal) to M, and suppose that the values of $f(x)$ can be made arbitrarily close to M by taking small enough values of x. Then M is the **limit of f as x approaches negative infinity**, written $\lim\limits_{x \to -\infty} f(x) = M$.

Derivatives

The **instantaneous rate of change** of a function f when $x = a$ is

$$\lim_{h \to 0} \frac{f(a + h) - f(a)}{h},$$

provided that this limit exists.

The **tangent line** to the graph of $y = f(x)$ at the point $(a, f(a))$ is the line through this point and having slope $\lim\limits_{h \to 0} \dfrac{f(a + h) - f(a)}{h}$, provided that this limit exists.

The **derivative** of the function f is the function denoted f' whose value at the number x is $f'(x) = \lim\limits_{h \to 0} \dfrac{f(x + h) - f(x)}{h}$, provided that this limit exists.

Rules for Derivatives

(Assume that all indicated derivatives exist.)

Constant Function If $f(x) = k$, where k is any real number, then $f'(x) = 0$.

Power Rule If $f(x) = x^n$, for any real number n, then $f'(x) = n \cdot x^{n-1}$.

Constant Times a Function Let k be a real number. Then the derivative of $y = k \cdot f(x)$ is $y' = k \cdot f'(x)$.

Sum-or-Difference Rule If $f(x) = u(x) \pm v(x)$, then $f'(x) = u'(x) \pm v'(x)$.

Product Rule If $f(x) = u(x) \cdot v(x)$, then $f'(x) = u(x) \cdot v'(x) + v(x) \cdot u'(x)$.

Quotient Rule If $f(x) = \dfrac{u(x)}{v(x)}$, and $v(x) \neq 0$, then $f'(x) = \dfrac{v(x) \cdot u'(x) - u(x) \cdot v'(x)}{[v(x)]^2}$.

Chain Rule Let $y = f[g(x)]$. Then $y' = f'[g(x)] \cdot g'(x)$.

Chain Rule (alternative form) If y is a function of u, say, $y = f(u)$, and if u is a function of x, say, $u = g(x)$, then $y = f(u) = f[g(x)]$, and

$$\frac{dy}{dx} = \frac{dy}{du} \cdot \frac{du}{dx}.$$

Generalized Power Rule Let u be a function of x, and let $y = u^n$ for any real number n. Then

$$y' = n \cdot u^{n-1} \cdot u'.$$

Exponential Function If $y = e^{g(x)}$, then $y' = g'(x) \cdot e^{g(x)}$.

Natural-Logarithm Function If $y = \ln|x|$, then $y' = \dfrac{1}{x}$.

If $y = \ln[g(x)]$, then $y' = \dfrac{g'(x)}{g(x)}$.

Continuity

A function f is **continuous** at $x = c$ if $f(c)$ is defined, $\lim\limits_{x \to c} f(x)$ exists, and $\lim\limits_{x \to c} f(x) = f(c)$.

Chapter 11 Review Exercises

In Exercises 1–4, determine graphically or numerically whether the limit exists. If the limit exists, find its (approximate) value.

1. $\lim_{x \to -3} f(x)$; $\lim_{x \to -3^-} f(x)$; $\lim_{x \to -3^+} f(x)$

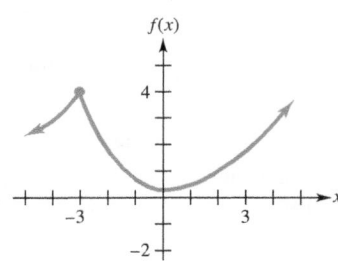

2. $\lim_{x \to -1} g(x)$; $\lim_{x \to -1^-} g(x)$; $\lim_{x \to -1^+} g(x)$

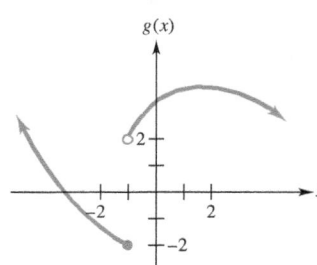

3. $\lim_{x \to 0} \dfrac{\sqrt{2-x} - \sqrt{2}}{x}$

4. $\lim_{x \to -1} \dfrac{10^x - .1}{x + 1}$

Find the given limit if it exists.

5. $\lim_{x \to 5} \dfrac{5x - 4}{x - 2}$

6. $\lim_{x \to -1} \dfrac{7 - 3x}{x - 4}$

7. $\lim_{x \to 3} \dfrac{x^2 - 9}{x + 3}$

8. $\lim_{x \to 7} \dfrac{49 - x^2}{x + 7}$

9. $\lim_{x \to 4} \dfrac{x^2 - 16}{x - 4}$

10. $\lim_{x \to -2} \dfrac{x^2 - x - 6}{x + 2}$

11. $\lim_{x \to 9} \dfrac{\sqrt{x} - 3}{x - 9}$

12. $\lim_{x \to 16} \dfrac{\sqrt{x} - 4}{x - 16}$

Find the given limit if it exists.

13. $\lim_{x \to 4^+} \sqrt{x^2 - x - 12}$

14. $\lim_{x \to 3^-} (5x + \sqrt{9 - x^2})$

15. $\lim_{x \to 7} \dfrac{|x - 7|}{x - 7}$

16. $\lim_{x \to -9} \dfrac{|x + 9|}{x + 9}$

17. $\lim_{x \to 6^-} \dfrac{x^2 + 1}{x - 6}$

18. $\lim_{x \to -5} \dfrac{8x}{(x + 5)^2}$

19. $\lim_{x \to \infty} \dfrac{9x + 1}{3x - 4x^2}$

20. $\lim_{x \to \infty} \dfrac{5x^2 - 8x + 3}{5 - 7x^3}$

21. $\lim_{x \to \infty} \dfrac{6x^2 - x + 50}{3 - 2x^2}$

22. $\lim_{x \to \infty} \dfrac{12x^3 + 3x^2 - 7x + 1}{6 - 3x - 4x^3}$

Use the accompanying graph to find the average rate of change of f on the given intervals.

23. $x = 0$ to $x = 4$

24. $x = 2$ to $x = 8$

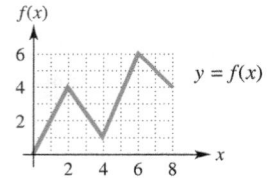

Find the average rate of change for each of the given functions.

25. $f(x) = 3x^2 - 5$, from $x = 1$ to $x = 5$

26. $g(x) = -x^3 + 2x^2 + 1$, from $x = -2$ to $x = 3$

27. $h(x) = \dfrac{6 - x}{2x + 3}$, from $x = 0$ to $x = 6$

28. $f(x) = e^{2x} + 5 \ln x$, from $x = 1$ to $x = 7$

Use the definition of the derivative to find the derivative of each of the given functions.

29. $y = 2x + 3$

30. $y = 4 - 3x$

31. $y = 2x^2 - x - 1$

32. $y = x^2 + 2x$

Find the slope of the tangent line to the given curve at the given value of x. Find the equation of each tangent line.

33. $y = x^2 - 6x$; at $x = 2$

34. $y = 8 - x^2$; at $x = 1$

35. $y = \dfrac{-2}{x + 5}$; at $x = -2$

36. $y = \sqrt{6x - 2}$; at $x = 3$

37. Business Suppose hardware store customers are willing to buy $T(p)$ boxes of nails at p dollars per box, where

$$T(p) = .06p^4 - 1.25p^3 + 6.5p^2 - 18p + 200$$
$$(0 < p \le 11).$$

(a) Find the average rate of change in demand for a change in price from \$5 to \$8.

(b) Find the instantaneous rate of change in demand when the price is \$5.

(c) Find the instantaneous rate of change in demand when the price is \$8.

38. Suppose the average rate of change of a function $f(x)$ from $x = 1$ to $x = 4$ is 0. Does this mean that f is constant between $x = 1$ and $x = 4$? Explain.

Find the derivative of each of the given functions.

39. $y = 6x^2 - 7x + 3$

40. $y = x^3 - 5x^2 + 1$

41. $y = 4x^{9/2}$

42. $y = -4x^{-5}$

43. $f(x) = x^{-6} + \sqrt{x}$

44. $f(x) = 8x^{-3} - 5\sqrt{x}$

45. $y = (4t^2 + 9)(t^3 - 5)$

46. $y = (-5t + 3)(t^3 - 4t)$

47. $y = 8x^{3/4}(5x + 1)$

48. $y = 40x^{-1/4}(x^2 + 1)$

49. $f(x) = \dfrac{4x}{x^2 - 8}$ **50.** $g(x) = \dfrac{-5x^2}{3x + 1}$

51. $y = \dfrac{\sqrt{x} - 6}{3x + 7}$ **52.** $y = \dfrac{\sqrt{x} + 9}{x - 4}$

53. $y = \dfrac{x^2 - x + 1}{x - 1}$ **54.** $y = \dfrac{2x^3 - 5x^2}{x + 2}$

55. $f(x) = (4x - 2)^4$ **56.** $k(x) = (5x - 1)^6$

57. $y = \sqrt{2t - 5}$ **58.** $y = -3\sqrt{8t - 1}$

59. $y = 2x(3x - 4)^3$ **60.** $y = 5x^2(2x + 3)^5$

61. $f(u) = \dfrac{3u^2 - 4u}{(2u + 3)^3}$ **62.** $g(t) = \dfrac{t^3 + t - 2}{(2t - 1)^5}$

63. $y = -6e^{2x}$ **64.** $y = 8e^{.5x}$

65. $y = e^{-2x^3}$ **66.** $y = -5e^{x^2}$

67. $y = 5x \cdot e^{2x}$ **68.** $y = -7x^2 \cdot e^{-3x}$

69. $y = \ln(x^2 + 4x - 1)$ **70.** $y = \ln(4x^3 + 2x)$

71. $y = \dfrac{\ln 6x}{x^2 - 1}$ **72.** $y = \dfrac{\ln(3x + 5)}{x^2 + 5x}$

Find all points of discontinuity for the given graphs.

73.

74.

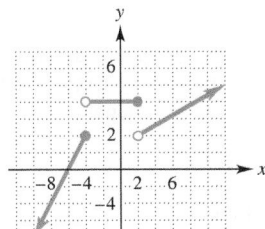

Are the given functions continuous at the given points?

75. $f(x) = \dfrac{x - 6}{x + 5}; x = 6, x = -5, x = 0$

76. $f(x) = \dfrac{x^2 - 9}{x + 3}; x = 3, x = -3, x = 0$

77. $h(x) = \dfrac{2 - 3x}{2 - x - x^2}; x = -2, x = \dfrac{2}{3}, x = 1$

78. $f(x) = \dfrac{x^2 - 4}{x^2 - x - 6}; x = 2, x = 3, x = 4$

Work these problems.

79. Business Shipping charges at an online pet supply store are 10% of the total purchase price except that there is a minimum

charge of $5 and orders over $100 receive free shipping. The accompanying figure shows the charge, $S(x)$, for shipping an order in the amount of x dollars. Find the given limits.

(a) $\lim\limits_{x \to 50} S(x)$ **(b)** $\lim\limits_{x \to 100} S(x)$

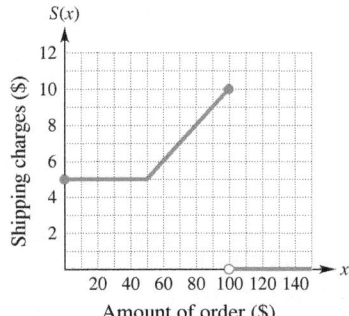

80. Business The Iowa Department of Revenue held a back-to-school sales tax holiday (during which clothing and footwear were exempt from state sales tax) on August 3–4, 2012. Suppose that the accompanying figure shows the sales tax receipts $T(x)$ (in dollars) from a certain apparel store at time x, where $x = 1$ corresponds to August 1. Find the given limits.

(a) $\lim\limits_{x \to 2} T(x)$ **(b)** $\lim\limits_{x \to 3} T(x)$

(c) $\lim\limits_{x \to 4} T(x)$ **(d)** $\lim\limits_{x \to 5} T(x)$

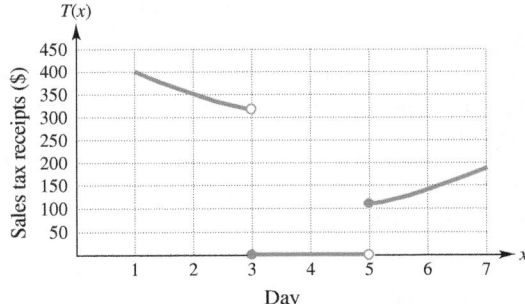

81. Business An airport car rental agency charges $65 per day (or fraction of a day) to rent a full-size car, plus a one-time airport surcharge of $5. Let $C(x)$ be the cost of renting a full-size car from this agency for x days. Find the given quantities.

(a) $C(2)$ **(b)** $\lim\limits_{x \to 2^-} C(x)$

(c) $\lim\limits_{x \to 2^+} C(x)$ **(d)** $\lim\limits_{x \to 2} C(x)$

82. Business The average cost (in dollars per hundred brochures) of printing x hundred glossy brochures (one page, two-sided, tri-fold) can be approximated by $\overline{C}(x) = \dfrac{450 + 115x}{x}$. Find $\lim\limits_{x \to \infty} \overline{C}(x)$.

83. Social Science Throughout the world, the percentage of seats in national parliaments (in a single chamber or lower chamber) held by women is shown in the figure on the next page. Find the average rate of change of the percent of women in national parliaments between the years 2000 and 2004. (Data from: www.worldbank.org.)

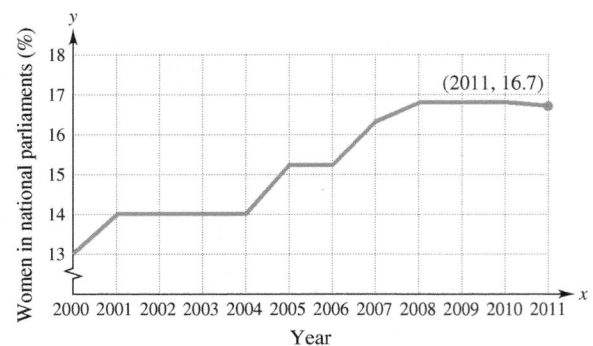

84. **Social Science** Use the figure in the preceding exercise to find the average rate of change of the percent of women in national parliaments between the years 2004 and 2011.

85. **Business** The amount of revenue (in thousands of dollars) generated by Google, Inc. can be approximated by $f(x) = 306x^2 + 133x - 1139$, where $x = 2$ corresponds to the year 2002. Find the instantaneous rate of change of revenue with respect to time in the year 2012. (Data from: www.morningstar.com.)

86. **Natural Science** Suppose that $D(x)$ represents the depth of a certain lake (in feet) at a distance x feet from the bank (in the direction toward the center of the lake). Explain what each of the given equations means in practical terms for a person standing in the lake.

    (a) $D(20) = 5$ (b) $D'(20) = .3$

87. **Social Science** The youth age dependency ratio in the United States, the proportion of youth dependents (people younger than 15) per 100 working-age population (people ages 15–64), can be approximated by $f(x) = .024x^2 - .47x + 32.33$, where $x = 0$ corresponds to the year 2000. Find the youth age dependency ratio and the rate of change of this number in the given year. (Data from: www.worldbank.org.)

    (a) 2007   (b) 2014

88. **Finance** Total gross domestic savings (in billions of dollars) can be approximated by $S(x) = .836x^4 - 20.3x^3 + 152x^2 - 333x + 1697$, where $x = 0$ corresponds to the year 2000. How is the total gross domestic savings changing in the year 2010? (Data from: www.worldbank.org.)

89. **Business** The number of cell phone subscriptions (in millions) in India can be approximated by
$$f(t) = 4.8e^{.5t},$$
where $t = 0$ corresponds to the year 2000. Find the number of cell phone subscriptions in India and the rate of change of this number in the year 2011. (Data from: www.worldbank.org.)

90. **Health** Based on historical data and future projections for the period 1970–2020, life expectancy (in years) for a person born in the United States in year x can be approximated by
$$L(x) = 15.08 \ln x + 7.3,$$
where $x = 70$ corresponds to the year 1970. (Data from: United States Census Bureau.)

    (a) Find the projected life expectancy for a person born in 2020.

    (b) If another person is born one year later, approximately how would her or his life expectancy differ from the person born in 2020?

91. **Business** A popular food truck that drives to various locations to sell lunch items has determined that the cost (in hundreds of dollars) of making x hundred sandwiches can be approximated by
$$C(x) = \frac{250x + 45}{2x + 40}.$$

    (a) Find the marginal-cost function.

    (b) If the food truck operators are currently making 1000 sandwiches per week, find the approximate cost of making an additional 100 sandwiches.

92. **Business** Consider the cost function given in the previous exercise.

    (a) Find the average-cost function.

    (b) Find the marginal average-cost function.

    (c) If the food truck operators are currently making 1000 sandwiches per week, approximately how will the average cost change if they make an additional 100 sandwiches?

93. **Business** The daily demand function for coffee at the campus coffee cart can be approximated by $p = \sqrt{25 - .1x}$, where p is the price (in dollars) and x is the number of cups of coffee demanded.

    (a) Find the revenue function.

    (b) Find the marginal revenue function.

    (c) If the demand is currently 90 cups of coffee, find the revenue.

    (d) If the demand is currently 90 cups of coffee, find the approximate revenue from selling one additional cup of coffee.

94. **Business** The cost function for the coffee cart described in the previous exercise can be approximated by $C(x) = 120 + .75x$, where $C(x)$ is the cost (in dollars) of producing x cups of coffee.

    (a) Find the profit function.

    (b) Find the marginal profit function.

    (c) If the demand is currently 120 cups of coffee, find the approximate profit from selling one additional cup of coffee.

95. **Business** Consider the demand equation given in Exercise 93.

    (a) Solve the demand equation for x in terms of p.

    (b) Find the rate of change of demand with respect to price.

    (c) If the price is currently $3 per cup, approximately what effect would raising the price by $1 have on the demand?

96. **Business** Sales at a fireworks outlet (in thousands of dollars) on day x can be approximated by $S(x) = 1 + 5xe^{-.3x}$, where $x = 1$ corresponds to July 1. Find the amount of sales and rate of change of sales on the given day.

    (a) July 2   (b) July 4

97. Business Use the graph of $y = S(x)$ shown in Exercise 79 to answer the given questions.

(a) At what x-values is the function S not continuous?

(b) At what x-values is the function S not differentiable?

98. Business The monthly cost of a popular cell phone plan is $50 for the first 450 minutes of airtime plus $.50 per minute (or fraction of a minute) for usage over 450 minutes. Let $C(x)$ be the cost of using x minutes of airtime. Find the given quantities.

(a) $C(400)$

(b) $\lim\limits_{x \to 400} C(x)$

(c) Is $C(x)$ continuous at $x = 400$?

(d) $C(460)$

(e) $\lim\limits_{x \to 460} C(x)$

(f) Is $C(x)$ continuous at $x = 460$?

99. Natural Science Under certain conditions, the length of the monkeyface prickleback, a west-coast game fish, can be approximated by

$$L = 71.5(1 - e^{-.1t})$$

and its weight by

$$W = .01289 \cdot L^{2.9},$$

where L is the length in cm, t is the age in years, and W is the weight in grams.[*]

(a) Find the approximate length of a five-year-old monkeyface.

(b) Find how fast the length of a five-year-old monkeyface is increasing.

(c) Find the approximate weight of a five-year-old monkeyface. (*Hint:* Use your answer from part (a).)

(d) Find the rate of change of the weight with respect to length for a five-year-old monkeyface.

(e) Using the chain rule and your answers to parts (b) and (d), find how fast the weight of a five-year-old monkeyface is increasing.

---

[*]William H. Marshall and Tina Wyllie Echeverria, "Characteristics of the Monkeyface Prickleback," *California Fish and Game* 78, no. 2 (spring 1992).

Case Study 11 Price Elasticity of Demand

Any retailer who sells a product or a service is concerned with how a change in price affects demand for the article. The sensitivity of demand to price changes varies with different items. For smaller items, such as soft drinks, food staples, and lightbulbs, small percentage changes in price will not affect the demand for the item much. However, sometimes a small percentage change in price on big-ticket items, such as cars, homes, and furniture, can have significant effects on demand.

One way to measure the sensitivity of changes in price to demand is by the ratio of percent change in demand to percent change in price. If q represents the quantity demanded and p the price of the item, this ratio can be written as

$$\frac{\Delta q/q}{\Delta p/p},$$

where Δq represents the change in q and Δp represents the change in p. The ratio is usually negative, because q and p are positive, while Δq and Δp typically have opposite signs. (An *increase* in price causes a *decrease* in demand.) If the absolute value of this quantity is large, it shows that a small increase in price can cause a relatively large decrease in demand.

Applying some algebra, we can rewrite this ratio as

$$\frac{\Delta q/q}{\Delta p/p} = \frac{\Delta q}{q} \cdot \frac{p}{\Delta p} = \frac{p}{q} \cdot \frac{\Delta q}{\Delta p}.$$

Suppose $q = f(p)$. (Note that this is the inverse of the way our demand functions have been expressed so far; previously, we had $p = D(q)$.) Then $\Delta q = f(p + \Delta p) - f(p)$. It follows that

$$\frac{\Delta q}{\Delta p} = \frac{f(p + \Delta p) - f(p)}{\Delta p}.$$

As $\Delta p \to 0$, this quotient becomes

$$\lim\limits_{\Delta p \to 0} \frac{\Delta q}{\Delta p} = \lim\limits_{\Delta p \to 0} \frac{f(p + \Delta p) - f(p)}{\Delta p} = \frac{dq}{dp},$$

and

$$\lim\limits_{\Delta p \to 0} \frac{p}{q} \cdot \frac{\Delta q}{\Delta p} = \frac{p}{q} \cdot \frac{dq}{dp}.$$

The quantity

$$E = -\frac{p}{q} \cdot \frac{dq}{dp}$$

is positive because dq/dp is negative. E is called **elasticity of demand** and measures the instantaneous responsiveness of demand to price. For example, E may be .6 for physician services (expenses that have considerable price increases each year, but still have a high demand), but may be 2.3 for restaurant meals (highly enjoyable, but high-cost items and not necessities). These numbers indicate that the demand for physician services is much less responsive to price changes than the demand for restaurant meals. Another factor that impacts elasticity of demand is the availability of substitute products. For example, if one airline increases prices on a particular route but other airlines serving the route do not, then rather than paying the higher prices, consumers could fly with a different airline (the substitute product).

If $E < 1$, the relative change in demand is less than the relative change in price, and the demand is called **inelastic.** If $E > 1$, the relative change in demand is greater than the relative change in price, and the demand is called **elastic.** When $E = 1$, the percentage changes in price and demand are relatively equal, and the demand is said to have **unit elasticity.**

Sometimes elasticity is counterintuitive. The addiction to illicit drugs is an excellent example. The quantity of the drug demanded by addicts, if anything, increases, no matter what the cost. Thus, illegal drugs are an inelastic commodity.

Example 1 Suppose that the demand for flat screen televisions is expressed by the equation

$$q = -.025p + 20.45,$$

where q is the annual demand (in millions of televisions) and p is the price of the product (in dollars).

(a) Calculate and interpret the elasticity of demand when $p = \$200$ and when $p = \$500$.

Solution Since $q = -.025p + 20.45$, we have $dq/dp = -.025$, so that

$$E = -\frac{p}{q} \cdot \frac{dq}{dp}$$

$$= -\frac{p}{-.025p + 20.45} \cdot (-.025)$$

$$= \frac{.025p}{-.025p + 20.45}.$$

Let $p = 200$ to get

$$E = \frac{.025(200)}{-.025(200) + 20.45} \approx .324.$$

Since $.324 < 1$, the demand was inelastic, and a percentage change in price resulted in a smaller percentage change in demand. For example, a 10% increase in price will cause a 3.24% decrease in demand.

If $p = 500$, then

$$E = \frac{.025(500)}{-.025(500) + 20.45} \approx 1.57.$$

Since $1.57 > 1$, the price is elastic. At this point, a percentage increase in price resulted in a greater percentage decrease in demand. A 10% increase in price resulted in a 15.7% decrease in demand.

(b) Determine the price at which demand had unit elasticity $(E = 1)$. What is the significance of this price?

Solution Demand had unit elasticity at the price p that made $E = 1$, so we must solve the equation

$$E = \frac{.025p}{-.025p + 20.45} = 1$$

$$.025p = -.025p + 20.45$$

$$.05p = 20.45$$

$$p = 409.$$

Demand had unit elasticity at a price of \$409 per flat screen television. Unit elasticity indicates that the changes in price and demand are about the same.

The definitions from the preceding discussion can be expressed in the manner that follows.

Elasticity of Demand

Let $q = f(p)$, where q is the demand at a price p. The **elasticity of demand** is as follows:

Demand is **inelastic** if $E < 1$.

Demand is **elastic** if $E > 1$.

Demand has **unit elasticity** if $E = 1$.

Exercises

1. The monthly demand for beef in a given region can be expressed by the equation $q = -3.003p + 675.23$, where q is the monthly demand in tons and p is the price in dollars per 100 pounds. Determine the elasticity of demand when the price is \$70.[*]

2. Acme Stationery sells designer-brand pens. The demand equation for annual sales of these pens is $q = -1000p + 70,000$, where p is the price per pen. Normally, the pens sell for \$30 each. They are very popular, and Acme has been thinking of raising the price by one third.[†]

   (a) Find the elasticity of demand if $p = \$30$.

   (b) Find the elasticity of demand if the price is raised by one third. Is raising the price a good idea?

3. The monthly demand for lodging in a certain city is given by $q = -2481.52p + 472,191.2$, where p is the nightly rate.[§]

   (a) Find E when $p = \$100$ and when $p = \$75$.

   (b) At what price is there unit elasticity?

4. The following multiple-choice question is a released sample question from the Major Field Test in Economics.[**] The demand for a good is given by $q = 100 - 4p^2$, where $q = $ quantity demanded per unit of time and $p = $ the price per unit. At a price of \$4, the absolute value of the price elasticity of demand is approximately equal to which of the following?

   (a) ∞ **(b)** 36.0   **(c)** 3.6

   (d) 1.0   **(e)** 0.28

5. What must be true about demand if $E = 0$ everywhere?

---

[*]Adapted from *How Demand and Supply Determine Price*, Agricultural Marketing Manual, Alberta, Canada, February 1999.

[†]Taken from R. Horn, *Economics 331: Warm-up Problems: Supply, Demand, Elasticity.*

[§]Extracted from Bjorn Hanson, *Price Elasticity of Lodging Demand* (Pricewaterhouse-Coopers, 2000).

[**]The Major Field Tests are developed by ETS (http://www.ets.org/Media/Tests/MFT/pdf/2008/MFT_Economics_Sample_Items_08.pdf).

Extended Project

Sensitivity to higher prices was evident in the tobacco market following increases in taxes that included large disparities in tax rates for cigarettes and pipe tobacco versus roll-your-own tobacco. Data for prices and quantities demanded are summarized in the following table for the year prior to and following the implementation of the tax increases.[*] In this project, the price data includes only the cost of the tax rather than the total cost of the product plus tax since the increases in taxes were the significant aspect of the changes in price.

Year	Cigarettes		Roll-Your-Own Tobacco		Pipe Tobacco	
	Price (dollars per thousand sticks)	Quantity (billions of sticks)	Price (dollars per pound)	Quantity (thousands of pounds)	Price (dollars per pound)	Quantity (thousands of pounds)
2008	19.50	337.64	1.10	19,673	1.10	3150
2010	50.33	296.23	24.78	6152	2.83	20,817

(a) The data show that the percent increase in the tax on cigarettes was $\dfrac{50.33 - 19.50}{19.50} = 158\%$. Find the percent increase for pipe tobacco and roll-your-own tobacco. Were the increases similar for all products or were there large disparities?

(b) For cigarettes, use a linear model (the equation of a line) to express the quantity demanded as a function of price.

(c) Repeat part (b) for roll-your-own tobacco.

(d) For cigarettes, determine the elasticity of demand $E = -\dfrac{p}{q}\dfrac{dq}{dp}$ at the lower price prior to the tax increases and also at the higher price following the tax increases. Was the elasticity of demand for cigarettes inelastic ($E < 1$) or elastic ($E > 1$) at the lower price? At the higher price?

(e) Repeat part (d) for roll-your-own tobacco.

(f) Factors that impact elasticity of demand include price, the necessity of the product, and availability of substitute products. What is a possible explanation for the large difference in elasticity of demand for cigarettes and roll-your-own tobacco at the higher price?

(g) You work for a tobacco store that sells a wide variety of products including those listed in the table above. Your employer has asked you to write a report that summarizes the elasticity of demand information you have calculated, provides a possible explanation for the large differences in elasticity of demand for cigarettes and roll-your-own tobacco after the price increases, and comments on the implications for the tobacco store.

---

[*]Tobacco Taxes: Large Disparities in Rates for Smoking Products Trigger Significant Market Shifts to Avoid Higher Taxes, United States Government Accountability Office Report to Congressional Committees, April 2012.

Applications of the Derivative

Functions and their derivatives can be used to solve a variety of optimization problems. For example, automotive engineers want to design engines with maximum fuel efficiency. A manufacturer wants to have a box that requires the smallest amount of cardboard (and hence is cheapest). A hospital or a business may want to determine the optimum intervals at which supplies should be ordered to minimize the total cost of ordering, delivery, and storage. Every business wants to maximize its profit. See Exercise 39 on page 714, Exercises 55 and 59 on page 715, and Exercise 53 on page 741.

In the last chapter, the derivative was defined and interpreted, and formulas were developed for the derivatives of many functions. In this chapter, we investigate the connection between the derivative of a function and the graph of the function. In particular, we shall see how to use the derivative to determine algebraically the maximum and minimum values of a function, as well as the intervals on which the function is increasing or decreasing.

12.1 Derivatives and Graphs

Informally, we say that a function is **increasing** on an interval if its graph is *rising* from left to right over the interval and that a function is **decreasing** on an interval if its graph is *falling* from left to right over the interval.

Example 1   For which x-intervals is the function graphed in Figure 12.1 increasing? For which intervals is it decreasing?

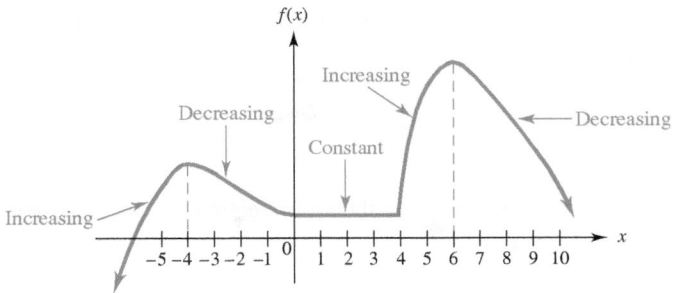

Figure 12.1

Solution Moving from left to right, the function is increasing up to -4, then decreasing from -4 to 0, constant (neither increasing nor decreasing) from 0 to 4, increasing from 4 to 6, and, finally, decreasing from 6 on. In interval notation, the function is increasing on $(-\infty, -4)$ and $(4, 6)$, decreasing on $(-4, 0)$ and $(6, \infty)$, and constant on $(0, 4)$. ✓

In order to examine the connection between the graph of a function f and the derivative of f, it is sometimes helpful to think of the graph of f as a roller-coaster track, with a roller-coaster car moving from left to right along the graph, as shown in Figure 12.2. At any point along the graph, the floor of the car (a straight-line segment) represents the tangent line to the graph at that point.

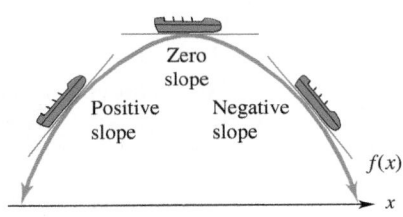

Figure 12.2

The slope of the tangent line is positive when the car travels uphill (the function is *increasing*), and the slope of the tangent line is negative when the car travels downhill (the function is *decreasing*). Since the slope of the tangent line at the point $(x, f(x))$ is given by the derivative $f'(x)$, we have the following useful facts.

Increasing and Decreasing Functions

Suppose a function f has a derivative at each point in an open interval. Then

1. if $f'(x) > 0$ for each x in the interval, f is *increasing* on the interval;

2. if $f'(x) < 0$ for each x in the interval, f is *decreasing* on the interval;

3. if $f'(x) = 0$ for each x in the interval, f is *constant* on the interval.

Checkpoint 1

For what values of x is the function whose graph is shown increasing? decreasing?

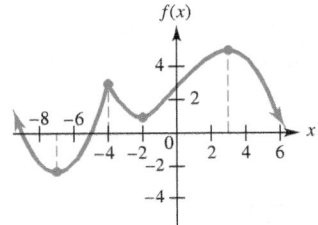

Answers to Checkpoint exercises are found at the end of the section.

Example 2 Find the intervals on which the function

$$f(x) = x^3 + 3x^2 - 9x + 4,$$

whose graph is shown in Figure 12.3, is increasing, decreasing, and constant.

Solution The graph in Figure 12.3 does not clearly show the intervals on which f is increasing or decreasing. To get more precise information, we first find the derivative:

$$f'(x) = 3x^2 + 6x - 9.$$

$$f(x) = x^3 + 3x^2 - 9x + 4$$

Figure 12.3

According to the box preceding the example, the function f is increasing on the intervals where $f'(x) > 0$ and decreasing on the intervals where $f'(x) < 0$. So we must solve the following inequalities:

$$f'(x) > 0 \quad \text{and} \quad f'(x) < 0$$
$$3x^2 + 6x - 9 > 0 \qquad\qquad 3x^2 + 6x - 9 < 0.$$

As shown in Section 2.5, the first step is to solve the equation $f'(x) = 0$:

$$3x^2 + 6x - 9 = 0$$
$$3(x^2 + 2x - 3) = 0$$
$$3(x + 3)(x - 1) = 0$$
$$x = -3 \quad \text{or} \quad x = 1.$$

Now use either graphical or algebraic methods to solve the inequalities.

Graphical   The graph of the derivative $f'(x) = 3x^2 + 6x - 9$ in Figure 12.4 lies above the x-axis on the intervals $(-\infty, -3)$ and $(1, \infty)$, meaning that $f'(x) > 0$ on these intervals. Similarly, $f'(x) < 0$ on $(-3, 1)$ because the graph of $f'(x)$ is below the x-axis on $(-3, 1)$.

Algebraic   The numbers -3 and 1 divide the x-axis into three intervals: $(-\infty, -3)$, $(-3, 1)$, and $(1, \infty)$. Determine the sign of $f'(x)$ on each interval by testing a number in that interval, as summarized next.

Interval	$(-\infty, -3)$	$(-3, 1)$	$(1, \infty)$
Test Value in Interval	-4	0	2
Value of $f'(x) = 3x^2 + 6x - 9$	15	-9	15
Graph of f'	Above x-axis	Below x-axis	Above x-axis
Sign of $f'(x)$	$f'(x) > 0$	$f'(x) < 0$	$f'(x) > 0$
Conclusion about f	f increasing	f decreasing	f increasing

Regardless of method, the conclusion is the same: The original function f is increasing on $(-\infty, -3)$ and $(1, \infty)$, which are the intervals where $f'(x) > 0$, and decreasing on $(-3, 1)$, where $f'(x) < 0$. ✓ 2

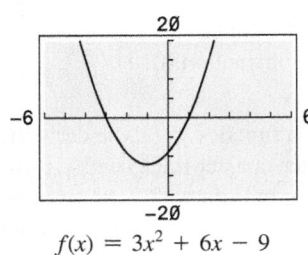

20

-6 6

-20

$f(x) = 3x^2 + 6x - 9$

Figure 12.4

✓ **Checkpoint 2**

Find all intervals on which $f(x) = 4x^3 + 3x^2 - 18x + 1$ is increasing or decreasing.

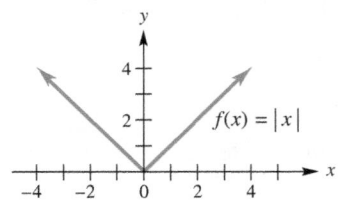

y

4

2 $f(x) = |x|$

-4 -2 0 2 4 x

Figure 12.5

Critical Numbers

In Example 2, the numbers for which $f'(x) = 0$ were essential for determining exactly where the function was increasing and decreasing. The situation is a bit different with the absolute-value function $f(x) = |x|$, whose graph is shown in Figure 12.5. Clearly, f is decreasing on the left of $x = 0$ and increasing on the right of $x = 0$. But as we saw on pages 613–614, the derivative of $f(x) = |x|$ does not exist at $x = 0$. These examples suggest that the points where the derivative is 0 or undefined play an important role.

In view of the preceding discussion, we have the following definition.

Critical Numbers

If f is a function, then a number c for which $f(c)$ is defined and

$$\text{either } f'(c) = 0 \quad \text{or} \quad f'(c) \text{ does not exist}$$

is called a **critical number** of f. The corresponding point $(c, f(c))$ on the graph of f is called a **critical point**.

The procedure used in Example 2, which applies to all functions treated in this text, can now be summarized in the manner that follows.

Increasing/Decreasing Test

To find the intervals on which a function f is increasing or decreasing, do the following:

Step 1 Compute the derivative f'.

Step 2 Find the critical numbers of f.

Step 3 Solve the inequalities $f'(x) > 0$ and $f'(x) < 0$ graphically or algebraically (by testing a number in each of the intervals determined by the critical numbers).

The solutions of $f'(x) > 0$ are intervals on which f is increasing, and the solutions of $f'(x) < 0$ are intervals on which f is decreasing.

Maxima and Minima

We have seen that the graph of a typical function may have "peaks" or "valleys," as illustrated in Figure 12.6.

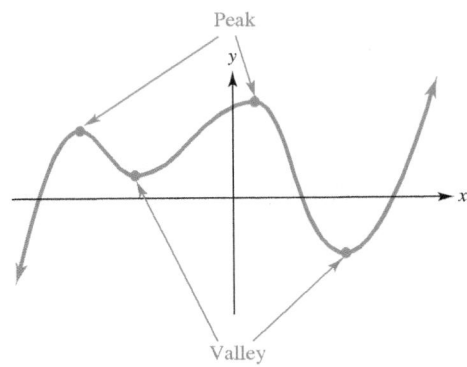

Figure 12.6

Peaks and valleys are sometimes called **turning points** of the graph, because as you go from left to right, the graph changes from increasing to decreasing at a peak and from decreasing to increasing at a valley.

A peak is the highest point in its neighborhood, but not necessarily the highest point on the graph. Similarly, a valley is the lowest point in its neighborhood, but not necessarily the lowest point on the graph. Consequently, a peak is called a *local maximum* and a valley a *local minimum.* More precisely, we have the following definitions.

Local Extrema

Let c be a number in the domain of a function f. Then

1. f has a **local maximum** at c if $f(x) \leq f(c)$ for all x near c;

2. f has a **local minimum** at c if $f(x) \geq f(c)$ for all x near c.

The function f is said to have a **local extremum** at c if it has a local maximum or minimum there.

NOTE The plurals of *maximum, minimum,* and *extremum* are, respectively, *maxima, minima,* and *extrema.*

Example 3 Identify the local extrema of the function whose graph is shown in Figure 12.7.

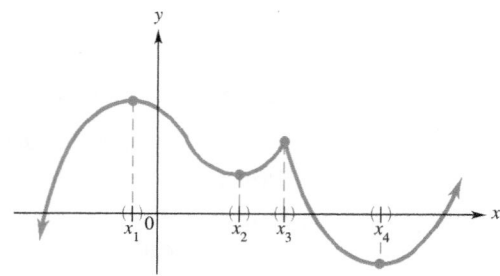

Figure 12.7

✓ **Checkpoint 3**

Identify the x-values of all points where the given graphs have local maxima and local minima.

(a)

(b)

(c)

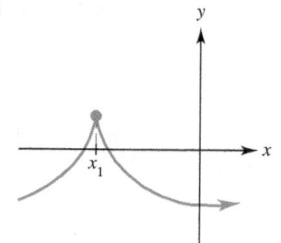

Solution The function has local maxima at x_1 and x_3 and local minima at x_2 and x_4. ✓ 3

The *exact* location of a local extremum (rather than a calculator's approximation) can normally be found by using derivatives. To see why this is so, let f be a function and, once again, think of the graph of f as a roller-coaster track, as shown in Figure 12.8.

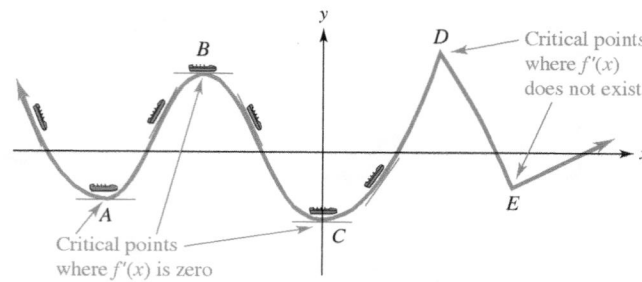

Figure 12.8

As the car passes through the local extrema at A, B, and C, the tangent line is horizontal and has slope 0. At D and E, however, a real roller-coaster car would have trouble. It would fly off the track at D and be unable to make the 90° change of direction at E. Notice that the graph does not have tangent lines at points D and E. (See the discussion of the existence of derivatives in Section 11.4.) Thus, a point $(c, f(c))$ where a local extremum occurs has the following property: The tangent line has slope 0, *or* there is no tangent line—that is, $f'(c) = 0$ or $f'(c)$ does not exist. In other words, c is a critical number.

Local Extrema and Critical Numbers

If f has a local extremum at $x = c$, then c is a critical number of f.

🛑 **CAUTION** This result says that every local extremum occurs at a critical number, *not* that every critical number produces a local extremum. Thus, the critical numbers provide a list of *possibilities*: If there is a local extremum, it must occur at a number on the list, but the list may include numbers at which there is no local extremum.

↗ **TECHNOLOGY TIP** Most graphing calculators have a maximum/minimum finder that can approximate local extrema to a high degree of accuracy. Check your instruction manual.

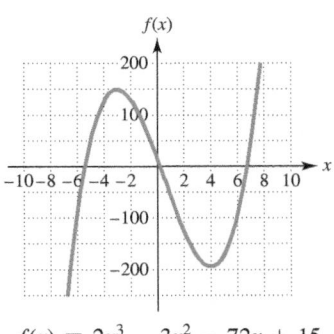

$f(x) = 2x^3 - 3x^2 - 72x + 15$

Figure 12.9

Figure 12.10

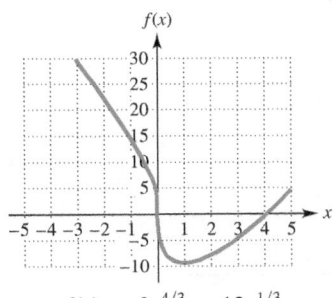

$f(x) = 3x^{4/3} - 12x^{1/3}$

Figure 12.11

✓ **Checkpoint 4**

Find the critical numbers for each of the given functions.

(a) $\frac{1}{3}x^3 - x^2 - 15x + 6$

(b) $6x^{2/3} - 4x$

Example 4   Find the critical numbers of the given functions.

(a) $f(x) = 2x^3 - 3x^2 - 72x + 15$

Solution   We have $f'(x) = 6x^2 - 6x - 72$, so $f'(x)$ exists for every x. Setting $f'(x) = 0$ shows that

$$6x^2 - 6x - 72 = 0$$
$$6(x^2 - x - 12) = 0$$
$$x^2 - x - 12 = 0$$
$$(x + 3)(x - 4) = 0$$
$$x + 3 = 0 \quad \text{or} \quad x - 4 = 0$$
$$x = -3 \quad \text{or} \quad x = 4.$$

Therefore, -3 and 4 are the critical numbers of f; these are the only places where local extrema could occur. The graph of f in Figure 12.9 shows that there is a local maximum at $x = -3$ and a local minimum at $x = 4$.

(b) $f(x) = x^3$

Solution   The derivative $f'(x) = 3x^2$ exists for every x. Setting $f'(x) = 0$ shows that $3x^2 = 0$ exactly when $x = 0$. Therefore, $x = 0$ is the only critical number of f and the only possible location for a local maximum or minimum. In this case, however, we know what the graph of f looks like. (See Figure 12.10.) The graph shows that there is no local maximum or minimum at $x = 0$.

(c) $f(x) = 3x^{4/3} - 12x^{1/3}$

Solution   We first compute the derivative:

$$f'(x) = 3 \cdot \frac{4}{3}x^{1/3} - 12 \cdot \frac{1}{3}x^{-2/3}$$

$$= 4x^{1/3} - \frac{4}{x^{2/3}}$$

$$= \frac{4x^{1/3}x^{2/3}}{x^{2/3}} - \frac{4}{x^{2/3}}$$

$$= \frac{4x - 4}{x^{2/3}}. \qquad \longleftarrow \quad f'(x) = 0 \text{ when } 4x - 4 = 0.$$
$$\longleftarrow \quad f'(x) \text{ does not exist when } x^{2/3} = 0.$$

The derivative fails to exist when $x = 0$, since the denominator is zero there. Since the original function f is defined when $x = 0$, 0 is a critical number of f. If $x \neq 0$, then $f'(x)$ is 0 only when the numerator $4x - 4 = 0$, that is, when $x = 1$. Therefore, the critical numbers of f are 0 and 1. These numbers are the *possible* locations for local extrema. However, the graph of f in Figure 12.11 suggests that there is a local minimum at $x = 1$, but no local extremum at $x = 0$. ✓ 4

The First-Derivative Test

When all the critical numbers of a function f have been found, you must then determine which ones lead to local extrema. Sometimes this can be done graphically, as in Example 4. It can also be done algebraically by using the following observation:

> At a local maximum, f changes from increasing to decreasing, and at a local minimum, f changes from decreasing to increasing, as illustrated in Figure 12.12 on the next page.

When f changes from increasing to decreasing, its derivative f' changes from positive to negative. Similarly, when f changes from decreasing to increasing, f' changes from negative to positive. These facts lead to the following test for local extrema; a formal proof of the test is omitted.

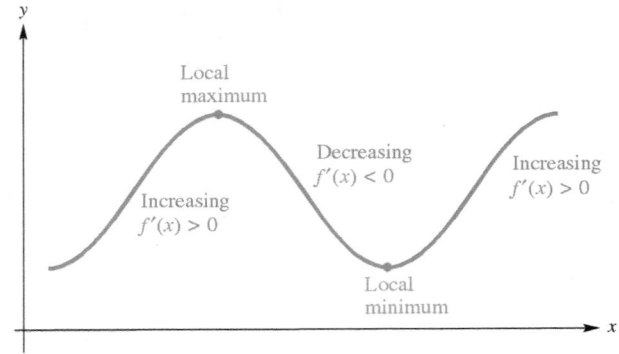

Figure 12.12

First-Derivative Test

Assume that $a < c < b$ and that c is the only critical number for a function f in the interval $[a, b]$. Assume that f is differentiable for all x in $[a, b]$, except possibly at $x = c$.

1. If $f'(a) > 0$ and $f'(b) < 0$, then there is a local maximum at c.

2. If $f'(a) < 0$ and $f'(b) > 0$, then there is a local minimum at c.

3. If $f'(a)$ and $f'(b)$ are both positive or both negative, then there is no local extremum at c.

The sketches in the following table show how the first-derivative test works (assume the same conditions on a, b, and c as those stated in the box):

$f(x)$ has . . .	Sign of $f'(a)$	Sign of $f'(b)$	Sketches	
Local Maximum	+	−		
Local Minimum	−	+		
No Local Extrema	+	+		
No Local Extrema	−	−		

The local extrema of the functions in Example 4(a) and 4(c) were determined graphically (once the critical numbers had been found algebraically). Examples 5 and 6 show how the first-derivative test can be used in place of graphing.

Example 5 Use the first-derivative test to find the local extrema of

$$f(x) = 2x^3 - 3x^2 - 72x + 15.$$

Solution Example 4(a) shows that the critical numbers of f are -3 and 4. To use the first-derivative test on -3, we must choose an interval $[a, b]$ containing -3, but not containing the other critical number. We shall use $a = -4$ and $b = 0$. Many other choices of a and b are possible, but we try to select ones that will make the computations easy. Since

$$f'(x) = 6x^2 - 6x - 72 = 6(x^2 - x - 12) = 6(x + 3)(x - 4),$$

it follows that

$$f'(-4) = 6(-4 + 3)(-4 - 4) = 6(-1)(-8) > 0$$

and

$$f'(0) = 6(0 + 3)(0 - 4) = 6(3)(-4) < 0.$$

(Note that it is not necessary to finish calculating the exact value of $f'(x)$ in order to determine its sign.) Thus, the value of the derivative is positive to the left of -3 and negative to the right of -3, as shown in Figure 12.13. By part 1 of the first-derivative test, there is a local maximum at $x = -3$, and it is $f(-3) = 150$.

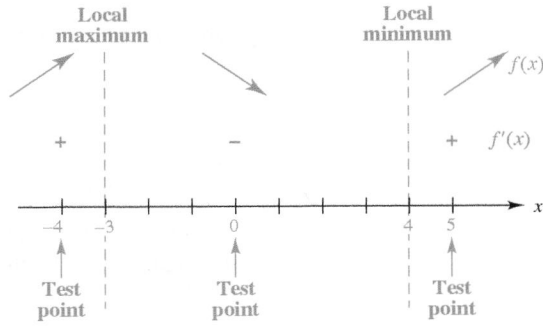

Figure 12.13

Similarly, we can use $a = 0$ and $b = 5$ to test the critical number $c = 4$. We just saw that $f'(0) < 0$; also,

$$f'(5) = 6(5 + 3)(5 - 4) = 6(8)(1) > 0.$$

Hence, by part 2 of the first-derivative test, there is a local minimum at $x = 4$, given by $f(4) = -193.$ ✓₅

✔ **Checkpoint 5**

Find the location of all local extrema of the given functions.

(a) $f(x) = 2x^2 + 12x - 15$

(b) $g(x) = \dfrac{1}{3}x^3 - x^2 - 8x + 57$

Example 6 Use the first-derivative test to find the local extrema of

$$f(x) = 3x^{4/3} - 12x^{1/3}.$$

Solution Example 4(c) shows that the critical numbers of f are 0 and 1. We can use the intervals $[-1, 1/2]$ and $[1/2, 2]$ to test these critical numbers:

$$f'(x) = \frac{4x - 4}{x^{2/3}} = \frac{4x - 4}{\sqrt[3]{x^2}}$$

$$f'(-1) = \frac{4(-1) - 4}{\sqrt[3]{(-1)^2}} = \frac{-4 - 4}{1} < 0$$

$$f'\left(\frac{1}{2}\right) = \frac{4(1/2) - 4}{\sqrt[3]{(1/2)^2}} = \frac{-2}{\sqrt[3]{1/4}} < 0$$

$$f'(2) = \frac{4(2) - 4}{\sqrt[3]{2^2}} = \frac{4}{\sqrt[3]{4}} > 0.$$

Checkpoint 6

Find any local extrema for
$f(x) = x^3 + 4x^2 - 3x + 5$.

Since $f'(x)$ is negative at both -1 and $\frac{1}{2}$, part 3 of the first-derivative test shows that there is no local extremum at $x = 0$. Since $f'(\frac{1}{2}) < 0$ and $f'(2) > 0$, there is a local minimum at $x = 1$, by part 2 of the first-derivative test. These results are shown schematically in Figure 12.14. ✓6

Figure 12.14

Although graphing technology sometimes eliminates the need to use the first-derivative test, this is not always the case, as the next example illustrates.

Example 7   Find all local extrema of $f(x) = x^2 e^{5x}$.

Solution   Although the graph of f in Figure 12.15 suggests that there are no local extrema, algebraic analysis shows otherwise. Using the product rule for derivatives, we have

$$f'(x) = x^2(5e^{5x}) + e^{5x}(2x) = 5x^2 e^{5x} + 2xe^{5x},$$

which exists for every x.

So the critical numbers are the solutions of

$$5x^2 e^{5x} + 2xe^{5x} = 0$$
$$e^{5x}(5x^2 + 2x) = 0$$
$$e^{5x}(5x + 2)x = 0.$$

Since e^{5x} is never 0, this derivative can equal 0 only when

$$5x + 2 = 0 \qquad \text{or} \qquad x = 0$$
$$x = -2/5 = -.4 \qquad \text{or} \qquad x = 0.$$

We choose the interval $[-1, -.2]$ to test $-.4$ and the interval $[-.2, 1]$ to test 0. Using a calculator to compute values of $y_1 = f'(x)$, we obtain Figure 12.16. By the first-derivative test, there is a local maximum at $x = -.4$ and there is a local minimum at $x = 0$, as indicated schematically in Figure 12.17 on the next page. ✓7 ✓8

Checkpoint 7

Find a viewing window on a graphing calculator that clearly shows the local maximum and minimum of the function f in Example 7.

Checkpoint 8

Find all local extrema of
$g(x) = x^3 e^x$.

Figure 12.15

Figure 12.16

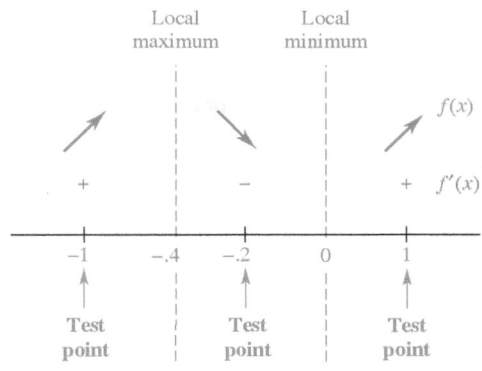

Figure 12.17

Example 8 **Business** Sales (in thousands of dollars) for Huttig Building Products, Inc. can be approximated by

$$S(x) = 8x^3 - 180x^2 + 1170x - 1260 \quad (3 \le x \le 11),$$

where $x = 3$ corresponds to the year 2003. Determine when sales were increasing and when sales were decreasing. Also find all local extrema of the sales function. (Data from: www.morningstar.com.)

Solution To determine the critical numbers, we find the derivative

$$S'(x) = 24x^2 - 360x + 1170.$$

Since the derivative exists for every x, the only critical numbers occur where the derivative is zero. Solve $S'(x) = 0$ using the quadratic formula:

$$24x^2 - 360x + 1170 = 0$$

$$x = \frac{-(-360) \pm \sqrt{(-360)^2 - 4(24)(1170)}}{2(24)} \approx \begin{cases} 4.8 \\ 10.2. \end{cases}$$ ← The critical numbers are approximately 4.8 and 10.2.

Since the domain of the sales function is $[3, 11]$, both critical numbers lie within the domain. We choose the interval $[4, 5]$ to test the critical number 4.8, and the interval $[5, 11]$ to test the critical number 10.2:

$$S'(4) = 114 > 0$$
$$S'(5) = -30 < 0$$
$$S'(11) = 114 > 0.$$

Therefore, sales are increasing on the intervals $(3, 4.8)$ and $(10.2, 11)$ and decreasing on the interval $(4.8, 10.2)$. By the first-derivative test, there is a local maximum at $x = 4.8$ and a local minimum at $x = 10.2$. In other words, sales reach a local maximum toward the end of 2004 and a local minimum near the beginning of 2010. The local maximum value is $S(4.8) \approx 1093.5$ (sales of approximately \$1,093,500) and the local minimum value is $S(10.2) \approx 436.5$ (sales of approximately \$436,500), as can be seen in Figure 12.18. ✓₉

✓ **Checkpoint 9**

If a sales function is given by $S(x) = x^3 - 21x^2 + 120x$, determine when sales are decreasing.

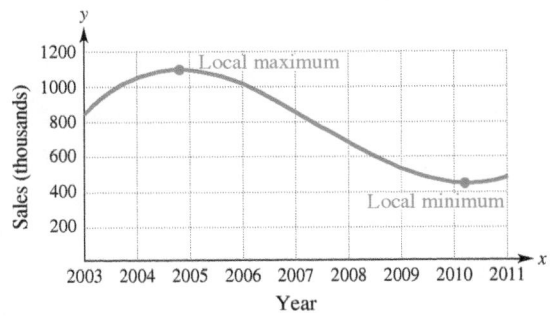

Figure 12.18

12.1 Exercises

For each function, list the intervals on which the function is increasing, the intervals on which it is decreasing, and the location of all local extrema. (See Examples 1 and 3.)

1.

2.

3.

4.

5.

6.

7.

8.
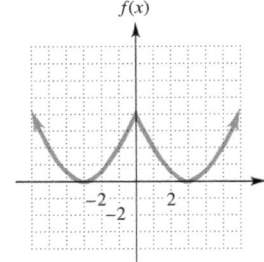

Find the intervals on which each function is increasing or decreasing. (See Example 2.)

9. $f(x) = 2x^3 - 5x^2 - 4x + 2$

10. $f(x) = 4x^3 - 9x^2 - 12x + 7$

11. $f(x) = \dfrac{x + 1}{x + 3}$

12. $f(x) = \dfrac{x^2 + 4}{x}$

13. $f(x) = \sqrt{x^2 + 9}$

14. $f(x) = \sqrt{6 - x}$

15. $f(x) = 2x^3 + 3x^2 - 12x + 5$

16. $f(x) = 4x^3 - 15x^2 - 72x + 5$

The graph of the derivative function f' is given; list the critical numbers of the function f.

17.

18.
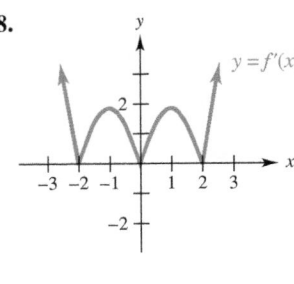

Determine the location of each local extremum of the function. (See Examples 4–7.)

19. $f(x) = x^3 + 3x^2 - 3$

20. $f(x) = x^3 - x^2 - 5x + 1$

21. $f(x) = x^3 + 6x^2 + 9x + 2$

22. $f(x) = x^3 - 3x^2 - 24x + 5$

23. $f(x) = \dfrac{4}{3}x^3 - \dfrac{21}{2}x^2 + 5x + 3$

24. $f(x) = -\dfrac{2}{3}x^3 - \dfrac{1}{2}x^2 - 3x - 4$

25. $f(x) = \dfrac{2}{3}x^3 - x^2 - 12x + 2$

26. $f(x) = \dfrac{4}{3}x^3 + 10x^2 - 24x - 3$

27. $f(x) = \dfrac{3}{2}x^4 + 4x^3 - 24x^2 + 20$

28. $f(x) = -3x^4 - 4x^3 + 12x^2 - 1$

In Exercises 29–40, use the first-derivative test to determine the location of each local extremum and the value of the function at this extremum. (See Examples 5–7.)

29. $f(x) = x^{11/5} - x^{6/5} + 1$ **30.** $f(x) = (7 - 2x)^{2/3} - 2$

31. $f(x) = -(3 - 4x)^{2/5} + 4$ **32.** $f(x) = x^4 + \dfrac{1}{x}$

33. $f(x) = \dfrac{x^3}{x^3 + 1}$ **34.** $f(x) = \dfrac{x^2 - 2x + 1}{x - 3}$

35. $f(x) = xe^{-x}$ **36.** $f(x) = -xe^x$

37. $f(x) = x \cdot \ln|x|$ **38.** $f(x) = x - \ln|x|$

39. $f(x) = xe^{3x} - 2$ **40.** $f(x) = x^3e^{4x} + 1$

Use the maximum/minimum finder on a graphing calculator to determine the approximate location of all local extrema of these functions.

41. $f(x) = .2x^4 - x^3 - 12x^2 + 99x - 5$

42. $f(x) = x^5 - 12x^4 - x^3 + 232x^2 + 260x - 600$

43. $f(x) = .01x^5 + .2x^4 - x^3 - 6x^2 + 5x + 40$

44. $f(x) = .1x^5 + 3x^4 - 4x^3 - 11x^2 + 3x + 2$

Work the given exercises.

45. Business The amount invested (in billions of dollars) in research and development by Microsoft Corporation during 2002–2011 is shown in the accompanying figure. On what intervals is the function increasing? decreasing? (Data from: www.morningstar.com.)

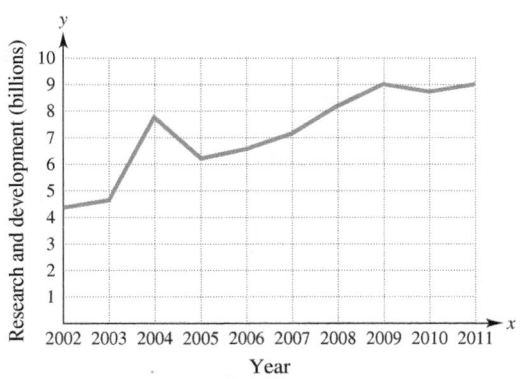

46. Business Operating profits (in billions of dollars) for the New York Times Company during 2002–2011 are shown in the accompanying figure. On what intervals is the function increasing? decreasing? (Data from: www.morningstar.com.)

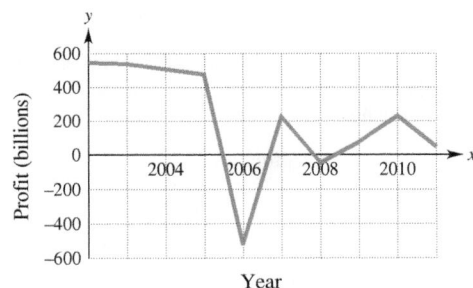

47. Business The graph approximates the net sales (in billions of dollars) for the home improvement retailer Lowe's Companies, Inc., for the period 2007–2012. (Data from: www.morningstar.com.)

(a) In what year does it appear there is a local minimum?

(b) In what year does it appear there is a local maximum?

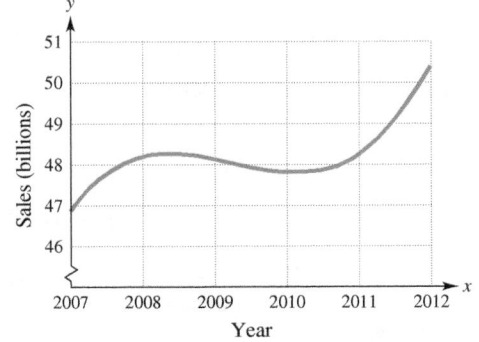

48. Business The average interest rate on a 3-month certificate of deposit is approximated in the accompanying figure. (Data from: www.federalreserve.gov.)

(a) At the start of 2009, approximately what was the interest rate on a 3-month certificate of deposit?

(b) During the year 2009, was this interest rate increasing or decreasing?

(c) In which years was the slope 0 at some point?

(d) In what year does it appear there was a local minimum?

(e) In what year does it appear there was a local maximum?

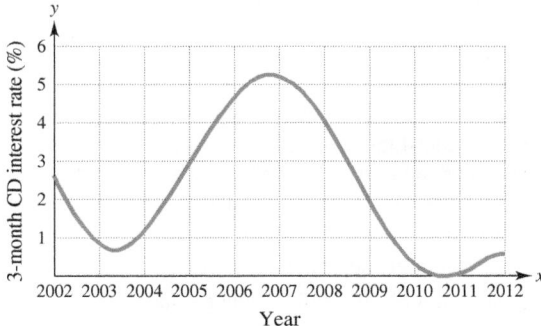

49. Social Science The graph shows the average number of 911 calls for police service for the Cleveland Police Department during the 24-hour day, with $x = 0$ corresponding to the hour 12:00 to 12:59 A.M.*

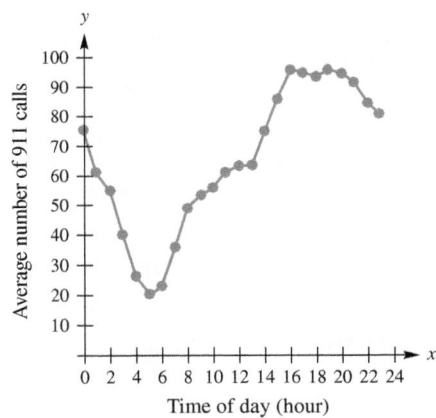

(a) List the intervals on which the average number of 911 calls is increasing.

(b) List the intervals on which the average number of 911 calls is decreasing.

(c) List the times of day at which this function has a local maximum or minimum.

50. Business The seasonally adjusted national unemployment rate (as a percent) is approximated in the accompanying figure. (Data from: www.dol.gov.)

(a) At the start of 2008, approximately what was the unemployment rate?

(b) During the year 2008, was the unemployment rate increasing or decreasing?

---

*Holcomb, J., and Radke Sharpe, N. "Forecasting Police Calls during Peak Times for the City of Cleveland," *Case Studies in Business, Industry, and Government Statistics*, 1(1), 2007, pp. 47–53.

(c) In what year does it appear there was a local minimum?

(d) In what year does it appear there was a local maximum?

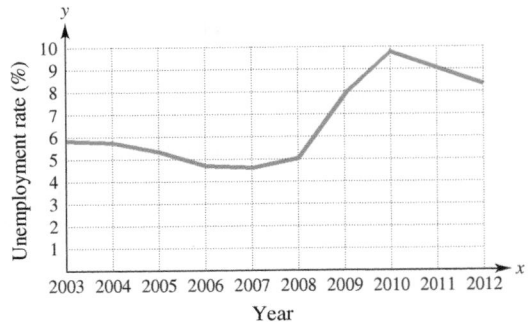

51. Physical Science A Boston Red Sox pitcher stands on top of the 37-foot-high left-field wall (the "Green Monster") in Fenway Park and fires a fastball straight up. The position function that gives the height of the ball (in feet) at time t seconds is given by $s(t) = -16t^2 + 140t + 37$.* Find

(a) the maximum height of the ball;

(b) the time when the ball hits the ground;

(c) the velocity of the ball when it hits the ground.

52. Business Revenue (in billions of dollars) from sales at Office Depot can be approximated by

$$f(x) = -.19x^2 + 2.4x + 7.3 \qquad (2 \le x \le 11),$$

where $x = 2$ corresponds to the year 2002. Find the locations of all local extrema and the value of the function at each extremum. (Data from: www.morningstar.com.)

53. Social Science According to projections by the United Nations, the population of the People's Republic of China (in billions) can be approximated by the function

$$f(x) = -.000164x^2 + .014532x + 1.1385$$
$$(0 \le x \le 60),$$

where $x = 0$ corresponds to the year 1990. In what year will China reach its maximum population, and what will that population be? (Data from: esa.un.org/unpp.)

54. Business The number of full-time employees (in thousands) for Lowe's Company, Inc. can be approximated by

$$f(x) = -1.3x^2 + 25.7x + 38.2 \qquad (6 \le x \le 12),$$

where $x = 6$ corresponds to the year 2006. Find the locations of all local extrema and the value of the function at each extremum. (Data from: www.mergentonline.com.)

Work these exercises. You may need to use the quadratic formula to find some critical numbers. (See Example 8.)

55. Natural Science The number of salmon swimming upstream to spawn is approximated by

$$S(x) = -x^3 + 3x^2 + 400x + 5000 \qquad (6 \le x \le 20),$$

where x represents the temperature of the water in degrees Celsius. Find the water temperature that produces the maximum number of salmon swimming upstream.

56. Business The number of common stock holders (in thousands) for Barnes and Noble, Inc. can be approximated by

$$f(x) = -2.6x^3 + 52x^2 - 270x + 2452 \qquad (3 \le x \le 12),$$

where $x = 3$ corresponds to the year 2003. Find the locations of all local extrema and the value of the function at each extremum. (Data from: www.morningstar.com.)

57. Natural Science The microbe concentration $B(x)$, in appropriate units, of Lake Tom depends approximately on the oxygen concentration x, again in appropriate units, according to the function

$$B(x) = x^3 - 7x^2 - 160x + 1800 \qquad (0 \le x \le 20).$$

(a) Find the oxygen concentration that will lead to the minimum microbe concentration.

(b) What is the minimum microbe concentration?

58. Finance The United States' gross savings as a percent of gross domestic product can be approximated by

$$f(x) = .3x^3 - 6.8x^2 + 48.6x - 95.9 \qquad (5 \le x \le 10),$$

where $x = 5$ corresponds to the year 2005. Find the locations of all local extrema and the value of the function at each extremum. (Data from: www.worldbank.com.)

59. Natural Science The function

$$A(x) = .004x^3 - .05x^2 + .16x + .05$$

approximates the blood alcohol concentration in an average person's bloodstream x hours after drinking 8 ounces of 100-proof whiskey. The function applies only to the interval [0, 6].

(a) On what time intervals is the blood alcohol concentration increasing?

(b) On what intervals is it decreasing?

60. Business Taxes on goods and services as a percent of revenue can be approximated by

$$f(x) = .015x^3 - .23x^2 + .9x + 2.5 \qquad (1 \le x \le 10),$$

where $x = 1$ corresponds to the year 2001. Find the locations of all local extrema and the value of the function at each extremum. (Data from: www.worldbank.com.)

61. Business The function

$$f(x) = -.547x^3 + 16.072x^2 - 102.955x + 658.046$$

approximates the number of construction workers (in thousands) employed in the construction industry in California during 1990–2010, where $x = 0$ corresponds to the year 1990. Find the locations of all local extrema. (Data from: St. Louis Federal Reserve.)

62. Natural Science In the summer, the activity level of a certain type of lizard varies according to the time of day. A biologist has determined that the activity level is given by the function

$$a(t) = .008t^3 - .27t^2 + 2.02t + 7 \quad (0 \le t \le 24),$$

where t is the number of hours after noon. When is the activity level highest? When is it lowest?

Work the following exercises.

63. Social Science The standard normal probability function is used to describe many different populations. Its graph is the well-known normal curve. This function is defined by

$$f(x) = \frac{1}{\sqrt{2\pi}} e^{-x^2/2}.$$

Give the intervals where the function is increasing and decreasing.

64. Business The number of hourly hits (in thousands) on a company's website x hours after a certain news story breaks can be approximated by

$$H(x) = 1 + 30xe^{-.5x}.$$

Find the locations of all local extrema and the value of the function at each extremum.

65. Social Science A group of researchers found that people prefer training films of moderate length; shorter films contain too little information, while longer films are boring. For a training film on the care of exotic birds, the researchers determined that the ratings people gave for the film could be approximated by

$$R(t) = \frac{20t}{t^2 + 100},$$

where t is the length of the film (in minutes). Find the film length that received the highest rating.

66. Natural Science A marshy region used for agricultural drainage has become contaminated with selenium. It has been determined that flushing the area with clean water will reduce the selenium for a while, but it will then begin to build up again. A biologist has found that the percentage of selenium in the soil x months after the flushing begins is given by

$$f(x) = \frac{x^2 + 36}{2x} \quad (1 \le x \le 12).$$

When will the selenium be reduced to a minimum? What is the minimum percentage?

67. Health The number of people $P(t)$ (in hundreds) infected t days after an epidemic begins is approximated by

$$P(t) = \frac{10 \ln(.19t + 1)}{.19t + 1}.$$

When will the number of people infected start to decline?

68. Natural Science The percent of concentration of a drug in the bloodstream x hours after the drug is administered is given by

$$K(x) = \frac{4x}{3x^2 + 27}.$$

(a) On what time intervals is the concentration of the drug increasing?

(b) On what intervals is it decreasing?

69. Business The amount of revenue generated (in millions of dollars) from taxes on alcohol in Connecticut can be approximated by the function

$$g(x) = 4.63 + 60.66x - 33.98x^2 + 8.686x^3 - 1.1526x^4$$
$$+ .08246x^5 - .0030185x^6 + .00004435x^7 \quad (2 \le x \le 18),$$

where $x = 2$ corresponds to the year 1992. (Data from: St. Louis Federal Reserve.)

(a) Using a graphing calculator or software, plot $g(x)$.

(b) How many local extrema appear in the graph?

(c) Use the maximum/minimum finder to approximate the values of the extrema.

70. Consider the function*

$$g(x) = \frac{1}{x^{12}} - 2\left(\frac{1000}{x}\right)^6.$$

(a) Using a graphing calculator, try to find any local minima, or tell why finding a local minimum is difficult for this function.

(b) Find any local minima, using the techniques of calculus.

(c) On the basis of your results in parts (a) and (b), describe circumstances under which local extrema are easier to find by using the techniques of calculus than with a graphing calculator.

✓ Checkpoint Answers

1. Increasing on $(-7, -4)$ and $(-2, 3)$; decreasing on $(-\infty, -7)$, $(-4, -2)$, and $(3, \infty)$

2. Increasing on $(-\infty, -3/2)$ and $(1, \infty)$; decreasing on $(-3/2, 1)$

3. **(a)** Local maximum at x_2; local minima at x_1 and x_3
   (b) No local maximum; local minimum at x_1
   (c) Local maximum at x_1; no local minimum

4. **(a)** $-3, 5$ **(b)** $0, 1$

5. **(a)** Local minimum at -3
   (b) Local maximum at -2; local minimum at 4

6. Local maximum at -3: $f(-3) = 23$; local minimum at $1/3$:
   $$f\left(\frac{1}{3}\right) = \frac{121}{27}$$

7. There are many possibilities, including $-2 \le x \le 2$ and $-.1 \le y \le .1$.

8. Local minimum at $x = -3$; no local extremum at $x = 0$

9. Decreasing on $(4, 10)$

*From Ed Dubinsky, "Is Calculus Obsolete?" *Mathematics Teacher*, 88, no. 2 (February 1995): 146–148.

12.2   The Second Derivative

The first derivative of a function indicates when the function is increasing or decreasing. In many applications, however, this information isn't enough. For example, Figure 12.19 shows the prices of two different stocks over a period of months. Both stocks are worth $5 per share at the beginning and are continually increasing in price.

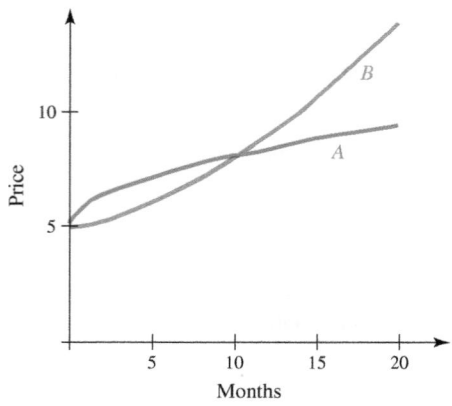

Figure 12.19

It is easy to see from the graph that stock B is the better long-term investment. In real life, however, you see only *part* of the graph (the past performance of a stock). How can that help you to predict future performance? To answer this question, look at the graphs again. Both are always increasing, but after the first few months, stock B increases at a faster rate than stock A. So the *rate* of increase plays a crucial role here.

In mathematical terms, if the price of the stock in month x is $f(x)$, then the derivative $f'(x)$ tells you when the price is increasing (or decreasing). The *rate* of increase (or decrease) of the derivative function f' is given by *its* derivative. In other words, the rate at which the stock price is increasing (or decreasing) is given by the derivative of the derivative of the price function. In order to deal with such situations, we need some additional terminology and notation.

Higher Derivatives

If a function f has a derivative f', then the derivative of f', if it exists, is the **second derivative** of f, written f''. The derivative of f'', if it exists, is called the **third derivative** of f, and so on. By continuing this process, we can find **fourth derivatives** and other higher derivatives. For example, if $f(x) = x^4 + 2x^3 + 3x^2 - 5x + 7$, then

$$f'(x) = 4x^3 + 6x^2 + 6x - 5, \quad \text{First derivative of } f$$

$$f''(x) = 12x^2 + 12x + 6, \quad \text{Second derivative of } f$$

$$f'''(x) = 24x + 12, \quad \text{Third derivative of } f$$

$$f^{(4)}(x) = 24. \quad \text{Fourth derivative of } f$$

✓ **Checkpoint 1**

Let $f(x) = 4x^3 - 12x^2 + x - 1$. Find

(a) $f''(0)$;

(b) $f''(4)$;

(c) $f''(-2)$.

The second derivative of $y = f(x)$ can be written in any of the following notations:

$$f''(x), \quad y'', \quad \frac{d^2y}{dx^2}, \quad \text{or} \quad D_x^2[f(x)].$$

The third derivative can be written in a similar way. For $n \geq 4$, the nth derivative is written $f^{(n)}(x)$.

Example 1 Find the second derivative of the given functions.

(a) $f(x) = 8x^3 - 9x^2 + 6x + 4$

Solution Here, $f'(x) = 24x^2 - 18x + 6$. The second derivative is the derivative of $f'(x)$, or

$$f''(x) = 48x - 18.$$

(b) $y = \dfrac{4x + 2}{3x - 1}$

Solution Use the quotient rule to find y':

$$y' = \frac{(3x - 1)(4) - (4x + 2)(3)}{(3x - 1)^2} = \frac{12x - 4 - 12x - 6}{(3x - 1)^2} = \frac{-10}{(3x - 1)^2}.$$

Use the quotient rule again to find y'':

$$y'' = \frac{(3x - 1)^2(0) - (-10)(2)(3x - 1)(3)}{[(3x - 1)^2]^2}$$

$$= \frac{60(3x - 1)}{(3x - 1)^4} = \frac{60}{(3x - 1)^3}.$$

(c) $y = xe^x$

Solution Using the product rule gives

$$\frac{dy}{dx} = x \cdot e^x + e^x \cdot 1 = xe^x + e^x.$$

Differentiate this result to get $\dfrac{d^2y}{dx^2}$:

$$\frac{d^2y}{dx^2} = (xe^x + e^x) + e^x = xe^x + 2e^x = (x + 2)e^x. \quad \boxed{2}$$

✓ **Checkpoint 2**

Find the second derivatives of the given functions.

(a) $y = -9x^3 + 8x^2 + 11x - 6$

(b) $y = -2x^4 + 6x^2$

(c) $y = \dfrac{x + 2}{5x - 1}$

(d) $y = e^x + \ln x$

Applications

In the previous chapter, we saw that the first derivative of a function represents the rate of change of the function. The second derivative, then, represents the rate of change of the first derivative. This fact has a variety of applications. For one such application, we take another look at stocks A and B from the beginning of this section.

Example 2 **Finance** Suppose that, over a 10-month period, the price of stock A is given by $f(x) = x^{1/2} + 5$ and the price of stock B is given by $g(x) = .1x^{3/2} + 5$.

(a) When are stocks A and B increasing in price?

Solution The first derivatives of the price functions are, respectively,

$$f'(x) = \frac{1}{2}x^{-1/2} = \frac{1}{2\sqrt{x}} \quad \text{and} \quad g'(x) = .1\left(\frac{3}{2}x^{1/2}\right) = \frac{.3}{2}\sqrt{x}.$$

Both derivatives are always positive (because $\sqrt{x}$ is positive for $x > 0$). So both price functions are increasing for all $x > 0$.

(b) At what rate are these stock prices increasing in the 10th month? What does this suggest about their future performance?

Solution The rate at which $f'(x) = \dfrac{1}{2}x^{-1/2}$ and $g'(x) = \dfrac{.3}{2}x^{1/2}$ are increasing is given by *their* derivatives (the second derivatives of f and g):

$$f''(x) = \frac{1}{2} \cdot \frac{-1}{2}x^{-3/2} = \frac{-1}{4\sqrt{x^3}} \quad \text{and} \quad g''(x) = \frac{.3}{2} \cdot \frac{1}{2}x^{-1/2} = \frac{3}{40\sqrt{x}}.$$

When $x = 10$,

$$f''(10) = \frac{-1}{4\sqrt{10^3}} \approx -.0079 \quad \text{and} \quad g''(10) = \frac{3}{40\sqrt{10}} \approx .0237.$$

The rate of increase for stock A is negative, meaning that its price is increasing at a decreasing rate. The rate of increase for stock B is positive, meaning that its price is increasing at an increasing rate. In other words, the price of stock A is increasing more and more slowly, while the price of stock B is increasing faster and faster. This result suggests that stock B is probably a better investment for the future.

The preceding discussion assumes that present trends continue (which is not guaranteed in the stock market). If they do continue for another 10 months, then Figure 12.19 shows what will happen to the stocks during this period.

Although Example 2 is much simpler than real life, second derivatives are actually used by some investors. According to an article in the *Wall Street Journal* on August 1, 2001 (when the market was in a downturn), "many investors hope it will help them get into the market ahead of any big rallies. In essence, the second-derivative approach involves looking at such things as profit warnings, analysts' earning estimates and equipment orders (including cancellations) for signs that the downward momentum is slowing."

The second derivative also plays a role in the physics of a moving particle. If a function describes the position of a moving object (along a straight line) at time t, then the first derivative gives the velocity of the object. That is, if $y = s(t)$ describes the position (along a straight line) of the object at time t, then $v(t) = s'(t)$ gives the velocity at time t.

The rate of change of velocity is called **acceleration**. Since the second derivative gives the rate of change of the first derivative, the acceleration is the derivative of the velocity. Thus, if $a(t)$ represents the acceleration at time t, then

$$a(t) = \frac{d}{dt}v(t) = s''(t).$$

Example 3   **Physical Science**   Suppose that an object is moving along a straight line, with its position, in feet, at time t, in seconds, given by

$$s(t) = t^3 - 2t^2 - 7t + 9.$$

(a) Find the velocity at any time t.

Solution   The velocity is given by

$$v(t) = s'(t) = 3t^2 - 4t - 7.$$

(b) Find the acceleration at any time t.

Solution   Acceleration is given by

$$a(t) = v'(t) = s''(t) = 6t - 4.$$

(c) When the object stops, its velocity is zero. For $t \geq 0$, when does that occur?

Solution   Set $v(t) = 0$:

$$3t^2 - 4t - 7 = 0$$
$$(3t - 7)(t + 1) = 0$$
$$3t - 7 = 0 \quad \text{or} \quad t + 1 = 0$$
$$t = \frac{7}{3} \qquad\qquad t = -1.$$

 Checkpoint 3

Rework Example 3 if
$s(t) = t^4 - t^3 + 10.$

Since we want $t \geq 0$, only $t = \frac{7}{3}$ is acceptable here. The object will stop in $\frac{7}{3}$ seconds.

Concavity

We shall now see how the second derivative provides information about how the graph of a function "bends." A graph is **concave upward** on an interval if it bends upward over the interval and **concave downward** if it bends downward, as shown in Figure 12.20. The graph is concave downward on the interval (a, b) and concave upward on the interval (b, c).* A point on the graph where the concavity changes (such as the point where $x = b$ in Figure 12.20) is called a **point of inflection**.

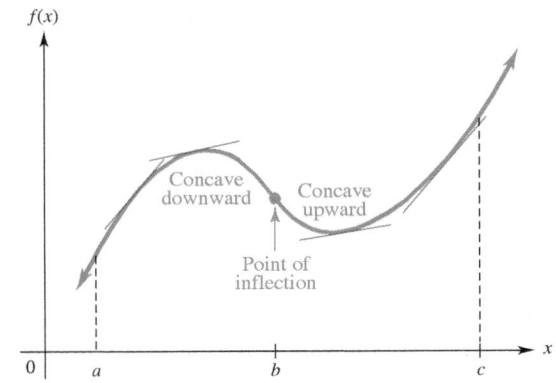

Figure 12.20

A function that is increasing on an interval may have either kind of concavity; the same is true for a decreasing function. Some of the possibilities are illustrated in Figure 12.21.

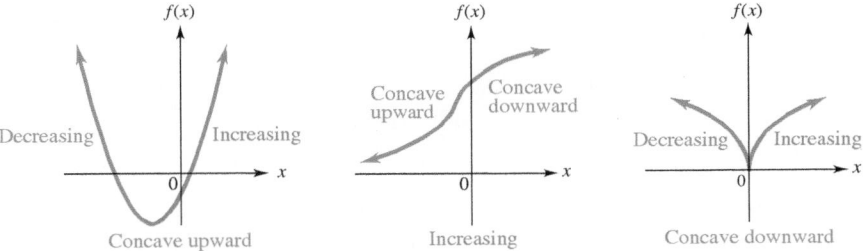

Figure 12.21

Next, we examine the relationship between the second derivative of a function f and the concavity of the graph of f. We have seen that when the derivative of any function is positive, that function is increasing. Consequently, if the *second* derivative of f (the derivative of the first derivative) is positive, then the *first* derivative of f is increasing. Since the first derivative gives the slope of the tangent line to the graph of f at each point, the fact that the first derivative is increasing means that the tangent-line slopes are increasing as you move from left to right along the graph of f, as illustrated in Figure 12.22.

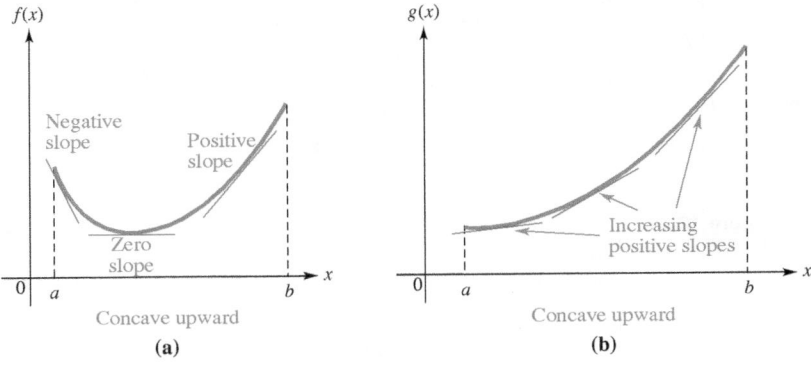

Figure 12.22

---

*Figure 12.20 also illustrates the formal definition of concavity: A function is *concave downward* on an interval if its graph lies below the tangent line at each point in the interval and *concave upward* if its graph is above the tangent line at each point in the interval.

In Figure 12.22(a), the slopes of the tangent lines increase from negative at the left, to 0 in the center, to positive at the right. In Figure 12.22(b), the slopes are all positive, but are increasing as the tangent lines get steeper. Note that both graphs in Figure 12.22 are *concave upward.*

Similarly, when the second derivative is negative, the first derivative (slope of the tangent line) is decreasing, as illustrated in Figure 12.23. In Figure 12.23(a), the tangent-line slopes decrease from positive, to 0, to negative. In Figure 12.23(b), the slopes get more and more negative as the tangent lines drop downward more steeply. Note that both graphs are *concave downward.*

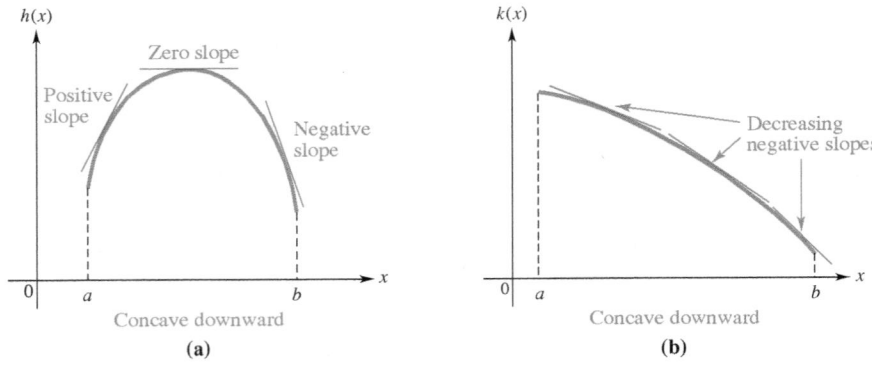

Figure 12.23

The preceding discussion suggests the following result.

Concavity Test

Let f be a function whose first and second derivatives exist at all points in the interval (a, b).

1. If $f''(x) > 0$ for all x in (a, b), then f is concave upward on (a, b).

2. If $f''(x) < 0$ for all x in (a, b), then f is concave downward on (a, b).

Example 4   Find the intervals over which the given function is concave upward or downward, and find any points of inflection.

(a) $f(x) = .5x^3 - 2x^2 + 5x + 1$

Figure 12.24

Solution   The graph of f (Figure 12.24) suggests that f is concave upward to the right of the y-axis, but the concavity near the y-axis is not clear. Even in a window where the concavity is visible, the location of the point of inflection is not clear. (Try it!) So we use the test in the preceding box. The first derivative is $f'(x) = 1.5x^2 - 4x + 5$, and the second derivative is $f''(x) = 3x - 4$. The function is concave upward when $f''(x) > 0$—that is, when

$$3x - 4 > 0$$
$$3x > 4$$
$$x > \frac{4}{3}.$$

Similarly, f is concave downward when $3x - 4 < 0$—that is, when $x < \frac{4}{3}$. Therefore, f is concave downward on $\left(-\infty, \frac{4}{3}\right)$ and concave upward on $\left(\frac{4}{3}, \infty\right)$, with a point of inflection when $x = \frac{4}{3}$.

(b) $g(x) = x^{1/3}$

Solution   The graph of g in Figure 12.25 suggests that g is concave upward when $x < 0$ and concave downward when $x > 0$. We can confirm this conclusion algebraically by noting that $g'(x) = \frac{1}{3}x^{-2/3}$ and

$$g''(x) = -\frac{2}{9}x^{-5/3} = \frac{-2}{9\sqrt[3]{x^5}}.$$

When $x < 0$, the denominator of $g''(x)$ is negative (why?), so $g''(x)$ is positive and g is concave upward on $(-\infty, 0)$. When $x > 0$, the denominator of $g''(x)$ is positive, so $g''(x)$ is negative and g is concave downward on $(0, \infty)$. The graph changes concavity at $(0, 0)$, which is a point of inflection.

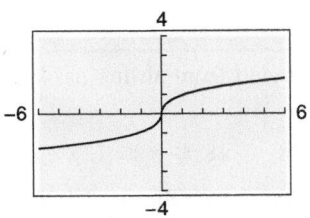

Figure 12.25

In Example 4(a), the point of inflection on the graph of f occurs at $x = \frac{4}{3}$, the number at which the second derivative $f''(x) = 3x - 4$ is 0. In Example 4(b), the point of inflection occurs when $x = 0$, the number at which the second derivative $g''(x) = \frac{-2}{9\sqrt[3]{x^5}}$ does not exist. These facts suggest the following result.

> If a function f has a point of inflection at $x = c$, then $f''(c) = 0$ or $f''(c)$ does not exist.

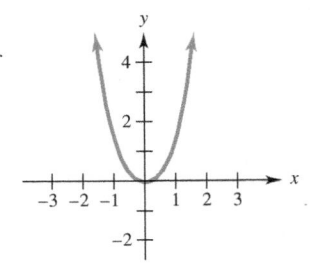

Figure 12.26

✓ **Checkpoint 4**

Find the intervals where the given functions are concave upward. Identify any inflection points.

(a) $f(x) = 6x^3 - 24x^2 + 9x - 3$

(b) $f(x) = 2x^2 - 4x + 8$

CAUTION The converse of the preceding statement is not always true: The second derivative may be 0 at a point that is not a point of inflection. For example, if $f(x) = x^4$, then $f'(x) = 4x^3$ and $f''(x) = 12x^2$. Hence, $f''(x) = 0$ when $x = 0$. However, the graph of $f(x)$ in Figure 12.26 is always concave upward, so it has no point of inflection at $x = 0$ (or anywhere else). ✓ 4

The **law of diminishing returns** in economics is related to the idea of concavity. The graph of the function f in Figure 12.27 shows the output y from a given input x. For instance, the input might be advertising costs and the output the corresponding revenue from sales.

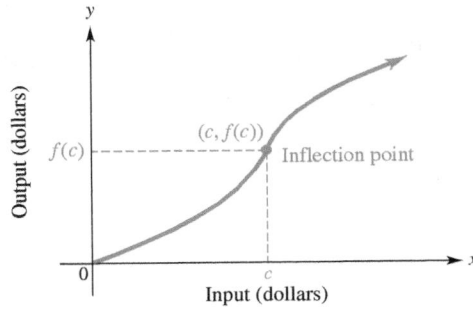

Figure 12.27

The graph in Figure 12.27 shows an inflection point at $(c, f(c))$. For $x < c$, the graph is concave upward, so the rate of change of the slope is increasing. This indicates that the output y is increasing at a faster rate with each additional dollar spent. When $x > c$, however, the graph is concave downward, the rate of change of the slope is decreasing, and the increase in y is smaller with each additional dollar spent. Thus, further input beyond c dollars produces diminishing returns. The point of inflection at $(c, f(c))$ is called the **point of diminishing returns**. Any investment beyond the value c is not considered a good use of capital.

Example 5   **Business**   The revenue $R(x)$ generated from airline passengers is related to the number of available seat miles x by

$$R(x) = -.928x^3 + 31.492x^2 - 326.80x + 1143.88 \qquad (8 \le x \le 12),$$

where x is measured in hundreds of billions of miles and $R(x)$ is in billions of dollars. Is there a point of diminishing returns for this function? If so, what is it? (Data from: Air Transport Association of America.)

Solution   Since a point of diminishing returns occurs at an inflection point, we must find $R''(x)$. We have

$$R'(x) = 3(-.928)x^2 + 2(31.492)x - 326.80$$
$$= -2.784x^2 + 62.984x - 326.80$$

and

$$R''(x) = 2(-2.784)x + 62.984$$
$$= -5.568x + 62.984,$$

which exists for every x.

When we set $R''(x) = 0$ and solve for x, we obtain

$$-5.568x + 62.984 = 0$$
$$-5.568x = -62.984$$
$$x \approx 11.31.$$

Test a number in the interval $(8, 11.31)$ to see that $R''(x)$ is positive there. Then test a number in the interval $(11.31, 12)$ to see that $R''(x)$ is negative in that interval. Since the sign of $R''(x)$ changes from positive to negative at $x = 11.31$, the graph changes from concave upward to concave downward at that point, and there is a point of diminishing returns at the inflection point $(11.31, 133.54)$. Increasing capacity beyond 1.131 trillion seat miles would not pay off. ✓ 5

✓ **Checkpoint 5**

The revenue $R(x)$ generated from sales of a certain product is related to the amount x spent on advertising by

$$R(x) = \frac{1}{75,000}(125x^3 - x^4)$$
$$(0 < x \le 100),$$

where x and $R(x)$ are in thousands of dollars. What is the point of diminishing returns?

Maxima and Minima

If a function f has a local maximum at c and $f'(c)$ is defined, then the graph of f is necessarily concave downward near $x = c$. Similarly, if f has a local minimum at d and $f'(d)$ exists, then the graph is concave upward near $x = d$, as shown in Figure 12.28.

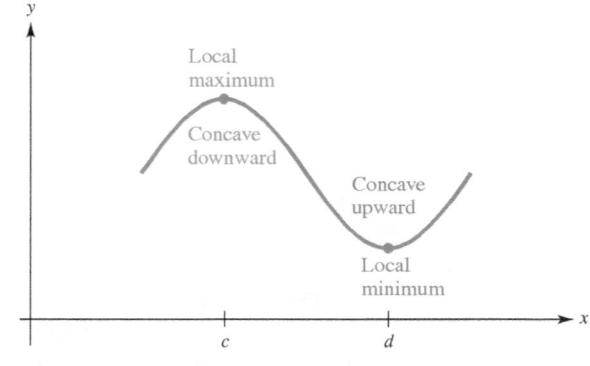

Figure 12.28

These facts should make the following result plausible.

The Second-Derivative Test

Let c be a critical number of the function f such that $f'(c) = 0$ and $f''(x)$ exists for all x in some open interval containing c.

1. If $f''(c) > 0$, then f has a local minimum at c.

2. If $f''(c) < 0$, then f has a local maximum at c.

3. If $f''(c) = 0$, then this test gives no information; use the first-derivative test.

Example 6   **Business**   The number of bicycle trips (in thousands) made in month x by Capital Bikeshare members in Washington, DC can be approximated by

$$g(x) = .27x^3 - 7.5x^2 + 63x - 42 \qquad (1 \le x \le 17),$$

where $x = 1$ corresponds to the month of January, 2011. Find all local extrema of this function, and interpret your answers. (Data from: www.capitalbikeshare.com.)

Solution   First find the critical numbers. The first derivative is

$$g'(x) = .81x^2 - 15x + 63.$$

Since $g'(x)$ always exists, critical numbers can occur only where $g'(x) = 0$. We find the solutions to $.81x^2 - 15x + 63 = 0$ using the quadratic formula

$$x = \frac{-(-15) \pm \sqrt{(-15)^2 - 4(.81)(63)}}{2(.81)}$$

$$= \frac{15 \pm \sqrt{20.88}}{1.62} \approx \begin{cases} 6.4 \\ 12.1 \end{cases} \quad \longleftarrow \quad \text{The critical numbers are approximately 6.4 and 12.1.}$$

Now use the second-derivative test on each critical number. The second derivative is

$$g''(x) = 2(.81)x - 15$$
$$= 1.62x - 15.$$

For the critical number 6.4, we have

$$g''(6.4) = 1.62(6.4) - 15 = -4.632 < 0,$$

which means that there is a local maximum at $x = 6.4$. The local maximum value is

$$g(6.4) = .27(6.4)^3 - 7.5(6.4)^2 + 63(6.4) - 42 \approx 124.8.$$

For the critical number 12.1, we have

$$g''(12.1) = 1.62(12.1) - 15 = 4.602 > 0,$$

hence there is a local minimum at $x = 12.1$. The local minimum value is

$$g(12.1) \approx 100.5.$$

In practical terms, this means that Bikeshare use was at a high of 124,800 trips near the middle of June ($x = 6.4$) and at a low of 100,500 trips near the beginning of December ($x = 12.1$). ✓6

✓**Checkpoint 6**

Use the second-derivative test to find all local maxima and local minima for $f(x) = x^3 - 3x^2 - 6x$.

NOTE The second-derivative test works only for those critical numbers c which make $f'(c) = 0$. This test does not work for those critical numbers c for which $f'(c)$ does not exist (since $f''(c)$ would not exist there either). Also, the second-derivative test does not work for critical numbers c that make $f''(c) = 0$. In both of these cases, use the first-derivative test.

12.2 Exercises

For each of these functions, find $f''(x), f''(0), f''(2),$ and $f''(-3)$.
(See Examples 1 and 2.)

1. $f(x) = x^3 - 6x^2 + 1$

2. $f(x) = -2x^3 + 5x^2 - 10x + 13$

3. $f(x) = (x + 3)^4$ 4. $f(x) = (2x + 1)^4$

5. $f(x) = \dfrac{x^2}{1 + x}$ 6. $f(x) = \dfrac{-x}{1 - x^2}$

7. $f(x) = \sqrt{x + 4}$ 8. $f(x) = \sqrt{2x + 9}$

9. $f(x) = -x^{2/3}$ 10. $f(x) = 5x^{4/5}$

11. $f(x) = 2e^x$ 12. $f(x) = 13 - 5e^x$

13. $f(x) = 6e^{2x}$ 14. $f(x) = 2 + e^{-x}$

15. $f(x) = \ln(2x + 1)$ 16. $f(x) = \ln(3x - 1)$

17. $f(x) = \dfrac{\ln|x|}{x}$ 18. $f(x) = x \ln|x|$

In Exercises 19 and 20, P(t) is the price of a certain stock at time t
during a particular day. (See Example 2.)

19. **Finance**   If the price of the stock is falling faster and faster,
are $P'(t)$ and $P''(t)$ positive or negative? Explain your answer.

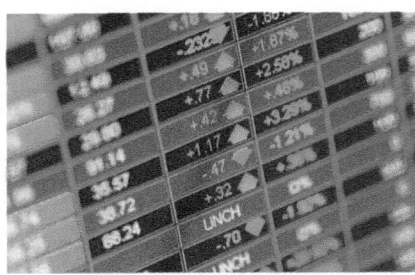

20. **Finance**   When the stock reaches its highest price during the
day, are $P'(t)$ and $P''(t)$ positive or negative? Explain your answer.

Physical Science   *Each of the functions in Exercises 21–24*
gives the position at time t of a particle moving along a line. Find
the velocity and acceleration functions. Then find the velocity and
acceleration at $t = 0$ and $t = 4$. Assume that time is measured in
seconds and distance is measured in centimeters. Velocity will be
in centimeters per second (cm/sec) and acceleration in centime-
ters per second per second (cm/sec²). (See Example 3.)

21. $s(t) = 6t^2 + 5t$ 22. $s(t) = 7t^2 + 2t + 10$

23. $s(t) = 3t^3 - 4t^2 + 8t - 9$

24. $s(t) = 3t^3 - 6t^2 + 8t - 4$

Find the largest open intervals on which each function is concave
upward or concave downward, and find the location of any points
of inflection. (See Example 4.)

25. $f(x) = x^3 + 3x - 5$

26. $f(x) = -x^3 + 8x - 7$

27. $f(x) = x^3 + 4x^2 - 6x + 3$

28. $f(x) = 5x^3 + 12x^2 - 32x - 14$

29. $f(x) = \dfrac{2}{x - 4}$ 30. $f(x) = \dfrac{-2}{x + 1}$

31. $f(x) = x^4 + 8x^3 - 30x^2 + 24x - 3$

32. $f(x) = x^4 + 8x^3 + 18x^2 + 12x - 84$

Business   *In Exercises 33–36, find the point of diminishing re-*
turns for the given functions, where R(x) represents revenue, in
thousands of dollars, and x represents the amount spent on adver-
tising, in thousands of dollars. (See Example 5.)

33. $R(x) = 10,000 - x^3 + 42x^2 + 800x; 0 \le x \le 20$

34. $R(x) = 1000 + 36x^2 - x^3$

35. $R(x) = \dfrac{4}{27}(-x^3 + 66x^2 + 1050x - 400); 0 \le x \le 25$

36. $R(x) = x + 13x^2 - \dfrac{x^3}{3}$

Find all critical numbers of the functions in Exercises 37–48.
Then use the second-derivative test on each critical number to
determine whether it leads to a local maximum or minimum.
(See Example 6.)

37. $f(x) = -2x^3 - 3x^2 - 72x + 1$

38. $f(x) = \dfrac{2}{3}x^3 + \dfrac{1}{2}x^2 - x - \dfrac{1}{4}$

39. $f(x) = (x - 3)^5$ 40. $f(x) = (2x - 1)^5$

41. $f(x) = x^4 - 8x^2$ 42. $f(x) = x^4 - 32x^2 + 7$

43. $f(x) = x + \dfrac{4}{x}$ 44. $f(x) = x - \dfrac{1}{x^2}$

45. $f(x) = \dfrac{x^2 + 9}{2x}$ 46. $f(x) = \dfrac{x^2 + 16}{2x}$

47. $f(x) = \dfrac{2 - x}{2 + x}$ 48. $f(x) = \dfrac{x + 2}{x - 1}$

In Exercises 49–52, the rule of the derivative of a function f is
given (but not the rule of f itself). Find the location of all local
extrema and points of inflection of the function f.

49. $f'(x) = (x - 1)(x - 2)(x - 4)$

50. $f'(x) = (x^2 - 1)(x - 2)$

51. $f'(x) = (x - 2)^2(x - 1)$

52. $f'(x) = (x - 1)^2(x - 3)$

53. In each part, list the points $(A–F)$ on the graph of f on the next
page that satisfy the given conditions.

  (a) $f'(x) > 0$ and $f''(x) > 0$

  (b) $f'(x) < 0$ and $f''(x) > 0$

(c) $f'(x) = 0$ and $f''(x) < 0$

(d) $f'(x) = 0$ and $f''(x) > 0$

(e) $f'(x) < 0$ and $f''(x) = 0$

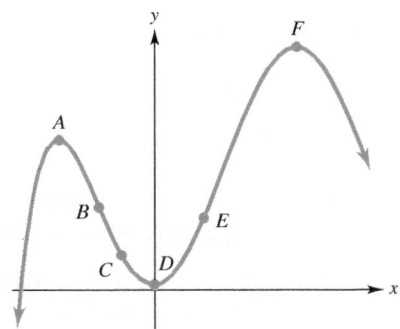

54. In each part, list the point (A–E) on the graph of f that satisfy the given conditions.

(a) $f'(x) > 0$ and $f''(x) > 0$

(b) $f'(x) < 0$ and $f''(x) > 0$

(c) $f'(x) = 0$ and $f''(x) < 0$

(d) $f'(x) = 0$ and $f''(x) > 0$

(e) $f'(x) < 0$ and $f''(x) = 0$

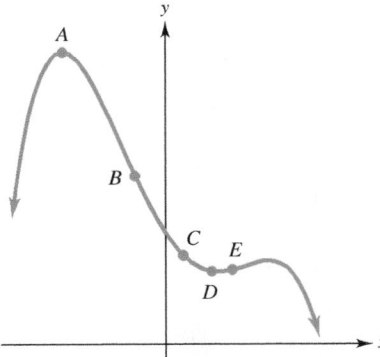

Work these problems. (See Example 2.)

55. Finance The price of Honda Motor Co., Ltd., stock over the 12-week period at the beginning of 2012 can be approximated by the function

$$f(x) = 30.2x^{.1},$$

where $x = 1$ designates the beginning of week 1. (Data from: www.morningstar.com.)

(a) When is the stock increasing in price?

(b) At what rate is the stock increasing at the beginning of the 2nd week?

(c) At what rate is the stock increasing at the beginning of the 12th week?

56. Finance The price of Apple, Inc., stock over the 12-week period at the beginning of 2012 can be approximated by the function

$$f(x) = 386e^{.036x},$$

where $x = 1$ designates the beginning of week 1. (Data from: www.morningstar.com.)

(a) When is the stock increasing in price?

(b) At what rate is the stock increasing at the beginning of the 2nd week?

(c) At what rate is the stock increasing at the beginning of the 12th week?

Work these problems. (See Example 3.)

57. Physical Science When an object is dropped straight down, its position, in feet, after t seconds is given by

$$s(t) = -16t^2.$$

Note that negative velocity indicates downward motion. Find the velocity at each of the following times.

(a) After 3 seconds

(b) After 5 seconds

(c) After 8 seconds

(d) Find the acceleration. (The answer here is a constant, the acceleration due to the influence of gravity alone.)

58. Physical Science If an object is thrown directly upward with a velocity of 256 ft/sec, its height, in feet, above the ground after t seconds is given by $s(t) = 256t - 16t^2$. Find the velocity and the acceleration after t seconds. What is the maximum height the object reaches? When does it hit the ground?

Work these problems. (See Example 5.)

59. Business A local automobile dealer has found that advertising produces sales, but that too much advertising tends to "turn consumers off," resulting in reduced sales. On the basis of past experience, the dealer expects that the number $V(x)$ of vehicles sold during a month is related to the amount spent on advertising by the function

$$V(x) = -.1x^3 + 2.2x^2 + 1.2x + 15 \qquad (0 \le x \le 20),$$

where x is the amount spent on advertising (in tens of thousands of dollars). What is the point of diminishing returns?

60. Business The revenue $R(x)$ (in millions of dollars) generated from cattle farming can be approximated by the function

$$R(x) = -3.21x^3 + 62.14x^2 + 172.92x + 48.65$$
$$(0 \le x \le 14),$$

where x represents the number of farms (in millions). What is the point of diminishing returns? (Data from: U.S. Department of Agriculture.)

Work these problems. You may need to use the quadratic formula to find some of the critical numbers. (See Example 6.)

61. Finance The U.S. gross domestic product (in billions of dollars) can be modeled by

$$f(x) = 19x^3 - 500x^2 + 4536x \qquad (4 \le x \le 12),$$

where $x = 4$ corresponds to the year 2004. Find and interpret the point of inflection. (Data from: www.bea.gov.)

62. Finance Personal consumption expenditures in the United States (in billions of dollars) can be modeled by

$$f(x) = 12x^3 - 312x^2 + 2870x + 668 \qquad (4 \le x \le 12),$$

where $x = 4$ corresponds to the year 2004. Find and interpret the point of inflection. (Data from: www.bea.gov.)

63. **Business** The male employment-population ratio (the percent of all men who are employed) can be approximated by

$$f(x) = .086x^3 - 2.22x^2 + 17.5x + 29,$$

where $x = 4$ corresponds to the year 2004. Use the second-derivative test to determine in what years the percent of employed men was at a local maximum or minimum. (Data from: Federal Reserve Economic Data.)

64. **Business** The price of Starbucks Corporation stock in year x can be approximated by

$$f(x) = .467x^3 - 10.4x^2 + 72.8x - 135 \quad (3 \le x \le 12),$$

where $x = 3$ corresponds to the year 2003. Use the second-derivative test to determine in what years the price was at a local maximum or minimum. (Data from: www.morningstar.com.)

Work these exercises.

65. **Social Science** The population of Wyoming (in thousands) is projected to be

$$f(x) = 18 \ln(x) + 478 \quad (5 \le x \le 20),$$

where $x = 5$ corresponds to the year 2005. (Data from: www.census.gov.)

(a) Is the population of Wyoming projected to increase or decrease through 2020?

(b) Determine whether the graph of this population function is concave up or concave down, and explain what that means for Wyoming.

66. **Finance** U.S. government consumption expenditures and gross investment (in billions of dollars) can be approximated by

$$f(x) = 519 \ln(x) + 1768 \quad (9 \le x \le 12),$$

where $x = 9$ corresponds to the year 2009. (Data from: www.bea.gov.)

(a) Was government consumption increasing or decreasing during this period?

(b) Determine whether the graph of the government consumption function is concave up or concave down, and explain what that means in practical terms.

67. **Business** One store's revenue from selling x cell phones is given by

$$R(x) = (200x)e^{-.01x}.$$

(a) How many phones should be sold to maximize revenue?

(b) What is the maximum revenue?

(c) When revenue is at a maximum, what is the average price per phone?

68. **Health** The birth weight (in pounds) of a newly born infant can be modeled by the function

$$f(t) = .0011t^{2.4} \quad (17 \le t \le 45),$$

where t is the number of weeks of gestation. (Data from: www.irss.unc.edu.)

(a) Are there any local extrema in the interval? If so, where?

(b) Is there a point of inflection? If so, what is it?

69. **Health** A flu outbreak occurs in a small community. Researchers estimate that the percentage of the population infected by the flu is approximated by

$$p(t) = \frac{30t^3 - t^4}{1200} \quad (0 \le t \le 30),$$

where t is the number of days after the flu was first observed.

(a) After how many days is the percentage of the population with the flu at a maximum?

(b) What is the maximum percentage of the population with the flu?

✓**Checkpoint Answers**

1. (a) -24 (b) 72 (c) -72

2. (a) $y'' = -54x + 16$ (b) $y'' = -24x^2 + 12$
   (c) $y'' = \dfrac{110}{(5x-1)^3}$ (d) $y'' = e^x - \dfrac{1}{x^2}$

3. (a) $v(t) = 4t^3 - 3t^2$
   (b) $a(t) = 12t^2 - 6t$
   (c) At 0 and $\frac{3}{4}$ second

4. (a) Concave upward on $(\frac{4}{3}, \infty)$; point of inflection is $(\frac{4}{3}, -\frac{175}{9})$
   (b) $f''(x) = 4$, which is always positive; function is always concave upward, no inflection point

5. $(62.5, 203.45)$

6. Local maximum of about 2.39 at $x \approx -.73$; local minimum of about -18.39 at $x \approx 2.73$

12.3 Optimization Applications

In most applications, the domains of the functions involved are restricted to numbers in a particular interval. For example, a factory that can produce a maximum of 40 units (because of market conditions, availability of labor, etc.) might have this cost function:

$$C(x) = -3x^3 + 135x^2 + 3600x + 12,000 \quad (0 \le x \le 40).$$

Even though the rule of C is defined for all numbers x, only the numbers in the interval $[0, 40]$ are relevant, because the factory cannot produce a negative number of units or more than 40 units. In such applications, we often want to find a smallest or largest quantity—for instance, the minimum cost or the maximum profit—when x is restricted to the relevant interval. So we begin with the mathematical description of such a situation.

Let f be a function that is defined for all x in the closed interval $[a, b]$. Let c be a number in the interval. We say that f has an **absolute maximum on the interval** at c if

$$f(x) \leq f(c) \quad \text{for all } x \text{ with } a \leq x \leq b,$$

that is, if $(c, f(c))$ is the highest point on the graph of f over the interval $[a, b]$. Similarly, f has an **absolute minimum on the interval** at c if

$$f(x) \geq f(c) \quad \text{for all } x \text{ with } a \leq x \leq b,$$

that is, if $(c, f(c))$ is the lowest point on the graph of f over the interval $[a, b]$.

✓ **Checkpoint 1**

Find the location of the absolute maximum and absolute minimum of the function f in Figure 12.29 on the interval $[-2, \frac{1}{2}]$.

Example 1   Figure 12.29 shows the graph of a function f. Consider the function f on the interval $[-2, 6]$. Since we are interested only in the interval $[-2, 6]$, the values of the function outside this interval are irrelevant. On the interval $[-2, 6]$, f has an absolute minimum at 3 (which is also a local minimum) and an absolute maximum at 6 (which is not a local maximum of the entire function). ✓₁

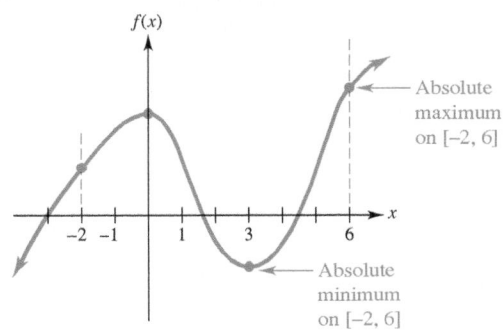

Figure 12.29

The absolute maximum in Example 1 occurred at $x = 6$, which is an endpoint of the interval, and the absolute minimum occurred at $x = 3$, which is a critical number of f (because f has a local minimum there). Similarly, in Checkpoint 1, the absolute maximum occurred at a critical number and the absolute minimum at an endpoint. These examples illustrate the following result, whose proof is omitted.

Extreme-Value Theorem

If a function f is continuous on a closed interval $[a, b]$, then f has both an absolute maximum and an absolute minimum on the interval. Each of these values occurs either at an endpoint of the interval or at a critical number of f.

⚠ **CAUTION** The extreme-value theorem may not hold on intervals that are not closed (that is, intervals that exclude one or both endpoints). For example, $f(x) = 1/x$ does not have an absolute maximum on the interval $(0, 1)$; the values of $f(x)$ get larger and larger as x approaches 0, as you can easily verify with a calculator.

Example 2   Use the extreme-value theorem to find the absolute extrema of $f(x) = 4x + \dfrac{36}{x}$ on the interval $[1, 6]$.

Solution According to the extreme-value theorem, we need consider only the critical numbers of f and the endpoints, 1 and 6, of the interval. Begin by finding the derivative and determining the critical numbers:

$$f'(x) = 4 - \frac{36}{x^2} = 0$$

$$\frac{4x^2 - 36}{x^2} = 0.$$

Since $f'(x)$ is not defined only at $x = 0$, $f'(x)$ exists for every x in the interval $[1, 6]$. The derivative is zero when the numerator is zero:

$$4x^2 - 36 = 0$$
$$4x^2 = 36$$
$$x^2 = 9$$
$$x = -3 \quad \text{or} \quad x = 3.$$

Since -3 is not in the interval $[1, 6]$, disregard it; 3 is the only critical number of interest. By the extreme-value theorem, the absolute maximum and minimum must occur at critical numbers or endpoints—that is, at 1, 3, or 6. Evaluate f at these three numbers to see which ones give the largest and smallest values:

x-Value	Value of Function
1	40 ← Absolute maximum
3	24 ← Absolute minimum
6	30

✓**Checkpoint 2**

Find the absolute maximum and absolute minimum values for $f(x) = -x^2 + 4x - 8$ on $[-4, 4]$.

A graphing calculator or other graphing technology sometimes makes it easy to find absolute extrema without taking the derivative. Technology, however, has its limits, so you should confirm your results algebraically whenever feasible.

Example 3 Find the absolute extrema of $g(x) = -.02x^3 + 600x - 20,000$ on $[60, 135]$.

Solution The graph of g on $[60, 135]$ in Figure 12.30 shows that the absolute maximum occurs at the local maximum, which is close to $x = 100$. The absolute minimum occurs at one of the endpoints, but you cannot determine which one from the graph.

Figure 12.30

We first determine the critical number exactly. Since $g'(x) = -.06x^2 + 600$ exists for every x, the critical numbers are the solutions of

$$-.06x^2 + 600 = 0.$$

We solve as follows:

$$-.06x^2 = -600$$
$$x^2 = 10,000$$
$$x = -100 \quad \text{or} \quad x = 100.$$

We disregard $x = -100$ because it is not in [60, 135]. According to the extreme-value theorem, we only need to evaluate g at the endpoints and the critical number 100, as shown in the next table. The absolute maximum of 20,000 occurs at $x = 100$ (as we suspected from the graph), and the absolute minimum of 11,680 occurs at $x = 60$.

x-Value	Value of Function	
60	11,680	← Absolute minimum
100	20,000	← Absolute maximum
135	11,792.5	✓ 3

✓ **Checkpoint 3**

Find the absolute extrema of
$g(x) = x^3 - 15x^2 + 48x + 50$ on $[1, 6]$.

Absolute Extrema on Other Intervals

The extreme-value theorem is very useful on closed intervals, but may be *false* on an open interval. For example, the function

$$f(x) = \frac{x}{(x + 2)(x - 3)}$$

has vertical asymptotes at $x = -2$ and $x = 3$. On the open interval $(-2, 3)$ between the asymptotes, the function has neither an absolute maximum nor an absolute minimum, as shown in Figure 12.31. The graph rises higher and higher near $x = -2$ and falls lower and lower near $x = 3$.

It is sometimes possible to identify an absolute maximum or minimum on an interval that is not closed by using the following theorem, whose proof is omitted.

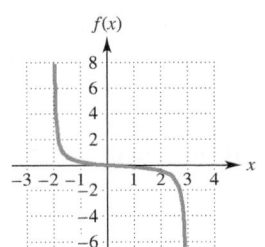

Figure 12.31

Critical-Point Theorem

Suppose that a function f is continuous on an interval I and that f has exactly one critical number in the interval I, say, $x = c$.*

If f has a local maximum at $x = c$, then this local maximum is the absolute maximum of f on the interval I.

If f has a local minimum at $x = c$, then this local minimum is the absolute minimum of f on the interval I.

Example 4   Consider the function $f(x) = x^3 - 3x + 1$.

(a) Without graphing, show that f has an absolute minimum on the interval $(0, 2)$.

Solution   The derivative is $f'(x) = 3x^2 - 3$, which is defined everywhere, so the critical numbers are the solutions of $f'(x) = 0$:

$$3x^2 - 3 = 0$$
$$3x^2 = 3$$
$$x^2 = 1$$
$$x = -1 \quad \text{or} \quad x = 1.$$

The only critical number in the interval $(0, 2)$ is $x = 1$. Use the second-derivative test to determine whether there is a local extremum at $x = 1$:

$$f'(x) = 3x^2 - 3$$
$$f''(x) = 6x$$
$$f''(1) = 6(1) = 6 > 0.$$

Hence, f has a local minimum at $x = 1$. Therefore, by the critical-point theorem, the absolute minimum of f on the interval $(0, 2)$ occurs at $x = 1$.

---

*I may be open, closed, or neither.

Figure 12.32

 (b) Confirm the result of part (a) by graphing.

Solution The graph of f in Figure 12.32 shows that $(1, -1)$ is the lowest point on the graph in the interval $(0, 2)$.

Applications

When solving applied problems that involve maximum and minimum values, follow these guidelines:

> ## Solving Applied Problems
>
> **Step 1** Read the problem carefully. Make sure you understand what is given and what is asked for.
>
> **Step 2** If possible, sketch a diagram and label the various parts.
>
> **Step 3** Decide which variable is to be maximized or minimized. Express that variable as a function of *one* other variable. Be sure to determine the domain of this function.
>
> **Step 4** Find the critical numbers for the function in Step 3.
>
> **Step 5** If the domain is a closed interval, apply the extreme-value theorem: evaluate the function at the endpoints and at each critical number to see which yields the absolute maximum or minimum. If the domain is a (not necessarily closed) interval in which there is exactly one critical number, $x = c$, apply the critical-point theorem: if f has a local extremum at $x = c$, then this local extremum is the absolute extremum.

⊘ **CAUTION** Do not skip Step 5 in the preceding box. If you are looking for a maximum and you find a single critical number in Step 4, do not automatically assume that the maximum occurs there. It may occur at an endpoint or may not exist at all.

Example 5 **Business** The annual cost (in thousands of dollars) of manufacturing x thousand sets of wireless earbuds is given by

$$C(x) = .001x^3 + 3x + 100,$$

and no more than 60,000 earbuds can be produced in a year.

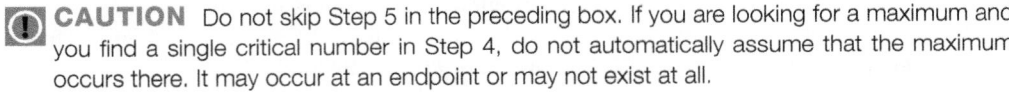 **(a)** Find the average cost function.

Solution As we saw in Section 11.6, the average cost function $\overline{C}$ is given by

$$\overline{C}(x) = \frac{C(x)}{x} = \frac{.001x^3 + 3x + 100}{x}$$

$$= .001x^2 + 3 + \frac{100}{x}.$$

(b) How many sets of earbuds should be made in order to minimize the average cost per set? What is the minimum average cost?

Solution The average cost function $\overline{C}(x) = .001x^2 + 3 + 100x^{-1}$ is defined for $0 < x \leq 60$ (since the function is undefined at $x = 0$ and no more than 60,000 earbuds can be produced in a year). The derivative of the average cost function is

$$\overline{C}'(x) = .001(2x) + 100(-x^{-2})$$

$$= .002x - \frac{100}{x^2}$$

$$= \frac{.002x^3 - 100}{x^2}.$$

The critical numbers occur at the numbers in the domain of the average cost function where the value of the derivative $\overline{C}'(x)$ is zero or does not exist. Since $\overline{C}'(x)$ always exists for $0 < x \leq 60$, the only critical numbers occur where $\overline{C}'(x)$ is zero:

$$\overline{C}'(x) = 0$$

$$\frac{.002x^3 - 100}{x^2} = 0 \quad\longleftarrow$$

A rational expression can be zero only when the numerator is zero.

$$.002x^3 - 100 = 0 \quad\longleftarrow$$

$$.002x^3 = 100$$

$$x^3 = \frac{100}{.002} = 50{,}000$$

$$x = \sqrt[3]{50{,}000} \approx 36.840. \quad\longleftarrow$$

The critical number is $x \approx 36.840$ or 36,840 earbuds.

Since $\overline{C}(x)$ is defined on $0 < x \leq 60$, which is *not* a closed interval, we *cannot* use the extreme-value theorem. However, since there is exactly one critical number in the interval $0 < x \leq 60$, we can apply the critical-point theorem. Use the second-derivative test to determine whether a local minimum occurs at this critical number:

$$\overline{C}'(x) = .002x - 100x^{-2}$$

$$\overline{C}''(x) = .002 - 100(-2x^{-3}) = .002 + \frac{200}{x^3}.$$

The value of the second derivative $\overline{C}''(x)$ is positive for all $x > 0$, so in particular, $\overline{C}''(36.840) > 0$, hence $\overline{C}$ has a local minimum at $x \approx 36.840$. By the critical-point theorem, an absolute minimum occurs at $x \approx 36.840$. Therefore, 36,840 sets of earbuds should be made in order to minimize the average cost per set. The minimum average cost is $\overline{C}(36.840) = 7.072$. In other words, the minimum average cost is \$7072 per 1000 earbuds or \$7.07 per set of earbuds. ✓ 4

✓ **Checkpoint 4**

For the cost function given by $C(x) = .02x^3 + 7x + 5000$, find the production level that leads to the minimum average cost.

Example 6   An open box is to be made by cutting a square from each corner of a 12-inch-by-12-inch piece of metal and then folding up the sides. The finished box must be at least 1.5 inches deep, but not deeper than 3 inches. What size square should be cut from each corner in order to produce a box of maximum volume?

Solution   Let x represent the length of a side of the square that is cut from each corner, as shown in Figure 12.33(a). The width of the box is $12 - 2x$, as is the length. As shown in Figure 12.33(b), the depth of the box is x inches.

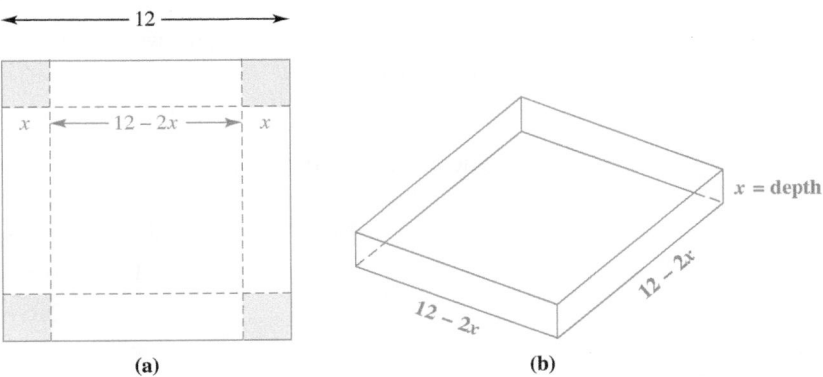

(a)   (b)

Figure 12.33

We must maximize the volume $V(x)$ of the box, which is given by

$$\text{Volume} = \text{length} \cdot \text{width} \cdot \text{height}$$

$$V(x) = (12 - 2x) \cdot (12 - 2x) \cdot x = 144x - 48x^2 + 4x^3.$$

Since the height x must be between 1.5 and 3 inches, the domain of this volume function is the closed interval [1.5, 3]. First find the critical numbers by setting the derivative equal to 0 (since the derivative always exists):

$$V'(x) = 12x^2 - 96x + 144 = 0$$
$$12(x^2 - 8x + 12) = 0$$
$$12(x - 2)(x - 6) = 0$$
$$x - 2 = 0 \quad \text{or} \quad x - 6 = 0$$
$$x = 2 \quad \text{or} \quad x = 6.$$

✓ **Checkpoint 5**

An open box is to be made by cutting squares from each corner of a 20-cm-by-32-cm piece of metal and folding up the sides. Let x represent the length of the side of the square to be cut out. Find

(a) an expression for the volume $V(x)$ of the box;

(b) $V'(x)$;

(c) the value of x that leads to maximum volume (*Hint*: The solutions of the equation $V'(x) = 0$ are 4 and 40/3);

(d) the maximum volume.

Since 6 is not in the domain, the only critical number of interest here is $x = 2$. By the extreme-value theorem, the maximum volume must occur at $x = 2$ or at the endpoints $x = 1.5$ or $x = 3$.

x	$V(x)$	
1.5	121.5	
2	128	← Absolute maximum
3	108	

The preceding table shows that the box has maximum volume when $x = 2$ inches and that this maximum volume is 128 cubic inches. ✓ 5

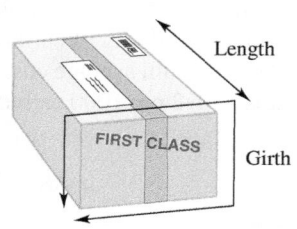

Figure 12.34

Example 7   **Business**   The U.S. Postal Service requires that boxes sent by Priority Mail have a length plus girth of no more than 108 inches, as shown in Figure 12.34. Find the dimensions of the box with largest volume that can be sent by Priority Mail, assuming that its width and height are equal.

Solution   Let x be the width and y the length of the box. Since width and height are the same, the volume of the box is

$$V = y \cdot x \cdot x = yx^2.$$

Now express V in terms of just *one* variable. Use the facts that the girth is $x + x + x + x = 4x$ and that the length plus girth is 108, so that

$$y + 4x = 108, \quad \text{or equivalently,} \quad y = 108 - 4x.$$

Substitute for y in the expression for V to get

$$V = yx^2 = (108 - 4x)x^2 = 108x^2 - 4x^3.$$

Since x and y are dimensions, we must have $x > 0$ and $y > 0$. Now, $y = 108 - 4x > 0$ implies that

$$4x < 108, \quad \text{or equivalently,} \quad x < 27.$$

Therefore, the domain of the volume function V (the set of values of x that make sense in the situation) is the open interval (0, 27). Since its derivative always exists, we find the critical numbers for V by setting its derivative equal to 0 and solving the equation:

$$V' = 216x - 12x^2 = 0$$
$$x(216 - 12x) = 0$$
$$x = 0 \quad \text{or} \quad 12x = 216$$
$$x = 18.$$

Use the second-derivative test to check $x = 18$, the only critical number in the domain of V. Since $V'(x) = 216x - 12x^2$,

$$V''(x) = 216 - 24x.$$

Hence, $V''(18) = 216 - 24 \cdot 18 = -216$, and V has a local maximum when $x = 18$. By the critical-point theorem, the absolute maximum of V on $(0, 27)$ is at $x = 18$. In this case, $y = 108 - 4 \cdot 18 = 36$. Therefore, a box with dimensions 18 inches by 18 inches by 36 inches satisfies postal regulations and yields the maximum volume of $18^2 \cdot 36 = 11,664$ cubic inches.

Example 8 **Business** A landscape gardener wants to build an 8000-square-foot rectangular display garden along the side of a river. The garden will be fenced on three sides. (No fence is necessary along the river.) She plans to use ornamental steel fencing at $12 per foot on the side opposite the river and chain-link fencing at $3 per foot on the other two sides. What dimensions for the garden will minimize her costs?

Solution First draw a sketch of the situation and label the sides of the garden, as in Figure 12.35.

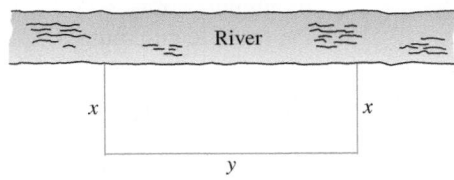

Figure 12.35

We see that $2x$ feet of fencing (at $3 per foot) are needed for the parallel sides and y feet (at $12 per foot) for the side opposite the river. So the cost is

$$C = 2x(3) + y(12) = 6x + 12y.$$

We must find the values of x and y that make C as small as possible. First, however, we must express C in terms of a single variable. Since the garden is to have an area of 8000 square feet and the area of a rectangle is its length times its width, we have

$$xy = \text{area} = 8000$$

$$y = \frac{8000}{x}.$$

Substituting this expression for y in the cost function, we obtain

$$C = 6x + 12y = 6x + 12\left(\frac{8000}{x}\right) = 6x + \frac{96,000}{x}.$$

Since x is a length, it is positive. Hence, the domain of the cost function is the open interval $(0, \infty)$, and we need look only at the critical numbers. The derivative is

$$C'(x) = 6 - 96,000x^{-2} = 6 - \frac{96,000}{x^2}.$$

Since $C'(x)$ exists for all x in the domain, the critical numbers are the solutions of

$$6 - \frac{96,000}{x^2} = 0$$

$$6x^2 - 96,000 = 0 \qquad \text{Multiply both sides by } x^2.$$

$$6x^2 = 96,000$$

$$x^2 = 16,000$$

$$x = \pm\sqrt{16,000} \approx \pm 126.5.$$

The only critical number in the domain $(0, \infty)$ is $x = \sqrt{16,000}$.

Next we apply the second-derivative test. Since $C''(x) = -96,000(-2x^{-3}) = 192,000/x^3$ is positive for all $x > 0$, a local minimum must occur at the critical number $x = \sqrt{16,000}$. Since this is the only critical number in the domain, the critical-point theorem ensures that an absolute minimum occurs there. Therefore, the garden with the least expensive fence has dimensions

$$x = \sqrt{16,000} \approx 126.5 \text{ ft and } y = \frac{8000}{x} = \frac{8000}{\sqrt{16,000}} \approx 63.2 \text{ ft.}$$

The preceding examples illustrate some of the factors that may affect applications in the real world. First, you must be able to find a function that models the situation. The rule of this function may be defined for values of x that do not make sense in the context of the application, so the domain must be restricted to the relevant values of x.

The techniques of calculus apply to functions that are defined and continuous at every real number in some interval, so the maximum or minimum for the mathematical model (function) may not be feasible in the setting of the problem. For instance, if $C(x)$ has a minimum at $x = 80\sqrt{3}$ (≈ 138.564), where $C(x)$ is the cost of hiring x employees, then the real-life minimum occurs at either 138 or 139, whichever one leads to lower cost.

Economic Lot Size

Suppose that a company manufactures a constant number of units of a product per year and that the product can be manufactured in several batches of equal size during the year. On the one hand, if the company were to manufacture the item only once per year, it would minimize setup costs, but incur high warehouse costs. On the other hand, making many small batches would increase setup costs. Calculus can be used to find the number of batches per year that should be manufactured in order to minimize total cost. This number is called the **economic lot size**.

Figure 12.36 shows several of the possibilities for a product having an annual demand of 12,000 units. The top graph shows the results if only one batch of the product is made annually; in this case, an average of 6000 items will be held in a warehouse. If four batches

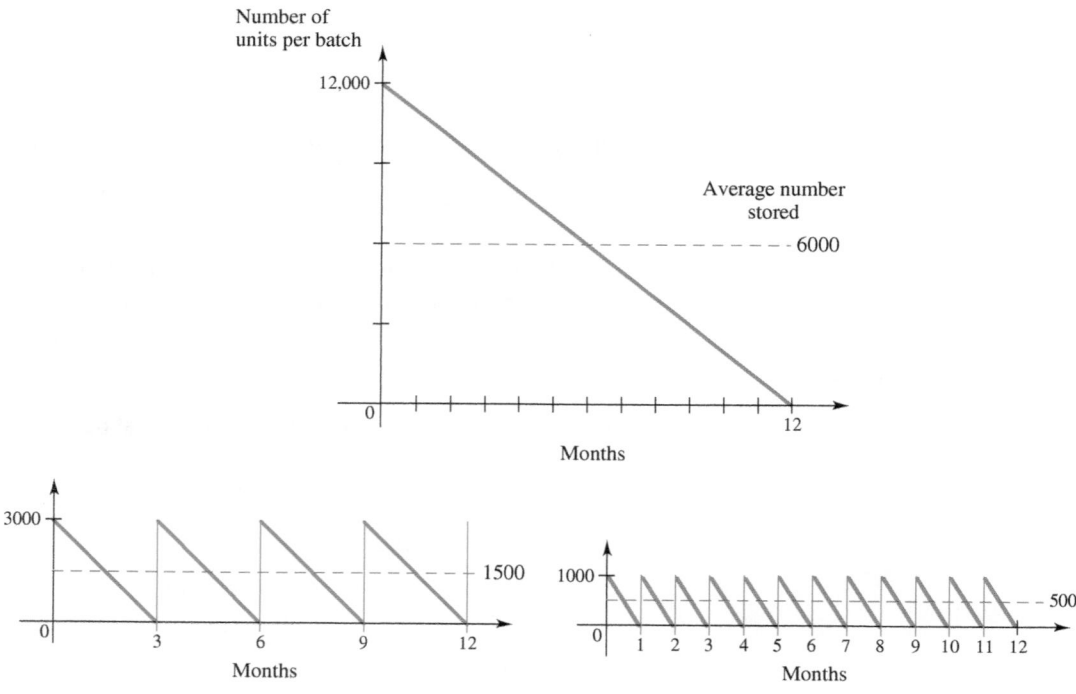

Figure 12.36

(of 3000 each) are made at equal time intervals during a year, the average number of units in the warehouse falls to only 1500. If 12 batches are made, an average of 500 items will be in the warehouse.

The following variables will be used in our discussion of economic lot size:

x = number of batches to be manufactured annually;

k = cost of storing one unit of the product for one year;

a = fixed setup cost to manufacture the product;

b = variable cost of manufacturing a single unit of the product;

M = total number of units produced annually.

The company has two types of costs associated with the production of its product: a cost associated with manufacturing the item and a cost associated with storing the finished product.

During a year, the company will produce x batches of the product, with M/x units of the product produced per batch. Each batch has a fixed cost a and a variable cost b per unit, so the manufacturing cost per batch is

$$a + b\left(\frac{M}{x}\right).$$

There are x batches per year, so the total annual manufacturing cost is

$$\left[a + b\left(\frac{M}{x}\right)\right]x. \tag{1}$$

Each batch consists of M/x units, and demand is constant; therefore, it is common to assume an average inventory of

$$\frac{1}{2}\left(\frac{M}{x}\right) = \frac{M}{2x}$$

units per year. The cost to store one unit of the product for a year is k, so the total storage cost is

$$k\left(\frac{M}{2x}\right) = \frac{kM}{2x}. \tag{2}$$

The total production cost is the sum of the manufacturing and storage costs, or the sum of expressions (1) and (2). If $T(x)$ is the total cost of producing x batches,

$$T(x) = \left[a + b\left(\frac{M}{x}\right)\right]x + \frac{kM}{2x} = ax + bM + \left(\frac{kM}{2}\right)x^{-1}.$$

Now find the value of x that will minimize $T(x)$. (Remember that a, b, k, and M are constants.) To do so, first find $T'(x)$:

$$T'(x) = a - \frac{kM}{2}x^{-2}.$$

Set this derivative equal to 0 and solve for x (remember that $x > 0$):

$$a - \frac{kM}{2}x^{-2} = 0$$

$$a = \frac{kM}{2x^2}$$

$$2ax^2 = kM$$

$$x^2 = \frac{kM}{2a}$$

$$x = \sqrt{\frac{kM}{2a}}. \tag{3}$$

The second-derivative test can be used to show that $\sqrt{kM/(2a)}$ is the annual number of batches that gives the minimum total production cost.

> **Example 9** **Business** A garden supplier has steady annual demand for 50,000 cubic feet of potting soil. The cost accountant for the company says that it costs $2.50 to store 1 cubic foot of potting soil for 1 year and $850 to set up the production facility to mix the ingredients for the potting soil. Find the number of batches of potting soil that should be produced for the minimum total production cost.
>
> **Solution** Use equation (3), given previously:
>
> $$x = \sqrt{\frac{kM}{2a}}$$
>
> $$x = \sqrt{\frac{(2.50)(50,000)}{2(850)}} \qquad \text{Let } k = 2.50, M = 50,000, \text{ and } a = 850.$$
>
> $$x \approx 9.$$
>
> Nine batches of potting soil per year will lead to minimum production costs.

✓ **Checkpoint 6**

In Example 9, suppose annual demand is 95,000 cubic feet, the annual cost of storage is $2.75 per cubic foot, and setup costs are $1100. Find the number of batches that should be made annually to minimize total costs.

12.3 Exercises

Find the location of the absolute maximum and absolute minimum of the function on the given interval. (See Example 1.)

1. $[0, 4]$

2. $[2, 5]$

3. $[-1, 2]$

4. $[-4, 2]$

5. $[-8, 0]$

6. $[-4, 4]$

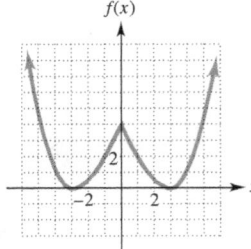

Find the absolute extrema of each function on the given interval. (See Examples 2 and 3.)

7. $f(x) = x^4 - 18x^2 + 1; [-4, 4]$

8. $f(x) = x^4 - 32x^2 - 7; [-5, 6]$

9. $f(x) = \dfrac{8 + x}{8 - x}; [4, 6]$

10. $f(x) = \dfrac{1 - x}{3 + x}; [0, 3]$

11. $f(x) = \dfrac{x}{x^2 + 2}; [-1, 4]$

12. $f(x) = \dfrac{x - 1}{x^2 + 1}; [0, 5]$

13. $f(x) = (x^2 + 18)^{2/3}; [-3, 2]$

14. $f(x) = (x^2 + 4)^{1/3}; [-1, 2]$

15. $f(x) = \dfrac{1}{\sqrt{x^2 + 1}}; [-1, 1]$

16. $f(x) = \dfrac{3}{\sqrt{x^2 + 4}}; [-2, 2]$

If possible, find an absolute extremum of each function on the given interval. (See Example 4.)

17. $g(x) = 2x^3 - 3x^2 - 12x + 1; (0, 4)$

18. $g(x) = x^3 - 2x^2 - 4x + 1; \quad (0, \infty)$

19. $g(x) = \dfrac{1}{x}; (0, \infty)$

20. $g(x) = 6x^{2/3} - 4x; (0, \infty)$

21. $g(x) = xe^{2-x^2}; (-\infty, 0)$

22. $g(x) = 2xe^{3-x}; (-\infty, \infty)$

23. $g(x) = \dfrac{x}{e^x}; (0, 3)$

24. $g(x) = \dfrac{x^2 + 1}{x}; (0, \infty)$

Work these problems. (See Example 5.)

25. Business The daily cost of producing x high-performance wheels for racing bicycles is given by

$$C(x) = .01x^3 - 1.5x^2 + 175x,$$

and no more than 100 wheels can be produced each day. What production level will give the lowest *average* cost per wheel? What is the minimum *average* cost?

26. Business The monthly cost of producing x thousand ultimate flying discs is given by

$$C(x) = 9750e^{.04x},$$

and at most 30,000 discs can be produced in a month. What production level will give the lowest *average* cost per disc? What is the minimum *average* cost?

Work these exercises.

27. Business The number of employees of Amazon.com, Inc., can be approximated by

$$f(x) = 627x^2 - 3530x + 11{,}500 \qquad (0 \le x \le 11),$$

where $x = 0$ corresponds to the year 2000. What was the maximum number of people employed by Amazon.com during this period? The minimum? (Data from: www.mergentonline.com.)

28. Social Science The number of people in attendance (in thousands) at National Football League games can be approximated by

$$f(x) = -59x^2 + 688x + 20{,}086 \qquad (1 \le x \le 10),$$

where $x = 1$ corresponds to the year 2001. What was the maximum number of people in attendance at NFL games during this period? The minimum number? (Data from: *The Statistical Abstract of the United States*: 2012.)

29. Business Revenue generated by admissions to motion picture theaters (in millions of dollars) can be approximated by

$$f(x) = 17.7x^3 - 245x^2 + 986x + 8485 \qquad (0 \le x \le 9),$$

where $x = 0$ corresponds to the year 2000. What was the maximum revenue from admissions to motion picture theaters during this period? The minimum revenue? (Data from: *The Statistical Abstract of the United States*: 2012.)

30. Health The number of heart transplants can be approximated by

$$f(x) = 7.2x^3 - 153.5x^2 + 1078x - 307 \qquad (4 \le x \le 10),$$

where $x = 4$ corresponds to the year 2004. What was the maximum number of heart transplants performed during this period? The minimum number? (Data from: *The Statistical Abstract of the United States*: 2012.)

31. Business A manufacturer produces gas grills that sell for $400 each. The total cost of producing x grills is approximated by the function $C(x) = 525{,}000 - 30x + .012x^2$.

(a) Write the revenue function in this situation.

(b) Write the profit function in this situation.

(c) What number of grills should be made to guarantee maximum profit? What will that profit be?

32. Business Saltwater taffy can be sold wholesale for $45 per thousand individual candies. The cost of producing x thousand candies is $C(x) = .001x^3 + .045x^2 - 1.75x$.

(a) What is the revenue function in this situation?

(b) What is the profit function in this situation?

(c) What number of candies will produce the largest possible profit?

33. Natural Science A lake polluted by bacteria is treated with an antibacterial chemical. After t days, the number N of bacteria per ml of water is approximated by

$$N(t) = 20\left(\frac{t}{12} - \ln\left(\frac{t}{12}\right)\right) + 30 \qquad (1 \le t \le 15).$$

(a) When during this period will the number of bacteria be a minimum?

(b) What is this minimum number of bacteria?

(c) When during the period will the number of bacteria be a maximum?

(d) What is this maximum number of bacteria?

34. Social Science The number of people in attendance (in thousands) at NCAA women's sports can be approximated by

$$f(x) = 1000 \ln(x) - 10x + 8800 \qquad (1 \le x \le 10),$$

where $x = 1$ corresponds to the year 2001. What was the maximum number of people in attendance at NCAA women's sports during this period? The minimum number? (Data from: *The Statistical Abstract of the United States*: 2012.)

35. Health A disease has hit College Station, Texas. The percentage of the population infected t days after the disease has arrived is approximated by $p(t) = 10te^{-t/8}$ for $0 \le t \le 40$.

(a) After how many days is the percentage of infected people a maximum?

(b) What is this maximum percentage of the population infected?

36. Business The projected unemployment rate (as a percent) can be approximated by

$$f(x) = (5.1x - 40.8)e^{-.5x+4} + 5.8 \qquad (8 \le x \le 14),$$

where $x = 8$ corresponds to the year 2008. What was the maximum unemployment rate during this period? The minimum? (Data from: *The Statistical Abstract of the United States*: 2012.)

Work these problems. (See Examples 6 and 7.)

37. Business An open box is to be made by cutting a square from each corner of a 3-foot-by-8-foot piece of cardboard and then folding up the sides. What size square should be cut from each corner in order to produce a box of maximum volume?

38. Business An artist makes a closed box with a square base. The box is to have a volume of 16,000 cubic centimeters. The material for the top and bottom of the box costs 3 cents per square centimeter, while the material for the sides costs 1.5 cents per square centimeter. Find the dimensions of the box that will lead to the minimum total cost. What is the minimum total cost?

39. Business A watch manufacturing firm needs to design an open-topped box with a square base. The box must hold 32 cubic inches. Find the dimensions of the box that can be built with the minimum amount of materials.

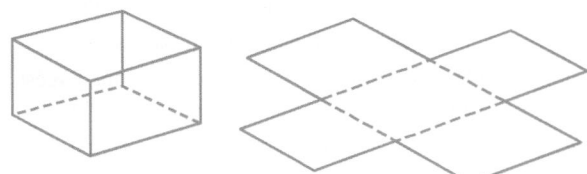

40. Business A company wishes to manufacture a rectangular box with a volume of 36 cubic feet that is open on top and that is twice as long as it is wide. Find the dimensions of the box produced from the minimum amount of material.

41. Business A cylindrical box will be tied up with ribbon as shown in the accompanying figure. The longest piece of ribbon available is 130 cm long, and 10 cm of that is required for the bow. Find the radius and height of the box with the largest possible volume.

42. Business A cylindrical can of volume 58 cubic inches (approximately 1 quart) is to be designed. For convenient handling, it must be at least 1 inch high and 2 inches in diameter. What dimensions (radius of top, and height of can) will use the least amount of material?

Work these problems. (See Example 8.)

43. Business A farmer has 1200 m of fencing. He wants to enclose a rectangular field bordering a river, with no fencing needed along the river. Let x represent the width of the field.

(a) Write an expression for the length of the field.

(b) Find the area of the field.

(c) Find the value of x leading to the maximum area.

(d) Find the maximum area.

44. Business A rectangular field is to be enclosed with a fence. One side of the field is against an existing fence, so that no fence is needed on that side. If material for the fence costs $2 per foot for the two ends and $4 per foot for the side parallel to the existing fence, find the dimensions of the field of largest area that can be enclosed for $1000.

45. Business A fence must be built to enclose a rectangular area of 20,000 ft². Fencing material costs $3 per foot for the two sides facing north and south and $6 per foot for the other two sides. Find the cost of the least expensive fence.

46. Business A rectangular field is to be enclosed on all four sides with a fence. Fencing material costs $3 per foot for two opposite sides and $6 per foot for the other two sides. Find the maximum area that can be enclosed for $2400.

47. Business A mathematics book is to contain 36 square inches of printed matter per page, with margins of 1 inch along the sides and $1\frac{1}{2}$ inches along the top and bottom. Find the dimensions of the page that will lead to the minimum amount of paper being used for a page.

48. Business A fence must be built in a large field to enclose a rectangular area of 15,625 m². One side of the area is bounded by an existing fence; no fence is needed there. Material for the fence costs $2 per meter for the two ends and $4 per meter for the side opposite the existing fence. Find the cost of the least expensive fence.

Work these problems.

49. Business If the price charged for a candy bar is $p(x)$ cents, where

$$p(x) = 100 - \frac{x}{10},$$

then x thousand candy bars will be sold in a certain city.

(a) Find an expression for the total revenue from the sale of x thousand candy bars. (*Hint:* Find the product of $p(x)$, x, and 1000.)

(b) Find the value of x that leads to the maximum revenue.

(c) Find the maximum revenue.

50. Business A company makes plastic buckets for children to play with on beaches. The buckets sell for $75 per hundred. The total cost (in dollars) of making x hundred buckets is $C(x) = 5x^2 - 20x + 12$. Assume that the company can sell all the buckets it makes. How many buckets should be made to maximize profit?

51. Business We can use the function

$$f(x) = 55.44(54.3x - 143.9)e^{-.15x}$$

to model the revenue (in millions of U.S. dollars) from the cell phone industry in India, where $x = 2$ corresponds to the year

2002. According to this model, in what year does revenue reach its maximum? (Data from: www.researchinchina.com.)

52. Business A rock-and-roll band travels from engagement to engagement in a large bus. While traveling x miles per hour, this bus burns fuel at the rate of $G(x)$ gallons per mile, where

$$G(x) = \frac{1}{50}\left(\frac{200}{x} + \frac{x}{15}\right).$$

(a) If fuel costs $3 per gallon, find the speed that will produce the minimum total cost for a 250-mile trip.

(b) Find the minimum total cost.

53. Natural Science Homing pigeons avoid flying over large bodies of water, preferring to fly around them instead. (One possible explanation is the fact that extra energy is required to fly over water because air pressure drops over water in the daytime.) Assume that a pigeon released from a boat 1 mile from the shore of a lake (point B in the accompanying figure) flies first to point P on the shore and then along the straight edge of the lake to reach its home at L. Assume that L is 2 miles from point A, the point on the shore closest to the boat, and that a pigeon needs $\frac{4}{3}$ as much energy to fly over water as over land. Find the location of point P if the pigeon uses the least possible amount of energy.

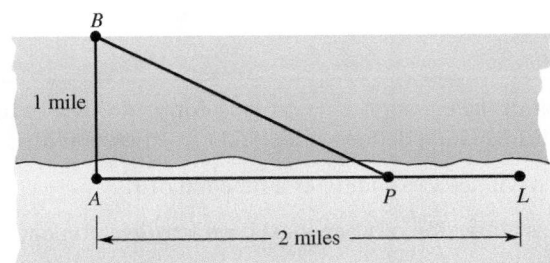

54. Business A company wishes to run a utility cable from point A on the shore to an installation at point B on the island. The island is 6 miles from the shore (at point C), and point A is 9 miles from point C. It costs $400 per mile to run the cable on land and $500 per mile underwater. Assume that the cable starts at A, runs along the shoreline, and then angles and runs underwater to the island. Find the point at which the line should begin to angle in order to yield the minimum total cost. (*Hint*: The length of the line underwater is $\sqrt{x^2 + 36}$.) See the accompanying figure.

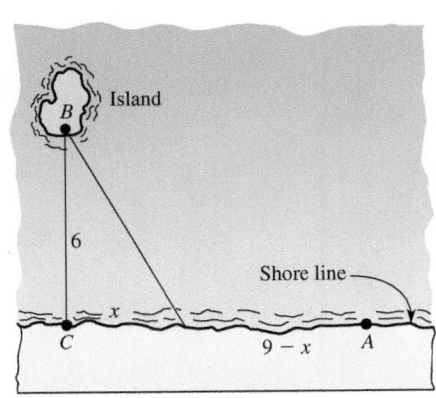

The remaining exercises refer to economic lot size. (See Example 9.)

55. Business A manufacturer of porcelain sinks has an annual demand of 12,300 sinks. It costs $2.25 to store a sink for a year, and it costs $350 to set up a factory to produce each batch. Find the number of batches of sinks that should be produced for the minimum total production cost.

56. Business How many sinks per batch will be produced in the previous exercise?

57. Business A regional market has a steady annual demand for 15,900 cases of beer. It costs $3.25 to store a case for a year. The market pays $5.50 for each order that is placed. Find the number of orders for cases of beer that should be placed each year. (*Hint*: Use the formula for economic lot size, with ordering cost in place of setup cost.)

58. Business Find the number of cases per order in the previous exercise.

59. Business A large hospital has an annual demand for 50,000 booklets on healthy eating. It costs $.75 to store one booklet for a year, and it costs $80 to place an order for a new batch of booklets. Find the optimum number of copies per order.

60. Business A restaurant has an annual demand for 900 bottles of a California wine. It costs $1 to store one bottle for one year, and it costs $5 to place a reorder. Find the number of orders that should be placed annually.

61. Business Choose the correct answer:* The economic order quantity formula assumes that

(a) Purchase costs per unit differ due to quantity discounts.

(b) Costs of placing an order vary with the quantity ordered.

(c) The periodic demand for the goods is known.

(d) Erratic usage rates are cushioned by safety stocks.

✓ Checkpoint Answers

1. Absolute maximum at 0; absolute minimum at -2

2. Absolute maximum of -4 at $x = 2$; absolute minimum of -40 at $x = -4$

3. Absolute maximum of 94 at $x = 2$; absolute minimum of 14 at $x = 6$

4. $x = 50$

5. (a) $V(x) = 640x - 104x^2 + 4x^3$

　　(b) $V'(x) = 640 - 208x + 12x^2$

　　(c) $x = 4$

　　(d) $V(4) = 1152$ cubic centimeters

6. 11 batches

*From Uniform CPA Examinations and Unofficial Answers. Copyright © May 1991 American Institute of Certified Public Accountants, Inc. (AICPA). Reproduced by permission of American Institute of Certified Public Accountants, Inc. (AICPA).

12.4 Implicit Differentiation

So far we have studied functions of the form $y = f(x)$ that are *explicitly* defined. This means that y appears only once in the equation and it appears by itself (not in combination with other functions) on one side of the equation. For example, the following equations define y explicitly as a function of x:

y appears once by itself and only on one side.
$$y = 5x - 1;$$
$$y = 2x^2 - 3x + 100;$$
$$y = 7e^x.$$

In the above examples, y appears alone on the left side of the equation. If we substitute a given value of x, each equation above yields the corresponding value of y (the function value).

It is sometimes necessary or convenient to consider **implicitly defined functions**. For example, the following equations define y implicitly as a function of x:

y appears in combination with other functions.
$$x + y = 7;$$
$$e^y = 2x + 5;$$
$$y = y^3 + x. \longleftarrow \text{ y appears more than once.}$$

If we substitute a given value of x, we would need to do some algebra to solve each equation above in order to find the corresponding value of y.

Example 1   The graph of the equation $x^2 + y^2 = 1$ for $y \geq 0$ is a semicircle (the top half of the unit circle). This equation defines y implicitly as a function of x.

(a) Rewrite the equation so that it defines y explicitly as a function of x.

Solution   To write y explicitly as a function of x, we must have y by itself on one side of the equation:

$$x^2 + y^2 = 1$$
$$y^2 = 1 - x^2 \quad \text{Subtract } x^2 \text{ from both sides.}$$
$$y = \pm\sqrt{1 - x^2} \quad \text{Take the square root of both sides.}$$
$$y = \sqrt{1 - x^2} \quad \text{We are given that } y \geq 0.$$

The last equation defines y explicitly as a function of x.

(b) Find the derivative of y with respect to x.

Solution   To differentiate the last equation above, we first use rules of exponents to rewrite the square root as a power:

$$y = (1 - x^2)^{\frac{1}{2}}.$$

We are now able to find the derivative:

$$\frac{dy}{dx} = \frac{1}{2}(1 - x^2)^{-\frac{1}{2}}\frac{d}{dx}(1 - x^2) \quad \text{Chain rule: } \frac{d}{dx}(u^{\frac{1}{2}}) = \frac{1}{2}u^{-\frac{1}{2}} \cdot \frac{du}{dx}$$

$$= \frac{1}{2}(1 - x^2)^{-\frac{1}{2}}(-2x)$$

$$= \frac{1}{2}\frac{1}{\sqrt{1 - x^2}}(-2x) \quad \text{Rules of exponents}$$

$$= \frac{-x}{\sqrt{1 - x^2}}. \quad \text{Simplify.}$$

Rather than solving the equation in the last example for y explicitly in terms of x, it would be more convenient if we could differentiate the original function that was implicitly defined. We now introduce the method for doing so, called **implicit differentiation**.

Implicit Differentiation

To find $\dfrac{dy}{dx}$ when y is defined implicitly as a function of x:

Step 1 Differentiate both sides of the equation with respect to x. Remember to use the chain rule since y is a function of x.

Step 2 Solve the resulting equation for $\dfrac{dy}{dx}$.

Example 2 Given that $x^2 + y^2 = 1$, find $\dfrac{dy}{dx}$ by implicit differentiation.

Solution When using implicit differentiation, there is no need to solve the equation explicitly for y.

Step 1 The first step is to differentiate both sides of the equation with respect to x. Recall that $\dfrac{d}{dx}[f(x)]$ is another notation for the derivative of $f(x)$ with respect to x.

$$\frac{d}{dx}(x^2 + y^2) = \frac{d}{dx}(1)$$

$$\frac{d}{dx}(x^2) + \frac{d}{dx}(y^2) = \frac{d}{dx}(1)$$

$$2x + 2y\frac{dy}{dx} = 0. \qquad \text{Chain rule: } \frac{d}{dx}(u^2) = 2u\frac{du}{dx}$$

Clearly, the derivative of x^2 *with respect to x* is $2x$, that is, $\dfrac{d}{dx}(x^2) = 2x$. However, when differentiating y^2 *with respect to x*, we must remember that y is an implicitly defined function of x, say $y = u(x)$. Thus y^2 is actually a composition of functions, $y^2 = [u(x)]^2$. Therefore, to find the derivative, we must apply the chain rule:

$$\frac{d}{dx}(y^2) = \frac{d}{dx}([u(x)]^2) = 2[u(x)]\frac{d}{dx}[u(x)] = 2y\frac{dy}{dx}.$$

Step 2 Since our goal is to find the derivative of y with respect to x, we now solve for $\dfrac{dy}{dx}$:

$$2x + 2y\frac{dy}{dx} = 0$$

$$2y\frac{dy}{dx} = -2x \qquad \text{Move terms without } \frac{dy}{dx} \text{ to the right side.}$$

$$\frac{dy}{dx} = -\frac{2x}{2y} \qquad \text{Divide both sides by } 2y.$$

$$\frac{dy}{dx} = -\frac{x}{y}. \qquad \text{Simplify.}$$

✓ **Checkpoint 1**

Find $\dfrac{dy}{dx}$ for $x^4 + y^5 = 6$.

Note that in Example 1 we found that $y = \sqrt{1 - x^2}$ and $\dfrac{dy}{dx} = \dfrac{-x}{\sqrt{1 - x^2}}$. In Example 2

we found that $\dfrac{dy}{dx} = -\dfrac{x}{y}$. These answers are equivalent since $\dfrac{dy}{dx} = -\dfrac{x}{y} = \dfrac{-x}{\sqrt{1 - x^2}}$. It is

often much easier to find a derivative by implicit differentiation (as in Example 2) rather than to solve an equation explicitly for the desired variable and then take the derivative (as in Example 1).

Example 3   Find $\dfrac{dy}{dx}$ given that $e^{1-5x} + e^y = 7x - 8y$.

Solution

Step 1 Take the derivative of both sides of the equation with respect to x:

$$\frac{d}{dx}(e^{1-5x}) + \frac{d}{dx}(e^y) = \frac{d}{dx}(7x) - \frac{d}{dx}(8y)$$

$$e^{1-5x}(-5) + e^y\frac{dy}{dx} = 7 - 8\frac{dy}{dx} \qquad \text{Chain rule: } \frac{d}{dx}(e^u) = e^u\frac{du}{dx}$$

$$-5e^{1-5x} + e^y\frac{dy}{dx} = 7 - 8\frac{dy}{dx}. \qquad \text{Simplify.}$$

Step 2 Solve the last equation for $\dfrac{dy}{dx}$:

$$-5e^{1-5x} + e^y\frac{dy}{dx} = 7 - 8\frac{dy}{dx}$$

$$e^y\frac{dy}{dx} = 7 - 8\frac{dy}{dx} + 5e^{1-5x} \qquad \text{Move terms without } \frac{dy}{dx} \text{ to the right side.}$$

$$e^y\frac{dy}{dx} + 8\frac{dy}{dx} = 7 + 5e^{1-5x} \qquad \text{Move terms involving } \frac{dy}{dx} \text{ to the left side.}$$

$$\frac{dy}{dx}(e^y + 8) = 7 + 5e^{1-5x} \qquad \text{Factor out } \frac{dy}{dx}.$$

$$\frac{dy}{dx} = \frac{7 + 5e^{1-5x}}{e^y + 8}. \qquad \text{Divide both sides by } e^y + 8. \quad \boxed{\checkmark 2}$$

✓ **Checkpoint 2**

Find $\dfrac{dy}{dx}$ for $e^{9x^2} - e^y = 6y^{10}$.

Note that when finding $\dfrac{dy}{dx}$ by implicit differentiation, the answer will typically involve both x and y. This is to be expected and it is acceptable to leave the answer in this form.

Example 4   Find $\dfrac{dy}{dx}$ for $10x^5y^8 = 3y + \pi$.

Solution

Step 1 First we take the derivative of both sides of the equation with respect to x. Because y is implicitly a function of x, the left side of the equation is a product of two functions of x. Therefore we will need the product rule to differentiate the left side of the equation:

$$\frac{d}{dx}[10x^5y^8] = \frac{d}{dx}[3y + \pi]$$

$$[10x^5]\frac{d}{dx}[y^8] + [y^8]\frac{d}{dx}[10x^5] = \frac{d}{dx}[3y + \pi] \quad \text{Product rule}$$

$$[10x^5]\left[8y^7\frac{dy}{dx}\right] + [y^8][50x^4] = 3\frac{dy}{dx} \quad \text{Chain rule}$$

$$80x^5y^7\frac{dy}{dx} + 50x^4y^8 = 3\frac{dy}{dx}. \quad \text{Simplify.}$$

Step 2   Solve the last equation for $\dfrac{dy}{dx}$:

$$80x^5y^7\frac{dy}{dx} + 50x^4y^8 = 3\frac{dy}{dx}$$

$$80x^5y^7\frac{dy}{dx} = 3\frac{dy}{dx} - 50x^4y^8 \quad \text{Move terms without } \frac{dy}{dx} \text{ to the right side.}$$

$$80x^5y^7\frac{dy}{dx} - 3\frac{dy}{dx} = -50x^4y^8 \quad \text{Move terms involving } \frac{dy}{dx} \text{ to the left side.}$$

$$\frac{dy}{dx}(80x^5y^7 - 3) = -50x^4y^8 \quad \text{Factor out } \frac{dy}{dx}.$$

$$\frac{dy}{dx} = -\frac{50x^4y^8}{80x^5y^7 - 3}. \quad \text{Divide both sides by } 80x^5y^7 - 3. \quad \boxed{\checkmark 3}$$

✓ **Checkpoint 3**

Find $\dfrac{dy}{dx}$ for $3x^6y^7 = 5$.

Example 5   Find $\dfrac{dy}{dx}$ at the point $(0, 4)$ given that $\sqrt{y} - \ln(3x + 1) = 2$.

Solution

Step 1   We want to take the derivative of both sides of the equation with respect to x. First we must rewrite $\sqrt{y}$ as $y^{\frac{1}{2}}$, so the given equation becomes

$$y^{\frac{1}{2}} - \ln(3x + 1) = 2.$$

Now differentiating with respect to x yields

$$\frac{1}{2}y^{-\frac{1}{2}}\left(\frac{dy}{dx}\right) - \frac{1}{3x + 1}(3) = 0 \quad \text{Chain rule}$$

$$\frac{1}{2\sqrt{y}}\frac{dy}{dx} - \frac{3}{3x + 1} = 0. \quad \text{Rules of exponents}$$

Step 2   Since we want to find $\dfrac{dy}{dx}$ at the given point $(0, 4)$, it is easier to substitute these values in the equation above prior to solving it. Substituting $x = 0$ and $y = 4$ in the equation above yields

$$\frac{1}{2\sqrt{4}}\frac{dy}{dx} - \frac{3}{3(0) + 1} = 0 \quad \text{Substitute.}$$

$$\frac{1}{2 \cdot 2}\frac{dy}{dx} - \frac{3}{1} = 0 \quad \text{Simplify.}$$

$$\frac{1}{4}\frac{dy}{dx} - 3 = 0. \quad \text{Simplify.}$$

It is now easy to solve the last equation for $\frac{dy}{dx}$. Thus at the point $(0, 4)$ we have

$$\frac{1}{4}\frac{dy}{dx} = 3$$

$$\frac{dy}{dx} = 12. \quad \text{Solve for } \frac{dy}{dx}. \quad \boxed{\checkmark_4}$$

✓ **Checkpoint 4**

Find $\frac{dy}{dx}$ at the point $(0, 1)$ for
$x^4 + 7x + \ln y = 0$.

Example 6   Find an equation of the tangent line to the curve $xe^y = 1$ at the point $(1, 0)$.

Solution   To find the slope of the tangent line, we must find $\frac{dy}{dx}$. Using implicit differentiation, we first differentiate both sides of the equation with respect to x:

$$\frac{d}{dx}(xe^y) = \frac{d}{dx}(1)$$

$$x\frac{d}{dx}(e^y) + e^y\frac{d}{dx}(x) = 0 \qquad \text{Product rule}$$

$$x\left(e^y\frac{dy}{dx}\right) + e^y(1) = 0 \qquad \text{Chain rule}$$

$$xe^y\frac{dy}{dx} + e^y = 0. \qquad \text{Simplify.}$$

Since we want to find $\frac{dy}{dx}$ at the point $(1, 0)$, it is easier to substitute $x = 1$ and $y = 0$ into the equation above before solving the equation:

$$1 \cdot e^0 \cdot \frac{dy}{dx} + e^0 = 0 \qquad \text{Substitute.}$$

$$\frac{dy}{dx} + 1 = 0 \qquad \text{Simplify.}$$

$$\frac{dy}{dx} = -1. \qquad \text{Solve for } \frac{dy}{dx}.$$

Thus the slope of the tangent line at $(1, 0)$ is $m = -1$.

To find the equation of the tangent line at the point $(x_1, y_1) = (1, 0)$, we use point-slope form:

$$y - y_1 = m(x - x_1) \qquad \text{Point-slope form}$$
$$y - 0 = -1(x - 1) \qquad \text{Substitute.}$$
$$y = -x + 1. \qquad \text{Simplify.}$$

✓ **Checkpoint 5**

Find the equation of the tangent line to $x^2 + y^2 = 1$ at the point $(0, 1)$.

The graph of the curve $xe^y = 1$ and its tangent line $y = -x + 1$ at the point $(1, 0)$ are shown in Figure 12.37. $\boxed{\checkmark_5}$

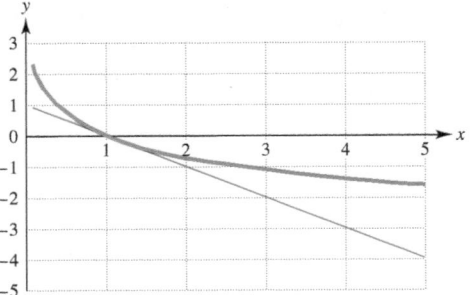

Figure 12.37

Example 7 **Business** The demand function for bumper stickers for an elementary school is given by

$$p = 9 - q^2,$$

where p is the price (in dollars) and q is the quantity demanded (in hundreds).

(a) Find the derivative of q with respect to p by implicit differentiation.

Solution

Step 1 Differentiate both sides of the equation with respect to p:

$$\frac{d}{dp}(p) = \frac{d}{dp}(9) - \frac{d}{dp}(q^2)$$

$$1 = 0 - 2q\frac{dq}{dp} \qquad \text{Chain rule: } \frac{d}{dp}(q^2) = 2q\frac{dq}{dp}$$

$$1 = -2q\frac{dq}{dp}. \qquad \text{Simplify.}$$

Step 2 Solve for $\frac{dq}{dp}$:

$$1 = -2q\frac{dq}{dp}$$

$$-\frac{1}{2q} = \frac{dq}{dp} \qquad \text{Divide both sides by } -2q.$$

$$\frac{dq}{dp} = -\frac{1}{2q}. \qquad \text{Reverse the equation.}$$

(b) Find the derivative of q with respect to p when the demand is 200 bumper stickers.

Solution Substituting $q = 2$ (since q is measured in hundreds) in $\frac{dq}{dp} = \frac{-1}{2q}$ shows that

$$\frac{dq}{dp} = -\frac{1}{2\cdot 2} = -\frac{1}{4} = -.25$$

hundred bumper stickers per dollar.

This means that when the demand is 200 bumper stickers, increasing the price by \$1 will reduce the demand by approximately 25 bumper stickers (one quarter of a hundred). ✓6

✓**Checkpoint 6**

Find $\frac{dq}{dp}$ by implicit differentiation for $p = 15 - 10q^3$.

Example 8 **Business** A baseball team finds that the relationship between the amount a (in thousands of dollars) spent on pop-up ads on a popular search engine and the amount of online sales s (in thousands of dollars) of team paraphernalia can be approximated by

$$s^2 = 125a^3 + 100.$$

(a) Find the sales when the team is spending \$1000 on advertising.

Solution Given that \$1000 is being spent on advertising ($a = 1$), we need to find the corresponding value of s. Substituting $a = 1$ into $s^2 = 125a^3 + 100$ yields

$$s^2 = 125(1)^3 + 100$$
$$s^2 = 225$$
$$s = \pm\sqrt{225}$$
$$s = \sqrt{225} \qquad \text{Sales cannot be negative.}$$
$$s = 15.$$

This means that spending \$1000 on advertising generates \$15,000 in online sales.

(b) Find the rate of change of sales with respect to advertising when the team is spending $1000 on advertising.

Solution

Step 1   Differentiate both sides of the given equation with respect to a:

$$\frac{d}{da}(s^2) = \frac{d}{da}(125a^3 + 100)$$

$$2s\left(\frac{ds}{da}\right) = 375a^2. \qquad \text{Chain rule}$$

Step 2   Substituting $a = 1$ and $s = 15$ into the last equation and solving for $\frac{ds}{da}$ yields

$$2(15)\left(\frac{ds}{da}\right) = 375(1)^2 \qquad \text{Substitute.}$$

$$30\frac{ds}{da} = 375 \qquad \text{Simplify.}$$

$$\frac{ds}{da} = 12.5. \qquad \text{Solve for } \frac{ds}{da}.$$

✓ **Checkpoint 7**

Suppose the sales function in Example 8 was given by $s^4 = 16a^3$. Find the derivative of sales with respect to advertising when $a = 1$.

Therefore, when the team is spending $1000 on advertising, spending an additional $1000 on advertising would yield approximately an additional $12,500 in online sales. ✓⁷

12.4 Exercises

Find $\frac{dy}{dx}$ by implicit differentiation. (See Examples 2–4.)

1. $x + y = 100$

2. $-15x + y = 77$

3. $x^4 + y^4 = 13$

4. $x^3 + y^5 = 97$

5. $10x^3 - 2y^5 = -6$

6. $5x^4 - 3y^2 = 1$

7. $x^2y^5 = 19$

8. $x^3y^4 = 33$

9. $5\sqrt{x} = 2\sqrt{y} + 1$

10. $3\sqrt{y} = \sqrt{x} - 49$

11. $5x^2 = 1 - e^y$

12. $5y^2 = 1 - e^x$

13. $2xe^y = 7$

14. $x^3e^y = 13$

15. $3 \ln x = 4 - \ln y$

16. $2 \ln y = 7x^6 + 5$

17. $8y \ln x = 15$

18. $7y^2 \ln x = 2$

Find $\frac{dy}{dx}$ at the given point. (See Example 5.)

19. $2x^2 - 3y^3 = 5x - 3y$ at $(0, 1)$

20. $3x^3 - 5y^2 = 10x - 5y$ at $(0, 1)$

21. $\sqrt{x^3} = \sqrt[3]{y^2}$ at $(1, 1)$

22. $\sqrt{2x - 1} = \sqrt[3]{2y - 1}$ at $(1, 1)$

23. $7x^2y^5 = 1 - x^2 - y$ at $(0, 1)$

24. $5x^6y^2 = 6 - 2x - 6y^2$ at $(0, 1)$

25. $2xe^{5y} = 2$ at $(1, 0)$

26. $x^2e^{1-y} = 1$ at $(1, 1)$

27. $x \ln y = 1$ at $(1, e)$

28. $y \ln x = 1$ at $(e, 1)$

Find the equation of the tangent line to the curve at the given point. (See Example 6.)

29. $x^2 + y^2 = 25$ at $(0, 5)$

30. $x^2 + y^2 = 9$ at $(0, -3)$

31. $y^3 = 8x^4$ at $(1, 2)$

32. $y^5 = 32x^4$ at $(1, 2)$

33. $5x - xy + y^2 = 5$ at $(1, 1)$

34. $x^3 + 3xy^2 + 3x^2y + y^3 = 8$ at $(1, 1)$

Work these exercises. (See Example 1.)

35. Consider $xe^y = 1$.

(a) Find $\frac{dy}{dx}$ by first solving the given equation explicitly for y in terms of x and then differentiating y.

(b) Find $\frac{dy}{dx}$ by implicit differentiation.

(c) Compare your answers from parts (a) and (b).

36. Consider $e^y = x$.

(a) Find $\frac{dy}{dx}$ by first solving the given equation explicitly for y in terms of x and then differentiating y.

(b) Find $\dfrac{dy}{dx}$ by implicit differentiation.

(c) Compare your answers from parts (a) and (b).

Work these exercises. (See Example 7.)

37. Business The demand for tee times at a public golf course can be approximated by

$$p = 200 - \frac{q}{2},$$

where p is the price of the greens fee (in dollars) and q is the quantity demanded. Use implicit differentiation to find $\dfrac{dq}{dp}$ when $q = 200$ and explain what your answer means in practical terms.

38. Business The demand for entry to a popular rock climbing gym can be approximated by

$$p = 25 - \frac{q}{10},$$

where p is the admission price (in dollars) and q is the quantity demanded. Use implicit differentiation to find $\dfrac{dq}{dp}$ when $q = 150$ and explain what your answer means in practical terms.

39. Business A casino hotel manager has approximated demand for two-room suites to be

$$p = 5000 - \frac{q^2}{20},$$

where p is the price (in dollars) and q is the quantity demanded. Use implicit differentiation to find and interpret $\dfrac{dq}{dp}$ when $q = 5$.

40. Business A food truck owner has approximated demand for burritos by

$$10p + 3q^2 = 75,$$

where p is the price (in dollars) and q is the quantity demanded (in hundreds). Use implicit differentiation to find and interpret $\dfrac{dq}{dp}$ when $q = 3$.

41. Business A night club has approximated the demand for their Thursday night drink special by

$$p^2 + 100q^2 = 100,$$

where p is the price (in dollars) and q is the quantity demanded (in thousands). Find and interpret $\dfrac{dq}{dp}$ when the price is \$6 and the demand is 800 drinks.

42. Business The demand to download a hit single by a certain band can be approximated by

$$100p^2 + 9q^2 = 900,$$

where p is the price (in dollars) and q is the quantity demanded (in thousands). Find and interpret $\dfrac{dq}{dp}$ when the price is \$1.80 and the demand is 8000 downloads.

Work these exercises.

43. Business For Wal-Mart Stores, Inc., the relationship between revenue R (in billions) and number of employees n (in millions) can be approximated by

$$R^2 = 18,000n^3.$$

Find $\dfrac{dR}{dn}$ when $n = 1.8$ and $R = 324$. (Data from: www. mergentonline.com.)

44. Business For the equation given in the previous exercise, find $\dfrac{dn}{dR}$ when $n = 1.8$ and $R = 324$.

45. Business For PepsiCo, Inc., the relationship between revenue R (in millions) and number of employees n (in thousands) can be approximated by

$$4R^2 = 961n^3.$$

Find $\dfrac{dR}{dn}$ when $n = 160$ and $R = 31,370$. (Data from: www. mergentonline.com.)

46. Business For the equation given in the previous exercise, find $\dfrac{dn}{dR}$ when $n = 160$ and $R = 31,370$.

47. Health The amount A of a certain drug (in mg) that remains in the blood stream t hours after taking a 100 mg tablet can be approximated by

$$Ae^{.2t} = 99.$$

Use implicit differentiation to find and interpret $\dfrac{dA}{dt}$ when $t = 12$ and $A = 9$.

48. Business At a certain online printing service, the cost y (in dollars) of purchasing x thousand business cards can be approximated by

$$xy + y = 90x.$$

Use implicit differentiation to find and interpret $\dfrac{dy}{dx}$ when $x = 1$ and $y = 45$.

✓ Checkpoint Answers

1. $\dfrac{dy}{dx} = -\dfrac{4x^3}{5y^4}$ **2.** $\dfrac{dy}{dx} = \dfrac{18xe^{9x^2}}{60y^9 + e^y}$

3. $\dfrac{dy}{dx} = -\dfrac{6y}{7x}$ **4.** $\dfrac{dy}{dx} = -7$

5. $y = 1$ **6.** $\dfrac{dq}{dp} = -\dfrac{1}{30q^2}$

7. $\dfrac{ds}{da} = 1.5$

12.5 Related Rates

In many applications, two quantities that are related to each other are also changing over time. For example, the revenue R generated by a business is related to the number of employees n the business has. Both revenue and number of employees also change over time. Therefore it makes sense to consider their derivatives with respect to time, $\frac{dR}{dt}$ and $\frac{dn}{dt}$. Since R and n are related, their rates of change $\frac{dR}{dt}$ and $\frac{dn}{dt}$ are also related. These are called **related rates.**

In general, whenever two quantities A and B vary over time and are related to each other, their derivatives $\frac{dA}{dt}$ and $\frac{dB}{dt}$ are called related rates. If we have information about A and B and one of these rates of change, we can determine how the other quantity is changing. The following box summarizes the procedure for solving related rates problems.

Related Rates Applications

1. Determine an equation that relates the two variables of interest. This equation may be given or may need to be developed from information in the problem. If the equation includes an extraneous variable (other than the two variables of interest), eliminate it using given information that holds at all times.
2. Differentiate both sides of the equation found in Step 1 with respect to time. Remember to use the chain rule since each variable is a function of time.
3. Substitute given values that hold at the particular time of interest and solve for the desired rate of change.

Example 1 **Business** For Wal-Mart Stores, Inc., the relationship between revenue R (in billions) and number of employees n (in millions) can be approximated by

$$R^2 = 18{,}000n^3.$$

In 2011, Wal-Mart Stores, Inc., generated revenue of approximately $408 billion, had 2,100,000 employees, and was adding employees at the rate of 100,000 employees per year. Find the rate of change of revenue with respect to time in 2011. (Data from: www.mergentonline.com.)

Solution Since revenue R and number of employees n are related, the derivatives $\frac{dR}{dt}$ and $\frac{dn}{dt}$ are related rates.

Step 1 We are given the relationship between R and n:

$$R^2 = 18{,}000n^3.$$

Step 2 Our goal is to find $\frac{dR}{dt}$, the rate of change of revenue with respect to time.

Differentiate both sides of the equation in Step 1 with respect to time. Remember to use the chain rule since both R and n are functions of time:

$$\frac{d}{dt}(R^2) = \frac{d}{dt}(18{,}000n^3) \qquad \text{Differentiate both sides with respect to } t.$$

$$2R\frac{dR}{dt} = 18{,}000(3n^2)\frac{dn}{dt} \qquad \text{Chain rule}$$

$$2R\frac{dR}{dt} = 54{,}000n^2\frac{dn}{dt}. \qquad \text{Simplify.}$$

Step 3 Next we substitute the given values for the year 2011. Since the revenue was $408 billion and the number of employees was 2,100,000, we know that $R = 408$ (in billions) and $n = 2.1$ (in millions). Since the company was *adding* 100,000 employees per year (or .1 million employees per year), the *rate of change* of the number of employees with respect to time was $\dfrac{dn}{dt} = .1$ (in millions per year).

Substituting these values into the equation above and solving for $\dfrac{dR}{dt}$ yields

$$2(408)\frac{dR}{dt} = 54{,}000(2.1)^2(.1) \qquad \text{Substitute.}$$

$$\frac{dR}{dt} = \frac{54{,}000(2.1)^2(.1)}{2(408)} \approx 29. \qquad \text{Solve for } \frac{dR}{dt}.$$

In 2011, the revenue for Wal-Mart Stores, Inc., was increasing at a rate of about $29 billion per year. ✔₁

✓ **Checkpoint 1**

Given that $R^3 = 25n^4$, find $\dfrac{dR}{dt}$ when $n = 5, R = 25$, and $\dfrac{dn}{dt} = 2$.

⊘ **CAUTION** In Example 1, it was important that we first differentiated both sides of the equation and then substituted in the given values for the specified time (the year 2011). It would not be accurate to first substitute the values for 2011 since these values do not hold at all times. It is easy to catch this common mistake since, if we substituted the given values first, both sides of the equation would involve only constants (no variables), so the derivative of each side would be zero.

Example 2 Suppose x and y both vary over time and are related by the equation $3x^3 + 12y = 10xy$. Find $\dfrac{dy}{dt}$ given that $x = 2, y = 3$, and $\dfrac{dx}{dt} = -4$.

Solution

Step 1 We are given the equation relating x and y:

$$3x^3 + 12y = 10xy.$$

Step 2 Since both x and y vary over time, we differentiate both sides of the given equation with respect to t. Remember to use the product rule on the right side of the equation and also to use the chain rule since both x and y are functions of time. This yields

$$\overbrace{9x^2\frac{dx}{dt} + 12\frac{dy}{dt} = (10x)\left(\frac{dy}{dt}\right) + (y)\left(10\frac{dx}{dt}\right).}^{\text{Product Rule}}$$

Chain rule

Step 3 Substitute the given values of $x = 2, y = 3$, and $\dfrac{dx}{dt} = -4$ into the equation above and then solve for the desired derivative $\dfrac{dy}{dt}$:

$$9(2)^2(-4) + 12\frac{dy}{dt} = (10(2))\left(\frac{dy}{dt}\right) + (3)(10(-4)) \qquad \text{Substitute.}$$

$$-144 + 12\frac{dy}{dt} = 20\frac{dy}{dt} - 120 \qquad \text{Simplify.}$$

$$12\frac{dy}{dt} - 20\frac{dy}{dt} = -120 + 144 \qquad \text{Isolate terms with } \frac{dy}{dt} \text{ on the left.}$$

$$-8\frac{dy}{dt} = 24 \qquad \text{Simplify.}$$

$$\frac{dy}{dt} = -\frac{24}{8} = -3. \qquad \text{Solve for } \frac{dy}{dt}. ✔₂$$

✓ **Checkpoint 2**

Given the equation in Example 2 and that $x = 2, y = 3$, and $\dfrac{dy}{dt} = -3$, find $\dfrac{dx}{dt}$.

Example 3 **Health** A cancerous tumor in the shape of a sphere is undergoing radiation treatment. The radius of the tumor is decreasing at the rate of 2 millimeters per week. How fast is the volume of the tumor changing when the radius of the tumor is 10 millimeters?

The volume (in cubic millimeters) of a sphere of radius r (in millimeters) is given by $V = \dfrac{4}{3}\pi r^3$.

Solution

Step 1   The relationship between the volume and radius of the tumor was given:

$$V = \frac{4}{3}\pi r^3.$$

Step 2   To find $\dfrac{dV}{dt}$, differentiate both sides of the given equation with respect to time (remember to use the chain rule since r is a function of time):

$$\frac{dV}{dt} = \frac{4}{3}\pi(3r^2)\frac{dr}{dt} \quad \text{Chain rule}$$

$$\frac{dV}{dt} = 4\pi r^2\frac{dr}{dt}. \quad \text{Simplify.}$$

Step 3   Substitute the given values of $r = 10$ and $\dfrac{dr}{dt} = -2$ (since the radius is decreasing by 2 mm per week) into the equation above to find that

$$\frac{dV}{dt} = 4\pi(10)^2(-2) = -800\pi \approx -2513. \quad \text{Substitute and simplify.}$$

The volume of the tumor is decreasing at a rate of about 2513 cubic millimeters per week.

Checkpoint 3

The volume (in cubic centimeters) of a cube of side length x centimeters is given by $V = x^3$. Find $\dfrac{dV}{dt}$ given that $x = 5$ cm and $\dfrac{dx}{dt} = 4$ cm per minute.

Example 4 **Social Science** A metropolitan area is approximately in the shape of a circle and the population density is roughly constant throughout. Because the metropolitan area is already densely populated, it is growing outwards in all directions to accommodate population growth of 13,000 people per year. When the radius of the metropolitan area is r miles, its population is approximated by $P = 5000\pi r^2$. Find the rate of change of the radius of the metropolitan area with respect to time when the radius is 4 miles.

Solution

Step 1   We are given the relationship $P = 5000\pi r^2$ between the population and the radius of the metropolitan area.

Step 2   To find $\dfrac{dr}{dt}$, we differentiate both sides of the given equation with respect to time:

$$\frac{dP}{dt} = 5000\pi(2r)\frac{dr}{dt} \quad \text{Chain rule}$$

$$\frac{dP}{dt} = 10{,}000\pi r\frac{dr}{dt}. \quad \text{Simplify.}$$

Step 3   Substitute the given values of $\dfrac{dP}{dt} = 13{,}000$ (since the population is increasing by 13,000 people per year) and $r = 4$ into the equation above and solve for $\dfrac{dr}{dt}$:

$$13{,}000 = 10{,}000\pi(4)\frac{dr}{dt} \quad \text{Substitute.}$$

$$\frac{dr}{dt} = \frac{13{,}000}{10{,}000\pi(4)} \approx .10 \quad \text{Solve for } \frac{dr}{dt}.$$

Checkpoint 4

The area of a circle is $A = \pi r^2$ square inches where r is the radius of the circle in inches. Find $\dfrac{dr}{dt}$ given that $r = 3$ inches and $\dfrac{dA}{dt} = 10$ square inches per minute.

The radius of the metropolitan area is growing at the rate of about .10 mile per year.

In Examples 1–4, we were given the relationship between two quantities of interest (such as revenue and number of employees). In some application problems, it is necessary to determine the relationship between two quantities using information given in the problem. The next example illustrates this.

Example 5 **Physical Science** A woman is flying a kite at a constant altitude of 120 feet. How fast is the kite traveling at the instant when 130 feet of string have already been let out and the woman is letting out the string at a rate of 10 feet per second?

Solution

Step 1 We need to determine a relationship between the variables of interest. Drawing a diagram such as the one in Figure 12.38 is often helpful.

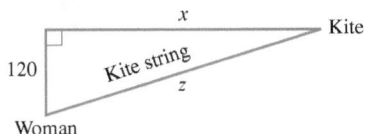

Figure 12.38

Using the Pythagorean Theorem, we see that $x^2 + 120^2 = z^2$.

Step 2 We want to find $\dfrac{dx}{dt}$, the speed of the kite (which is flying horizontally at a constant altitude). Differentiating both sides of the equation in Step 1 with respect to t yields

$$2x\frac{dx}{dt} + 0 = 2z\frac{dz}{dt} \qquad \text{Chain rule}$$

$$x\frac{dx}{dt} = z\frac{dz}{dt}. \qquad \text{Simplify.}$$

Step 3 We were given that the speed at which the string is being let out is $\dfrac{dz}{dt} = 10$ feet per second. We were also given that the length of string that has been let out is $z = 130$ feet, but we need to find the corresponding value of x. Substituting $z = 130$ into the equation $x^2 + 120^2 = z^2$ yields

$$x^2 + 120^2 = 130^2$$
$$x^2 + 14{,}400 = 16{,}900$$
$$x^2 = 16{,}900 - 14{,}400$$
$$x^2 = 2500$$
$$x = \pm\sqrt{2500}$$
$$x = 50. \qquad \text{Since } x \text{ cannot be negative.}$$

We now substitute $x = 50$, $z = 130$, and $\dfrac{dz}{dt} = 10$ into $x\dfrac{dx}{dt} = z\dfrac{dz}{dt}$, which yields

$$50\frac{dx}{dt} = 130(10) \qquad \text{Substitute.}$$

$$\frac{dx}{dt} = \frac{130(10)}{50} = 26. \qquad \text{Solve for } \frac{dx}{dt}.$$

Therefore, the kite is flying at 26 feet per second.

✓ **Checkpoint 5**

Suppose that in Example 5 the kite was flying at a constant altitude of 40 feet and the string was being let out at a rate of 6 feet per second. Find the speed of the kite when 50 feet of string have been let out.

Example 6 **Physical Science** In a certain automatic coffee maker, hot water passes through coffee grounds in a conical filter and then pours out the bottom of the cone into a coffee pot. However, the cone has become blocked so that no coffee is flowing into the coffee pot and water is rising in the filter. The shape of the filter is such that the radius of the surface of the water in the cone is always half of the height of the water in the cone. If water is entering the cone at a rate of 6 cubic centimeters per second, how fast is the height of the water rising when the height of the water is 2 cm?

Solution

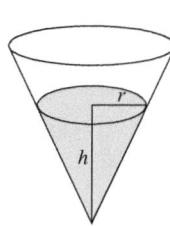

Figure 12.39

Step 1 The volume V of water in the cone (in cubic centimeters) when the radius of the surface of the water is r centimeters and the height of the water is h centimeters is

$V = \frac{1}{3}\pi r^2 h$ (see Figure 12.39). However, we need a relationship between V and h that does not involve r. We say that r is an extraneous variable and we need to eliminate r from the equation using information that holds at all times. Since we are given that the radius of the surface of the water in the cone is always half of the height of the water, we may substitute $r = \frac{1}{2}h = \frac{h}{2}$ into the equation above:

$$V = \frac{1}{3}\pi \left(\frac{h}{2}\right)^2 h = \frac{1}{3}\pi \left(\frac{h^2}{4}\right)h = \frac{1}{12}\pi h^3.$$

Step 2 Now that we have a relation between V and h, we differentiate both sides of the equation with respect to time:

$$\frac{dV}{dt} = \frac{1}{12}\pi(3h^2)\frac{dh}{dt} \quad \text{Chain rule}$$

$$\frac{dV}{dt} = \frac{1}{4}\pi h^2 \frac{dh}{dt}. \quad \text{Simplify.}$$

Step 3 Finally, we substitute the given values of $\frac{dV}{dt} = 6$ (since the volume of water entering the cone is 6 cm³ per second) and $h = 2$ into the equation above and solve for $\frac{dh}{dt}$:

$$6 = \frac{1}{4}\pi(2)^2\frac{dh}{dt} \quad \text{Substitute.}$$

$$\frac{dh}{dt} = \frac{6}{\pi} \approx 1.9. \quad \text{Solve for } \frac{dh}{dt}.$$

When the height of water in the cone is 2 cm, water is rising in the cone at a rate of about 1.9 cm per second. ✓6

✓ **Checkpoint 6**

Water is draining from a cone whose height is three times the radius. Find $\frac{dV}{dr}$ at the instant when $r = 5$ cm

and $\frac{dr}{dt} = -2$ cm per minute.

Example 7 **Business** At a local clothing store, the daily demand for a certain brand of blue jeans is given by $p = 200 - 2x$, where p is the price in dollars and x is the quantity demanded. The cost of purchasing these jeans at wholesale is $25 per pair (ignore any fixed costs). If daily demand for this brand of jeans is currently 35 pairs of jeans and declining by 2 pairs per day, how is the profit changing?

Solution

Step 1 We must determine an equation that relates profit and the quantity demanded. Since profit is the difference between revenue and cost, we must find the revenue and cost functions. The revenue generated by selling x pairs of jeans is the product of the price per item and the number of items demanded:

$$R = xp = x(200 - 2x) = 200x - 2x^2.$$

The cost of purchasing x pairs of jeans at the wholesale price of \$25 per pair is

$$C = 25x.$$

Therefore, the profit when x pairs of jeans are demanded is

$$P = R - C = (200x - 2x^2) - (25x) = 175x - 2x^2.$$

Step 2 Differentiate both sides of the equation in Step 1 with respect to time.

$$\frac{dP}{dt} = 175\frac{dx}{dt} - 4x\frac{dx}{dt}. \quad \text{Chain rule}$$

Step 3 Substitute the given values of $x = 35$ and $\dfrac{dx}{dt} = -2$ (since demand is decreasing by 2 pairs of jeans per day):

$$\frac{dP}{dt} = 175(-2) - 4(35)(-2) = -70. \quad \text{Substitute and simplify.}$$

✓**Checkpoint 7**

Suppose that in Example 7 $p = 50 - x$ and $C = 10x$. Find $\dfrac{dP}{dt}$ when $x = 15$ and $\dfrac{dx}{dt} = -1$.

This means that when the daily demand is 35 pairs of jeans and dropping at 2 pairs per day, the profit is decreasing by \$70 per day. ◢ 7

12.5 Exercises

Given that x and y are functions of time, find the indicated rate of change. (See Example 2.)

1. Find $\dfrac{dy}{dt}$ when $x = 1, y = 2,$ and $\dfrac{dx}{dt} = 3,$ given that $y^3 = 2x^4 + 6.$

2. Find $\dfrac{dx}{dt}$ when $x = 1, y = 2,$ and $\dfrac{dy}{dt} = 2,$ given that $y^3 = 2x^4 + 6.$

3. Find $\dfrac{dx}{dt}$ when $x = 0, y = 1,$ and $\dfrac{dy}{dt} = 5,$ given that $2x^5 + x = y^2 - 1.$

4. Find $\dfrac{dy}{dt}$ when $x = 0, y = 1,$ and $\dfrac{dx}{dt} = 10,$ given that $2x^5 + x = y^2 - 1.$

5. Find $\dfrac{dx}{dt}$ when $x = 2, y = 2,$ and $\dfrac{dy}{dt} = -1,$ given that $xy = x + y.$

6. Find $\dfrac{dy}{dt}$ when $x = 2, y = 2,$ and $\dfrac{dx}{dt} = 1,$ given that $xy = x + y.$

Given that x and y are functions of time, find the indicated rate of change. (See Example 5.)

7. Find $\dfrac{dy}{dt}$ when $x = 1$ and $\dfrac{dx}{dt} = -4,$ given that $x^3 + y^3 = 9.$

8. Find $\dfrac{dx}{dt}$ when $x = 1$ and $\dfrac{dy}{dt} = 1,$ given that $x^3 + y^3 = 9.$

9. Find $\dfrac{dx}{dt}$ when $y = 1$ and $\dfrac{dy}{dt} = 1,$ given that $x^3 = 9y^5 - 1.$

10. Find $\dfrac{dy}{dt}$ when $y = 1$ and $\dfrac{dx}{dt} = \dfrac{15}{4},$ given that $x^3 = 9y^5 - 1.$

Work these exercises. (See Examples 1, 3, and 4.)

11. **Business** For PepsiCo, Inc., the relationship between revenue R (in millions) and number of employees n (in thousands) can be approximated by

    $$4R^2 = 961n^3.$$

    In 2007, PepsiCo, Inc., generated revenue of \$39 billion, had 185,000 employees, and was adding employees at the rate of 13,000 employees per year. Find the rate of change of revenue with respect to time. (Data from: www.mergentonline.com.)

12. **Business** Using the equation in the previous exercise, find the rate of change of the number of employees with respect to time given that PepsiCo generated revenue of \$39 billion, had 185,000 employees, and revenue was increasing at a rate of \$4 billion per year.

13. **Social Science** During the 2012 National Football League regular season, a team's winning percentage W (wins divided by total games, expressed as a decimal) and turnover differential T (turnovers taken away minus turnovers given away) can be roughly approximated by the equation $5T - 211W = 105.$ Suppose that a team's turnover differential dropped by 2 turnovers one week. (Data from: www.nfl.com.)

    (a) Would you expect the team's winning percentage to increase or decrease?

    (b) Find the rate of change of winning percentage with respect to time.

14. **Health** A man who is 5 foot 10 inches tall is losing weight at the rate of 4 pounds per month. For a person of this height, the relationship between body mass index B and weight w (in pounds) is given by $4900B = 703w.$ Find the rate of change of body mass index with respect to time.

15. **Physical Science** A parked car dripping transmission fluid is creating a circular puddle whose area (in square inches) is $A = \pi r^2$ where r is the radius of the circle in inches. Find the rate at which the area of the puddle is increasing at the instant when the radius is 3 inches and increasing at a rate of 2 inches per minute.

16. **Business** An oil production company is concerned about an oil slick that is forming on the surface of the water in the Gulf of Mexico. The slick is roughly in the shape of a circle with area $A = \pi r^2$ square kilometers where r is the radius in kilometers. Find the rate at which the area of the oil slick is changing at the instant when the radius is 2 kilometers and increasing at .3 kilometer per day.

17. **Health** The radius of an inoperable spherical tumor is increasing by .5 millimeter per month. How fast is the volume of the tumor changing when the radius is 30 millimeters? The volume of a sphere of radius r is given by $V = \frac{4}{3}\pi r^3$.

18. **Health** An angioplasty balloon is roughly in the shape of a sphere and being inflated at 25 cubic millimeters per second. How fast is the radius of the balloon changing when the radius is 1 millimeter? The volume of a sphere of radius r is given by $V = \frac{4}{3}\pi r^3$.

Work these exercises. (See Example 5.)

19. **Social Science** At a certain point during a football game, the quarterback is standing motionless while the intended receiver is running directly downfield toward the goal line. Let z represent the distance between quarterback and receiver as measured by a straight line. The lateral distance between quarterback and receiver is constant at 6 yards. Let x represent the downfield distance between quarterback and receiver (see the accompanying figure). Find $\frac{dz}{dt}$ at the instant when $x = 8$ yards and $\frac{dx}{dt} = 3$ yards per second.

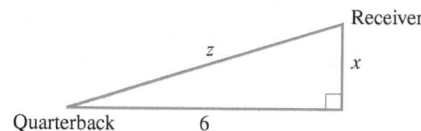

20. **Physical Science** An aircraft flying at a constant altitude of 5 miles and a constant speed of 325 mph is heading away from John F. Kennedy airport in New York. Its path is being tracked by an air traffic controller on the ground. (Ignore the height of air traffic control tower.) How fast is the distance between aircraft and air traffic controller changing at the instant when this distance is 13 miles?

21. **Business** An architectural firm must decide on the size of a scale model to present to a client. The area of the base A (in ft^2) is related to the weight of the model W (in lbs) according to the equation $W^2 = 9A^3$. If the area of the base is currently 4 ft^2 and is increased by 2 ft^2 (while keeping the model to scale), determine the corresponding change in the weight of the model.

22. **Social Science** During a six-game hitless slump early in the season, the number of hits for a certain softball player remained constant at 5. The relationship between her batting average B and number of at bats A is given by $B = \frac{5}{A}$. Determine how her batting average was changing when she had 20 at bats and went to the plate one more time and struck out.

Work these exercises. (See Example 6.)

23. **Physical Science** Sand falling through an hourglass is forming a conical pile such that the height is always twice the radius. Find $\frac{dV}{dt}$ at the instant when $r = 1$ cm and $\frac{dr}{dt} = 2$ cm per minute.

24. **Physical Science** Water from a drinking fountain is filling a paper cup. The cup is in the shape of a cone whose radius is half of its height. Find $\frac{dV}{dt}$ at the instant when $h = 2$ cm and $\frac{dh}{dt} = 4$ cm per minute.

25. **Business** A brewpub is brewing beer in a large cylindrical container with radius 3 meters. Beer is being removed from the container at a rate of 10 cubic meters per hour. Find the rate at which the height of beer in the container is changing. The volume of a cylinder is given by $V = \pi r^2 h$, where r is the radius and h is the height of the cylinder.

26. **Physical Science** The baby pool at a city park is being filled for the season at a rate of 60 cubic feet of water per minute. The pool is in the shape of a cylinder with radius 10 feet. Find the rate at which the height of the water in the pool is increasing. The volume of a cylinder is given by $V = \pi r^2 h$, where r is the radius and h is the height of the cylinder.

Work these exercises.

27. **Business** The campus bookstore has estimated that its profit (in dollars) from selling x hundred basketball conference championship t-shirts is given by

$$P = -48x^2 + 576x - 528.$$

The demand is currently 400 t-shirts, but euphoria over the championship is subsiding so the demand is dropping by 100 t-shirts per day. How is the profit changing with respect to time?

28. **Business** Following a tweet by a celebrity, hourly demand for downloading a certain ring tone is currently 9000 and increasing by 2000 downloads per hour. Determine how the profit is changing assuming that the profit (in dollars) from selling x thousand downloads is given by

$$P = -x^2 + 2000x - 50,000.$$

29. **Business** During a local political race, the demand x (in thousands) for campaign buttons is related to the price p (in dollars) by the equation

$$25p^2 + 49x^2 = 1225.$$

If the quantity demanded is currently 3000 at a price of $5.60 and demand is increasing by 400 buttons per month, find the rate of change of price with respect to time.

30. Business The cost (in hundreds of dollars) of producing x electronic readers is given by

$$C(x) = 1000 + \sqrt{2x^2 + 3x + 25}.$$

If the quantity demanded is currently 50,000 and increasing by 1000 per month, find the rate of change of cost with respect to time.

31. Social Science The home ownership rate H (as a percent) in the United States is approximately related to the violent crime rate C (number of violent crimes per 100,000 population) according to the equation $C = 600{,}000e^{-.105H}$. In a certain year, home ownership was 68.8% and decreasing by .1% per year. How was the violent crime rate changing at that time? (Data from: Bureau of Justice Statistics and Federal Reserve Economic Data.)

32. Finance The personal savings rate (savings as a percent of disposable personal income) P is approximately related to the unemployment rate U according to the equation

$$2.9 \ln(U) = P + 1.5.$$

In 2010, unemployment was at 9.6% and decreasing by .7% per year. Find the rate of change of the personal savings rate with respect to time. (Data from: Federal Reserve Economic Data.)

✓**Checkpoint Answers**

1. About 13.33

2. $\dfrac{dx}{dt} = -4$

3. $300 \text{ cm}^3/\text{min}$

4. About .53 inch per minute

5. 10 feet per second

6. About $-471.2 \text{ cm}^3/\text{min}$

7. $-\$10$ per day

12.6 Curve Sketching

In earlier sections, we saw that the first and second derivatives of a function provide a variety of information about the graph of the function, such as the location of its local extrema, the concavity of the graph, and the intervals on which it is increasing and decreasing. This information can be very helpful for interpreting misleading screen images on a graphing calculator or computer. It also enables us to make reasonably accurate graphs of many functions by hand if graphing technology is not available.

When graphing functions by hand, you should use the following guidelines. It may not always be feasible to carry out all the steps, but you should do as many as necessary, in any convenient order, to obtain a reasonable graph.

To sketch the graph of a function $y = f(x)$, execute the following steps:

1. Find the y-intercept (if it exists) by letting $x = 0$ and computing $y = f(0)$.

2. Find the x-intercepts (if any) by letting $y = 0$ and solving the equation $f(x) = 0$ if doing so is not too difficult.

3. If f is a rational function, find any vertical asymptotes by finding the numbers for which the denominator is 0, but the numerator is nonzero. Find any horizontal asymptotes by using the techniques of Section 3.6, as summarized in the box on page 172.

4. Find $f'(x)$ and $f''(x)$.

5. Locate any critical numbers by solving the equation $f'(x) = 0$ and determining where $f'(x)$ does not exist, but $f(x)$ does. Find the local extrema by using the first- or second-derivative test. Find the intervals where f is increasing or decreasing by solving the inequalities $f'(x) > 0$ and $f'(x) < 0$.

6. Locate potential points of inflection by solving the equation $f''(x) = 0$ and determining where $f''(x)$ does not exist, but $f(x)$ does. Find the intervals where f is concave upward or downward by solving the inequalities $f''(x) > 0$ and $f''(x) < 0$. Use this information to determine the points of inflection.

7. Use the preceding results and any other information that may be available to determine the general shape of the graph.

(*continued*)

8. Plot the intercepts, critical points, points of inflection, and other points as needed. Connect the points with a smooth curve, using correct concavity and being careful not to draw a connected graph through points where the function is not defined.

9. If feasible, verify your results with a graphing calculator or computer. If there are significant differences between your graph and the calculator's, check for mistakes in the hand-drawn graph or adjust the calculator viewing window appropriately.

Example 1   Graph $f(x) = 2x^3 - 3x^2 - 12x + 1$.

Solution

Step 1   The y-intercept is $f(0) = 2 \cdot 0^3 - 3 \cdot 0^2 - 12 \cdot 0 + 1 = 1$.

Step 2   To find the x-intercepts, we must solve the equation

$$2x^3 - 3x^2 - 12x + 1 = 0.$$

There is no easy way to do this by hand, so skip this step. Since $f(x)$ is a polynomial function, the graph has no asymptotes, so we can also skip Step 3.

Step 4   The first derivative is $f'(x) = 6x^2 - 6x - 12$, and the second derivative is $f''(x) = 12x - 6$.

Step 5   The first derivative is defined for all x, so the only critical numbers are the solutions of $f'(x) = 0$:

$$6x^2 - 6x - 12 = 0$$
$$x^2 - x - 2 = 0 \quad \text{Divide both sides by 6.}$$
$$(x + 1)(x - 2) = 0 \quad \text{Factor.}$$
$$x = -1 \quad \text{or} \quad x = 2.$$

Using the second-derivative test on the critical number $x = -1$, we have

$$f''(-1) = 12(-1) - 6 = -18 < 0.$$

Hence, there is a local maximum when $x = -1$, that is, at the point $(-1, f(-1)) = (-1, 8)$. Similarly,

$$f''(2) = 12(2) - 6 = 18 > 0,$$

so there is a local minimum when $x = 2$ (at the point $(2, f(2)) = (2, -19)$).

Next, we determine the intervals on which f is increasing or decreasing by solving the inequalities

$$f'(x) > 0 \qquad \text{and} \qquad f'(x) < 0$$
$$6x^2 - 6x - 12 > 0 \qquad \qquad 6x^2 - 6x - 12 < 0.$$

The critical numbers divide the x-axis into three regions. Testing a number from each region, as indicated in Figure 12.40, we conclude that f is increasing on the intervals $(-\infty, -1)$ and $(2, \infty)$ and decreasing on $(-1, 2)$.

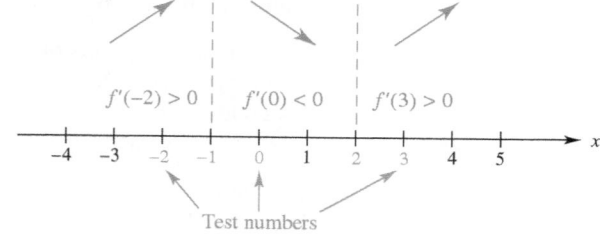

Figure 12.40

Step 6 The second derivative is defined for all x, so the possible points of inflection are determined by the solutions of $f''(x) = 0$:

$$12x - 6 = 0$$

$$x = \frac{1}{2}.$$

Determine the concavity of the graph by solving

$$f''(x) > 0 \qquad \text{and} \qquad f''(x) < 0$$

$$12x - 6 > 0 \qquad\qquad 12x - 6 < 0$$

$$x > \frac{1}{2} \qquad\qquad x < \frac{1}{2}.$$

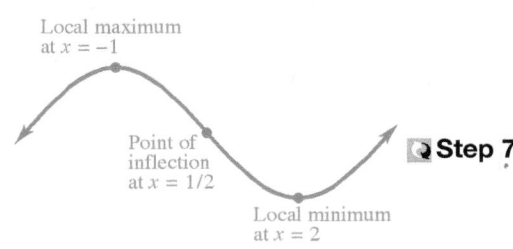

Local maximum
at $x = -1$

Point of
inflection
at $x = 1/2$

Local minimum
at $x = 2$

Figure 12.41

Therefore, f is concave upward on the interval $(\frac{1}{2}, \infty)$ and concave downward on $(-\infty, \frac{1}{2})$. Consequently, the only point of inflection is $(\frac{1}{2}, f(\frac{1}{2})) = (\frac{1}{2}, -5.5)$.

Step 7 Since f is a third-degree polynomial function, we know from Section 3.6 that when x is very large in absolute value, its graph must resemble the graph of its highest-degree term, $2x^3$; that is, the graph must rise sharply on the right side and fall sharply on the left. Combining this fact with the information obtained in the preceding steps, we see that the graph of f must have the general shape shown in Figure 12.41.

Step 8 Now we plot the points determined in Steps 1, 5, and 6, together with a few additional points, to obtain the graph in Figure 12.42.

Checkpoint 1

Step 9 Use technology to verify that the graph in Figure 12.42 is correct.

Checkpoint 2

Sketch the graph of

$$f(x) = x^3 - 3x^2.$$

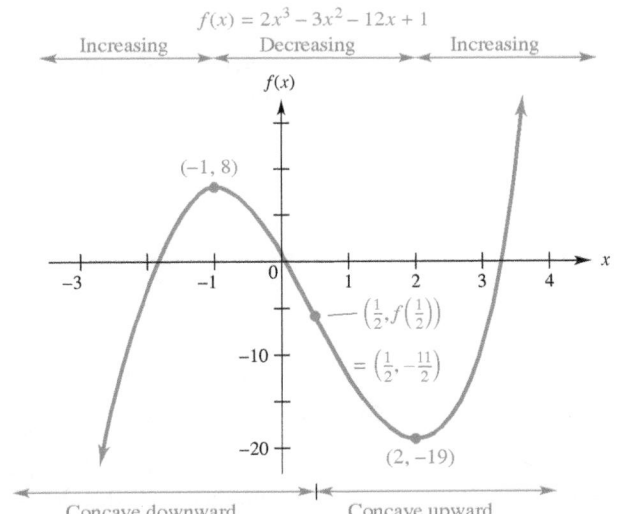

Figure 12.42

Example 2   Graph

$$f(x) = \frac{3x^2}{x^2 + 5}.$$

Solution

Step 1 The y-intercept is $f(0) = 0/5 = 0$.

Step 2 To find the x-intercepts, note that $f(x)$ is always defined, because $x^2 + 5$ is always positive. Hence, $f(x) = 0$ when the numerator $3x^2 = 0$; this occurs when $x = 0$. So the point $(0, f(0)) = (0, 0)$ is both the x- and y-intercept.

⚟ Step 3   This is a rational function, but its denominator is always nonzero (why?), so there are no vertical asymptotes. Using the techniques presented in Section 3.7, we see that

$$f(x) = \frac{3x^2}{x^2 + 5} = \frac{\dfrac{3x^2}{x^2}}{\dfrac{x^2}{x^2} + \dfrac{5}{x^2}} = \frac{3}{1 + \dfrac{5}{x^2}}.$$

When x is very large in absolute value, so is x^2; thus, $5/x^2$ is very close to 0, and hence $f(x)$ is very close to $3/(1 + 0) = 3$. Consequently, the horizontal line $y = 3$ is a horizontal asymptote.

Step 4   The first derivative is

$$f'(x) = \frac{(x^2 + 5)(6x) - (3x^2)(2x)}{(x^2 + 5)^2} = \frac{30x}{(x^2 + 5)^2}.$$

The second derivative is

$$f''(x) = \frac{(x^2 + 5)^2\, 30 - (30x)(2)(x^2 + 5)(2x)}{(x^2 + 5)^4}.$$

Factor $30(x^2 + 5)$ out of the numerator:

$$f''(x) = \frac{30(x^2 + 5)[(x^2 + 5) - (x)(2)(2x)]}{(x^2 + 5)^4}.$$

Divide a factor of $(x^2 + 5)$, out of the numerator and denominator and simplify the numerator:

$$f''(x) = \frac{30[(x^2 + 5) - (x)(2)(2x)]}{(x^2 + 5)^3}$$

$$= \frac{30[(x^2 + 5) - 4x^2]}{(x^2 + 5)^3}$$

$$= \frac{30(5 - 3x^2)}{(x^2 + 5)^3}.$$

Step 5   Since $f'(x) = \dfrac{30x}{(x^2 + 5)^2}$ and $x^2 + 5 \neq 0$ for all x, $f'(x)$ is always defined. $f'(x) = 0$ when its numerator, $30x$, is 0; this occurs when $x = 0$. The critical number 0 divides the x-axis into two regions (Figure 12.43). Testing a number in each region shows that f is decreasing on $(-\infty, 0)$ and increasing on $(0, \infty)$. By the first-derivative test, f has a local minimum at $x = 0$.

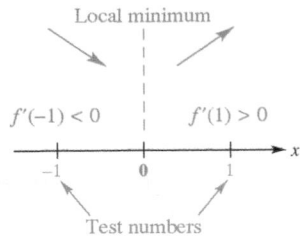

Local minimum

$f'(-1) < 0$ $f'(1) > 0$

-1 0 1 x

Test numbers

Figure 12.43

Step 6   Since $f''(x) = \dfrac{30(5 - 3x^2)}{(x^2 + 5)^3}$ and $x^2 + 5 \neq 0$ for all x, $f''(x)$ is always defined. $f''(x) = 0$ when

$$30(5 - 3x^2) = 0$$
$$3x^2 = 5$$
$$x = \pm\sqrt{5/3} \approx \pm 1.29.$$

Testing a point in each of the three intervals defined by these points shows that f is concave downward on $(-\infty, -1.29)$ and $(1.29, \infty)$ and concave upward on $(-1.29, 1.29)$. The graph has inflection points at $(\pm\sqrt{5/3}, f(\pm\sqrt{5/3})) \approx (\pm 1.29, .75)$.

Step 7 The information about the shape of the graph obtained in Steps 5 and 6 is summarized in the following chart:

Interval	$(-\infty, -1.29)$	$(-1.29, 0)$	$(0, 1.29)$	$(1.29, \infty)$
Sign of f'	$-$	$-$	$+$	$+$
Sign of f''	$-$	$+$	$+$	$-$
f Increasing or Decreasing	Decreasing	Decreasing	Increasing	Increasing
Concavity of f	Downward	Upward	Upward	Downward
Shape of Graph	$\frown\!\!\searrow$	$\smile$	$\smile$	$\frown$

Step 8 Plot some points (several are needed near the origin), including the intercept at the origin, and use the fact that $y = 3$ is a horizontal asymptote to obtain the graph in Figure 12.44. ☑ 3

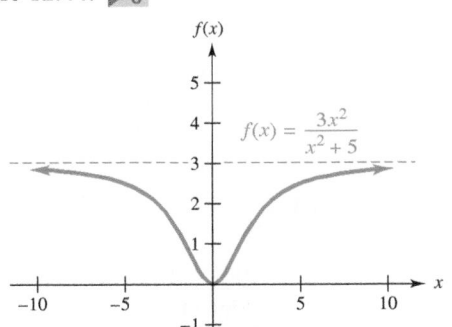

Figure 12.44

✓ Checkpoint 3 ↗

Step 9 Use technology to verify that the graph in Figure 12.44 is correct.

Example 3   Graph $f(x) = x + 1/x$.

Solution

Step 1 Since $x = 0$ is not in the domain of the function (why?), there is no y-intercept.

Step 2 To find the x-intercepts, solve $f(x) = 0$:

$$x + \frac{1}{x} = 0$$

$$x = -\frac{1}{x}$$

$$x^2 = -1.$$

Since x^2 is never negative, there is also no x-intercept.

Step 3 Note that the rule of f can be written as

$$f(x) = x + \frac{1}{x} = \frac{x^2 + 1}{x}.$$

When $x = 0$, the denominator is 0, but the numerator is nonzero, so there is a vertical asymptote at $x = 0$. Since the numerator of $f(x)$ is of a higher degree than the denominator, there is no horizontal asymptote.

Step 4 Because $f(x) = x + 1/x = x + x^{-1}$, we have

$$f'(x) = 1 - x^{-2} = 1 - \frac{1}{x^2},$$

so

$$f''(x) = 2x^{-3} = \frac{2}{x^3}.$$

Step 5 $f'(x) = 0$ when

$$\frac{1}{x^2} = 1$$
$$x^2 = 1$$
$$x = 1 \quad \text{or} \quad x = -1.$$

Hence, $x = -1$ and $x = 1$ are critical numbers. The derivative does not exist when $x = 0$, but the function is not defined there either, so $x = 0$ is not a critical number. Evaluating $f'(x)$ in each of the regions determined by the critical numbers and the asymptote shows that f is increasing on $(-\infty, -1)$ and $(1, \infty)$ and decreasing on $(-1, 0)$ and $(0, 1)$, as summarized in the chart in Step 7. By the first-derivative test, f has a relative maximum of $y = f(-1) = -2$ when $x = -1$ and a relative minimum of $y = f(1) = 2$ when $x = 1$.

Step 6 The second derivative $f''(x) = 2/x^3$ is never equal to 0 and does not exist when $x = 0$. (The function itself also does not exist at 0.) Because of this, there may be a change in concavity, but not an inflection point, when $x = 0$. The second derivative is negative when x is negative, making f concave downward on $(-\infty, 0)$. Also, $f''(x) > 0$ when $x > 0$, making f concave upward on $(0, \infty)$, as indicated in the chart in Step 7.

Step 7 The preceding information is summarized in the following chart:

Interval	$(-\infty, -1)$	$(-1, 0)$	$(0, 1)$	$(1, \infty)$
Sign of f'	+	−	−	+
Sign of f''	−	−	+	+
f Increasing or Decreasing	Increasing	Decreasing	Decreasing	Increasing
Concavity of f	Downward	Downward	Upward	Upward
Shape of Graph	⌢	⌢	⌣	⌣

We can determine the shape of the graph when x is very large in absolute value by noting that as x gets very large, the second term of its rule, $1/x$, gets very small, so that $f(x) = x + 1/x \approx x$. Hence, the graph gets closer and closer to the straight line $y = x$ as x becomes larger and larger. The line $y = x$ is called an **oblique**, or **slant asymptote**.

Step 8 Plot several points and use the preceding information to obtain the graph of $f(x)$ in Figure 12.45.

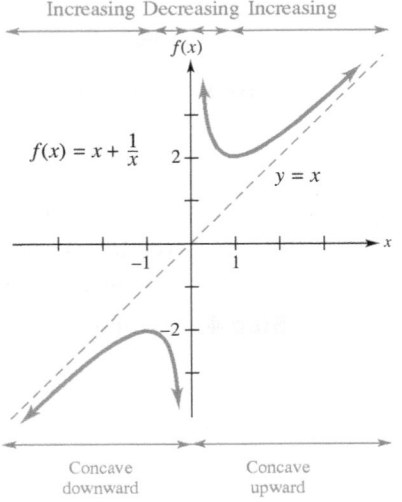

✓ **Checkpoint 4**

Step 9 Use technology to verify that the graph in Figure 12.45 is correct.

Figure 12.45

12.6 Exercises

Sketch the graph of the function. Identify any local extrema and points of inflection. (See Examples 1–3.)

1. $f(x) = -x^2 - 10x - 25$ 2. $f(x) = x^2 - 12x + 36$

3. $f(x) = 3x^3 - 3x^2 + 1$ 4. $f(x) = 2x^3 - 4x^2 + 2$

5. $f(x) = -2x^3 - 9x^2 + 108x - 10$

6. $f(x) = -2x^3 - 9x^2 + 60x - 8$

7. $f(x) = 2x^3 + \dfrac{7}{2}x^2 - 5x + 3$

8. $f(x) = x^3 - \dfrac{15}{2}x^2 - 18x - 1$

9. $f(x) = (x + 3)^4$ 10. $f(x) = x^3$

11. $f(x) = x^4 - 18x^2 + 5$ 12. $f(x) = x^4 - 8x^2$

13. $f(x) = x - \dfrac{1}{x}$ 14. $f(x) = 2x + \dfrac{8}{x}$

15. $f(x) = \dfrac{x^2 + 25}{x}$ 16. $f(x) = \dfrac{x^2 + 4}{x}$

17. $f(x) = \dfrac{x - 1}{x + 1}$ 18. $f(x) = \dfrac{x}{1 + x}$

Sketch the graph of the function. Identify any local extrema and inflection points.

19. $y = x - \ln|x|$

20. $y = \dfrac{\ln x}{x}$

21. $y = xe^{-x}$

22. $f(x) = xe^{-\frac{x}{2}}$

 In Exercises 23–28, sketch the graph of a function f that has all of the properties listed. There are many correct answers, and your graph need not be given by an algebraic formula.

23. (a) The domain of f is $[0, 10]$.
    (b) $f'(x) > 0$ and $f''(x) > 0$ for all x in the domain of f.

24. (a) The domain of f is $[0, 10]$.
    (b) $f'(x) > 0$ and $f''(x) < 0$ for all x in the domain of f.

25. (a) Continuous and differentiable for all real numbers
    (b) Increasing on $(-\infty, -3)$ and $(1, 4)$
    (c) Decreasing on $(-3, 1)$ and $(4, \infty)$
    (d) Concave downward on $(-\infty, -1)$ and $(2, \infty)$
    (e) Concave upward on $(-1, 2)$
    (f) $f'(-3) = f'(4) = 0$
    (g) Inflection points at $(-1, 3)$ and $(2, 4)$

26. (a) Continuous for all real numbers
    (b) Increasing on $(-\infty, -2)$ and $(0, 3)$
    (c) Decreasing on $(-2, 0)$ and $(3, \infty)$
    (d) Concave downward on $(-\infty, 0)$ and $(0, 5)$
    (e) Concave upward on $(5, \infty)$
    (f) $f'(-2) = f'(3) = 0$

27. (a) Continuous for all real numbers
    (b) Decreasing on $(-\infty, -6)$ and $(1, 3)$
    (c) Increasing on $(-6, 1)$ and $(3, \infty)$
    (d) Concave upward on $(-\infty, -6)$ and $(3, \infty)$
    (e) Concave downward on $(-6, 3)$
    (f) y-intercept at $(0, 2)$

28. (a) Continuous and differentiable everywhere except at $x = -1$, where it has a vertical asymptote
    (b) Decreasing everywhere it is defined
    (c) Concave downward on $(-\infty, -1)$ and $(1, 2)$
    (d) Concave upward on $(-1, 1)$ and $(2, \infty)$

Work these exercises.

29. **Business** The accompanying figure shows the *product life cycle* graph, with typical products marked on it. It illustrates the fact that a new product is often purchased at a faster and faster rate as people become familiar with it. In time, saturation is reached and the purchase rate stays constant until the product is made obsolete by newer products, after which it is purchased less and less often. (Data from: www.tutor2u.net/business/marketing/products_lifecycle.asp.)

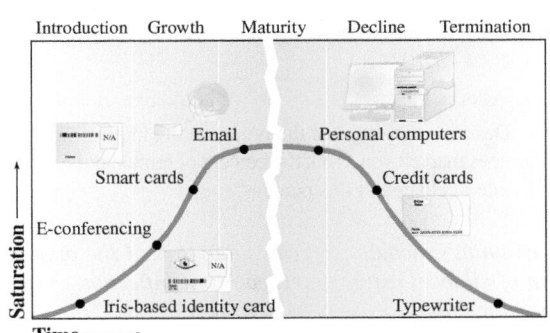

Which product on the left side of the graph is closest to the left-hand point of inflection? What does the point of inflection mean here?

30. Refer to the graph in Exercise 29. Which product on the right side of the graph is closest to the right-hand point of inflection? What does the point of inflection mean here?

31. **Business** The revenue function (in millions of dollars) for Priceline.com, Inc., can be approximated by

    $$R(x) = 57x^2 - 396x + 1448 \qquad (0 \le x \le 11),$$

    where $x = 0$ corresponds to the year 2000. Find the location of all local extrema and points of inflection. (Data from: www.morningstar.com.)

32. **Business** The cost function (in millions of dollars) for Priceline.com, Inc., can be approximated by

    $$C(x) = 16x^2 - 150x + 1060 \qquad (0 \le x \le 11),$$

    where $x = 0$ corresponds to the year 2000. Find the location of all local extrema and points of inflection. (Data from: www.morningstar.com.)

33. **Social Science** The percent of the population registered to vote in the presidential election among those who are 18 and over and whose educational attainment is a bachelor's degree or higher can be approximated by

$$V(x) = \frac{315}{x^{0.3}} \quad (72 \le x \le 112),$$

where $x = 72$ corresponds to the year 1972. (Data from: www.census.gov.)

   (a) Approximately what percent of this population was registered to vote in 1972? 2012?

   (b) What is the sign of the first derivative over the 40-year period 1972–2012?

   (c) What is the sign of the second derivative over this period?

   (d) Describe the shape of the graph on the interval (72, 112). What does that tell you about voter registration and the rate of change of voter registration among this population?

34. **Health** The percent of female graduates in health fields can be approximated by

$$H(x) = 78.9x^{.016} \quad (1 \le x \le 10),$$

where $x = 1$ corresponds to the year 2001. (Data from: www.worldbank.org.)

   (a) Approximately what percent of graduates in health fields were female in 2001? 2010?

   (b) What is the sign of the first derivative over the period 2001–2010?

   (c) What is the sign of the second derivative over this period?

   (d) Describe the shape of the graph on the interval (1, 10). What does that tell you about the percent of female graduates and the rate of change of this percent?

Use a graphing calculator or computer to find the approximate location of all local extrema and points of inflection of the given revenue functions.

35. **Business** The revenue (in millions of dollars) for Lifepoint Hospitals, Inc., can be approximated by

$$R(x) = -7x^3 + 110x^2 - 143x + 580 \quad (0 \le x \le 11),$$

where $x = 0$ corresponds to the year 2000. (Data from: www.morningstar.com.)

36. **Business** The revenue (in billions of dollars) for Southwest Airlines, Inc., can be approximated by

$$R(x) = .073x^3 - 1.57x^2 + 11.66x - 20 \quad (4 \le x \le 11),$$

where $x = 4$ corresponds to the year 2004. (Data from: www.morningstar.com.)

37. **Business** The revenue (in millions of dollars) for Coca-Cola Bottling Company Consolidated can be approximated by

$$R(x) = .7x^4 - 21.1x^3 + 222.3x^2 - 917x + 2503 \quad (3 \le x \le 12),$$

where $x = 3$ corresponds to the year 2003. (Data from: www.morningstar.com.)

38. **Business** The revenue (in millions of dollars) for Dream-Works Animation SKG, Inc., can be approximated by

$$R(x) = 5.37x^4 - 176.76x^3 + 2115x^2 - 10,817x + 20,436 \quad (4 \le x \le 11),$$

where $x = 4$ corresponds to the year 2004. (Data from: www.morningstar.com.)

39. **Business** The revenue (in billions of dollars) for J. C. Penney Company, Inc., is approximated by

$$R(x) = -.0432x^4 + .8586x^3 - 5.226x^2 + 7.58x + 31.4 \quad (0 \le x \le 9),$$

where $x = 0$ corresponds to the year 2000. (Data from: www.morningstar.com.)

40. **Business** The revenue (in billions of dollars) for Polo Ralph Lauren Corporation is approximated by

$$R(x) = -.0046x^3 + .090x^2 - .101x + 2.1 \quad (0 \le x \le 9).$$

where $x = 0$ corresponds to the year 2000. (Data from: www.morningstar.com.)

Use a graphing calculator or computer to find the approximate location of all local extrema and points of inflection of the given functions.

41. **Physical Science** The pressure of the oil in a reservoir tends to drop with time. By taking sample pressure readings for a particular oil reservoir, petroleum engineers have found that the change in pressure is given by

$$P(t) = t^3 - 18t^2 + 81t \quad (0 \le t \le 15),$$

where t is time in years from the date of the first reading.

42. **Health** The cost–benefit curve for pollution control is given by

$$y = \frac{9.2x}{106 - x} \quad (0 < x \le 100),$$

where y is the cost, in thousands of dollars, or removing x percent of a specified industrial pollutant.

43. **Social Science** The enrollment (in millions) in U.S. public high schools is modeled by

$$g(x) = -.000039x^4 + .002393x^3 - .03311x^2 - .0845x + 14.3 \quad (0 \le x \le 35),$$

where $x = 0$ corresponds to the year 1975. (Data from: U.S. Center for Educational Statistics.)

44. **Health** The function

$$f(x) = .000000143x^4 + .0000178x^3 - .00145x^2 - .9279x + 77.8 \quad (0 \le x \le 100)$$

gives a person's average remaining life expectancy (in years), where x is the current age (in years). (Data from: National Center for Health Statistics.)

✓ Checkpoint Answers

1.

2.

3.

4.

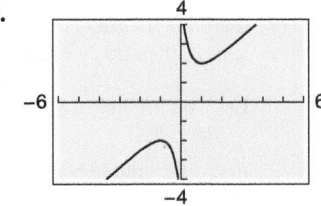

CHAPTER 12 Summary and Review

Key Terms and Symbols

12.1 increasing function on an interval
decreasing function on an interval
critical number
critical point
local maximum (maxima)
local minimum (minima)
local extremum (extrema)
first-derivative test

12.2 $f''(x)$ or y'' or $\dfrac{d^2y}{dx^2}$ or $D_x^2[f(x)]$, second derivative of f
$f'''(x)$, third derivative of f
$f^{(n)}(x)$, nth derivative of f
acceleration
concave upward

concave downward
point of inflection
point of diminishing returns
second-derivative test

12.3 absolute maximum on an interval
absolute minimum on an interval
extreme-value theorem

critical-point theorem
economic lot size

12.4 implicitly defined function
implicit differentiation

12.5 related rates

12.6 curve sketching
oblique asymptote

Chapter 12 Key Concepts

Increasing and Decreasing Functions   If $f'(x) > 0$ for each x in an interval, then f is **increasing** on the interval; if $f'(x) < 0$ for each x in the interval, then f is **decreasing** on the interval; if $f'(x) = 0$ for each x in the interval, then f is **constant** on the interval.

Critical Numbers   If f is a function, then a number c for which $f(c)$ is defined and either $f'(c) = 0$ or $f'(c)$ does not exist is called a crucial number of f. The corresponding point $(c, f(c))$ on the graph of f is called a critical point.

Local Extrema   Let c be a number in the domain of a function f. Then f has a **local maximum** at c if $f(x) \le f(c)$ for all x near c, and f has a **local minimum** at c if $f(x) \ge f(c)$ for all x near c. If f has a local extremum at c, then c is a critical number of f.

First-Derivative Test   Let f be a differentiable function for all x in $[a, b]$, except possibly at $x = c$. Assume that $a < c < b$ and that c is the only critical number for f in $[a, b]$. If $f'(a) > 0$ and $f'(b) < 0$, then there is a local maximum at c. If $f'(a) < 0$ and $f'(b) > 0$, then there is a local minimum at c.

Concavity   Let f have derivatives f' and f'' for all x in (a, b). Then f is **concave upward** on (a, b) if $f''(x) > 0$ for all x in (a, b), f is **concave downward** on (a, b) if $f''(x) < 0$ for all x in (a, b), and f has a **point of inflection** at $x = c$ if $f''(x)$ changes sign at $x = c$.

Second-Derivative Test   Let c be a critical number of f such that $f'(c) = 0$ and $f''(x)$ exists for all x in some open interval containing c. If $f''(c) > 0$, then there is a local minimum at c. If $f''(c) < 0$, then there is a local maximum at c. If $f''(c) = 0$, then the test gives no information.

Absolute Extrema	Let c be in an interval $[a, b]$ where f is defined. Then f has an **absolute maximum** on the interval at c if $f(x) \le f(c)$ for all x in $[a, b]$, and f has an **absolute minimum** on the interval at c if $f(x) \ge f(c)$ for all x in $[a, b]$.
Extreme-Value Theorem	If a function f is continuous on a closed interval $[a, b]$, then f has both an absolute maximum and an absolute minimum on the interval. Each of these values occurs either at an endpoint of the interval or at a critical number of f.
Critical-Point Theorem	Suppose that a function f is continuous on an interval I (which may be open, closed, or neither) and that f has exactly one critical number in the interval I, say, $x = c$. If f has a local maximum at $x = c$, then this local maximum is the absolute maximum of f on the interval I. If f has a local minimum at $x = c$, then this local minimum is the absolute minimum of f on the interval I.
Implicit Differentiation	Let y be implicitly defined as a function of x by a given equation. To find $\dfrac{dy}{dx}$ by implicit differentiation, first differentiate both sides of the equation with respect to x, then solve for $\dfrac{dy}{dx}$.
Related Rates	To solve a related rates problem, first determine an equation that relates only the two variables of interest. Next, differentiate both sides of the equation with respect to time. Finally, substitute the given values, and solve for the desired rate of change.

Chapter 12 Review Exercises

1. When the rule of a function is given, how can you determine where it is increasing and where it is decreasing?

2. When the rule of a function is given, how can you determine where the local extrema are located? State two algebraic ways to test whether a local extremum is a maximum or a minimum.

3. What is the difference between a local extremum and an absolute extremum? Can a local extremum be an absolute extremum? Is a local extremum necessarily an absolute extremum?

4. What information about a graph can be found from the first derivative? from the second derivative?

Find the largest open intervals on which the given functions are increasing or decreasing.

5. $f(x) = x^2 + 9x - 9$

6. $f(x) = -3x^2 - 3x + 11$

7. $g(x) = 2x^3 - x^2 - 4x + 7$

8. $g(x) = -4x^3 - 5x^2 + 8x + 1$

9. $f(x) = \dfrac{4}{x - 4}$

10. $f(x) = \dfrac{-6}{3x - 5}$

Find the locations and the values of all local maxima and minima for the given functions.

11. $f(x) = 2x^3 - 3x^2 - 36x + 10$

12. $f(x) = 2x^3 - 3x^2 - 12x + 2$

13. $f(x) = x^4 - \dfrac{8}{3}x^3 - 6x^2 + 2$

14. $f(x) = x \cdot e^x$

15. $f(x) = 3x \cdot e^{-x}$

16. $f(x) = \dfrac{e^x}{x - 1}$

Find the second derivatives of the given functions; then find $f''(1)$ and $f''(-2)$.

17. $f(x) = 2x^5 - 5x^3 + 3x - 1$

18. $f(x) = \dfrac{3 - 2x}{x + 3}$

19. $f(x) = -5e^{2x}$ 20. $f(x) = \ln|5x + 2|$

Sketch the graph of each of the given functions. List the location of each local extremum and point of inflection, the intervals on which the function is increasing and decreasing, and the intervals on which it is concave upward and concave downward.

21. $f(x) = -2x^3 - \dfrac{1}{2}x^2 - x - 3$

22. $f(x) = -\dfrac{4}{3}x^3 + x^2 + 30x - 7$

23. $f(x) = x^4 - \dfrac{4}{3}x^3 - 4x^2 + 1$

24. $f(x) = -\dfrac{2}{3}x^3 + \dfrac{9}{2}x^2 + 5x + 1$

25. $f(x) = \dfrac{x - 1}{2x + 1}$ 26. $f(x) = \dfrac{2x - 5}{x + 3}$

27. $f(x) = -4x^3 - x^2 + 4x + 5$

28. $f(x) = x^3 + \dfrac{5}{2}x^2 - 2x - 3$

29. $f(x) = x^4 + 2x^2$ 30. $f(x) = 6x^3 - x^4$

31. $f(x) = \dfrac{x^2 + 4}{x}$ 32. $f(x) = x + \dfrac{8}{x}$

Find the locations and values of all absolute maxima and absolute minima for the given functions on the given intervals.

33. $f(x) = -x^2 + 6x + 1;\ [2, 4]$

34. $f(x) = 4x^2 - 4x - 7;\ [-1, 3]$

35. $f(x) = x^3 + 2x^2 - 15x + 3; [-.5, 3.3]$

36. $f(x) = -2x^3 - x^2 + 4x - 1; [-3, 1]$

If possible, find an absolute extremum of each function on the given interval.

37. $g(x) = x^3 + 6x^2 - 15x + 1; (0, 9)$

38. $g(x) = x^3 + 6x^2 - 15x + 1; (-9, 0)$

39. $g(x) = xe^{-x/3}; (-\infty, \infty)$

40. $g(x) = -5xe^{-2x}; (-\infty, \infty)$

Find $\dfrac{dy}{dx}$ by implicit differentiation.

41. $10xy = 2x + 5y$ 　　　**42.** $12xy = 4y + 3x$

43. $ye^x - 10x = y$ 　　　**44.** $5ye^x + x^2 = -10y$

Find the equation of the tangent line to the curve at the given point.

45. $5 - y^3 = 6 - 2x^6$ at $(1, 1)$

46. $5 - y^2 = 6 - 2x^4$ at $(1, 1)$

Work these exercises. You may need the quadratic formula to find some of the critical numbers.

47. Finance The federal funds rate (as a percent) is shown in the accompanying figure (as recorded on January 1 of each year). Is the federal funds rate increasing or decreasing in the following year? (Data from: www.federalreserve.gov.)

(a) 2002 　　　 (b) 2006 　　　 (c) 2008

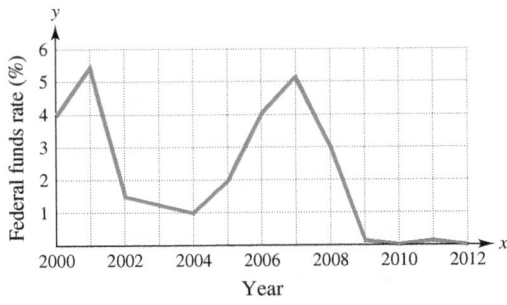

48. Business The graph approximates the revenue (in billions of dollars) for the Walt Disney Company for the period 2007–2011. (Data from: www.morningstar.com.)

(a) In what year does it appear there is a local minimum?

(b) In what year does it appear there is a local maximum?

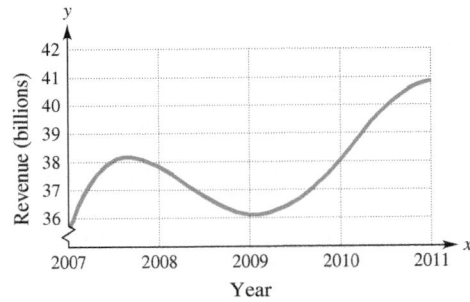

49. Social Science The population of Arizona (in millions) is projected to be

$$f(x) = 5.18e^{.024x} \quad (0 \le x \le 30),$$

where $x = 0$ corresponds to the year 2000. (Data from: www.census.gov.)

(a) Is the population of Arizona projected to increase or decrease through 2030?

(b) Determine whether the graph of this population function is concave up or concave down and explain what that means for Arizona.

50. Social Science The gold medal height (in meters) in the women's Olympic high jump can be approximated by

$$f(x) = 39 \ln x + .21 \quad (28 \le x \le 112),$$

where $x = 28$ corresponds to the year 1928. (Data from: www.olympic.org.)

(a) According to this model, is the winning height increasing or decreasing during this period?

(b) Determine whether the graph of the winning height is concave up or concave down and explain what that means about the high jump.

51. Social Science The number of women in the United States Senate can be approximated by

$$f(x) = .012x^2 - 1.75x + 63.85 \quad (59 \le x \le 111),$$

where $x = 59$ corresponds to the year 1959. (Data from: womenincongress.house.gov.)

(a) What was the number of female senators in 1959? 2011?

(b) What was the absolute minimum number of female senators during this period? The absolute maximum?

52. Business The percent (by volume) of all beer sales made up of craft beers (by small and independent breweries) can be modeled by

$$f(x) = .08x^2 - x + 7 \quad (7 \le x \le 11),$$

where $x = 7$ corresponds to the year 2007. (Data from: Brewers Association.)

(a) What percent of beer sales did craft beers capture in 2007? 2011?

(b) What was the absolute minimum percent during this period? The absolute maximum?

53. Business The profit (in millions of U.S. dollars) generated by the German footwear corporation Adidas can be approximated by

$$f(x) = -4x^3 + 81x^2 - 78x + 2528 \quad (0 \le x \le 11),$$

where $x = 0$ corresponds to the year 2000. What was the absolute maximum profit for Adidas during this period? The absolute minimum profit? (Data from: www.morningstar.com.)

54. Health The number of children and youth (in thousands) with speech or language impairments served under the Individuals with Disabilities Education Act can be approximated by

$$f(x) = -.46x^3 + 3.5x^2 + 7.1x + 1089 \quad (0 \le x \le 9),$$

where $x = 0$ corresponds to the year 2000. What was the absolute maximum number of children and youth served for these impairments during this period? The absolute minimum number? (Data from: The Statistical Abstract of the United States: 2012.)

55. **Finance** The price of JPMorgan Chase & Co. stock over a 16-week period in 2012 can be approximated by the function

$$f(x) = .029x^3 - .8x^2 + 5.3x + 35.3,$$

where $x = 1$ designates the beginning of week 1. (Data from: www.morningstar.com.)

   (a) When is this stock decreasing in price during this period?

   (b) Find all local extrema of the stock price during this period.

56. **Finance** The price of The Goldman Sachs Group, Inc., stock over a 32-week period in 2012 can be approximated by the function

$$f(x) = .012x^3 - .64x^2 + 8.9x + 84,$$

where $x = 1$ designates the beginning of week 1. (Data from: www.morningstar.com.)

   (a) When is this stock decreasing in price during this period?

   (b) Find all local extrema of the stock price during this period.

57. **Social Science** Long-term unemployment (expressed as a percent of the total unemployed) can be approximated by

$$f(x) = .0293x^4 - .46x^3 + 2x^2 - x + 6 \quad (0 \le x \le 10),$$

where $x = 0$ corresponds to the year 2000. What was the absolute maximum percent of long-term unemployment during this period? The absolute minimum percent? (Data from: www.worldbank.org.)

58. **Social Science** The lending interest rate (as a percent) charged by banks on loans to prime customers can be modeled by

$$f(x) = .00542x^5 - .127x^4 + .953x^3 - 2.24x^2 - .64x + 9.23$$
$$(0 \le x \le 10),$$

where $x = 0$ corresponds to the year 2000. What was the absolute maximum lending rate during this period? The absolute minimum? (Data from: www.worldbank.org.)

Work these exercises.

59. **Business** A landscaper needs to design an enclosed rectangular garden with one side against an existing garage, with no fence needed there. Find the dimensions of the rectangular space of maximum area that can be enclosed with 500 meters of fence.

60. **Business** If the garden described in the previous exercise needs fencing on all four sides, find the dimensions of the maximum rectangular area that can be made with 500 meters of fence.

61. **Business** The packaging department of a corporation is designing a box with a square base and top. The volume is to be 27 cubic meters. To reduce the cost, the surface area of the box is to be minimized. What dimensions (height, length, and width) should the box have?

62. **Business** A company plans to package its product in a cylinder that is open at one end. The cylinder is to have a volume of 27π cubic inches. What radius should the circular bottom of the cylinder have in order to minimize the cost of the material?

(*Hint*: The volume of a circular cylinder is $\pi r^2 h$, where r is the radius of the circular base and h is the height; the surface area of an open cylinder is $2\pi rh + \pi r^2$.)

63. **Business** A cell phone manufacturer produces 145,000 phones a year. It costs \$3.25 to store each phone for one year and \$230 to produce each batch. Find the number of batches that should be produced annually.

64. **Business** How many phones need to be produced for each batch in the previous exercise?

65. **Business** A chocolate maker has annual demand of 250,000 pounds per year. It costs \$1.25 to store a pound of chocolate for a year and \$350 to produce a batch. Find the number of batches to be produced annually.

66. How many pounds should be produced for each batch in the previous exercise?

Find the indicated rate of change.

67. Find $\dfrac{dx}{dt}$ when $x = 0$, $y = 1$, and $\dfrac{dy}{dt} = 5$, given that $2x^5 + x = y^2 - 1$.

68. Find $\dfrac{dy}{dt}$ when $x = 0$, $y = 1$, and $\dfrac{dx}{dt} = 10$, given that $2x^5 + x = y^2 - 1$.

Work these exercises.

69. **Natural Science** The relationship between temperature F measured in degrees Fahrenheit and temperature C measured in degrees Celsius is given by $F = \dfrac{9}{5}C + 32$.

   (a) If the temperature in Fahrenheit is dropping by 4 degrees per hour $\left(\dfrac{dF}{dt} = -4\right)$, find $\dfrac{dC}{dt}$, the rate of change of temperature in degrees Celsius per hour.

   (b) If the temperature in Celsius is rising by 3 degrees per hour $\left(\dfrac{dC}{dt} = 3\right)$, find $\dfrac{dF}{dt}$, the rate of change of temperature in degrees Fahrenheit per hour.

70. **Health** A personal trainer instructs clients interested in high-intensity cardiac training to workout at 80% of their maximum heart rate. This desired heart rate H (in beats per minute) is related to age A (in years) according to the formula $4A + 5H = 880$. As a client becomes one year older, how much should her desired heart rate change?

71. **Business** Suppose that the daily profit (in dollars) from selling x large cups of latte at the Crestwood Coffee Company can be approximated by $P = -\dfrac{x^2}{360} + 6x - 300$. At the start of final exams, the demand is $x = 450$ cups and increasing at a rate of $\dfrac{dx}{dt} = 90$ cups per day. Find $\dfrac{dP}{dt}$ at the start of final exams.

72. **Business** The demand x for cold bottles of water from a street vendor outside a sports stadium can be approximated by $3x + 160p^2 = 1440$, where p is the price in dollars. If the street

vendor increases the price from $2.00 per bottle to $2.50 per bottle, how would she expect the demand to change?

73. **Social Science**   A woman rowing a single skull is racing at 221 meters per minute in a straight line. A spectator is watching from shore, 10 meters in a perpendicular direction from the path of the competitor. How fast is the distance between the spectator and competitor changing at the instant when this distance is 26 meters?

74. **Social Science**   A baseball player hits the ball and runs toward first base. Let x represent the distance in feet between the player and first base and z represent the distance in feet between the player and second base (measured by a straight line, not by the path the player must run). Find $\dfrac{dz}{dt}$ at the instant when $x = 45, z = 45\sqrt{5}$, and $\dfrac{dx}{dt} = -9$ ft/sec. Note that a baseball diamond is a square that is 90 feet on each side.

Case Study 12 A Total Cost Model for a Training Program*

In this application, we set up a mathematical model for determining the total cost required to set up a training program. Then we use calculus to find the time interval between training programs that produces the minimum total cost. The model assumes that the demand for trainees is constant and that the fixed cost of training a batch of trainees is known. Also, it is assumed that people who are trained, but for whom no job is readily available, will be paid a fixed amount per month while waiting for a job to open up.

The model uses the following variables:

D = demand for trainees per month;

N = number of trainees per batch;

C_1 = fixed cost of training a batch of trainees;

C_2 = variable cost of training per trainee per month;

C_3 = salary paid monthly to a trainee who has not yet been given a job after training;

m = time interval in months between successive batches of trainees;

t = length of training program in months;

$Z(m)$ = total monthly cost of program.

The total cost of training a batch of trainees is given by $C_1 + NtC_2$. However, $N = mD$, so that the total cost per batch is $C_1 + mDtC_2$.

After training, personnel are given jobs at the rate of D per month. Thus, $N - D$ of the trainees will not get a job the first month, $N - 2D$ will not get a job the second month, and so on. The $N - D$ trainees who do not get a job the first month produce total costs of $(N - D)C_3$, those not getting jobs during the second month produce costs of $(N - 2D)C_3$, and so on. Since $N = mD$, the costs during the first month can be written as

$$(N - D)C_3 = (mD - D)C_3 = (m - 1)DC_3,$$

while the costs during the second month are $(m - 2)DC_3$, and so on. The total cost for keeping the trainees without a job is thus

$$(m - 1)DC_3 + (m - 2)DC_3$$
$$+ (m - 3)DC_3 + \cdots + 2DC_3 + DC_3,$$

which can be factored to give

$$DC_3[(m - 1) + (m - 2) + (m - 3) + \cdots + 2 + 1].$$

The expression in brackets is the sum of the terms of an arithmetic sequence discussed in most algebra texts. Using formulas for arithmetic sequences, we can show that the expression in brackets is equal to $m(m - 1)/2$, so we have

$$DC_3\left[\frac{m(m - 1)}{2}\right] \tag{1}$$

as the total cost for keeping jobless trainees.

The total cost per batch is the sum of the training cost per batch, $C_1 + mDtC_2$, and the cost of keeping trainees without a proper job, given by equation (1). Since we assume that a batch of trainees is trained every m months, the total cost per month, $Z(m)$, is given by

$$Z(m) = \frac{C_1 + mDtC_2}{m} + \frac{DC_3\left[\dfrac{m(m - 1)}{2}\right]}{m}$$
$$= \frac{C_1}{m} + DtC_2 + DC_3\left(\frac{m - 1}{2}\right).$$

Exercises

1. Find $Z'(m)$.

2. Solve the equation $Z'(m) = 0$. As a practical matter, it is usually required that m be a positive integer. If m does not come out to be an integer, then m^+ and m^-, the two integers closest to m, must be chosen. Calculate both $Z(m^+)$ and $Z(m^-)$; the smaller of the two provides the optimum value of Z.

3. Suppose a company finds that its demand for trainees is three per month, that a training program requires 12 months, that the fixed cost of training a batch of trainees is $15,000, that the marginal cost per trainee per month is $100, and that trainees are paid $900 per month after training, but before going to work. Use your result from Exercise 2 to find m.

4. Since m is not an integer, find m^+ and m^-.

5. Calculate $Z(m^+)$ and $Z(m^-)$.

6. What is the optimum time interval between successive batches of trainees? How many trainees should be in a batch?

*Based on "A Total Cost Model for a Training Program," by P. L. Goyal and S. K. Goyal, Faculty of Commerce and Administration, Concordia University. Used with permission.

Extended Project

A pharmaceutical company is planning to gradually expand its service area over the next year and needs to hire and train new sales representatives. The company is considering two options for training programs. The first option is to bring new employees from various sales regions to the company headquarters for an intensive two-week training program with top company experts. This option is expensive due to travel and lodging costs. The second option involves online training through the use of webinars. Although this option avoids travel expenses, the same level of intensity is not possible and the training requires four weeks to be effective. The details for the two options are below.

	On-site Training	Online Training
D	4	4
C_1	6000	6000
C_2	3500	2000
C_3	3000	3000
t	.5	1

(a) For the on-site training option, what is the optimum time interval between successive batches of trainees? How many trainees should be in a batch? What is the total monthly cost of this training program?

(b) Repeat part (a) for the online training option.

(c) Your employer has asked you to write a report summarizing your findings about the cost of the two training options over the next year, and to make and justify a recommendation about which program to select.

Integral Calculus

13

CHAPTER

CHAPTER OUTLINE

Social scientists use integral calculus to estimate the total population size from a rate-of-growth function. Natural scientists use similar techniques to approximate the growth of animal populations. In business and finance, integrals are used to find total revenue from marginal revenue functions. Integral calculus is also used to determine the point where profitability fails for a company. See Example 10 on page 752, Exercises 3 and 23 on page 793, and Exercise 38 on page 806.

The derivative and its applications, which were studied in Chapters 11 and 12, are part of what is called *differential calculus.* This chapter is devoted to the other main branch of calculus, *integral calculus.* Integrals are used to find areas, to determine the lengths of curved paths, to solve complicated probability problems, to calculate the location of an object (such as the height of a space shuttle) from its velocity, and in a variety of other ways. Such topics may seem quite different from those studied earlier, but the fundamental theorem of calculus in Section 13.4 will reveal a surprisingly close connection between differential and integral calculus.

13.1 Antiderivatives

Functions used in applications in previous chapters have provided information about the *total amount* of a quantity, such as cost, revenue, profit, temperature, gallons of oil, or distance. Derivatives of these functions provided information about the rate of change of

745

these quantities and allowed us to answer important questions about the extrema of the functions. It is not always possible to find ready-made functions that provide information about the total amount of a quantity, but it is often possible to collect enough data to come up with a function that gives the *rate of change* of a quantity. We know that derivatives give the rate of change when the total amount is known. In this section, we shall see that this process can be reversed: When the rate of change is known, a function that gives the total amount can be obtained by a process called *antidifferentiation*. Here is the basic definition.

Antiderivatives

If $F(x)$ and $f(x)$ are functions such that $F'(x) = f(x)$, then $F(x)$ is said to be an **anti-derivative** of $f(x)$.

Example 1

(a) If $F(x) = 10x$, then $F'(x) = 10$, so $F(x) = 10x$ is an antiderivative of $f(x) = 10$.

(b) For $F(x) = x^5$, $F'(x) = 5x^4$, which means that $F(x) = x^5$ is an antiderivative of $f(x) = 5x^4$.

Example 2   Find an antiderivative of $f(x) = 2x$.

Solution   By remembering formulas for derivatives, it is easy to see that $F(x) = x^2$ is an antiderivative of $f(x)$ because $F'(x) = 2x = f(x)$. Note that $G(x) = x^2 + 2$ and $H(x) = x^2 - 4$ are also antiderivatives of $f(x)$, because

$$G'(x) = 2x + 0 = f(x) \quad \text{and} \quad H'(x) = 2x - 0 = f(x).$$

Any two of the antiderivatives of $f(x) = 2x$ that were found in Example 2 differ by a constant. For instance, $G(x) - F(x) = 2$ and $H(x) - G(x) = -6$. The same thing is true in the general case.

✓ Checkpoint 1

Find an antiderivative for each of the given expressions.

(a) $3x^2$

(b) $5x$

(c) $8x^7$

Answers to Checkpoint exercises are found at the end of the section.

If $F(x)$ and $G(x)$ are both antiderivatives of $f(x)$, then there is a constant C such that

$$F(x) - G(x) = C.$$

(Two antiderivatives of a function can differ only by a constant.)

The statement in the box reflects a geometric fact about derivatives, namely, that the derivative of a function gives the slope of the tangent line at any number x. For example, if you graph the three antiderivatives of $f(x) = 2x$ found in Example 2, you will see that the graphs all have the same shape because, at any x-value, their tangent lines all have the same slope, as shown in Figure 13.1.

The family of all antiderivatives of the function f is indicated by

$$\int f(x)\, dx.$$

The symbol $\int$ is the **integral sign,** $f(x)$ is the **integrand,** and $\int f(x)\, dx$ is called an **indefinite integral.** Since any two antiderivatives of $f(x)$ differ by a constant (which means that one is a constant plus the other), we can describe the indefinite integral as follows.

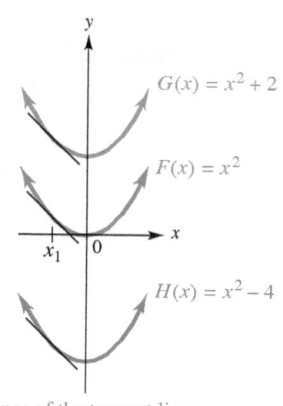

Slopes of the tangent lines at $x = x_1$ are the same.

Figure 13.1

Indefinite Integral

If $F'(x) = f(x)$, then

$$\int f(x)\, dx = F(x) + C,$$

for any real number C.

For example, with this notation,

$$\int 2x\, dx = x^2 + C.$$

NOTE The dx in the indefinite integral $\int f(x)\, dx$ indicates that x is the variable of the function whose antiderivative is to be found, in the same way that dy/dx denotes the derivative when y is a function of the variable x. For example, in the indefinite integral $\int 2ax\, dx$, the variable of the function is x, whereas in the indefinite integral $\int 2ax\, da$, the variable is a.

The symbol $\int f(x)\, dx$ was created by G. W. Leibniz (1646–1716) in the latter part of the 17th century. The $\int$ is an elongated S from *summa*, the Latin word for *sum*. The word *integral* as a term in calculus was coined by Jakob Bernoulli (1654–1705), a Swiss mathematician who corresponded frequently with Leibniz. The relationship between sums and integrals will be clarified in Section 13.3.

Because finding an antiderivative is the inverse of finding a derivative, each formula for derivatives leads to a rule for antiderivatives. For instance, the power rule for derivatives tells us that

$$\text{if } F(x) = x^4, \qquad \text{then } F'(x) = 4x^3.$$

Consequently,

$$\text{if } F(x) = \frac{1}{4}x^4, \qquad \text{then } F'(x) = \frac{1}{4}(4x^3) = x^3.$$

In other words, an antiderivative of $f(x) = x^3$ is $F(x) = \frac{1}{4}x^4$. Similarly,

$$\text{if } G(x) = \tfrac{1}{8}x^8, \text{ then } G'(x) = \tfrac{1}{8}(8x^7) = x^7,$$

so $G(x) = \frac{1}{8}x^8$ is an antiderivative of $g(x) = x^7$. The same pattern holds in the general case: To find the antiderivative of x^n, increase the exponent by 1 and divide by that same number.

Power Rule for Antiderivatives

For any real number $n \neq -1$,

$$\int x^n\, dx = \frac{1}{n+1}x^{n+1} + C.$$

This result can be verified by differentiating the expression on the right in the box:

$$\frac{d}{dx}\left(\frac{1}{n+1}x^{n+1} + C\right) = \frac{n+1}{n+1}x^{(n+1)-1} + 0 = x^n.$$

748   **CHAPTER 13** Integral Calculus

(If $n = -1$, the expression in the denominator is 0, and the power rule cannot be used. We will see later how to find an antiderivative in this case.)

> **Example 3** Find each antiderivative.
>
> **(a)** $\int x^5\, dx$
>
> **Solution** Use the power rule with $n = 5$:
>
> $$\int x^5 dx = \frac{1}{5+1}x^{5+1} + C = \frac{1}{6}x^6 + C.$$
>
> **(b)** $\int \frac{1}{t^2}\, dt$
>
> **Solution** First, write $1/t^2$ as t^{-2}. Then
>
> $$\int \frac{1}{t^2}\, dt = \int t^{-2}\, dt = \frac{1}{-2+1}t^{-2+1} = \frac{t^{-1}}{-1} + C = \frac{-1}{t} + C.$$
>
> **(c)** $\int \sqrt{u}\, du$
>
> **Solution** Since $\sqrt{u} = u^{1/2}$,
>
> $$\int \sqrt{u}\, du = \int u^{1/2}du = \frac{1}{1/2+1}u^{1/2+1} + C = \frac{1}{3/2}u^{3/2} + C = \frac{2}{3}u^{3/2} + C.$$
>
> To check this result, differentiate $(2/3)u^{3/2} + C$; the derivative is $u^{1/2}$, the original function.
>
> **(d)** $\int dx$
>
> **Solution** Writing dx as $1 \cdot dx$, and using the fact that $x^0 = 1$ for any nonzero number x, we obtain
>
> $$\int dx = \int 1\, dx = \int x^0 dx = \frac{1}{1}x^1 + C = x + C.$$

✓**Checkpoint 2**

Find each of the following.

(a) $\int x^6\, dx$

(b) $\int \sqrt[4]{x}\, dx$

(c) $\int 8\, dx$

As shown in Chapter 11, the derivative of the product of a constant and a function is the product of the constant and the derivative of the function. A similar rule applies to antiderivatives. Also, since derivatives of sums and differences are found term by term, antiderivatives can also be found term by term.

Properties of Antiderivatives

Let $f(x)$ and $g(x)$ be functions that have antiderivatives and let k be any real number.

Constant-multiple rule: $\int k \cdot f(x)\, dx = k\int f(x)\, dx.$

Sum-or-difference rule: $\int [f(x) \pm g(x)]\, dx = \int f(x)\, dx \pm \int g(x)\, dx.$

⚠ **CAUTION** The constant-multiple rule requires that k be a *number*. The rule does not apply to a *variable*. For example,

$$\int x\sqrt{x-1}\, dx \neq x\int \sqrt{x-1}\, dx.$$

Example 4   Find each of the given antiderivatives.

(a) $\int 4x^7\, dx$

Solution   By the constant-multiple rule and the power rule,

$$\int 4x^7 = 4\int x^7\, dx = 4\left(\frac{1}{8}x^8\right) + C = \frac{1}{2}x^8 + C.$$

Since C represents any real number, it is not necessary to multiply it by 4 in the next-to-last step.

(b) $\int \frac{10}{z^6}\, dz$

Solution   Convert to negative exponents and use the constant-multiple rule and the power rule:

$$\int \frac{10}{z^6}\, dz = \int 10z^{-6}\, dz$$

$$= 10\int z^{-6}\, dz \qquad \text{Constant-multiple rule}$$

$$= 10\left(\frac{z^{-5}}{-5}\right) + C \qquad \text{Power rule}$$

$$= \frac{-2}{z^5} + C.$$

(c) $\int (5y^2 - 6y + 2)\, dy$

By extending the sum-or-difference rule to more than two terms, we get

$$\int (5y^2 - 6y + 2)\, dy = \int 5y^2\, dy - \int 6y\, dy + \int 2\, dy$$

$$= 5\int y^2\, dy - 6\int y\, dy + 2\int dy$$

$$= 5\left(\frac{y^3}{3}\right) - 6\left(\frac{y^2}{2}\right) + 2y + C$$

$$= \frac{5}{3}y^3 - 3y^2 + 2y + C.$$

✓ **Checkpoint 3**

Find each of the following.

(a) $\int (-6x^8)\, dx$

(b) $\int 7x^{2/3}\, dx$

(c) $\int \frac{5}{x^3}\, dx$

(d) $\int (5x^4 - 3x^2 + 8)\, dx$

(e) $\int \left(4\sqrt[3]{x} + \frac{2}{x^2}\right) dx$

Only one constant C is needed in the answer, because the three constants from the term-by-term antiderivatives are combined. ✓₃

The nice thing about working with antiderivatives is that you can always check your work by taking the derivative of the result. For instance, in Example 4(c), check that $\frac{5}{3}y^3 - 3y^2 + 2y + C$ is the required antiderivative by taking the derivative:

$$\frac{d}{dy}\left(\frac{5}{3}y^3 - 3y^2 + 2y + C\right) = 5y^2 - 6y + 2.$$

The result is the original function to be integrated, so the work checks out.

Example 5   Find each of the given antiderivatives.

(a) $\int \dfrac{x^2 + 1}{\sqrt{x}}\, dx$

Solution   First rewrite the integrand as follows:

$$\int \frac{x^2 + 1}{\sqrt{x}}\, dx = \int \left(\frac{x^2}{\sqrt{x}} + \frac{1}{\sqrt{x}} \right) dx$$

$$= \int \left(\frac{x^2}{x^{1/2}} + \frac{1}{x^{1/2}} \right) dx$$

$$= \int \left(x^{3/2} + x^{-1/2} \right) dx. \qquad \text{Quotient rule for exponents}$$

Now find the antiderivative:

$$\int \left(x^{3/2} + x^{-1/2} \right) dx = \int x^{3/2}\, dx + \int x^{-1/2}\, dx$$

$$= \frac{x^{5/2}}{5/2} + \frac{x^{1/2}}{1/2} + C$$

$$= \frac{2}{5}x^{5/2} + 2x^{1/2} + C.$$

(b) $\int (x^2 - 1)^2\, dx$

Solution   Square the integrand first and then find the antiderivative.

$$\int (x^2 - 1)^2\, dx = \int (x^4 - 2x^2 + 1)\, dx$$

$$= \int x^4\, dx - \int 2x^2\, dx + \int 1\, dx$$

$$= \frac{x^5}{5} - \frac{2x^3}{3} + x + C \quad \checkmark_4$$

✓ **Checkpoint 4**

Find each of the following.

(a) $\int \dfrac{\sqrt{x} + 1}{x^2}\, dx$

(b) $\int (\sqrt{x} + 2)^2\, dx$

As shown in Chapter 11, the derivative of $f(x) = e^x$ is $f'(x) = e^x$. Also, the derivative of $f(x) = e^{kx}$ is $f'(x) = k \cdot e^{kx}$. These results lead to the following formulas for antiderivatives of exponential functions.

Antiderivatives of Exponential Functions

If k is a real number, $k \neq 0$, then

$$\int e^x\, dx = e^x + C;$$

$$\int e^{kx}\, dx = \frac{1}{k} \cdot e^{kx} + C.$$

Example 6   Here are some antiderivatives of exponential functions:

(a) $\int 8e^x\, dx = 8 \int e^x\, dx = 8e^x + C;$

(b) $\int e^{8t}\,dt = \dfrac{1}{8}e^{8t} + C;$

(c) $\int 3e^{(5/6)u}\,du = 3\left(\dfrac{1}{5/6}e^{(5/6)u}\right) + C = 3\left(\dfrac{6}{5}\right)e^{(5/6)u} + C$

$$= \dfrac{18}{5}e^{(5/6)u} + C.\ \checkmark_5$$

✓ Checkpoint 5

Find each of the following.

(a) $\int (-7e^x)\,dx$

(b) $\int e^{5x}\,dx$

(c) $\int (e^{4x} - 4e^x)\,dx$

(d) $\int (-11e^{-x})\,dx$

The antiderivative formula $\int x^n\,dx = \dfrac{x^{n+1}}{n+1} + C$ does not hold when $n = -1$, because the denominator is 0 in that case. Nevertheless, the function $g(x) = x^{-1}$ does have an antiderivative. Recall that the derivative of $f(x) = \ln|x|$ is $f'(x) = 1/x = x^{-1}$.

Antiderivative of x^{-1}

$$\int x^{-1}\,dx = \int \dfrac{1}{x}\,dx = \ln|x| + C, \qquad \text{where } x \neq 0.$$

CAUTION The domain of the logarithmic function is the set of positive real numbers. However, $y = x^{-1} = 1/x$ has the set of all nonzero real numbers as its domain, so the absolute value of x *must* be used in the antiderivative.

Example 7   Here are some antiderivatives involving logarithmic functions:

(a) $\int \dfrac{4}{x}\,dx = 4\int \dfrac{1}{x}\,dx = 4\cdot\ln|x| + C;$

(b) $\int \left(-\dfrac{5}{x} + e^{-2x}\right)dx = -5\cdot\ln|x| - \dfrac{1}{2}e^{-2x} + C.\ \checkmark_6$

✓ Checkpoint 6

Find each of the following.

(a) $\int (-9/x)\,dx$

(b) $\int (8e^{4x} - 3x^{-1})\,dx$

Applications

In the preceding examples, a family of antiderivative functions was found. In many applications, however, the given information allows us to determine the value of the constant C. The next three examples illustrate this idea.

Example 8   **Business**   The rate of increase in the number of cell phone subscriptions worldwide (in millions per year) can be approximated by

$$S'(x) = 56x + 166,$$

where $x = 0$ corresponds to the year 2000. There were 5960 million cell phone subscriptions worldwide in 2011. Find the function $S(x)$ that gives the number of subscribers (in millions) in year x. (Data from: www.worldbank.org.)

Solution   Since $S'(x)$ gives the rate of change of subscribers, the number of subscribers is given by

$$S(x) = \int (56x + 166)\,dx$$

$$= \dfrac{56}{2}x^2 + 166x + C$$

$$= 28x^2 + 166x + C.$$

To find the value of C, use the fact that in 2011 ($x = 11$) there were 5960 million subscribers, which says that $S(11) = 5960$. This information gives an equation that can be solved for C:

$$S(x) = 28x^2 + 166x + C$$
$$S(11) = 28(11)^2 + 166(11) + C$$
$$5960 = 28(11)^2 + 166(11) + C$$
$$5960 = 5214 + C$$
$$C = 746.$$

Thus, the number of subscribers in year x is

$$S(x) = 28x^2 + 166x + 746. \quad ☑_7$$

 Checkpoint 7

Find $S(x)$ given that
$S'(x) = 7x + 3$ and $S(4) = 76$.

Example 9 **Business** Suppose the marginal revenue from selling x units of a product is given by $40/e^{.05x} + 10$.

(a) Find the revenue function.

Solution The marginal revenue is the derivative of the revenue function, so

$$\frac{dR}{dx} = \frac{40}{e^{.05x}} + 10$$

$$R = \int \left(\frac{40}{e^{.05x}} + 10 \right) dx = \int (40e^{-.05x} + 10)\, dx$$

$$= 40 \left(\frac{-1}{.05} \right) e^{-.05x} + 10x + C = -800e^{-.05x} + 10x + C,$$

where C is a constant. If $x = 0$, then $R = 0$ (no items sold means no revenue), and

$$0 = -800e^0 + 10(0) + C$$
$$800 = C.$$

Thus,

$$R = -800e^{-.05x} + 10x + 800$$

is the revenue function.

(b) Find the demand function for this product.

Solution Recall that $R = xp$, where p is the demand function. Hence,

$$-800e^{-.05x} + 10x + 800 = xp$$
$$\frac{-800e^{-.05x} + 10x + 800}{x} = p.$$

Checkpoint 8

The marginal cost at a level of production of x items is

$$C'(x) = 2x^3 + 6x - 5.$$

The fixed cost is $800. Find the cost function $C(x)$.

The demand function is $p = \dfrac{-800e^{-.05x} + 10x + 800}{x}.$ ☑_8

Example 10 **Social Science** The population of the Southern region of the United States was 100.6 million in 2000. Its growth rate (in millions per year) is approximated by

$$f(t) = 1.3078e^{.013t},$$

where $t = 0$ corresponds to the year 2000. (Data from: www.census.gov.)

(a) Find the function $F(t)$ that gives the population (in millions) in year t.

Solution   The derivative of the population function $F(t)$ is the rate at which the population is growing, namely $F'(t) = f(t) = 1.3078e^{.013t}$. Therefore,

$$F(t) = \int 1.3078e^{.013t}dt = 1.3078\left(\frac{1}{.013}\right)e^{.013t} + C = 100.6e^{.013t} + C.$$

✓**Checkpoint 9**

Suppose a population growth rate (in millions per year) is given by $f(t) = 5e^{.04t}$ and that the population is 125 million in the year $t = 0$.

(a) Find the population function $F(t)$ in millions.

(b) Find the population in year $t = 10$.

Since the population was 100.6 million in 2000 (that is, when $t = 0$), we have

$$100.6 = F(0) = 100.6e^{.013(0)} + C = 100.6e^0 + C = 100.6 + C,$$

so that $C = 0$. Therefore, the population function is $F(t) = 100.6e^{.013t}$.

(b) What is the population projected to be in the year 2018?

Solution   Since 2018 corresponds to $t = 18$, the population is projected to be

$$F(18) = 100.6e^{.013(18)} = 100.6e^{.234} \approx 127.1 \text{ million.}$$ ✓9

13.1 Exercises

1. What must be true of $F(x)$ and $G(x)$ if both are antiderivatives of $f(x)$?

2. How is the antiderivative of a function related to the function?

3. In your own words, describe what is meant by an integrand.

4. Explain why the restriction $n \neq -1$ is necessary in the rule

$$\int x^n \, dx = \frac{1}{n+1}x^{n+1} + C.$$

Find each of the given antiderivatives. (See Examples 3–7.)

5. $\int 12x \, dx$

6. $\int 25r^2 dr$

7. $\int 8p^3 dp$

8. $\int 5t^5 dt$

9. $\int 105 \, dx$

10. $\int 35 dt$

11. $\int (5z - 1) \, dz$

12. $\int (2m^2 + 3) \, dm$

13. $\int (z^2 - 4z + 6) \, dz$

14. $\int (2y^2 + 10y + 7) \, dy$

15. $\int (x^3 - 14x^2 + 22x + 8) \, dx$

16. $\int (5x^3 + 5x^2 - 10x - 6) \, dx$

17. $\int 6\sqrt{y} \, dy$

18. $\int 8z^{1/2} \, dz$

19. $\int (6t\sqrt{t} + 3\sqrt[4]{t}) \, dt$

20. $\int (12\sqrt{x} - x\sqrt{x}) \, dx$

21. $\int (56t^{1/2} + 18t^{7/2}) \, dt$

22. $\int (10u^{3/2} - 8u^{5/2}) \, du$

23. $\int \frac{24}{x^3} \, dx$

24. $\int \frac{-20}{x^2} \, dx$

25. $\int \left(\frac{1}{y^3} - \frac{2}{\sqrt{y}}\right) dy$

26. $\int \left(\frac{3 + 2u}{\sqrt{u}}\right) du$

27. $\int (6x^{-3} + 2x^{-1}) \, dx$

28. $\int (3x^{-1} - 10x^{-2}) \, dx$

29. $\int 4e^{3u} \, du$

30. $\int -e^{-3x} \, dx$

31. $\int 3e^{-.8x} \, dx$

32. $\int -4e^{.2v} \, dv$

33. $\int \left(\frac{6}{x} + 4e^{-.5x}\right) dx$

34. $\int \left(\frac{9}{x} - 3e^{-.4x}\right) dx$

35. $\int \frac{1 + 2t^4}{t} \, dt$

36. $\int \frac{2y^{1/2} - 3y^2}{y^3} \, dy$

37. $\int \left(e^{2u} + \frac{4}{u}\right) du$

38. $\int \left(\frac{2}{v} - e^{3v}\right) dv$

39. $\int (5x + 1)^2 \, dx$

40. $\int (2y - 1)^2 \, dy$

41. $\int \frac{\sqrt{x} + 1}{\sqrt[3]{x}} \, dx$

42. $\int \frac{1 - 2\sqrt[3]{z}}{\sqrt[3]{z}} \, dz$

43. Find the equation of the curve whose tangent line has a slope of

$$f'(x) = x^{2/3}$$

if the point $(1, \frac{3}{5})$ is on the curve.

44. The slope of the tangent line to a curve is given by

$$f'(x) = 6x^2 - 4x - 3.$$

If the point $(0, 1)$ is on the curve, find the equation of the curve.

Work the given problems. (See Examples 8 and 10.)

45. Health   Total healthcare expenditures in the United States (in billions of dollars) are increasing at a rate of $f(x) = 9.42x + 87.14$, where $x = 0$ corresponds to the year 2000. Total healthcare expenditures were $1589.92 billion in 2002. (Data from: U.S. Centers for Medicare & Medicaid Services.)

   (a) Find a function that gives the total healthcare expenditures in year x.

   (b) What will total healthcare expenditures be in 2014?

46. Business   The total U.S. sales of bicycles and bicycle-related equipment was $5.0 billion in 2000. The rate at which this number was changing since 2000 is approximated by

$$f(x) = .054x - .12,$$

where $x = 0$ corresponds to 2000. (Data from: *Statistical Abstract of the United States*: 2004–2005.)

   (a) Find a function that gives the sales in billions of dollars in year x.

   (b) Estimate the total sales in 2014.

47. Business   Imports (in billions of U.S. dollars) from Canada to the United States have changed at a rate given by $g(x) = .21x^2 + .36x + 11.38$, where x is the number of years since 2000. The United States imported $216.63 billion worth of goods in 2001. (Data from: U.S. Census Bureau.)

   (a) Find a function giving the value of imports in year x.

   (b) What was the value of imports from Canada in 2007?

48. Social Science   The number of motor vehicles per 1000 people in Mexico has changed at a rate approximated by

$$V'(x) = -2.4x^2 + 32x - 85 \quad (3 \le x \le 10),$$

where $x = 3$ corresponds to the year 2003. There were 202.4 motor vehicles per 1000 people in Mexico in 2003. (Data from: www.worldbank.org.)

   (a) Find the function $V(x)$ giving the number of motor vehicles per 1000 people in Mexico in year x.

   (b) Find the number of motor vehicles per thousand people in Mexico in 2010.

Work the given problems. (See Example 9.)

49. Business   The marginal profit at a sales level of x hundred items of a product is $P'(x) = 4 - 6x + 3x^2$, and the "profit" when no items are sold is $-$40$. Find the profit function.

50. Business   The marginal revenue from a product is given by $R'(x) = 50 - 3x - x^2$. Find the demand function for the product.

Business   *Find the cost function for each of the given marginal cost functions.*

51. $C'(x) = x^{2/3} + 5$; 8 units cost $58.

52. $C'(x) = x^{1/2}$; 16 units cost $70.

53. $C'(x) = x^2 - 2x + 3$; 3 units cost $25.

54. $C'(x) = .2x^2 + .4x + .8$; 6 units cost $32.50.

55. $C'(x) = -\dfrac{40}{e^{.05x}} + 100$; 5 units cost $1400.

56. $C'(x) = 1.2e^{.02x}$; 2 units cost $105.

Work the given problems.

57. Social Science   The number of federal background checks performed is increasing at a rate (in thousands per year) approximated by

$$f(t) = 150.5e^{.035t},$$

where $t = 0$ corresponds to the year 2000. The number of federal background checks performed in 2000 was 4,300,000 (in other words, 4300 thousand background checks). (Data from: www.fbi.gov.)

   (a) Find the function that gives the number of federal background checks (in thousands) in year t.

   (b) How many background checks are projected to be performed in 2017?

58. Natural Science   If the rate of excretion of a biochemical compound is given by

$$f'(t) = .01e^{-.01t},$$

the total amount excreted by time t (in minutes) is $f(t)$.

   (a) Find an expression for $f(t)$.

   (b) If 0 units are excreted at time $t = 0$, how many units are excreted in 10 minutes?

59. Social Science   Recently, there were approximately 200 million licensed drivers in the United States. Sixteen-year-olds had 20 accidents per 100 drivers. The rate at which the number of accidents per 100 drivers changed as the driver's age increased was approximated by

$$g(x) = -\frac{10.2}{x} \quad (16 \le x \le 80),$$

where x is the age of the driver (in years). (Data from: National Safety Council.)

   (a) Find a function that gives the number of accidents per 100 drivers of age x years. (Round the constant C to two decimal places.)

   (b) Approximately how many accidents per 100 drivers did drivers of age 18 have? of age 20? of age 50? of age 70?

   (c) What reasons might account for your answers in part (b)?

Checkpoint Answers

1. Only one possible antiderivative is given for each.

    (a) x^3 (b) $\dfrac{5}{2}x^2$ (c) x^8

2. (a) $\dfrac{1}{7}x^7 + C$ (b) $\dfrac{4}{5}x^{5/4} + C$ (c) $8x + C$

3. (a) $-\dfrac{2}{3}x^9 + C$ (b) $\dfrac{21}{5}x^{5/3} + C$

    (c) $-\dfrac{5}{2}x^{-2} + C$ or $-\dfrac{5}{2x^2} + C$ (d) $x^5 - x^3 + 8x + C$

    (e) $3x^{4/3} - \dfrac{2}{x} + C$

4. (a) $-\dfrac{2}{\sqrt{x}} - \dfrac{1}{x} + C$ (b) $\dfrac{x^2}{2} + \dfrac{8}{3}x^{3/2} + 4x + C$

5. (a) $-7e^x + C$ (b) $\dfrac{1}{5}e^{5x} + C$

    (c) $\dfrac{1}{4}e^{4x} - 4e^x + C$ (d) $11e^{-x} + C$

6. (a) $-9 \cdot \ln|x| + C$ (b) $2e^{4x} - 3 \cdot \ln|x| + C$

7. $S(x) = \dfrac{7}{2}x^2 + 3x + 8$ 8. $C(x) = \dfrac{1}{2}x^4 + 3x^2 - 5x + 800$

9. (a) $F(t) = 125e^{.04t}$ (b) $F(10) \approx 186.5$ million

13.2 Integration by Substitution

In Section 13.1, we saw how to find the antiderivatives of a few simple functions. The antiderivatives of more complicated functions can sometimes be found by a process called *integration by substitution*. The technique depends on the following concept: If $u = f(x)$, then the **differential** of u, written du, is defined as

$$du = f'(x)\,dx.$$

Checkpoint 1

Find du for the given functions.

(a) $u = 9x$

(b) $u = 5x^3 + 2x^2$

(c) $u = e^{-2x}$

For example, if $u = 6x^4$, then $du = 24x^3 dx$. ✓

Differentials have many useful interpretations that are studied in more advanced courses. We shall use them only as a convenient notational device when finding an antiderivative such as

$$\int (3x^2 + 4)^4 6x\,dx.$$

The function $(3x^2 + 4)^4\,6x$ is reminiscent of the chain rule, so we shall try to use differentials and the chain rule in *reverse* to find the antiderivative. Let $u = 3x^2 + 4$; then $du = 6x\,dx$. Now substitute u for $3x^2 + 4$ and du for $6x\,dx$ in the indefinite integral:

$$\int (3x^2 + 4)^4\,6x\,dx = \int \overbrace{(3x^2 + 4)^4}^{u}\overbrace{(6x\,dx)}^{du}$$

$$= \int u^4\,du.$$

This last integral can now be found by the power rule:

$$\int u^4\,du = \frac{u^5}{5} + C.$$

Finally, substitute $3x^2 + 4$ for u into the antiderivative above to get:

$$\frac{u^5}{5} + C = \frac{(3x^2 + 4)^5}{5} + C.$$

We can check the accuracy of this result by using the chain rule to take the derivative. We get

$$\frac{d}{dx}\left[\frac{(3x^2 + 4)^5}{5} + C\right] = \frac{1}{5} \cdot 5(3x^2 + 4)^4\,(6x) + 0$$

$$= (3x^2 + 4)^4\,6x,$$

which is the original function.

This method of integration is called **integration by substitution.** As just shown, it is simply the chain rule for derivatives in reverse. The results can always be verified by differentiation.

Example 1 Find

$$\int (4x + 5)^9 \, dx.$$

Solution We choose $4x + 5$ as u. Then $du = 4 \, dx$. We are missing the constant 4. Using the fact that $4(1/4) = 1$, we can rewrite the integral:

$$\int (4x + 5)^9 \, dx = \frac{1}{4} \cdot 4 \int (4x + 5)^9 \, dx$$

$$= \frac{1}{4} \int \underbrace{(4x + 5)^9}_{u} \underbrace{(4 \, dx)}_{du} \qquad k \int f(x) \, dx = \int kf(x) \, dx$$

$$= \frac{1}{4} \int u^9 \, du \qquad \text{Substitute.}$$

$$= \frac{1}{4} \cdot \frac{u^{10}}{10} + C = \frac{u^{10}}{40} + C \qquad \text{Find the antiderivative.}$$

$$= \frac{(4x + 5)^{10}}{40} + C. \qquad \text{Substitute.}$$

✓ Checkpoint 2

Find the given antiderivatives.

(a) $\int 8x(4x^2 - 1)^5 \, dx$

(b) $\int (3x - 8)^4 \, dx$

(c) $\int 18x^2(x^3 - 7)^{3/2} \, dx$

⊘ **CAUTION** When changing the x-problem to the u-problem, make sure that the change is complete—that is, that no x's are left in the u-problem.

Example 2 Find

$$\int x^2 \sqrt{x^3 + 5} \, dx.$$

Solution Rewrite the function as $x^2(x^3 + 5)^{1/2}$. An expression raised to a power is usually a good choice for u, so we let $u = x^3 + 5$; then $du = 3x^2 \, dx$. The integrand does not contain the constant 3, which is part of du. One way to take care of this is to solve the differential $du = 3x^2 \, dx$ for $x^2 \, dx$:

$$du = 3x^2 \, dx$$

$$\frac{1}{3} du = x^2 \, dx.$$

Substitute u for $x^3 + 5$ and $\frac{1}{3} du$ for $x^2 \, dx$:

$$\int x^2 \sqrt{x^3 + 5} \, dx = \int \sqrt{x^3 + 5} \underbrace{(x^2 \, dx)}_{du} = \int \sqrt{u} \cdot \frac{1}{3} du.$$

Now use the constant-multiple rule to bring the $\frac{1}{3}$ outside the integral sign and then find the antiderivative:

$$\int x^2 \sqrt{x^3 + 5} \, dx = \int \sqrt{u} \cdot \frac{1}{3} du = \frac{1}{3} \int u^{1/2} \, du$$

$$= \frac{1}{3} \cdot \frac{u^{3/2}}{3/2} + C = \frac{2}{9} u^{3/2} + C.$$

✓ Checkpoint 3

Find the given antiderivatives.

(a) $\int 4x(6x^2 + 3)^2 \, dx$

(b) $\int x\sqrt{x^2 + 16} \, dx$

Since $u = x^3 + 5$,

$$\int x^2 \sqrt{x^3 + 5} \, dx = \frac{2}{9}(x^3 + 5)^{3/2} + C.$$

CAUTION The substitution method given in the preceding examples *will not always work.* For example, we might try to find

$$\int x^3\sqrt{x^5 + 1}\, dx$$

by substituting $u = x^5 + 1$, so that $du = 5x^4\, dx$. However, there is no *constant* that can be inserted inside the integral sign to give $5x^4$. This integral, and a great many others, cannot be evaluated by substitution.

With practice, choosing u will become easy if you keep two principles in mind. First, u should equal some expression in the integral that, when replaced with u, tends to make the integral simpler. Second, and more importantly, u must be an expression whose derivative is also present in the integral. The substitution should include as much of the integral as possible, so long as its derivative is still present. In Example 2, we could have chosen $u = x^3$, but $u = x^3 + 1$ is better, because it has the same derivative as x^3 and captures more of the original integral. If we carry this reasoning further, we might try $u = \sqrt{x^3 + 1} = (x^3 + 1)^{1/2}$, but this is a poor choice because $du = (1/2)(x^3 + 1)^{-1/2}(3x^2)\, dx$, an expression not present in the original integral.

Example 3 Find

$$\int \frac{x^2 + 5}{(x^3 + 15x)^2}\, dx.$$

Solution Let $u = x^3 + 15x$, so that $du = (3x^2 + 15)\, dx = 3(x^2 + 5)\, dx$. The integrand is missing the 3, so multiply by $\frac{3}{3}$, putting 3 inside the integral sign and $\frac{1}{3}$ outside:

$$\int \frac{x^2 + 5}{(x^3 + 15x)^2}\, dx = \frac{1}{3}\int \frac{3(x^2 + 5)}{(x^3 + 15x)^2}\, dx$$

$$= \frac{1}{3}\int \frac{du}{u^2} = \frac{1}{3}\int u^{-2}\, du$$

$$= \frac{1}{3}\cdot\frac{u^{-1}}{-1} + C = \frac{-1}{3u} + C.$$

Substituting $x^3 + 15x$ for u gives

$$\int \frac{x^2 + 5}{(x^3 + 15x)^2}\, dx = \frac{-1}{3(x^3 + 15x)} + C.$$

✓**Checkpoint 4**

Find the given antiderivatives.

(a) $\int z(z^2 + 1)^2\, dz$

(b) $\int \frac{x^2 + 3}{\sqrt{x^3 + 9x}}\, dx$

Recall that if $f(x)$ is a function, then by the chain rule, the derivative of the exponential function $y = e^{f(x)}$ is

$$\frac{dy}{dx} = e^{f(x)}\cdot f'(x).$$

Both the function $f(x)$ and its derivative appear on the right. This suggests that the antiderivative of a function of the form $e^{f(x)}\cdot f'(x)$ can be found by letting u be the exponent.

Example 4 Find

$$\int 2e^{x^2}x\, dx.$$

Let $u = x^2$, so that $du = 2x\, dx$. Then

$$\int 2e^{x^2}x\, dx = \int e^{x^2}2x\, dx$$

$$= \int e^u\, du$$

$$= e^u + C = e^{x^2} + C.$$

Check this answer by using the chain rule to take the derivative:

$$\frac{d}{dx}(e^{x^2} + C) = e^{x^2}(2x) + 0 = 2e^{x^2}x.$$

Example 5   Find the given antiderivatives.

(a) $\int e^{-12x}\, dx$

Solution   Choose $u = -12x$, so $du = -12\, dx$. Multiply the integral by $(-\frac{1}{12})(-12)$, and use the rule for $\int e^u\, du$:

$$\int e^{-12x}\, dx = -\frac{1}{12} \cdot -12 \int e^{-12x}\, dx$$

$$= -\frac{1}{12} \int e^{-12x}(-12\, dx)$$

$$= -\frac{1}{12} \int e^u\, du \qquad \text{Substitute.}$$

$$= -\frac{1}{12}e^u + C \qquad \text{Find the antiderivative.}$$

$$= -\frac{1}{12}e^{-12x} + C. \qquad \text{Substitute.}$$

(b) $\int 6x^2 \cdot e^{x^3}\, dx$

Solution   Let $u = x^3$, the exponent on e. Then $du = 3x^2\, dx$, and $(\frac{1}{3})\, du = x^2\, dx$. So

$$\int 6x^2 \cdot e^{x^3}\, dx = \int 6e^{x^3}(x^2\, dx)$$

$$= \int 6e^u\left(\frac{1}{3}\, du\right) \qquad \text{Substitute.}$$

$$= 2 \int e^u\, du \qquad \text{Constant-multiple rule}$$

$$= 2e^u + C \qquad \text{Find the antiderivative.}$$

$$= 2e^{x^3} + C. \qquad \text{Substitute.} \quad \boxed{\checkmark\, 5}$$

✓ **Checkpoint 5**

Find the given antiderivatives.

(a) $\int e^{5x}\, dx$

(b) $\int 10xe^{3x^2}\, dx$

(c) $\int 2x^3 e^{x^4-1}\, dx$

Recall that an antiderivative of $f(x) = 1/x$ is $\ln|x|$. The next example uses $\int x^{-1}\, dx = \ln|x| + C$ and the method of substitution.

Example 6   Find the following.

(a) $\int \frac{dx}{9x + 6}$

Solution   Choose $u = 9x + 6$, so $du = 9\, dx$. Multiply by $(\frac{1}{9})(9)$:

$$\int \frac{dx}{9x + 6} = \frac{1}{9} \cdot 9 \int \frac{dx}{9x + 6} = \frac{1}{9} \int \frac{1}{9x + 6}(9\, dx)$$

$$= \frac{1}{9} \int \frac{1}{u}\, du = \frac{1}{9} \ln|u| + C = \frac{1}{9} \ln|9x + 6| + C.$$

(b) $\displaystyle\int \frac{(2x-3)\,dx}{x^2-3x}$

Solution Let $u = x^2 - 3x$, so that $du = (2x-3)\,dx$. Then

$$\int \frac{(2x-3)\,dx}{x^2-3x} = \int \frac{du}{u} = \ln|u| + C = \ln|x^2 - 3x| + C. \quad ✓_6$$

The techniques used in the preceding examples can be summarized as follows.

> ### Substitution Method
>
> Let $u(x)$ be some function of x.
>
> | Form of the Integral | Form of the Antiderivative |
> |---|---|
> | 1. $\displaystyle\int [u(x)]^n \cdot u'(x)\,dx,\, n \neq -1$ | $\dfrac{[u(x)]^{n+1}}{n+1} + C$ |
> | 2. $\displaystyle\int e^{u(x)} \cdot u'(x)\,dx$ | $e^{u(x)} + C$ |
> | 3. $\displaystyle\int \dfrac{u'(x)\,dx}{u(x)}$ | $\ln|u(x)| + C$ |

A slightly more complicated substitution technique is needed in some cases.

Example 7 Find

$$\int x\sqrt[3]{1-x}\,dx.$$

Solution Let $u = 1 - x$. Then $x = 1 - u$ and $dx = -du$. Now substitute:

$$\int x\sqrt[3]{1-x}\,dx = \int (1-u)\sqrt[3]{u}(-du) = \int (u-1)u^{1/3}\,du$$

$$= \int (u^{4/3} - u^{1/3})\,du = \frac{3u^{7/3}}{7} - \frac{3u^{4/3}}{4} + C$$

$$= \frac{3}{7}(1-x)^{7/3} - \frac{3}{4}(1-x)^{4/3} + C. \quad ✓_7$$

Applications

Integration by substitution enables you to handle a wider variety of real-life applications.

Example 8 **Business** The rate of change of retail spending per capita in health and personal care stores (in hundreds of dollars per year) can be approximated by

$$S'(x) = \frac{2.1}{\sqrt{4.2x + 30.4}},$$

where $x = 0$ corresponds to the year 2000. Retail spending per capita in such stores in 2000 was \$551. (Data from: www.census.gov.)

✓ Checkpoint 6

Find the given antiderivatives.

(a) $\displaystyle\int \frac{4\,dx}{x-6}$

(b) $\displaystyle\int \frac{(3x^2+5)\,dx}{x^3+5x+4}$

✓ Checkpoint 7

Find $\displaystyle\int x(x+1)^{2/3}\,dx$.

(a) Find the function giving retail spending per capita in health and personal care stores (in hundreds of dollars).

Solution The retail spending per capita function is

$$S(x) = \int S'(x)\,dx = \int \frac{2.1}{\sqrt{4.2x + 30.4}}\,dx.$$

Let $u = 4.2x + 30.4$. Then $du = 4.2\,dx$ and so $\frac{1}{4.2}\,du = dx$. Thus we have

$$
\begin{aligned}
S(x) &= \int \frac{2.1}{\sqrt{4.2x + 30.4}}\,dx \\
&= \int \frac{2.1}{\sqrt{u}}\left(\frac{1}{4.2}\,du\right) && \text{Substitute.}\\
&= \frac{2.1}{4.2}\int \frac{1}{\sqrt{u}}\,du && \text{Constant-multiple rule}\\
&= \frac{1}{2}\int u^{-\frac{1}{2}}\,du && \text{Property of exponents}\\
&= \frac{1}{2}\frac{u^{-\frac{1}{2}+1}}{-\frac{1}{2} + 1} + C && \text{Find the antiderivative.}\\
&= \frac{1}{2}\cdot\frac{2}{1}u^{\frac{1}{2}} + C && \text{Simplify.}\\
&= \sqrt{u} + C \\
&= \sqrt{4.2x + 30.4} + C. && \text{Substitute.}
\end{aligned}
$$

Find the value of C by using the fact that retail spending per capita was \$551 in 2000; that is, $S(0) = 5.51$ (recall that $S(x)$ is in hundreds of dollars). Thus,

$$
\begin{aligned}
S(x) &= \sqrt{4.2x + 30.4} + C \\
S(0) &= \sqrt{4.2(0) + 30.4} + C \\
5.51 &= 5.5136 + C \\
C &\approx 0.
\end{aligned}
$$

Therefore retail spending per capita in health and personal care stores is given by

$$S(x) = \sqrt{4.2x + 30.4}.$$

(b) If this trend continues, will retail spending per capita in health and personal care stores exceed \$1000 by 2018?

Solution The retail spending per capita in the year 2018 ($x = 18$) is given by

$$S(18) = \sqrt{4.2(18) + 30.4} = \sqrt{106} \approx 10.30 \text{ (in hundreds of dollars)}.$$

Thus retail spending per capita is approximately \$1030 by the year 2018, which is in excess of \$1000. ✓ 8

Checkpoint 8

Find $S(x)$, given that
$$S'(x) = \frac{15}{\sqrt{5x + 1}} \text{ and } S(0) = 6.$$

Example 9 **Social Science** To determine the top 100 popular songs of each year, Jim Quirin and Barry Cohen developed a function that represents the rate of change on the charts of *Billboard* magazine required for a song to earn a "star" on the *Billboard* "Hot 100" survey.[*] They developed the function

$$f(x) = \frac{A}{B + x},$$

where $f(x)$ represents the rate of change in position on the charts, x is the position on the "Hot 100" survey, and A and B are appropriate constants. The function

$$F(x) = \int f(x)\, dx$$

is defined as the "Popularity Index." Find $F(x)$.

Integrating $f(x)$ gives

$$F(x) = \int f(x)\, dx$$

$$= \int \frac{A}{B + x}\, dx$$

$$= A \int \frac{1}{B + x}\, dx. \qquad \text{Constant-multiple rule}$$

Let $u = B + x$, so that $du = dx$. Then

$$F(x) = A \int \frac{1}{u}\, du = A \ln u + C$$

$$= A \ln(B + x) + C.$$

(The absolute value is not necessary, since $B + x$ is always positive here.)

13.2 Exercises

1. Integration by substitution is related to what differentiation method? What type of integrand suggests using integration by substitution?

2. For each of the given integrals, decide what expression should be u. Then find du.

   (a) $\displaystyle \int (3x^2 - 5)^4 2x\, dx$ (b) $\displaystyle \int \sqrt{1 - x}\, dx$

   (c) $\displaystyle \int \frac{x^2}{2x^3 + 1}\, dx$ (d) $\displaystyle \int (8x - 8)(4x^2 - 8x)\, dx$

Use substitution to find the given indefinite integrals. (See Examples 1–6 for Exercises 3–36 and Example 7 for Exercises 37–40.)

3. $\displaystyle \int 3(12x - 1)^2\, dx$

4. $\displaystyle \int 5(4 + 9t)^3\, dt$

5. $\displaystyle \int \frac{5}{(3t - 6)^2}\, dt$

6. $\displaystyle \int \frac{4}{\sqrt{5u - 1}}\, du$

7. $\displaystyle \int \frac{x + 1}{(x^2 + 2x - 4)^{3/2}}\, dx$

8. $\displaystyle \int \frac{3x^2 - 2}{(2x^3 - 4x)^{5/2}}\, dx$

9. $\displaystyle \int r^2 \sqrt{r^3 + 3}\, dr$

10. $\displaystyle \int y^3 \sqrt{y^4 - 8}\, dy$

11. $\displaystyle \int (-4e^{5k})\, dk$

12. $\displaystyle \int (-2e^{-3z} dz)$

13. $\displaystyle \int 4w^3 e^{2w^4}\, dw$

14. $\displaystyle \int 10ze^{-z^2}\, dz$

15. $\displaystyle \int (2 - t)e^{4t - t^2}\, dt$

16. $\displaystyle \int (3 - x^2)e^{9x - x^3}\, dx$

17. $\displaystyle \int \frac{e^{\sqrt{y}}}{\sqrt{y}}\, dy$

18. $\displaystyle \int \frac{e^{1/z^2}}{z^3}\, dz$

19. $\displaystyle \int \frac{-5}{12 + 6x}\, dx$

20. $\displaystyle \int \frac{9}{3 - 4x}\, dx$

21. $\displaystyle \int \frac{e^{2t}}{e^{2t} + 1}\, dt$

22. $\displaystyle \int \frac{e^{5w+1}}{2 - e^{5w+1}}\, dw$

23. $\displaystyle \int \frac{x + 2}{(2x^2 + 8x)^3}\, dx$

24. $\displaystyle \int \frac{4y - 2}{(y^2 - y)^4}\, dy$

25. $\displaystyle \int 5\left(\frac{1}{r} + r\right)\left(1 - \frac{1}{r^2}\right) dr$

26. $\displaystyle \int \left(\frac{2}{a} - a\right)\left(\frac{-2}{a^2} - 1\right) da$

27. $\displaystyle \int \frac{x^2 + 1}{(x^3 + 3x)^{2/3}}\, dx$

28. $\displaystyle \int \frac{B^3 - 1}{(2B^4 - 8B)^{3/2}}\, dB$

29. $\displaystyle \int \frac{6x + 7}{3x^2 + 7x + 8}\, dx$

30. $\displaystyle \int \frac{x^2}{x^3 + 5}\, dx$

31. $\displaystyle \int 2x(x^2 + 5)^3\, dx$

32. $\displaystyle \int 2y^2(y^3 - 8)^3\, dy$

33. $\displaystyle \int (\sqrt{x^2 + 12x})(x + 6)\, dx$

34. $\displaystyle \int (\sqrt{x^2 - 6x})(x - 3)\, dx$

35. $\displaystyle \int \frac{1}{x(\ln x)}\, dx$

36. $\displaystyle \int \frac{1}{x(\ln x)^2}\, dx$

37. $\displaystyle\int \frac{5u}{\sqrt{u-1}}\, du$ **38.** $\displaystyle\int \frac{2x}{(x+5)^6}\, dx$

39. $\displaystyle\int t\sqrt{5t-1}\, dt$ **40.** $\displaystyle\int 3r\sqrt{6-r}\, dr$

Work these problems. Round the constant C to two decimal places.

41. Business A company has found that the rate of change in the cost of a new production line (in thousands of dollars per year) is

$$C'(x) = \frac{60x}{5x^2+1},$$

where x is the number of years the line is in use.

(a) If the fixed costs are \$10,000, find the total cost function for the production line.

(b) The company will add a new production line if the total cost of this one for the first five years stays below \$40,000. Should the company add the new line?

42. Business The rate of expenditure (in dollars per year) for maintenance of a particular machine is given by

$$M'(x) = \sqrt{x^2+8x}(2x+8),$$

where x is time measured in years. Total maintenance costs through the fourth year are \$540.

(a) Find the total maintenance function.

(b) How many years must pass before the total maintenance costs reach \$2000?

43. Business Net sales for Costco Wholesale Corporation are changing at a rate (in billions of dollars per year) approximated by

$$f(x) = 2.944e^{.092x},$$

where $x = 0$ corresponds to the year 2000. Net sales were \$32 billion in 2000. (Data from: www.morningstar.com.)

(a) Find the function giving net sales in year x.

(b) Find the net sales (to the nearest billion) in 2012.

44. Business The rate of growth of profits (in millions of dollars per year) in year x from a new manufacturing process is approximated by

$$f(x) = xe^{-x^2}.$$

The total profit in the third year of the new process is \$10,000.

(a) Find the total profit function. (Remember that profits are given in millions of dollars.)

(b) As time goes on, what will happen to the total profit?

45. Business The marginal revenue (in thousands of dollars per unit) from the sale of x digital music players is given by

$$MR(x) = 1.8x(x^2 + 27,000)^{-2/3}.$$

The revenue from 150 players is \$32,000.

(a) Find the revenue function.

(b) What is the revenue from selling 250 players?

(c) How many players must be sold to produce revenue of at least \$100,000?

46. Business The number of jobs in the mining industry is changing at a rate (in thousands of jobs per year) approximated by

$$f(x) = \frac{53}{x+1},$$

where $x = 0$ corresponds to the year 2000. There were 520,000 mining industry jobs in 2000. (Data from: U.S. Bureau of Labor Statistics.)

(a) Find the function giving the number of mining industry jobs in year x.

(b) Find the projected number of mining industry jobs in the year 2020.

47. Business The rate of change in the number of urban transit vehicles such as buses and light-rail trains, in thousands per year, is approximated by

$$g(x) = .00040674x(x - 1970)^{.4} \quad (x \geq 1970),$$

where x is the year. In 1970, the number of such vehicles was 61,298. (Data from: U.S. Bureau of Transportation Statistics.)

(a) Find a function that gives the approximate number of urban transit vehicles in year x. (*Hint:* Example 7.)

(b) Estimate the number of urban transit vehicles in 2015.

48. Business For Nike Inc., the rate of change of revenue with respect to the number of employees (in billions of dollars of revenue per million employees) can be approximated by

$$f(x) = \frac{44}{2x+1},$$

where x is the number of employees in millions. When the number of employees was 34.4 million, the revenue was \$19 billion dollars. (Data from: www.mergentonline.com.)

(a) Find the revenue (in billions) as a function of x.

(b) Find the revenue (to the nearest billion) when there were 44 million employees.

✓ Checkpoint Answers

1. (a) $du = 9\, dx$ (b) $du = (15x^2 + 4x)\, dx$

  (c) $du = -2e^{-2x}\, dx$

2. (a) $\dfrac{(4x^2-1)^6}{6} + C$ (b) $\dfrac{(3x-8)^5}{15} + C$

  (c) $\dfrac{12(x^3-7)^{5/2}}{5} + C$

3. (a) $\dfrac{1}{9}(6x^2 + 3)^3 + C$ (b) $\dfrac{1}{3}(x^2 + 16)^{3/2} + C$

4. (a) $\dfrac{(z^2+1)^3}{6} + C$ (b) $\dfrac{2}{3}\sqrt{x^3 + 9x} + C$

5. (a) $\dfrac{1}{5}e^{5x} + C$ (b) $\dfrac{5}{3}e^{3x^2} + C$

  (c) $\dfrac{1}{2}e^{x^4-1} + C$

6. (a) $4\ln|x-6| + C$ (b) $\ln|x^3 + 5x + 4| + C$

7. $\dfrac{3}{8}(x+1)^{8/3} - \dfrac{3}{5}(x+1)^{5/3} + C$

8. $S(x) = 6\sqrt{5x+1}$

13.3   Area and the Definite Integral

Suppose a car travels along a straight road at a constant speed of 50 mph. The speed of the car at time t is given by the constant function $v(t) = 50$, whose graph is a horizontal straight line, as shown in Figure 13.2(a).

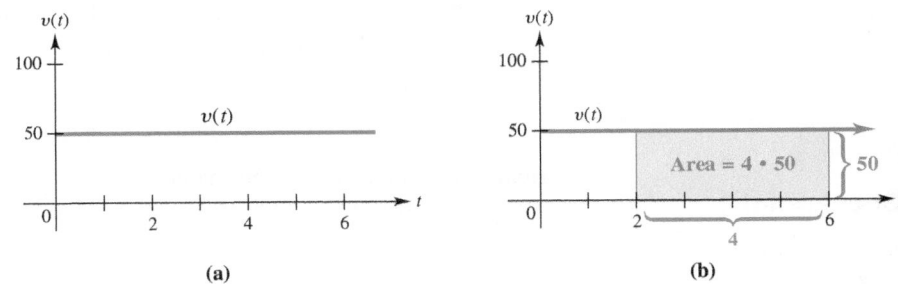

(a)   (b)

Figure 13.2

How far does the car travel from time $t = 2$ to $t = 6$? Since this is a 4-hour period, the answer, of course, is $4 \cdot 50 = 200$ miles. Note that 200 is precisely the *area* under the graph of the speed function $v(t)$ and above the t-axis from $t = 2$ to $t = 6$, as shown in Figure 13.2(b).

As we saw in Chapter 12, the speed function $v(t)$ is the rate of change of distance with respect to time—that is, the rate of change of the distance function $s(t)$ (which gives the distance traveled by the car at time t). Now, the distance traveled from time $t = 2$ to $t = 6$ is the amount that the distance has changed from $t = 2$ to $t = 6$. In other words, the *total change* in distance from $t = 2$ to $t = 6$ is the area under the graph of the speed (rate of change) function from $t = 2$ to $t = 6$.

A more complicated argument (omitted here) shows that a similar situation holds in the general case.

Total Change in $F(x)$

Let f be a function such that f is continuous on the interval $[a, b]$ and $f(x) \geq 0$ for all x in $[a, b]$. If $f(x)$ is the rate of change of a function $F(x)$, then the **total change in $F(x)$** as x goes from a to b is the area between the graph of $f(x)$ and the x-axis from $x = a$ to $x = b$.

Example 1   **Business**   Figure 13.3 shows the graph of the function that gives the rate of change of the annual maintenance charges for a certain machine. The rate function is increasing because maintenance tends to cost more as the machine gets older. Estimate the total maintenance charges over the 10-year life of the machine.

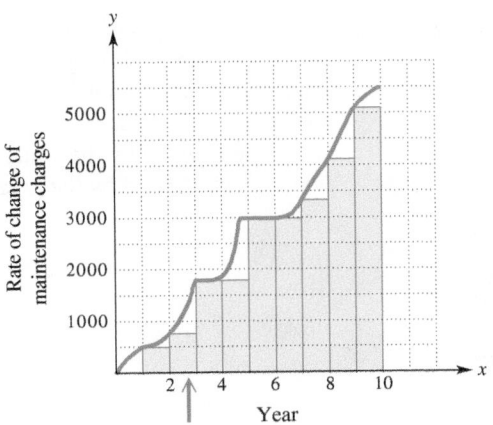

Figure 13.3

Solution This is the situation described in the preceding box, with $F(x)$ being the maintenance cost function and $f(x)$, whose graph is given, the rate-of-change function. The total maintenance charges are the total change in $F(x)$ from $x = 0$ to $x = 10$—that is, the area between the graph of the rate function and the x-axis from $x = 0$ to $x = 10$. We can approximate this area by using the shaded rectangles in Figure 13.3. For instance, the rectangle marked with an arrow has base 1 (from year 2 to year 3) and height 750 (the rate of change at $x = 2$), so its area is $1 \times 750 = 750$. Similarly, each of the other rectangles has base 1 and height determined by the rate of change at the beginning of the year. Consequently, we estimate the area to be the sum

$$1 \cdot 0 + 1 \cdot 500 + 1 \cdot 750 + 1 \cdot 1800 + 1 \cdot 1800 + 1 \cdot 3000 + 1 \cdot 3000$$
$$+ 1 \cdot 3400 + 1 \cdot 4200 + 1 \cdot 5200 = 23{,}650.$$

Hence, the total maintenance charges over the 10 years are at least \$23,650. (The unshaded areas under the rate graph have not been accounted for in this estimate). ✔1

✓ Checkpoint 1

Use Figure 13.3 to estimate the maintenance charge during

(a) the first 6 years of the machine's life;

(b) the first 8 years of the machine's life.

Area

The preceding examples show that the area between a graph and the x-axis has useful interpretations. In this section and the next, we develop a means of measuring such areas precisely when the function is given by an algebraic formula. The underlying idea is the same as in Example 1: Use rectangles to approximate the area under the graph.

> **Example 2** Find the area under the graph of $f(x) = \sqrt{4 - x^2}$ from $x = 0$ to $x = 2$, shown in Figure 13.4.

Figure 13.4

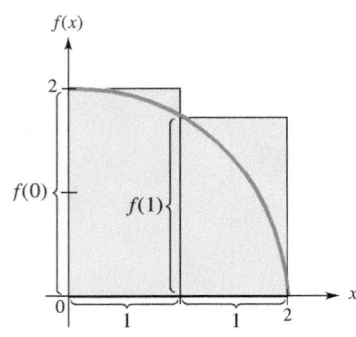

Figure 13.5

Solution A very rough approximation of the area of this region can be found by using two rectangles, as in Figure 13.5. The height of the rectangle on the left is $f(0) = 2$, and the height of the rectangle on the right is $f(1) = \sqrt{3}$. The width of each rectangle is 1, making the total area of the two rectangles

$$1 \cdot f(0) + 1 \cdot f(1) = 2 + \sqrt{3} \approx 3.7321 \text{ square units.}$$

As Figure 13.5 suggests, this approximation is greater than the actual area. To improve the accuracy of the approximation, we could divide the interval from $x = 0$ to $x = 2$ into four equal parts, each of width $\frac{1}{2}$, as shown in Figure 13.6. As before, the height of each rectangle is given by the value of f at the left-hand side of the rectangle, and its area is the width, $\frac{1}{2}$, multiplied by the height. The total area of the four rectangles is

$$\frac{1}{2} \cdot f(0) + \frac{1}{2} \cdot f\left(\frac{1}{2}\right) + \frac{1}{2} \cdot f(1) + \frac{1}{2} \cdot f\left(\frac{3}{2}\right)$$

$$= \frac{1}{2}(2) + \frac{1}{2}\left(\frac{\sqrt{15}}{2}\right) + \frac{1}{2}(\sqrt{3}) + \frac{1}{2}\left(\frac{\sqrt{7}}{2}\right)$$

$$= 1 + \frac{\sqrt{15}}{4} + \frac{\sqrt{3}}{2} + \frac{\sqrt{7}}{4} \approx 3.4957 \text{ square units.}$$

Figure 13.6

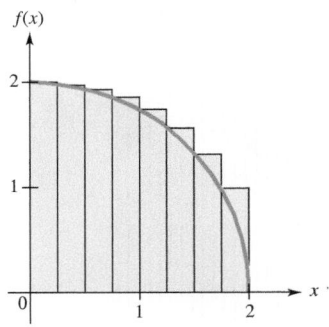

Figure 13.7

n	Area
125	3.15675
2000	3.14257
8000	3.14184
32,000	3.14165
128,000	3.14160
512,000	3.14159

✓ **Checkpoint 2**

Calculate the sum

$$\frac{1}{4} \cdot f(0) + \frac{1}{4} \cdot f\left(\frac{1}{4}\right) + \cdots$$

$$+ \frac{1}{4} \cdot f\left(\frac{7}{4}\right),$$

using the following information:

x	f(x)
0	2
1/4	1.98431
1/2	1.93649
3/4	1.85405
1	1.73205
5/4	1.56125
3/2	1.32288
7/4	.96825

This approximation looks better, but it is still greater than the actual area desired. To improve the approximation, divide the interval from $x = 0$ to $x = 2$ into eight parts with equal widths of $\frac{1}{4}$. (See Figure 13.7.) The total area of all these rectangles is

$$\frac{1}{4} \cdot f(0) + \frac{1}{4} \cdot f\left(\frac{1}{4}\right) + \frac{1}{4} \cdot f\left(\frac{1}{2}\right) + \frac{1}{4} \cdot f\left(\frac{3}{4}\right) + \frac{1}{4} \cdot f(1) + \frac{1}{4} \cdot f\left(\frac{5}{4}\right)$$

$$+ \frac{1}{4} \cdot f\left(\frac{3}{2}\right) + \frac{1}{4} \cdot f\left(\frac{7}{4}\right). \quad \boxed{\checkmark}_2$$

This process of approximating the area under the curve by using more and more rectangles to get a better and better approximation can be extended. To do this, divide the interval from $x = 0$ to $x = 2$ into n equal parts. Each of these n intervals has width

$$\frac{2 - 0}{n} = \frac{2}{n},$$

so each rectangle has width $2/n$ and height determined by the value of the function $f(x) = \sqrt{4 - x^2}$ at the left side of the rectangle. A computer was used to find approximations of the area for several values of n given in the table at the side.

As the number n of rectangles gets larger and larger, the sum of their areas gets closer and closer to the actual area of the region. In other words, the actual area is the *limit* of these sums as n gets larger and larger without bound, which can be written

$$\text{Area} = \lim_{n \to \infty} (\text{sum of areas of } n \text{ rectangles}).$$

The table suggests that this limit is a number whose decimal expansion begins $3.14159\ldots$, which is the same as the beginning of the decimal approximation of π. Therefore, it seems plausible that

$$\text{Area} = \lim_{n \to \infty} (\text{sum of areas of } n \text{ rectangles}) = \pi.$$

It can be shown that the region whose area was found in Example 2 is one-fourth of the interior of a circle of radius 2 with center at the origin (see Figure 13.4). Hence, its area is

$$\frac{1}{4}(\pi r^2) = \frac{1}{4}(\pi \cdot 2^2) = \pi,$$

which agrees with our answer in Example 2.

The method used in Example 2 can be generalized to find the area bounded by the curve $y = f(x)$, the x-axis, and the vertical lines $x = a$ and $x = b$, as shown in Figure 13.8, on the following page. To approximate this area, we could divide the region under the curve first into 10 rectangles (Figure 13.8(a)) and then into 20 rectangles (Figure 13.8(b)). In each case, the sum of the areas of the rectangles gives an approximation of the area under the curve.

We can get better and better approximations by increasing the number n of rectangles. Here is a description of the general procedure: Let n be a positive integer. Divide the interval from a to b into n pieces of equal length. The symbol Δx is traditionally used to denote the length of each piece. Since the length of the entire interval is $b - a$, each of the n pieces has length

$$\Delta x = \frac{b - a}{n}.$$

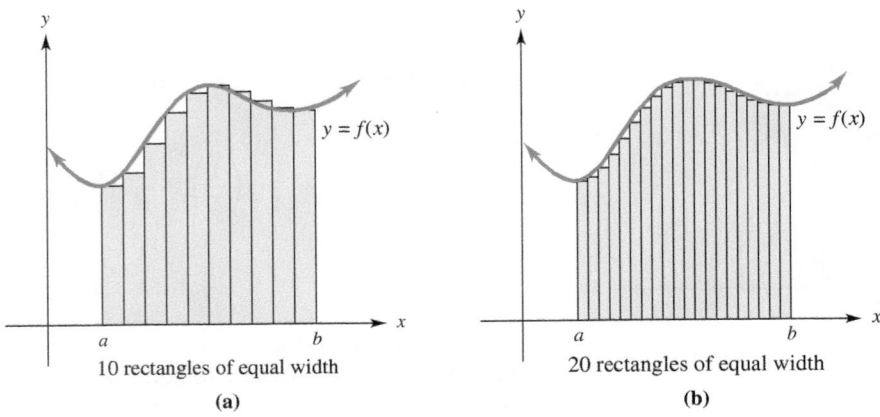

Figure 13.8

Use each of these pieces as the base of a rectangle, as shown in Figure 13.9, where the endpoints of the n intervals are labeled $x_1, x_2, x_3, \ldots, x_{n+1}$. A typical rectangle, the one whose lower left corner is at x_i, has red shading. The base of this rectangle is Δx, and its height is the height of the graph over x_i, namely, $f(x_i)$, so

$$\text{Area of } i\text{th rectangle} = f(x_i) \cdot \Delta x.$$

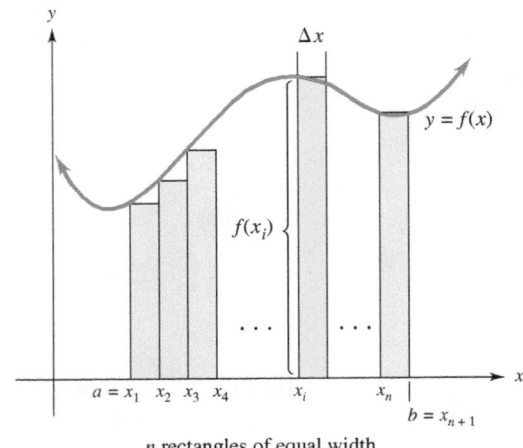

n rectangles of equal width

Figure 13.9

The total area under the curve is approximated by the sum of the areas of all n of the rectangles, namely,

$$f(x_1) \cdot \Delta x + f(x_2) \cdot \Delta x + f(x_3) \cdot \Delta x + \cdots + f(x_n) \cdot \Delta x.$$

The exact area is defined to be the limit of this sum (if it exists) as the number of rectangles gets larger and larger, without bound. Hence,

$$\text{Exact area} = \lim_{n \to \infty} (f(x_1) \cdot \Delta x + f(x_2) \cdot \Delta x + f(x_3) \cdot \Delta x + \cdots + f(x_n) \cdot \Delta x)$$
$$= \lim_{n \to \infty} ([f(x_1) + f(x_2) + f(x_3) + \cdots + f(x_n)] \cdot \Delta x).$$

This limit is called the *definite integral* of $f(x)$, from a to b and is denoted by the symbol

$$\int_a^b f(x)\, dx.$$

The preceding discussion can be summarized as follows.

The Definite Integral

If f is a continuous function on the interval $[a, b]$, then the **definite integral** of f from a to b is the number

$$\int_a^b f(x)\, dx = \lim_{n \to \infty}[(f(x_1) + f(x_2) + f(x_3) + \cdots + f(x_n))\, \Delta x],$$

where $\Delta x = (b - a)/n$ and x_i is the left-hand endpoint of the ith interval.

For instance, the area of the region in Example 2 could be written as the definite integral

$$\int_0^2 \sqrt{4 - x^2}\, dx = \pi.$$

Although the definition in the box is obviously motivated by the problem of finding areas, it is applicable to many other situations, as we shall see in later sections. In particular, *the definition of the definite integral is valid even when $f(x)$ takes negative values* (that is, when the graph goes below the x-axis). In that case, however, the resulting number is not the area between the graph and the x-axis. In this section, we shall deal only with the area interpretation of the definite integral.

The elongated "S" in the notation for the definite integral stands for the word "Sum," which plays a crucial role in the definition. This notation looks very similar to that used for antiderivatives (also called *indefinite* integrals) in earlier sections. The connection between the definite integral and antiderivatives, which is the reason for the similar terminology and notation, will be explained in the next section.

CAUTION The symbols $\int f(x)\, dx$ and $\int_a^b f(x)\, dx$ have totally different meanings—the a and b make all the difference. The indefinite integral $\int f(x)\, dx$ denotes a set of *functions* (the antiderivatives of $f(x)$), whereas the definite integral $\int_a^b f(x)\, dx$ represents a *number* (which can be interpreted as the area under the graph when $f(x) \geq 0$).

Example 3   Approximate $\int_1^4 4x\, dx$, which is the area under the graph of $f(x) = 4x$, above the x-axis, and between $x = 1$ and $x = 4$, by using six rectangles of equal width whose heights are the values of the function at the left endpoint of each rectangle.

Solution   We want to find the area of the shaded region in Figure 13.10.

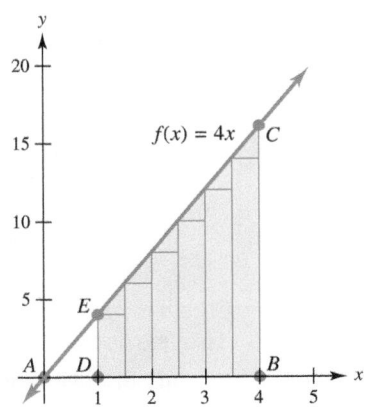

Figure 13.10

The heights of the six rectangles given by $f(x_i)$ are as follows:

i	x_i	$f(x_i)$
1	$x_1 = 1$	$f(1) = 4$
2	$x_2 = 1.5$	$f(1.5) = 6$
3	$x_3 = 2$	$f(2) = 8$
4	$x_4 = 2.5$	$f(2.5) = 10$
5	$x_5 = 3$	$f(3) = 12$
6	$x_6 = 3.5$	$f(3.5) = 14$

The width of each rectangle is $\Delta x = \dfrac{4-1}{6} = \dfrac{1}{2} = .5$. The sum of the areas of the six rectangles is

$$f(x_1)\Delta x + f(x_2)\Delta x + f(x_3)\Delta x + f(x_4)\Delta x + f(x_5)\Delta x + f(x_6)\Delta x$$
$$= f(1)\Delta x + f(1.5)\Delta x + f(2)\Delta x + f(2.5)\Delta x + f(3)\Delta x + f(3.5)\Delta x$$
$$= (4)(.5) + (6)(.5) + (8)(.5) + (10)(.5) + (12)(.5) + (14)(.5)$$
$$= 27.$$

We can check the accuracy of this approximation by noting that the area of the shaded region in Figure 13.10 is the difference of the areas of triangle ABC and triangle ADE. Triangle ABC has base 4 and height 16, and triangle ADE has base 1 and height 4. Using the formula for the area of a triangle, $A = \frac{1}{2}bh$, we see that the area of the shaded region is

$$\text{Area } ABC - \text{Area } ADE = (1/2)(4)(16) - (1/2)(1)(4) = 32 - 2 = 30.$$

So our approximation is a bit low. Using more rectangles will produce a better approximation of the area. ✔3

✔ Checkpoint 3

Divide the region of Figure 13.10 into 12 rectangles of equal width whose heights are the values of the function at the left endpoint of each rectangle.

(a) Complete this table.

i	x_i	$f(x_i)$
1	1	4
2	1.25	
3	1.5	
4	1.75	
5	2	
6	2.25	
7		
8		
9		
10		
11		
12		

(b) Use the results from the table to approximate $\int_1^4 4x\, dx$.

🖈 Technology and Definite Integrals

The preceding examples illustrate the difficulty of evaluating definite integrals by direct computation. In the next section, an algebraic evaluation technique that works in many cases will be developed. In all cases, technology can be used to evaluate definite integrals. Computer programs and calculators that have symbolic capabilities, such as Maple, Mathematica, the TI-89, and the TI-Nspire will generally produce exact results. Other graphing calculators and spreadsheets usually provide highly accurate approximations.

TECHNOLOGY TIP   There are two ways to approximate a definite integral with a graphing calculator, each of which is illustrated here for $\int_{-2}^{1}(x^3 - 5x + 6)\, dx$.

1. Approximate the limit in the definition by computing the sum for a large value of n, say, $n = 100$. Then $\Delta x = (b - a)/n = (1 - (-2))/100 = 3/100 = .03$, and the sum is

$$[f(x_1) + f(x_2) + f(x_3) + \cdots + f(x_n)] \cdot \Delta x$$
$$= [f(x_1) + f(x_2) + f(x_3) + \cdots + f(x_{100})](.03).$$

To compute this sum automatically on most TI calculators, look in the submenus of the LIST menu and enter

$$\text{sum(seq}(x^3 - 5x + 6, x, -2, 1 - .03, .03)) \times (.03).$$

Left endpoint   Right endpoint $-\Delta x$ Δx

On other calculators, use the RECTANGLE program in Appendix A of this text. In each case, the calculator produces the approximation 21.8393.

2. Use **numerical integration.** This feature approximates the definite integral by using more complicated summing techniques than used previously (which typically involve trapezoids or regions with parabolic boundaries). On the new edition of the TI-84+, go to the MATH menu and enter fnInt. The screen will then show a definite integral with blanks to fill in.

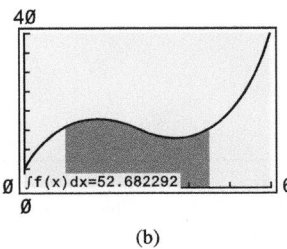

(a)

(b)

Figure 13.11

Alternatively, enter the function as Y1, and graph the function. Then go to the CALC menu, enter $\int f(x)\,dx$, and follow the on-screen instructions. On older TI calculators, look in the MATH or CALC menu and enter

$$\text{fnInt}(x^3 - 5x + 6, x, -2, 1).$$

On the Casio, use the $\int dx$ key on the keyboard and enter

$$\int (x^3 - 5x + 6, -2, 1).$$

In each case, the calculator approximates the integral as 21.75, which actually is its exact value, as we shall see in the next section.

Example 4   Figure 13.11(a) shows the graph of

$$f(x) = x^3 - 8x^2 + 18x + 5.$$

The area under the graph from $x = 1$ to $x = 4.5$, which is shown in Figure 13.11(b), is given by

$$\int_1^{4.5} (x^3 - 8x^2 + 18x + 5)\,dx.$$

(a) Use a calculator and the definition presented earlier, together with 100 rectangles, to approximate this integral.

Solution   For $n = 100$ rectangles, $\Delta x = (b - a)/n = (4.5 - 1)/100 = .035$. The left-hand endpoints of the bases of the rectangles are 1, 1.035, 1.07, 1.105, 1.14, . . . , 4.43, and 4.465. (The right-hand endpoint of the base of the last rectangle is 4.5.) We must compute the following sum:

$$[f(1) + f(1.035) + f(1.07) + \cdots + f(4.43) + f(4.465)](.035).$$

Compute the sum by doing Checkpoint 4 in the margin. ☑ 4

(b) Approximate the integral by using numerical integration on a calculator.

Solution   The numerical integration program in the MATH menu of the TI-84+ (see part 2 of the previous Technology Tip) produces the answer in Figure 13.12. This answer is more accurate than the estimate in part (a) and is correct to seven decimal places, as the techniques in the next section will show. Alternatively, sketching the graph and using the CALC menu produces the result in Figure 13.11(b).

At the beginning of this section, we saw that if $f(x)$ (with $f(x) \geq 0$) is the rate of change of a function $F(x)$, then the total change in $F(x)$ as x goes from a to b is the area between the graph of $f(x)$ and the x-axis from $x = a$ to $x = b$. In other words,

$$\text{Total change in } F(x) = \int_a^b f(x)\,dx.$$

✓ Checkpoint 4 ➚

If $f(x) = x^3 - 8x^2 + 18x + 5$, use the first part of the previous Technology Tip to compute the sum

$$[f(1) + f(1.035) + f(1.07)$$
$$+ \cdots + f(4.465)](.035).$$

Figure 13.12

Example 5   **Business**   The marginal cost (in dollars per snowboard) for manufacturing x snowboards is given by

$$MC(x) = \frac{(x - 600)^2}{450}.$$

Find the amount added to the total cost when production goes from 350 to 400 snowboards.

Solution   The amount added is the total change in cost from $x = 350$ to $x = 400$. Since the marginal cost function is the derivative of the cost function,

$$\text{Total change} = \int_{350}^{400} \frac{(x - 600)^2}{450}\,dx.$$

✓ **Checkpoint 5** ✈

If the marginal revenue from selling x of the snowboards in Example 5 is given by

$$MR(x) = .001x^2 + .35x,$$

find the total change in revenue when production goes from 350 to 400 snowboards.

Numerical integration (Figure 13.13) shows that the total change in cost from $x = 350$ to $x = 400$ is \$5648.15. ✓ 5

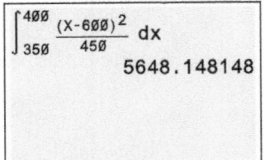

Figure 13.13

13.3 Exercises

In Exercises 1–4, estimate the required areas by using rectangles whose height is given by the value of the function at the left side of each rectangle. (See Example 1.)

1. **Business** The accompanying graph shows the rate of use of electrical energy (in millions of kilowatts) in a certain city on a very hot day. Estimate the total usage of electricity on that day. Let the width of each rectangle be 2 hours.

2. **Business** According to the U.S. Energy Information Administration, the rate of residential energy consumption (in quadrillion BTUs per year) is projected to be as shown in the accompanying graph. Estimate the total residential energy consumption that is projected for the period from 2015 to 2040 by using rectangles of width 5 years.

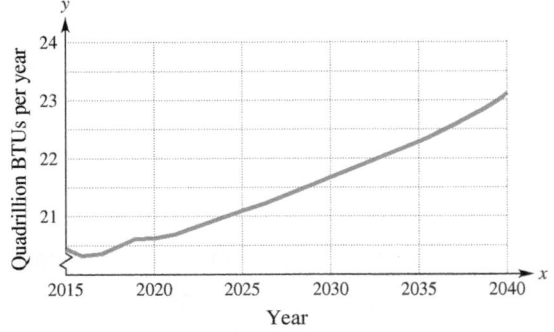

3. **Business** The accompanying graph shows the rate of coal consumption (in millions of short tons per year) in the United States. Estimate total coal consumption for the 12-year period from 2000 to 2012 by using rectangles of width 2 years. (Data from: U.S. Energy Information Administration.)

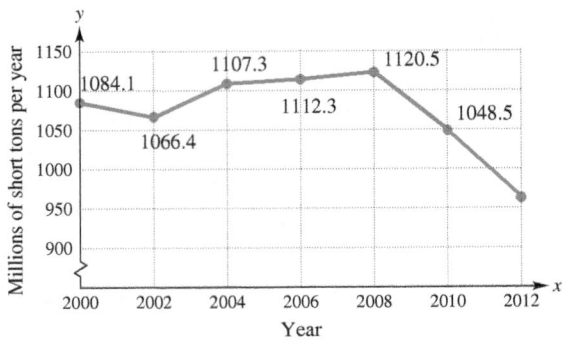

4. **Natural Science** The accompanying graph shows the rate of inhalation of oxygen by a person riding a bicycle very rapidly for 10 minutes. Estimate the total volume of oxygen inhaled in the first 20 minutes after the beginning of the ride. Use rectangles of width 1 minute.

5. Explain the difference between an indefinite integral and a definite integral.

6. Complete the following statement:

$$\int_0^3 (x^2 + 2) \, dx = \lim_{n \to \infty} \underline{\qquad}, \text{ where } \Delta x = \underline{\qquad}.$$

Approximate the area under each curve and above the x-axis on the given interval, using rectangles whose height is the value of the function at the left side of the rectangle.

(a) *Use two rectangles. (See Examples 2 and 3.)*

(b) *Use four rectangles.*

✈ **(c)** *Use a graphing calculator (or other technology) and 40 rectangles. (See Example 4.)*

7. $f(x) = 3x + 8; [0, 4]$ **8.** $f(x) = 9 - 2x; [0, 4]$

9. $f(x) = 4 - x^2; [-2, 2]$ **10.** $f(x) = x^2 + 5; [-2, 2]$

11. $f(x) = e^{2x} - .5; [0, 2]$ **12.** $f(x) = e^{-3x}; [0, 2]$

13. $f(x) = \dfrac{60}{x + 5}; [-2, 2]$ **14.** $f(x) = \dfrac{2}{x + 1}; [1, 9]$

Work the given exercises. (See Example 3.)

15. Find $\int_0^5 (5 - x)\, dx$ by using the formula for the area of a triangle.

16. Consider the region below $f(x) = x/2$, above the x-axis, between $x = 0$ and $x = 4$. Let x_i be the left endpoint of the ith subinterval.

    (a) Use four rectangles to approximate the area of the region.

    (b) Use eight rectangles to approximate the area of the region.

    (c) Find $\int_0^4 f(x)\, dx$ by using the formula for the area of a triangle.

✈ *Use the numerical integration feature on a graphing calculator to approximate the value of the definite integral. (See Example 4.)*

17. $\displaystyle\int_{-5}^{0} (x^3 + 6x^2 - 10x + 2)\, dx$

18. $\displaystyle\int_{-1}^{2} (-x^4 + 3x^3 - 4x^2 + 20)\, dx$

19. $\displaystyle\int_{2}^{7} 5 \ln (2x^2 + 1)\, dx$ **20.** $\displaystyle\int_{1}^{5} 3x \ln x\, dx$

21. $\displaystyle\int_{0}^{3} 4x^2 e^{-3x}\, dx$ **22.** $\displaystyle\int_{0}^{1} 3x^2 e^{x^3}\, dx$

✈ **Business** *A marginal revenue function MR(x) (in dollars per unit) is given. Use numerical integration on a graphing calculator or computer to find the total revenue over the given range. (See Example 5.)*

23. $MR(x) = .04x^3 - .5x^2 + 2x \quad (0 \le x \le 99)$

24. $MR(x) = .04x^4 - .5x^3 + 2x^2 - x \quad (0 \le x \le 60)$

25. $MR(x) = \dfrac{175}{1 + 3e^{-.7x}} - 20 \quad (0 \le x \le 310)$

26. $MR(x) = \dfrac{50}{1 + e^{-.1x}} \quad (0 \le x \le 200)$

✈ *Use numerical integration on a graphing calculator or computer to work these exercises. (See Example 5.)*

27. **Business** The rate of residential energy consumption (in trillion BTUs per year) is projected to be

$$f(x) = 2.17x^2 - 9.74x + 19,956 \quad (15 \le x \le 40),$$

where $x = 15$ corresponds to the year 2015. Find the total residential energy consumption that is projected for the period from 2015 to 2040. (Data from: U.S. Energy Information Administration.)

28. **Physical Science** The speed of a car at time x hours after starting on a trip is given by $52 - e^{-x/2}$ mph. Use the fact that speed is the derivative of distance to find the total distance traveled by the car from time $x = 2$ to $x = 5$.

Physical Science *The graphs for Exercises 29 and 30 show the speed, in miles per hour, at time t, in seconds, when a car accelerates from a dead stop. To find the total distance traveled by the car in reaching 100 miles per hour, we must estimate the definite integral*

$$\int_{0}^{T} v(t)\, dt,$$

where T represents the number of seconds it takes for the car to reach 100 mph.

    Use the graphs to estimate this distance by adding the areas of rectangles with width 5 seconds and whose height is the value of the function at the left side of the rectangle. To adjust your answer to miles per hour, divide by 3600 (the number of seconds in an hour). You then have the number of miles that the car traveled in reaching 100 mph. Finally, multiply by 5280 feet per mile to convert the answers to feet.

29. Estimate the distance traveled by the car in the following graph:

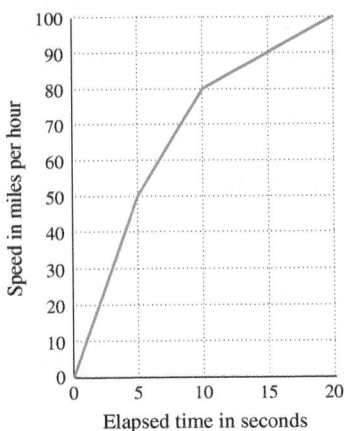

30. Estimate the distance traveled by the car in the following graph:

31. Two cars start from rest at a traffic light and accelerate for several minutes. The accompanying graph shows the speed of each car (in feet per second) as a function of time (in seconds). Car A is the one that initially has the greater speed.[*]

   (a) How far has car A traveled after 2 seconds? (*Hint:* Use formulas from geometry.)

   (b) When is car A farthest ahead of car B?

   (c) Estimate the farthest that car A gets ahead of car B. For car A, use formulas from geometry. For car B, use $n = 4$ and the value of the function at the midpoint of each interval for the height of the rectangle.

   (d) Give a rough estimate of when car B catches up with car A.

32. The booklet *All About Lawns*, published by Ortho Books, gives the following instructions for measuring the area of an irregularly shaped region.

   Irregular Shapes   (within 5% accuracy)
   Measure a long (L) axis of the area. Every 10 feet along the length line, measure the width at right angles to the length line. Total widths and multiply by 10.

   $$\text{Area} = (A_1A_2 + B_1B_2 + C_1C_2 \text{ etc.}) \times 10$$
   $$A = (40' + 60' + 32') \times 10$$
   $$A = 132' \times 10'$$
   $$A = 1320 \text{ square feet}$$

[*]Based on an example given by Steve Monk of the University of Washington.

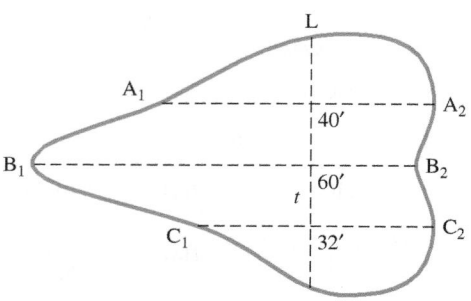

How does this method relate to the discussion in this section?

✓ Checkpoint Answers

1. **(a)** $7850   **(b)** $14,250

2. 3.33982 square units

3. **(a)**

i	x_i	$f(x_i)$
1	1	4
2	1.25	5
3	1.5	6
4	1.75	7
5	2	8
6	2.25	9
7	2.5	10
8	2.75	11
9	3	12
10	3.25	13
11	3.5	14
12	3.75	15

   (b) 28.5

4. 52.6977   **5.** $13,604.17

13.4   The Fundamental Theorem of Calculus

We now develop the connection between definite integrals and antiderivatives, which will explain the similar notation for these two concepts. More importantly, it provides a way to calculate definite integrals exactly.

In the last section, we saw that when $f(x)$ is the rate of change of the function $F(x)$ and $f(x) \geq 0$ on $[a, b]$, the definite integral has this interpretation:

$$\int_a^b f(x)\, dx = \text{total change in } F(x) \text{ as } x \text{ changes from } a \text{ to } b. \qquad (*)$$

The total change in $F(x)$ as x changes from a to b is the difference between the value of F at the end and the value of F at the beginning—that is, $F(b) - F(a)$. So equation (*) can be stated as

$$\int_a^b f(x)\, dx = F(b) - F(a).$$

Now, $f(x)$ is the rate of change of $F(x)$, which means that $f(x)$ is the derivative of $F(x)$, or equivalently, $F(x)$ is an antiderivative of $f(x)$. This relationship is an example of the following result.

Fundamental Theorem of Calculus

Suppose f is continuous on the interval $[a, b]$ and F is *any* antiderivative of f. Then

$$\int_a^b f(x)\, dx = F(b) - F(a).$$

The proof of the fundamental theorem is discussed at the end of this section. For now, we shall concentrate on applying it. Note these facts:

1. The fundamental theorem applies to every continuous function $f(x)$. It does not require that $f(x) \geq 0$.

2. If the antiderivative $F(x)$ is replaced by $F(x) + C$ for any constant C, the conclusion of the fundamental theorem is the same because C is eliminated in the final answer:

$$\int_a^b f(x)\, dx = (F(b) + C) - (F(a) + C)$$

$$= F(b) - F(a).$$

3. The variable used in the integrand does not matter. Each of the following integrals represents the number $F(b) - F(a)$:

$$\int_a^b f(x)\, dx = \int_a^b f(t)\, dt = \int_a^b f(u)\, du.$$

4. The definition of $\int_a^b f(x)\, dx$ assumed that $a < b$—that is, that the lower limit of integration is the smaller number. When $a > b$, we make this definition:

$$\int_a^b f(x)\, dx = -\int_b^a f(x)\, dx.$$

For example, $\int_3^1 x^2\, dx = -\int_1^3 x^2\, dx$. Similarly, when the limits of integration are the same, we define $\int_a^a f(x)\, dx$ to be 0. The fundamental theorem is valid for such integrals.

The fundamental theorem of calculus certainly deserves its name, since it is the key connection between differential calculus and integral calculus, which were originally developed separately without knowledge of this connection between them. Most importantly for our purposes, it provides an algebraic means to evaluate definite integrals exactly.

Applying the Fundamental Theorem

When evaluating definite integrals, the number $F(b) - F(a)$ is sometimes denoted by the symbol

$$F(x)\Big|_a^b$$

For example, if $F(x) = x^3$, then

$$F(x)\Big|_1^2 \quad \text{means } F(2) - F(1) = 2^3 - 1^3 = 7. \quad ✓_1$$

✓ **Checkpoint 1**

Let $C(x) = x^3 + 4x^2 - x + 3$.
Find the following.

(a) $C(x)\Big|_1^5$

(b) $C(x)\Big|_3^4$

Example 1   Evaluate each of the given integrals.

(a) $\displaystyle\int_1^2 4t^3\, dt.$

Solution   We know that $F(t) = t^4$ is an antiderivative of $4t^3$. By the fundamental theorem,

$$\int_1^2 4t^3\, dt = t^4\Big|_1^2 = 2^4 - 1^4 = 15.$$

(b) $\displaystyle\int_0^5 e^{2x}\, dx$

Solution   By the antiderivative rules in Section 13.1, we know that an antiderivative of e^{2x} is $\frac{1}{2}e^{2x}$. Therefore,

$$\int_0^5 e^{2x}\, dx = \frac{1}{2}e^{2x}\Big|_0^5 = \frac{1}{2}e^{10} - \frac{1}{2}e^0 = \frac{1}{2}e^{10} - \frac{1}{2}. \quad ✓_2$$

✓ **Checkpoint 2**

Evaluate each of the given integrals.

(a) $\displaystyle\int_4^6 5z\, dz$

(b) $\displaystyle\int_0^1 e^{3t}\, dt$

(c) $\displaystyle\int_1^9 \sqrt{z}\, dz$

To evaluate more complicated integrals, we need the following properties.

Properties of Definite Integrals

For any real numbers a and b for which the definite integrals exist,

1. $\displaystyle\int_a^b k \cdot f(x)\, dx = k \cdot \int_a^b f(x)\, dx$, for any real constant k
(constant multiple of a function);

2. $\displaystyle\int_a^b [f(x) \pm g(x)]\, dx = \int_a^b f(x)\, dx \pm \int_a^b g(x)\, dx$
(sum or difference of functions);

3. $\displaystyle\int_a^b f(x)\, dx = \int_a^c f(x)\, dx + \int_c^b f(x)\, dx$, for any real number c.

Properties 1 and 2 follow directly from the similar properties of antiderivatives. Property 3 won't be proved here, but Figure 13.14, on the following page, illustrates it when $f(x) > 0$ and $a < c < b$. In this case,

$$\int_a^b f(x)\, dx = \text{area of the entire shaded region}$$

$$= \text{area of blue region} + \text{area of red region}$$

$$= \int_a^c f(x)\, dx + \int_c^b f(x)\, dx.$$

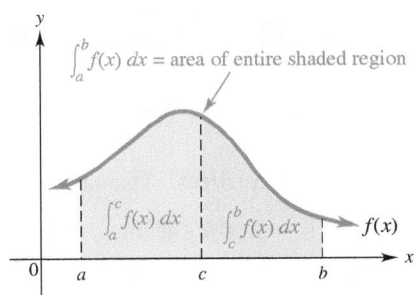

Figure 13.14

Example 2   Evaluate

$$\int_{1}^{7} (4x^2 - 6x + 7)\, dx.$$

Solution   To evaluate this integral, use property 2 of definite integrals to obtain

$$\int_{1}^{7} (4x^2 - 6x + 7)\, dx = \int_{1}^{7} 4x^2\, dx - \int_{1}^{7} 6x\, dx + \int_{1}^{7} 7\, dx.$$

Next, find an antiderivative for each of the three functions on the right-hand side:

$$4x^2 \text{ has antiderivative } 4\frac{x^3}{3} = \frac{4}{3}x^3;$$

$$6x \text{ has antiderivative } 6\frac{x^2}{2} = 3x^2;$$

$$7 \text{ has antiderivative } 7x.$$

Using the fundamental theorem on the three integrals on the right-hand side above, we see that

$$\int_{1}^{7} (4x^2 - 6x + 7)\, dx = \frac{4}{3}x^3 \Big|_{1}^{7} - 3x^2 \Big|_{1}^{7} + 7x \Big|_{1}^{7}$$

$$= \frac{4}{3}(7^3 - 1^3) - 3(7^2 - 1^2) + 7(7 - 1)$$

$$= \frac{4}{3}(343 - 1) - 3(49 - 1) + 7(6)$$

$$= 456 - 144 + 42 = 354. \quad \boxed{\checkmark}_3$$

✓**Checkpoint 3**

Evaluate each definite integral.

(a) $\displaystyle\int_{1}^{3} (4x + 3x^2)\, dx$

(b) $\displaystyle\int_{-2}^{3} (6k^2 - 2k + 1)\, dk$

✓**Checkpoint 4**

Evaluate the given integrals.

(a) $\displaystyle\int_{3}^{5} \frac{dx}{x}$

(b) $\displaystyle\int_{2}^{7} \frac{4}{x}\, dx$

Example 3   Find

$$\int_{1}^{2} \frac{dy}{y}.$$

Solution   In Section 13.1, we saw that an antiderivative of $\frac{1}{y}$ is $\ln|y|$. Hence,

$$\int_{1}^{2} \frac{dy}{y} = \ln|y| \Big|_{1}^{2} = \ln|2| - \ln|1| \approx .6931 - 0 = .6931. \quad \boxed{\checkmark}_4$$

Example 4 Evaluate

$$\int_0^5 x\sqrt{25 - x^2}\, dx.$$

Solution Use substitution to find the antiderivative. Let $u = 25 - x^2$, so that $du = -2x\, dx$. The integrand is missing the -2, so multiply by $\dfrac{-2}{-2}$, putting -2 inside the integral and $-\dfrac{1}{2}$ outside:

$$\int x\sqrt{25 - x^2}\, dx = -\frac{1}{2}\int \sqrt{25 - x^2}(-2x\, dx)$$

$$= -\frac{1}{2}\int \sqrt{u}\, du \qquad\qquad \text{Substitute.}$$

$$= -\frac{1}{2}\int u^{1/2}\, du \qquad\qquad \text{Fractional exponent}$$

$$= -\frac{1}{2}\cdot\frac{u^{3/2}}{3/2} \qquad\qquad \text{Use antiderivative formula.}$$

$$= -\frac{1}{2}\cdot\frac{2}{3}u^{3/2} = -\frac{1}{3}u^{3/2} \qquad \text{Simplify.}$$

$$= -\frac{1}{3}(25 - x^2)^{3/2}. \qquad\qquad \text{Express in terms of } x.$$

Now evaluate the definite integral:

$$\int_0^5 x\sqrt{25 - x^2}\, dx = -\frac{1}{3}(25 - x^2)^{3/2}\Big|_0^5$$

$$= -\frac{1}{3}(25 - 5^2)^{3/2} - \left[-\frac{1}{3}(25 - 0^2)^{3/2}\right]$$

$$= 0 + \frac{1}{3}\cdot 25^{3/2} = \frac{125}{3}. \quad ✓5$$

 Checkpoint 5

Find $\displaystyle\int_0^2 \frac{x}{x^2 + 1}\, dx.$

🚫 **CAUTION** When using substitution, be sure to express the antiderivative in terms of x before evaluating it. In Example 4, for instance, if you evaluate the antiderivative $-\dfrac{1}{3}u^{3/2}$ at 5 and 0, you get a wrong answer.

Area

When the graph of $f(x)$ lies above the x-axis between a and b, the definite integral $\displaystyle\int_a^b f(x)\, dx$ gives the area between the graph of $f(x)$ and the x-axis from a to b. Now consider a function f whose graph lies below the x-axis from a to b. The shaded area in Figure 13.15, on the following page, can be approximated by sums of areas of rectangles, that is, by sums of the form

$$f(x_1)\cdot \Delta x + f(x_2)\cdot \Delta x + f(x_3)\cdot \Delta x + \cdots + f(x_n)\cdot \Delta x,$$

with one difference: Since $f(x)$ is negative, the sum represents the negative of the sum of the areas of the rectangles. Consequently, the definite integral $\displaystyle\int_a^b f(x)\, dx$, which is the limit of such sums as n gets larger and larger, is the *negative* of the shaded area in Figure 13.15.

Figure 13.15

✓ **Checkpoint 6**

Find each shaded area.

(a)

(b)
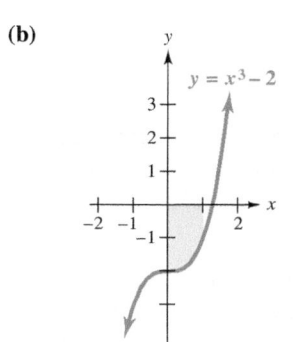

Example 5 Find the area between the x-axis and the graph

$$f(x) = \frac{1}{2}x^2 - 4x \qquad \text{from} \qquad x = 2 \text{ to } x = 8.$$

Solution That region, which is shaded in Figure 13.16, lies below the x-axis, and the definite integral gives the negative of its area:

$$\int_2^8 \left(\frac{1}{2}x^2 - 4x\right) dx = \left(\frac{x^3}{6} - 2x^2\right)\Big|_2^8 = \left(\frac{512}{6} - 128\right) - \left(\frac{8}{6} - 8\right) = -36.$$

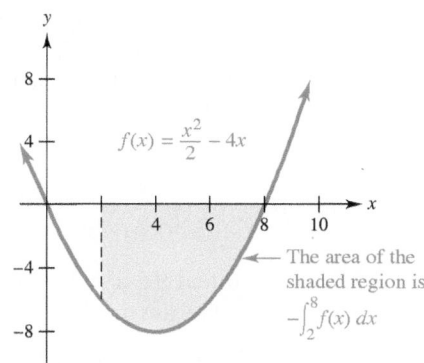

Figure 13.16

Therefore, the area of the region is 36. ✓ 6

Example 6 Find the area between the graph of $f(x) = 6x^2 - 7x - 3$ and the x-axis from $x = 0$ to $x = 2$, which is the shaded region in Figure 13.17.

Solution To find the total area, compute the area under the x-axis and the area over the x-axis separately. Start by finding the x-intercepts of the graph by solving

$$6x^2 - 7x - 3 = 0$$
$$(2x - 3)(3x + 1) = 0$$
$$x = 3/2 \qquad \text{or} \qquad x = -1/3.$$

Figure 13.17

Since we are concerned just with the graph between 0 and 2, the only relevant x-intercept is $\frac{3}{2}$. The area below the x-axis is the negative of

$$\int_0^{3/2} (6x^2 - 7x - 3)\, dx = \left(2x^3 - \frac{7}{2}x^2 - 3x\right)\Big|_0^{3/2}$$

$$= \left(2\left(\frac{3}{2}\right)^3 - \frac{7}{2}\left(\frac{3}{2}\right)^2 - 3\left(\frac{3}{2}\right)\right) - (0 - 0 - 0) = -\frac{45}{8}.$$

So the area of the lower region is $\frac{45}{8}$. The area above the x-axis is

$$\int_{3/2}^2 (6x^2 - 7x - 3)\, dx = \left(2x^3 - \frac{7}{2}x^2 - 3x\right)\Big|_{3/2}^2$$

$$= \left(2(2)^3 - \frac{7}{2}(2)^2 - 3(2)\right) - \left(2\left(\frac{3}{2}\right)^3 - \frac{7}{2}\left(\frac{3}{2}\right)^2 - 3\left(\frac{3}{2}\right)\right)$$

$$= \frac{13}{8}.$$

The area of the upper region is $\frac{13}{8}$, and the total area between the graph and the x-axis is

$$\frac{45}{8} + \frac{13}{8} = \frac{58}{8} = 7.25 \text{ square units.}$$

CAUTION If you attempt to find the area in Example 6 by using a single integral over the entire interval [0, 2], you will get a wrong answer, as shown in Checkpoint 7. It is essential to compute the upper and lower areas separately, using the two integrals over [0, $\frac{3}{2}$] and [$\frac{3}{2}$, 2].

✓ **Checkpoint 7**

Evaluate $\int_0^2 (6x^2 - 7x - 3)\, dx.$

Although it may be helpful, it is not necessary to graph a function in order to find the entire area between its graph and the x-axis. As Example 6 shows, the procedure depends only on finding the x-intercepts of the graph that are the limits of integration on the various integrals. Here is a summary of the procedure used there.

Finding Area

To find the area bounded by $y = f(x)$, the vertical lines $x = a$ and $x = b$, and the x-axis, use the following steps:

Step 1 Sketch a graph if convenient.

Step 2 Find any x-intercepts in [a, b]. These divide the total region into subregions.

Step 3 The definite integral will be *positive* for subregions above the x-axis and *negative* for subregions below the x-axis. Use separate integrals to find the areas of the subregions.

Step 4 The total area is the sum of the areas of all of the subregions.

We have seen a variety of interpretations of certain definite integrals in terms of area. We now present an interpretation that applies to all definite integrals. Consider, for example, $\int_0^2 (6x^2 - 7x - 3)\, dx$. By property 3 of definite integrals,

$$\int_0^2 (6x^2 - 7x - 3)\, dx = \int_0^{3/2} (6x^2 - 7x - 3)\, dx + \int_{3/2}^2 (6x^2 - 7x - 3)\, dx.$$

Each of the integrals on the right-hand side was evaluated in Example 6. Using those results, we see that

$$\int_0^2 (6x^2 - 7x - 3)\, dx = -\frac{45}{8} + \frac{13}{8} = \frac{13}{8} - \frac{45}{8}.$$

As Example 6 shows, this last difference is precisely

(area above the x-axis) − (area below the x-axis).

The same result holds in the general case.

If f is a continuous function on $[a, b]$, then

$$\int_a^b f(x)\, dx = \left(\begin{array}{c}\text{area between the}\\ \text{graph and the x-axis}\\ \textit{above} \text{ the axis}\end{array}\right) - \left(\begin{array}{c}\text{area between the}\\ \text{graph and the x-axis}\\ \textit{below} \text{ the axis}\end{array}\right)$$

Applications

In the last section, we saw that the area under the graph of a rate-of-change function $f'(x)$ from $x = a$ to $x = b$ gives the total change in $f(x)$ from a to b. We can now use the fundamental theorem to compute this change.

Example 7 **Business** Data and projections from the U.S. Energy Information Administration were used to generate the following model for the rate of consumption of marketed renewable energy (in trillion BTUs per year), where $x = 10$ corresponds to the beginning of the year 2010:

$$C'(x) = -1.86x^2 + 386x + 4400 \quad (10 \le x \le 35).$$

At this consumption rate, what is the amount of energy that will be used between the beginning of 2010 and the beginning of 2030?

Solution The amount of marketed renewable energy used is the total change in consumption from year 10 to year 30, so it is given by the definite integral

$$\int_{10}^{30} C'(x) = \int_{10}^{30} (-1.86x^2 + 386x + 4400)\, dx$$

$$= \left(-\frac{1.86}{3}x^3 + \frac{386}{2}x^2 + 4400x\right)\Big|_{10}^{30} \quad \text{Find the antiderivative.}$$

$$= (-.62x^3 + 193x^2 + 4400x)\Big|_{10}^{30} \quad \text{Simplify.}$$

$$= (-.62(30)^3 + 193(30)^2 + 4400(30))$$
$$- (-.62(10)^3 + 193(10)^2 + 4400(10)) = 226{,}280.$$

Therefore, 226,280 trillion BTUs of marketable renewable energy are projected to be used between 2010 and 2030. ✓8

✓ **Checkpoint 8**

Use the function in Example 7 to find the amount of marketable renewable energy projected to be used between the beginning of 2010 and the beginning of 2020.

In Chapter 10, you may have studied the normal probability distribution. There are many other distributions that can be used to model probability. One of these is the exponential distribution, which has the general form

$$f(x) = ae^{-ax} \quad (0 \le x < \infty),$$

where a is a positive constant that changes with the particular model. With this distribution—and, indeed, all probability distributions—the function is greater than or equal to zero, and the area between the curve and the x-axis equals 1. Figure 13.18 shows the graph of $f(x)$ for several values of a.

Figure 13.18

The next example shows how to use the exponential distribution and the fundamental theorem of calculus to estimate probabilities.

> **Example 8**   **Natural Science**   Biology students were interested in analyzing the amount of time hummingbirds spend at feeders before flying away. They found that an exponential model $f(x) = ae^{-ax}$ with $a = \frac{1}{4}$ approximated the probability of feeding time very well. Use the model to determine the probability that a hummingbird will feed for less than 5 seconds.
>
> **Solution**   With $a = \frac{1}{4}$, we can calculate the probability of feeding for less than 5 seconds by determining the area beneath the curve
>
> $$f(x) = \frac{1}{4}e^{-x/4}$$
>
> from $x = 0$ to $x = 5$ seconds. Figure 13.19 shows this area shaded in blue.

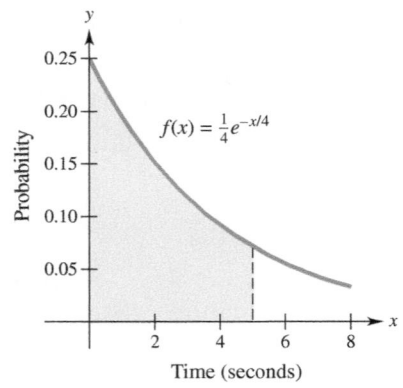

Figure 13.19

Thus, we have

$$\int_0^5 \frac{1}{4}e^{-x/4}\,dx = -e^{-x/4}\Big|_0^5 = -e^{-5/4} - (-e^0) \approx -.2865 + 1 = .7135.$$

Therefore, the probability that a hummingbird feeds for less than 5 seconds at the feeder is .7135.

✓**Checkpoint 9**

A different biology class developed an exponential model for hummingbird feeding time with $a = .303$. With this model, find the probability that a hummingbird feeds for between 1 and 4 seconds.

Proof of the Fundamental Theorem

Although we cannot give a rigorous proof of the fundamental theorem of calculus here, we can indicate why it is true in an important case. Suppose $f(x) > 0$ when $a \leq x \leq b$, so that the definite integral represents the area under the curve and above the x-axis.

Define a new function $A(x)$ by this rule:

$$A(x) = \text{area between the graph of } f(x) \text{ and the } x\text{-axis from } a \text{ to } x,$$

as shown in Figure 13.20. For instance, if the area under the graph from a to 4 is 35, then $A(4) = 35$.

We now show that $A(x)$ is an antiderivative of $f(x)$. We must show that

$$A'(x) = \lim_{h \to 0} \frac{A(x + h) - A(x)}{h}$$

is actually $f(x)$. Look at the situation geometrically. When h is a small positive number, $A(x + h)$ is the area under the graph of f from a to $x + h$, and $A(x)$ is the area from a to x. Consequently, $A(x + h) - A(x)$ is the area of the shaded strip in Figure 13.21. This area can be approximated with a rectangle having base h and height $f(x)$. The area of the rectangle is $h \cdot f(x)$, and

$$A(x + h) - A(x) \approx h \cdot f(x).$$

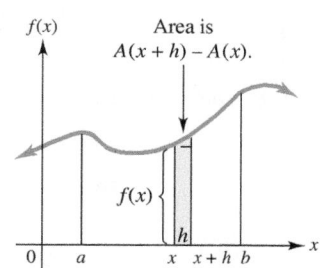

Figure 13.20   **Figure 13.21**

Dividing both sides by h gives

$$\frac{A(x + h) - A(x)}{h} \approx f(x).$$

This approximation improves as h gets smaller and smaller. Take the limit on the left as h approaches 0:

$$\lim_{h \to 0} \frac{A(x + h) - A(x)}{h} = f(x).$$

The limit is simply $A'(x)$, so

$$A'(x) = f(x).$$

This result means that A is an antiderivative of f, as we set out to show.

Since $A(x)$ is the area under the graph of f from a to x, it follows that $A(a) = 0$ and $A(b)$ is the area under the graph from a to b. But this last area is the definite integral $\int_a^b f(x)\, dx$. Putting these facts together, we have

$$\int_a^b f(x)\, dx = A(b) = A(b) - 0 = A(b) - A(a).$$

This argument suggests that the fundamental theorem is true when $f(x) > 0$ and the area function $A(x)$ is used as the antiderivative. Other arguments, which are omitted here, handle the case when $f(x)$ may not be positive and any antiderivative $F(x)$ is used.

13.4 Exercises

Evaluate each of the given definite integrals. (See Examples 1–4.)

1. $\displaystyle\int_{-1}^{3} (6x^2 - 7x + 8)\, dx$ **2.** $\displaystyle\int_{0}^{2} (-3x^2 + 6x + 5)\, dx$

3. $\displaystyle\int_{0}^{2} 3\sqrt{4u + 1}\, du$ **4.** $\displaystyle\int_{4}^{14} \sqrt{2r + 8}\, dr$

5. $\displaystyle\int_{0}^{1} 3(t^{1/2} + 4t)\, dt$ **6.** $\displaystyle\int_{0}^{4} -(3x^{3/2} - x^{1/2})\, dx$

7. $\displaystyle\int_{1}^{4} (10y\sqrt{y} + 3\sqrt{y})\, dy$ **8.** $\displaystyle\int_{4}^{9} (4\sqrt{r} - .5r\sqrt{r})\, dr$

9. $\displaystyle\int_{4}^{7} \frac{11}{(x - 3)^2}\, dx$ **10.** $\displaystyle\int_{1}^{4} \frac{-3}{(2p + 1)^2}\, dp$

11. $\displaystyle\int_{1}^{5} (6n^{-1} + n^{-4})\, dn$ **12.** $\displaystyle\int_{2}^{3} (3x^{-1} - 5x^{-4})\, dx$

13. $\displaystyle\int_{0}^{5} 6e^{2x}\, dx$ **14.** $\displaystyle\int_{1}^{2} 8e^{5x}\, dx$

15. $\displaystyle\int_{2}^{3} \left(.1e^{-.1A} + \frac{3}{A}\right) dA$ **16.** $\displaystyle\int_{1}^{2} \left(\frac{-1}{B} + 3e^{.2B}\right) dB$

17. $\displaystyle\int_{-1}^{0} y(2y^2 - 3)^5\, dy$ **18.** $\displaystyle\int_{0}^{2} m^2(5m^3 - 2)^3\, dm$

19. $\displaystyle\int_{1}^{64} \frac{\sqrt{z} - 2}{\sqrt[3]{z}}\, dz$ **20.** $\displaystyle\int_{1}^{8} \frac{9 - y^{1/3}}{y^{2/3}}\, dy$

21. $\displaystyle\int_{1}^{3} \frac{\ln x}{4x}\, dx$ **22.** $\displaystyle\int_{1}^{9} \frac{\sqrt{\ln x}}{x}\, dx$

23. $\displaystyle\int_{0}^{8} x^{1/3}\sqrt{x^{4/3} + 9}\, dx$ **24.** $\displaystyle\int_{0}^{4} 9x^{1/2}\sqrt{x^{3/2} + 1}\, dx$

25. $\displaystyle\int_{0}^{1} \frac{4e^t}{(3 + e^t)^2}\, dt$ **26.** $\displaystyle\int_{0}^{1} \frac{4e^t}{(e^t + 5)^3}\, dt$

27. $\displaystyle\int_{1}^{49} \frac{(1 + \sqrt{x})^{4/3}}{\sqrt{x}}\, dx$ **28.** $\displaystyle\int_{2}^{8} \frac{(1 + x^{1/3})^6}{x^{2/3}}\, dx$

29. $\displaystyle\int_{2}^{3} \frac{4x^3 + 6}{x^4 + 6x + 9}\, dx$ **30.** $\displaystyle\int_{0}^{2} \frac{18x^2 - 24x + 6}{x^3 - 2x^2 + x + 12}\, dx$

31. Suppose the function in Example 6, $f(x) = 6x^2 - 7x - 3$ from $x = 0$ to $x = 2$, represented the annual rate of profit of a company over a two-year period. What might the negative integral for the first year and a half indicate? What integral would represent the overall profit for the two-year period?

32. In your own words, describe how the fundamental theorem of calculus relates definite and indefinite integrals.

Find the area of each shaded region. (See Examples 5 and 6.)

33.

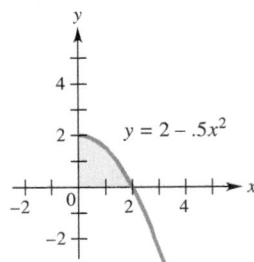

$y = 2 - .5x^2$

34.

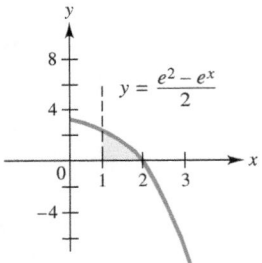

$y = \dfrac{e^2 - e^x}{2}$

35.

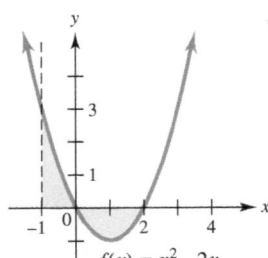

$f(x) = x^2 - 2x$

36.

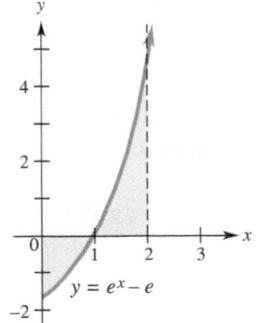

$y = e^x - e$

Use the definite integral to find the area between the x-axis and
f(x) over the indicated interval. Check first to see if the graph
crosses the x-axis in the given interval. (See Examples 5 and 6.)

37. $f(x) = 9 - x^2$; $[0, 4]$ **38.** $f(x) = x^2 - 3x - 4$; $[0, 5]$

39. $f(x) = x^3 - 1$; $[-1, 2]$ **40.** $f(x) = x^3 - 4x$; $[-2, 4]$

41. $f(x) = e^{2x} - 1$; $[-2, 1]$ **42.** $f(x) = 1 - e^{-3x}$; $[-1, 2]$

43. $f(x) = x^2 e^{-x^3/2}$; $[0, 3]$ **44.** $f(x) = 5xe^{x^2}$; $[0, 1]$

45. $f(x) = \dfrac{1}{x}$; $[1, e]$ **46.** $f(x) = \dfrac{2}{x}$; $[e, e^2]$

47. $f(x) = \dfrac{12(\ln x)^3}{x}$; $[1, 4]$

48. $f(x) = \dfrac{-(6x - 4)}{(3x^2 - 4x + 4)}$; $[-1, .5]$

◨ *Use property 3 of definite integrals to find* $\displaystyle\int_1^4 f(x)\, dx$ *for the given*

functions.

49. $f(x) = \begin{cases} 2x + 3 & \text{if } x \le 2 \\ -.5x + 8 & \text{if } x > 2 \end{cases}$

50. $f(x) = \begin{cases} x^2 - 2 & \text{if } x \le 3 \\ -x^2 + 16 & \text{if } x > 3 \end{cases}$

Work these problems. (See Example 7.)

51. Business De Win Enterprises has found that its expenditure
rate (in hundreds of dollars per day) on a certain type of job is
given by

$$E(x) = 4x + 2,$$

where x is the number of days since the start of the job.

(a) Find the total expenditure if the job takes 10 days.

(b) How much will be spent on the job from the 10th to the
25th day?

52. Business A worker new to a job will improve efficiency
with time so that it takes fewer hours to produce an item with
each day on the job, up to a certain point. Suppose the rate of
change of the number of hours it takes a worker in a certain factory to produce the xth item is given by

$$H'(x) = 20 - 2x.$$

(a) What is the total number of hours required to produce the
first 5 items?

(b) What is the total number of hours required to produce the
first 10 items?

53. Business The rate of depreciation (in dollars per year) for a
certain truck is

$$f(t) = \frac{6000(.3 + .28t)}{(1 + .3t + .14t^2)^2},$$

where t is in years and $t = 0$ is the year of purchase. Find the
total depreciation at the end of 3 years.

54. Health The rate of change of healthcare expenditures in the
United States (in billions of dollars per year) is approximated by

$$f(x) = 122.5x + 1400,$$

where $x = 0$ corresponds to the year 2000. According to this
model, what was the total amount spent on healthcare from the
beginning of 2010 to the beginning of 2012. (Data from: Centers for Medicare and Medicaid Services.)

55. Social Science The 2010 U.S. Census gives an age distribution approximated by

$$f(x) = -.81x^2 + 38x + 3904,$$

where x is age in years and $f(x)$ gives the number of people in
thousands who are of age x. The population of an age group can
be found by integrating this function over the interval for that
age group.[*] (Data from: www.census.gov.)

(a) Find $\displaystyle\int_{20}^{30} f(x)\, dx$. What does this integral represent?

(b) Find $\displaystyle\int_{0}^{90} f(x)\, dx$. What does this integral represent?

(c) The Millennial Generation (also known as Generation Y)
includes people who were between 10 and 30 years old at
the time of the census. Find the number of Millennials.

56. Business The rate of nuclear energy generation in the United
States (in billion kilowatt hours per year) is approximated by

$$f(x) = -.49x^2 + 9.4x + 755,$$

where $x = 0$ corresponds to the year 2000. How much nuclear
energy was generated between the beginning of 2000 and the
beginning of 2010? (Data from: U.S. Energy Information
Administration.)

57. Business The rate of residential consumption of geothermal
energy in the United States (in trillion BTUs per year) is approximated by

$$f(x) = 8e^{.148x},$$

where $x = 0$ corresponds to the year 2000. How much geothermal power was consumed between the beginning of 2000 and
the beginning of 2010? (Data from: U.S. Energy Information
Administration.)

58. Health A colony of *H. pylori* bacteria grows at the rate (in
milligrams per hour)

$$w' = \sqrt[3]{2t + 5},$$

where w is the weight (in milligrams) after t hours. Find the
change in weight of the colony from $t = 0$ to $t = 4$ hours.

---

[*]Exercise suggested by Ralph DeMarr, University of New Mexico.

Work these exercises.

59. Natural Science An oil tanker is leaking oil at a rate given in barrels per hour by

$$L'(t) = \frac{70 \ln(t + 1)}{t + 1},$$

where t is the time in hours after the tanker hits a hidden rock (when $t = 0$).

(a) Find the total number of barrels that the ship will leak on the first day.

(b) Find the total number of barrels that the ship will leak on the second day.

(c) What is happening over the long run to the amount of oil leaked per day?

60. Business Suppose that the rate of consumption of a natural resource is

$$c'(t) = ke^{rt},$$

where t is time in years, r is a constant, and k is the rate of consumption in the year when $t = 0$. Assume that $r = .04$.

(a) In 2010 ($t = 0$), an oil company sells 1.2 billion barrels of oil. Set up a definite integral for the amount of oil that the company will sell in the 10 subsequent years.

(b) Evaluate the definite integral of part (a).

61. Business The inflow of revenue to Dell Inc. (in billions of dollars per year) is approximated by

$$f(x) = 3.2 + 28\ln x \qquad (x \geq 3),$$

where $x = 0$ corresponds to the year 2000. (Data from: www.dell.com.)

(a) Use the product rule to find the derivative of $y = x(\ln|x| - 1)$.

(b) Use your answer to part (a) to determine Dell's total net revenue from January 1, 2004 to January 1, 2009.

62. Education The rate at which students are receiving Pell grants (in thousands per year) is approximately given by

$$N(x) = 19x^3 - 240x^2 + 1015x + 3740,$$

where $x = 0$ corresponds to the year 2000. Find the total number of students who received Pell grants between the

beginning of 2000 and the beginning of 2010. (Data from: www.finaid.org.)

Business *A model for the amount of time it takes for the first customer to arrive at a coffee shop in the morning is modeled by the exponential distribution and the function*

$$f(x) = \frac{1}{3}e^{-x/3}.$$

(See Example 8.)

63. Find the probability that the first customer arrives in the first 5 minutes.

64. Find the probability that the first customer arrives between 1 and 3 minutes after the shop opens.

Business *A company tests batteries for cordless drills. It finds that after the first 3 hours, the life of the battery can be modeled by an exponential distribution and the function*

$$f(x) = \frac{1}{8}e^{-x/8}.$$

65. Find the probability that the battery will last between 5 and 8 hours. (*Hint:* Be sure to take into account the first three hours.)

66. Find the probability that the battery lasts more than 7 hours.

✓**Checkpoint Answers**

1. (a) 216   (b) 64

2. (a) 50   (b) $\frac{1}{3}e^3 - \frac{1}{3}$ (c) 52/3

3. (a) 42   (b) 70

4. (a) .51083   (b) 5.01105

5. $\frac{1}{2}\ln 5$

6. (a) 8/3   (b) 7/4

7. −4   8. 97,560 trillion BTUs

9. .4410

13.5 Applications of Integrals

If a function gives the rate of change of a quantity, then the area between the graph of the rate function and the x-axis is the total amount of the quantity. This fact has numerous applications, some of which are explored here.

Example 1 **Business** When you buy a used car, you may be offered the opportunity to buy a warranty that covers repair costs for a certain period. A company that provides such warranties uses current data and past experience to determine that the annual rate of repair costs for a particular model is given in year x by

$$r(x) = 120\, e^{.4x}.$$

What will the total repair costs be for one year and for three years?

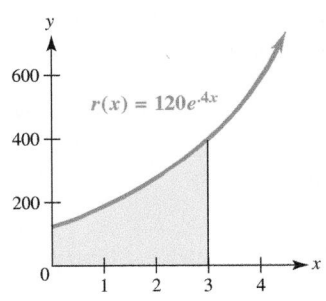

Figure 13.22

Solution The total repair costs are represented by the area under the rate curve over the appropriate interval. For the first three years, the area is shown in Figure 13.22 and is given by the integral

$$\int_0^3 120\, e^{.4x}\, dx = \frac{120}{.4} e^{.4x}\Big|_0^3 = 300\, e^{.4x}\Big|_0^3$$

$$= 300\, e^{.4(3)} - 300\, e^{.4(0)}$$

$$= 300\, e^{1.2} - 300 \approx \$696.04.$$

Similarly, the total repair costs for one year are

$$\int_0^1 120\, e^{.4x}\, dx = 300 e^{.4x}\Big|_0^1 = 300\, e^{.4} - 300 \approx \$147.55.$$

In order to make a profit, the company must charge more than \$147.55 for a one-year warranty and more than \$696.04 for a three-year warranty. ✓ 1

✓ **Checkpoint 1**

In Example 1, find the total repair costs for

(a) two years;

(b) four years.

Example 2   **Business**   The rate at which revenue is generated (in billions of dollars per year) by McDonald's Corp. can be approximated by

$$f(x) = 1.1x + 14,$$

where $x = 0$ corresponds to the year 2000. (Data from: www.morningstar.com.)

(a) What was the total revenue generated over the 5-year period from the beginning of 2008 to the end of 2012?

Solution Since the end of 2012 coincides with the start of 2013, the total revenue generated is the area under the graph of $f(x)$ and above the x-axis from $x = 8$ to $x = 13$, as shown in Figure 13.23. This area is given by

$$\int_8^{13} (1.1x + 14)\, dx = \left(\frac{1.1}{2}x^2 + 14x\right)\Big|_8^{13}$$

$$= (.55x^2 + 14x)\Big|_8^{13}$$

$$= [.55(13)^2 + 14(13)] - [.55(8)^2 + 14(8)]$$

$$= [92.95 + 182] - [35.2 + 112] = 127.75.$$

So the total revenue generated in this period was approximately \$127.75 billion.

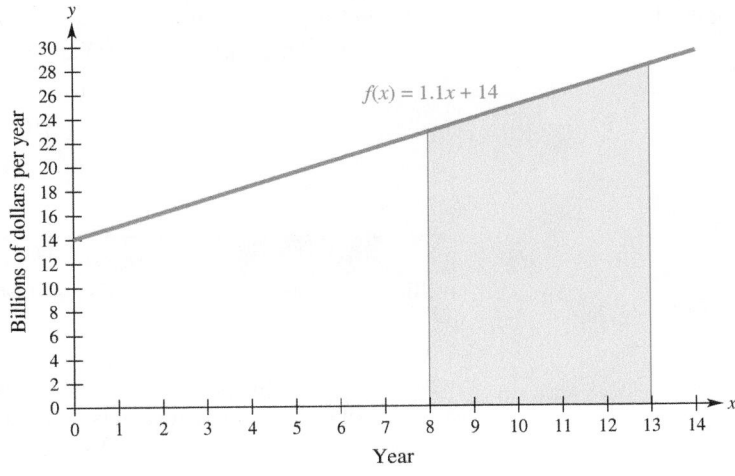

Figure 13.23

(b) In what year (starting in 2000) did the total revenue reach $195 billion?

Solution   The total revenue from $x = 0$ to $x = t$ is given by $\int_0^t (1.1x + 14)\,dx$. So we must find t such that

$$\int_0^t (1.1x + 14)\,dx = 195.$$

$$\left(\frac{1.1}{2}x^2 + 14x\right)\Big|_0^t = 195$$

$$(.55x^2 + 14x)\Big|_0^t = 195$$

$$[.55(t)^2 + 14(t)] - 0 = 195$$

$$.55t^2 + 14t - 195 = 0.$$

Using the quadratic formula, we obtain the solutions $t = 10$ and $t \approx -35.45$. Only the positive solution is meaningful here. Hence, total revenue reached $195 billion when $t = 10$ (at the beginning of 2010). ✓2

✓ Checkpoint 2

In Example 2, find

(a) the total revenue from the beginning of 2000 to the end of 2011;

(b) the time when total revenue (starting in 2000) reached $250 billion.

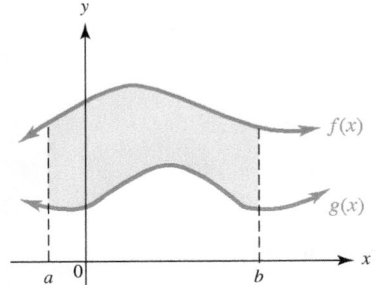

Figure 13.24

Area between Two Curves

In some applications, it is necessary to find the area between two curves. For example, the area between the graphs of $f(x)$ and $g(x)$ from $x = a$ to $x = b$ in Figure 13.24 is shaded. This area is the area under the graph of $f(x)$ *minus* the area under the graph of $g(x)$, that is,

$$\int_a^b f(x)\,dx - \int_a^b g(x)\,dx,$$

which can be written as

$$\int_a^b [f(x) - g(x)]\,dx.$$

Similar arguments in other cases (even when the graphs are not above the x-axis) produce the following important result.

Area between Two Curves

If f and g are continuous functions and $f(x) \geq g(x)$ on the interval $[a, b]$, then the area between the graphs of $f(x)$ and $g(x)$ from $x = a$ to $x = b$ is given by

$$\int_a^b [f(x) - g(x)]\,dx.$$

Example 3   **Business**   The rate at which revenue is generated from sales (in millions of dollars per year) for General Mills, Inc., can be approximated by

$$f(x) = 796x + 7010,$$

where $x = 0$ corresponds to the year 2000. The rate at which costs are incurred (in millions of dollars per year) can be approximated by

$$g(x) = -36x^2 + 1034x + 2620.$$

Find the total profit earned between $x = 0$ and $x = 13$. (Data from: www.morningstar.com.)

Solution The rate of revenue and rate of cost functions are graphed in Figure 13.25. Total revenue during this period is the area under the rate of revenue curve, and total cost is the area under the rate of cost curve. So the profit is the area between the two curves from $x = 0$ to $x = 13$, as shown in Figure 13.26.

Figure 13.25

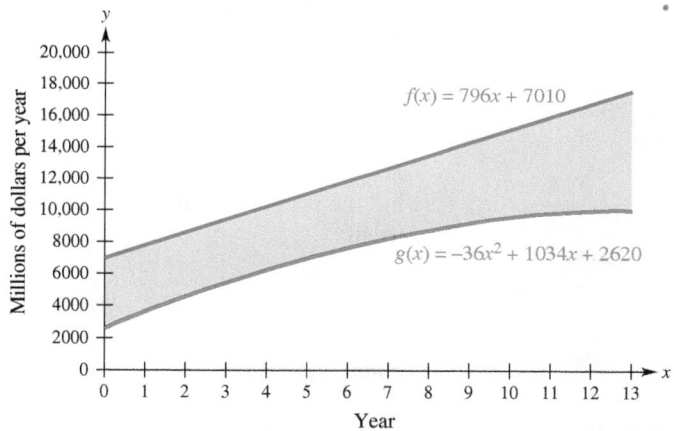

Figure 13.26

This area is

$$\int_0^{13} [f(x) - g(x)]\, dx = \int_0^{13} [(796x + 7010) - (-36x^2 + 1034x + 2620)]\, dx$$

$$= \int_0^{13} (36x^2 - 238x + 4390)\, dx$$

$$= \left(\frac{36}{3}x^3 - \frac{238}{2}x^2 + 4390x \right) \Big|_0^{13}$$

$$= (12x^3 - 119x^2 + 4390x) \Big|_0^{13}$$

$$= (12(13)^3 - 119(13)^2 + 4390(13)) - 0$$

$$= 63{,}323.$$

The profit was approximately $63,323,000,000 or $63.323 billion.

✓ **Checkpoint 3**

In Example 3, find the total profit earned between $x = 10$ and $x = 13$.

If revenue, cost, and profit are denoted by $R(x)$, $C(x)$, and $P(x)$, respectively, then

$$P(x) = R(x) - C(x),$$

so that

$$P'(x) = R'(x) - C'(x).$$

As we saw in Chapter 12, maximal profit occurs at a value of x for which $P'(x) = 0$. The previous equation shows that $P'(x) = 0$ exactly when $R'(x) = C'(x)$. In other words, maximal profit occurs when marginal revenue and marginal cost are equal.

Example 4   **Business**   A manufacturer produces a fabric similar to nylon. The product has been selling well, with a marginal revenue (in hundreds of dollars per hundred bolts) given by

$$R'(x) = -.3x^2 + 9x + 11,$$

where x is measured in hundreds of bolts of fabric. The marginal cost (in hundreds of dollars per hundred bolts) is given by

$$C'(x) = 2x + 6.$$

(a) To maximize profit, how many bolts should the company produce?

Solution   The manufacturer should continue production until the marginal costs equal the marginal revenue. Find this point by solving the equation $R'(x) = C'(x)$ as follows:

$$-.3x^2 + 9x + 11 = 2x + 6$$
$$-3x^2 + 90x + 110 = 20x + 60 \qquad \text{Multiply by 10.}$$
$$-3x^2 + 70x + 50 = 0.$$

Find the positive solution by using a graphing calculator (Figure 13.27) or the quadratic formula:

$$x = \frac{-70 - \sqrt{(70)^2 - 4(-3)(50)}}{2(-3)} \approx 24.0.$$

To maximize profit, the company should produce 2400 bolts of the fabric.

(b) What will the profit be on 2400 bolts?

Solution   To find the profit on 2400 bolts, find the area between the graphs of the marginal revenue and marginal cost functions, shown in Figure 13.28.

Figure 13.27

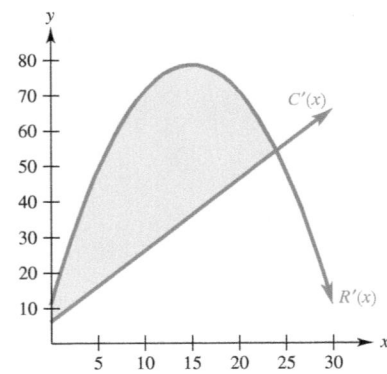

Figure 13.28

The area (profit) is

$$\text{Profit} = \int_0^{24} [R'(x) - C'(x)]\, dx$$

$$= \int_0^{24} [(-.3x^2 + 9x + 11) - (2x + 6)]\, dx$$

$$= \int_0^{24} (-.3x^2 + 7x + 5)\, dx \qquad\qquad \text{Combine terms.}$$

$$= \left(\frac{-.3x^3}{3} + \frac{7x^2}{2} + 5x \right)\Bigg|_0^{24} \qquad\qquad \text{Find the antiderivative.}$$

$$= 753.6.$$

The profit on 2400 bolts will be $75,360.

Example 5   **Business**   A company is considering a new manufacturing process in one of its plants. The new process provides substantial initial savings, with the savings declining with time x according to the rate-of-savings function

$$S'(x) = 100 - x^2,$$

where x is measured in years and $S'(x)$ in thousands of dollars per year. At the same time, the cost of operating the new process increases with time x according to the rate-of-cost function (in thousands of dollars per year)

$$C'(x) = x^2 + \frac{14}{3}x.$$

(a) To maximize its savings, for how many years should the company use the new process?

Solution   Figure 13.29 shows the graphs of the rate-of-savings and the rate-of-cost functions. As was the case in Example 4, maximum savings will occur when the rate of savings equals the rate of cost, that is, the time at which these graphs intersect.

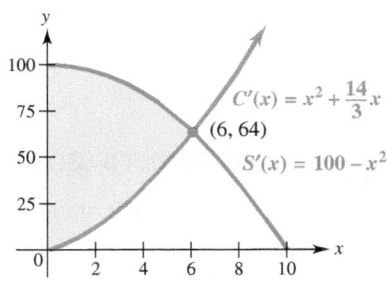

Figure 13.29

The graphs intersect when

$$S'(x) = C'(x),$$

or

$$100 - x^2 = x^2 + \frac{14}{3}x.$$

Solve this equation as follows:

$$0 = 2x^2 + \frac{14}{3}x - 100$$

$$0 = 3x^2 + 7x - 150 \qquad \text{Multiply by } \tfrac{3}{2}.$$

$$0 = (x - 6)(3x + 25) \qquad \text{Factor.}$$

Set each factor equal to 0 and solve both equations to get

$$x = 6 \qquad \text{or} \qquad x = -\frac{25}{3}.$$

Only 6 is a meaningful solution here. Alternatively, the intersection point can be found by using the intersection finder on a calculator, as in Figure 13.30. The company should use the new process for 6 years.

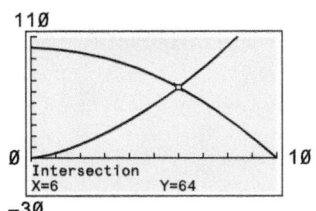

110

0
Intersection
X=6   Y=64
-30

Figure 13.30

(b) Taking the additional costs into account, how much will the company actually save during the 6-year period?

Solution   The actual savings (or net savings) are the difference between the savings and the additional costs. Total savings are given by the area under the rate-of-savings curve, and total additional costs are given by the area under the rate-of-cost curve, from $x = 0$ to $x = 6$. So total net savings are given by the difference between these two areas—that is, by the shaded area in Figure 13.29. This area is given by the integral

$$\text{Net savings} = \int_0^6 [S'(x) - C'(x)]\, dx$$

$$= \int_0^6 \left[(100 - x^2) - \left(x^2 + \frac{14}{3}x \right) \right] dx$$

$$= \int_0^6 \left(100 - \frac{14}{3}x - 2x^2 \right) dx \qquad \text{Combine terms.}$$

$$= 100x - \frac{7}{3}x^2 - \frac{2}{3}x^3 \Big|_0^6 \qquad \text{Find the antiderivative.}$$

$$= 100(6) - \frac{7}{3}(36) - \frac{2}{3}(216) = 372.$$

The company will save a total of $372,000 over the 6-year period. ✔4 ✔5

✔**Checkpoint 4**

In Example 5, find the total net savings if pollution control regulations permit the new process for only 4 years.

✔**Checkpoint 5**

If a company's rate-of-savings and rate-of-cost functions are, respectively,

$$S'(x) = 150 - 2x^2$$

and

$$C'(x) = x^2 + 15x,$$

where $S'(x)$ and $C'(x)$ give amounts in thousands of dollars per year, find the given quantities.

(a) Number of years to maximize savings

(b) Net savings during the period in part (a)

Consumers' and Producers' Surplus

The market determines the price at which a product is sold. As indicated earlier, the point of intersection of the demand curve and the supply curve for a product gives the equilibrium price. At the equilibrium price, consumers will purchase the same amount of the product that the manufacturers want to sell. Some consumers, however, will be willing to spend more for an item than the equilibrium price. The total of the differences between the equilibrium price of the item and the higher prices all those individuals would be willing to pay is called the **consumers' surplus.**

In Figure 13.31, the (red and blue) colored area under the demand curve is the total amount consumers are willing to spend for q_0 items. The red area under the line $y = p_0$ shows the total amount consumers actually will spend at the equilibrium price of p_0. The blue area represents the consumers' surplus. As the figure suggests, the consumers' surplus is given by the area between the two curves $p = D(q)$ and $p = p_0$, so its value can be found with a definite integral as follows.

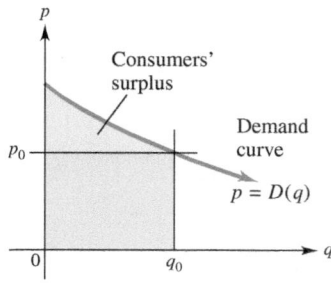

p

Consumers'
surplus

Demand
curve

p_0

$p = D(q)$

0   q_0 *q*

Figure 13.31

Consumers' Surplus

If $D(q)$ is a demand function with equilibrium price p_0 and equilibrium demand q_0, then

$$\textbf{Consumers' surplus} = \int_0^{q_0} [D(q) - p_0]\, dq.$$

Similarly, if some manufacturers would be willing to supply a product at a price *lower* than the equilibrium price p_0, the total of the differences between the equilibrium price and the lower prices at which the manufacturers would sell the product is called the **producers' surplus**. Figure 13.32 shows the (red) area under the supply curve from $q = 0$ to $q = q_0$, which is the minimum total amount the manufacturers are willing to realize from the sale of q_0 items. The (red and blue) total area under the line $p = p_0$ is the amount actually realized. The difference between these two areas, the producers' surplus (blue), is also given by a definite integral.

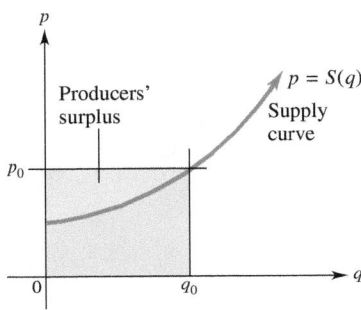

Figure 13.32

Producers' Surplus

If $S(q)$ is a supply function with equilibrium price p_0 and equilibrium supply q_0, then

$$\textbf{Producers' surplus} = \int_0^{q_0} [p_0 - S(q)]\, dq.$$

Example 6 **Business** Suppose the price (in dollars per ton) for oat bran is

$$D(q) = 900 - 20q - q^2$$

when the demand for the product is q tons. Also, suppose the function

$$S(q) = q^2 + 10q$$

gives the price (in dollars per ton) when the supply is q tons. Find the consumers' surplus and the producers' surplus.

Solution We begin by finding the equilibrium quantity by setting the two equations equal:

$$D(q) = S(q)$$
$$900 - 20q - q^2 = q^2 + 10q$$
$$0 = 2q^2 + 30q - 900$$
$$0 = q^2 + 15q - 450$$
$$0 = (q - 15)(q + 30)$$
$$q = 15 \quad \text{or} \quad q = -30.$$

Either factor (as shown above) or use the quadratic formula to see that the only positive solution of this equation is $q = 15$. At the equilibrium point where the supply and demand are both $q_0 = 15$ tons, the price is

$$\text{Equilibrium price} = p_0 = S(q_0) = S(15) = 15^2 + 10(15) = 375,$$

or $375. Verify that the same answer is found by computing $D(15)$. The consumers' surplus, represented by the blue area shown in Figure 13.33, is

$$\text{Consumers' surplus} = \int_0^{q_0} [D(q) - p_0]\, dq = \int_0^{15} [(900 - 20q - q^2) - 375]\, dq$$

$$= \int_0^{15} (525 - 20q - q^2)\, dq.$$

Evaluating this definite integral gives

$$\left(525q - 10q^2 - \frac{1}{3}q^3\right)\Big|_0^{15} = \left[525(15) - 10(15)^2 - \frac{1}{3}(15)^3\right] - 0$$

$$= 4500.$$

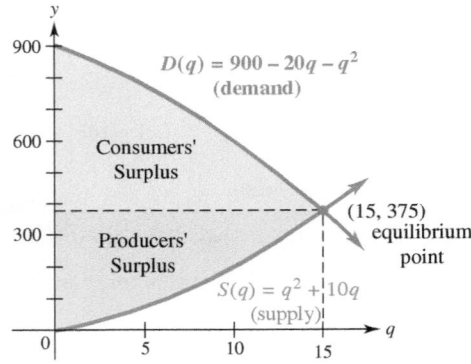

Figure 13.33

Here, the consumers' surplus is $4500. The producers' surplus (the red area in Figure 13.33) is given by

$$\text{Producers' surplus} = \int_0^{q_0} [p_0 - S(q)]\, dq = \int_0^{15} [375 - (q^2 + 10q)]\, dq$$

$$= \int_0^{15} (375 - q^2 - 10q)\, dq$$

$$= \left(375q - \frac{1}{3}q^3 - 5q^2\right)\Big|_0^{15}$$

$$= \left[375(15) - \frac{1}{3}(15)^3 - 5(15)^2\right] - 0$$

$$= 3375.$$

The producers' surplus is $3375. ✓ 6

✓ **Checkpoint 6**

Given the demand function $D(q) = 12 - .07q$ and the supply function $S(q) = .05q$, where $D(q)$ and $S(q)$ are in dollars, find

(a) the equilibrium point;

(b) the consumers' surplus;

(c) the producers' surplus.

13.5 Exercises

Business *Work the given exercises. (See Examples 1 and 2.)*

1. A car-leasing firm must decide how much to charge for maintenance on the cars it leases. After careful study, the firm determines that the rate of maintenance, $M(x)$, on a new car will approximate $M(x) = 60(1 + x^2)$ dollars per year, where x is the number of years the car has been in use. What total maintenance cost can the company expect for a 2-year lease? What minimum amount should be added to the monthly lease payments to pay for maintenance on a 2-year lease?

2. Using the function of Exercise 1, find the total maintenance cost during the first three years. What minimum monthly charge should be added to cover a 3-year lease?

3. Over the previous decade, about 13 billion tickets were sold at U.S. movie theaters. The marginal revenue from box-office receipts (in billions of dollars per billion tickets) was approximated by

$$MR(x) = .56x + 3.1,$$

where x is the number of tickets sold (in billions). What was the total revenue from selling these 13 billion tickets? (Data from: www.boxofficemojo.com.)

4. The marginal revenue from retail prescription drug sales (in billions of dollars per billion prescriptions) is approximated by

$$MR(x) = .01151e^{3.8362x},$$

where x is the number of prescriptions sold (in billions). (Data from: *The Statistical Abstract of the United States: 2009.*)

(a) What was the total revenue for the first 3.4 billion prescriptions?

(b) What was the total revenue from 3 billion to 3.4 billion prescriptions?

(c) After how many prescriptions were sold did total revenue reach $900 billion?

5. A company is considering a new manufacturing process. It knows that the rate of savings (in dollars per year) from the process will be about $S(t) = 1000(t + 2)$, where t is the number of years the process has been in use. Find the total savings during the first year. Find the total savings during the first six years.

6. Assume that the new process in Exercise 5 costs $16,000. About when will it pay for itself?

7. A company is introducing a new product. Production is expected to grow slowly because of difficulties in the start-up process. It is expected that the rate of production will be approximated by $P(x) = 1000e^{.2x}$, where x is the number of years since the introduction of the product. Will the company be able to supply 20,000 units during the first four years?

8. About when will the company of Exercise 7 be able to supply its 15,000th unit?

9. The rate of sales (in millions of dollars per year) for Heinz Co. (of ketchup fame) can be approximated by

$$f(x) = 366x + 6900,$$

where $x = 3$ corresponds to the year 2003. According to this model, what were the total sales from the beginning of 2010 to the end of 2012 (use $x = 10$ and $x = 13$ as limits of integration)? (Data from: www.morningstar.com.)

10. The rate of the cost of sales (in millions of dollars per year) for Heinz Co. can be approximated by

$$g(x) = 242x + 4400,$$

where $x = 3$ corresponds to the year 2003. According to this model, what was the total cost of sales from the beginning of 2010 to the end of 2012 (use $x = 10$ and $x = 13$ as limits of integration)? (Data from: www.morningstar.com.)

11. For Apple Inc., the rate of net sales (in billions of dollars per year) can be approximated by

$$f(x) = 3.8e^{.28x},$$

where $x = 0$ corresponds to the year 2000. According to this model, what were the total net sales from the beginning of 2000 to the end of 2012? (Data from: www.morningstar.com.)

12. For Apple Inc., the rate of the cost of sales (in billions of dollars per year) can be approximated by

$$g(x) = 2.9e^{.258x},$$

where $x = 0$ corresponds to the year 2000. According to this model, what was the total cost of sales from the beginning of 2000 to the end of 2012? (Data from: www.morningstar.com.)

Find the area between the two curves. (See Example 3.)

13. $y = 3x$ and $y = x^2 - 4$ from $x = -1$ to $x = 3$

14. $y = x^2 - 30$ and $y = 10 - 3x$ from $x = 1$ to $x = 5$

15. $y = x^2$ and $y = x^3$ from $x = 0$ to $x = \frac{1}{2}$

16. $y = 6x^2$ and $y = 8x^3$ from $x = 0$ to $x = 2$

17. $y = e^x$ and $y = x$ from $x = 0$ to $x = 1$

18. $y = e^x$ and $y = 3 - e^x$ from $x = -3$ to $x = 0$

Use a graphing calculator to approximate the area between the graphs of each pair of functions on the given interval.

19. $y = \ln x$ and $y = 2xe^x$; $[1, 4]$

20. $y = \ln x$ and $y = 4 - x^2$; $[2, 5]$

21. $y = \sqrt{9 - x^2}$ and $y = \sqrt{x + 1}$; $[-1, 2]$

22. $y = \sqrt{4 - 4x^2}$ and $y = \sqrt{\dfrac{9 - x^2}{7}}$; $[-.5, .5]$

Work these problems. (See Examples 3–5.)

23. **Business** Suppose a company wants to introduce a new machine that will produce annual savings in dollars per year at the rate given by

$$S'(x) = 150 - x^2,$$

where x is the number of years of operation of the machine, while producing annual costs in dollars per year at the rate of

$$C'(x) = x^2 + \frac{11}{4}x.$$

(a) To maximize its net savings, for how many years should the company use this new machine?

(b) What are the net savings during the first year of use of the machine?

(c) What are the net savings over the period determined in part (a)?

24. Natural Science A new smog-control device will reduce the output of sulfur oxides from automobile exhausts. It is estimated that the rate of savings (in millions of dollars per year) to the community from the use of this device in year x will be approximated by

$$S'(x) = -x^2 + 4x + 8.$$

The new device cuts down on the production of sulfur oxides, but it causes an increase in the production of nitrous oxides. The rate of costs (in millions of dollars per year) to the community in year x is approximated by

$$C'(x) = \frac{3}{25}x^2.$$

(a) To maximize net savings, for how many years should the new device be used?

(b) What will be the net savings over the period found in part (a)?

25. Business A factory at Harold Levinson Industries has installed a new process that will produce an increased rate of revenue (in thousands of dollars per year) of

$$r(t) = 104 - .4e^{t/2},$$

where t is time measured in years. The new process produces additional costs (in thousands of dollars per year) at the rate of

$$c(t) = .3e^{t/2}.$$

(a) To maximize this additional profit, how long should the new process be used?

(b) Find the additional profit during this period.

26. Business Richardson Construction Company has an expenditure rate of $E(x) = e^{.15x}$ dollars per day on a particular paving job and an income rate of $I(x) = 120.3 - e^{.15x}$ dollars per day on the same job, where x is the number of days from the start of the job. The company's profit on that job will equal total income less total expenditures. Profit will be maximized if the job ends at the optimum time, which is the point where the two curves meet. Find the following:

(a) the optimum number of days for the job to last;

(b) the total income for the optimum number of days;

(c) the total expenditures for the optimum number of days;

(d) the maximum profit for the job.

27. Business After t years, an oil refinery is producing at the rate of

$$P(t) = \frac{20}{1.2t + 1.6}$$

trillions of gallons per year. At the same time, the oil is consumed at a rate of $C(t) = t + .8$ trillions of gallons per year.

(a) In how many years will the rate of consumption equal the rate of production?

(b) What is the total excess production before consumption and production are equal?

28. Business The rate of expenditure (in dollars per year) for maintenance of a certain machine is given by

$$m(x) = x^2 + 6x,$$

where x is time measured in years. The machine produces a rate of savings (in dollars per year) given by

$$s(x) = 360 - 2x^2.$$

(a) In how many years will the maintenance rate equal the savings rate?

(b) What will be the net savings over this period?

29. Natural Science Polluted fluid from a factory begins to enter a lake at the rate

$$f(t) = 8(1 - e^{-.25t}),$$

where t is time (in hours) and $f(t)$ is in gallons per hour. At the same time, a pollution filter begins to remove the pollution at the rate of

$$g(t) = .2t,$$

where t is in hours and $g(t)$ is in gallons per hour.

(a) How much pollution is in the lake after 20 hours?

(b) At what time will the rate at which pollution enters the lake equal the rate at which pollution is being removed?

(c) How much pollution is in the lake at the time found in part (b)?

(d) At what time will all the pollution be removed from the lake?

30. Natural Science Suppose that, over a 4-hour period on a certain evening, an individual is consuming alcohol at the rate

$$f(x) = 1 - e^{-x},$$

where x is in hours and $f(x)$ is in ounces per hour. At the same time, this individual is metabolizing alcohol at the rate

$$m(x) = .6$$

ounces per hour. (Note that one 12-ounce beer that is 5% alcohol by volume contains .6 ounce of pure alcohol.)

(a) What was the total amount of alcohol consumed during the 4-hour period?

(b) What was the total amount of alcohol metabolized during the 4-hour period?

(c) How much alcohol remains in the body at $x = 4$ hours?

Business *Work the given supply-and-demand exercises, where the price is given in dollars. (See Example 6.)*

31. Suppose the supply function of a certain item is given by

$$S(q) = \frac{7}{5}q$$

and the demand function is given by

$$D(q) = -\frac{3}{5}q + 10.$$

(a) Graph the supply and demand curves.

(b) Find the point at which supply and demand are in equilibrium.

(c) Find the consumers' surplus.

(d) Find the producers' surplus.

32. Find the consumers' surplus and the producers' surplus for an item having supply function

$$S(q) = 3q^2$$

and demand function

$$D(q) = 120 - \frac{q^2}{6}.$$

33. Suppose the supply function for concrete is given by

$$S(q) = 100 + 3q^{3/2} + q^{5/2}$$

and that supply and demand are in equilibrium at $q = 9$. Find the producers' surplus.

34. Find the producers' surplus if the supply function for digital cameras sold by an office supply chain is given by

$$S(q) = q^{5/2} + 2.1q^{3/2} + 48.$$

Assume that supply and demand are in equilibrium at $q = 16$.

35. Find the consumers' surplus if the demand function for a particular wine is given by

$$D(q) = \frac{15,500}{(3.2q + 7)^3}$$

and if supply and demand are in equilibrium at $q = 5$.

36. Find the consumers' surplus if the demand function for grass seed is given by

$$D(q) = \frac{80}{(3q + 1)^2},$$

assuming that supply and demand are in equilibrium at $q = 3$.

37. Suppose the supply function of a certain item is given by

$$S(q) = e^{q/2} - 1$$

and the demand function is given by

$$D(q) = 400 - e^{q/2}.$$

(a) Graph the supply and demand curves.

(b) Find the point at which supply and demand are in equilibrium.

(c) Find the consumers' surplus.

(d) Find the producers' surplus.

38. Repeat the four parts in Exercise 37 for the supply function

$$S(q) = q^2 + \frac{11}{4}q$$

and the demand function

$$D(q) = 150 - q^2.$$

Work the given exercises.

39. An artist sketches the curves $y = 3\sqrt{x}$ and $y = 2x$ on a sheet of poster board and then cuts out the area between the curves. What is that area?

40. A computer-guided laser cuts out the area between the curves $y = 3\sqrt{x}$ and $y = 3x^2$ on a piece of sheet metal. What is that area?

41. **Business** If a large truck has been driven x thousand miles, the rate of repair costs in dollars per mile is given by

$$r(x) = .04x^{3/2}.$$

Find the total repair costs if the truck is driven

(a) 100,000 miles;   (b) 400,000 miles.

42. **Social Science** The rate of volunteerism in the United States (in millions of volunteers per year) can be approximated by

$$f(x) = 49x^{.112},$$

where $x = 7$ corresponds to the year 2007. What was the total number of volunteers (to the nearest million) between the start of 2007 and the end of 2011 (use $x = 7$ and $x = 12$ as limits of integration). (Data from: U.S. Bureau of Labor Statistics.)

43. **Natural Science** From 1905 to 1920, most of the predators of the Kaibab Plateau of Arizona were killed by hunters. This allowed the deer population there to grow rapidly until the deer had depleted their food sources, which caused a rapid decline in their population. The rate of change of this deer population during that time span is approximated by the function

$$D(t) = \frac{25}{2}t^3 - \frac{5}{8}t^4 \qquad (0 \le t \le 25),$$

where t is the time in years and $t = 0$ corresponds to the year 1905.

(a) Find the function for the deer population if there were 4000 deer in 1905.

(b) What was the population in 1920?

(c) When was the population at a maximum?

(d) What was the maximum population?

44. **Health** For a certain drug, the rate of release into the bloodstream of the active ingredient, in the appropriate units, is given by

$$R(t) = \frac{4}{3t} + \frac{2}{t^2},$$

where t is measured in hours after the drug is administered. Find the total amount released

(a) from $t = 1$ to 10 hours;

(b) from $t = 10$ to 20 hours.

45. **Business** A worker new to a job will improve efficiency with time, so that it takes fewer hours to produce an item with each day on the job, up to a certain point. Suppose the rate of change of the number of hours it takes a worker in a certain factory to produce the xth item is given by

$$H(x) = 20 - 2x.$$

The production rate per item is a maximum when $\int_0^T H(x)\, dx$ is a maximum.

(a) How many items must be made to achieve the maximum production rate? Assume that 0 items are made in 0 hours.

(b) What is the maximum production rate per item?

46. Social Science Suppose that all the people in a country are ranked according to their incomes, starting at the bottom. Let x represent the fraction of the country making the lowest income $(0 \leq x \leq 1)$; $x = .4$ therefore represents the lower 40% of all income producers. Let $I(x)$ represent the proportion of the total income earned by the lowest x of all the people. Thus, $I(.4)$ represents the fraction of total income earned by the lowest 40% of the population. Suppose

$$I(x) = .9x^2 + .1x.$$

Find and interpret the following:

(a) $I(.1)$;   **(b)** $I(.5)$;   **(c)** $I(.9)$.

If income were distributed uniformly, we would have $I(x) = x$. The area under this line of complete equality is $\frac{1}{2}$. As $I(x)$ dips farther below $y = x$, there is less equality of income distribution. This inequality can be quantified by the ratio of the area between $I(x)$ and $y = x$ to $\frac{1}{2}$. This ratio is called the *coefficient of inequality* and equals $2\int_0^1 (x - I(x))\, dx$.

(d) Graph $I(x) = x$ and $I(x) = .9x^2 + .1x$ for $0 \leq x \leq 1$ on the same axes.

(e) Find the area between the curves. What does this area represent?

✓ Checkpoint Answers

1. **(a)** $367.66   **(b)** $1185.91

2. **(a)** $247.2 billion   **(b)** $t \approx 12.1$

3. $19.323 billion   **4.** $320,000

5. **(a)** 5   **(b)** $437,500

6. **(a)** $q = 100$ **(b)** $350   **(c)** $250

13.6 Tables of Integrals (Optional)

Although the fundamental theorem of calculus is a powerful tool, it cannot be used unless you can find the antiderivative of the function to be integrated. Sometimes this is difficult or even impossible. For instance,

$$\int_0^1 e^{x^2}\, dx$$

cannot be evaluated exactly. In such cases, the only option is to employ various approximation methods (such as those used by graphing calculators).

Even when a function has an antiderivative, the methods presented in earlier sections may not be adequate for finding it. Computer algebra programs, some graphing calculators (such as the TI-89 and TI-Nspire), and Internet resources such as Wolfram Alpha (www.wolframalpha.com) can find the antiderivatives of a wide variety of functions. Tables of integrals provide another resource. One such table is Table 3 in Appendix B at the back of this text. The following examples illustrate its use.

Example 1   Find

$$\int \frac{1}{\sqrt{x^2 + 16}}\, dx.$$

Solution   By inspecting the table, we see that if $a = 4$, this antiderivative is the same as entry 5 of the table, which is

$$\int \frac{1}{\sqrt{x^2 + a^2}}\, dx = \ln|x + \sqrt{x^2 + a^2}| + C.$$

Substituting 4 for a in this entry, we get

$$\int \frac{1}{\sqrt{x^2 + 16}}\, dx = \ln|x + \sqrt{x^2 + 16}| + C.$$

This last result could be verified by taking the derivative of the right-hand side of this last equation. ✓₁

✓ Checkpoint 1

Find the given antiderivatives.

(a) $\displaystyle\int \frac{4}{\sqrt{x^2 + 100}}\, dx$

(b) $\displaystyle\int \frac{-9}{\sqrt{x^2 - 4}}\, dx$

Example 2   Find

$$\int \frac{8}{16 - x^2}\, dx.$$

Solution   Convert this antiderivative into the one given in entry 7 of the table by writing the 8 in front of the integral sign (permissible only with constants) and by letting $a = 4$. Doing this gives

$$8 \int \frac{1}{16 - x^2}\, dx = 8 \left[\frac{1}{2 \cdot 4} \ln \left| \frac{4 + x}{4 - x} \right| \right] + C$$

$$= \ln \left| \frac{4 + x}{4 - x} \right| + C. \ \checkmark_2$$

✓ **Checkpoint 2**

Find the given antiderivatives.

(a) $\int \dfrac{1}{x^2 - 4}\, dx$

(b) $\int \dfrac{-6}{x \sqrt{25 - x^2}}\, dx$

Example 3   Find

$$\int \sqrt{4x^2 + 9}\, dx.$$

Solution   This antiderivative seems most similar to entry 15 of the table. However, entry 15 requires that the coefficient of the x^2 term be 1. We can satisfy that requirement here by factoring out the 4:

$$\int \sqrt{4x^2 + 9}\, dx = \int \sqrt{4 \left(x^2 + \frac{9}{4} \right)}\, dx$$

$$= \int 2 \sqrt{x^2 + \frac{9}{4}}\, dx$$

$$= 2 \int \sqrt{x^2 + \left(\frac{3}{2} \right)^2}\, dx$$

✓ **Checkpoint 3**

Find the given antiderivatives.

(a) $\int \dfrac{3}{16x^2 - 1}\, dx$

(b) $\int \dfrac{-1}{9 - 100x^2}\, dx$

Now use entry 15 with $a = \frac{3}{2}$:

$$\int \sqrt{4x^2 + 9}\, dx = 2 \left[\frac{x}{2} \sqrt{x^2 + \frac{9}{4}} + \frac{(9/4)}{2} \ln \left| x + \sqrt{x^2 + \frac{9}{4}} \right| \right] + C$$

$$= x \sqrt{x^2 + \frac{9}{4}} + \frac{9}{4} \ln \left| x + \sqrt{x^2 + \frac{9}{4}} \right| + C. \ \checkmark_3$$

13.6 Exercises

Use the table of integrals to find each antiderivative. (See Examples 1–3.)

1. $\int \dfrac{-7}{\sqrt{x^2 + 36}}\, dx$

2. $\int \dfrac{9}{\sqrt{x^2 + 9}}\, dx$

3. $\int \dfrac{6}{x^2 - 9}\, dx$

4. $\int \dfrac{-9}{x^2 - 16}\, dx$

5. $\int \dfrac{-4}{x\sqrt{9 - x^2}}\, dx$

6. $\int \dfrac{3}{x\sqrt{121 - x^2}}\, dx$

7. $\int \dfrac{-5x}{3x + 1}\, dx$

8. $\int \dfrac{2x}{4x - 5}\, dx$

9. $\int \dfrac{13}{3x(3x - 5)}\, dx$

10. $\int \dfrac{-4}{3x(2x + 7)}\, dx$

11. $\int \dfrac{4}{4x^2 - 1}\, dx$

12. $\int \dfrac{-6}{9x^2 - 1}\, dx$

13. $\int \dfrac{3}{x\sqrt{1 - 9x^2}}\, dx$

14. $\int \dfrac{-5}{x\sqrt{1 - 16x^2}}\, dx$

15. $\int \dfrac{15x}{2x + 3}\, dx$

16. $\int \dfrac{11x}{6 - x}\, dx$

17. $\int \dfrac{-x}{(5x - 1)^2}\, dx$

18. $\int \dfrac{-6}{x(4x + 3)^2}\, dx$

19. $\int \dfrac{3x^4 \ln|x|}{4}\, dx$

20. $\int 4x^2 \ln|x|\, dx$

21. $\int \dfrac{7 \ln|x|}{x^2}\, dx \left(\textit{Hint:} \dfrac{1}{x^2} = x^{-2} \right)$

22. $\int \dfrac{-3 \ln|x|}{x^3}\, dx$

23. $\displaystyle\int 6xe^{3x}\,dx$

24. $\displaystyle\int xe^{-2x}\,dx$

Use Table 3 in Appendix B to solve the given problems.

25. Business The rate of change of revenue in dollars per computer from the sale of x computers is

$$R'(x) = \frac{5000}{\sqrt{x^2 + 25}}.$$

Find the total revenue from the sale of the first 20 computers.

26. Health The rate of reaction to a drug is given by

$$r'(x) = 2x^2 e^{-x},$$

where x is the number of hours since the drug was administered. Find the total reaction to the drug from $x = 1$ to $x = 5$.

27. Natural Science The rate of growth of a microbe population is given by

$$m'(x) = 25xe^{2x},$$

where x is time in days. What is the total accumulated growth after 3 days?

28. Social Science The rate (in hours per item) at which a worker in a certain job produces the xth item is

$$h'(x) = \sqrt{x^2 + 16}.$$

What is the total number of hours it will take this worker to produce the first seven items?

✓**Checkpoint Answers**

1. (a) $4 \ln\left|x + \sqrt{x^2 + 100}\right| + C$

 (b) $-9 \ln\left|x + \sqrt{x^2 - 4}\right| + C$

2. (a) $\dfrac{1}{4} \ln\left|\dfrac{x - 2}{x + 2}\right| + C$ (b) $\dfrac{6}{5} \ln\left|\dfrac{5 + \sqrt{25 - x^2}}{x}\right| + C$

3. (a) $\dfrac{3}{8} \ln\left|\dfrac{x - \frac{1}{4}}{x + \frac{1}{4}}\right| + C$ (b) $-\dfrac{1}{60} \ln\left|\dfrac{\frac{3}{10} + x}{\frac{3}{10} - x}\right| + C$

13.7 Differential Equations

A **differential equation** is an equation that involves an unknown function $y = f(x)$ and a finite number of its derivatives. Solving the differential equation for y would give the unknown function. Differential equations have been important in the physical sciences and engineering for several centuries. More recently, they have been used in the social sciences, life sciences, and economics to solve a variety of problems involving population growth, biological balance, interest rates, and more.

Up to now, we have considered only equations whose solutions are *numbers*. The solutions of differential equations, however, are *functions*. For example, the solutions of the differential equation

$$\frac{dy}{dx} = 3x^2 - 2x \tag{1}$$

consist of all functions y that satisfy the equation. Since the left side of the equation is the derivative of y with respect to x, the equation says that the derivative of y is $3x^2 - 2x$, which means that y is an *antiderivative* of $3x^2 - 2x$. In other words, the solutions are all functions y such that

$$y = \int (3x^2 - 2x)\,dx = x^3 - x^2 + C. \tag{2}$$

Each different value of C in equation (**2**) leads to a different solution of equation (**1**), showing that a differential equation can have an infinite number of solutions. Equation (**2**) is the **general solution** of the differential equation (**1**). Some of the solutions of equation (**1**) are graphed in Figure 13.34, on the following page. ✓₁

Equation (**1**) has the form

$$\frac{dy}{dx} = f(x),$$

so its solution suggests the following generalization.

✓**Checkpoint 1**

Find the general solution of

(a) $dy/dx = 4x$;

(b) $dy/dx = -x^3$;

(c) $dy/dx = 2x^2 - 5x$.

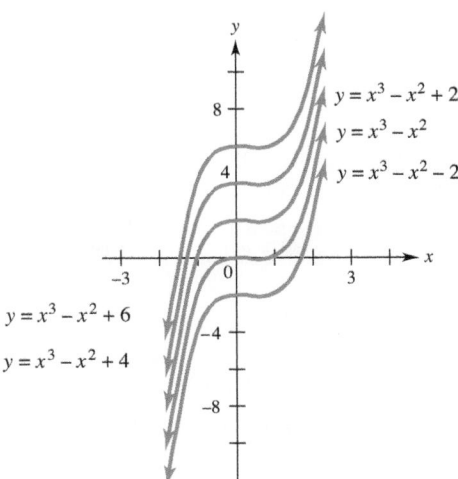

Figure 13.34

General Solution of $dy/dx = f(x)$

The general solution of the differential equation $dy/dx = f(x)$ is

$$y = \int f(x)\,dx.$$

Example 1   The population P of a flock of birds is growing exponentially so that

$$\frac{dP}{dx} = 20e^{.05x},$$

where x is time in years. Find P in terms of x if there were 20 birds in the flock initially.

Solution   Solve the differential equation:

$$P = \int 20e^{.05x}\,dx$$

$$= \frac{20}{.05}e^{.05x} + C$$

$$= 400e^{.05x} + C.$$

Since P is 20 when x is 0,

$$20 = 400e^{0} + C$$
$$-380 = C,$$

and

$$P = 400e^{.05x} - 380.$$

✓ **Checkpoint 2**

Find the particular solution in Example 1 if there were 100 birds in the flock after 2 years.

In Example 1, the given information was used to produce a solution with a specific value of C. Such a solution is called a **particular solution** of the given differential equation. The given information, $P = 20$ when $x = 0$, is called an **initial condition.** A differential equation together with an initial condition is called an initial value problem. ✓₂

Sometimes a differential equation must be rewritten in the form

$$\frac{dy}{dx} = f(x)$$

before it can be solved.

Example 2   Find the particular solution of

$$\frac{dy}{dx} - 3x = 7,$$

given that $y = 2$ when $x = -2$.

Solution   Add $3x$ to both sides of the equation to get

$$\frac{dy}{dx} = 3x + 7.$$

The general solution is

$$y = \int (3x + 7) \, dx$$

$$y = \frac{3x^2}{2} + 7x + C.$$

Substituting 2 for y and -2 for x gives

$$2 = \frac{3(-2)^2}{2} + 7(-2) + C$$

$$C = 10.$$

The particular solution is $y = \dfrac{3x^2}{2} + 7x + 10.$ ✔3

✓ **Checkpoint 3**

Find the particular solution of

$$2\frac{dy}{dx} - 4 = 9x^2,$$

given that $y = 4$ when $x = 1$.

Marginal productivity is the rate at which production changes (increases or decreases) for a unit change in investment. Thus, marginal productivity can be expressed as the first derivative of the function that gives production in terms of investment.

Example 3   **Business**   Suppose the marginal productivity of a manufacturing process is given by

$$P'(x) = 3x^2 - 10, \tag{3}$$

where x is the amount of the investment in hundreds of thousands of dollars. If the process produces 100 units with the present investment of $300,000 (that is, $x = 3$), how would production increase if the investment were increased to $500,000?

Solution   To obtain an equation for production, we solve the differential equation $P'(x) = 3x^2 - 10$. The general solution is:

$$P(x) = \int (3x^2 - 10) \, dx$$

$$= x^3 - 10x + C.$$

To find C, use the given initial values—that is, $P(3) = 100$:

$$100 = 3^3 - 10(3) + C$$

$$C = 103.$$

Production is thus represented by

$$P(x) = x^3 - 10x + 103,$$

and if investment is increased to \$500,000, production becomes

$$P(5) = 5^3 - 10(5) + 103 = 178.$$

An increase to \$500,000 in investment will increase production from 100 units to 178 units. ✔ 4

✓ **Checkpoint 4**

In Example 3, if marginal productivity is changed to

$$P'(x) = 3x^2 + 8x,$$

with the same initial conditions,

(a) find an equation for production;

(b) find the increase in production if investment increases to \$500,000.

Separation of Variables

The solution method used so far in this section is essentially the same as that in Sections 13.1 and 13.2, where we studied antiderivatives. But not all differential equations can be solved so easily. Suppose, for example, that y is a function of x such that

$$\frac{dy}{dx} = \frac{-6x}{y}.$$

We cannot simply find the antiderivative since the right side involves both variables. Nevertheless, there is a solution method that we now develop.

Consider a differential equation of the form

$$\frac{dy}{dx} = \frac{f(x)}{g(y)}. \tag{4}$$

(The example in the preceding paragraph is the case when $f(x) = -6x$ and $g(y) = y$.) Up to this point, we have used the symbol dy/dx to denote the derivative function of the function y. In advanced courses, it is shown that dy/dx can also be interpreted as a quotient of two differentials, dy divided by dx. (You may recall that differentials were used in integration by substitution.) Then we can multiply both sides of equation **(4)** by $g(y)\, dx$ to obtain

$$g(y)\, dy = f(x)\, dx.$$

In this form, all terms involving y (including dy) are on one side of the equation, and all terms involving x (and dx) are on the other side. Such a differential equation is said to be **separable,** since the variables x and y can be separated. A separable differential equation may be solved by integrating each side after separating the variables.

Example 4 Find the general solution of

$$\frac{dy}{dx} = -\frac{6x}{y}.$$

Solution Separate the variables by multiplying both sides by $y\, dx$:

$$y\, dy = -6x\, dx.$$

To solve this equation, take antiderivatives on each side:

$$\int y\, dy = \int -6x\, dx$$

$$\frac{y^2}{2} + C_1 = -3x^2 + C_2$$

$$3x^2 + \frac{y^2}{2} = C_2 - C_1.$$

Find the general solution of

$$\frac{dy}{dx} = \frac{5x^2}{y}.$$

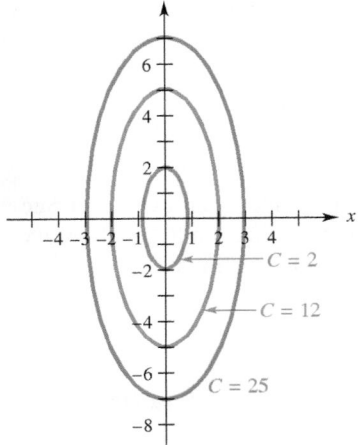

Figure 13.35

We can replace the constant $C_2 - C_1$ with a single constant C to obtain

$$3x^2 + \frac{y^2}{2} = C.^*$$

Since powers of y are involved, it is better to leave the solution in this form rather than trying to solve for y. For each positive constant C, the graph of the solution is an ellipse, as shown in Figure 13.35. ✓5

Example 5   **Business**   Sales at a small store are now $20,000 and are continuously increasing at an annual rate of 5%.

(a) Find a function $y = f(t)$ that gives the amount of sales y at time t years.

Solution   To say that sales are continuously increasing at an annual rate of 5% means that the rate of increase at any time t is

$$5\% \text{ of } y, \quad \text{that is,} \quad .05y.$$

Since the rate of increase is dy/dt, we have

$$\frac{dy}{dt} = .05y.$$

To solve this differential equation for y, begin by separating the variables in order to have all terms involving y (including dy) on the left and all terms involving t (including dt) on the right. Multiply both sides of the preceding equation by $\frac{dt}{y}$ (note that $y \neq 0$) to obtain

$$\frac{dy}{y} = .05 \, dt.$$

Now take antiderivatives on both sides and use properties of logarithms and exponents to simplify the result:

$$\int \frac{dy}{y} = \int .05 \, dt$$

$$\ln|y| = .05t + C$$

$$\ln y = .05t + C \qquad |y| = y \text{ since } y \text{ is positive}$$

$$e^{\ln y} = e^{.05t + C}$$

$$y = e^{.05t + C} \qquad \text{Property of logarithms (page 202)}$$

$$y = e^{.05t}e^C. \qquad \text{Property of exponents (page 36)}$$

If we denote the constant e^C by M, the sales function has the form

$$y = Me^{.05t},$$

the same as the exponential growth functions considered in Section 4.2. To find the value of M, use the fact that $y = 20{,}000$ when $t = 0$, that is,

$$20{,}000 = Me^{.05(0)} = Me^0 = M.$$

Therefore, the sales function is $y = Me^{.05t} = 20{,}000e^{.05t}.$

(b) What was the amount of sales after 4.5 years?

Solution   Evaluate y when $t = 4.5$:

$$y = 20{,}000e^{.05(4.5)} \approx \$25{,}046.45.$$

---

*From now on, we will add just one constant, with the understanding that it represents the difference between the two constants obtained from the two antiderivatives.

(c) After how many years did sales reach $30,000?

Solution To find when the sales will be $30,000, we solve the following equation for t:

$$y = 30,000 \qquad \text{Sales} = \$30,000.$$
$$20,000e^{.05t} = 30,000$$
$$e^{.05t} = \frac{30,000}{20,000} = 1.5 \qquad \text{Divide both sides by 20,000.}$$
$$\ln(e^{.05t}) = \ln(1.5) \qquad \text{Take the natural log of both sides.}$$
$$.05t = \ln(1.5) \qquad \text{Properties of logarithms}$$
$$t = \frac{\ln(1.5)}{.05} \approx 8.1. \qquad \text{Solve for } t.$$

Thus sales reach $30,000 after about 8.1 years.

(d) If the trend continues, when will sales be twice the current amount?

Solution Since the sales are currently $M = 20,000$, to find when the sales will be twice the current level, we solve the following equation for t:

$$y = 2M \qquad \text{Sales} = \text{twice current sales.}$$
$$Me^{.05t} = 2M$$
$$e^{.05t} = 2 \qquad \text{Divide both sides by } M.$$
$$\ln(e^{.05t}) = \ln(2) \qquad \text{Take the natural log of both sides.}$$
$$.05t = \ln(2) \qquad \text{Properties of logarithms}$$
$$t = \frac{\ln(2)}{.05} \approx 13.9. \qquad \text{Solve for } t.$$

Thus sales will double in about 13.9 years. Note that the time it takes for sales to double does not depend on the current level of sales M. We can see this in our work above since M was eliminated from the equation in the third step of the solution. ✓6

✓ Checkpoint 6

Suppose that sales are currently $5000 and continuously increasing at an annual rate of 10%.

(a) What will the amount of sales be in 4 years?

(b) When will sales be double the current level?

We can now explain how the exponential growth and decay functions presented in Section 4.2 were obtained. In the absence of inhibiting conditions, a population y (which might be human, animal, bacterial, etc.) grows in such a way that the rate of change of the population is proportional to the population at time x; that is, there is a constant k such that

$$\frac{dy}{dx} = ky.$$

The constant k is called the **growth-rate constant.** Example 5 is the case when $k = .05$. The same argument used there (with k in place of .05) shows that the population y at time x is given by

$$y = Me^{kx},$$

where M is the population at time $x = 0$. A positive value of k indicates growth while a negative value indicates decay.

Example 6 Social Science Women first participated in the Games of the Olympiad in 1900 when they accounted for 2.2% of athletes. Since that time, the percent of women athletes has increased at a continuous rate of approximately 2.68%. According to this model, what percent of Olympic athletes were women in 2012? (Data from: www.olympic.org.)

Solution   If y represents the percent of Olympic athletes who were women in year x and k is the growth-rate constant, then y satisfies the differential equation

$$\frac{dy}{dx} = ky.$$

As in Example 5, the solution to this differential equation is

$$y = Me^{kx}.$$

We were given that the growth-rate constant is $k = .0268$ (that is, 2.68% expressed as a decimal). Since M is the initial value of the function, if we let $x = 0$ correspond to the year 1900, then $M = 2.2$. So we have

$$y = 2.2e^{.0268x}.$$

To find the percent of women Olympic athletes in 2012, evaluate y at $x = 112$:

$$y = 2.2e^{.0268(112)} \approx 44.3\%. \quad \checkmark_7$$

✓ **Checkpoint 7**

Given that $\dfrac{dy}{dx} = .2y$ and
$y(0) = 50$, find $y(10)$.

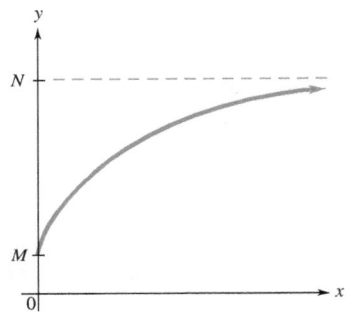

Figure 13.36

Limited Growth

As a model of population growth, the equation $y = Me^{kx}$ is not realistic over the long run for most populations. As shown by graphs of functions of the form $y = Me^{kx}$, with both M and k positive, growth would be unbounded. Additional factors, such as space restrictions or a limited amount of food, tend to inhibit the growth of populations as time goes on. In an alternative model that assumes a maximum population of size N, the rate of growth of a population is proportional to how close the population is to that maximum. These assumptions lead to the differential equation

$$\frac{dy}{dx} = k(N - y)$$

and the limited-growth function mentioned in Chapter 4. Graphs of limited-growth functions look like the graph in Figure 13.36, where M is the initial population.

Example 7   **Natural Science**   Researchers believe that a certain lake can support no more than 3000 fish. There are approximately 500 fish in the lake at present, with a continuous annual growth constant of .25.

(a) Write and solve a differential equation for the rate of growth of this population.

Solution   Let $N = 3000$ and $k = .25$. The rate of growth of the population y is given by

$$\frac{dy}{dx} = k(N - y)$$

$$\frac{dy}{dx} = .25(3000 - y).$$

To solve for y, first separate the variables. (Assume $y < 3000$, so that $3000 - y \neq 0$.)

$$\frac{dy}{3000 - y} = .25\, dx \qquad \text{Multiply both sides by } \frac{dx}{3000 - y}.$$

$$\int \frac{dy}{3000 - y} = \int .25\, dx \qquad \text{Take antiderivatives on both sides.}$$

$$-\ln(3000 - y) = .25x + C$$
$$\ln(3000 - y) = -.25x - C$$
$$3000 - y = e^{-.25x-C} = (e^{-.25x})(e^{-C}).$$

The absolute-value bars are not needed for $\ln(3000 - y)$ because y must be less than 3000 for this population, so that $3000 - y$ is always positive. Let $e^{-C} = B$. Then

$$3000 - y = Be^{-.25x}$$
$$y = 3000 - Be^{-.25x}.$$

Find B by using the fact that $y = 500$ when $x = 0$:

$$500 = 3000 - Be^0$$
$$500 = 3000 - B$$
$$B = 2500.$$

Notice that the value of B is the difference between the maximum population and the initial population. Substituting 2500 for B in the equation for y gives

$$y = 3000 - 2500e^{-.25x}.$$

(b) What will the fish population be in four years?

Solution In four years, the population will be

$$y = 3000 - 2500e^{-.25(4)} = 3000 - 2500e^{-1}$$
$$\approx 2080.3,$$

or about 2080 fish.

(c) After how many years will the population of fish be 2000?

Solution   To find when the population will be 2000, we solve the following equation for x:

$y = 2000$	Population = 2000.
$3000 - 2500e^{-.25x} = 2000$	
$-2500e^{-.25x} = -1000$	Subtract 3000 from both sides.
$e^{-.25x} = \dfrac{-1000}{-2500} = .4$	Divide both sides by -2500.
$\ln(e^{-.25x}) = \ln(.4)$	Take the natural log of both sides.
$-.25x = \ln(.4)$	Properties of logarithms
$x = \dfrac{\ln(.4)}{-.25} \approx 3.7.$	Solve for x.

So the population will reach 2000 fish after about 3.7 years. ✓₈

✓ **Checkpoint 8**

An animal population is growing at a continuous rate of 4%. The habitat will support no more than 10,000 animals. There are 3000 animals present now.

(a) Write an equation giving the population y in x years.

(b) Estimate the animal population in five years.

(c) When will the population be 6500?

13.7 Exercises

Find general solutions for the given differential equations. (See Examples 1 and 4.)

1. $\dfrac{dy}{dx} = -3x^2 + 7x$

2. $\dfrac{dy}{dx} = 5 - 9x^2$

3. $\dfrac{dy}{dx} = 6e^{-2x}$

4. $\dfrac{dy}{dx} = 3e^{-4x}$

5. $3x^3 - 2\dfrac{dy}{dx} = 0$

6. $3x^2 - 3\dfrac{dy}{dx} = 8$

7. $y\dfrac{dy}{dx} = x$

8. $y\dfrac{dy}{dx} = x^2 - 1$

9. $\dfrac{dy}{dx} = 4xy$

10. $\dfrac{dy}{dx} = x^2y$

11. $\dfrac{dy}{dx} = 4x^3y - 3x^2y$

12. $\dfrac{dy}{dx} = 2xy - 6x^2y$

13. $\dfrac{dy}{dx} = \dfrac{1}{3y^2}$

14. $\dfrac{x}{3y^2} = \dfrac{dy}{dx}$

15. $\dfrac{dy}{dx} = \dfrac{y}{x}, x > 0$ **16.** $\dfrac{dy}{dx} = \dfrac{y}{x^2}$

17. $\dfrac{dy}{dx} = y - 7$ **18.** $\dfrac{dy}{dx} = y - 4$

19. $\dfrac{dy}{dx} = 1 - y$ **20.** $\dfrac{dy}{dx} = 9 - y$

21. $\dfrac{dy}{dx} = \dfrac{7e^x}{e^y}$ **22.** $\dfrac{dy}{dx} = y^2 e^x$

Find particular solutions for the given equations. (See Examples 2 and 5.)

23. $\dfrac{dy}{dx} + 2x = 3x^2; y = 4$ when $x = 0$

24. $\dfrac{dy}{dx} = 8x^3 - 3x^2 + 2x; y = -1$ when $x = 1$

25. $\dfrac{dy}{dx}(x^3 + 28) = \dfrac{6x^2}{y}; y^2 = 6$ when $x = -3$

26. $\dfrac{2y}{x-3}\dfrac{dy}{dx} = \sqrt{x^2 - 6x}; y^2 = 40$ when $x = 8$

27. $\dfrac{dy}{dx} = \dfrac{x^2}{y}; y = 4$ when $x = 0$

28. $\dfrac{dy}{dx} = \dfrac{5x^4}{2y}; y = 1$ when $x = 0$

29. $(5x + 3)y = \dfrac{dy}{dx}; y = 1$ when $x = 0$

30. $x\dfrac{dy}{dx} - y\sqrt{x} = 0; y = 1$ when $x = 0$

31. $\dfrac{dy}{dx} = \dfrac{7x + 1}{y - 3}; y = 4$ when $x = 0$

32. $\dfrac{dy}{dx} = \dfrac{x^2 + 5}{2y - 1}; y = 11$ when $x = 0$

33. What is the difference between a general solution and a particular solution of a differential equation?

34. What is meant by a separable differential equation?

Work the given problems. (See Example 3.)

35. **Business** The marginal productivity of a manufacturing process is given by

$$\frac{dy}{dx} = \frac{3x^2 - 4x}{25},$$

where x is the amount of investment (in thousands of dollars) and y is the number of units produced per month (in hundreds). Production is 2300 units when investment is $5000. Find the production level if investment is increased to

(a) $8000;   **(b)** $11,000.

36. **Business** The marginal productivity of a process is given by

$$\frac{dy}{dx} = -\frac{40}{32 - 4x},$$

where x represents the investment (in thousands of dollars) and y is the number of units produced per month. Find the productivity for each of the given investments if productivity is 100 units when the investment is $1000.

(a) $3000   **(b)** $5000

(c) Can investments ever reach $8000 according to this model? Why?

Work these problems. (See Examples 5 and 6.)

37. **Social Science** Girls on the Run is a program for third through eighth graders that has grown rapidly in size according to the differential equation

$$\frac{dy}{dx} = .4y,$$

where y is the number of girls served in year x. Let $x = 0$ correspond to the year 2000 when 1330 girls participated. (Data from: www.GirlsOnTheRun.org.)

(a) Solve the differential equation for y.

(b) To the nearest thousand, find the number of Girls on the Run in 2010.

38. **Natural Science** The once endangered Bald Eagle (the only eagle unique to North America) has made a dramatic recovery in the lower 48 states that can be modeled by the differential equation

$$\frac{dy}{dx} = .07y,$$

where y is the number of breeding pairs in year x. Let $x = 0$ correspond to the year 1963 when there were only 487 breeding pairs. (Data from: U.S. Fish and Wildlife Service.)

(a) Solve the differential equation for y.

(b) To the nearest thousand, find the number of pairs of Bald Eagles in 2006.

39. **Natural Science** The sell-by dating of dairy products depends on the solution of a differential equation. The rate of growth of bacteria in such products increases with time. If y is the number of bacteria (in thousands) present at a time t (in days), then the rate of growth of bacteria can be expressed as dy/dt, and we have

$$\frac{dy}{dt} = kt,$$

where k is an appropriate constant. For a certain product, $k = 8$ and $y = 50$ (in thousands) when $t = 0$.

(a) Solve the differential equation for y.

(b) Suppose the maximum allowable value for y is 550 (thousand). How should the product be dated?

40. **Social Science** According to projections by the United States Census Bureau, the population of the United States will be about 321 million in 2015 and population growth can be approximated by the differential equation

$$\frac{dy}{dx} = .0063y,$$

where y is the population in millions and x is in years with $x = 0$ corresponding to the year 2015.

(a) Solve the differential equation for *y*.

(b) Find the projected population of the United States in 2050 ($x = 35$).

41. Business Sales of a particular product have been declining continuously at the rate of 15% per year.

(a) Express the rate of sales decline as a differential equation.

(b) Find the general solution for the equation in part (a).

(c) When will sales decrease to 25% of their original level?

42. Natural Science The amount of a tracer dye injected into the bloodstream decreases exponentially, with a decay constant of 3% per minute. If 6 cc are present initially, how many cc are present after 8 minutes? (Here, *k* will be negative.)

43. Finance If inflation grows continuously at a rate of 4%, how long will it take for $1 to lose half its value?

44. Business If the value *y* of an antique Italian violin has a continuous annual growth rate of 5% and is worth $100,000 today, how long will it be until it is worth twice its current value?

Work these exercises.

45. Social Science Suppose the rate at which a rumor spreads—that is, the number of people who have heard the rumor over a certain period of time—increases with the number of people who have heard it. If *y* is the number of people who have heard the rumor, then

$$\frac{dy}{dt} = ky,$$

where *t* is the time in days and *k* is a constant.

(a) If *y* is 1 when $t = 0$, and *y* is 5 when $t = 2$, find *k*.

Using the value of *k* from part (a), find *y* for each of the following times:

(b) $t = 3$; **(c)** $t = 5$; **(d)** $t = 10$.

46. Finance A life insurance company invests $5000 to fund a death benefit of $20,000. Growth in the investment over time can be modeled by the differential equation

$$\frac{dA}{dt} = Ai,$$

where *i* is the interest rate and $A(t)$ is the amount invested at time *t* (in years). Calculate the interest rate that the investment must earn in order for the company to fund the death benefit in 24 years. (Choose one of the following.)[*]

(a) $\dfrac{-\ln 2}{12}$ **(b)** $\dfrac{-\ln 2}{24}$ **(c)** $\dfrac{\ln 2}{24}$

(d) $\dfrac{\ln 2}{12}$ **(e)** $\dfrac{\ln 2}{6}$

47. Social Science A company has found that the rate at which a person new to the assembly line produces items is

$$\frac{dy}{dx} = 7.5e^{-.3x},$$

where *x* is the number of days the person has worked on the line. How many items can a new worker be expected to produce on the seventh day if the worker produces none when $x = 0$?

48. Social Science Repeat the previous exercise given that

$$\frac{dy}{dx} = 3.4e^{-.2x}.$$

Work these problems. (See Example 7.)

49. Natural Science The rate at which the number of bacteria in a culture is changing (in thousands of bacteria per hour) after the introduction of a bactericide is given by

$$\frac{dy}{dx} = 30 - y,$$

where *y* is the number of bacteria (in thousands) present at time *x* in hours. Find the number of bacteria present at each of the given times if there were one thousand bacteria present at time $x = 0$.

(a) $x = 2$ **(b)** $x = 7$ **(c)** $x = 10$

50. Natural Science An isolated fish population is limited to 4000 by the amount of food available. If there are now 320 fish and the population is growing continuously at the rate of 2% per year, find the population at the end of 10 years.

Physical Science *Newton's law of cooling states that the rate of change of temperature of an object is proportional to the difference in temperature between the object and the surrounding medium. Thus, if T is the temperature of the object after t hours and C is the (constant) temperature of the surrounding medium, then*

$$\frac{dT}{dt} = -k(T - C),$$

where k is a constant. When a dead body is discovered within 48 hours of the death and the temperature of the medium (air or water, for example) has been fairly constant, Newton's law of cooling can be used to determine the time of death.[†] (The medical examiner does not actually solve the equation for each case, but uses a table that is based on the formula.) Use Newton's law of cooling to work the given problems.

51. Assume that the temperature of a body at death is 98.6°F, the temperature of the surrounding air is 68°F, and the body temperature is 90°F at the end of one hour.

(a) Find an equation that gives the body temperature *T* after *t* hours.

(b) What was the temperature of the body after two hours?

(c) When will the temperature of the body be 75°F?

(d) Approximately when will the temperature of the body be within .01° of the surrounding air?

52. Repeat Exercise 51 under these conditions: The temperature of the surrounding air is 38°F, and after one hour, the body temperature is 81°.

---

[*]Problem 46 is from the May 2003 Course 1 Examination of the *Education and Examination Committee of the Society of Actuaries*. Reprinted by permission of the Society of Actuaries.

[†]Dennis Callas and David J. Hildreth, "Snapshots of Applications in Mathematics," *College Mathematics Journal* 26, No. 2 (March 1995).

Business *Elasticity of demand was discussed in Case 11 at the end of Chapter 11, where it was defined as*

$$E = -\frac{p}{q} \cdot \frac{dq}{dp}$$

for demand q and price p. Find the general demand equation q = f(p) for each of the given elasticity functions. (Hint: Set each elasticity function equal to $-\frac{p}{q} \cdot \frac{dq}{dp}$ *and then solve for q. Write the constant of integration as C.)*

53. $E = 2$

54. $E = \frac{4p^2}{q^2}$

✓**Checkpoint Answers**

1. (a) $y = 2x^2 + C$

(b) $y = -\frac{1}{4}x^4 + C$

(c) $y = \frac{2}{3}x^3 - \frac{5}{2}x^2 + C$

2. $P = 400e^{.05x} - 342$

3. $y = \frac{3}{2}x^3 + 2x + \frac{1}{2}$

4. (a) $P(x) = x^3 + 4x^2 + 37$

(b) Production goes from 100 units to 262 units, an increase of 162 units.

5. $\frac{y^2}{2} - \frac{5x^3}{3} = C$

6. (a) \$7459.12

(b) About 6.9 years

7. $y(10) \approx 369.5$

8. (a) $y = 10,000 - 7000e^{-.04x}$

(b) About 4269 animals

(c) About 17.3 years

CHAPTER 13 Summary and Review

Key Terms and Symbols

13.1 $\int f(x)\,dx$, indefinite integral of f
antiderivative
integral sign
integrand
power rule
constant-multiple rule

sum-or-difference rule

13.2 differential
integration by substitution

13.3 $\int_a^b f(x)\,dx$, definite integral of f
total change in $F(x)$

13.4 Fundamental Theorem of Calculus
$$F(x)\Big|_a^b = F(b) - F(a)$$

13.5 consumers' surplus
producers' surplus

13.6 tables of integrals

13.7 differential equation
general solution
particular solution
initial condition
marginal productivity
separable differential equation
growth-rate constant

Chapter 13 Key Concepts

Antiderivative $F(x)$ is an antiderivative of $f(x)$ if $F'(x) = f(x)$.

Indefinite Integral   If $F'(x) = f(x)$, then $\int f(x)\,dx = F(x) + C$, for any real number C.

Properties of Integrals $\int k \cdot f(x)\,dx = k \cdot \int f(x)\,dx$, for any real number k.

$$\int [f(x) \pm g(x)]\,dx = \int f(x)\,dx \pm \int g(x)\,dx.$$

Rules for Integrals   For $u = f(x)$ and $du = f'(x)\,dx$,

$$\int u^n\,du = \frac{u^{n+1}}{n+1} + C; \quad \int e^u\,du = e^u + C; \quad \int u^{-1}\,du = \int \frac{du}{u} = \ln|u| + C.$$

Definite Integral   If f is continuous on $[a, b]$, the definite integral of f from a to b is

$$\int_a^b f(x)\,dx = \lim_{n \to \infty} ([f(x_1) + f(x_2) + f(x_3) + \cdots + f(x_n)] \cdot \Delta x),$$

provided that this limit exists, where $\Delta x = \dfrac{b - a}{n}$ and x_i is the left endpoint of the ith interval.

Total Change in $F(x)$	Let f be continuous on $[a, b]$ and $f(x) \geq 0$ for all x in $[a, b]$. If $f(x)$ is the rate of change of $F(x)$, then the total change in $F(x)$ as x goes from a to b is given by $$\int_a^b f(x)\, dx.$$
Fundamental Theorem of Calculus	Let f be continuous on $[a, b]$ and let F be any antiderivative of f. Then $$\int_a^b f(x)\, dx = F(x)\Big|_a^b = F(b) - F(a).$$
General Solution of $\dfrac{dy}{dx} = f(x)$	The general solution of the differential equation $dy/dx = f(x)$ is $$y = \int f(x)\, dx.$$
General Solution of $\dfrac{dy}{dx} = ky$	The general solution of the differential equation $dy/dx = ky$ is $$y = Me^{kx}.$$

Chapter 13 Review Exercises

Find each indefinite integral.

1. $\displaystyle\int (x^2 - 8x - 7)\, dx$ **2.** $\displaystyle\int (6 - x^2)\, dx$

3. $\displaystyle\int 7\sqrt{x}\, dx$ **4.** $\displaystyle\int \frac{\sqrt{x}}{8}\, dx$

5. $\displaystyle\int (x^{1/2} + 3x^{-2/3})\, dx$ **6.** $\displaystyle\int (8x^{4/3} + x^{-1/2})\, dx$

7. $\displaystyle\int \frac{-6}{x^3}\, dx$ **8.** $\displaystyle\int \frac{9}{x^4}\, dx$

9. $\displaystyle\int -3e^{2x}\, dx$ **10.** $\displaystyle\int 8e^{-x}\, dx$

11. $\displaystyle\int \frac{10}{x - 3}\, dx$ **12.** $\displaystyle\int \frac{-14}{x + 2}\, dx$

13. $\displaystyle\int \frac{1}{3 - x}\, dx$ **14.** $\displaystyle\int \frac{5}{2 - x}\, dx$

15. $\displaystyle\int \frac{3x}{x^2 - 1}\, dx$ **16.** $\displaystyle\int \frac{-6x}{4 - x^2}\, dx$

17. $\displaystyle\int \frac{12x^2\, dx}{(x^3 + 5)^4}$ **18.** $\displaystyle\int (x^2 - 5x)^4(2x - 5)\, dx$

19. $\displaystyle\int \frac{4x - 5}{2x^2 - 5x}\, dx$ **20.** $\displaystyle\int \frac{8(2x + 9)}{x^2 + 9x + 1}\, dx$

21. $\displaystyle\int 5xe^{3x^2}\, dx$ **22.** $\displaystyle\int 4xe^{-3x^2+7}\, dx$

23. $\displaystyle\int \frac{x^2}{e^{3x^3}}\, dx$ **24.** $\displaystyle\int \frac{-2x}{e^{x^2}}\, dx$

25. $\displaystyle\int \frac{3(\ln x)^5}{x}\, dx$ **26.** $\displaystyle\int \frac{10(\ln(5x + 3))^2}{5x + 3}\, dx$

27. $\displaystyle\int \sqrt{2x + 9}\, dx$ **28.** $\displaystyle\int \sqrt{1 + 5x}\, dx$

29. Explain how rectangles are used to approximate the area under a curve.

30. (a) Use five rectangles to approximate the area between the graph of $f(x) = 16x^2 - x^4 + 2$ and the x-axis from $x = -2$ to $x = 3$.

(b) Use numerical integration to approximate this area.

31. Repeat Exercise 30 using six rectangles for the function $g(x) = -x^4 + 12x^2 + x + 5$ from $x = -3$ to $x = 3$.

32. Use four rectangles to approximate the area under the graph of $f(x) = 2x + 3$ and above the x-axis from $x = 0$ to $x = 4$. Let the height of each rectangle be the value of the function on the left side.

33. Find $\displaystyle\int_0^4 (2x + 3)\, dx$ by using the formula $A = \frac{1}{2}(B + b)h$ for the area of a trapezoid, where B and b are the lengths of the parallel sides and h is the distance between them. Compare with Exercise 32. If the answers are different, explain why.

34. Explain under what circumstances substitution is useful in integration.

Find each definite integral.

35. $\displaystyle\int_0^4 (x^3 - x^2)\, dx$ **36.** $\displaystyle\int_0^1 (5 - 10x + 15x^2)\, dx$

37. $\displaystyle\int_2^5 (6x^{-2} + x^{-3})\, dx$ **38.** $\displaystyle\int_2^3 (5x^{-2} + 7x^{-4})\, dx$

39. $\displaystyle\int_1^5 15x^{-1}\, dx$ **40.** $\displaystyle\int_1^6 \frac{8x^{-1}}{3}\, dx$

41. $\displaystyle\int_0^4 2e^{-5x}\,dx$

42. $\displaystyle\int_1^2 \frac{7}{2}e^{4x}\,dx$

43. $\displaystyle\int_{\sqrt{5}}^5 2x\sqrt{x^2-3}\,dx$

44. $\displaystyle\int_0^1 x\sqrt{5x^2+4}\,dx$

45. $\displaystyle\int_1^6 \frac{8x+12}{x^2+3x+9}\,dx$

46. $\displaystyle\int_0^3 \frac{6x}{x^2+1}\,dx$

47. $\displaystyle\int_1^e \frac{9(\ln x)^2}{x}\,dx$

48. $\displaystyle\int_1^4 \frac{3(\ln x)^5}{x}\,dx$

Find the area between the x-axis and f(x) over each of the given intervals.

49. $f(x) = e^x;\ [0, 2]$

50. $f(x) = 1 + e^{-x};\ [0, 4]$

Business   *Find the cost function for each of the marginal cost functions in Exercises 51–54.*

51. $C'(x) = 10 - 5x$; fixed cost is $4.

52. $C'(x) = 2x + 3x^2$; 2 units cost $12.

53. $C'(x) = 3\sqrt{2x-1}$; 13 units cost $270.

54. $C'(x) = \dfrac{6}{x+1}$; fixed cost is $18.

Work the given exercises.

55. Business   The rate of change of sales of a new brand of tomato soup, in thousands per month, is given by

$$S(x) = \sqrt{x} + 3,$$

where x is the time in months that the new product has been on the market. Find the total sales after 9 months.

56. Business   The curve shown in the accompanying figure gives the rate at which an investment accumulates income (in dollars per year). Use rectangles of width 2 units and height determined by the value of the function at the left endpoint to approximate the total income accumulated over 10 years.

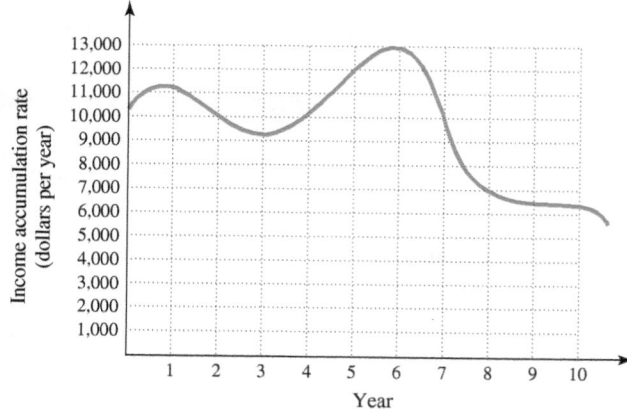

57. Business   A manufacturer of electronic equipment requires a certain rare metal. He has a reserve supply of 4,000,000 units that he will not be able to replace. If the rate at which the metal is used is given by

$$f(t) = 100,000e^{.03t},$$

where t is the time in years, how long will it be before he uses up the supply? (*Hint:* Find an expression for the total amount used in t years, and set it equal to the known reserve supply.)

58. Natural Science   The rate of change of the population of a rare species of Australian spider is given by

$$f'(t) = 150 - \sqrt{3.2t + 4},$$

where $f(t)$ is the number of spiders present at time t, measured in months. Find the total number of additional spiders in the first 10 months.

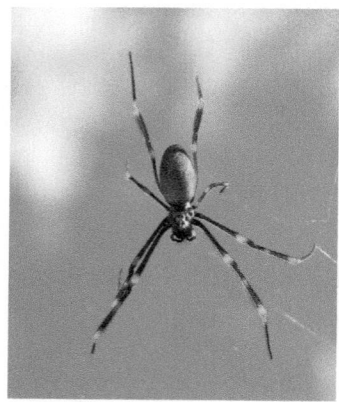

59. Business   The rate at which profit was generated (in billions of dollars per year) by PepsiCo Inc., can be approximated by

$$f(x) = .51x + 3.14,$$

where $x = 0$ corresponds to the year 2000. What were the total profits generated over the 13-year period from the beginning of 2000 to the end of 2012 (use $x = 0$ and $x = 13$ as limits of integration)? (Data from: www.morningstar.com.)

60. Business   The rate of consumption of solar energy (in trillions of BTUs per year) can be approximated by

$$f(x) = 1.3x^2 - 8.4x + 64,$$

where $x = 0$ corresponds to the year 2000. Estimate the total consumption of solar energy of the 12-year period from the beginning of 2000 to the end of 2011 (use $x = 0$ and $x = 12$ as limits of integration). (Data from: U.S. Energy Information Administration.)

61. Business   The rate at which profit was generated (in billions of Japanese yen per year) by Nintendo Co., Ltd., can be approximated by

$$f(x) = -44x^2 + 740x - 2350,$$

where $x = 0$ corresponds to the year 2000. What were the total profits (in billions of Japanese yen) generated over the 4-year period from the beginning of 2008 to the end of 2011? (Data from: www.morningstar.com.)

62. Social Science   The rate at which assaults were committed in the United States (in thousands per year) can be approximated by

$$f(x) = -.47x^3 + 6.7x^2 - 34x + 925,$$

where $x = 0$ corresponds to the year 2000. What was the total number of assaults committed from the beginning of 2000 to the end of 2010? (Data from: www.fbi.gov.)

63. **Business** A company has installed new machinery that will produce a savings rate (in thousands of dollars per year) of

$$S'(x) = 225 - x^2,$$

where x is the number of years the machinery is to be used. The rate of additional costs (in thousands of dollars per year) to the company because of the new machinery is expected to be

$$C'(x) = x^2 + 25x + 150.$$

To maximize net savings, for how many years should the company use the new machinery? Find the net savings (in thousands of dollars) over this period.

64. Explain what consumers' surplus and producers' surplus are.

65. **Business** Suppose that the supply function of some commodity is

$$S(q) = q^2 + 5q + 100$$

and the demand function for the commodity is

$$D(q) = 350 - q^2.$$

(a) Find the producers' surplus.

(b) Find the consumers' surplus.

66. **Natural Science** The rate of infection of a disease (in people per month) is given by the function

$$I'(t) = \frac{100t}{t^2 + 2},$$

where t is the time in months since the disease broke out. Find the total number of infected people over the first four months of the disease.

67. **Business** Suppose waiting times (in minutes) in a teller line at a bank can be estimated by an exponential distribution and the function

$$f(x) = \frac{1}{2}e^{-x/2}.$$

(a) Find the probability that a customer in line waits less than 2 minutes.

(b) Find the probability that a customer in line waits more than 3 minutes.

68. **Natural Science** Suppose the amount of time between blinks of an eye for a given individual can be modeled by an exponential distribution and the function

$$f(t) = .44e^{-.44t},$$

where t is measured in seconds.

(a) Find the probability that the person will take between 1 and 2 seconds between blinks.

(b) Find the probability that the person will take more than 4 seconds between blinks.

Use technology or a table of integrals to find the given antiderivatives.

69. $\displaystyle\int \frac{1}{\sqrt{x^2 - 64}}\, dx$

70. $\displaystyle\int \frac{10}{x\sqrt{25 + x^2}}\, dx$

71. $\displaystyle\int \frac{18}{x^2 - 9}\, dx$

72. $\displaystyle\int \frac{15x}{2x - 5}\, dx$

Find general solutions for the given differential equations.

73. $\dfrac{dy}{dx} = 2x^3 + 6x + 5$

74. $\dfrac{dy}{dx} = x^2 + \dfrac{5x^4}{8}$

75. $\dfrac{dy}{dx} = \dfrac{3x + 1}{y}$

76. $\dfrac{dy}{dx} = \dfrac{e^x + x}{y - 1}$

Find particular solutions for the given differential equations.

77. $\dfrac{dy}{dx} = 5(e^{-x} - 1); y = 17$ when $x = 0$

78. $\dfrac{dy}{dx} = \dfrac{x}{x^2 - 3} + 7; y = 52$ when $x = 2$

79. $(5 - 2x)y = \dfrac{dy}{dx}; y = 2$ when $x = 0$

80. $\sqrt{x}\,\dfrac{dy}{dx} = xy; y = 4$ when $x = 1$

81. **Social Science** According to projections by the U.S. Census Bureau, the rate of growth of the Hispanic population in the United States can be modeled by the differential equation

$$\frac{dy}{dx} = .0192y,$$

where y is the population (in millions) in year x. Let $x = 0$ correspond to the year 2015 when the Hispanic population is projected to be 57 million.

(a) Solve the differential equation for y.

(b) What is the projected Hispanic population in the year 2050 ($x = 35$)?

82. **Business** You can purchase a collectible Rickenbacker 325 Capri electric guitar for $3000 today. Suppose that its value y has a continuous growth rate of 4%. How long will it be until it is worth twice its current value?

83. **Social Science** The percentage y of 3- to 5-year-old children enrolled in preprimary programs in year x approximately satisfies the differential equation

$$\frac{dy}{dx} = .05(70 - y).$$

Let $x = 0$ correspond to the year 1965 when enrollment was 27%. (Data from: National Center for Education Statistics.)

(a) Solve the differential equation for y.

(b) If this trend continues, what percent of 3- to 5-year-old children will be enrolled in preprimary programs in 2015 ($x = 50$)?

84. **Business** The rate at which a new worker in a certain factory produces items is given by

$$\frac{dy}{dx} = .2(125 - y),$$

where y is the number of items produced by the worker per day, x is the number of days worked, and the maximum production per day is 125 items. Assume that the worker produced 20 items the first day on the job ($x = 0$).

(a) Find the number of items the new worker will produce after 10 days.

(b) According to the function that is the solution of the differential equation, can the worker ever produce 125 items in a day?

85. Physical Science   A roast at a temperature of 40° is put in a 300° oven. After 1 hour, the roast has reached a temperature of 150°. Newton's law of cooling states that

$$\frac{dT}{dt} = k(T - T_F),$$

where T is the temperature of an object at time t, the surrounding medium has temperature T_F, and k is a constant.

(a) Use Newton's law of cooling to find the temperature of the roast after 2.5 hours.

(b) How long does it take for the roast to reach a temperature of 250°?

86. Business   The marginal profit (in hundreds of dollars per hundred books) of a small bookstore is given by

$$\frac{dy}{dx} = 2.4e^{.1x},$$

where x is the number of books sold (in hundreds). Assume that profits were 0 initially.

(a) Find the profit when 800 books are sold.

(b) Find the profit when 1200 books are sold.

Case Study 13 Bounded Population Growth

The population growth model $\frac{dP}{dt} = kP$, whose solution is the exponential growth function $P = P_0 e^{kt}$, can work well in a situation where a population is changing rapidly over a short period of time. But the model may not be useful in the long term. Exponential functions grow very large very quickly and will eventually exceed any values that the population under consideration may actually attain. For this reason, the exponential function is said to be *unbounded*. A more realistic growth model would take into account any natural bounds on the population size.

For example, consider a population of cattle or sheep that lives and grazes on a piece of farmland. Sheep, in particular, obtain the majority of their food intake from foraging in their environment. The sheep happily graze on the grass, plants, and weeds without exhausting the supply. This allows time for the plant life to grow back, and the eating–growing cycle continues. If the farmer populates the farmland with too many sheep, however, the plants may be eaten too quickly, failing to grow enough before some of the sheep develop health problems and possibly die. The maximum number of animals the farmland can comfortably sustain over a long period of time is called the *carrying capacity* of the land.

One model used for bounded population growth is the *logistic differential equation*

$$\frac{dP}{dt} = kP(C - P),$$

where k is a positive proportionality constant and C is the carrying capacity of the environment under consideration. When the population satisfies

$$0 < P < C,$$

the expression $kP(C - P)$ will be positive, and a positive derivative indicates that the population is increasing. If the population P exceeds the carrying capacity C, the factor $C - P$ becomes negative and

$$\frac{dP}{dt} < 0,$$

indicating that the population is decreasing, which must be the case when the carrying capacity is exceeded. The model thus agrees with the expected behavior of a bounded population.

For example, given an initial population of 10 sheep on land with carrying capacity $C = 200$ and a proportionality factor $k = .005$, the logistic differential equation becomes

$$\frac{dP}{dt} = .005P(200 - P).$$

Separating variables and integrating gives

$$\int \frac{1}{P(200 - P)}\, dP = \int .005\, dt. \tag{1}$$

The right side of equation **(1)** is easily integrated:

$$\int .005\, dt = .005t + K. \tag{2}$$

The left side of equation **(1)** does not match the standard integration formulas, but can be integrated by using the following identity, which you are asked to verify in Exercise 1:

$$\frac{1}{P(C - P)} = \frac{1/C}{P} + \frac{1/C}{C - P}. \tag{3}$$

Applying this identity with $C = 200$ allows the left-hand side of equation **(1)** to be easily integrated:

$$\int \frac{1}{P(200 - P)}\, dP = \int \frac{1/200}{P}\, dP + \int \frac{1/200}{200 - P}\, dP$$

$$= \frac{1}{200}\ln(P) - \frac{1}{200}\ln(200 - P). \tag{4}$$

Substituting equations **(2)** and **(4)** into equation **(1)** shows that

$$\frac{1}{200}\ln(P) - \frac{1}{200}\ln(200 - P) = .005t + K. \tag{5}$$

In Exercise 2, you are asked to solve equation (5) for $P(t)$ and use the fact that $P(0) = 10$ to obtain the population function

$$P(t) = \frac{200e^t}{e^t + 19}. \qquad (6)$$

After one year, the population would consist of $P(1) = 25$ sheep.

The graph of the population function in the accompanying figure illustrates the typical S-shaped curve for a population modeled by the logistic differential equation. The population increases rapidly at first, and then the rate of increase decreases as the population approaches the carrying capacity of its environment.

Before the logistic model can be applied, an estimate of the carrying capacity is needed. In the case of cattle and sheep, veterinary and agricultural science, along with hundreds of years of recorded experience, tell a farmer how much livestock can survive comfortably on a given plot of land. A much more difficult problem is to determine the carrying capacity of a population when many factors contribute to the carrying capacity.

Exercises

1. Verify equation (3).

2. Use the techniques of Section 13.7 and the fact that $P(0) = 10$ to solve equation (5).

3. The carrying capacity of Atlantic harp seals has been estimated to be $C = 10$ million seals. Let $t = 0$ correspond to the year 1980 when this seal population was estimated to be about 2 million. (Data from: Fisheries and Oceans Canada.)

    (a) Use a logistic growth model $\frac{dP}{dt} = kP(C - P)$ with $k = .007$ to find a population function similar to the one given in equation (6).

    (b) According to this model, what is the seal population in the year 2012? The year 2018?

    (c) If the model remains accurate, when will the seal population reach 8 million?

Extended Project

The logistic growth model $\frac{dP}{dt} = kP(C - P)$ can be applied to the population of the world. You will need to do some research to find the current world population and an estimate of the carrying capacity of the Earth. (Internet sites for the U.S. Census Bureau and the United Nations may be helpful.) Let $t = 0$ correspond to the current year. Use $k = .0011$ and the values you found for the current world population and carrying capacity to find a function for the population of the world. If the model remains accurate, what will the world population be in 2020? When will the world population reach 9 billion? According to the model, will the world population ever reach 20 billion? Write a report explaining your findings. Include the logistic growth model, the values you found for the current population and carrying capacity (including your sources), the estimates you found for future world population, and an explanation that the model is an estimate and has limitations.

Multivariate Calculus

14

CHAPTER

Divers must take into account both water depths and dive times to determine safe water pressures and avoid compression sickness. Anyone who is active outside during cold weather may experience windchill (which is determined by air temperature and wind speed). The profit a business makes is dependent on a variety of factors, such as the cost of materials, wages, competitive price pressures, and interest rates. Accurate models of these and other real-life situations require functions of two or more variables. See Exercise 60 on page 835, Exercise 62 on page 836, and Exercise 32 on page 844.

Many of the ideas developed for functions of one variable also apply to functions of more than one variable. In particular, the fundamental idea of the derivative generalizes in a very natural way to functions of more than one variable.

14.1 Functions of Several Variables

Recall from Section 3.1 that a **function** consists of a set of inputs called the **domain,** a set of outputs called the **range,** and a **rule** by which each input determines exactly one output. For all of the functions studied previously in this text, both the inputs and outputs were real numbers. We now extend the concept of function to the case when the inputs are *ordered pairs* of real numbers.

Suppose, for example, that a gourmet popsicle company makes fruity and creamy popsicles. It costs $10 per dozen to produce fruit-based popsicles and $15 per dozen to make cream-based popsicles. So the cost of producing x dozen fruity popsicles and y dozen creamy popsicles is $10x + 15y$. We can think of this cost function as a function of *two* variables whose rule is

$$C(x, y) = 10x + 15y.$$

For instance, the cost of producing 250 dozen fruity popsicles and 100 dozen creamy popsicles is denoted $C(250, 100)$ and is found by letting $x = 250$ and $y = 100$ in the rule of the function:

$$C(250, 100) = 10 \cdot 250 + 15 \cdot 100 = 2500 + 1500 = \$4000.$$

Here is the general definition.

> A **function of two variables** consists of
>
> a set of inputs that are *ordered pairs* of real numbers (the **domain**);
>
> a set of outputs that are real numbers (the **range**); and
>
> a rule by which each input pair produces exactly one output number.

Essentially the same definition works for functions of three, four, or more variables—just change the inputs to ordered *triples* of real numbers for functions of three variables, to ordered *quadruples* of real numbers for functions of four variables, and so on. Functions of more than one variable are called **multivariate functions.**

Many familiar formulas can be considered as the rules of multivariate functions. For example,

- the volume V of a cone is given by a function of two variables,

$$V(r, h) = \frac{1}{3}\pi r^2 h,$$

where r is the radius of the base and h is the height of the cone;

- the future value A of an amount deposited at compound interest is given by a function of three variables,

$$A(P, i, n) = P(1 + i)^n,$$

where P is the amount deposited, i is the interest rate per period, and n is the number of periods.

Unless otherwise stated, the domain of a multivariate function defined by a formula or equation is assumed to be the set of all inputs for which the rule of the function produces a real number as output.

Example 1 Let $f(x, y) = 4x^2 + 2xy + 9/y$, and find each of the given quantities.

(a) $f(-1, 3)$

Solution Replace x with -1 and y with 3:

$$f(-1, 3) = 4(-1)^2 + 2(-1)(3) + \frac{9}{3} = 4 - 6 + 3 = 1.$$

✓ **Checkpoint 1**

Let $f(x, y) = x^3 - 5x^2 + xy$. Find

(a) $f(2, 4)$;

(b) $f(-2, 3)$.

Answers to Checkpoint exercises are found at the end of the section.

(b) The domain of f

Solution Because of the quotient $9/y$, it is not possible to replace y with 0, so the domain of the function f consists of all ordered pairs (x, y) such that $y \neq 0$. ✓

Example 2 Social Science In major league baseball, a pitcher's earned run average is the mean number of earned runs given up per nine innings pitched. Unearned runs, which result from defensive errors, are excluded from this statistic.

(a) Write the rule of the function $f(r, p)$ that gives the earned run average (ERA) for a pitcher who allowed r earned runs in p innings pitched.

Solution Since the pitcher has given up r earned runs in p innings, this corresponds to a mean of $\dfrac{r}{p}$ earned runs per inning. Since the ERA is defined to be the mean number of earned runs allowed in nine innings, the rule for the function is $f(r, p) = \dfrac{9r}{p}$.

(b) The pitcher with the lowest ERA in the 2012 season was Clay Buchholz of the Boston Red Sox. He pitched 44.2 innings and allowed only 5 runs, all of which were earned. Find his ERA. (Data from: www.mlb.com.)

Solution Replace r with 5 and p with 44.2 to get

$$f(5, 44.2) = \frac{9(5)}{44.2} \approx 1.02 \text{ earned runs per nine innings.}$$

✓**Checkpoint 2**

Find the earned run average for Mark Buehrle of the Toronto Blue Jays, who pitched 35 innings in 2012 and gave up 27 runs, 2 of which were unearned.

Graphing Equations in Three Variables

Equations in two variables, such as $3x + 2y = 5$, are graphed by using an x-axis and a y-axis to locate points in a plane. The plane determined by the x- and y-axes is called the **xy-plane.** In order to graph an equation in three variables, such as $2x + y + z = 6$, a third axis is needed—the z-axis, which goes through the origin in the xy-plane and is perpendicular to both the x-axis and the y-axis.

Figure 14.1 shows one possible way to draw the three axes. In Figure 14.1, the yz-plane is in the plane of the page, with the x-axis perpendicular to the plane of the page.

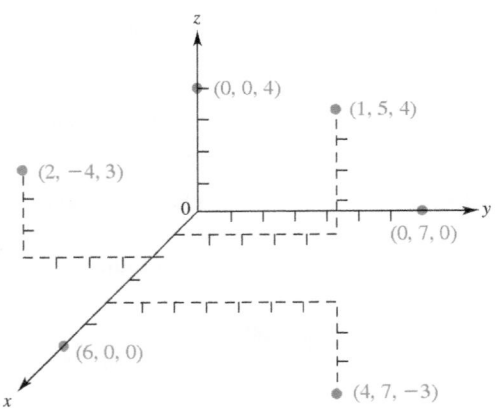

Figure 14.1

✓**Checkpoint 3**

Locate (3, 2, 4) on the coordinate system shown here.

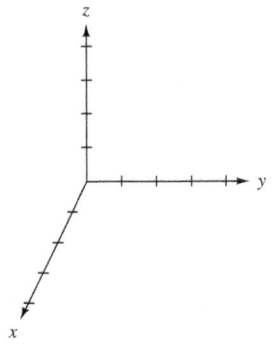

Just as we graphed ordered pairs earlier, we can now graph **ordered triples** of the form (x, y, z). For example, to locate the point corresponding to the ordered triple $(2, -4, 3)$, start at the origin and go 2 units along the positive x-axis. Then go 4 units in a negative direction (to the left), parallel to the y-axis. Finally, go up 3 units, parallel to the z-axis. The point representing $(2, -4, 3)$ is shown in Figure 14.1, along with several other points. The region of three-dimensional space where all coordinates are positive is called the **first octant.** ✓₃

Some simple equations in three variables can be graphed by hand. In Chapter 2, we saw that the graph of $ax + by = c$ (where a, b, and c are constants and not both a and b are zero) is a straight line. This result generalizes to three dimensions.

Planes

If a, b, c, and d are real numbers, with a, b, and c not all zero, then the graph of

$$ax + by + cz = d$$

is a plane.

Example 3   Graph $2x + y + z = 6$.

Solution   By the result shown in the preceding box, the graph of this equation is a plane. Earlier, we graphed straight lines by finding x- and y-intercepts. A similar idea helps graph a plane. To find the x-intercept—the point where the graph crosses the x-axis—let $y = 0$ and $z = 0$:

$$2x + 0 + 0 = 6$$
$$x = 3.$$

The point $(3, 0, 0)$ is on the graph. To find the y-intercept, let $x = 0$ and $z = 0$, which gives the point $(0, 6, 0)$. Letting $x = 0$ and $y = 0$ leads to the point $(0, 0, 6)$, which is the z-intercept. The plane through these three points includes the triangular surface shown in Figure 14.2. This region is the first-octant part of the plane that is the graph of $2x + y + z = 6$.

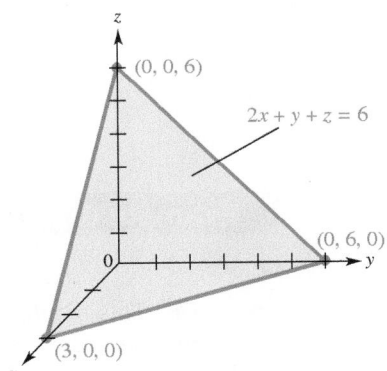

Figure 14.2

Throughout this discussion, we assume that all equations involve three variables. Consequently, an equation such as $x + z = 6$ is understood to have a y-term with zero coefficient: $x + 0y + z = 6$.

Example 4   Graph $x + z = 6$.

Solution   To find the x-intercept, let $z = 0$, giving $(6, 0, 0)$. If $x = 0$, we get the z-intercept $(0, 0, 6)$. Because there is no y in the equation $x + z = 6$, there can be no y-intercept. A plane that has no y-intercept is parallel to the y-axis. The first-octant portion of the graph of $x + z = 6$ is shown in Figure 14.3.

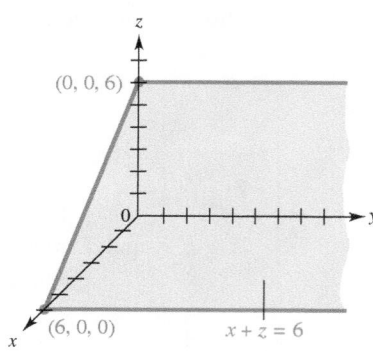

Figure 14.3

Example 5 Graph the three planes whose equations are respectively

$$x = 0, \quad y = 0, \quad \text{and} \quad z = 0.$$

Solution The graph of $x = 0$ consists of all points with first coordinate 0. These are the points in the **yz-plane** shown in Figure 14.4. Similarly, the graph of $y = 0$ consists of all points with second coordinate 0, that is, all points in the **xz-plane** in Figure 14.4. Finally, the graph of $z = 0$ consists of all points with third coordinate 0—the **xy-plane** in Figure 14.4.

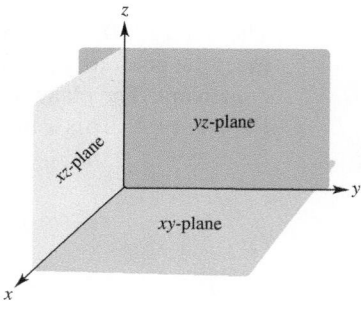

Figure 14.4

Example 6 Graph each of the given equations.

(a) $x = 3$

Solution This graph, which goes through $(3, 0, 0)$, can have no y-intercept and no z-intercept. It is, therefore, a plane parallel to the y-axis and the z-axis and, therefore, to the yz-plane. The first-octant portion of the graph is shown in Figure 14.5.

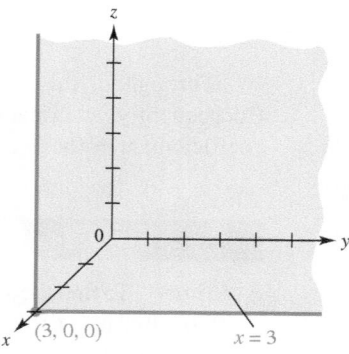

Figure 14.5

(b) $y = 4$

Solution This graph goes through $(0, 4, 0)$ and is parallel to the xz-plane. The first-octant portion of the graph is shown in Figure 14.6.

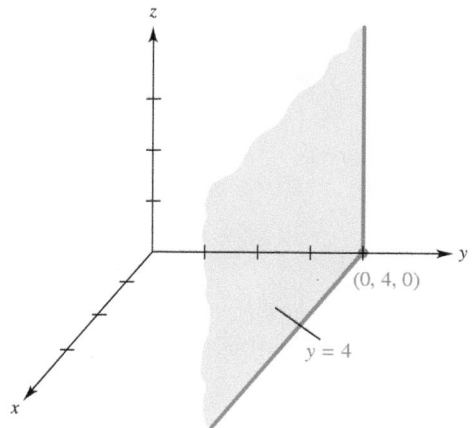

Figure 14.6

(c) $z = 1$.

✓ Checkpoint 4

Describe each graph and give any intercepts.

(a) $2x + 3y - z = 4$

(b) $x + y = 3$

(c) $z = 2$

Solution The graph is a plane parallel to the xy-plane and passing through $(0, 0, 1)$. Its first-octant portion is shown in Figure 14.7. ✓ 4

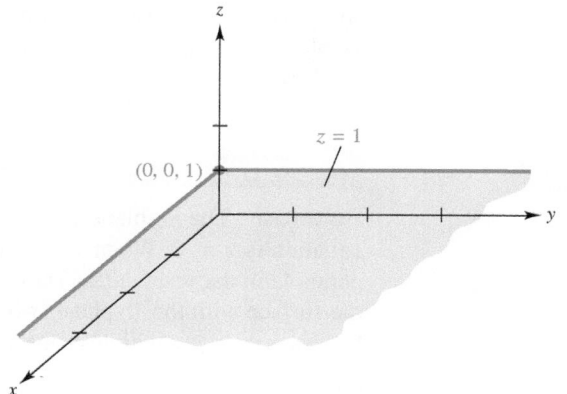

Figure 14.7

Graphing Functions of Two Variables

The graph of a function of one variable, $y = f(x)$, is a curve in the plane. If x_0 is in the domain of f, the point $(x_0, f(x_0))$ on the graph lies directly above or directly below (or possibly on) the number x_0 on the x-axis, as shown in Figure 14.8.

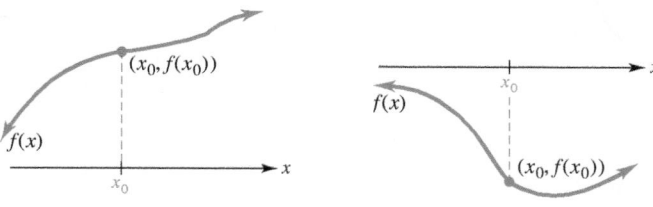

Figure 14.8

The graph of a function of two variables, $z = f(x, y)$, is a **surface** in three-dimensional space. If (x_0, y_0) is in the domain of f, the point $(x_0, y_0, f(x_0, y_0))$ lies directly above or directly below (or possibly on) the point (x_0, y_0) in the xy-plane, as shown in Figure 14.9.

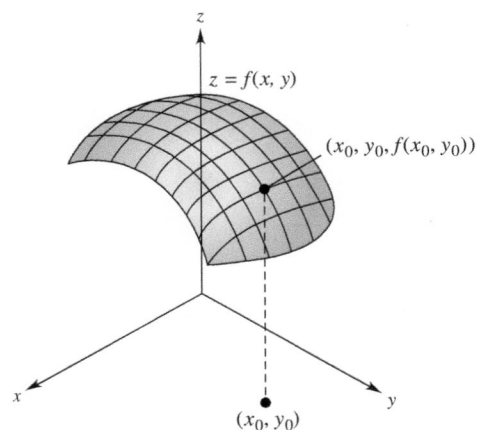

Figure 14.9

Computer software is available for drawing the graphs of functions of two independent variables, but you can sometimes get a good picture of a graph without it by finding various **traces**—the curves that result when a surface is cut by a plane. The **xy-trace** is the intersection of the surface with the xy-plane. The **yz-trace** and **xz-trace** are defined similarly. You can also determine the intersection of the surface with planes parallel to the xy-plane. Such planes are of the form $z = k$, where k is a constant, and the curves that result when they cut the surface are called **level curves.**

Example 7   Graph $z = x^2 + y^2$.

Solution   The yz-plane is the plane in which every point has first coordinate 0, so its equation is $x = 0$. When $x = 0$, the equation becomes $z = y^2$, which is the equation of a parabola in the yz-plane, as shown in Figure 14.10(a). Similarly, to find the intersection of the surface with the xz-plane (whose equation is $y = 0$), let $y = 0$ in the equation. It then becomes $z = x^2$, which is the equation of a parabola in the xz-plane (shown in Figure 14.10(a)). The xy-trace (the intersection of the surface with the plane $z = 0$) is the single point $(0, 0, 0)$, because $x^2 + y^2$ is never negative and is equal to 0 only when $x = 0$ and $y = 0$.

(a)

(b)

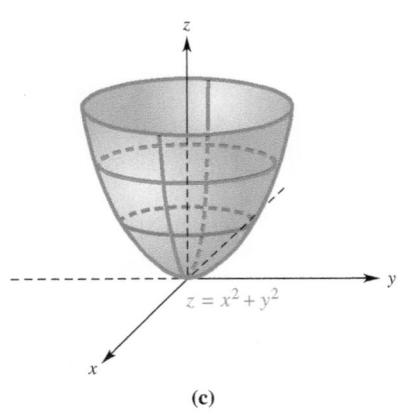

(c)

Figure 14.10

Next, we find the level curves by intersecting the surface with the planes $z = 1, z = 2$, $z = 3$, etc. (all of which are parallel to the xy-plane). In each case, the result is a circle,

$$x^2 + y^2 = 1, \qquad x^2 + y^2 = 2, \qquad x^2 + y^2 = 3,$$

and so on, as shown in Figure 14.10(b). Drawing the traces and level curves on the same set of axes suggests that the graph of $z = x^2 + y^2$ is the bowl-shaped figure, called a **paraboloid,** that is shown in Figure 14.10(c).

Figure 14.11 shows the level curves from Example 7 plotted in the xy-plane. The picture can be thought of as a topographical map that describes the surface generated by $z = x^2 + y^2$, just as the topographical map in Figure 14.12 describes the surface of the land in a part of New York State.

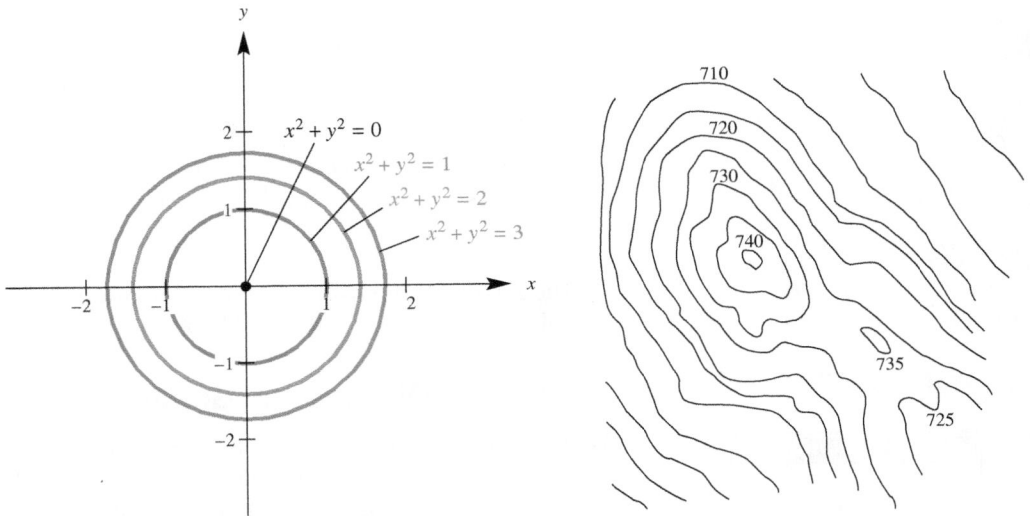

Figure 14.11   **Figure 14.12**

Applications

One application of level curves in economics occurs with production functions. A **production function** $z = f(x, y)$ is a function that gives the quantity z of an item produced as a function of x and y, where x is the amount of labor and y is the amount of capital (in appropriate units) needed to produce z units. If the production function has the special form $z = P(x, y) = Ax^a y^{1-a}$, where A and a are constants and $0 < a < 1$, the function is called a **Cobb–Douglas production function.**

Example 8   Find the level curve at a production of 100 items for the Cobb–Douglas production function $z = x^{2/3} y^{1/3}$.

Solution   Let $z = 100$ and solve for y to get

$$100 = x^{2/3} y^{1/3}$$

$$\frac{100}{x^{2/3}} = y^{1/3}.$$

Now reverse the equation and cube both sides to express y as a function of x:

$$(y^{1/3})^3 = \frac{100^3}{(x^{2/3})^3}$$

$$y = \frac{1,000,000}{x^2}.$$

✓ **Checkpoint 5**

Find the equation of the level curve for the production of 100 items if the production function is $z = 5x^{1/4}y^{3/4}$.

The level curve of height 100 is graphed in three dimensions in Figure 14.13(a) and on the familiar xy-plane in Figure 14.13(b). The points on the graph correspond to those values of x and y that lead to the production of 100 items. ☑5

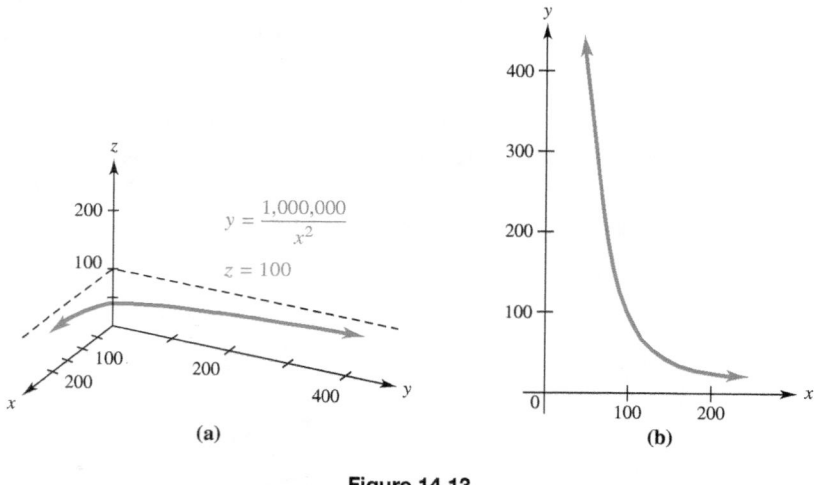

Figure 14.13

The curve in Figure 14.13 is called an *isoquant*, for *iso* (equal) and *quant* (amount). In Example 8, the "amounts" all "equal" 100.

Other Three-Dimensional Graphs

Figure 14.14

The graphing techniques discussed up to now may not always be effective. So technology is normally used to graph equations in three variables. Figure 14.14 shows the graph of $z = x^2 + y^2$, which was discussed in Example 7, on a TI-89 graphing calculator. (Most graphing calculators cannot do three-dimensional graphing.) Figure 14.15 shows the same graph drawn by the computer program Maple™. The computer-generated graph has more detail than a graphing calculator can produce.

Paraboloid,
$$z = x^2 + y^2$$

---
xy-trace: point
yz-trace: parabola
xz-trace: parabola

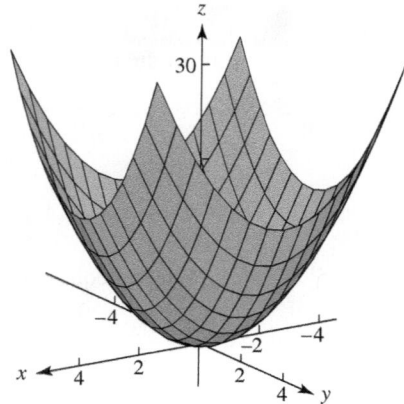

Figure 14.15

Figure 14.16 shows some other computer-generated graphs.

Ellipsoid,

$$\frac{x^2}{a^2} + \frac{y^2}{b^2} + \frac{z^2}{c^2} = 1$$

xy-trace: ellipse
yz-trace: ellipse
xz-trace: ellipse

Hyperboloid of Two Sheets,

$$-x^2 - y^2 + z^2 = 1$$

xy-trace: none
yz-trace: hyperbola
xz-trace: hyperbola

Hyperbolic Paraboloid,

$$x^2 - y^2 = z$$
(sometimes called a **saddle**)

xy-trace: two intersecting lines
yz-trace: parabola
xz-trace: parabola

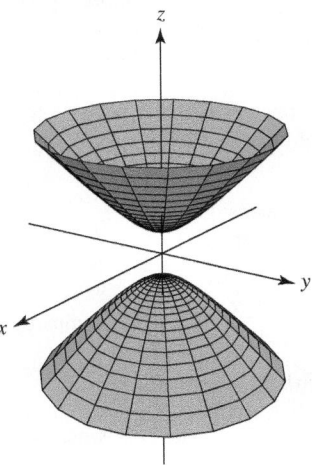

Figure 14.16

14.1 Exercises

For each of the given functions, find $f(2, -1)$, $f(-4, 1)$, $f(-2, -3)$, *and* $f(0, 8)$. *(See Examples 1 and 2.)*

1. $f(x, y) = 5x + 2y - 4$ **2.** $f(x, y) = 2x^2 - xy + y^2$

3. $f(x, y) = \sqrt{y^2 + 2x^2}$ **4.** $f(x, y) = \dfrac{3x + 4y}{\ln|x|}$

5. Let $g(x, y) = -x^2 - 4xy + y^3$. Find the following:

  (a) $g(-2, 4)$;   **(b)** $g(-1, -2)$;

  (c) $g(-2, 3)$;   **(d)** $g(5, 1)$.

6. Let $f(x, y) = \dfrac{\sqrt{9x + 5y}}{\log x}$. Find the following:

  (a) $f(10, 2)$;   **(b)** $f(100, 1)$;

  (c) $f(1000, 0)$;   **(d)** $f\left(\dfrac{1}{10}, 5\right)$.

Find the domain of the given function. (See Example 1.)

7. $f(x, y) = x^2 + y^2$ **8.** $B(h, w) = \dfrac{w}{h^2}$

9. $f(x, y) = \sqrt{x} - \sqrt{y}$ **10.** $K(r, s, t) = \dfrac{\sqrt{r} - s}{t + 1}$

11. $h(u, v, w) = \left|\dfrac{u + v}{v - w}\right|$ **12.** $g(x, y, z) = \dfrac{3x + 4y}{\ln z}$

Write the rule of the function. (See Example 2.)

13. Write the rule of a function that gives the perimeter of a rectangle of length l and width w.

14. Write the rule of a function that gives the area of a triangle of base b and height h.

15. Finance Write the rule of a function that gives the future value of an ordinary annuity of n payments, with payment R per period and interest rate i per period.

16. Finance Write the rule of a function that gives the present value of an annuity of n payments, with payment R per period and interest rate i per period.

17. Business If labor (x) costs \$200 per unit, materials (y) cost \$100 per unit, and capital (z) costs \$50 per unit, write a function for total cost.

18. Social Science Write the rule of the function that gives the batting average a of a baseball player who has had h hits in b at bats.

19. What are the *xy*-, *xz*-, and *yz*-traces of a graph?

20. What is a level curve?

Graph the first-octant portion of each of the given planes. (See Examples 3, 4, and 6.)

21. $3x + 2y + z = 12$ **22.** $2x + 3y + 3z = 18$

23. $x + y = 4$

24. $y + z = 3$

25. $z = 4$

26. $y = 3$

Graph the level curves in the first octant at heights of $z = 0$, $z = 2$, and $z = 4$ for the given equations. (See Example 7.)

27. $3x + 2y + z = 18$

28. $x + 3y + 2z = 8$

29. $y^2 - x = -z$

30. $2y - \dfrac{x^2}{3} = z$

Business *Find the level curve at a production of 500 for each of the production functions in Exercises 31 and 32. Graph each function on the xy-plane. (See Example 8.)*

31. The production function z for the United States was once estimated as $z = x^{.7}y^{.3}$, where x stands for the amount of labor and y stands for the amount of capital.

32. A study published in the *Journal of Political Economy* considered a production function of the form $z = x^{.6}y^{.4}$, where x represents the amount of labor and y the amount of capital.[*]

33. **Business** For the function in Exercise 31, what is the effect on z of doubling x? of doubling y? of doubling both x and y?

34. **Social Science** For the function in Exercise 18, what is the effect on a of doubling h? of doubling b? of doubling both h and b?

Work these exercises.

35. **Business** The production of digital cameras is given by

$$P(x, y) = 100\left(\frac{3}{5}x^{-2/5} + \frac{2}{5}y^{-2/5}\right)^{-5},$$

where x is the amount of labor in work-hours and y is the amount of capital.

(a) What is the production when 32 work-hours and 1 unit of capital are provided?

(b) Find the production when 1 work-hour and 32 units of capital are provided.

(c) If 32 work-hours and 243 units of capital are used, what is the production output?

Natural Science *The temperature–humidity index (THI), sometimes called the discomfort index, is given by*

$$f(d, w) = 15 + .4(d + w),$$

where d is the "dry-bulb temperature" (essentially the ambient-air temperature) and w is the "wet-bulb temperature" (which reflects the relative humidity as well as the temperature). When the THI is 75 or more, most people are uncomfortable. Find the THI and determine whether most people feel comfortable or uncomfortable under the given conditions.

36. **(a)** $d = 72°$ and $w = 70°$

(b) $d = 72°$ and $w = 78°$

37. **(a)** $d = 85°$ and $w = 60°$

(b) $d = 85°$ and $w = 70°$

38. $d = 90°$ and $w = 60°$

Finance *The multiplier function*

$$M(n, i, t) = \frac{(1 + i)^n(1 - t) + t}{[1 + (1 - t)i]^n}$$

compares the growth of an Individual Retirement Account (IRA) with the growth of the same amount (at the same interest rate for the same period of time) in an ordinary savings account. The savings account is subject to federal income tax, but the IRA is tax free (until money is withdrawn). The three variables are the number of years n; the annual interest rate i; and the marginal income tax rate t of the saver. When $M > 1$, the IRA grows faster than the savings account. In each of the next two exercises, find the multiplier and determine which account grows faster.

39. Money can be invested for 25 years at 5%, and the marginal income tax rate is 33%.

40. Money is invested for 40 years at 6%, and the marginal income tax rate is 28%.

41. **Natural Science** An article entitled "How Dinosaurs Ran" explains that the locomotion of different-sized animals can be compared when they have the same Froude number, defined as

$$F = \frac{v^2}{gl},$$

where v is the dinosaur's velocity, g is the acceleration due to gravity (9.81 m/sec^2), and l is the dinosaur's leg length.[†]

(a) One result described in the article is that different animals change from a trot to a gallop at the same Froude number, roughly 2.56. Find the velocity at which this change occurs for a ferret, with a leg length of .09 m, and a rhinoceros, with a leg length of 1.2 m.

(b) Ancient footprints in Texas of a sauropod, a large herbivorous dinosaur, are roughly 1 m in diameter, corresponding to a leg length of roughly 4 m. By comparing the stride divided by the leg length with that of various modern creatures, it can be determined that the Froude number for these dinosaurs is roughly .025. How fast were the sauropods traveling?

42. **Business** Extra postage is charged for parcels sent by U.S. mail that are more than 108 inches in length and girth combined. (Girth is the distance around the parcel perpendicular to its length. See the accompanying figure.) Express the combined length and girth as a function of L, W, and H.

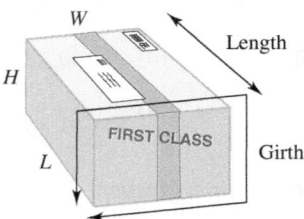

43. **Natural Science** Using data collected by the U.S. Forest Service, we can estimate the annual number of deer–vehicle accidents for any given county in Ohio with the function

$$A(L, T, U, C) = 53.02 + .383L + .0015T + .0028U - .0003C,$$

---

[*]Storesletten, Kjetil, "Sustaining Fiscal Policy Through Immigration," *Journal of Political Economy*, Vol. 108, No. 2, April 2000, pp. 300–323.

[†]R. MacNeill Alexander, "How Dinosaurs Ran," *Scientific American* 264 (April 1991): 4.

where A is the estimated number of accidents, L is the road length in kilometers, T is the total county land area in hundred acres (Ha), U is the urban land area in hundred acres, and C is the number of hundred acres of cropland.[*]

(a) Use this formula to estimate the number of deer–vehicle accidents for Mahoning County, where $L = 266$ km, $T = 107{,}484$ Ha, $U = 31{,}697$ Ha, and $C = 24{,}870$ Ha.

(b) Given the magnitude and nature of the input numbers, which of the variables have the greatest potential to influence the number of deer–vehicle accidents? Explain your answer.

44. Natural Science Using data collected by the U.S. Forest Service, we can estimate the annual number of deer that are harvested for any given county in Ohio with the function

$$N(R, C) = 329.32 + .0377R - .0171C,$$

where N is the estimated number of harvested deer, R is the rural land area in hundred acres (Ha), and C is the number of hundred acres of cropland.[*] Use this formula to estimate the number of harvested deer for Tuscarawas County, where $R = 141{,}319$ Ha and $C = 37{,}960$ Ha.

By considering traces, match each equation in Exercises 45–50 with its graph in (a)–(f).

45. $z = x^2 + y^2$

46. $z^2 - y^2 - x^2 = 1$

47. $x^2 - y^2 = z$

48. $z = y^2 - x^2$

49. $\dfrac{x^2}{16} + \dfrac{y^2}{25} + \dfrac{z^2}{4} = 1$

50. $z = 5(x^2 + y^2)^{-1/2}$

(a)

(b)

(c)

(d)

(e)

(f)

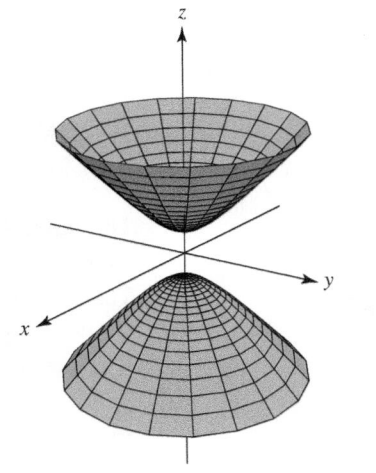

[*]Aaron Iverson and Louis Iverson, "Spatial and Temporal Trends of Deer Harvest and Deer–Vehicle Accidents in Ohio," *Ohio Journal of Science* 99 (1999): 84–94.

✓**Checkpoint Answers**

1. (a) −4 **(b)** −34

2. About 6.43 ERA **3.**

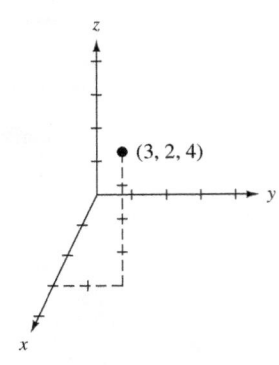

4. (a) A plane; $(2, 0, 0)$, $(0, 4/3, 0)$, $(0, 0, -4)$

   (b) A plane parallel to the z-axis; $(3, 0, 0)$, $(0, 3, 0)$

   (c) A plane parallel to the x-axis and the y-axis; $(0, 0, 2)$

5. $y = \dfrac{20^{4/3}}{x^{1/3}}$

14.2 Partial Derivatives

A start-up cell phone accessory company makes only two products: colorful phone chargers and decorative phone covers that are almost indestructible. The profits of the firm are given by

$$P(x, y) = 40x^2 - 10xy + 5y^2 - 80,$$

where x is the number of units of chargers sold and y is the number of units of covers sold. How will a change in x or y affect P?

Suppose that sales of chargers have been steady at 10 units; only the sales of covers vary. The management would like to find the marginal profit with respect to y, the number of covers sold. Recall that marginal profit is given by the derivative of the profit function. Here, x is fixed at 10. Using this information, we begin by finding a new function, $f(y) = P(10, y)$. Let $x = 10$ to get

$$f(y) = P(10, y) = 40(10)^2 - 10(10)y + 5y^2 - 80$$
$$= 3920 - 100y + 5y^2.$$

The function $f(y)$ shows the profit from the sale of y covers, assuming that x is fixed at 10 units. Find the derivative df/dy to get the marginal profit with respect to y:

$$\frac{df}{dy} = -100 + 10y.$$

In this example, the derivative of the function $f(y)$ was taken with respect to y only; we assumed that x was fixed. To generalize, let $z = f(x, y)$. An intuitive definition of the *partial derivatives* of f with respect to x and y follows.

Partial Derivatives (Informal Definition)[*]

The **partial derivative of f with respect to x** is the derivative of f obtained by treating x as a variable and y as a constant.

The **partial derivative of f with respect to y** is the derivative of f obtained by treating y as a variable and x as a constant.

---

[*]A formal definition is given at the end of the section.

The symbols $f_x(x, y)$ (no prime used), $\partial z/\partial x$, and $\partial f/\partial x$ are used to represent the partial derivative of $z = f(x, y)$ with respect to x, with similar symbols used for the partial derivative with respect to y. The symbol $f_x(x, y)$ is often abbreviated as just f_x, with $f_y(x, y)$ abbreviated f_y.

Example 1   Let $f(x, y) = 4x^2 - 9xy + 6y^3$. Find f_x and f_y.

Solution   To find f_x, treat x as a variable and y as a constant. Then find the derivative term by term. The derivative of $4x^2$ is $8x$. The term $-9xy$ can be written as $(-9y)x$. Since y is being treated as a constant, this term is the constant $-9y$ times x, and its derivative with respect to x is $-9y$. The last term, $6y^3$, is a constant, so its derivative is 0. In sum,

$$f(x, y) = 4x^2 - 9xy + 6y^3$$
$$f_x = 8x - 9y + 0$$
$$f_x = 8x - 9y.$$

To find f_y, treat y as a variable and x as a constant. Proceeding term by term to find the derivative, we have

$$f(x, y) = 4x^2 - 9xy + 6y^3$$
$$f_y = 0 - 9x + 18y^2$$
$$f_y = -9x + 18y^2. \;\checkmark_1$$

✓**Checkpoint 1**

Find f_x and f_y.

(a) $f(x, y) = -x^2y + 3xy + 2xy^2$

(b) $f(x, y) = x^3 + 2x^2y + xy$

Example 2   Find the indicated partial derivatives.

(a) Find f_x and f_y for $f(x, y) = e^x + e^{y^3} + e^{5x} + e^{xy}$.

Solution   Recall that if $y = e^x$, then $y' = e^x$. By the chain rule, if $y = e^{g(x)}$, then $y' = g'(x)e^{g(x)}$. Treating x as a variable and y as a constant and differentiating f term by term we obtain

$$f(x, y) = e^x + e^{y^3} + e^{5x} + e^{xy}$$
$$f_x = e^x + 0 + 5e^{5x} + ye^{xy}.$$

Similarly, treating y as the variable and x as a constant we see that

$$f(x, y) = e^x + e^{y^3} + e^{5x} + e^{xy}$$
$$f_y = 0 + 3y^2e^{y^3} + 0 + xe^{xy}.$$

(b) Find f_x and f_y for $f(x, y) = 8ye^{2x+3y}$.

Solution   To find f_x, we treat $8y$ as a constant, so we have

$$f_x = 8y(2e^{2x+3y}) = 16ye^{2x+3y}.$$

To find f_y, we must use the product rule since both factors of f involve the variable y. Therefore,

$$f_y = (8y)\frac{d}{dy}(e^{2x+3y}) + (e^{2x+3y})\frac{d}{dy}(8y)$$

$$f_y = (8y)(3e^{2x+3y}) + (e^{2x+3y})(8)$$
$$f_y = 24ye^{2x+3y} + 8e^{2x+3y}. \;\checkmark_2$$

✓**Checkpoint 2**

Find f_x and f_y, given that
$f(x, y) = 5x^3e^{10x-2y^4}$.

Example 3   Let $f(x, y) = \ln(x^2 + y)$. Find f_x and f_y.

Solution   Recall the formula for the derivative of a natural logarithmic function. If $y = \ln(g(x))$, then $y' = g'(x)/g(x)$. Using this formula and treating y as a constant, we obtain

$$f_x = \frac{\frac{d}{dx}(x^2 + y)}{x^2 + y} = \frac{2x}{x^2 + y}.$$

Similarly, treating x as a constant leads to the following result:

$$f_y = \frac{\frac{d}{dy}(x^2 + y)}{x^2 + y} = \frac{1}{x^2 + y}.$$ ✓₃

✓**Checkpoint 3**

Find f_x and f_y, given that
$f(x, y) = \ln(2x + 3y)$.

The notation

$$f_x(a, b) \qquad \text{or} \qquad \frac{\partial f}{\partial x}(a, b)$$

represents the value of a partial derivative when $x = a$ and $y = b$, as shown in the next example.

Example 4   Let $f(x, y) = 2x^2 + 3xy^3 + 2y + 5$. Find the following.

(a) $f_x(-1, 2)$

Solution First, find f_x by holding y constant in $f(x, y)$:

$$f(x, y) = 2x^2 + 3xy^3 + 2y + 5$$
$$f_x = 4x + 3y^3.$$

Now let $x = -1$ and $y = 2$:

$$f_x(-1, 2) = 4(-1) + 3(2)^3 = -4 + 24 = 20.$$

(b) $\dfrac{\partial f}{\partial y}(-4, -3)$

Solution Hold x constant in $f(x, y)$ to find $\dfrac{\partial f}{\partial y}$:

$$f(x, y) = 2x^2 + 3xy^3 + 2y + 5$$
$$\frac{\partial f}{\partial y} = 9xy^2 + 2.$$

Then

✓**Checkpoint 4**

Let $f(x, y) = x^2 + xy^2 + 5y - 10$.
Find the given partial derivatives.

(a) $f_x(2, 1)$

(b) $\dfrac{\partial f}{\partial y}(-1, 0)$

$$\frac{\partial f}{\partial y}(-4, -3) = 9(-4)(-3)^2 + 2 = 9(-36) + 2 = -322.$$ ✓₄

The derivative of a function of one variable can be interpreted as the slope of the tangent line to the graph at that point. With some modification, the same is true of partial derivatives of functions of two variables. At a point on the graph of a function of two variables, $z = f(x, y)$, there may be many tangent lines, all of which lie in the same tangent plane, as shown in Figure 14.17, on the following page.

In any particular direction, however, there will be only one tangent line. We now demonstrate how to use partial derivatives to find the slope of the tangent lines in the x- and y-directions.

Figure 14.18, on the following page, shows a surface $z = f(x, y)$ and a plane that is parallel to the xz-plane. The equation of the plane is $y = b$. (This equation corresponds to holding y fixed.)

Every point (x, y, z) on the plane has $y = b$. Hence, every point on the curve that is the intersection of the plane and the surface must have the form $(x, b, f(x, b))$. Thus, the curve is the graph of $z = f(x, b)$. Since b is a constant, $z = f(x, b)$ is a function of the single variable x, whose derivative with respect to x is $f_x(x, b)$. When this derivative is evaluated at $x = a$, it gives the slope of the tangent line to the curve at the point $(a, b, f(a, b))$—that

Figure 14.17

Figure 14.18

is, the tangent line to the surface in the x-direction at the point $(a, b, f(a, b))$. In the same way, the partial derivative with respect to y will give the slope of the tangent line to the surface in the y-direction at the point $(a, b, f(a, b))$.

Rate of Change

The derivative of $y = f(x)$ gives the rate of change of y with respect to x. In the same way, if $z = f(x, y)$, then f_x gives the rate of change of z with respect to x if y is held constant and f_y gives the rate of change of z with respect to y if x is held constant.

Example 5   **Natural Science**   Suppose that the temperature of the water at the point on a river where a nuclear power plant discharges its hot wastewater is approximated by

$$T(x, y) = 2x + 5y + xy - 40.$$

Here, x represents the temperature of the river water in degrees Celsius before it reaches the power plant and y is the number of megawatts (in hundreds) of electricity being produced by the plant.

(a) Find and interpret $T_x(9, 5)$.

Solution   First, find the partial derivative T_x:

$$T_x = 2 + y.$$

This partial derivative gives the rate of change of T with respect to x. Replacing x with 9 and y with 5 gives

$$T_x(9, 5) = 2 + 5 = 7.$$

Just as the marginal cost is the approximate cost of one more item, this result, 7, is the approximate change in temperature of the output water if the input water temperature changes by 1 degree from $x = 9$ to $x = 9 + 1 = 10$ while y remains constant at 5 (500 megawatts of electricity produced).

(b) Find and interpret $T_y(9, 5)$.

Solution   The partial derivative T_y is

$$T_y = 5 + x.$$

This partial derivative gives the rate of change of T with respect to y, with

$$T_y(9, 5) = 5 + 9 = 14.$$

This result, 14, is the approximate change in temperature resulting from a 1-unit increase in production of electricity from $y = 5$ to $y = 5 + 1 = 6$ (from 500 to 600 megawatts) while the input water temperature x remains constant at 9°C. ✓₅

✓ **Checkpoint 5**

Use the function of Example 5 to find and interpret the given partial derivatives.

(a) $T_x(5, 4)$

(b) $T_y(8, 3)$

As mentioned in the previous section, if $P(x, y)$ gives the output P produced by x units of labor and y units of capital, then $P(x, y)$ is a production function. The partial derivatives of this production function have practical implications. For example, $\partial P/\partial x$ gives the **marginal productivity** of labor. This represents the rate at which the output is changing with respect to changes in labor for a fixed capital investment. That is, if capital investment is held constant and labor is increased by 1 work hour, $\partial P/\partial x$ will yield the approximate change in the production level. Likewise, $\partial P/\partial y$ gives the marginal productivity of capital, which represents the rate at which the output is changing with respect to changes in capital for a fixed labor value. So if the labor force is held constant and the capital investment is increased by 1 unit, $\partial P/\partial y$ will approximate the corresponding change in the production level.

Example 6   **Business**   A company that manufactures computers has determined that its production function is given by

$$P(x, y) = 500x + 800y + 3x^2y - \frac{11x^3}{15} - \frac{y^4}{4},$$

where x is the size of the labor force (in thousands of work hours per week) and y is the amount of capital (in units of $1000) invested. Find the marginal productivity of labor and the marginal productivity of capital when $x = 50$ and $y = 20$, and interpret the results.

Solution   The marginal productivity of labor is found by taking the derivative of P with respect to x:

$$\frac{\partial P}{\partial x} = 500 + 6xy - \frac{33x^2}{15}$$

$$\frac{\partial P}{\partial x}(50, 20) = 500 + 6(50)(20) - \frac{33(50^2)}{15}$$

$$= 1000.$$

Thus, if capital investment is held constant at $20,000 and labor is increased from 50 thousand to 51 thousand work hours per week, production will increase by about 1000 units. In the same way, the marginal productivity of capital is $\partial P/\partial y$:

$$\frac{\partial P}{\partial y} = 800 + 3x^2 - y^3$$

$$\frac{\partial P}{\partial y}(50, 20) = 800 + 3(50)^2 - 20^3$$

$$= 300.$$

If work hours are held constant at 50 thousand hours per week and capital investment is increased from $20,000 to $21,000, production will increase by about 300 units. ✓₆

✓ **Checkpoint 6**

Suppose a production function is given by $P(x, y) = 10x^2y + 100x + 400y - 5xy^2$, where x and y are defined as in Example 6. Find the marginal productivity of labor and capital when $x = 20$ and $y = 10$.

Second-Order Partial Derivatives

The second derivative of a function of one variable is very useful in determining local maxima and minima. **Second-order partial derivatives** (partial derivatives of a partial derivative) are used in a similar way for functions of two or more variables. The situation is somewhat more complicated, however, with more independent variables. For example, $f(x, y) = 4x + x^2y + 2y$ has two first-order partial derivatives:

$$f_x = 4 + 2xy \quad \text{and} \quad f_y = x^2 + 2.$$

Because each of these partial derivatives has two partial derivatives, one with respect to x and one with respect to y, there are *four* second-order partial derivatives of the function f.

The same is true for any function $z = f(x, y)$. The following schematic diagram shows the partial derivatives and the second-order partial derivatives of f and the various notations used for each:

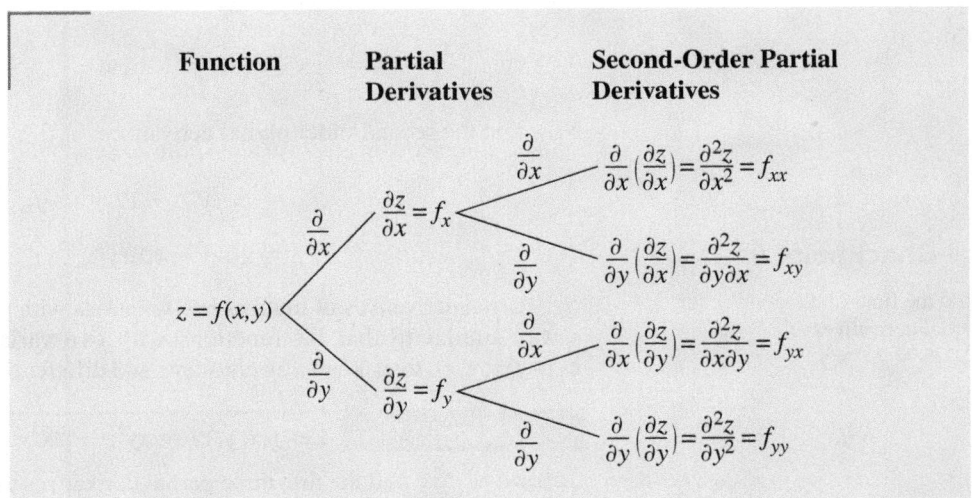

Function	Partial Derivatives	Second-Order Partial Derivatives

As shown in the diagram, f_{xx} is used as an abbreviation for $f_{xx}(x, y)$, with f_{yy}, f_{xy}, and f_{yx} used in a similar way. The symbol f_{xx} is read, "the partial derivative of f_x with respect to x," and f_{xy} is read, "the partial derivative of f_x with respect to y." Also, the symbol $\partial^2 z/\partial y^2$ is read, "the partial derivative of $\partial z/\partial y$ with respect to y."

NOTE For most functions found in applications, and for all the functions in this text, the second-order partial derivatives f_{xy} and f_{yx} are equal. Therefore, we need not be particular about the order in which these derivatives are found.

Example 7 Find all second-order partial derivatives of

$$f(x, y) = -4x^3 - 3x^2y^3 + 2y^2.$$

Solution First find f_x and f_y:

$$f_x = -12x^2 - 6xy^3 \quad \text{and} \quad f_y = -9x^2y^2 + 4y.$$

To find f_{xx}, take the partial derivative of f_x with respect to x:

$$f_{xx} = -24x - 6y^3.$$

Now find f_{yy} by taking the partial derivative of f_y with respect to y:

$$f_{yy} = -18x^2y + 4.$$

Next, find f_{xy} by taking the partial derivative of f_x with respect to y:

$$f_{xy} = -18xy^2.$$

Finally, find f_{yx} by taking the partial derivative of f_y with respect to x:

$$f_{yx} = -18xy^2.$$

Observe that $f_{xy} = f_{yx}$. ✓₇

✓ **Checkpoint 7**

Let $f(x, y) = 4x^2y^2 - 9xy + 8x^2 - 3y^4$. Find all second-order partial derivatives.

Example 8   Let

$$f(x, y) = \sqrt{x} + \frac{1}{y} - 2x^3y^5.$$

Find all second-order partial derivatives.

Solution   Using laws of exponents, rewrite the function as

$$f(x, y) = x^{\frac{1}{2}} + y^{-1} - 2x^3y^5.$$

Then the first-order partial derivatives are

$$f_x = \frac{1}{2}x^{-\frac{1}{2}} - 6x^2y^5 \quad \text{and} \quad f_y = -y^{-2} - 10x^3y^4.$$

Now find the second-order partial derivatives:

$$f_{xx} = -\frac{1}{4}x^{-\frac{3}{2}} - 12xy^5; \quad f_{xy} = -30x^2y^4;$$

$$f_{yy} = 2y^{-3} - 40x^3y^3; \quad f_{yx} = -30x^2y^4. \quad \boxed{8}$$

✓ **Checkpoint 8**

Find the first- and second-order partial derivatives of $f(x, y) = 4x^6\sqrt{y}$.

Partial derivatives of multivariate functions with more than two variables are found in a way similar to that for functions with two variables. For example, to find f_x for $w = f(x, y, z)$, treat y and z as constants and differentiate with respect to x.

Example 9   Let $f(x, y, z) = xy^2z + 2x^2y - 4xz^2$. Find f_x, f_y, f_z, f_{xy}, and f_{yz}.

Solution   We find the first three partial derivatives as follows:

$$f_x = y^2z + 4xy - 4z^2$$
$$f_y = 2xyz + 2x^2$$
$$f_z = xy^2 - 8xz$$

To find f_{xy}, differentiate f_x with respect to y:

$$f_{xy} = 2yz + 4x$$

In the same way, differentiate f_y with respect to z to get

$$f_{yz} = 2xy. \quad \boxed{9}$$

✓ **Checkpoint 9**

Let $f(x, y, z) = xyz + x^2yz + xy^2z^3$. Find f_x, f_y, f_z, and f_{xz}.

For those who may be interested, we close this section with the formal definition of partial derivatives. As you can see, it is very similar to the definition of the derivative of a function of one variable.

Partial Derivatives (Formal Definition)

Let $z = f(x, y)$ be a function of two variables. Then the **partial derivative of f with respect to x** is

$$f_x(x, y) = \lim_{h \to 0} \frac{f(x + h, y) - f(x, y)}{h},$$

and the **partial derivative of f with respect to y** is

$$f_y(x, y) = \lim_{h \to 0} \frac{f(x, y + h) - f(x, y)}{h},$$

provided that these limits exist.

Similar definitions could be given for functions of more than two independent variables.

14.2 Exercises

For each of the given functions, find the following. (See Examples 1 and 4.)

(a) $\dfrac{\partial z}{\partial x}$ (b) $\dfrac{\partial z}{\partial y}$ (c) $f_x(2,3)$ (d) $f_y(1,-2)$

1. $z = f(x, y) = 8x^3 - 4x^2y + 9y^2$

2. $z = f(x, y) = -3x^2 - 2xy^2 + 5y^3$

In Exercises 3–14, find f_x and f_y. Then find $f_x(2, -1)$ and $f_y(-4, 3)$. Leave the answers in terms of e in Exercises 5–8 and 13 and 14. (See Examples 1–4.)

3. $f(x, y) = 6y^3 - 4xy + 5$

4. $f(x, y) = -3x^4y^3 + 10$

5. $f(x, y) = e^{2x+y}$ **6.** $f(x, y) = -4e^{x-y}$

7. $f(x, y) = \dfrac{-2}{e^{x+2y}}$ **8.** $f(x, y) = \dfrac{6}{e^{4x-y}}$

9. $f(x, y) = \dfrac{x + 3y^2}{x^2 + y^3}$ **10.** $f(x, y) = \dfrac{8x^2y}{x^3 - y}$

11. $f(x, y) = \ln|1 + 5x^3y^2|$

12. $f(x, y) = \ln|4x^2y + 3x|$

13. $f(x, y) = x^2e^{2xy}$ **14.** $f(x, y) = ye^{5x+2y}$

Find all second-order partial derivatives of the given functions. (See Examples 7 and 8.)

15. $f(x, y) = 4x^2y^2 - 16x^2 + 4y$

16. $R(x, y) = 4x^2 - 5xy^3 + 12x^2y^2$

17. $h(x, y) = -3y^2 - 4x^2y^2 + 7xy^2$

18. $P(x, y) = -16x^3 + 3xy^2 - 12x^4y^2$

19. $r(x, y) = \dfrac{6y}{x + y}$ **20.** $k(x, y) = \dfrac{-7x}{2x + 3y}$

21. $z = 4xe^y$ **22.** $z = -3ye^x$

23. $r = \ln|2x + y|$ **24.** $r = \ln|7x - 5y|$

25. $z = x \ln(xy)$ **26.** $z = (y + 1) \ln(x^3y)$

In Exercises 27 and 28, evaluate $f_{xy}(1, 2)$ and $f_{yy}(3, 1)$.

27. $f(x, y) = x \ln(xy)$ **28.** $f(x, y) = (y + 1) \ln(x^3y)$

Find values of x and y such that both $f_x(x, y) = 0$ and $f_y(x, y) = 0$.

29. $f(x, y) = 6x^2 + 6y^2 + 6xy + 36x - 5$

30. $f(x, y) = 50 + 4x - 5y + x^2 + y^2 + xy$

31. $f(x, y) = 9xy - x^3 - y^3 - 6$

32. $f(x, y) = 2200 + 27x^3 + 72xy + 8y^2$

Find $f_x, f_y, f_z,$ and f_{yz} for the given functions. In Exercises 33 and 34, also find $f_y(3, 4, -2)$ and $f_{yz}(1, -1, 0)$. (See Example 9.)

33. $f(x, y, z) = x^2 + yz + z^4$

34. $f(x, y, z) = 3x^5 - x^2 + y^5$

35. $f(x, y, z) = \dfrac{6x - 5y}{4z + 5}$

36. $f(x, y, z) = \dfrac{2x^2 + xy}{yz - 2}$

37. $f(x, y, z) = \ln(x^2 - 5xz^2 + y^4)$

38. $f(x, y, z) = \ln(8xy + 5yz - x^3)$

39. How many partial derivatives does a function in three variables have? How many second-order partial derivatives does it have? Explain why.

40. Suppose $z = f(x, y)$ describes the cost to build a certain structure, where x represents the labor costs and y represents the cost of materials. Describe what f_x and f_y represent.

Work the following applied problems. (See Example 5.)

41. Business Suppose that the manufacturing cost of a calculator is approximated by

$$M(x, y) = 40x^2 + 30y^2 - 10xy + 30,$$

where x is the cost of electronic chips and y is the cost of labor. Find the given partial derivatives.

(a) $M_y(4, 2)$ (b) $M_x(3, 6)$

(c) $(\partial M/\partial x)(2, 5)$ (d) $(\partial M/\partial y)(6, 7)$

42. Business The revenue from the sale of x units of a tranquilizer and y units of an antibiotic is given by

$$R(x, y) = 5x^2 + 9y^2 - 4xy.$$

Suppose 9 units of tranquilizer and 5 units of antibiotic are sold. Use partial derivatives to answer these questions.

(a) What is the *approximate* effect on revenue if 10 units of tranquilizer and 5 units of antibiotic are sold?

(b) What is the *approximate* effect on revenue if the amount of antibiotic sold is increased to 6 units, while tranquilizer sales remain constant?

43. Business A car dealership estimates that the total weekly sales of its most popular model are a function of the car's list price p (in dollars) and the interest rate i (as a percent) offered by the manufacturer. The weekly sales are given by

$$f(p, i) = 99p - .5pi - .0025p^2.$$

(a) Find the weekly sales if the average list price is \$19,400 and the manufacturer is offering an 8% interest rate.

(b) Find and interpret $f_p(p, i)$ and $f_i(p, i)$.

(c) What would be the approximate effect on weekly sales if the price is \$19,400 and interest rates rise from 8% to 9%?

44. Health The reaction to x units of a drug t hours after it was administered is given by

$$R(x, t) = x^2(a - x)t^2e^{-t},$$

for $0 \le x \le a$ (where a is a constant). Find the given partial derivatives.

(a) $\dfrac{\partial R}{\partial x}$ (b) $\dfrac{\partial R}{\partial t}$

(c) Interpret your answers to parts (a) and (b).

45. Business A bicycle manufacturer produces two kinds of frames, aluminum and carbon fiber. The cost function for these products is $C(x, y) = 500x + 1100y + 20,000$, where x is the number of aluminum frames and y is the number of carbon fiber frames produced.

(a) What is the marginal cost of producing one additional aluminum frame when the production of carbon fiber models is held constant?

(b) What is the marginal cost of producing one additional carbon fiber frame when the production of aluminum models is held constant?

46. Social Science Early in the 2013 Major League Baseball season, Robinson Cano of the New York Yankees had 38 hits in 119 at bats. Batting average is calculated using the function $f(h, b) = \dfrac{h}{b}$, where h is the number of hits and b is the number of at bats. (Data from: www.mlb.com.)

(a) Find Cano's batting average at this point in the season.

(b) Suppose that Cano had managed to get one more hit in his 119 at bats to date (so that his number of hits is increased by one, but his number of at bats remains constant). Use an appropriate partial derivative to approximate how his batting average would be different.

(c) Suppose that Cano strikes out in his next at bat (so that his number of at bats is increased by one, but his number of hits remains constant). Use an appropriate partial derivative to approximate the change in his batting average.

47. Business Suppose that the cost function for the company discussed in the first paragraph of this section is given by:

$$C(x, y) = 600x + 120y + 4000,$$

where x is the number of units of phone chargers and y is the number of units of phone covers produced.

(a) In $C(x, y)$, what does 4000 represent?

(b) Find $\partial C/\partial x$ and $\partial C/\partial y$. What do these quantities represent?

48. Business A radio-controlled plane manufacturer produces two models, the Basic and the Ultra. Its cost function for these products is

$$C(x, y) = 125x + 400y + 10,000,$$

where x is the number of Basic models and y is the number of Ultra models produced.

(a) What is the marginal cost of producing an Ultra model when the production of Basics is held constant?

(b) What is the marginal cost of producing a Basic model when the production of Ultras is held constant?

49. Natural Science The surface area of a human (in square meters) is approximated by

$$A(M, H) = .202M^{.425}H^{.725},$$

where M is the mass of the person (in kilograms) and H is the height (in meters). Find the *approximate* change in surface area under the given conditions.

(a) The mass changes from 72 kg to 73 kg, while the height remains 1.8 m.

(b) The mass remains stable at 70 kg, while the height changes from 1.6 m to 1.7 m.

Work the following applied problems. (See Example 6.)

50. Business Suppose the production function of a company is given by

$$P(x, y) = 100\sqrt{x^2 + y^2},$$

where x represents units of labor and y represents units of capital. (See Example 5.) Find the following when $x = 4$ and $y = 3$.

(a) The marginal productivity of labor

(b) The marginal productivity of capital

51. Business A manufacturer of automobile batteries estimates that total production in thousands of units is given by

$$f(x, y) = 3x^{1/3}y^{2/3},$$

where x is the number of units of labor and y is the number of units of capital utilized.

(a) Find and interpret $f_x(64, 125)$ and $f_y(64, 125)$ if the current level of production uses 64 units of labor and 125 units of capital.

(b) What would be the *approximate* effect on production of increasing labor to 65 units while holding capital at the current level?

(c) Suppose that sales have been good and management wants to increase either capital or labor by 1 unit. Which option would result in a larger increase in production?

52. Business A manufacturer estimates that production (in hundreds of units) is a function of the respective amounts x and y of labor and capital used, as follows:

$$f(x, y) = \left[\frac{1}{3}x^{-1/3} + \frac{2}{3}y^{-1/3}\right]^{-3}.$$

(a) Find the number of units produced when 27 units of labor and 64 units of capital are utilized.

(b) Find and interpret $f_x(27, 64)$ and $f_y(27, 64)$.

(c) What would be the *approximate* effect on production of increasing labor by 1 unit?

(d) What would be the *approximate* effect on production of increasing capital by 1 unit?

53. Business The production function z for the United States was once estimated as

$$z = x^{.7}y^{.3},$$

where x stands for the amount of labor and y stands for the amount of capital. Find the marginal productivity of labor (that is, find $\partial z / \partial x$) and of capital (that is, find $\partial z / \partial y$.)

54. **Business** A similar production function for Canada is

$$z = x^{.4}y^{.6},$$

with x, y, and z as in Exercise 53. Find the marginal productivity of labor and of capital.

Work these exercises.

55. **Natural Science** In one method of computing the quantity of blood pumped through the lungs in 1 minute, a researcher first finds each of the following (in milliliters):

$b = $ quantity of oxygen used by the body in 1 minute;

$a = $ quantity of oxygen per liter of blood that has just gone through the lungs;

$v = $ quantity of oxygen per liter of blood that is about to enter the lungs.

In 1 minute,

Amount of oxygen used $=$ amount of oxygen per liter

$\times$ number of liters of blood pumped.

If C is the number of liters pumped through the blood in 1 minute, then

$$b = (a - v) \cdot C; \quad \text{or} \quad C = \frac{b}{a - v}.$$

(a) Find C if $a = 160$, $b = 200$, and $v = 125$.

(b) Find C if $a = 180$, $b = 260$, and $v = 142$.

(c) Find $\partial C / \partial b$.   (d) Find $\partial C / \partial v$.

56. **Physical Science** The gravitational attraction F on a body a distance r from the center of the earth, where r is greater than the radius of the earth, is a function of the mass m of the body and the distance r. Specifically,

$$F = \frac{mgR^2}{r^2},$$

where R is the radius of the earth and g is the force of gravity—about 32 feet per second per second (ft/sec^2).

(a) Find and interpret F_m and F_r.

🖎 (b) Show that $F_m > 0$ and $F_r < 0$. Why is this reasonable?

57. **Social Science** A developmental mathematics instructor at a large university has determined that a student's probability of success in the university's pass/fail remedial algebra course is a function of s, n, and a, where s is the student's score on the departmental placement exam, n is the number of semesters of mathematics passed in high school, and a is the student's mathematics SAT score. The instructor estimates that p, the probability of passing the course (in percent), will be

$$p = f(s, n, a) = .078a + 4(sn)^{1/2}$$

for $200 \le a \le 800$, $0 \le s \le 10$, and $0 \le n \le 8$. Assume that this model has some merit.

(a) If a student scores 8 on the placement exam, has passed 6 semesters of high school math, and has an SAT score of 450, what is the probability that the student will pass the course?

(b) Find p for a student with 3 semesters of high school mathematics, a placement score of 3, and an SAT score of 320.

(c) Find and interpret $f_n(3, 3, 320)$ and $f_a(3, 3, 320)$.

58. **Finance** The price p (in dollars) of a zero-coupon discount bond is calculated according to the formula $p = \dfrac{v}{(1 + r)^m}$, where v is the face value of the bond (in dollars), r is the annual interest rate (expressed as a decimal), and m is the time to maturity (in years). The modified duration of the bond is defined to be the partial derivative of the price with respect to interest rate divided by the negative of the price. In other words,

$$\text{modified duration} = \frac{p_r}{-p}.$$

Modified duration can be interpreted as the percent by which the price of the bond will change with a 1% change in interest rate. Bonds with longer-dated maturities will be more sensitive to interest rate shifts. Calculate the modified duration of the following bonds.[*]

(a) $r = 5\%$; $m = 1$ year

(b) $r = 5\%$; $m = 10$ years

59. **Health** A weight-loss counselor has prepared a program of diet and exercise for a client. If the client sticks to the program, the weight loss that can be expected (in pounds per week) is given by

$$\text{Weight loss} = f(n, c) = \frac{1}{8}n^2 - \frac{1}{5}c + \frac{1937}{8},$$

where c is the average daily calorie intake for the week and n is the number of 40-minute aerobic workouts per week.

(a) How many pounds can the client expect to lose by eating an average of 1200 calories per day and participating in four 40-minute workouts in a week?

(b) Find and interpret $\partial f / \partial n$.

(c) The client currently averages 1100 calories per day and does three 40-minute workouts each week. What would be the *approximate* impact on weekly weight loss of adding a fourth workout per week?

60. **Natural Science** In 1908, J. Haldane constructed diving tables that give a relationship between the water pressure on body tissues for various water depths and dive times. The tables were used by divers and virtually eliminated the occurrence of decompression sickness. The pressure in atmospheres for a no-stop dive is given by the formula

$$p(l, t) = 1 + \frac{l}{33}(1 - e^{-.1386t}),$$

where t is in minutes, l is in feet, and p is in atmospheres (atm).[†]

(a) Find the pressure at 33 feet for a 10-minute dive.

(b) Find $p_l(33, 10)$ and $p_t(33, 10)$.

---

[*]This exercise was suggested by Nathaniel J. Black.

[†]The estimates provided by the formula are conservative. Consult modern diving tables before making a dive. See David Westbrook, "The Mathematics of Scuba Diving," *UMAP Journal* 18, no. 2 (1997): 2–19.

(c) Haldane estimated that decompression sickness for no-stop dives could be avoided if the diver's tissue pressure did not exceed 2.15 atmospheres. Find the maximum amount of time (including the time going down and coming back up) that a diver could stay down if he or she wants to dive to a depth of 66 feet.

61. Health The body mass index (BMI) is a number that can be calculated for any individual as follows: Multiply a person's weight by 703 and divide by the person's height squared. That is,

$$B = \frac{703w}{h^2},$$

where w is in pounds and h is in inches. The National Heart, Lung and Blood Institute uses the BMI to determine whether a person is "overweight" ($25 \le B < 30$) or "obese" ($B \ge 30$). (Data from: National Institutes of Health.)

(a) Calculate the BMI for a person who weighs 220 pounds and is 74 inches tall.

(b) Calculate $\dfrac{\partial B}{\partial w}$ and $\dfrac{\partial B}{\partial h}$.

62. Natural Science In 1941, explorers Paul Siple and Charles Passel discovered that the amount of heat lost when an object is exposed to cold air depends on both the temperature of the air and the velocity of the wind. They developed the windchill index as a way to measure the danger of frostbite while performing outdoor activities. On the basis of new findings and additional data, the windchill index was recalculated in 2001. The new index is given by

$$W(V, T) = 35.74 + .6215T - 35.75V^{.16} + (.4275T)V^{.16},$$

where V is the wind speed in miles per hour and T is the Fahrenheit temperature for wind speeds between 4 and 45 mph.[*]

[*]Joint Action Group of the National Weather Service and the Meteorological Services of Canada, press release, August 2001.

(a) Find the windchill for a wind speed of 20 mph and 10°F.

(b) A weather report indicates that the windchill is −22°F and the actual outdoor temperature is 5°F. Use a graphing calculator to find the corresponding wind speed to the nearest mile per hour.

(c) Find and interpret $W_V(20, 10)$ and $W_T(20, 10)$.

(d) Using the table command on a graphing calculator or a spreadsheet, develop a windchill chart for wind speeds of 5, 10, 15, and 20 mph and temperatures of 0°, 5°, 15°, and 25°.

✓ Checkpoint Answers

1. **(a)** $f_x = -2xy + 3y + 2y^2; f_y = -x^2 + 3x + 4xy$
 (b) $f_x = 3x^2 + 4xy + y; f_y = 2x^2 + x$

2. $f_x = 15x^2e^{10x-2y^4} + 50x^3e^{10x-2y^4}; f_y = -40x^3y^3e^{10x-2y^4}$

3. $f_x = \dfrac{2}{2x + 3y}; f_y = \dfrac{3}{2x + 3y}$

4. **(a)** 5 **(b)** 5

5. **(a)** $T_x(5, 4) = 6$; the approximate increase in output temperature if the input temperature increases from 5 to 6 degrees

 (b) $T_y(8, 3) = 13$; the approximate increase in output temperature if the production of electricity increases from 300 to 400 megawatts

6. The marginal productivity of labor is 3600. The marginal productivity of capital is 2400.

7. $f_{xx} = 8y^2 + 16$
 $f_{yy} = 8x^2 - 36y^2$
 $f_{xy} = 16xy - 9$
 $f_{yx} = 16xy - 9$

8. $f_x = 24x^5y^{\frac{1}{2}}; f_y = 2x^6y^{-\frac{1}{2}}; f_{xx} = 120x^4y^{\frac{1}{2}}; f_{yy} = -x^6y^{-\frac{3}{2}};$
 $f_{xy} = f_{yx} = 12x^5y^{-\frac{1}{2}}$

9. $f_x = yz + 2xyz + y^2z^3$
 $f_y = xz + x^2z + 2xyz^3$
 $f_z = xy + x^2y + 3xy^2z^2$
 $f_{xz} = y + 2xy + 3y^2z^2$

14.3 Extrema of Functions of Several Variables

One of the most important applications of calculus is finding maxima and minima of functions. Earlier, we studied this idea extensively for functions of a single variable; now we shall see that extrema can be found for functions of two variables. In particular, an extension of the second-derivative test can be derived and used to identify maxima or minima. We begin with the definitions of local maxima and minima.

Local Maxima and Minima

Let (a, b) be in the domain of a function f.

1. f has a **local maximum** at (a, b) if there is a circular region in the xy-plane with (a, b) in its interior such that
$$f(a, b) \geq f(x, y)$$
for all points (x, y) in the circular region.

2. f has a **local minimum** at (a, b) if there is a circular region in the xy-plane with (a, b) in its interior such that
$$f(a, b) \leq f(x, y)$$
for all points (x, y) in the circular region.

As before, the term *local extremum* is used for either a local maximum or a local minimum. Examples of a local maximum and a local minimum are given in Figures 14.19 and 14.20, respectively.

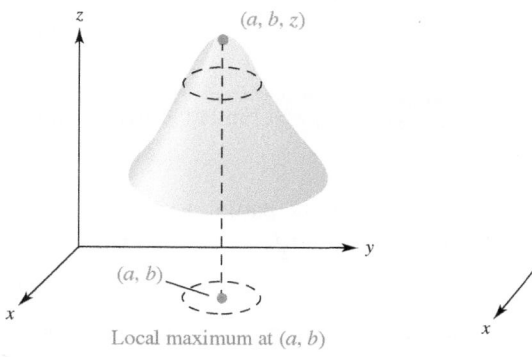

Local maximum at (a, b)

Figure 14.19

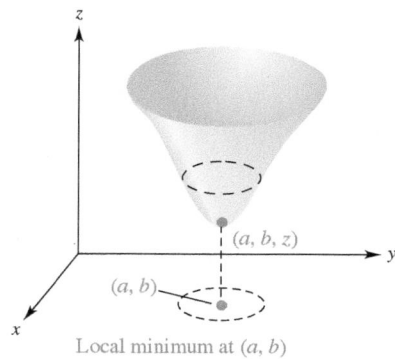

Local minimum at (a, b)

Figure 14.20

NOTE With functions of a single variable, we made a distinction between local extrema and absolute extrema. The methods for finding absolute extrema are quite involved for functions of two variables, so we will discuss only local extrema.

As suggested by Figure 14.21, at a local maximum the tangent line parallel to the x-axis (if it exists) has a slope of 0, as does the tangent line parallel to the y-axis (if it exists). (Notice the similarity to functions of one variable.) That is, if the function $z = f(x, y)$ has a local extremum at (a, b), then $f_x(a, b) = 0$ and $f_y(a, b) = 0$, as stated in the following theorem.

Tangent is horizontal.

Tangent is horizontal.

(a, b)

Figure 14.21

Location of Extrema

If a function $z = f(x, y)$ has a local maximum or local minimum at the point (a, b), and $f_x(a, b)$ and $f_y(a, b)$ both exist, then
$$f_x(a, b) = 0 \quad \text{and} \quad f_y(a, b) = 0.$$

Just as with functions of one variable, the fact that the slopes of the tangent lines are 0 is no guarantee that a local extremum has been located. For example, Figure 14.22 shows the graph of $z = f(x, y) = x^2 - y^2$. Both $f_x(0, 0) = 0$ and $f_y(0, 0) = 0$, and yet $(0, 0)$ leads to neither a local maximum nor a local minimum for the function. The point $(0, 0, 0)$ on the graph of this function is called a **saddle point;** it is a minimum when approached from one direction (in this case, the x-direction), but a maximum when approached from another direction (in this case, the y-direction). A saddle point is neither a maximum nor a minimum.

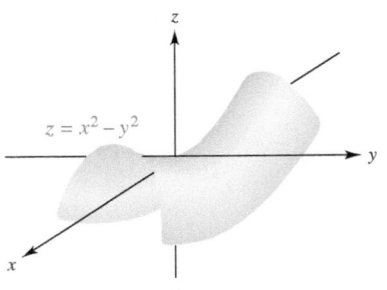

Figure 14.22

For a function $f(x, y)$, the points (a, b) such that $f_x(a, b) = 0$ and $f_y(a, b) = 0$ (or such that $f_x(a, b)$ or $f_y(a, b)$ does not exist) are called **critical points.**

Example 1   Find all critical points for

$$f(x, y) = 6x^2 + 6y^2 + 6xy + 36x - 54y - 5.$$

Solution   Since the partial derivatives always exist, we must find all points (a, b) such that $f_x(a, b) = 0$ and $f_y(a, b) = 0$. Here,

$$f_x = 12x + 6y + 36 \quad \text{and} \quad f_y = 12y + 6x - 54.$$

Set each of these two partial derivatives equal to 0:

$$12x + 6y + 36 = 0 \quad \text{and} \quad 12y + 6x - 54 = 0.$$

These two equations form a system of linear equations that we can rewrite as

$$12x + 6y = -36$$
$$6x + 12y = 54.$$

To solve this system by elimination, multiply the first equation by -2 and then add the equations:

$$\begin{array}{rcl} -24x - 12y &=& 72 \\ 6x + 12y &=& 54 \\ \hline -18x &=& 126 \\ x &=& -7. \end{array}$$

Substituting $x = -7$ in the first equation of the system, we have

$$12(-7) + 6y = -36$$
$$6y = 48$$
$$y = 8.$$

✓ **Checkpoint 1**

Find all critical points for the given functions.

(a) $f(x, y) = 4x^2 + 3xy + 2y^2 + 7x - 6y - 6$

(b) $f(x, y) = e^{-2x} + xy$

Therefore, $(-7, 8)$ is the solution of the system. Since this is the only solution, $(-7, 8)$ is the only critical point for the given function. By the previous theorem, if the function has a local extremum, it must occur at $(-7, 8)$. ✓₁

The results of the next theorem can be used to decide whether $(-7, 8)$ in Example 1 leads to a local maximum, a local minimum, or neither. The proof of this theorem is beyond the scope of this course.

Test for Local Extrema

Suppose $f(x, y)$ is a function such that f_{xx}, f_{yy}, and f_{xy} all exist. Let (a, b) be a critical point for which

$$f_x(a, b) = 0 \quad \text{and} \quad f_y(a, b) = 0.$$

Let M be the number defined by

$$M = f_{xx}(a, b) \cdot f_{yy}(a, b) - [f_{xy}(a, b)]^2.$$

1. If $M > 0$ and $f_{xx}(a, b) < 0$, then f has a **local maximum** at (a, b).
2. If $M > 0$ and $f_{xx}(a, b) > 0$, then f has a **local minimum** at (a, b).
3. If $M < 0$, then f has a **saddle point** at (a, b).
4. If $M = 0$, the test gives **no information.**

The following chart summarizes the conclusions of the theorem:

	$f_{xx}(a, b) < 0$	$f_{xx}(a, b) > 0$
$M > 0$	Local maximum	Local minimum
$M = 0$	No information	
$M < 0$	Saddle point	

Example 2   Example 1 showed that the only critical point of the function

$$f(x, y) = 6x^2 + 6y^2 + 6xy + 36x - 54y - 5$$

is $(-7, 8)$. Does $(-7, 8)$ lead to a local maximum, a local minimum, or neither?

Solution   We can find out by using the test for local extrema. From Example 1,

$$f_x(-7, 8) = 0 \quad \text{and} \quad f_y(-7, 8) = 0.$$

Now find the various second-order partial derivatives used in finding M. From $f_x = 12x + 6y + 36$ and $f_y = 12y + 6x - 54$, we have

$$f_{xx} = 12, \quad f_{yy} = 12, \quad \text{and} \quad f_{xy} = 6.$$

(If these second-order partial derivatives had not all been constants, we would have had to evaluate them at the point $(-7, 8)$.) Now,

$$M = f_{xx}(-7, 8) \cdot f_{yy}(-7, 8) - [f_{xy}(-7, 8)]^2 = 12 \cdot 12 - 6^2 = 108.$$

Since $M > 0$ and $f_{xx}(-7, 8) = 12 > 0$, Part 2 of the theorem applies, showing that $f(x, y) = 6x^2 + 6y^2 + 6xy + 36x - 54y - 5$ has a local minimum at $(-7, 8)$. The value of this local minimum is $f(-7, 8) = -347$.

✓**Checkpoint 2**

Find any local maxima or minima for the functions defined in Checkpoint 1.

Example 3   Find all points where the function

$$f(x, y) = 9xy - x^3 - y^3 - 6$$

has any local maxima or local minima.

Solution   First find any critical points. Here,

$$f_x = 9y - 3x^2 \quad \text{and} \quad f_y = 9x - 3y^2.$$

Set each of these partial derivatives equal to 0:

$$
\begin{array}{ll}
f_x = 0 & f_y = 0 \\
9y - 3x^2 = 0 & 9x - 3y^2 = 0 \\
9y = 3x^2 & 9x = 3y^2 \\
3y = x^2. & 3x = y^2.
\end{array}
$$

The last two equations provide some useful information. Since $3y = x^2$ and $x^2 \geq 0$, we must have $y \geq 0$. Similarly, since $3x = y^2$ and $y^2 \geq 0$, we must have $x \geq 0$. Consequently,

any critical point (x, y) of f must satisfy $x \geq 0$ and $y \geq 0$.

The substitution method can be used to solve the system of equations

$$
\begin{aligned}
3y &= x^2 \\
3x &= y^2.
\end{aligned}
$$

The first equation, $3y = x^2$, can be rewritten as $y = x^2/3$. Substitute this expression into the second equation to get

$$3x = y^2 = \left(\frac{x^2}{3}\right)^2$$

$$3x = \frac{x^4}{9}.$$

Solve this equation as follows:

$$
\begin{array}{ll}
27x = x^4 & \text{Multiply both sides by 9.} \\
x^4 - 27x = 0 & \\
x(x^3 - 27) = 0. & \text{Factor} \\
\quad x = 0 \quad \text{or} \quad x^3 - 27 = 0 & \text{Set each factor equal to 0.} \\
\qquad\qquad\qquad\quad x^3 = 27 & \\
\qquad\qquad\qquad\quad\ x = 3 & \text{Take the cube root on each side.}
\end{array}
$$

Use these values of x, along with the equation $3x = y^2$, to find y:

$$
\begin{array}{ll}
\text{If } x = 0, & \text{If } x = 3, \\
3x = y^2 & 3x = y^2 \\
3(0) = y^2 & 3(3) = y^2 \\
0 = y^2 & 9 = y^2 \\
0 = y. & 3 = y \quad \text{or} \quad -3 = y.
\end{array}
$$

So the solutions for the system of equations are $(0, 0)$, $(3, 3)$ and $(3, -3)$. However, as we saw earlier, a critical point here must have *both* coordinates nonnegative. Hence, the only critical points of f are $(0, 0)$ and $(3, 3)$.

To see if either critical point produces an extremum, use the test for local extrema. Here,

$$f_x = 9y - 3x^2 \quad \text{and} \quad f_y = 9x - 3y^2.$$

Hence,

$$f_{xx} = -6x, \quad f_{yy} = -6y, \quad \text{and} \quad f_{xy} = 9.$$

Test each of the critical points.

For $(0, 0)$,

$$f_{xx}(0, 0) = -6(0) = 0, \quad f_{yy}(0, 0) = -6(0) = 0, \quad \text{and} \quad f_{xy}(0, 0) = 9,$$

so that $M = 0 \cdot 0 - 9^2 = -81$. Since $M < 0$, there is a saddle point at $(0, 0)$.

For (3, 3),

$$f_{xx}(3, 3) = -6(3) = -18, \qquad f_{yy}(3, 3) = -6(3) = -18, \qquad \text{and} \qquad f_{xy}(3, 3) = 9,$$

so that $M = (-18)(-18) - 9^2 = 243$. Since $M > 0$ and $f_{xx}(3, 3) = -18 < 0$, there is a local maximum at (3, 3). If you examine Figure 14.23 carefully, you will see both the local maximum at (3, 3) and the saddle point at (0, 0). ✓3

✓ **Checkpoint 3**

Find any local extrema for

$$f(x, y) = \frac{2\sqrt{2}}{3}x^3 - xy$$
$$+ \frac{1}{3}y^3 - 10.$$

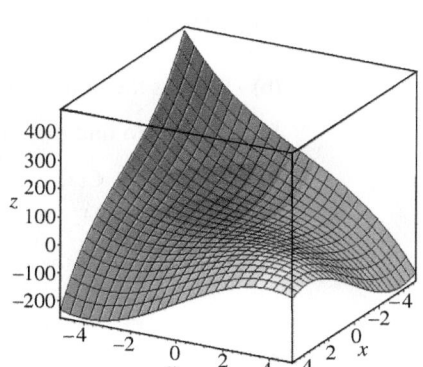

Figure 14.23

Example 4   **Business**   A company is developing a new soft drink. The cost in dollars to produce a batch of the drink is approximated by

$$C(x, y) = 2200 + 27x^3 - 72xy + 8y^2,$$

where x is the number of kilograms of sugar per batch and y is the number of grams of flavoring per batch.

(a)   Find the amounts of sugar and flavoring that result in a local minimum cost for a batch.

Solution   Start with the following partial derivatives:

$$C_x = 81x^2 - 72y \qquad \text{and} \qquad C_y = -72x + 16y.$$

Set each of these expressions equal to 0 and solve for y:

$$81x^2 - 72y = 0 \qquad\qquad -72x + 16y = 0$$
$$-72y = -81x^2 \qquad\qquad 16y = 72x$$
$$y = \frac{9}{8}x^2. \qquad\qquad\qquad y = \frac{9}{2}x.$$

From the equation on the left, $y \geq 0$. Since $(9/8)x^2$ and $(9/2)x$ both are equal to y, they are equal to each other. Set $(9/8)x^2$ and $(9/2)x$ equal and solve the resulting equation for x:

$$\frac{9}{8}x^2 = \frac{9}{2}x$$
$$9x^2 = 36x$$
$$9x^2 - 36x = 0$$
$$9x(x - 4) = 0$$
$$9x = 0 \quad \text{or} \quad x - 4 = 0$$
$$x = 0 \quad \text{or} \quad x = 4.$$

Substitute $x = 0$ and $x = 4$ into $y = (9/2)x$ to find the corresponding y values:

$$y = \left(\frac{9}{2}\right)(0) = 0 \qquad \text{and} \qquad y = \left(\frac{9}{2}\right)(4) = 18.$$

✓**Checkpoint 4**

Compute M for the critical point $(0, 0)$ for the function in Example 4. What do you conclude?

So the critical points are $(0, 0)$ and $(4, 18)$. Verify that $(0, 0)$ does not produce a minimum. ✓4 Now check to see if the critical point $(4, 18)$ leads to a local minimum. Note that

$$C_{xx} = 162x, \qquad C_{yy} = 16, \qquad \text{and} \qquad C_{xy} = -72.$$

At $(4, 18)$, $C_{xx}(4, 18) = 162(4) = 648$, $C_{yy}(4, 18) = 16$, and $C_{xy}(4, 18) = -72$. Therefore,

$$M = (648)(16) - (-72)^2 = 5184.$$

Since $M > 0$ and $C_{xx}(4, 18) > 0$, the cost at $(4, 18)$ is a minimum.

(b) What is the minimum cost?

Solution To find the minimum cost, go back to the cost function and evaluate $C(4, 18)$:

$$C(x, y) = 2200 + 27x^3 - 72xy + 8y^2$$
$$C(4, 18) = 2200 + 27(4)^3 - 72(4)(18) + 8(18)^2 = 1336.$$

The minimum cost for a batch is $1336.

➤ **TECHNOLOGY TIP** Spreadsheet programs have built-in solvers that are able to optimize many functions of two or more variables. The Excel Solver is located on the Data tab in the Analysis group. (If the Solver command or the Analysis group is not available, you need to load the Solver Add-in program—see Excel Help for details.) The Solver requires that cells be identified ahead of time for each variable in the problem. It also requires that another cell be identified where the function to be optimized, in terms of the variable cells, is placed. In Example 4, for instance, we could identify cells A1 and B1 to represent the variables x and y, respectively. The Solver requires that we place a guess for the answer in these cells. Thus, for our initial value or guess, we place the number 5 in each of these cells. The function must be placed in a cell in terms of cells A1 and B1. If we choose cell A3 to represent the function, then we would type "=2200 + 27*A1^3 − 72*A1*B1 + 8*B1^2" in cell A3.

We now click on the Data tab and choose Solver from the Analysis group to find a solution that either maximizes or minimizes the value of cell A3, depending on which option we choose. Figure 14.24 illustrates the Solver box in Excel 2013 (Microsoft Corporation Excel © 2013) and the items placed in it.

Figure 14.24

To obtain a solution, click on Solve. When Excel shows a dialog box with "Keep Solver Solution" as the default, click OK. The rounded solution $x = 4$ and $y = 18$ is located in cells A1 and B1, respectively. The minimum cost $C(4, 18) = 1336$ is located in cell A3.

Note: One must be careful when using the Excel Solver, because it will not find a "maximum or minimum" of a function if the initial guess is the exact place in which a saddle point occurs. For example, in the preceding problem, if our initial guess was (0, 0), the Solver would have returned the value of (0, 0) as the place where a minimum occurs. But (0, 0) is a saddle point. Thus, it is always a good idea to run the Solver for two different initial values and compare the solutions.

14.3 Exercises

1. Compare and contrast the way critical points are found for functions with one variable and for functions with more than one variable.

2. Compare and contrast the second-derivative test for $y = f(x)$ and the test for local extrema for $z = f(x, y)$.

Find all points where the given functions have any local extrema. Give the values of any local extrema. Identify any saddle points. (See Examples 1–3.)

3. $f(x, y) = 2x^2 + 4xy + 6y^2 - 8x - 10$

4. $f(x, y) = x^2 + xy + y^2 - 6x - 3$

5. $f(x, y) = x^2 - xy + y^2 + 2x + 2y + 6$

6. $f(x, y) = 2x^2 + 3xy + 2y^2 - 5x - 5y$

7. $f(x, y) = 3xy + 6y - 5x$

8. $f(x, y) = 5xy - 7x^2 - y^2 + 3x - 6y - 4$

9. $f(x, y) = 4xy - 10x^2 - 4y^2 + 8x + 8y + 9$

10. $f(x, y) = 4y^2 + 2xy + 6x + 4y - 8$

11. $f(x, y) = x^2 + xy + y^2 - 3x - 5$

12. $f(x, y) = x^2 + xy - 2x - 2y + 2$

13. $f(x, y) = x^2 - y^2 - 2x + 4y - 7$

14. $f(x, y) = 4x + 2y - x^2 + xy - y^2 + 3$

15. $f(x, y) = 2x^3 + 2y^2 - 12xy + 15$

16. $f(x, y) = 2x^2 + 4y^3 - 24xy + 18$

17. $f(x, y) = x^2 + 4y^3 - 6xy - 1$

18. $f(x, y) = 2y^3 + 5x^2 + 60xy + 25$

19. $f(x, y) = e^{xy}$ **20.** $f(x, y) = e^{x^2 - y^2}$

21. $f(x, y) = x^{10} - e^{10y}$ **22.** $f(x, y) = x^2 + e^y$

Figures (a)–(f) show the graphs of the functions defined in Exercises 23–28, respectively. Find all local extrema for each function, and then match the equation with its graph.

23. $z = -3xy + x^3 - y^3 + \dfrac{1}{8}$

24. $z = \dfrac{3}{2}y - \dfrac{1}{2}y^3 - x^2y + \dfrac{1}{16}$

25. $z = y^4 - 2y^2 + x^2 - \dfrac{17}{16}$

26. $z = -2x^3 - 3y^4 + 6xy^2 + \dfrac{1}{16}$

27. $z = -x^4 + y^4 + 2x^2 - 2y^2 + \dfrac{1}{16}$

28. $z = -y^4 + 4xy - 2x^2 + \dfrac{1}{16}$

(a)

(b)

(c)

(d)

(e)

(f)

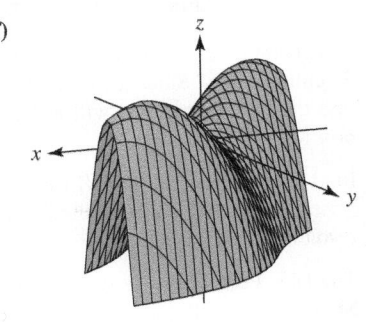

Business *In the following exercises, find the local maximum or local minimum, as requested. (See Example 4.)*

29. The labor cost in dollars for manufacturing a digital camera can be approximated by

$$L(x, y) = \frac{3}{2}x^2 + y^2 - 2x - 2y - 2xy + 68,$$

where x is the number of hours required by a skilled craftsperson and y is the number of hours required by a semiskilled person. Find values of x and y that minimize the labor charge. Find the minimum labor charge.

30. Suppose that the profit of a certain firm is approximated by

$$P(x, y) = 1000 + 24x - x^2 + 80y - y^2,$$

where x is the cost of a unit of labor and y is the cost of a unit of goods. Find values of x and y that maximize the profit. Find the maximum profit.

31. The most significant expenses for a particular house cleaning service are transportation and labor costs. Daily profit (in dollars) for the business is approximated by

$$P(x, y) = 600 - 2x^3 + 6xy - y^2,$$

where x is the cost of a gallon of gasoline and y is the hourly wage paid to housekeeping employees. Find the maximum profit and the costs of gasoline and labor that produce the maximum profit.

32. The total profit from one acre of a certain crop depends on the amounts spent on fertilizer, x, and hybrid seed, y, according to the model

$$P(x, y) = -x^2 + 3xy + 160x - 5y^2 + 200y + 2,600,000.$$

Find values of x and y that lead to maximum profit. Find the maximum profit.

33. The total cost required to produce x units of electrical tape and y units of packing tape is given by

$$C(x, y) = 2x^2 + 3y^2 - 2xy + 2x - 126y + 3800.$$

Find the number of units of each kind of tape that should be produced so that the total cost is a minimum. Find the minimum total cost.

34. The total revenue, in thousands of dollars, from the sale of x spas and y solar heaters is approximated by

$$R(x, y) = 12 + 74x + 85y - 3x^2 - 5y^2 - 5xy.$$

Find the number of each that should be sold to produce maximum revenue. Find the maximum revenue.

35. A rectangular closed box is to be built at minimum cost to hold 27 cubic meters. Since the cost will depend on the surface area, find the dimensions that will minimize the surface area of the box.

36. Find the dimensions that will minimize the surface area (and hence the cost) of a rectangular fish aquarium, open on top, with a volume of 32 cubic feet.

37. The U.S. Postal Service requires that any box sent by Priority Mail have a length plus girth (distance around) totaling no more than 108 inches. (See Example 7 in Section 12.3 for a special case.) Find the dimensions of the box with maximum volume that can be sent by Priority Mail.

38. A box that is sent through the U.S. mail by parcel post must have a length plus girth of no more than 130 inches. Find the dimensions of the box with maximum volume that can be sent by parcel post. (See Exercise 37.)

39. Find the dimensions of the circular tube with maximum volume that can be sent by U.S. Priority Mail. (See Exercise 37.)

40. A piece of carry-on luggage on most airlines (such as American, Delta, and Continental) must satisfy the condition that the sum of its length, width, and height is no more than 45 inches. If no other restrictions apply, find the dimensions of the piece of carry-on luggage with maximum volume that can be brought on these airlines.[*]

41. The monthly revenue, in hundreds of dollars, from the production of x thousand tons of grade A iron ore and y thousand tons of grade B iron ore is given by

$$R(x, y) = 2xy + 2y + 12,$$

and the corresponding cost, in hundreds of dollars, is given by

$$C(x, y) = 2x^2 + y^2.$$

Find the amount of each grade of ore that will produce maximum profit.

42. The revenue and cost (in thousands of dollars) from the manufacture of x thousand specialty cupcakes and y thousand pies are, respectively,

$$R(x, y) = 12xy + 5 - 2x^2 \quad \text{and} \quad C(x, y) = x^2 + 2y^3.$$

How many units of each product will produce the maximum profit? What is the maximum profit?

43. The profit (in thousands of dollars) that Aunt Mildred's Metalworks earns from producing x tons of steel and y tons of aluminum can be approximated by

$$P(x, y) = 36xy - x^3 - 8y^3.$$

Find the amounts of steel and aluminum that maximize the profit, and find the value of the maximum profit.

44. **Health** Research has shown that the total change in color, E (measured in the form of energy as kJ/mol), when blanched potato strips are fried can be estimated by the function

$$E(t, T) = 436.16 - 10.57t - 5.46T - .02t^2 + .02T^2 + .08Tt,$$

where T is the temperature (in degrees Centigrade) and t is the frying time (in minutes).[†]

(a) Find the value of E prior to cooking. Assume that $T = 0$.

(b) Estimate the total change in color of a potato strip that has been cooked for 10 minutes at 180°C.

(c) Determine the critical point of this function and whether a maximum, minimum, or saddle point occurs at that point.

---

[*]Depending on the plane and the airline, additional restrictions may apply (for instance, that the luggage fit under the seat or in the overhead compartment).

[†]Hindra, F., and Oon-Doo Baik, "Kinetics of Quality Changes During Food Frying," *Critical Reviews in Food Science and Nutrition*, Vol. 46, 2006, pp. 239–358.

✓ **Checkpoint Answers**

1. (a) $(-2, 3)$ (b) $(0, 2)$

2. (a) Local minimum at $(-2, 3)$

  (b) Neither a local minimum nor a local maximum at $(0, 2)$

3. Local minimum at $\left(\dfrac{1}{2}, \dfrac{\sqrt{2}}{2} \right)$; saddle point at $(0, 0)$

4. $M = -5184$, so there is a saddle point at $(0, 0)$.

14.4 Lagrange Multipliers

It is often necessary to solve optimization problems (such as finding the maximum profit or the minimum cost). We have seen two techniques for doing this with functions of two variables:

1. Change the given problem into an equivalent one-variable problem by making a suitable substitution (as in Example 7 of Section 12.3).

2. Use the test for local extrema (as in Example 4 of Section 14.3).

The first technique works only when algebra can be used to express one variable in terms of the other. The second technique does not work when constraints are present (as is often the case in the real world). Finally, neither method applies to functions of three or more variables.

In this section, we present Lagrange's method for optimizing a function of two or more variables, subject to a constraint.* The method is used for problems of the form

Find the optimum value of the function $f(x, y)$,

subject to the constraint $g(x, y) = 0$;

that is, find the point (x, y) satisfying the constraint $g(x, y) = 0$, at which $f(x, y)$ has its optimum value. The optimum value may be either a maximum value or a minimum value, depending on the problem.

Here is a typical example:

Find the minimum value of $f(x, y) = x^2 + y^2$,

subject to the constraint $x + y - 4 = 0$.

In this case, $g(x, y) = x + y - 4$ and the optimum value is the minimum value. Graphically, the point (x, y, z) satisfying $x + y - 4 = 0$ at which $z = f(x, y)$ is smallest is the lowest point on the intersection of the graph of $z = x^2 + y^2$ and the plane $x + y - 4 = 0$, as shown in Figure 14.25, on the following page.† Note that this point is *not* the lowest point on the graph of $f(x, y) = x^2 + y^2$. The minimum value of $f(x, y)$ (with no constraint) occurs at $(0, 0, 0)$, which does not lie on the plane $x + y - 4 = 0$ given by the constraint.

Lagrange's method provides an algebraic way to solve problems such as this one. The key idea is to introduce an additional variable called the **Lagrange multiplier** and denoted by the lowercase Greek letter λ (lambda) and to use the *Lagrange function*

$$F(x, y, \lambda) = f(x, y) - \lambda \cdot g(x, y).$$

In our example,

$$F(x, y, \lambda) = (x^2 + y^2) - \lambda(x + y - 4)$$
$$= x^2 + y^2 - \lambda x - \lambda y + 4\lambda.$$

Lagrange's method (whose proof is beyond the scope of this text) uses the partial derivatives of the function F to find the point satisfying the constraint $g(x, y) = 0$ at which $f(x, y)$ has its optimum value (if such a point exists).

---

*Named for the French mathematician Joseph Louis Lagrange (1736–1813). The method is stated here for functions of two variables, but with obvious modifications, it is valid for any number of variables.

†These graphs were found in Example 7 and Exercise 23 of Section 14.1.

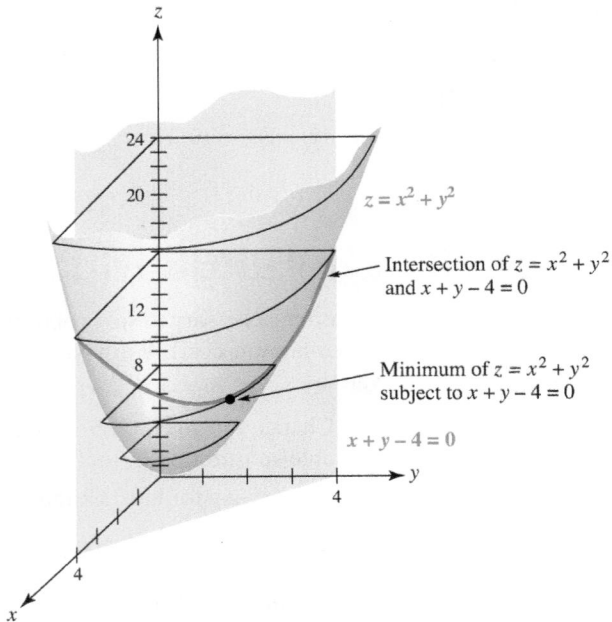

Figure 14.25

Lagrange's Method

To optimize the function $f(x, y)$ subject to the constraint $g(x, y) = 0$,

Step 1   Form the Lagrange function

$$F(x, y, \lambda) = f(x, y) - \lambda \cdot g(x, y).$$

Step 2   Find the partial derivatives of F: $F_x(x, y, \lambda)$, $F_y(x, y, \lambda)$, and $F_\lambda(x, y, \lambda)$.

Step 3   Solve the following system of equations:

$$F_x(x, y, \lambda) = 0$$
$$F_y(x, y, \lambda) = 0$$
$$F_\lambda(x, y, \lambda) = 0.$$

If the original problem has a solution, it will occur at a point (x, y) for which there exists a value of λ such that (x, y, λ) is a solution of the system in Step 3.

The points found in Step 3 of Lagrange's method provide a list of *possibilities*. If the optimum value exists, it must occur at a point on the list, but the list may contain points that do not produce an optimum value.[*] Thus, to apply Lagrange's method, we must know that the required maximum or minimum actually exists. In many applied problems, the given conditions make it clear that an optimum value must exist. In other cases, graphical information can sometimes be used to make this determination, as Example 1 illustrates. Unless stated otherwise, you may assume that the required optimum exists in each example and exercise of this section.

---

[*]This is similar to the situation with functions of one variable. Every local extremum must occur at a critical number (where the derivative is 0 or does not exist), but not every critical number produces a local extremum.

Example 1 Use Lagrange's method to find the minimum value of

$$f(x, y) = x^2 + y^2, \text{ subject to the constraint } x + y = 4.$$

Solution First, rewrite the constraint in the form $g(x, y) = 0$:

$$x + y - 4 = 0.$$

Then follow the steps in the preceding box.

Step 1 As we saw previously, the Lagrange function is

$$F(x, y, \lambda) = f(x, y) - \lambda \cdot g(x, y).$$
$$= x^2 + y^2 - \lambda x - \lambda y + 4\lambda.$$

Step 2 Find the partial derivatives of F:

$$F_x(x, y, \lambda) = 2x - \lambda$$
$$F_y(x, y, \lambda) = 2y - \lambda$$
$$F_\lambda(x, y, \lambda) = -x - y + 4.$$

Step 3 Set each partial derivative equal to 0 and solve the resulting system:

$$2x - \lambda = 0$$
$$2y - \lambda = 0$$
$$-x - y + 4 = 0. \tag{1}$$

Since this is a system of *linear* equations in x, y, and λ, it could be solved by the matrix techniques of Section 6.2. However, we shall use a different technique, one that can be used even when the equations of the system are not all linear. Begin by solving the first two equations for λ:

$$2x - \lambda = 0 \qquad\qquad 2y - \lambda = 0$$
$$\lambda = 2x \qquad\qquad\qquad \lambda = 2y.$$

Set the two expressions for λ equal to obtain

$$2x = 2y$$
$$x = y.$$

Now make the substitution $y = x$ in the third equation of the system **(1)**:

$$-x - y + 4 = 0$$
$$-x - x + 4 = 0$$
$$-2x = -4$$
$$x = 2.$$

Since $y = x$ and $\lambda = 2x$, we see that the only solution of system **(1)** is

$$x = 2, \qquad y = 2, \qquad \lambda = 2 \cdot 2 = 4.$$

Graphical considerations show that the original problem has a solution (see Figure 14.25 and the discussion preceding it), so we conclude that the minimum value of $f(x, y) = x^2 + y^2$, subject to the constraint $x + y = 4$, occurs when $x = 2$ and $y = 2$. The minimum value is

$$f(2, 2) = 2^2 + 2^2 = 8.$$

Example 2 A builder plans to construct a three-story building with a rectangular floor plan. The cost of the building, which depends on the dimensions of the floor plan, is given by

$$xy + 30x + 20y + 474{,}000,$$

where x and y are, respectively, the length and width of the rectangular floors. What length and width should be used if the building is to cost \$500,000 and have maximum area on each floor?

Solution   The area of each floor is given by $A(x, y) = xy$. Since the building is to cost \$500,000, we have the following constraint:

$$xy + 30x + 20y + 474,000 = 500,000$$

$$\underbrace{xy + 30x + 20y - 26,000}_{g(x, y)} = 0.$$

So we must find the maximum value of $A(x, y)$, subject to $g(x, y) = 0$.

Step 1   The Lagrange function is

$$F(x, y, \lambda) = A(x, y) - \lambda \cdot g(x, y).$$
$$= xy - \lambda(xy + 30x + 20y - 26,000)$$
$$= xy - \lambda xy - 30\lambda x - 20\lambda y + 26,000\lambda.$$

Step 2   The partial derivatives of F are

$$F_x(x, y, \lambda) = y - \lambda y - 30\lambda$$
$$F_y(x, y, \lambda) = x - \lambda x - 20\lambda$$
$$F_\lambda(x, y, \lambda) = -xy - 30x - 20y + 26,000.$$

Step 3   Set each partial derivative equal to 0 and solve the system of equations

$$y - \lambda y - 30\lambda = 0$$
$$x - \lambda x - 20\lambda = 0$$
$$-xy - 30x - 20y + 26,000 = 0 \qquad\qquad (2)$$

as follows. Solve the first two equations for λ:

$$\begin{array}{ll}
y - \lambda y - 30\lambda = 0 & \qquad x - \lambda x - 20\lambda = 0 \\
\quad y = \lambda y + 30\lambda & \qquad\quad x = \lambda x + 20\lambda \\
\quad y = (y + 30)\lambda & \qquad\quad x = (x + 20)\lambda \\
\quad \lambda = \dfrac{y}{y + 30} & \qquad\quad \lambda = \dfrac{x}{x + 20}.
\end{array}$$

Set the two expressions for λ equal and solve the resulting equation:

$$\frac{y}{y + 30} = \frac{x}{x + 20}$$

$$y(x + 20) = x(y + 30) \qquad \text{Multiply both sides by } (x + 20)(y + 30).$$
$$xy + 20y = xy + 30x$$
$$20y = 30x \qquad\qquad \text{Subtract } xy \text{ from both sides.}$$
$$y = 1.5x. \qquad\qquad \text{Divide both sides by 20.}$$

Make the substitution $y = 1.5x$ in the third equation of the system **(2)**:

$$-xy - 30x - 20y + 26,000 = 0$$
$$-x(1.5x) - 30x - 20(1.5x) + 26,000 = 0$$
$$-1.5x^2 - 60x + 26,000 = 0.$$

By the quadratic formula,

$$x = \frac{-(-60) \pm \sqrt{(-60)^2 - 4(-1.5)(26,000)}}{2(-1.5)} \approx \begin{cases} 113.17 \\ -153.17. \end{cases}$$

Since x is a length, the negative value does not apply. Since $y = 1.5x$,

$$y \approx 1.5(113.17) \approx 169.75.$$

We now have sufficient information. (There is no need to solve for λ.) Floors that measure 113.17 ft $\times$ 169.75 ft will result in the largest area per floor, which is

$$A(113.17, 169.75) = (113.17)(169.75) \approx 19{,}211 \text{ sq ft.}$$

NOTE In Examples 1 and 2, we solved the system by first solving each equation with a λ in it for λ. Then we set the expressions for λ equal and solved for one of the original variables. This is often a good approach, since we are not usually interested in the value of λ.

With a constrained function of two variables (as in the preceding examples), the Lagrange function has three variables, and a system of three equations in three variables must be solved. Next we consider constrained functions of three variables, in which case the Lagrange function has four variables and a system of four equations in four variables must be solved.

Example 3 Find three positive numbers x, y, and z whose sum is 50 and such that xyz^2 is as large as possible.

Solution We must find the maximum value of $f(x, y, z) = xyz^2$, subject to the constraint $x + y + z = 50$. Begin by writing the constraint as

$$\underbrace{x + y + z - 50}_{g(x, y, z)} = 0.$$

Step 1 The Lagrange function is

$$\begin{aligned} F(x, y, z, \lambda) &= f(x, y, z) - \lambda \cdot g(x, y, z) \\ &= xyz^2 - \lambda(x + y + z - 50) \\ &= xyz^2 - \lambda x - \lambda y - \lambda z + 50\lambda. \end{aligned}$$

Step 2 The partial derivatives of F are

$$\begin{aligned} F_x(x, y, z, \lambda) &= yz^2 - \lambda \\ F_y(x, y, z, \lambda) &= xz^2 - \lambda \\ F_z(x, y, z, \lambda) &= 2xyz - \lambda \\ F_\lambda(x, y, z, \lambda) &= -x - y - z + 50. \end{aligned}$$

Step 3 Set each partial derivative equal to 0 and solve the system of equations

$$\begin{aligned} yz^2 - \lambda &= 0 \\ xz^2 - \lambda &= 0 \\ 2xyz - \lambda &= 0 \\ -x - y - z + 50 &= 0. \end{aligned} \tag{3}$$

The first three equations are easily solved for λ:

$$\lambda = yz^2, \qquad \lambda = xz^2, \qquad \lambda = 2xyz.$$

Setting the expressions for λ equal produces three equations:

$$yz^2 = xz^2, \qquad yz^2 = 2xyz, \qquad xz^2 = 2xyz.$$

Solve the first two of these equations as follows:

$$yz^2 = xz^2 \qquad \text{First equation}$$

$$\frac{yz^2}{z^2} = \frac{xz^2}{z^2} \qquad \text{Divide both sides by } z^2.$$

$$y = x$$

$$yz^2 = 2xyz \qquad \text{Second equation}$$

$$\frac{yz^2}{yz} = \frac{2xyz}{yz} \qquad \text{Divide both sides by } yz.$$

$$z = 2x.$$

(This information is sufficient, so we need not solve the third equation.) Substitute these values into the last equation of the system (**3**):

$$-x - y - z + 50 = 0$$

$$-x - x - 2x + 50 = 0 \qquad \text{Substitute } y = x \text{ and } z = 2x.$$

$$-4x = -50$$

$$x = 12.5. \qquad \text{Divide both sides by } -4.$$

Since $y = x$ and $z = 2x$, the three numbers in the original problem are

$$x = 12.5, \qquad y = 12.5, \qquad \text{and} \qquad z = 2(12.5) = 25,$$

and the maximum value of $f(x, y, z) = xyz^2$ is $(12.5)(12.5)(25^2) = 97{,}656.25$.

Checkpoint 1

Find three positive numbers x, y, and z whose sum is 15 and whose product xyz is as large as possible.

Example 4 Find the dimensions of the closed rectangular box of maximum volume that can be constructed from 6 square feet of material.

Solution Let the dimensions of the box be x, y, and z, as shown in Figure 14.26. The volume of the box is given by

$$f(x, y, z) = xyz.$$

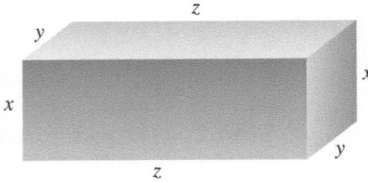

Figure 14.26

By considering the surface area of each side of the box in Figure 14.26, we obtain a constraint:

$$\text{Right end} + \text{left end} + \text{front} + \text{back} + \text{top} + \text{bottom} = 6$$

$$xy \quad + \quad xy \quad + \quad xz \quad + \quad xz \quad + \quad yz \quad + \quad yz \quad = 6$$

$$2xy + 2xz + 2yz = 6$$

$$xy + xz + yz = 3. \qquad \text{Divide both sides by 2.}$$

So we must find the maximum value of $f(x, y, z) = xyz$, subject to the constraint $xy + xz + yz - 3 = 0$.

Step 1 The Lagrange function is

$$F(x, y, z, \lambda) = f(x, y, z) - \lambda \cdot g(x, y, z).$$

$$= xyz - \lambda(xy + xz + yz - 3)$$

$$= xyz - \lambda xy - \lambda xz - \lambda yz + 3\lambda.$$

Step 2 The partial derivatives of F are

$$F_x(x, y, z, \lambda) = yz - \lambda y - \lambda z$$
$$F_y(x, y, z, \lambda) = xz - \lambda x - \lambda z$$
$$F_z(x, y, z, \lambda) = xy - \lambda x - \lambda y$$
$$F_\lambda(x, y, z, \lambda) = -xy - xz - yz + 3.$$

Step 3 Set each partial derivative equal to 0 and solve the system of equations

$$yz - \lambda y - \lambda z = 0$$
$$xz - \lambda x - \lambda z = 0$$
$$xy - \lambda x - \lambda y = 0$$
$$-xy - xz - yz + 3 = 0. \qquad (4)$$

Begin by solving each of the first three equations for λ:

$yz - \lambda y - \lambda z = 0$	$xz - \lambda x - \lambda z = 0$	$xy - \lambda x - \lambda y = 0$	First three equations
$-\lambda y - \lambda z = -yz$	$-\lambda x - \lambda z = -xz$	$-\lambda x - \lambda y = -xy$	Isolate terms with λ on the left.
$\lambda(y + z) = yz$	$\lambda(x + z) = xz$	$\lambda(x + y) = xy$	Multiply both sides by -1 and factor out λ.
$\lambda = \dfrac{yz}{y + z}$	$\lambda = \dfrac{xz}{x + z}$	$\lambda = \dfrac{xy}{x + y}$.	Solve for λ.

Set these expressions for λ equal, and simplify as follows (notice in the second and last steps that, since none of the dimensions of the box can be 0, we can divide both sides of each equation by x or z):

$$\frac{yz}{y + z} = \frac{xz}{x + z} \qquad \text{and} \qquad \frac{xz}{x + z} = \frac{xy}{x + y}$$

$$\frac{y}{y + z} = \frac{x}{x + z} \qquad\qquad\qquad \frac{z}{x + z} = \frac{y}{x + y}$$

$$y(x + z) = x(y + z) \qquad\qquad z(x + y) = y(x + z)$$

$$xy + yz = xy + xz \qquad\qquad zx + zy = yx + yz$$

$$yz = xz \qquad\qquad\qquad\qquad zx = yx$$

$$y = x \qquad\qquad\qquad\qquad\quad z = y.$$

(Setting the first and third expressions equal gives no additional information.) Thus, $x = y = z$. From the last equation in system **(4)**, with $x = y$ and $z = y$,

$$-xy - xz - yz + 3 = 0$$
$$-y^2 - y^2 - y^2 + 3 = 0$$
$$-3y^2 = -3$$
$$y^2 = 1$$
$$y = \pm 1.$$

The negative solution is not applicable, so the solution of the system of equations is $x = 1, y = 1, z = 1$. In other words, the box with maximum volume under the constraint is a cube that measures 1 ft on each side. ✓₂

✓**Checkpoint 2**

Find the dimensions of the open rectangular box (which does not have a top) of maximum volume that can be constructed from 12 square feet of material.

TECHNOLOGY TIP Finding extrema of a constrained function of one or more variables can be done with a spreadsheet. In addition to the requirements stated in the Technology Tip at the end of Section 14.3, the constraint must be input into the Excel Solver. To do this, we need to input the variable part of the constraint into a designated cell. In Example 4, for instance, suppose that A5 is the designated cell. Then, in cell A5, we would type "=A1*B1 + A1*C1 + B1*C1".

We now click on the Data tab and choose Solver from the Analysis group to find a solution that either maximizes or minimizes the value of cell A3, depending on which option we choose.

Figure 14.27 illustrates the Solver box in Excel 2013 (Microsoft Corporation Excel © 2013) and the items placed in it.

Figure 14.27

To obtain a solution, click on Solve. When Excel shows a dialog box with "Keep Solver Solution" as the default, click OK. The solution $x = 1, y = 1, z = 1$ is located in cells A1, B1, and C1, respectively. The maximum volume $f(1, 1, 1) = 1$ is located in cell A3.

Note: One must be careful when using the Solver because the solution may depend on the initial value. Thus, it is always a good idea to run the Solver for two different initial values and compare the solutions.

14.4 Exercises

Find the maxima and minima in Exercises 1–12. Assume all variables are positive. (See Examples 1 and 3.)

1. Maximum of $f(x, y) = 2xy$, subject to $x + y = 20$

2. Maximum of $f(x, y) = 4xy + 8$, subject to $x + y = 16$

3. Maximum of $f(x, y) = xy^2$, subject to $x + 4y = 15$

4. Maximum of $f(x, y) = 2xy^2$, subject to $x + y = 6$

5. Minimum of $f(x, y) = x^2 + 2y^2 - xy$, subject to $x + y = 8$

6. Minimum of $f(x, y) = 3x^2 + 4y^2 - xy - 2$, subject to $2x + y = 21$

7. Maximum of $f(x, y) = x^2 - 10y^2$, subject to $x - y = 18$

8. Maximum of $f(x, y) = 12xy - x^2 - 3y^2$, subject to $x + y = 16$

9. Maximum of $f(x, y) = e^{-x^2 - y^2}$, subject to $x + y = 2$

10. Minimum of $f(x, y) = e^{-xy}$, subject to $x + y = 10$

11. Maximum of $f(x, y, z) = xyz^2$, subject to $x + y + z = 6$

12. Minimum of $f(x, y, z) = xy + 2xz + 2yz$, subject to $xyz = 32$

13. Find positive numbers x and y such that $x + y = 21$ and $2xy^2$ is maximized.

14. Find positive numbers x and y such that $x + y = 24$ and $x^2y + 4$ is maximized.

15. Find three positive numbers whose sum is 102 and whose product is a maximum.

16. Find three positive numbers such that their sum is 75 and the sum of their squares is a maximum.

17. Explain Lagrange's method in your own words.

18. Explain the difference between the two methods we used in Sections 14.3 and 14.4 to solve extrema problems.

19. Why is it unnecessary to find the value of λ when using the method explained in this section?

20. Show that the three equations in Step 3 of the box on page 846 are equivalent to the three equations

$$f_x(x, y) = \lambda g_x(x, y),$$
$$f_y(x, y) = \lambda g_y(x, y),$$
$$g(x, y) = 0.$$

Business *Solve the given problems. (See Examples 2 and 4.)*

21. The profit from the sale of x units of radiators for automobiles and y units of radiators for generators is given by

$$P(x, y) = -x^2 - y^2 + 4x + 8y.$$

Find values of x and y that lead to a maximum profit if the firm must produce a total of 6 units of radiators.

22. The total cost to produce x small knitting kits and y large ones is given by

$$C(x, y) = 2x^2 + 6y^2 + 4xy + 10.$$

If a total of 10 kits must be made, how should production be allocated so that total cost is minimized?

23. A manufacturing firm estimates that its total production of automobile batteries, in thousands of units, is

$$f(x, y) = 3x^{1/3}y^{2/3},$$

where x is the number of units of labor and y is the number of units of capital utilized. Labor costs are $80 per unit, and capital costs are $150 per unit. How many units each of labor and capital will maximize production if the firm can spend $40,000 for these costs?

24. An outdoor outfitter estimates that its total production of 60-meter rock climbing ropes is

$$f(x, y) = 4x^{3/4}y^{1/4},$$

where x is the number of units of labor and y is the number of units of capital utilized. If $40,000 is available for labor and capital, and if the firm's costs are $100 per unit of labor and $200 per unit of capital, how many units of each will give the maximum production?

25. Because of terrain difficulties, two sides of a fence can be built for $6 per ft, while the other two sides cost $4 per ft. (See the accompanying sketch.) Find the field of maximum area that can be enclosed for $1200.

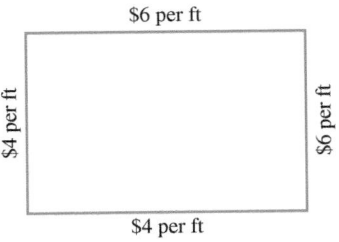

$6 per ft

$4 per ft

$6 per ft

$4 per ft

26. To enclose a yard, a fence is built against a large building, so that fencing material is used only on three sides. Material for the ends costs $8 per ft; material for the side opposite the building costs $6 per ft. Find the dimensions of the yard of maximum area that can be enclosed for $1200.

27. A farmer has 200 m of fencing. Find the dimensions of the rectangular field of maximum area that can be enclosed by this amount of fencing.

28. Find the area of the largest rectangular field that can be enclosed with 600 m of fencing. Assume that no fencing is needed along one side of the field.

Business *Work these exercises.*

29. A cylindrical can is to be made that will hold 250π cubic inches of candy. Find the dimensions of the can with minimum surface area.

30. An ordinary 12-oz soda pop can holds about 25 cubic inches. Find the dimensions of a can with minimum surface area.

Measure a can and see how close its dimensions are to the results you found.

31. A rectangular box with no top is to be built from 500 square meters of material. Find the dimensions of such a box that will enclose the maximum volume.

32. A 1-lb soda cracker box has a volume of 185 cubic inches. The end of the box is square. Find the dimensions of such a box that has minimum surface area.

33. Find the dimensions that will minimize the surface area (and hence the cost) of a rectangular fish aquarium, open on top, with a volume of 32 cubic feet.

34. A rectangular closed box is to be built at minimum cost to hold 27 cubic meters. Since the cost will depend on the surface area, find the dimensions that will minimize the surface area of the box.

35. A company needs to construct a box with an open top that will be used to transport 400 cubic yards of material, in several trips, from one place to another. Two of the sides and the bottom of the box can be made of a free, lightweight material, but only 4 square yards of the material is available. Because of the nature of the material to be transported, the two ends of the box must be made from a heavyweight material that costs $20 per square yard. Each trip costs 10 cents.

   (a) Let x, y, and z respectively denote the length, width, and height of the box. If we want to use all of the free material, show that the total cost in dollars is given by the function

   $$f(x, y, z) = \frac{40}{xyz} + 40yz,$$

   subject to the constraint $2xz + xy = 4$.

   (b) Use the Solver feature on a spreadsheet to find the dimensions of the box that minimize the transportation cost, subject to the given constraint.

36. **Social Science** The probability that the majority of a three-person jury will convict a guilty person is given by the formula

   $$P(r, s, t) = rs(1 - t) + (1 - r)st + r(1 - s)t + rst$$

   subject to the constraint

   $$r + s + t = \alpha,$$

   where r, s, and t represent each of the three jury members' probability of reaching a guilty verdict and α is some fixed constant that is generally less than or equal to the number of jurors.

   (a) Form the Lagrange function.

   (b) Find the values of r, s, and t that maximize the probability of convicting a guilty person when $\alpha = .75$.

   (c) Find the values of r, s, and t that maximize the probability of convicting a guilty person when $\alpha = 3$.

✓ **Checkpoint Answers**

1. $x = y = z = 5$

2. 2 ft × 2 ft × 1 ft

CHAPTER 14 Summary and Review

Key Terms and Symbols

14.1 $z = f(x, y)$, function of
two variables
multivariate function
xy-plane
ordered triple
first octant
surface
trace
level curves
paraboloid

production function
Cobb–Douglas production
function

14.2 f_x or $\dfrac{\partial f}{\partial x}$, partial derivative
of f with respect to x

$\dfrac{\partial}{\partial x}\left(\dfrac{\partial z}{\partial x}\right)$ or $\dfrac{\partial^2 z}{\partial x^2}$ or f_{xx},
second-order partial
derivative of f, partial

derivative of $\partial z/\partial x$ (or
f_x) with respect to x

$\dfrac{\partial}{\partial y}\left(\dfrac{\partial z}{\partial x}\right)$ or $\dfrac{\partial^2 z}{\partial y\partial x}$ or f_{xy},
second-order partial
derivative of f, partial
derivative of $\partial z/\partial x$ (or
f_x) with respect to y

14.3 saddle point
local maximum

local minimum
critical point

14.4 constraint
Lagrange multipliers
Lagrange function
Lagrange's method

Chapter 14 Key Concepts

Graphs of Multivariate Functions

The graph of $ax + by + cz = d$ is a **plane.**

The graph of $z = f(x, y)$ is a **surface** in three-dimensional space.

The graph of $z = ax^2 + by^2$ is a **paraboloid.**

Partial Derivatives

The **partial derivative of $f(x, y)$ with respect to x** is the derivative of f found by treating x as a variable and y as a constant.

The **partial derivative of $f(x, y)$ with respect to y** is the derivative of f found by treating y as a variable and x as a constant.

Second-Order Partial Derivatives

For a function $z = f(x, y)$, if all indicated partial derivatives exist, then

$$\frac{\partial}{\partial x}\left(\frac{\partial z}{\partial x}\right) = \frac{\partial^2 z}{\partial x^2} = f_{xx} \qquad \frac{\partial}{\partial y}\left(\frac{\partial z}{\partial y}\right) = \frac{\partial^2 z}{\partial y^2} = f_{yy}$$

$$\frac{\partial}{\partial y}\left(\frac{\partial z}{\partial x}\right) = \frac{\partial^2 z}{\partial y\partial x} = f_{xy} \qquad \frac{\partial}{\partial x}\left(\frac{\partial z}{\partial y}\right) = \frac{\partial^2 z}{\partial x\partial y} = f_{yx}.$$

Local Extrema

Let (a, b) be in the domain of a function f.

1. f has a **local maximum** at (a, b) if there is a circular region in the xy-plane with (a, b) in its interior such that

$$f(a, b) \geq f(x, y)$$

for all points (x, y) in the circular region.

2. f has a **local minimum** at (a, b) if there is a circular region in the xy-plane with (a, b) in its interior such that

$$f(a, b) \leq f(x, y)$$

for all points (x, y) in the circular region.

If $f(a, b)$ is a local extremum, and $f_x(a, b)$ and $f_y(a, b)$ both exist, then $f_x(a, b) = 0$ and $f_y(a, b) = 0$.

Test for Local Extrema

Suppose $f(x, y)$ is a function such that f_{xx}, f_{yy}, and f_{xy} all exist. Let (a, b) be a critical point for which $f_x(a, b) = 0$ and $f_y(a, b) = 0$. Let $M = f_{xx}(a, b) \cdot f_{yy}(a, b) - [f_{xy}(a, b)]^2$.

If $M > 0$ and $f_{xx}(a, b) < 0$, then f has a **local maximum** at (a, b).

If $M > 0$ and $f_{xx}(a, b) > 0$, then f has a **local minimum** at (a, b).

If $M < 0$, then f has a **saddle point** at (a, b).

If $M = 0$, the test gives **no information.**

Lagrange's Method

To optimize the function $f(x, y)$ subject to the constraint $g(x, y) = 0$, form the Lagrange function $F(x, y, \lambda) = f(x, y) - \lambda \cdot g(x, y)$ and find its partial derivatives $F_x(x, y, \lambda)$, $F_y(x, y, \lambda)$, and $F_\lambda(x, y, \lambda)$. Then solve the system of equations

$$F_x(x, y, \lambda) = 0, \qquad F_y(x, y, \lambda) = 0, \qquad F_\lambda(x, y, \lambda) = 0.$$

If the original problem has a solution, it will occur at a point (x, y) for which there exists a value of λ such that (x, y, λ) is a solution of the preceding system.

Chapter 14 Review Exercises

Find $f(-3, 1)$ and $f(5, -2)$ for each of the given functions.

1. $f(x, y) = 6y^2 - 5xy + 2x$

2. $f(x, y) = -3x + 2x^2y^2 + 5y$

3. $f(x, y) = \dfrac{2x - 4}{x + 3y}$ 4. $f(x, y) = \dfrac{12y - 6x}{x + 3y}$

5. $f(x, y) = 7x\sqrt{y}$ 6. $f(x, y) = x\sqrt{x^2 + y^2}$

7. Describe the graph of $2x + y + 4z = 12$.

8. Describe the graph of $y = 2$ on a three-dimensional grid.

Graph the first-octant portion of each plane.

9. $x + 2y + 4z = 4$ 10. $3x + 2y = 6$

11. $4x + 5y = 20$ 12. $x = 6$

13. Let $z = f(x, y) = -2x^2 + 5xy + y^2$. Find the following:

(a) $\dfrac{\partial z}{\partial x}$;   (b) $\dfrac{\partial z}{\partial y}(-1, 4)$;   (c) $f_{xy}(2, -1)$.

14. Let $z = f(x, y) = \dfrac{2y + x^2}{3y - x}$. Find the following:

(a) $\dfrac{\partial z}{\partial y}$;   (b) $\dfrac{\partial z}{\partial x}(0, 2)$;   (c) $f_{yy}(-1, 0)$.

15. Explain the difference between $\dfrac{\partial z}{\partial x}$ and $\dfrac{\partial z}{\partial y}$.

16. Explain the difference between f_{xx} and f_{xy}.

Find f_x and f_y.

17. $f(x, y) = 3y - 7x^2y^3$ 18. $f(x, y) = 4x^3y + 12xy^3$

19. $f(x, y) = \sqrt{3x^2 + 2y^2}$ 20. $f(x, y) = \sqrt{1 - 4xy^3}$

21. $f(x, y) = \dfrac{-x^2y}{5x + 8y^3}$ 22. $f(x, y) = \dfrac{3x^2 - 2y^2}{x^2 + 4y^2}$

23. $f(x, y) = x^3e^{3y}$ 24. $f(x, y) = (y + 1)^2e^{2x+y}$

25. $f(x, y) = \ln|x^2 - 4y^3|$ 26. $f(x, y) = \ln|1 + x^3y^2|$

Find f_{xx} and f_{xy}.

27. $f(x, y) = 4x^3y^2 - 8xy$ 28. $f(x, y) = -6xy^3 + 2x^2y$

29. $f(x, y) = \dfrac{2x + y}{x - 2y}$ 30. $f(x, y) = \dfrac{3x + y}{x - 1}$

31. $f(x, y) = x^2e^y$ 32. $f(x, y) = ye^{x^2}$

33. $f(x, y) = \ln(2 - x^2y)$ 34. $f(x, y) = \ln(1 + 3xy^2)$

35. **Business** The cost (in dollars) of repainting a car is given by
$$C(x, y) = 4x^2 + 5y^2 - 4xy + 50,$$
where x is the number of hours of labor and y is the number of gallons of paint used. Find the cost in the given cases.

   (a) 10 hours of labor and 8 gallons of paint are needed.

   (b) 12 hours of labor and 10 gallons of paint are needed.

   (c) 14 hours of labor and 14 gallons of paint are needed.

36. **Business** Write a function in terms of L, W, and H that gives the total material required to build the closed shipping box shown in the accompanying figure.

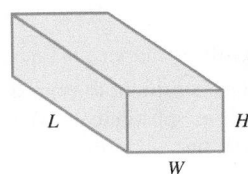

37. **Business** The manufacturing cost (in dollars) for a USB jump drive is given by
$$C(x, y) = \frac{x}{4} + y + \frac{xy}{4} + 1,$$
where x is its memory capacity (in gigabytes) and y is the number of hours of labor required. Find each of the following.

   (a) $\dfrac{\partial C}{\partial x}(32, 1)$ (b) $\dfrac{\partial C}{\partial y}(32, 1)$

38. **Business** The production function for a certain company is given by
$$z = x^{.7}y^{.3},$$
where x is the amount of labor (in appropriate units) and y is the amount of capital (in thousands of dollars). Find the marginal productivity of

   (a) labor;   (b) capital.

Find all points where these functions have any local extrema. Find any saddle points.

39. $z = x^2 + 2y^2 - 4y$

40. $z = x^2 + y^2 + 9x - 8y + 1$

41. $f(x, y) = x^2 + 5xy - 10x + 3y^2 - 12y$

42. $z = x^3 - 8y^2 + 6xy + 4$

43. $z = x^3 + y^2 + 2xy - 4x - 3y - 2$

44. $f(x, y) = 7x^2 + y^2 - 3x + 6y - 5xy$

45. $f(x, y) = e^{x^2+y^2}$ 46. $f(x, y) = e^{xy}$

47. Business   The total cost in dollars to manufacture x solar cells and y solar collectors is

$$C(x, y) = x^2 + 5y^2 + 4xy - 70x - 164y + 1800.$$

(a)   Find values of x and y that produce the minimum total cost.

(b)   Find the minimum total cost.

48. Business   The total profit from 1 acre of a certain crop depends on the amount spent on fertilizer, x, and on hybrid seed, y, according to the model

$$P(x, y) = .01(-x^2 + 3xy + 160x - 5y^2 + 200y + 2600).$$

The budget for fertilizer and seed is limited to \$280.

(a)   Use the budget constraint to express one variable in terms of the other. Then substitute into the profit function to get a function with one variable. Use the method shown in

Chapter 12 to find the amounts spent on fertilizer and seed that will maximize profit. What is the maximum profit per acre? (*Hint:* Throughout this problem, you may ignore the coefficient of .01 until you need to find the maximum profit.)

(b)   Find the amounts spent on fertilizer and seed that will maximize profit, using the method shown in Section 14.3. (*Hint:* You will not need to use the budget constraint.)

(c)   Discuss any relationships between these methods.

49.   Minimize $f(x, y) = x^2 + y^2$, subject to the constraint $x = y + 2$.

50.   Find positive numbers x and y that maximize the value of $f(x, y) = x^2 y$, subject to the constraint $x + y = 4$.

51.   Find positive numbers x and y whose sum is 80 such that $x^2 y$ is maximized.

52.   Find positive numbers x and y whose sum is 50 such that xy^2 is maximized.

53.   Notice in the previous two exercises that we specified that x and y must be positive numbers. Does a maximum exist without this requirement? Explain why or why not.

54.   Use Lagrange's method to find the amounts spent on fertilizer and seeds that will maximize profit in Exercise 48.

Case Study 14   Global Warming and the Method of Least Squares

The least-squares regression line for modeling data that is approximately linear was introduced in Section 2.3. The discussion there explained why least squares are used to measure how well a line fits the data. In this case study, we show how the theory of extrema of functions of several variables is used to construct the least-squares regression line.

Global warming is a term used to describe the phenomenon in recent years that the atmospheric temperature of Earth is slowly increasing over time. The National Oceanic and Atmospheric Administration (NOAA) has compiled a great deal of historical global temperature data. Data from recent years is compiled by satellite, but a variety of methods, including the analysis of temperature-sensitive phenomena such as tree-ring density, allows for temperature estimates from centuries past. The data is often presented in terms of temperature anomalies—that is, as deviations from some norm.

For example, the NOAA reports the following temperature anomalies:

Global Land Surface Average Temperature

Year	Temperature Anomaly (°C)	Temperature (°C)
1900	−0.15	8.35
1950	−0.34	8.16
2012	0.92	9.42

The baseline temperature against which the anomalies were determined is the average global temperature over land from the years 1880 to 2000, an average computed to be 8.5°C. Adding 8.5 to each anomaly gives the actual temperature.

Figure 1 shows a plot of the adjusted temperature data.

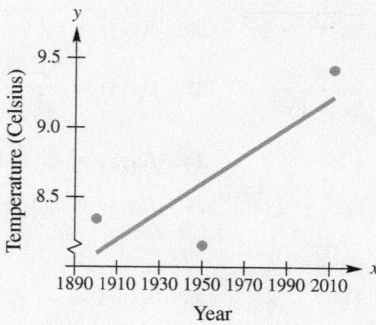

Figure 1   Global Land Surface Temperature

If the three points lie on a straight line, the rate at which the temperature is changing can be determined by the slope of that line. The points clearly are not on the same line, but can be approximated by a straight line, as in the figure. The purpose of the least-squares method is to find the best such approximation.

Figure 2 shows the vertical distance from each point to the approximating line.

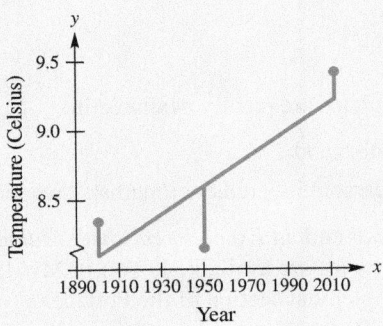

Figure 2 Deviations from Approximating Line

If the first point is (x_1, y_1) and the equation of the line is $y = mx + b$, then the first vertical distance is $y_1 - (mx_1 + b) = y_1 - mx_1 - b$. In the least-squares method, the values of m and b are determined so that the sum of the squares of these distances is minimized. For three points (x_1, y_1), (x_2, y_2), and (x_3, y_3), the following function of two variables must be minimized,

$$f(m, b) = (y_1 - mx_1 - b)^2 + (y_2 - mx_2 - b)^2$$
$$+ (y_3 - mx_3 - b)^2. \quad \textbf{(1)}$$

Using the points

$$(1900, 8.35), (1950, 8.16), \text{ and } (2012, 9.42),$$

we find that equation **(1)** becomes

$$f(m, b) = 3b^2 + 11{,}460{,}644m^2 + 11{,}724bm - 51.86b$$
$$- 101{,}460m + 225.045.$$

The partial derivatives of f with respect to m and b are

$$\frac{\partial f}{\partial m} = 22{,}921{,}288m + 11{,}724b - 101{,}460$$

and

$$\frac{\partial f}{\partial b} = 6b + 11{,}724m - 51.86.$$

The resulting critical point is approximately $m = .01$ and $b = -10.85$. The line of best fit for these data is $y = .01x - 10.85$ and is drawn in Figure 1.

According to these data, the global land temperature is increasing at a rate of approximately .01°C per year.

It is not fair to say that this calculation is evidence of global warming, as only three pieces of data were used. The data set was kept small to illustrate the least-squares method. This method can be generalized to use any amount of data and to fit more complicated functions, including exponential functions.

Exercises

1. Verify that the critical point $m = .01$ and $b = -10.85$ corresponds to a minimum of the function $f(m, b)$.

2. By differentiating equation **(1)** with respect to m and b without substituting the specific values for points (x_1, y_1), (x_2, y_2), and (x_3, y_3), the formulas

$$m = \frac{3(x_1y_1 + x_2y_2 + x_3y_3) - (x_1 + x_2 + x_3)(y_1 + y_2 + y_3)}{3(x_1^2 + x_2^2 + x_3^2) - (x_1 + x_2 + x_3)^2}$$

and

$$b = \frac{y_1 + y_2 + y_3}{3} - m\left(\frac{x_1 + x_2 + x_3}{3}\right)$$

can be derived. Show that these formulas give the same values for m and b given earlier.

3. The formulas in Exercise 2 generalize to any number of data points. For example, for four data points, the formulas for m and b respectively become

$$m = \frac{4(x_1y_1 + x_2y_2 + x_3y_3 + x_4y_4)}{4(x_1^2 + x_2^2 + x_3^2 + x_4^2) - (x_1 + x_2 + x_3 + x_4)^2}$$
$$- \frac{(x_1 + x_2 + x_3 + x_4)(y_1 + y_2 + y_3 + y_4)}{4(x_1^2 + x_2^2 + x_3^2 + x_4^2) - (x_1 + x_2 + x_3 + x_4)^2}$$

and

$$b = \frac{y_1 + y_2 + y_3 + y_4}{4} - m\left(\frac{x_1 + x_2 + x_3 + x_4}{4}\right).$$

Add the temperature data point $(2000, 9.13)$ to the preceding three and find the least-squares straight-line fit by using the formulas in Exercise 3. Plot the points, graph the line, and discuss the value of m.

Extended Project

Investigate the most recent data available for global land surface average temperature. Add these data to those given in the table above and then use the method of least squares to find the straight line that best fits these data. According to this linear model, what is the predicted global land surface average temperature for next year? Write a report summarizing the method of least squares, the given data and the most recent data you found, the resulting line of best fit, the interpretation of the slope of the line, and your prediction for the future.

Graphing Calculators

Basics

Instructions on using your graphing calculator are readily available in:

the instruction book for your calculator; and

the web site for this book at www.pearsonhighered.com/mathstatsresources/.

In addition, a *Graphing Calculator Manual* and an *Excel Spreadsheet Manual* specific for finite mathematics and applied calculus topics are available to you in MyMathLab. These manuals are described in the Student Supplement section of the Preface.

Programs

The following programs are available for TI and most Casio graphing calculators. You can download them from www.pearsonhighered.com/mathstatsresources/, and use the appropriate USB cable and software to install them in your calculator.

General

1. Fraction Conversion for Casio

   Chapter 1: Algebra and Equations

2. Quadratic Formula for TI-83

   Chapter 5: Mathematics of Finance

3. Present and Future Value of an Annuity

4. Loan Payment

5. Loan Balance after n Payments

6. Amortization Table for TI

   Chapter 6: Systems of Linear Equations and Matrices

7. RREF Program for Casio 9750GA+, 9850, and 9860G

   Chapter 7: Linear Programming

8. Simplex Method

9. Two-Stage Method

   Chapter 13: Integral Calculus

10. Rectangle Approximation of $\int_a^b f(x)\, dx$ (using left endpoints)

Programs 1, 2, 6, and 7 are built into most calculators other than those mentioned. Programs 3–5 are part of the TVM Solver on TI and most Casio models, although some students may find the versions here easier to use. Programs 8–10 are not built into any calculator.

Tables

Table 1   Formulas from Geometry

CIRCLE
Area: $A = \pi r^2$
Circumference: $C = 2\pi r$

RECTANGLE
Area: $A = lw$
Perimeter: $P = 2l + 2w$

PARALLELOGRAM
Area: $A = bh$
Perimeter: $P = 2a + 2b$

TRIANGLE
Area: $A = \dfrac{1}{2}bh$

SPHERE

Volume: $V = \dfrac{4}{3}\pi r^3$

Surface area: $A = 4\pi r^2$

RECTANGULAR BOX
Volume: $V = lwh$
Surface area: $A = 2lh + 2wh + 2lw$

CIRCULAR CYLINDER
Volume: $V = \pi r^2 h$
Surface area: $A = 2\pi r^2 + 2\pi rh$

TRIANGULAR CYLINDER
Volume: $V = \dfrac{1}{2}bhl$

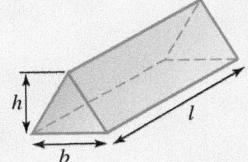

CONE

Volume: $V = \dfrac{1}{3}\pi r^2 h$

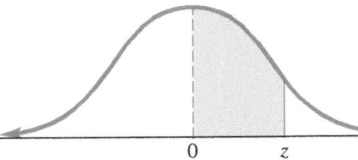

Table 2   Areas under the Normal Curve

The column under A gives the proportion of the area under the entire curve that is between $z = 0$ and a positive value of z.

z	A	z	A	z	A	z	A
.00	.0000	.48	.1844	.96	.3315	1.44	.4251
.01	.0040	.49	.1879	.97	.3340	1.45	.4265
.02	.0080	.50	.1915	.98	.3365	1.46	.4279
.03	.0120	.51	.1950	.99	.3389	1.47	.4292
.04	.0160	.52	.1985	1.00	.3413	1.48	.4306
.05	.0199	.53	.2019	1.01	.3438	1.49	.4319
.06	.0239	.54	.2054	1.02	.3461	1.50	.4332
.07	.0279	.55	.2088	1.03	.3485	1.51	.4345
.08	.0319	.56	.2123	1.04	.3508	1.52	.4357
.09	.0359	.57	.2157	1.05	.3531	1.53	.4370
.10	.0398	.58	.2190	1.06	.3554	1.54	.4382
.11	.0438	.59	.2224	1.07	.3577	1.55	.4394
.12	.0478	.60	.2258	1.08	.3599	1.56	.4406
.13	.0517	.61	.2291	1.09	.3621	1.57	.4418
.14	.0557	.62	.2324	1.10	.3643	1.58	.4430
.15	.0596	.63	.2357	1.11	.3665	1.59	.4441
.16	.0636	.64	.2389	1.12	.3686	1.60	.4452
.17	.0675	.65	.2422	1.13	.3708	1.61	.4463
.18	.0714	.66	.2454	1.14	.3729	1.62	.4474
.19	.0754	.67	.2486	1.15	.3749	1.63	.4485
.20	.0793	.68	.2518	1.16	.3770	1.64	.4495
.21	.0832	.69	.2549	1.17	.3790	1.65	.4505
.22	.0871	.70	.2580	1.18	.3810	1.66	.4515
.23	.0910	.71	.2612	1.19	.3830	1.67	.4525
.24	.0948	.72	.2642	1.20	.3849	1.68	.4535
.25	.0987	.73	.2673	1.21	.3869	1.69	.4545
.26	.1026	.74	.2704	1.22	.3888	1.70	.4554
.27	.1064	.75	.2734	1.23	.3907	1.71	.4564
.28	.1103	.76	.2764	1.24	.3925	1.72	.4573
.29	.1141	.77	.2794	1.25	.3944	1.73	.4582
.30	.1179	.78	.2823	1.26	.3962	1.74	.4591
.31	.1217	.79	.2852	1.27	.3980	1.75	.4599
.32	.1255	.80	.2881	1.28	.3997	1.76	.4608
.33	.1293	.81	.2910	1.29	.4015	1.77	.4616
.34	.1331	.82	.2939	1.30	.4032	1.78	.4625
.35	.1368	.83	.2967	1.31	.4049	1.79	.4633
.36	.1406	.84	.2996	1.32	.4066	1.80	.4641
.37	.1443	.85	.3023	1.33	.4082	1.81	.4649
.38	.1480	.86	.3051	1.34	.4099	1.82	.4656
.39	.1517	.87	.3079	1.35	.4115	1.83	.4664
.40	.1554	.88	.3106	1.36	.4131	1.84	.4671
.41	.1591	.89	.3133	1.37	.4147	1.85	.4678
.42	.1628	.90	.3159	1.38	.4162	1.86	.4686
.43	.1664	.91	.3186	1.39	.4177	1.87	.4693
.44	.1700	.92	.3212	1.40	.4192	1.88	.4700
.45	.1736	.93	.3238	1.41	.4207	1.89	.4706
.46	.1772	.94	.3264	1.42	.4222	1.90	.4713
.47	.1808	.95	.3289	1.43	.4236	1.91	.4719

Table 2   (*continued*)

z	A	z	A	z	A	z	A
1.92	.4726	2.42	.4922	2.92	.4983	3.42	.4997
1.93	.4732	2.43	.4925	2.93	.4983	3.43	.4997
1.94	.4738	2.44	.4927	2.94	.4984	3.44	.4997
1.95	.4744	2.45	.4929	2.95	.4984	3.45	.4997
1.96	.4750	2.46	.4931	2.96	.4985	3.46	.4997
1.97	.4756	2.47	.4932	2.97	.4985	3.47	.4997
1.98	.4762	2.48	.4934	2.98	.4986	3.48	.4998
1.99	.4767	2.49	.4936	2.99	.4986	3.49	.4998
2.00	.4773	2.50	.4938	3.00	.4987	3.50	.4998
2.01	.4778	2.51	.4940	3.01	.4987	3.51	.4998
2.02	.4783	2.52	.4941	3.02	.4987	3.52	.4998
2.03	.4788	2.53	.4943	3.03	.4988	3.53	.4998
2.04	.4793	2.54	.4945	3.04	.4988	3.54	.4998
2.05	.4798	2.55	.4946	3.05	.4989	3.55	.4998
2.06	.4803	2.56	.4948	3.06	.4989	3.56	.4998
2.07	.4808	2.57	.4949	3.07	.4989	3.57	.4998
2.08	.4812	2.58	.4951	3.08	.4990	3.58	.4998
2.09	.4817	2.59	.4952	3.09	.4990	3.59	.4998
2.10	.4821	2.60	.4953	3.10	.4990	3.60	.4998
2.11	.4826	2.61	.4955	3.11	.4991	3.61	.4999
2.12	.4830	2.62	.4956	3.12	.4991	3.62	.4999
2.13	.4834	2.63	.4957	3.13	.4991	3.63	.4999
2.14	.4838	2.64	.4959	3.14	.4992	3.64	.4999
2.15	.4842	2.65	.4960	3.15	.4992	3.65	.4999
2.16	.4846	2.66	.4961	3.16	.4992	3.66	.4999
2.17	.4850	2.67	.4962	3.17	.4992	3.67	.4999
2.18	.4854	2.68	.4963	3.18	.4993	3.68	.4999
2.19	.4857	2.69	.4964	3.19	.4993	3.69	.4999
2.20	.4861	2.70	.4965	3.20	.4993	3.70	.4999
2.21	.4865	2.71	.4966	3.21	.4993	3.71	.4999
2.22	.4868	2.72	.4967	3.22	.4994	3.72	.4999
2.23	.4871	2.73	.4968	3.23	.4994	3.73	.4999
2.24	.4875	2.74	.4969	3.24	.4994	3.74	.4999
2.25	.4878	2.75	.4970	3.25	.4994	3.75	.4999
2.26	.4881	2.76	.4971	3.26	.4994	3.76	.4999
2.27	.4884	2.77	.4972	3.27	.4995	3.77	.4999
2.28	.4887	2.78	.4973	3.28	.4995	3.78	.4999
2.29	.4890	2.79	.4974	3.29	.4995	3.79	.4999
2.30	.4893	2.80	.4974	3.30	.4995	3.80	.4999
2.31	.4896	2.81	.4975	3.31	.4995	3.81	.4999
2.32	.4898	2.82	.4976	3.32	.4996	3.82	.4999
2.33	.4901	2.83	.4977	3.33	.4996	3.83	.4999
2.34	.4904	2.84	.4977	3.34	.4996	3.84	.4999
2.35	.4906	2.85	.4978	3.35	.4996	3.85	.4999
2.36	.4909	2.86	.4979	3.36	.4996	3.86	.4999
2.37	.4911	2.87	.4980	3.37	.4996	3.87	.5000
2.38	.4913	2.88	.4980	3.38	.4996	3.88	.5000
2.39	.4916	2.89	.4981	3.39	.4997	3.89	.5000
2.40	.4918	2.90	.4981	3.40	.4997		
2.41	.4920	2.91	.4982	3.41	.4997		

Table 3   Integrals
(C is an arbitrary constant.)

1. $\int x^n \, dx = \dfrac{1}{n+1} x^{n+1} + C \qquad (n \neq -1)$

2. $\int e^{kx} \, dx = \dfrac{1}{k} e^{kx} + C$

3. $\int \dfrac{a}{x} \, dx = a \ln|x| + C$

4. $\int \ln|ax| \, dx = x(\ln|ax| - 1) + C$

5. $\int \dfrac{1}{\sqrt{x^2 + a^2}} \, dx = \ln\left|x + \sqrt{x^2 + a^2}\right| + C$

6. $\int \dfrac{1}{\sqrt{x^2 - a^2}} \, dx = \ln\left|x + \sqrt{x^2 - a^2}\right| + C$

7. $\int \dfrac{1}{a^2 - x^2} \, dx = \dfrac{1}{2a} \cdot \ln\left|\dfrac{a+x}{a-x}\right| + C \qquad (a \neq 0)$

8. $\int \dfrac{1}{x^2 - a^2} \, dx = \dfrac{1}{2a} \cdot \ln\left|\dfrac{x-a}{x+a}\right| + C \qquad (a \neq 0)$

9. $\int \dfrac{1}{x\sqrt{a^2 - x^2}} \, dx = -\dfrac{1}{a} \cdot \ln\left|\dfrac{a + \sqrt{a^2 - x^2}}{x}\right| + C \qquad (a \neq 0)$

10. $\int \dfrac{1}{x\sqrt{a^2 + x^2}} \, dx = -\dfrac{1}{a} \cdot \ln\left|\dfrac{a + \sqrt{a^2 + x^2}}{x}\right| + C \qquad (a \neq 0)$

11. $\int \dfrac{x}{ax + b} \, dx = \dfrac{x}{a} - \dfrac{b}{a^2} \cdot \ln|ax + b| + C \qquad (a \neq 0)$

12. $\int \dfrac{x}{(ax + b)^2} \, dx = \dfrac{b}{a^2(ax + b)} + \dfrac{1}{a^2} \cdot \ln|ax + b| + C \qquad (a \neq 0)$

13. $\int \dfrac{1}{x(ax + b)} \, dx = \dfrac{1}{b} \cdot \ln\left|\dfrac{x}{ax + b}\right| + C \qquad (b \neq 0)$

14. $\int \dfrac{1}{x(ax + b)^2} \, dx = \dfrac{1}{b(ax + b)} + \dfrac{1}{b^2} \cdot \ln\left|\dfrac{x}{ax + b}\right| \qquad (b \neq 0)$

15. $\int \sqrt{x^2 + a^2} \, dx = \dfrac{x}{2} \sqrt{x^2 + a^2} + \dfrac{a^2}{2} \cdot \ln\left|x + \sqrt{x^2 + a^2}\right| + C$

16. $\int x^n \cdot \ln|x| \, dx = x^{n+1} \left[\dfrac{\ln|x|}{n+1} - \dfrac{1}{(n+1)^2}\right] + C \qquad (n \neq -1)$

17. $\int x^n e^{ax} \, dx = \dfrac{x^n e^{ax}}{a} - \dfrac{n}{a} \cdot \int x^{n-1} e^{ax} \, dx + C \qquad (a \neq 0)$

APPENDIX C

Learning Objectives

After studying these objectives and solving the problems, students will be able to:

Chapter 1 Algebra and Equations

1.1 The Real Numbers

- Identify the properties of real numbers.
- Evaluate algebraic expressions using the proper order of operations.
- Calculate square roots correctly.
- Identify points on a number line.
- Shade inequality regions on a number line and use proper interval notation.
- Evaluate algebraic expressions involving absolute value.

1.2 Polynomials

- Identify the base and the exponent in exponential expressions.
- Evaluate expressions involving multiplication of exponential expressions.
- Calculate exponential expressions raised to a power.
- Understand the zero exponent.
- Add and subtract polynomials by combining like terms.

1.3 Factoring

- Find the greatest common factor in an expression.
- Factor quadratic expressions.
- Factor differences of cubes and sums of cubes.

1.4 Rational Expressions

- Simplify rational expressions.
- Use the multiplication, division, addition, and subtraction rules for rational expressions.
- Simplify complex fractions.

1.5 Exponents and Radicals

- Evaluate expressions involving division of exponential expressions, products to a power, and quotients raised to a power.
- Work with negative exponents.
- Evaluate roots of expressions and radical expressions.
- Rationalize the denominator of a fraction.

1.6 First-Degree Equations

- Solve a first-degree expression for an unknown quantity.

- Set up and solve a first-degree equation from an applied context.

1.7 Quadratic Equations

- Understand the zero factor and square root properties.
- Solve a quadratic equation using the quadratic formula.
- Set up and solve a quadratic equation from an applied context.

Chapter 2 Graphs, Lines, and Inequalities

2.1 Graphs

- Read and interpret graphs of two variables in real world contexts.
- Plot ordered pairs on a two-dimensional grid.
- Find the horizontal and vertical intercepts of a first-order equation.

2.2 Equations of Lines

- Calculate the slope of a line through two ordered pairs.
- Write a first order equation in slope-intercept form.
- Sketch graphs of first-order equations.
- Use the point-slope form of an equation.
- Recognize and graph equations of horizontal and vertical lines.

2.3 Linear Models

- Fit a line to ordered pairs of data given in real world contexts.
- Assess the fit of two linear models for given data in real world contexts.
- Use technology to fit a least squares regression line (optional).
- Use technology to calculate the correlation coefficient and interpret its meaning (optional).

2.4 Linear Inequalities

- Solve linear inequalities and shade solution regions.
- Solve absolute value inequalities and shade solution regions.

2.5 Polynomial and Rational Inequalities

- Solve quadratic inequalities, shade solution regions, and express the solution in interval notation.
- Solve higher order inequalities, shade solution regions, and express the solution in interval notation.

- Solve rational inequalities and express the solution in interval notation.

Chapter 3 Functions and Graphs

3.1 Functions

- Understand the definition of a function.
- Understand the meanings of domain and range of a function.
- Use correct function notation.
- Solve equations involving functions and piecewise functions.

3.2 Graphs of Functions

- Graph linear functions, piecewise linear functions, and absolute value functions.
- Graph a function by plotting points.
- Read and interpret graphs correctly.
- Use the vertical line test.

3.3 Applications of Linear Functions

- Create, graph and solve revenue, cost, and profit equations.
- Understand that rate of depreciation is the slope of the depreciation equation.
- Understand the relationship of slope to marginal cost and marginal revenue.
- Solve for break-even points using revenue and cost equations.
- Graph supply and demand curves.
- Solve supply and demand equations.

3.4 Quadratic Functions and Applications

- Graph quadratic functions.
- Determine the vertex of a quadratic graph.
- Understand the properties of quadratic graphs.
- Determine maximum or minimum profit, revenue, or cost from quadratic graphs.
- Solve for the equilibrium points of quadratic supply and demand curves using graphical and algebraic methods.
- Perform quadratic regression using technology (optional).

3.5 Polynomial Functions

- Understand the properties of graphs of polynomials.
- Graph polynomials using technology.
- Use polynomial models for estimation.

3.6 Rational Functions

- Graph rational functions.
- Solve real world applications using rational functions.

Chapter 4 Exponential and Logarithmic Functions

4.1 Exponential Functions

- Graph exponential functions with various bases.
- Evaluate exponential functions for values within the domain.
- Use technology to find the domain value for a given function value.

4.2 Applications of Exponential Functions

- Define an exponential growth function from given information in real world applications.
- Evaluate exponential functions for values within the domain from real world applications.
- Use technology to find the domain value for a given function value in real world applications.

4.3 Logarithmic Functions

- Evaluate logarithmic expressions of base 10, base e, and an arbitrary base a.
- Recognize that logarithms of negative numbers and 0 are not defined.
- Use the properties of logarithms to evaluate expressions.
- Translate exponential expressions to logarithmic expressions and vice versa.
- Graph logarithmic functions.
- Use technology to solve algebraic equations involving logarithmic expressions.

4.4 Logarithmic and Exponential Equations

- Solve algebraic equations involving logarithmic functions for unknown quantities.
- Solve algebraic equations involving exponential functions for unknown quantities.
- Solve algebraic equations involving logarithmic or exponential functions presented in real world applications.

Chapter 5 Mathematics of Finance

5.1 Simple Interest and Discount

- Determine unknown quantities using the simple interest formula, the future value for simple interest formula, and the present value for simple interest formula.

5.2 Compound Interest

- Determine unknown quantities using the compound interest formula, the future value for compound interest formula, and the present value for compound interest formula.
- Calculate the effective rate.

5.3 Annuities, Future Value, and Sinking Funds

- Determine unknown quantities using the future value of an ordinary annuity or an annuities due product.
- Determine unknown quantities involving a sinking fund.

5.4 Annuities, Present Value, and Amortization

- Determine unknown quantities using the present value of an ordinary annuity or an annuities due product.
- Calculate payment amounts, the remaining balance, and the amortization schedule of loans.

Chapter 6 Systems of Linear Equations and Matrices

6.1 Systems of Two Linear Equations in Two Variables

- Solve a system of linear equations with the substitution and elimination methods.
- Recognize dependent and inconsistent systems.

6.2 Larger Systems of Linear Equations

- Solve larger systems with the elimination method.
- Solve larger systems with the matrix method.
- Use technology to solve systems of linear equations.

6.3 Applications of Systems of Linear Equations

- Set up and solve a system of linear equations from a real world context.

6.4 Basic Matrix Operations

- Add and subtract matrices.
- Multiply a matrix by a scalar.

6.5 Matrix Products and Inverses

- Perform matrix multiplication.
- Recognize an identity matrix.
- Calculate a matrix inverse.

6.6 Applications of Matrices

- Solve a system of equations using the inverse of a matrix.
- Perform input-output analysis.
- Use matrices in coding and routing applications.

Chapter 7 Linear Programming

7.1 Graphing Linear Inequalities in Two Variables

- Graph a linear inequality in two variables and shade the solution region.
- Graph a system of linear inequalities and shade the solution region.
- Set up and solve a system of linear inequalities from a real world context.

7.2 Linear Programming: The Graphical Method

- Find graphically the maximum and minimum values of an objective function subject to linear constraints.

7.3 Applications of Linear Programming

- Solve graphically real world applications to maximization and minimization values of an objective function subject to linear constraints.

7.4 The Simplex Method: Maximization

- Convert a system of linear equations with an objective function to standard maximum form.
- Pivot and solve for the solution from standard maximum form.
- Use technology to perform the simplex method.

7.5 Maximization Applications

- Set up and solve, using the simplex method, real world applications involving maximization.

7.6 The Simplex Method: Duality and Minimization

- Construct the dual matrix to solve a minimization problem.
- Interpret the minimization solution correctly.
- Set up and solve, using the simplex method, real world applications involving minimization.

7.7 The Simplex Method: Nonstandard Problems

- Solve maximization and minimization problems with inequality constraints.
- Solve real world applications of nonstandard problems.

Chapter 8 Sets and Probability

8.1 Sets

- Recognize the elements of a set and set equality.
- Understand the definition of and the notation for a subset.
- Perform the operations of complement, union, and intersection on sets.

8.2 Applications of Venn Diagrams and Contingency Tables

- Draw Venn diagrams to represent sets.
- Shade Venn diagrams appropriately to represent operations on sets.

8.3 Introduction to Probability

- List the elements of a sample space.
- List the elements of an event.
- Perform set operations for events.
- Draw Venn diagrams to represent operations on events.
- Use the basic probability principle to find the probability of an event.

- Recognize disjoint events.
- Calculate the probability of an event from relative frequency.
- Understand the properties of probability.

8.4 Basic Concepts of Probability

- Use the addition and complement rules to calculate probability.
- Calculate the odds of an event.
- Apply probability rules to real world contexts.

8.5 Conditional Probability and Independent Events

- Calculate conditional probability.
- Use the multiplication rule to calculate probability.
- Create and use a tree diagram to illustrate real world applications of conditional contexts.
- Recognize independent events and use the multiplication rule for independent events.

8.6 Bayes' Formula

- Calculate probabilities using Bayes' formula.
- Create appropriate tree diagrams to model real world conditional contexts.

Chapter 9 Counting, Probability Distributions, and Further Topics in Probability

9.1 Probability Distributions and Expected Value

- Recognize a random variable and a probability distribution.
- Calculate the expected value of a probability distribution.

9.2 The Multiplication Principle, Permutations, and Combinations

- Use the multiplicative principle for counting.
- Use factorial notation for counting.
- Use permutations to count how many ways n objects can be taken r at a time if order does matter.
- Use combinations to count how many ways n objects can be taken r at a time if order does not matter.
- Choose the appropriate counting method in a variety of real world applications.

9.3 Applications of Counting

- Choose and use correctly the appropriate counting method in a variety of real world applications.

9.4 Binomial Probability

- Recognize the four conditions of a binomial experiment.
- Use the binomial formula appropriately to calculate the binomial probability distribution.
- Calculate the expected value of a binomial distribution.

9.5 Markov Chains

- Create a transition matrix to model conditional behavior.
- Find the long-range trend for a Markov chain.
- Apply Markov chain modeling for a variety of real world applications.

9.6 Decision Making

- Identify states of nature, strategies, and a payoff matrix to illuminate decision options and expected outcomes in a variety of real world applications.

Chapter 10 Introduction to Statistics

10.1 Frequency Distributions

- Tabulate grouped frequency distributions.
- Create histograms.
- Create stem-and-leaf plots.
- Assess the shape of a distribution.

10.2 Measures of Center

- Calculate mean, median, and mode.
- Calculate mean and median for grouped distributions.

10.3 Measures of Variation

- Calculate range, variance, and standard deviation.
- Calculate variance and standard deviation for grouped distributions.

10.4 Normal Distributions and Boxplots

- Explore properties of normal curves.
- Use the normal probability table for the standard normal distribution.
- Calculate z-scores.
- Use the z-scores and the standard normal probability chart to find probabilities for nonstandard normal distributions.
- Calculate quartiles.
- Create and interpret boxplots.

10.5 Normal Approximation to the Binomial Distribution

- Use the normal distribution to approximate binomial probabilities.

Chapter 11 Differential Calculus

11.1 Limits

- Understand the concept of the limit of a function and properties of limits.
- Find limits of functions using the numerical method, graphical method, and algebraic method.
- Find limits in problems involving real world applications.

11.2 One-Sided Limits and Limits Involving Infinity

- Understand one-sided limits and their relationship to two-sided limits.
- Understand that the limit of a function may equal positive or negative infinity.
- Find limits of functions at positive or negative infinity.
- Find one-sided limits and limits at infinity using the numerical method, graphical method, and algebraic method.
- Find one-sided limits and limits at infinity in problems involving real world applications.

11.3 Rates of Change

- Understand the average rate of change of a function in terms of its algebraic meaning and geometric meaning.
- Understand the instantaneous rate of change of a function and its relationship to average rate of change.
- Find average and instantaneous rates of change in a variety of real world applications, including the velocity of an object moving in a straight line.

11.4 Tangent Lines and Derivatives

- Understand the concept of the derivative of a function, including its algebraic interpretation and geometric interpretation.
- Find the derivative of a function at a given point using the definition.
- Use technology to find the numerical derivative of a function at a given point.
- Find the slope of the tangent line and the equation of the tangent line to the graph of a function at a given point.
- Apply the concept of the derivative at a point in a variety of real world problems.

11.5 Techniques for Finding Derivatives

- Find derivatives using the constant rule, power rule, constant times a function rule, and sum-or-difference rule.
- Understand marginal cost, marginal revenue, marginal profit, and demand functions.
- Apply understanding of derivatives to solve real world problems.

11.6 Derivatives of Products and Quotients

- Find derivatives using the product rule and quotient rule.
- Understand the concepts of average cost per item manufactured and marginal average cost.
- Apply understanding of derivatives to solve real world problems involving products and quotients of functions.

11.7 The Chain Rule

- Find derivatives using the chain rule and generalized power rule.

- Understand the concept of marginal-revenue product.
- Apply understanding of derivatives to solve real world problems involving composition of functions.

11.8 Derivatives of Exponential and Logarithmic Functions

- Find derivatives of exponential and logarithmic functions.
- Apply understanding of derivatives to solve real world problems involving exponential and logarithmic functions.

11.9 Continuity and Differentiability

- Understand the concept of continuity of a function at a point and on an interval.
- Understand that if the derivative of a function exists at a point, then the function is continuous at that point.

Chapter 12 Applications of the Derivative

12.1 Derivatives and Graphs

- Determine the intervals on which a function is increasing and decreasing.
- Find the critical numbers of a function.
- Find the local extrema of a function.
- Use local extrema to solve real world problems.

12.2 The Second Derivative

- Find the second derivative and higher-order derivatives of a function.
- Determine the intervals on which a function is concave up and concave down.
- Find the points of inflection of a function.
- Use second derivatives to solve real world problems, including finding the acceleration of an object moving in a straight line and the point of diminishing returns.

12.3 Optimization Applications

- Understand the extreme-value theorem and use it appropriately to find absolute extrema.
- Understand the critical-point theorem and use it appropriately to find absolute extrema.
- Calculate economic lot size.
- Solve optimization problems in real world contexts.

12.4 Implicit Differentiation

- Find derivatives using implicit differentiation.
- Find equations of tangent lines using implicit differentiation.
- Solve real world problems that require implicit differentiation.

12.5 Related Rates

- Solve real world problems involving related rates.

12.6 Curve Sketching

- Use calculus to aid in sketching the graph of a function.
- Find the oblique asymptote of a function, if it exists.
- Read and interpret graphs in real world contexts.

Chapter 13 Integral Calculus

13.1 Antiderivatives

- Understand the concept of the antiderivative of a function.
- Find antiderivatives of functions using the power rule, exponential function rule, constant-multiple rule, and sum-or-difference rule.
- Find antiderivatives involving real world contexts.

13.2 Integration by Substitution

- Find antiderivatives using the method of substitution.
- Find antiderivatives involving real world contexts.

13.3 Area and the Definite Integral

- Understand the concept of the definite integral of a function.
- Understand the concept of the total change of a function.
- Use numerical integration technology to calculate definite integrals.
- Apply understanding of definite integrals to solve real world problems.

13.4 The Fundamental Theorem of Calculus

- Understand and apply the fundamental theorem of calculus.
- Find the area between the graph of a function and the x-axis on a closed interval.
- Apply understanding of definite integrals to solve real world problems.

13.5 Applications of Integrals

- Find the area between the graphs of two functions.
- Find the consumers' surplus and producers' surplus.
- Apply understanding of definite integrals to solve real world problems.

13.6 Tables of Integrals (Optional)

- Find antiderivatives using tables of integrals.

13.7 Differential Equations

- Understand the concept of a differential equation.
- Find the general solution of a separable differential equation.
- Find a particular solution of a separable differential equation with an initial condition.
- Compute marginal productivity.
- Understand exponential growth and decay and limited-growth functions.
- Use differential equations to solve real world problems.

Chapter 14 Multivariate Calculus

14.1 Functions of Several Variables

- Understand the concept of a multivariate function.
- Plot ordered triples in three-dimensional space.
- Sketch level curves and traces of a function of two variables.
- Solve real world problems using functions of two variables, including the Cobb-Douglas production function.

14.2 Partial Derivatives

- Understand the concept of a partial derivative of a multivariate function.
- Find first-order and second-order partial derivatives of a multivariate function.
- Apply understanding of partial derivatives to solve real world problems.

14.3 Extrema of Functions of Several Variables

- Find the critical points of a function of two variables.
- Find the local extrema and saddle points of a function of two variables.
- Use local extrema to solve problems in real world contexts.

14.4 Lagrange Multipliers

- Understand the concept of a constraint on an optimization problem.
- Use the method of Lagrange multipliers to solve constrained optimization problems.
- Solve optimization problems in real world contexts.

Solutions to Prerequisite Skills Test and Calculus Readiness Test

Prerequisite Skills Test

1. We must find a common denominator before subtracting. Since 6 can be written as a fraction as $\frac{6}{1}$, then 2 can be the common denominator.

$$\frac{5}{2} - 6 = \frac{5}{2} - \frac{6}{1}$$
$$= \frac{5}{2} - \frac{6(2)}{2} = \frac{5}{2} - \frac{12}{2}$$
$$= \frac{5 - 12}{2} = \frac{-7}{2}.$$

2. Division of fraction implies that we multiply by the reciprocal. In this case, we multiply $\frac{1}{2}$ by the reciprocal of $\frac{2}{5}$, which is $\frac{5}{2}$. We obtain

$$\frac{1}{2} \div \frac{2}{5} = \frac{1}{2} \cdot \frac{5}{2} = \frac{1 \cdot 5}{2 \cdot 2} = \frac{5}{4}.$$

3. We rewrite 3 as a fraction as $\frac{3}{1}$ and then multiply by the reciprocal.

$$\frac{1}{3} \div \frac{3}{1} = \frac{1}{3} \cdot \frac{1}{3} = \frac{1 \cdot 1}{3 \cdot 3} = \frac{1}{9}.$$

4. We perform the operation inside the parenthesis first. We have

$$2 \div 6 = \frac{2}{6} = \frac{1}{3}.$$

Thus,

$$7 + 2 - 3(2 \div 6) = 7 + 2 - 3\left(\frac{1}{3}\right).$$

We then perform the multiplication and see that

$$3\left(\frac{1}{3}\right) = \frac{3}{1} \cdot \frac{1}{3} = \frac{3(1)}{1(3)} = \frac{3}{3} = 1.$$

So we now have

$$7 + 2 - 3\left(\frac{1}{3}\right) = 7 + 2 - 1.$$

Performing addition and subtraction from left to right, we obtain $9 - 1 = 8$.

5. We begin by performing the multiplication on the numerator. We obtain

$$\frac{2 \times 3 + 12}{1 + 5} - 1 = \frac{6 + 12}{1 + 5} - 1.$$

Next, we perform addition in the numerator and addition in the denominator.

$$\frac{6 + 12}{1 + 5} - 1 = \frac{18}{6} - 1.$$

Next, we perform the division and realize that $\frac{18}{6} = 3$, to obtain $3 - 1 = 2$.

6. False. We add the numerator values together to obtain

$$\frac{4 + 3}{3} = \frac{7}{3} \neq 5.$$

7. False. We obtain a common denominator of 35 to obtain

$$\frac{5}{7} + \frac{7}{5} = \frac{5(5)}{35} + \frac{7(7)}{35} = \frac{25}{35} + \frac{49}{35} = \frac{25 + 49}{35} = \frac{74}{35} \neq 1.$$

8. False. We write 1 as a fraction with the same denominator as $\frac{3}{5}$, namely $1 = \frac{5}{5}$. Thus, we have

$$\frac{3}{5} + 1 = \frac{3}{5} + \frac{5}{5} = \frac{8}{5} \neq \frac{6}{5}.$$

9. Since n represents the number of shoes that Alicia has, we can add 2 to n to obtain the number of shoes for Manuel. Thus we are looking for the expression $n + 2$ for the number of shoes for Manuel.

10. We can say x represents David's age. Since Selina's age is 6 more than David, Selina's age is $x + 6$. The two ages together then are

$$x + (x + 6) = 42.$$

If we combine like terms, we have

$$2x + 6 = 42.$$

We can solve for x by adding -6 to each side to obtain

$$2x + 6 - 6 = 42 - 6$$
$$2x = 36.$$

We then divide each side by 2 to obtain

$$x = 18.$$

Thus, David's age is 18 and Selina's age is $18 + 6 = 24$.

11. If the sweater is reduced by 20%, then its sale price is $100 - 20 = 80\%$ of the original price. To obtain the new price we first convert 80% to a decimal to obtain .80 and then multiply by the price of the sweater to obtain

$$.80(\$72) = \$57.60$$

12. When we plot points, the first coordinate is the value for the x-axis and the second value is for the y-axis. For points A, B, and C, we obtain

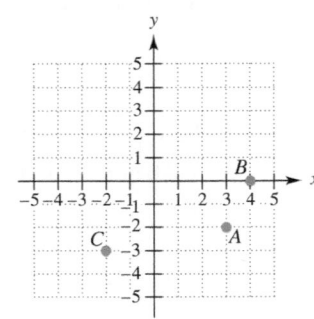

13. Similarly, we plot points D, E, and F to obtain

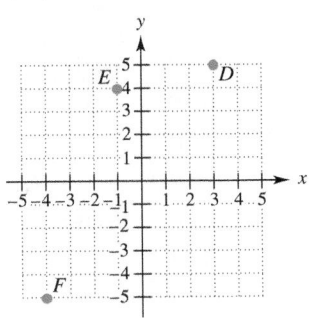

14. (a) 4.27659 has a value of 2 in the tenths place, and the value after that is 7, so we round up to obtain 4.3 to the nearest tenth.

(b) 245.984 has a 5 in the units place and a 9 in the tenths place, so we round up the units place to obtain 246 to the nearest unit.

15. (a) 16.38572 has an 8 in the hundredths place and a 5 in the thousandths place, so we round up to obtain 16.39 to the nearest hundredth.

(b) 1,763,304.42 has a 3 in the thousands place and the following digit is also a 3, so we do not round up and obtain 1,763,000 rounded to the nearest thousand.

16. (a) Writing 34 million dollars as a numerical value is $34 \cdot 1,000,000 = \$34,000,000$.

(b) Writing 2.2 thousand dollars as a numerical value is $2.2 \cdot 1000 = \$2,200$.

17. (a) 17 hundred thousand as a numerical value is $17 \cdot 100,000 = 1,700,000$.

(b) Three and a quarter billion as a numerical value is $3.25 \cdot 1,000,000,000 = 3,250,000,000$.

18. There is no solution to $\dfrac{5}{0}$ because a 0 in the denominator indicates the fraction is undefined.

19. Yes, it is. If a car is traveling 60 miles in one hour, it is traveling 60 miles in 60 minutes, which equates to 1 mile per minute.

20. -9 is greater than -900.

Calculus Readiness Test

1. $(7x^4 - 8x^3 + 2x^2 - 3) - (9x^4 - 2x^2 + 5x + 6)$

$= (7x^4 - 9x^4) + (-8x^3 - 0) + (2x^2 - (-2x^2)) + (0 - 5x) + (-3 - 6)$

$= -2x^4 - 8x^3 + 4x^2 - 5x - 9$

(See Section 1.2, Example 7.)

2. $\dfrac{-6}{3x + 4} + \dfrac{2}{x} = \dfrac{-6}{3x + 4} \cdot \dfrac{x}{x} + \dfrac{2}{x} \cdot \dfrac{3x + 4}{3x + 4} = \dfrac{-6x}{x(3x + 4)} + \dfrac{2(3x + 4)}{x(3x + 4)}$

$= \dfrac{-6x}{3x^2 + 4x} + \dfrac{6x + 8}{3x^2 + 4x} = \dfrac{8}{3x^2 + 4x}$

(See Section 1.4, Example 5.)

3. $(3x + 7)(5x - 8) = (3x)(5x) + (3x)(-8) + (7)(5x) + (7)(-8)$

$= 15x^2 - 24x + 35x - 56 = 15x^2 + 11x - 56$

(See Section 1.2, Example 10.)

4. $(7x + 3)(6x^2 + x - 8) = 7x(6x^2 + x - 8) + 3(6x^2 + x - 8)$

$= (42x^3 + 7x^2 - 56x) + (18x^2 + 3x - 24) = 42x^3 + 25x^2 - 53x - 24$

(See Section 1.2, Example 8.)

5. $\dfrac{(x^5y^{-5})^3}{(x^2\sqrt{y})^6} = \dfrac{(x^5)^3(y^{-5})^3}{(x^2)^6(y^{1/2})^6} = \dfrac{x^{15}y^{-15}}{x^{12}y^3} = \dfrac{x^{15}}{x^{12}y^3y^{15}} = \dfrac{x^{15-12}}{y^{3+15}} = \dfrac{x^3}{y^{18}}$

(See Section 1.5, Example 8.)

6. $(8x - 9)^2 = (8x - 9)(8x - 9) = 64x^2 - 72x - 72x + 81 = 64x^2 - 144x + 81$

(See Section 1.2, Example 10.)

7. $9x^2 - 49 = (3x)^2 - 7^2 = (3x + 7)(3x - 7)$

(See Section 1.3, Example 7.)

8. $9x - 4 = 8 + 7(x - 5)$

$\Rightarrow 9x - 4 = 8 + 7x - 35$

$\Rightarrow 9x - 7x = 8 - 35 - (-4)$

$\Rightarrow 2x = -23$

$\Rightarrow x = -\dfrac{23}{2}$

(See Section 1.6, Example 2.)

9. $3x^2 + 2x + 8 = 20x - 7$

$\Rightarrow 3x^2 + 2x - 20x + 8 + 7 = 0$

$\Rightarrow 3x^2 - 18x + 15 = 0$

$\Rightarrow 3(x^2 - 6x + 5) = 0$

$\Rightarrow 3(x - 5)(x - 1) = 0$

$\Rightarrow x - 5 = 0 \quad \text{or} \quad x - 1 = 0$

$\Rightarrow x = 5 \quad \text{or} \quad x = 1$

(See Section 1.7, Example 2.)

10. $x^2 - x - 6 < 0$

First solve $x^2 - x - 6 = 0 \Rightarrow (x + 2)(x - 3) = 0 \Rightarrow x = -2$ or $x = 3$. The numbers -2 and 3 divide the number line into three regions. Test one number in each region to determine that $(x + 2)(x - 3) < 0$ when $-2 < x < 3$.

(See Section 2.5, Example 3.)

11. $5e^{x-3} - 1 = 9$

$\Rightarrow 5e^{x-3} = 10$

$\Rightarrow e^{x-3} = 2$

$\Rightarrow \ln(e^{x-3}) = \ln(2)$

$\Rightarrow x - 3 = \ln(2)$

$\Rightarrow x = \ln(2) + 3$

(See Section 4.4, Example 6.)

12. $\ln(5x + 1) = 2$

$\Rightarrow e^{\ln(5x+1)} = e^2$

$\Rightarrow 5x + 1 = e^2$

$\Rightarrow 5x = e^2 - 1$

$\Rightarrow x = \dfrac{e^2 - 1}{5}$

(See Section 4.4, Example 2.)

13. $f(-2) = 5(-2)^3 - 3(-2)^2 + 9(-2) + 60$

$= 5(-8) - 3(4) + 9(-2) + 60$

$= -40 - 12 - 18 + 60$

$= -10$

(See Section 3.1, Example 8.)

14. $f(x) = 0$

$\Rightarrow 6x^2 - 7x - 20 = 0$

$\Rightarrow (3x + 4)(2x - 5) = 0$

$\Rightarrow 3x + 4 = 0 \quad \text{or} \quad 2x - 5 = 0$

$\Rightarrow x = -4/3 \quad \text{or} \quad x = 5/2$

(See Section 1.7, Example 2.)

15. $y - y_1 = m(x - x_1)$

$\Rightarrow y - (-3) = -5(x - 8)$

$\Rightarrow y + 3 = -5x + 40$

$\Rightarrow y = -5x + 37$

(See Section 2.2, Example 9.)

Answers to Selected Exercises

Chapter 1

Section 1.1 (Page 8)

1. True   **3.** Answers vary with the calculator, but 2,508,429,787/798,458,000 is the best.   **5.** Distributive property
7. Identity property of addition   **9.** Associative property of addition
11. Answers vary.   **13.** -39 **15.** -2 **17.** 45.6
19. About .9167   **21.** -12 **23.** 0   **25.** 4   **27.** -1
29. $\dfrac{2040}{523}, \dfrac{189}{37}, \sqrt{27}, \dfrac{4587}{691}, 6.735, \sqrt{47}$ **31.** $12 < 18.5$
33. $x \geq 5.7$ **35.** $z \leq 7.5$ **37.** $<$ **39.** $<$ **41.** a lies to the right of b or is equal to b.   **43.** $c < a < b$
45. ⟵————(————————)————⟶ -8 -1
47. ⟵——+——+——(——+——+——+——+——]——+——⟶ -4 -2 0 2 4
49. ⟵————————(————————————⟶ -2
51. -3 **53.** -19 **55.** $=$ **57.** $=$ **59.** $=$ **61.** $>$
63. $7 - a$ **65.** Answers vary.   **67.** Answers vary.   **69.** 1
71. 9   **73.** 7   **75.** 49.9   **77.** 3.8   **79.** 35.7
81. 2005, 2006, 2008, 2010, 2011   **83.** 2007, 2008, 2009, 2010, 2011

Section 1.2 (Page 16)

1. 1,973,822.685   **3.** 289.0991339   **5.** Answers vary.   **7.** 4^5
9. $(-6)^7$ **11.** $(5u)^{28}$ **13.** Degree 4; coefficients: $6.2, -5, 4, -3, 3.7$; constant term 3.7   **15.** 3   **17.** $-x^3 + x^2 - 13x$
19. $-6y^2 + 3y + 6$ **21.** $-6x^2 + 4x - 4$ **23.** $-18m^3 - 54m^2 + 9m$
25. $12z^3 + 14z^2 - 7z + 5$ **27.** $12k^2 + 16k - 3$
29. $6y^2 + 13y + 5$ **31.** $18k^2 - 7kq - q^2$
33. $4.34m^2 + 5.68m - 4.42$ **35.** $-k + 3$
37. $R = 5000x$; $C = 200,000 + 1800x$; $P = 3200x - 200,000$
39. $R = 9750x$; $C = -3x^2 + 3480x + 259,675$; $P = 3x^2 + 6270x - 259,675$ **41. (a)** \$265 million
(b) About \$212 million   **43. (a)** \$948 million
(b) About \$883 million   **45.** About \$1712 million
47. About \$1163 million   **49.** False   **51.** True   **53.** .866
55. .505   **57. (a)** Approximately 60,501,067 cu ft
(b) The shape becomes a rectangular box with a square base, with volume b^2h.   **(c)** Yes   **59. (a)** 0, 1, 2, 3, or no degree (if one is the negative of the other)   **(b)** 0, 1, 2, 3, or no degree (if they are equal)   **(c)** 6
61. Between 40,000 and 45,000 calculators

Section 1.3 (Page 23)

1. $12x(x - 2)$ **3.** $r(r^2 - 5r + 1)$ **5.** $6z(z^2 - 2z + 3)$
7. $(2y - 1)^2(14y - 4) = 2(2y - 1)^2(7y - 2)$
9. $(x + 5)^4(x^2 + 10x + 28)$ **11.** $(x + 1)(x + 4)$
13. $(x + 3)(x + 4)$ **15.** $(x + 3)(x - 2)$ **17.** $(x - 1)(x + 3)$
19. $(x - 4)(x + 1)$ **21.** $(z - 7)(z - 2)$ **23.** $(z + 4)(z + 6)$
25. $(2x - 1)(x - 4)$ **27.** $(3p - 4)(5p - 1)$ **29.** $(2z - 5)(2z - 3)$
31. $(2x + 1)(3x - 4)$ **33.** $(5y - 2)(2y + 5)$ **35.** $(2x - 1)(3x + 4)$
37. $(3a + 5)(a - 1)$ **39.** $(x + 9)(x - 9)$ **41.** $(3p - 2)^2$
43. $(r - 2t)(r + 5t)$ **45.** $(m - 4n)^2$ **47.** $(2u + 3)^2$
49. Cannot be factored   **51.** $(2r + 3v)(2r - 3v)$ **53.** $(x + 2y)^2$
55. $(3a + 5)(a - 6)$ **57.** $(7m + 2n)(3m + n)$
59. $(y - 7z)(y + 3z)$ **61.** $(11x + 8)(11x - 8)$
63. $(a - 4)(a^2 + 4a + 16)$ **65.** $(2r - 3s)(4r^2 + 6rs + 9s^2)$
67. $(4m + 5)(16m^2 - 20m + 25)$ **69.** $(10y - z)(100y^2 + 10yz + z^2)$

71. $(x^2 + 3)(x^2 + 2)$ **73.** $b^2(b + 1)(b - 1)$
75. $(x + 2)(x - 2)(x^2 + 3)$ **77.** $(4a^2 + 9b^2)(2a + 3b)(2a - 3b)$
79. $x^2(x^2 + 2)(x^4 - 2x^2 + 4)$ **81.** Answers vary.
83. Answers vary.

Section 1.4 (Page 29)

1. $\dfrac{x}{7}$ **3.** $\dfrac{5}{7p}$ **5.** $\dfrac{5}{4}$ **7.** $\dfrac{4}{w + 6}$ **9.** $\dfrac{y - 4}{3y^2}$ **11.** $\dfrac{m - 2}{m + 3}$
13. $\dfrac{x + 3}{x + 1}$ **15.** $\dfrac{3}{16a}$ **17.** $\dfrac{3y}{x^2}$ **19.** $\dfrac{5}{4c}$ **21.** $\dfrac{3}{4}$ **23.** $\dfrac{3}{10}$
25. $\dfrac{2(a + 4)}{a - 3}$ **27.** $\dfrac{k + 2}{k + 3}$ **29.** Answers vary.   **31.** $\dfrac{3}{35z}$
33. $\dfrac{4}{3}$ **35.** $\dfrac{20 + x}{5x}$ **37.** $\dfrac{3m - 2}{m(m - 1)}$ **39.** $\dfrac{37}{5(b + 2)}$
41. $\dfrac{33}{20(k - 2)}$ **43.** $\dfrac{7x - 1}{(x - 3)(x - 1)(x + 2)}$
45. $\dfrac{y^2}{(y + 4)(y + 3)(y + 2)}$ **47.** $\dfrac{x + 1}{x - 1}$ **49.** $\dfrac{-1}{x(x + h)}$
51. (a) $\dfrac{\pi x^2}{4x^2}$ **(b)** $\dfrac{\pi}{4}$ **53. (a)** $\dfrac{x^2}{25x^2}$ **(b)** $\dfrac{1}{25}$
55. $\dfrac{-7.2x^2 + 6995x + 230,000}{1000x}$ **57.** About \$2.95 million
59. No   **61.** \$3.99   **63.** \$10,537.68

Section 1.5 (Page 41)

1. 49   **3.** $16c^2$ **5.** $32/x^5$ **7.** $108u^{12}$ **9.** $1/7$
11. $-1/7776$ **13.** $-1/y^3$ **15.** $9/16$ **17.** b^3/a **19.** 7
21. About 1.55   **23.** -16 **25.** 81/16   **27.** $4^2/5^3$ **29.** 4^3
31. 4^8 **33.** z^3 **35.** $\dfrac{p}{9}$ **37.** $\dfrac{q^5}{r^3}$ **39.** $\dfrac{8}{25p^7}$
41. $2^{5/6}p^{3/2}$ **43.** $2p + 5p^{5/3}$ **45.** $\dfrac{1}{3y^{2/3}}$ **47.** $\dfrac{a^{1/2}}{49b^{5/2}}$
49. $x^{7/6} - x^{11/6}$ **51.** $x - y$ **53.** (f)   **55.** (h)   **57.** (g)
59. (c)   **61.** 5   **63.** 5   **65.** 21   **67.** $\sqrt{77}$ **69.** $5\sqrt{3}$
71. $-\sqrt{2}$ **73.** $15\sqrt{5}$ **75.** 3   **77.** $-3 - 3\sqrt{2}$
79. $4 + \sqrt{3}$ **81.** $\dfrac{7}{11 + 6\sqrt{2}}$ **83. (a)** 14   **(b)** 85   **(c)** 58.0
85. About \$10.2 billion   **87.** About \$10.6 billion   **89.** About 180.6
91. About 168.7   **93.** About 5.8 million   **95.** About 7.3 million
97. About 30.4 million   **99.** About 87.1 million

Section 1.6 (Page 50)

1. 4   **3.** 7   **5.** $-10/9$ **7.** 4   **9.** $\dfrac{40}{7}$ **11.** $\dfrac{26}{3}$ **13.** $-\dfrac{12}{5}$
15. $-\dfrac{59}{6}$ **17.** $-\dfrac{9}{4}$ **19.** $x = .72$ **21.** $r \approx -13.26$
23. $\dfrac{b - 5a}{2}$ **25.** $x = \dfrac{3b}{a + 5}$ **27.** $V = \dfrac{k}{P}$ **29.** $g = \dfrac{V - V_0}{t}$
31. $B = \dfrac{2A}{h} - b$ or $B = \dfrac{2A - bh}{h}$ **33.** $-2, 3$ **35.** $-8, 2$
37. $\dfrac{5}{2}, \dfrac{7}{2}$ **39.** 10 hrs   **41.** $23°$ **43.** $71.6°$ **45.** 2010

47. 2015   **49.** 2010   **51.** 2016   **53.** 2012   **55.** 2016
57. 4779 thousand   **59.** 3074 thousand   **61.** $205.41
63. $21,000   **65.** $70,000 for first plot; $50,000 for the second
67. About 409,091 per month   **69.** 25,772,733   **71.** $\dfrac{400}{3}$L
73. About 105 miles   **75.** 83 mph   **77.** 2.9 gallons of premium and 12.7 gallons of regular

Section 1.7 (Page 58)

1. $-4, 14$ **3.** $0, -6$ **5.** $0, 2$ **7.** $-7, -8$ **9.** $\dfrac{1}{2}, 3$
11. $-\dfrac{1}{2}, \dfrac{1}{3}$ **13.** $\dfrac{5}{2}, 4$ **15.** $-5, -2$ **17.** $\dfrac{4}{3}, -\dfrac{4}{3}$ **19.** $0, 1$
21. $2 \pm \sqrt{7}$ **23.** $\dfrac{1 \pm 2\sqrt{5}}{4}$ **25.** $\dfrac{-7 \pm \sqrt{41}}{4}$; $-.1492, -3.3508$
27. $\dfrac{-1 \pm \sqrt{5}}{4}$; $.3090, -.8090$ **29.** $\dfrac{-5 \pm \sqrt{65}}{10}$; $.3062, -1.3062$
31. No real-number solutions   **33.** $-\dfrac{5}{2}, 1$ **35.** No real-number
solutions   **37.** $-5, \dfrac{3}{2}$ **39.** 1   **41.** 2   **43.** $x \approx .4701$ or 1.8240
45. $x \approx -1.0376$ or $.6720$ **47. (a)** 30 mph   **(b)** About 35 mph
(c) About 44 mph   **49. (a)** 2007   **(b)** 2009
51. (a) About $7.6 trillion   **(b)** 2007   **53.** About 1.046 ft
55. (a) $x + 20$ **(b)** Northbound: $5x$; eastbound: $5(x + 20)$ or $5x + 100$
(c) $(5x)^2 + (5x + 100)^2 = 300^2$ **(d)** About 31.23 mph and 51.23 mph
57. (a) $150 - x$ **(b)** $x(150 - x) = 5000$ **(c)** Length 100 m; width 50 m
59. 9 ft by 12 ft   **61.** 6.25 sec   **63. (a)** About 3.54 sec   **(b)** 2.5 sec
(c) 144 ft   **65. (a)** 2 sec   **(b)** 3/4 sec or 13/4 sec   **(c)** It reaches the
given height twice: once on the way up and once on the way down.
67. $t = \dfrac{\sqrt{2Sg}}{g}$ **69.** $h = \dfrac{d^2\sqrt{kL}}{L}$
71. $R = \dfrac{-2Pr + E^2 \pm E\sqrt{E^2 - 4Pr}}{2P}$ **73. (a)** $x^2 - 2x = 15$
(b) $x = 5$ or $x = -3$ **(c)** $z = \pm\sqrt{5}$ **75.** $\pm\dfrac{\sqrt{6}}{2}$
77. $\pm\sqrt{\dfrac{3 + \sqrt{13}}{2}}$

Chapter 1 Review Exercises (Page 61)

Refer to Section	1.1	1.2	1.3	1.4	1.5	1.6	1.7
For Exercises	1–18, 81–84	19–24, 85–88	25–32	33–38, 89–90	39–60, 91–92	61–68, 93–94	69–80, 95–100

1. $0, 6$ **3.** $-12, -6, -\dfrac{9}{10}, -\sqrt{4}, 0, \dfrac{1}{8}, 6$
5. Commutative property of multiplication   **7.** Distributive property
9. $x \geq 9$ **11.** $-|3 - (-2)|, -|-2|, |6 - 4|, |8 + 1|$ **13.** -1
15.

[image: number line with open circle at −3, arrow pointing left; labeled −3]

17. $-\dfrac{7}{9}$ **19.** $4x^4 - 4x^2 + 11x$ **21.** $25k^2 - 4h^2$
23. $9x^2 + 24xy + 16y^2$ **25.** $k(2h^2 - 4h + 5)$
27. $a^2(5a + 2)(a + 2)$ **29.** $(12p + 13q)(12p - 13q)$
31. $(3y - 1)(9y^2 + 3y + 1)$ **33.** $\dfrac{9x^2}{4}$ **35.** 4   **37.** $\dfrac{(m - 1)^2}{3(m + 1)}$
39. $\dfrac{1}{5^3}$ or $\dfrac{1}{125}$ **41.** -1 **43.** 4^3 **45.** $\dfrac{1}{8}$ **47.** $\dfrac{7}{10}$ **49.** $\dfrac{1}{5^{2/3}}$
51. $3^{7/2}a^{5/2}$ **53.** 3   **55.** $3pq\sqrt[3]{2q^2}$ **57.** $-21\sqrt{3}$
59. $\sqrt{6} - \sqrt{3}$ **61.** $-\dfrac{1}{3}$ **63.** No solution   **65.** $x = \dfrac{3}{8a - 2}$

67. $-38, 42$ **69.** $-7 \pm \sqrt{5}$ **71.** $\dfrac{1}{2}, -2$ **73.** $-\dfrac{3}{2}, 7$
75. $\pm\dfrac{\sqrt{3}}{3}$ **77.** $r = \dfrac{-Rp \pm E\sqrt{Rp}}{p}$ **79.** $s = \dfrac{a \pm \sqrt{a^2 + 4K}}{2}$
81. 111%   **83.** $1118.75   **85. (a)** 2009   **(b)** 2012
87. 52.66 million   **89. (a)** 9.8824 million   **(b)** 2013
91. (a) About $19.79 billion   **(b)** About $31.27 billion   **93.** 11%
95. (a) 7182   **(b)** About 13.61 million   **97.** 3.2 feet
99. About 7.77 seconds

Case Study 1 (Page 64)

1. $218 + 508x$ **3.** Electric by $1880   **5.** $1529.10 + 50x$
7. LG by $29.10

Chapter 2

Section 2.1 (Page 72)

1. IV, II, I, III   **3.** Yes   **5.** No
7.

9.

11.

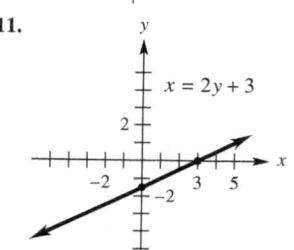

13. x-intercepts $-2.5, 3$; y-intercept 3   **15.** x-intercepts $-1, 2$;
y-intercept -2 **17.** x-intercept 4; y-intercept 3   **19.** x-intercept 12;
y-intercept -8 **21.** x-intercepts $3, -3$; y-intercept -9
23. x-intercepts $-5, 4$; y-intercept -20
25. no x-intercept; y-intercept 7
27.

29.

31.

33.

35.

37.

31.

39.

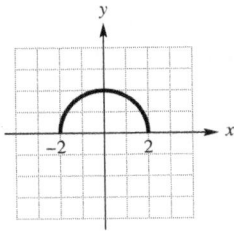

33. Perpendicular **35.** Parallel **37.** Neither **39. (a)** $\dfrac{2}{5}, \dfrac{9}{8}, -\dfrac{5}{2}$

(b) Yes **41.** $y = -\dfrac{2}{3}x$ **43.** $y = 3x - 3$ **45.** $y = 1$

47. $x = -2$ **49.** $y = 2x + 3$ **51.** $2y = 7x - 3$ **53.** $y = 5x$
55. $x = 6$ **57.** $y = 2x - 2$ **59.** $y = x - 6$ **61.** $y = -x + 2$
63. $1330.42 **65.** $6715.23 **67. (a)** $202.05 billion
(b) $270.5 billion **(c)** 2015 **69. (a)** 384.6 thousand
(b) 366.6 thousand **(c)** 2019 **71. (a)** $(5, 35.1), (11, 29.7)$
(b) $y = -.9x + 39.6$ **(c)** $31.5 billion **(d)** 2016
73. (a) $y = .035x + .40$ **(b)** $.82 **75. (a)** $y = -964.5x + 36,845$
(b) 31,058 **77. (a)** The average decrease in time over 1 year; times
are going down, in general. **(b)** 12.94 minutes

41. 2008; 20 million pounds **43.** 2011
45. (a) About $1,250,000 **(b)** About $1,750,000
(c) About $4,250,000 **47. (a)** About $500,000
(b) About $1,000,000 **(c)** About $1,500,000 **49.** Beef: about
59 pounds; Chicken: about 83 pounds; Pork: about 47.5 pounds
51. 2001 **53.** About $507 billion **55.** 2008–2015
57. $16.5; $21 **59.** $17.25; Day 14 **61.** No

63.

65.

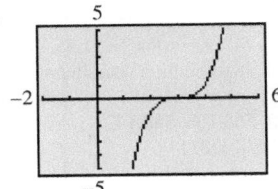

Section 2.3 (Page 93)

1. (a) $y = \dfrac{5}{9}(x - 32)$ **(b)** 10°C and 23.89°C **3.** 463.89°C

5. $y = 4.66x + 173.64$; 210.92; 243.54
7. $y = .0625x + 6$; 6.625 million **9.** 4 ft
11. (a) 22.2, –23.2, –12.6, 6.0, 7.6; –22.6, –41.4, –4.2, 41.0, 69.2;
sum $= 0$ **(b)** 1283.6; 8712 **(c)** Model 1 **13.** Yes
15. (a) $y = 5.90x + 146.59$ **(b)** $235.09 billion
17. (a) $y = -3.96x + 73.98$ **(b)** $10.62 billion
19. (a) $y = 2.37x - 2.02$ **(b)** $26.42 billion; $31.16 billion
21. (a) $y = -2.318x + 55.88$ **(b)** 41.972 thousand **(c)** early 2012
(d) $r \approx -.972$

67.

69. No;

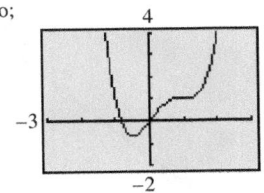

Section 2.4 (Page 100)

1. Answers vary.
3. $[-4, \infty)$

5. $(-\infty, 0)$

7. $\left(-\infty, \dfrac{10}{3}\right]$

9. $(-\infty, -8]$

71. $x \approx -1.1038$ **73.** $x \approx 2.1017$ **75.** $x \approx -1.7521$
77. About $6.99 trillion **79.** About $45.41 trillion

11. $(-\infty, 3)$

13. $(-1, \infty)$

Section 2.2 (Page 84)

1. $-\dfrac{3}{2}$ **3.** -2 **5.** $-\dfrac{5}{2}$ **7.** Not defined **9.** $y = 4x + 5$

15. $(-\infty, 1]$

17. $\left(\dfrac{1}{5}, \infty\right)$

11. $y = -2.3x + 1.5$ **13.** $y = -\dfrac{3}{4}x + 4$ **15.** $m = 2; b = -9$

17. $m = 3; b = -2$ **19.** $m = \dfrac{2}{3}; b = -\dfrac{16}{9}$ **21.** $m = \dfrac{2}{3}; b = 0$

23. $m = 1; b = 5$ **25. (a)** C **(b)** B **(c)** B **(d)** D

19. $(-5, 7)$

21. $\left[\dfrac{7}{3}, 5\right]$

27.

29.

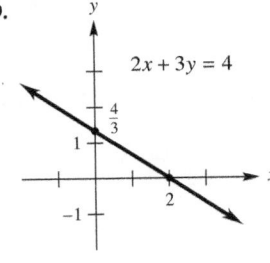

23. $\left[-\dfrac{11}{2}, \dfrac{7}{2}\right]$

25. $\left[-\dfrac{17}{7}, \infty\right)$

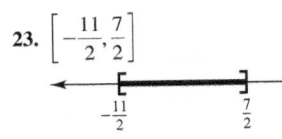

27. $x \geq 2$ **29.** $-3 < x \leq 5$ **31.** $x \geq 400$ **33.** $x \geq 50$
35. Impossible to break even
37. $(-\infty, -7)$ or $(7, \infty)$ **39.** $[-5, 5]$

41. All real numbers **43.** $\left(-\frac{3}{2}, \frac{5}{2}\right)$

45. $\left(-\infty, -\frac{3}{2}\right]$ or $\left[\frac{1}{4}, \infty\right)$

47. $76 \leq T \leq 90$ **49.** $40 \leq T \leq 82$
51. (a) $25.33 \leq R_L \leq 28.17; 36.58 \leq R_E \leq 40.92$
(b) $5699.25 \leq T_L \leq 6338.25; 8230.5 \leq T_E \leq 9207$ **53.** $35 \leq B \leq 43$
55. $0 < x \leq 8700; 8700 < x \leq 35,350; 35,350 < x \leq 85,650;$
$85,650 < x \leq 178,650; 178,650 < x \leq 388,350; x > 388,350$

Section 2.5 (Page 108)

1. $\left[-4, \frac{3}{2}\right]$ **3.** $(-\infty, -3)$ or $(-1, \infty)$

5. $\left[-2, \frac{1}{4}\right]$ **7.** $(-\infty, -1)$ or $\left(\frac{1}{4}, \infty\right)$

9. $[-6, 6]$ **11.** $(-\infty, 0)$ or $(16, \infty)$

13. $[-3, 0]$ or $[3, \infty)$ **15.** $[-7, -2]$ or $[2, \infty)$
17. $(-\infty, -5)$ or $(-1, 3)$ **19.** $\left(-\infty, -\frac{1}{2}\right)$ or $\left(0, \frac{4}{3}\right)$ **21.** No.
23. $(-.1565, 2.5565)$ **25.** $[-2.2635, .7556]$ or $[3.5079, \infty)$
27. $(.5, .8393)$ **29.** $(-\infty, 1)$ or $[4, \infty)$ **31.** $\left(\frac{7}{2}, 5\right)$
33. $(-\infty, 2)$ or $(5, \infty)$ **35.** $(-\infty, -1)$ **37.** $(-\infty, -2)$ or $(0, 3)$
39. $[-1, .5]$ **41.** $(8, \infty)$ **43.** $[52, 200]$ **45.** 2010 or higher
47. $[2006, 2011]$

Chapter 2 Review Exercises (Page 110)

Refer to Section	2.1	2.2	2.3	2.4	2.5
For Exercises	1–10	11–34	35–38	39–54	55–68

1. $(-2, 3), (0, -5), (3, -2), (4, 3)$
3.

5.

7.

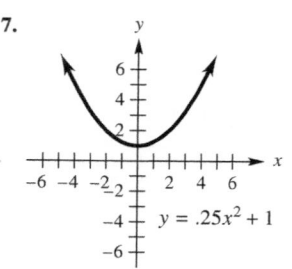

9. (a) About 11:30 AM to about 7:30 PM **(b)** From midnight until about 5 AM and after about 10:30 PM **11.** Answers vary. **13.** -3
15. $-\frac{1}{4}$ **17.** 3 **19.** 0 **21.** -3
23.

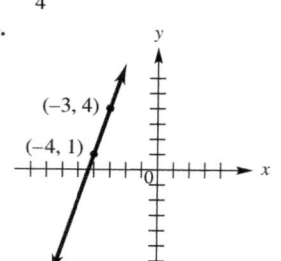

25. $3y = 2x - 13$ **27.** $4y = -5x + 17$
29. $x = -1$ **31.** $3y = 5x + 15$
33. (a) $y = .55x + 11.25$ **(b)** Positive; exports increased
(c) 18.95 million hectoliters
35. (a) $y = 1919x + 47,059$ **(b)** $y = 1917.38x + 47,051.26$
(c) $68,168; $68,142.44; least–squares regression line is closer;
(d) $75, 811.96
37. (a) $y = 10.72x + 98.8$
(b)

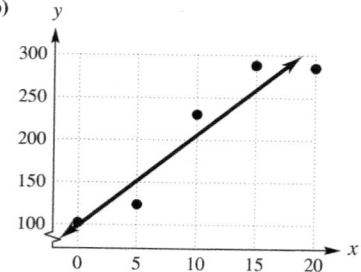

(c) Yes **(d)** $r \approx .953$ **39.** $\left(\frac{3}{8}, \infty\right)$ **41.** $\left(-\infty, \frac{1}{4}\right]$
43. $\left[-\frac{1}{2}, 2\right]$ **45.** $[-8, 8]$ **47.** $(-\infty, 2]$ or $[5, \infty)$
49. $\left[-\frac{9}{5}, 1\right]$ **51. (d)** **53. (a)** $y = 75.4x + 1496$ **(b)** 2013
55. $(-3, 2)$ **57.** $(-\infty, -5]$ or $\left[\frac{3}{2}, \infty\right)$
59. $(-\infty, -5]$ or $[-2, 3]$ **61.** $[-2, 0)$ **63.** $\left(-1, \frac{3}{2}\right)$
65. $[-19, -5)$ or $(2, \infty)$ **67.** 2011 and 2012

Case Study 2 Exercises (Page 113)

1. $y = -146.1x + 2330$
3. $-389.8, -212.7, 96.4, 331.5, 525.6, 195.7, -41.2, -221.1, -217.0,$
$-137.9, 73.2$

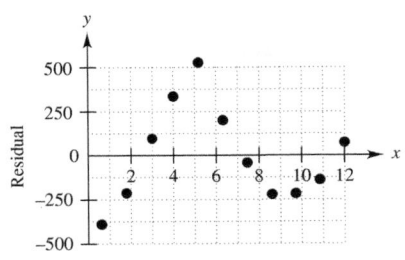

5. $y = .343x - 20.65$ **7.** $\hat{y} = \$-.07$; Cannot have a negative wage
9. $y = 0$; answers vary.

Chapter 3

Section 3.1 (Page 121)
1. Function   **3.** Function   **5.** Not a function   **7.** Function
9. $(-\infty, \infty)$ **11.** $(-\infty, \infty)$ **13.** $(-\infty, 0]$
15. All real numbers except 2   **17.** All real numbers except 2 and -2
19. All real numbers such that $x > -4$ and $x \neq 3$ **21.** $(-\infty, \infty)$
23. (a) 8 (b) 8 (c) 8 (d) 8   **25.** (a) 48 (b) 6 (c) 25.38
(d) 28.42   **27.** (a) $\sqrt{7}$ (b) 0 (c) $\sqrt{5.7}$ (d) Not defined
29. (a) 12 (b) 23 (c) 12.91 (d) 49.41   **31.** (a) $\dfrac{\sqrt{3}}{15}$
(b) Not defined (c) $\dfrac{\sqrt{1.7}}{6.29}$ (d) Not defined   **33.** (a) 13 (b) 9
(c) 6.5 (d) 24.01   **35.** (a) $6 - p$ (b) $6 + r$ (c) $3 - m$
37. (a) $\sqrt{4 - p}$ $(p \leq 4)$ (b) $\sqrt{4 + r}$ $(r \geq -4)$ (c) $\sqrt{1 - m}$ $(m \leq 1)$
39. (a) $p^3 + 1$ (b) $-r^3 + 1$ (c) $m^3 + 9m^2 + 27m + 28$
41. (a) $\dfrac{3}{p - 1}$ $(p \neq 1)$ (b) $\dfrac{3}{-r - 1}$ $(r \neq -1)$ (c) $\dfrac{3}{m + 2}$ $(m \neq -2)$
43. 2   **45.** $2x + h$
47.

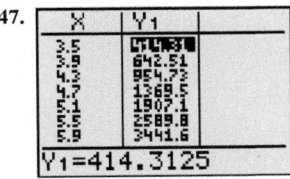

49. (a) \$1070 (b) \$4542.30 (c) \$8420.18   **51.** (a) \$–6.744 billion
(loss) (b) \$14.448 billion   **53.** (a) \$2347.9 million
(b) \$2299.9 million   **55.** $2050 - 500t$ **57.** (a) $c(x) = 1800 + .5x$
(b) $r(x) = 1.2x$ (c) $p(x) = .7x - 1800$
59.

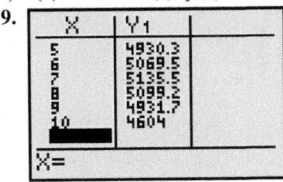

Section 3.2 (Page 131)
1.

3.

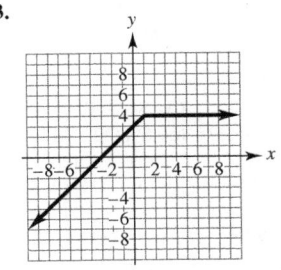

$$f(x) = \begin{cases} x + 3 & \text{if } x \leq 1 \\ 4 & \text{if } x > 1 \end{cases}$$

5.

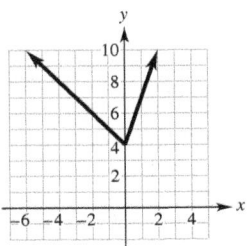

$$y = \begin{cases} 4 - x & \text{if } x \leq 0 \\ 3x + 4 & \text{if } x > 0 \end{cases}$$

7.

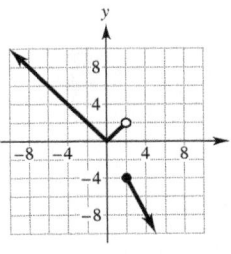

$$f(x) = \begin{cases} |x| & \text{if } x < 2 \\ -2x & \text{if } x \geq 2 \end{cases}$$

9.

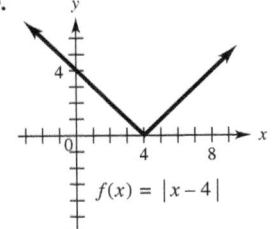

$f(x) = |x - 4|$

11.

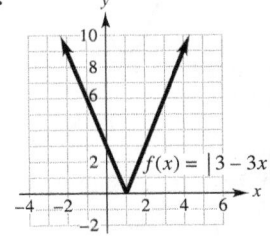

$f(x) = |3 - 3x|$

13.

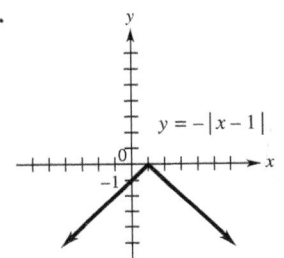

$y = -|x - 1|$

15.

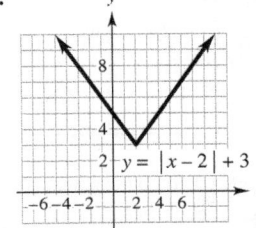

$y = |x - 2| + 3$

17.

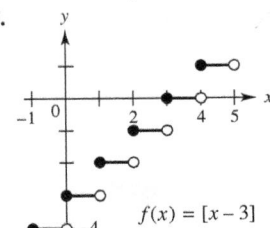

$f(x) = [x - 3]$

19.

$g(x) = [-x]$

21.

23.

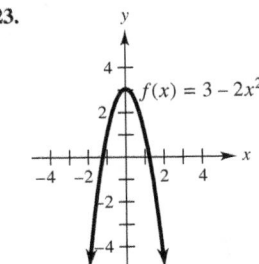

$f(x) = 3 - 2x^2$

25.

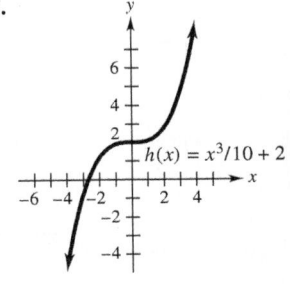

$h(x) = x^3/10 + 2$

27.

$g(x) = \sqrt{-x}$

29.

$f(x) = \sqrt[3]{x}$

(b) $7.879   **51. (a)** $f(x) = \begin{cases} 2x + 15.1 & \text{if } 0 \le x \le 30 \\ 10.5x - 240.1 & \text{if } x > 30 \end{cases}$

(b)

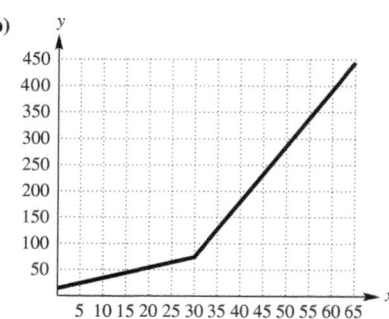

(c) 326.9   **(d)** 442.4   **53. (a)** No   **(b)** 1998, 2002, 2009   **(c)** 2009
55. (a) Yes   **(b)** The years 1990–2010   **(c)** [7750, 15400]
57. (a) 33; 44   **(b)** The figure has vertical line segments, which can't be part of the graph of a function. (Why?) To make the figure into the graph of f, delete the vertical line segments; then, for each horizontal segment of the graph, put a closed dot on the left end and an open circle on the right end (as in Figure 3.7).   **59. (a)** $34.99   **(b)** $24.99   **(c)** $64.99
(d) $74.99

(e)

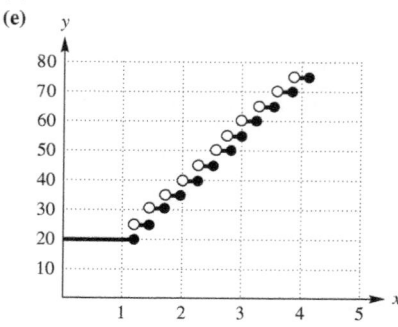

61. There are many correct answers, including

31.

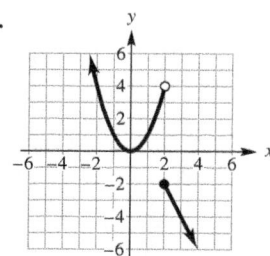

33. Function   **35.** Not a function   **37.** Function
39.

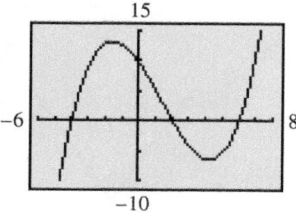

41. $(1, -1)$ is on the graph; $(1, 3)$ is not on the graph

43. $x = -4, 2, 6$ **45.** Peak at $(.5078, .3938)$; valleys at $(-1.9826, -4.2009)$ and $(3.7248, -8.7035)$
47.

49. (a)

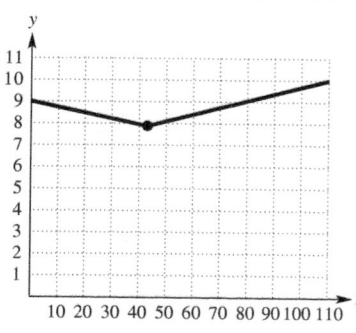

Section 3.3 (Page 142)
1. Let $C(x)$ be the cost of renting a saw for x hours; $C(x) = 25 + 5x$.
3. Let $C(x)$ be the cost (in dollars) for x half hours; $C(x) = 8 + 2.5x$.
5. $C(x) = 36x + 200$ **7.** $C(x) = 120x + 3800$ **9.** $48, $15.60, $13.80   **11.** $55.50, $11.40, $8.46   **13. (a)** $f(x) = -1916x + 16,615$
(b) 7035   **(c)** $1916 per year   **15. (a)** $f(x) = -11,875x + 120,000$
(b) [0, 8]   **(c)** $48,750   **17. (a)** $80,000   **(b)** $42.50   **(c)** $122,500;
$1,440,000   **(d)** $122.50; $45   **19. (a)** $C(x) = .097x + 1.32$
(b) $98.32   **(c)** $98.42   **(d)** $.097, or 9.7¢   **(e)** $.097, or 9.7¢
21. $R(x) = 1.77x + 2,310,000$ **23. (a)** $C(x) = 10x + 750$
(b) $R(x) = 35x$ **(c)** $P(x) = 25x - 750$ **(d)** $1750
25. (a) $C(x) = 18x + 300$ **(b)** $R(x) = 28x$ **(c)** $P(x) = 10x - 300$
(d) $700   **27. (a)** $C(x) = 12.50x + 20,000$ **(b)** $R(x) = 30x$
(c) $P(x) = 17.50x - 20,000$ **(d)** $-$18,250 (a loss)   **29.** $(3, -1)$
31. $\left(-\dfrac{11}{4}, -\dfrac{61}{4}\right)$ **33. (a)** 200,000 policies $(x = 200)$

(b)

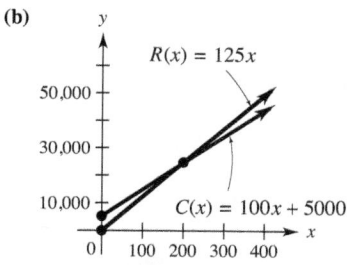

(c) Revenue: $12,500; cost: $15,000   **35. (a)** $C(x) = .126x + 1.5$
(b) $2.382 million   **(c)** About 17.857 units   **37.** Break-even
point is about 467 units; do not produce the item.   **39.** Break-even
point is about 1037 units; produce the item.   **41.** The percentage is
approximately 53% in 1998.

43. (a)

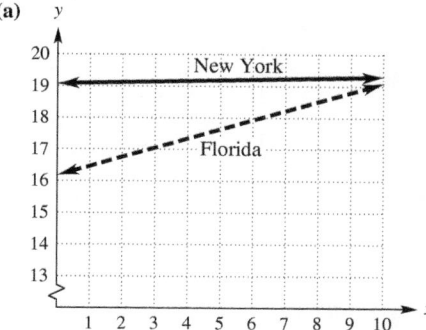

(b) No   **(c)** Yes; Late 2010   **45.** $140   **47.** 10 items
49. (a) $16   **(b)** $11   **(c)** $6   **(d)** 8 units   **(e)** 4 units   **(f)** 0 units
(g)

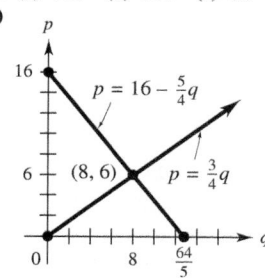

(h) 0 units   **(i)** $\frac{40}{3}$ units   **(j)** $\frac{80}{3}$ units   **(k)** See part (g).   **(l)** 8 units

(m) $6
51. (a)

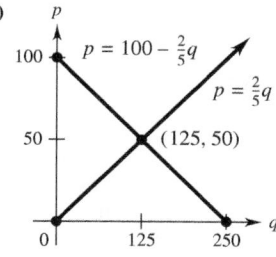

(b) 125 units   **(c)** 50¢   **(d)** $[0, 125]$ **53.** Total cost increases when
more items are made (because it includes the cost of all previously made
items), so the graph cannot move downward. No; the average cost can
decrease as more items are made, so its graph can move downward.

Section 3.4 (Page 154)

1. Upward   **3.** Downward   **5.** $(5, 7)$; downward
7. $(-1, -9)$; upward   **9.** i   **11.** k   **13.** j   **15.** f

17. $f(x) = \frac{1}{4}(x - 1)^2 + 2$ **19.** $f(x) = (x + 1)^2 - 2$ **21.** $(-3, 12)$

23. $(2, -7)$ **25.** x-intercepts 1, 3; y-intercept 9
27. x-intercepts $-1, -3$; y-intercept 6

29. $(-2, 0), x = -2$

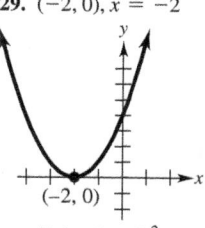

$f(x) = (x + 2)^2$

31. $(2, 2), x = 2$

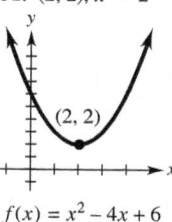

$f(x) = x^2 - 4x + 6$
$f(x) = (x - 2)^2 + 2$

33. 54   **35. (a)** 10 milliseconds   **(b)** 40 responses per millisecond
37. (a) 27 cases   **(b)** Answers vary.   **(c)** 15 cases
39. (a) About 12 books   **(b)** 10 books   **(c)** About 7 books   **(d)** 0 books
(e) 5 books   **(f)** About 7 books   **(g)** 10 books   **(h)** about 12 books
(i)

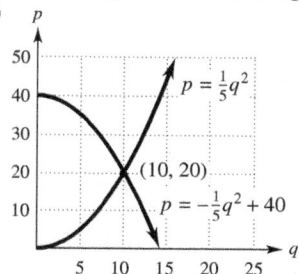

41. (a) $640   **(b)** $515   **(c)** $140
(d)

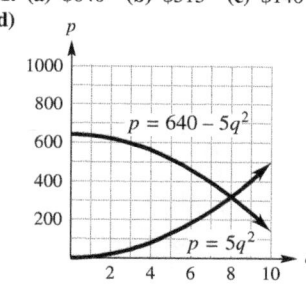

(e) 800 units   **(f)** $320   **43.** 80; $3600   **45.** 30; $1500
47. 20   **49.** 10
51. (a) $R(x) = (100 - x)(200 + 4x)$
$= 20,000 + 200x - 4x^2$
(b)

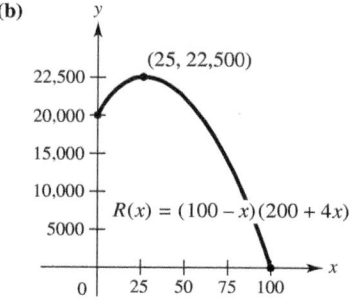

(c) 25 seats   **(d)** $22,500   **53.** 13 weeks; $96.10/hog
55. (a) $.013(x - 20)^2$ **(b)** About 4
57. (a) $f(x) = 3.9375(x - 4)^2 + 57.8$ **(b)** About $309.8 billion
59. 30   **61.** 200

$f(x) = .034x^2 - 1.87x + 26.16$;
about 4

$f(x) = 1.808x^2 - 5.185x + 50.72$;
about $248.85 billion

63. (a) 11.3 and 88.7   **(b)** 50   **(c)** $3000   **(d)** $x < 11.3$ or $x > 88.7$
(e) $11.3 < x < 88.7$

Section 3.5 (Page 165)

1.

$f(x) = x^4$

3.

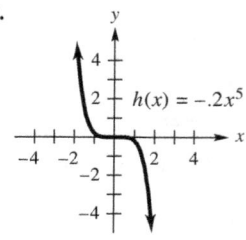

$h(x) = -.2x^5$

5. (a) Yes   **(b)** No   **(c)** No   **(d)** Yes   **7. (a)** Yes   **(b)** No
(c) Yes   **(d)** No   **9.** d   **11.** b   **13.** e

15.

17.

19.

21.

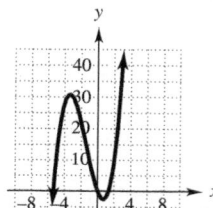

23. $-3 \le x \le 5$ and $-20 \le y \le 5$ **25.** $-3 \le x \le 4$ and
$-35 \le y \le 20$ **27. (a)** $933.33 billion   **(b)** $1200 billion
(c) $1145.8 billion   **(d)** $787.5 billion

(e)

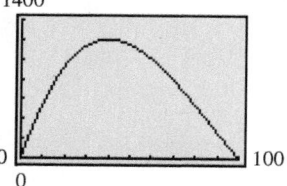

29. (a) $54.785 million; $64.843 million; $99.578 million

(b)

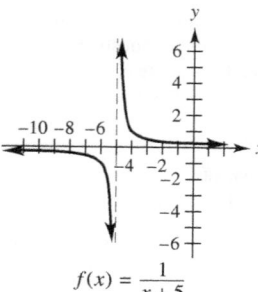

(c) Yes, because the slope is always positive.
31. (a) $53.615 million; $63.505 million; $97.33 million

(b)

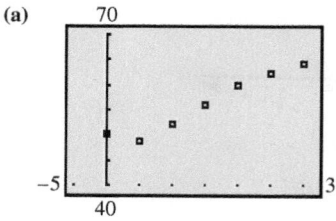

(c) Yes, the slope is always positive
33. $P(x) = .006x^3 - .13x^2 + .99x - 1.28$; $2.248 million

35. (a)

(b) $g(x) = -.0016x^3 + .0765x^2 - .425x + 50.0$

(c)   Yes

(d) 62.9528 million
37. (a) $R(x) = -.0668x^3 + 1.708x^2 - 12.15x + 120.1$

(b)   Yes

39. $P(x) = -.0313x^3 + .773x^2 - 4.83x + 17.1$

Section 3.6 (Page 175)

1. $x = -5, y = 0$ **3.** $x = -\dfrac{5}{2}, y = 0$

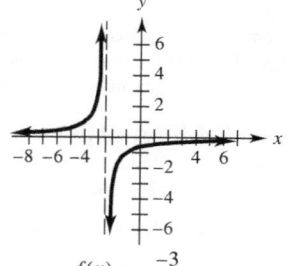

$f(x) = \dfrac{1}{x+5}$ $f(x) = \dfrac{-3}{2x+5}$

5. $x = 1, y = 3$

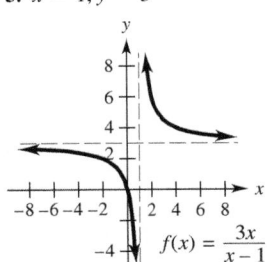

$f(x) = \dfrac{3x}{x-1}$

7. $x = 4, y = 1$

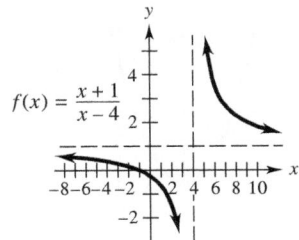

$f(x) = \dfrac{x+1}{x-4}$

9. $x = 3; y = -1$

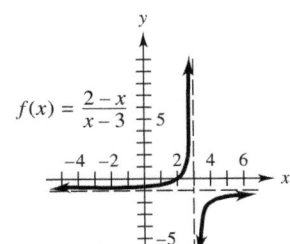

$f(x) = \dfrac{2-x}{x-3}$

11. $x = -2, y = \dfrac{3}{2}$

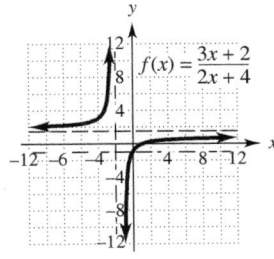

$f(x) = \dfrac{3x+2}{2x+4}$

13. $x = -4, x = 2, y = 0$

$h(x) = \dfrac{x+1}{x^2+2x-8}$

15. $x = -2, x = 2, y = 1$

$f(x) = \dfrac{x^2+4}{x^2-4}$

17. $x = -2, x = 1$ **19.** $x = -1, x = 5$
21. (a) \$4300 **(b)** \$10,033.33 **(c)** \$17,200 **(d)** \$38,700
(e) \$81,700 **(f)** \$210,700
(g) \$425,700 **(h)** No
(i)

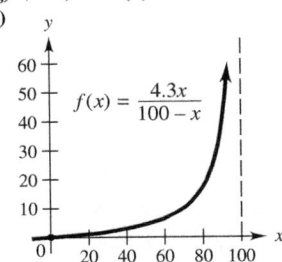

$f(x) = \dfrac{4.3x}{100-x}$

23. (a) $[0, \infty)$
(b)

$f(x) = \dfrac{x}{1+x}$

(c)

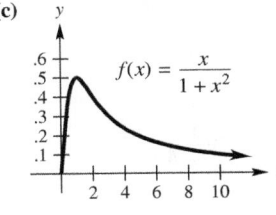

$f(x) = \dfrac{x}{1+x^2}$

(d) Increasing b makes the next generation smaller when this generation is
larger.   **25. (a)** 6 min **(b)** 1.5 min **(c)** .6 min **(d)** $A = 0$

(e)

$W = \dfrac{S(S-A)}{A}$

(f) W becomes negative. The waiting time approaches 0 as A approaches 3.
The formula does not apply for $A > 3$ because there will be no waiting if
people arrive more than 3 min apart.
27.

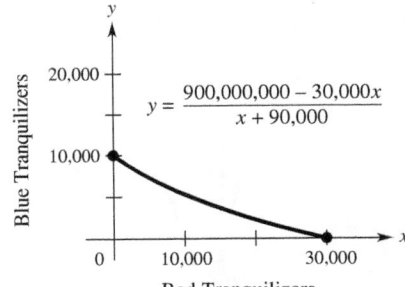

$y = \dfrac{900,000,000 - 30,000x}{x + 90,000}$

Blue Tranquilizers

Red Tranquilizers

30,000 reds; 10,000 blues
29. (a) $C(x) = 2.6x + 40,000$
(b) $\overline{C}(x) = \dfrac{2.6x + 40,000}{x} = 2.6 + \dfrac{40,000}{x}$
(c) $y = 2.6$; the average cost may get close to, but will never equal, \$2.60.
31. About 73.9
33. (a)

(b) They appear almost identical, because the parabola is an asymptote of
the graph.

Chapter 3 Review Exercises (Page 177)

Refer to Section	3.1	3.2	3.3	3.4	3.5	3.6
From Exercises	1–12	13–24	25–36	37–60	61–70	71–80

1. Not a function   **3.** Function   **5.** Not a function
7. (a) 23 **(b)** -9 **(c)** $4p - 1$ **(d)** $4r + 3$
9. (a) -28 **(b)** -12 **(c)** $-p^2 + 2p - 4$ **(d)** $-r^2 - 3$
11. (a) -13 **(b)** 3 **(c)** $-k^2 - 4k$ **(d)** $-9m^2 + 12m$
(e) $-k^2 + 14k - 45$ **(f)** $12 - 5p$

13.

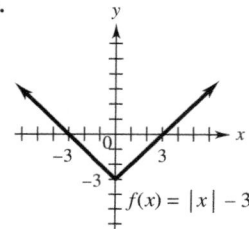

$f(x) = |x| - 3$

15.

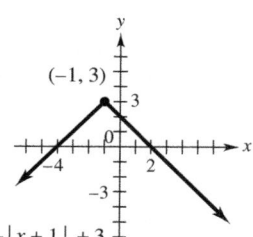

$(-1, 3)$

$f(x) = -|x + 1| + 3$

17.

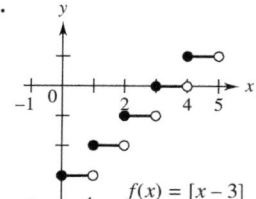

$f(x) = [x - 3]$

19.

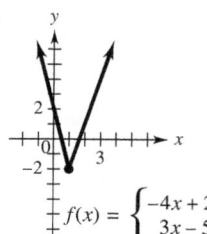

$f(x) = \begin{cases} -4x + 2 & \text{if } x \le 1 \\ 3x - 5 & \text{if } x > 1 \end{cases}$

21.

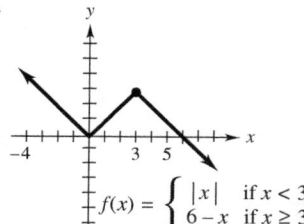

$f(x) = \begin{cases} |x| & \text{if } x < 3 \\ 6 - x & \text{if } x \ge 3 \end{cases}$

23.

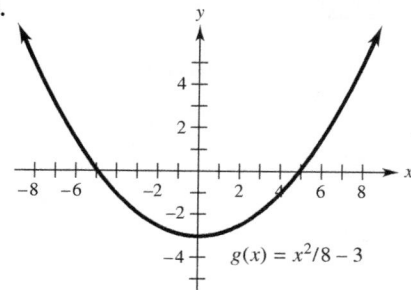

$g(x) = x^2/8 - 3$

25. (a)

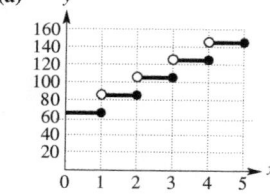

(b) Domain: $(0, \infty)$ range: $\{65, 85, 105, 125, \ldots\}$ **(c)** 2 days
27. (a) decreasing; relatively flat   **(b)** $f(x) = -1.4x + 30$ **(c)** 13.2%
29. (a) $C(x) = 30x + 60$ **(b)** $30   **(c)** $30.60
31. (a) $C(x) = 30x + 85$ **(b)** $30   **(c)** $30.85
33. (a) $18,000   **(b)** $R(x) = 28x$ **(c)** 4500 cartridges   **(d)** $126,000
35. Equilibrium quantity is 36 million subscribers at a price of $12.95 per
month.   **37.** Upward; $(2, 6)$ **39.** Downward; $(-1, 8)$

41.

Vertex $(0, -9)$

43.

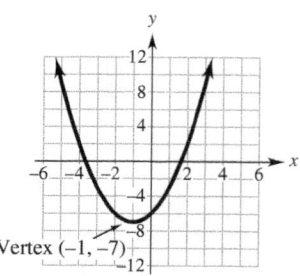

Vertex $(-1, -7)$

45.

Vertex $(-3, 14)$

47.

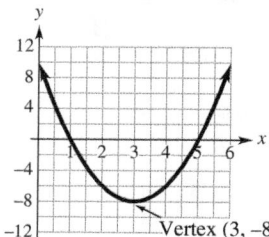

Vertex $(3, -8)$

49. Minimum value; -11 **51.** Maximum value; 7
53. 161 weeks; $97.16   **55.** 2027; about 1391 million
57. (a) $f(x) = 25.82(x - 5)^2 + 3672$ **(b)** $44,984
59. (a) $g(x) = 9.738x^2 + 389x + 1096$
(b) 35,000

(c) $38,320.45

61.

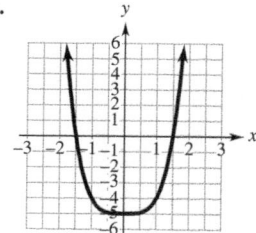

$f(x) = x^4 - 5$

63.

$f(x) = x(x - 4)(x + 1)$

65.

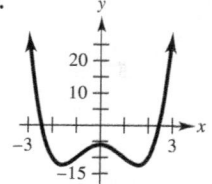

$f(x) = x^4 - 5x^2 - 6$

67. About 313,152; about $690.72 per thousand
69. (a) $404,963 million

(b) $373,222 million   **(c)** $297x^3 - 6901x^2 + 50,400x - 79,159$
(d) $31,741 million; $45,113 million
71. $x = 3, y = 0$ **73.** $x = 2, y = 0$

$$f(x) = \frac{1}{x-3}$$

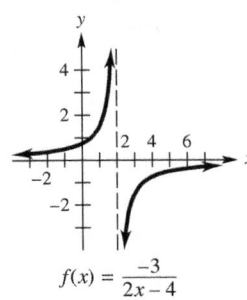

$$f(x) = \frac{-3}{2x-4}$$

75. $x = -\frac{1}{2}, x = \frac{3}{2}, y = 0$

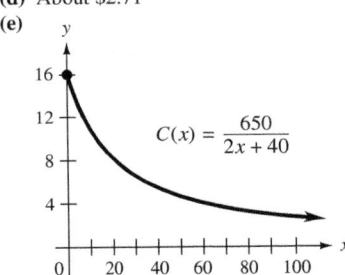

$$g(x) = \frac{5x-2}{4x^2 - 4x - 3}$$

77. (a) About $10.83   **(b)** About $4.64   **(c)** About $3.61
(d) About $2.71
(e)

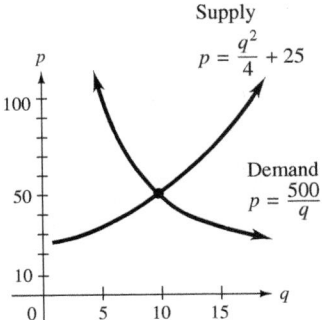

$$C(x) = \frac{650}{2x+40}$$

79. (a) $(10, 50)$

Supply
$$p = \frac{q^2}{4} + 25$$

Demand
$$p = \frac{500}{q}$$

(b) $(10, \infty)$ **(c)** $(0, 10)$

Case Study 3 Exercises (Page 182)

1. $f(x) = \frac{-20}{49}x^2 + 20$

3. $g(x) = \sqrt{625 - x^2}$; 50 ft

5. $h(x) = \sqrt{144 - x^2} + 8$; 8 ft   **7.** It will fit through the semicircular arch and Norman arch; to fit it through the parabolic arch, increase the width to 15 ft.

Chapter 4

Section 4.1 (Page 189)

1. Exponential   **3.** Quadratic   **5.** Exponential
7. (a) The graph is entirely above the x-axis and falls from left to right, crossing the y-axis at 1 and then getting very close to the x-axis.
(b) $(0, 1), (1, .6)$ **9. (a)** The graph is entirely above the x-axis and rises from left to right, less steeply than the graph of $f(x) = 2^x$.
(b) $(0, 1), (1, 2^{.5}) = (1, \sqrt{2})$ **11. (a)** The graph is entirely above the x-axis and falls from left to right, crossing the y-axis at 1 and then getting very close to the x-axis.   **(b)** $(0, 1), (1, e^{-1}) \approx (1, .367879)$
13.   **15.**

$f(x) = 3^x$

$f(x) = 2^{x/2}$

17.

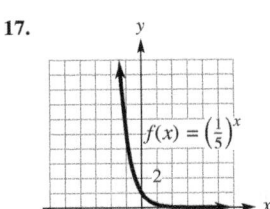

$f(x) = \left(\frac{1}{5}\right)^x$

19. (a)–(c)

$f(x) = 2^x$
$g(x) = 2^{x+3}$
$h(x) = 2^{x-4}$

(d) Answers vary.   **21.** 2.3   **23.** .75   **25.** .31
27. (a) $a > 1$ **(b)** Domain: $(-\infty, \infty)$; range: $(0, \infty)$
(c)

$(0, -1)$
$g(x) = -a^x$

(d) Domain: $(-\infty, \infty)$; range: $(-\infty, 0)$
(e)

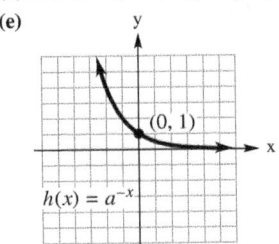

$(0, 1)$
$h(x) = a^{-x}$

(f) Domain: $(-\infty, \infty)$; range: $(0, \infty)$ **29. (a)** 3   **(b)** $\frac{1}{3}$ **(c)** 9   **(d)** 1

31.

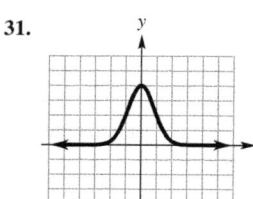

$$f(x) = 2^{-x^2 + 2}$$

33.

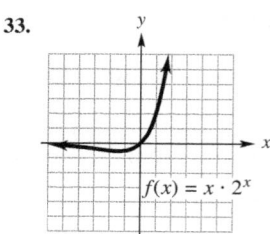

$$f(x) = x \cdot 2^x$$

35. (a)

t	0	1	2	3	4	5	6	7	8	9	10
y	1	1.06	1.12	1.19	1.26	1.34	1.42	1.50	1.59	1.69	1.79

(b)

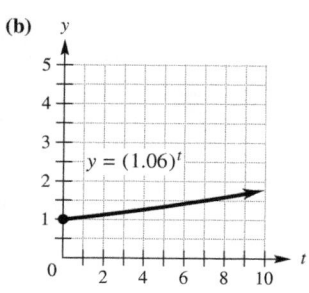

$$y = (1.06)^t$$

37. (a) About \$141,892   **(b)** About \$64.10
39. (a) About 175 million   **(b)** About 321 million
(c) About 355 million   **41. (a)** About .97 kg   **(b)** About .75 kg
(c) About .65 kg   **(d)** About 24,360 years   **43.** \$34,706.99
45. (a) About 6.2 billion   **(b)** About 6.5 billion   **(c)** About 8 billion
(d) Answers vary.   **47. (a)** China: About \$12.4 trillion; U.S: About
\$15.6 trillion   **(b)** China: About \$27.2 trillion; U.S: About \$22.4 trillion
(c) China: About \$515.3 trillion; U.S: About \$86.3 trillion   **(d)** 2016
49. (a) About 13.72 million   **(b)** About 28.9 million
(c) First quarter of 2012   **51. (a)** About 1.2 billion
(b) About 2.1 billion   **(c)** Fourth quarter of 2012
53. (a) About 12.6 mg   **(b)** About 7.9 mg   **(c)** In about 15.1 hours

Section 4.2 (Page 197)

1. (a) \$752.27   **(b)** \$707.39   **(c)** \$432.45   **(d)** \$298.98
(e) Answers vary.   **3. (a)** 2540   **(b)** About 9431 megawatts; about
59,177 megawatts   **5. (a)** $f(t) = 1000(1.046)^t$ **(b)** \$3078.17
(c) 2005   **7. (a)** $f(t) = 81.1(1.067)^t$ **(b)** About \$260.6 billion
(c) About \$410.3 billion   **9. (a)** Two-point: $f(t) = (.9763)^t$;
regression: $f(t) = .998(.976)^t$ **(b)** Two-point: \$.70; \$.65; regression:
\$.69; \$.64   **(c)** Two-point: 2038; regression: 2037
11. (a) Two-point: $f(t) = 257.6(.964)^t$; regression: $f(t) = 257.4(.963)^t$
(b) Two-point: about 165.9; about 143.3; regression: about 163.7; about
140.8   **(c)** Two-point: 2025; regression: 2025   **13. (a)** About 6 items
(b) About 23 items   **(c)** 25 items   **15.** $2.6°$ C   **17. (a)** .13
(b) .23   **(c)** About 2 weeks
19. (a) About \$594.0 billion; about \$802.4 billion
(b) 1000

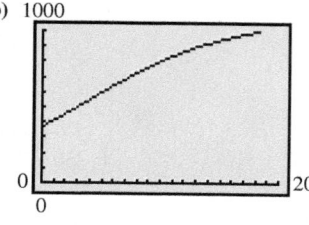

(c) 2011
21. (a) About \$91.89 billion; about \$96.86 billion

(b) 120

(c) No

Section 4.3 (Page 207)

1. a^y **3.** It is missing the value that equals b^y. If that value is x, the
expression should read $y = \log_b x$ **5.** $10^5 = 100,000$ **7.** $9^2 = 81$
9. $\log 96 = 1.9823$ **11.** $\log_3\left(\dfrac{1}{9}\right) = -2$ **13.** 3   **15.** 2
17. 3   **19.** -2 **21.** $\dfrac{1}{2}$ **23.** 8.77   **25.** 1.724
27. -4.991 **29.** Because $a^0 = 1$ for every valid base a.
31. $\log 24$ **33.** $\ln 5$ **35.** $\log\left(\dfrac{u^2 w^3}{v^6}\right)$ **37.** $\ln\left(\dfrac{(x+2)^2}{x+3}\right)$
39. $\dfrac{1}{2}\ln 6 + 2\ln m + \ln n$ **41.** $\dfrac{1}{2}\log x - \dfrac{5}{2}\log z$ **43.** $2u + 5v$
45. $3u - 2v$ **47.** 3.32112   **49.** 2.429777
51. Many correct answers, including, $b = 1, c = 2$.
53.

$$y = \ln(x+2)$$

55.

$$y = \log(x-3)$$

57. Answers vary.   **59.** $\ln 2.75 = 1.0116009$; $e^{1.0116009} = 2.75$
61. (a) 17.67 yr   **(b)** 9.01 yr   **(c)** 4.19 yr   **(d)** 2.25 yr
63. (a) \$2219.63
(b) 2500

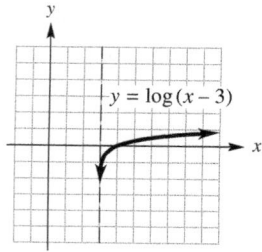

(c) Gradually increasing
65. (a) About 31.99 million; about 37.67 million
(b) 50

(c) Gradually increasing   **67.** 1.5887
69. (a) About \$441.15 billion; about \$737.74 billion   **(b)** 2027
71. (a) About 24.8 gallons; about 21.9   **(b)** 2021

Section 4.4 (Page 216)

1. 8   **3.** 9   **5.** 11   **7.** $\dfrac{11}{6}$ **9.** $\dfrac{4}{9}$ **11.** 10

13. 5.2378   **15.** 10   **17.** $\dfrac{4+b}{4}$ **19.** $\dfrac{10^{2-b}-5}{6}$

21. Answers vary.   **23.** 4   **25.** $-\dfrac{5}{6}$ **27.** -4 **29.** -2

31. 2.3219   **33.** 2.710   **35.** -1.825 **37.** .597253

39. $-.123$ **41.** $\dfrac{\log d + 3}{4}$ **43.** $\dfrac{\ln b + 1}{2}$ **45.** 4

47. No solution   **49.** $-4, 4$ **51.** 9   **53.** 1   **55.** 4, -4
57. ± 2.0789 **59.** 1.386   **61.** Answers vary.   **63. (a)** 2009
(b) 2012   **65. (a)** 1992 ($x \approx 92.1518$)   **(b)** Mid-2007 ($x \approx 107.7364$)
(c) Mid-2041 ($x \approx 141.6168$)   **67. (a)** 1995   **(b)** 2022
69. (a) 25 g   **(b)** About 4.95 yr   **71.** About 3689 yr old
73. (a) Approximately $79,432,823i_0$ **(b)** Approximately $251,189i_0$
(c) About 316.23 times stronger   **75. (a)** 21   **(b)** 100   **(c)** 105
(d) 120   **(e)** 140   **77. (a)** 27.5%   **(b)** $130.14

79. (a)

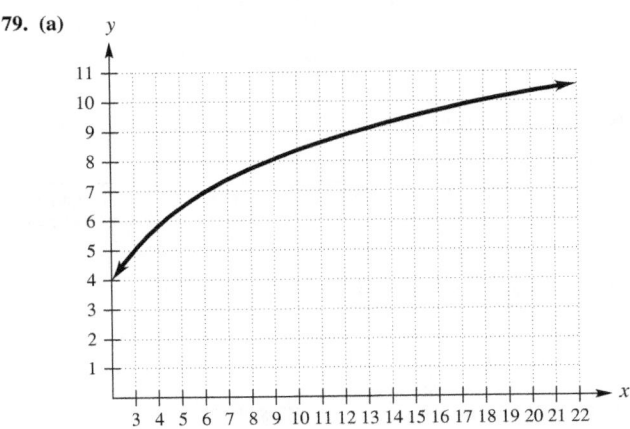

(b) 2002

Chapter 4 Review Exercises (Page 219)

Refer to Section	4.1	4.2	4.3	4.4
For Exercises	1–10	13–14, 55–58, 61–64	11–12, 15–40, 65–66	41–54, 59–60

1. (c)   **3. (d)**   **5.** $0 < a < 1$ **7.** All positive real numbers

9.

11.

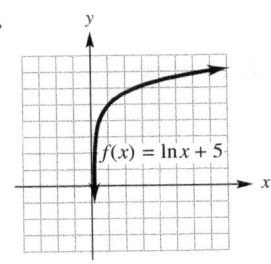

13. (a) About 412 thousand   **(b)** June 2012   **15.** $\log 340 = 2.53148$
17. $\ln 45 = 3.8067$ **19.** $10^4 = 10,000$ **21.** $e^{4.3957} = 81.1$
23. 5   **25.** 8.9   **27.** $\dfrac{1}{3}$ **29.** $\log 20x^6$ **31.** $\log\!\left(\dfrac{b^3}{c^2}\right)$
33. 4   **35.** 97   **37.** 5   **39.** 5   **41.** -2 **43.** -2
45. 1.416   **47.** -2.807 **49.** -3.305 **51.** .747
53. 28.463   **55. (a)** C   **(b)** A   **(c)** D   **(d)** B   **57. (a)** 10 g
(b) About 140 days   **(c)** About 243 days   **59. (a)** $10,000,000i_0$
(b) $3,162,278i_0$ **(c)** About 3.2 times stronger   **61.** 81.25° C
63. (a) $f(x) = 500(1.067)^x$ **(b)** $f(x) = 474.8(1.075)^x$
(c) Two-point: about 896 minutes; regession: about 910 minutes
(d) Two point and regression: May, 2013.

65. (a) $f(x) = 18 + 21.07 \ln x$ **(b)** $f(x) = 15.21 + 20.47 \ln x$
(c) Two point: about 64%; regression: about 60%
(d) Two point: 2016; regression: 2019

Case Study 4 Exercises (Page 224)

1.

3. 66.6 years   **5.** About $1383

7.

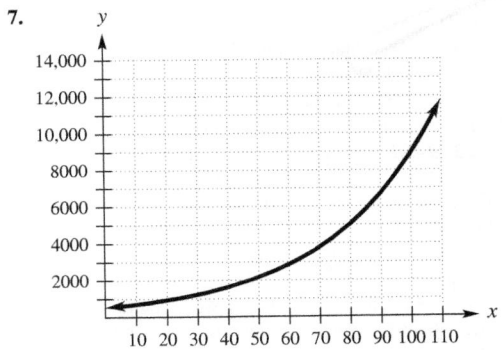

9. About $2131; about $8899

11.

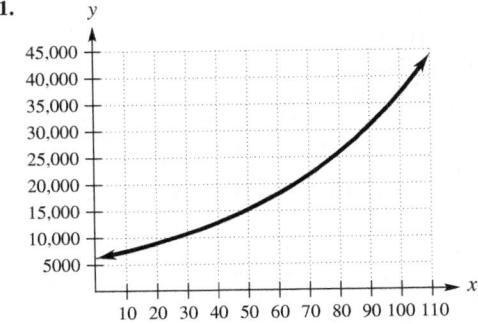

13. About $18,168; about $44,329

Chapter 5

Section 5.1 (Page 230)

1. Time and interest rate   **3.** $133   **5.** $217.48   **7.** $86.26
9. $158.82   **11.** $31.25; $187.50   **13.** $234.38; $4687.50
15. $81.25; $1625   **17.** $12,105   **19.** $6727.50
21. Answers vary.   **23.** $14,354.07   **25.** $15,089.46
27. $19,996.25; about .07501%   **29.** $15,491.86; about .105087%
31. $19,752; about 5.0223%   **33.** $15,117.92; about 5.0545%

35. (a) $9450 (b) $19,110 **37.** $3056.25 **39.** 5.0%
41. 4 months **43.** $1750.04 **45.** $5825.24 **47.** 3.5%
49. About 11.36% **51.** About 102.91%. Ouch! **53.** $13,725; yes
55. (a) $y_1 = 8t + 100$; $y_2 = 6t + 200$
(b) The graph of y_1 is a line with slope 8 and y-intercept 100. The graph of
y_2 is a line with slope 6 and y-intercept 200.

(c)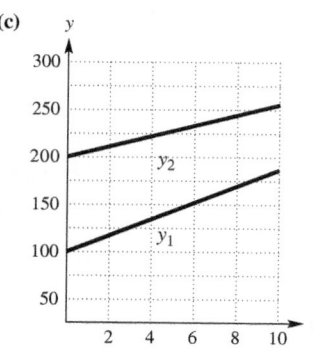

(d) The y-intercept of each graph indicates the amount invested. The slope
of each graph is the annual amount of interest paid.

Section 5.2 (Page 241)

1. Answers vary. **3.** Interest rate and number of compounding periods
5. Answers vary. **7.** $1265.32; $265.32 **9.** $1204.75; $734.75
11. $9297.93; $2797.93 **13.** $10,090.41; $90.41
15. $5081.63; $81.63 **17.** $107,896.09; $7,896.09 **19.** 3.75%
21. 5.25% **23.** $23,824.92; $3824.92 **25.** $31,664.54; $1664.54
27. $10,000 **29.** $20,000 **31.** 4.04% **33.** 5.095%
35. $8954.58 **37.** $11,572.58 **39.** $4203.64 **41.** $9963.10
43. $4606.57 **45.** $465.85 **47.** $1000 now **49.** $21,570.27
51. Treasury note **53.** $1000 now **55.** 3.59%
57. Flagstar, 4.45%; Principal, 4.46%; Principal paid a higher APY
59. About $2,259,696 **61.** About $21,043 **63.** 23.4 years
65. 14.2 years **67.** About 11.9 years **69.** (a) $16,659.95
(b) $21,472.67 **71.** (a)

Section 5.3 (Page 249)

1. 21.5786 **3.** $119,625.61 **5.** $23,242.87 **7.** $72,482.38
9. About $205,490 **11.** About $310,831 **13.** $797.36
15. $4566.33 **17.** $152.53 **19.** 5.19% **21.** 5.223%
23. Answers vary. **25.** $6603.39 **27.** $234,295.32
29. $26,671.23 **31.** $3928.88 **33.** $620.46 **35.** $265.71
37. $280,686.25 **39.** (a) $173,497.86 (b) $144,493.82
(c) $29,004.04 **41.** (a) $552,539.96 (b) $854,433.28
43. $32,426.46 **45.** $284,527.35 **47.** (a) $256.08 (b) $247.81
49. $863.68 **51.** (a) $1200 (b) $3511.58 **53.** 6.5%
55. (a) Answers vary. (b) $24,000 (c) $603,229 (d) $84,000
(e) $460,884

Section 5.4 (Page 261)

1. Answers vary. **3.** $8693.71 **5.** $1,566,346.66
7. $11,468.10 **9.** $38,108.61 **11.** $557.68 **13.** $6272.14
15. $119,379.35 **17.** $97,122.49 **19.** $48,677.34
21. $15,537.76 **23.** $9093.14 **25.** $446.31 **27.** $11,331.18
29. $589.31 **31.** $979.21 **33.** $925.29
35. $594.72; $13,818.25 **37.** $947.69; $151,223.33 **39.** $6.80
41. $42.04 **43.** $30,669,881 **45.** $24,761,633
47. (a) $1465.42 (b) $214.58 **49.** $2320.83
51. $414.18; $14,701.60 **53.** (a) $2717.36 (b) 2
55. (a) $969.75 (b) $185,658.15 (c) $143,510
57. About $8143.79 **59.** $406.53 **61.** $663.22

63.

Payment Number	Amount of Payment	Interest for Period	Portion to Principal	Principal at End of Period
0	–	–	–	$4000.00
1	$1207.68	$320.00	$887.68	3112.32
2	1207.68	248.99	958.69	2153.63
3	1207.68	172.29	1035.39	1118.24
4	1207.70	89.46	1118.24	0

65.

Payment Number	Amount of Payment	Interest for Period	Portion to Principal	Principal at End of Period
0	–	–	–	$7184.00
1	$189.18	$71.84	117.34	7066.66
2	189.18	70.67	118.51	6948.15
3	189.18	69.48	119.70	6828.45
4	189.18	68.28	120.90	6707.55

Chapter 5 Review Exercises (Page 265)

Refer to Section	5.1	5.2	5.3	5.4
For Exercises	1–14	15–28, 65–66, 71	32–41, 67–70, 75–76	29–31,42–64, 72–74,77–79

1. $292.08 **3.** $62.05 **5.** $285; $3420 **7.** $7925.67
9. Answers vary. **11.** $78,742.54 **13.** About 4.082%
15. $5634.15; $2834.15 **17.** $20,402.98; $7499.53 **19.** $8532.58
21. $15,000 **23.** 5.0625% **25.** $18,207.65 **27.** $1088.54
29. $9706.74 **31.** Answers vary. **33.** $162,753.15
35. $22,643.29 **37.** Answers vary. **39.** $2619.29 **41.** $916.12
43. $31,921.91 **45.** $14,222.42 **47.** $136,340.32
49. $1194.02 **51.** $38,298.04 **53.** $3581.11 **55.** $435.66
57. $85,459.20 **59.** $81.98 **61.** $502.49
63. (a) $7,233,333.33 (b) $136,427,623.40
65. $2298.58 **67.** $24,818.76; $2418.76 **69.** $12,538.59
71. $5596.62 **73.** $3560.61 **75.** $222,221.02 **77.** (d)

Case Study 5 Exercises (Page 268)

1. (a) $22,549.94 (b) $36,442.38 (c) $66,402.34
3. (a) $40,722.37 (b) $41,090.49 (c) $41,175.24 (d) $41,216.62
(e) $41,218.03 **5.** (a) About 4.603% (b) About 5.866%
(c) About 7.681%

Chapter 6

Section 6.1 (Page 275)

1. Yes **3.** $(-1,-4)$ **5.** $\left(\dfrac{2}{7}, -\dfrac{11}{7}\right)$ **7.** $\left(\dfrac{11}{5}, -\dfrac{7}{5}\right)$
9. $(28, 22)$ **11.** $(2, -1)$ **13.** No solution **15.** $(4y + 1, y)$
for any real number y **17.** $(5, 10)$ **19.** (a) About 51.8 weeks;
$959,091 (b) Answers vary. **21.** 2025 **23.** 2058
25. 145 adults; 55 children **27.** Plane: 550 mph; wind: 50 mph
29. 300 of Boeing; 100 of GE **31.** (a) $y = x + 1$
(b) $y = 3x + 4$ (c) $\left(-\dfrac{3}{2}, -\dfrac{1}{2}\right)$

Section 6.2 (Page 286)

1.
$$\begin{aligned} x \qquad\;\; - 3z &= 2 \\ 2x - 4y + 5z &= 1 \\ 5x - 8y + 7z &= 6 \\ 3x - 4y + 2z &= 3 \end{aligned}$$
3.
$$\begin{aligned} 3x \qquad + z + 2w + 18v &= 0 \\ -4x + y \qquad - w - 24v &= 0 \\ 7x - y + z + 3w + 42v &= 0 \\ 4x \qquad + z + 2w + 24v &= 0 \end{aligned}$$

5.
$$\begin{aligned} x + y + 2z + 3w &= 1 \\ -y - z - 2w &= -1 \\ 3x + y + 4z + 5w &= 2 \end{aligned}$$

7.
$$\begin{aligned} x + 12y - 3z + 4w &= 10 \\ 2y + 3z + w &= 4 \\ -z &= -7 \\ 6y - 2z - 3w &= 0 \end{aligned}$$

9. $(-68, 13, -6, 3)$ **11.** $\left(20, -9, \dfrac{15}{2}, 3\right)$ **13.** $\begin{bmatrix} 2 & 1 & 1 & \vline & 3 \\ 3 & -4 & 2 & \vline & -5 \\ 1 & 1 & 1 & \vline & 2 \end{bmatrix}$

15.
$$\begin{aligned} 2x + 3y + 8z &= 20 \\ x + 4y + 6z &= 12 \\ 3y + 5z &= 10 \end{aligned}$$
17. $\begin{bmatrix} 1 & 2 & 3 & \vline & -1 \\ 2 & 0 & 7 & \vline & -4 \\ 6 & 5 & 4 & \vline & 6 \end{bmatrix}$

19. $\begin{bmatrix} -4 & -3 & 1 & -1 & \vline & 2 \\ 0 & -4 & 7 & -2 & \vline & 10 \\ 0 & -2 & 9 & 4 & \vline & 5 \end{bmatrix}$ **21.** $\left(\dfrac{3}{2}, 17, -5, 0\right)$

23. $(12 - w, -3 - 2w, -5, w)$ for any real number w **25.** Dependent

27. Inconsistent   **29.** Independent   **31.** $\left(\dfrac{3}{2}, \dfrac{3}{2}, -\dfrac{3}{2}\right)$

33. $(-.8, -1.8, .8)$ **35.** $(100, 50, 50)$ **37.** $(0, 3.5, 1.5)$
39. $(-3, 4, 0)$ **41.** $(1, 0, -1)$ **43.** $(-93, -31, 10)$
45. No solution   **47.** $(192, 125.5, -148.5)$
49. $\left(\dfrac{1 - z}{2}, \dfrac{11 - z}{2}, z\right)$ for any real number z **51.** No solution
53. $(-7, 5)$ **55.** $(-1, 2)$ **57.** $(-3, z - 17, z)$ for any real number z
59. $(-11.5, 13.75, -2.25, -5)$ **61.** No solution
63. $\left(\dfrac{1}{2}, \dfrac{1}{3}, -\dfrac{1}{4}\right)$ **65.** 2012; 5000 people
67. 220 adults; 150 teenagers; 200 children
69.

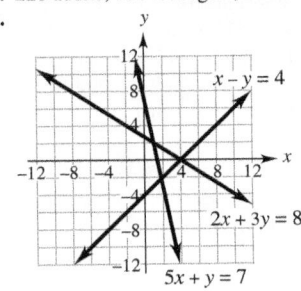

There is no point that is on all three lines.

71. $y = .75x^2 + .25x - .5$

Section 6.3 (Page 294)

1. 100 vans, 50 small trucks, 25 large trucks   **3.** 10 units of corn; 25 units of soybeans; 40 units of cottonseed   **5.** Shirt $1.99; slacks $4.99; sports coat $6.49   **7.** 220 adults; 150 teenagers; 200 preteens
9. $20,000 in AAA; $10,000 in B; none in A   **11.** 40 lb pretzels, 20 lb dried fruit, 80 lb nuts   **13.** Four possible solutions: (i) no cases of A and D; 12 cases of B; 8 cases of C; 9 of C; 1 of D; (ii) 1 of A; 8 of B; 9 of C; 1 of D; (iii) 2 of A; 4 of B; 10 of C; 2 of D; (iv) 3 of A; none of B; 11 of C; 3 of D
15. $13,750 in the mutual fund, $27,500 in bonds, and $28,750 in the franchise   **17. (a)** $b + c$ **(b)** .35, .45, .2; A is tumorous, B is bone, and C is healthy.
19. (a) $x_2 + x_3 = 700$
$x_3 + x_4 = 600$
(b) $(1000 - x_4, 100 + x_4, 600 - x_4, x_4)$ **(c)** 600; 0
(d) x_1: 1000; 400
x_2: 700; 100
x_3: 600; 0
(e) Answers vary.   **21.** 4 cups of Hearty Chicken Rotini, 5 cups of Hearty Chicken, and 6 cups of Chunky Chicken Noodle; serving size 1.5 cups
23. (a) $12,000 at 6%, $7000 at 7%, and $6000 at 10%
(b) $10,000 at 6%, $15,000 at 7%, and $5000 at 10%
(c) $20,000 at 6%, $10,000 at 7%, and $10,000 at 10%
25. (a) $f(x) = -.008x^2 + 1.6x + 140.8$ **(b)** 169.6 million

27. (a) $y = .01x^2 - .3x + 4.24$ **(b)** 15 platters; $1.99
29. (a) $C = -.0000108S^2 + .034896S + 22.9$ **(b)** About 864.7 knots

Section 6.4 (Page 303)

1. 2×3; $\begin{bmatrix} -7 & 8 & -4 \\ 0 & -13 & -9 \end{bmatrix}$ **3.** 3×3; square matrix; $\begin{bmatrix} 3 & 0 & -11 \\ -1 & -\frac{1}{4} & 7 \\ -5 & 3 & -9 \end{bmatrix}$ **5.** 2×1; column matrix; $\begin{bmatrix} -7 \\ -11 \end{bmatrix}$

7. B is a 5×3 zero matrix.   **9.** $\begin{bmatrix} -7 & 14 & 2 & 4 \\ 6 & -3 & 2 & -4 \end{bmatrix}$

11. $\begin{bmatrix} 3 & -1 & 2 \\ 3 & 1 & 5 \end{bmatrix}$ **13.** $\begin{bmatrix} -4 & -7 & 7 \\ 6 & 3 & -8 \end{bmatrix}$

15. Not defined   **17.** $\begin{bmatrix} -4 & 0 \\ 10 & 6 \end{bmatrix}$ **19.** $\begin{bmatrix} 0 & -8 \\ -16 & 24 \end{bmatrix}$

21. $\begin{bmatrix} 8 & 10 \\ 0 & -42 \end{bmatrix}$ **23.** $\begin{bmatrix} 4 & -\frac{7}{2} \\ 4 & \frac{21}{2} \end{bmatrix}$

25. $X + T = \begin{bmatrix} x & y \\ z & w \end{bmatrix} + \begin{bmatrix} r & s \\ t & u \end{bmatrix} = \begin{bmatrix} x + r & y + s \\ z + t & w + u \end{bmatrix}$; a 2×2 matrix

27. $X + (T + P) = \begin{bmatrix} x + (r + m) & y + (s + n) \\ z + (t + p) & w + (u + q) \end{bmatrix}$
$= \begin{bmatrix} (x + r) + m & (y + s) + n \\ (z + t) + p & (w + u) + q \end{bmatrix} = (X + T) + P$

29. $P + O = \begin{bmatrix} m + 0 & n + 0 \\ p + 0 & q + 0 \end{bmatrix} = \begin{bmatrix} m & n \\ p & q \end{bmatrix} = P$

31. Several possible correct answers, including

	Basketball	Hockey	Football	Baseball
Percent of no shows	16	16	20	18
Lost revenue per fan ($)	18.20	18.25	19	15.40
Lost annual revenue (millions $)	22.7	35.8	51.9	96.3

33.

	2009	2010	2011
Heart	2674	2874	2813
Lung	1799	1759	1630
Liver	15,094	15,394	15,330
Kidney	79,397	83,919	86,547

35. (a)

	Bread	Milk	Peanut Butter	Cold Cuts
I	88	48	16	112
II	105	72	21	147
III	60	40	0	50

(b) $\begin{bmatrix} 110 & 60 & 20 & 140 \\ 140 & 96 & 28 & 196 \\ 66 & 44 & 0 & 55 \end{bmatrix}$ **(c)** $\begin{bmatrix} 198 & 108 & 36 & 252 \\ 245 & 168 & 49 & 343 \\ 126 & 84 & 0 & 105 \end{bmatrix}$

37. (a) $A = \begin{bmatrix} 2.61 & 4.39 & 6.29 & 9.08 \\ 1.63 & 2.77 & 4.61 & 6.92 \\ .92 & .75 & .62 & .54 \end{bmatrix}$

(b) $B = \begin{bmatrix} 1.38 & 1.72 & 1.94 & 3.31 \\ 1.26 & 1.48 & 2.82 & 2.28 \\ .41 & .33 & .27 & .40 \end{bmatrix}$ **(c)** $\begin{bmatrix} 1.23 & 2.67 & 4.35 & 5.77 \\ .37 & 1.29 & 1.79 & 4.64 \\ .51 & .42 & .35 & .14 \end{bmatrix}$

Section 6.5 (Page 314)

1. 2×2; 2×2 **3.** 3×3; 5×5 **5.** AB does not exist; 3×2

7. columns; rows   **9.** $\begin{bmatrix} 5 \\ 9 \end{bmatrix}$ **11.** $\begin{bmatrix} -2 & 4 \\ 0 & -8 \end{bmatrix}$ **13.** $\begin{bmatrix} -4 & 1 \\ 2 & -3 \end{bmatrix}$

15. $\begin{bmatrix} 3 & -5 & 7 \\ -2 & 1 & 6 \\ 0 & -3 & 4 \end{bmatrix}$ **17.** $\begin{bmatrix} 16 & 10 \\ 2 & 28 \\ 58 & 46 \end{bmatrix}$

19. $AB = \begin{bmatrix} -30 & -45 \\ 20 & 30 \end{bmatrix}$, but $BA = \begin{bmatrix} 0 & 0 \\ 0 & 0 \end{bmatrix}$.

21. $(A + B)(A - B) = \begin{bmatrix} -7 & -24 \\ -28 & -33 \end{bmatrix}$, but $A^2 - B^2 = \begin{bmatrix} -37 & -69 \\ -8 & -3 \end{bmatrix}$.

23. $(PX)T = \begin{bmatrix} (mx + nz)r + (my + nw)t & (mx + nz)s + (my + nw)u \\ (px + qz)r + (py + qw)t & (px + qz)s + (py + qw)u \end{bmatrix}$.
$P(XT)$ is the same, so $(PX)T = P(XT)$.

25. $k(X + T) = k\begin{bmatrix} x + r & y + s \\ z + t & w + u \end{bmatrix}$
$= \begin{bmatrix} k(x + r) & k(y + s) \\ k(z + t) & k(w + u) \end{bmatrix}$
$= \begin{bmatrix} kx + kr & ky + ks \\ kz + kt & kw + ku \end{bmatrix}$
$= \begin{bmatrix} kx & ky \\ kz & kw \end{bmatrix} + \begin{bmatrix} kr & ks \\ kt & ku \end{bmatrix} = kX + kT$

27. No   **29.** Yes   **31.** Yes   **33.** $\begin{bmatrix} 2 & 3 \\ 1 & 2 \end{bmatrix}$ **35.** $\begin{bmatrix} 1 & 2 \\ 1 & 1 \end{bmatrix}$

37. No inverse   **39.** $\begin{bmatrix} -4 & -2 & 3 \\ -5 & -2 & 3 \\ 2 & 1 & -1 \end{bmatrix}$ **41.** $\begin{bmatrix} 2 & 1 & -1 \\ 8 & 2 & -5 \\ -11 & -3 & 7 \end{bmatrix}$

43. No inverse   **45.** $\begin{bmatrix} 6 & -5 & 8 \\ -1 & 1 & -1 \\ -1 & 1 & -2 \end{bmatrix}$ **47.** $\begin{bmatrix} \frac{1}{2} & -1 & -\frac{1}{2} & \frac{1}{2} \\ \frac{1}{2} & 4 & \frac{5}{2} & -\frac{1}{2} \\ -\frac{1}{4} & -\frac{1}{2} & -\frac{1}{4} & \frac{1}{4} \\ \frac{1}{2} & -2 & -\frac{3}{2} & \frac{1}{2} \end{bmatrix}$

49. (a) $A = \begin{bmatrix} 3719 & 727 & 521 & 313 \\ 4164 & 738 & 590 & 345 \\ 4566 & 744 & 652 & 374 \end{bmatrix}$

(b) $B = \begin{bmatrix} .019 & .007 \\ .011 & .011 \\ .019 & .006 \\ .024 & .008 \end{bmatrix}$ (c) $AB = \begin{bmatrix} 96 & 40 \\ 107 & 44 \\ 116 & 47 \end{bmatrix}$

(d) The rows represent the years 2000, 2010, 2020. Column 1 gives the total births (in millions) in those years and column 2 the total deaths (in millions)   (e) About 107 million; about 47 million

51. (a) $A = \begin{bmatrix} 195 & 143 & 1225 & 1341 \\ 210 & 141 & 1387 & 1388 \end{bmatrix}$ (b) $B = \begin{bmatrix} .016 & .006 \\ .011 & .014 \\ .023 & .008 \\ .013 & .007 \end{bmatrix}$

(c) $AB = \begin{bmatrix} 50 & 22 \\ 55 & 24 \end{bmatrix}$ (d) The rows represent the years 2010 and 2020.
Column 1 gives the total births (in millions) in those years and column 2 the total deaths (in millions).   (e) About 22 million; about 55 million

53. (a) $\begin{array}{r} \\ \text{Dept. 1} \\ \text{Dept. 2} \\ \text{Dept. 3} \\ \text{Dept. 4} \end{array} \begin{array}{cc} A & B \\ \begin{bmatrix} 254 & 290 \\ 199 & 240 \\ 170 & 216 \\ 174 & 170 \end{bmatrix} \end{array}$ (b) supplier A: \$797; supplier B: \$916; buy from A.

55. (a) $\begin{array}{r} \\ \text{Burgers} \\ \text{Fries} \\ \text{Drinks} \end{array} \begin{array}{ccc} \text{I} & \text{II} & \text{III} \\ \begin{bmatrix} 900 & 1500 & 1150 \\ 600 & 950 & 800 \\ 750 & 900 & 825 \end{bmatrix} \end{array} = S$

(b) $\begin{array}{ccc} \text{Burgers} & \text{Fries} & \text{Drinks} \\ [\; 3.00 & 1.80 & 1.20 \;] \end{array}$

(c) $PS = [4680 \quad 7290 \quad 5880]$ (d) \$17,850

Section 6.6 (Page 325)

1. $\begin{bmatrix} 2 \\ -2 \end{bmatrix}$ **3.** $\begin{bmatrix} \frac{1}{2} & 1 \\ \frac{3}{2} & 1 \end{bmatrix}$ **5.** $\begin{bmatrix} -7 \\ 15 \\ -3 \end{bmatrix}$ **7.** $(-63, 50, -9)$

9. $(-31, -131, 181)$ **11.** $(-48, 8, 12)$ **13.** $(1, 0, 2, 1)$ **15.** $\begin{bmatrix} -6 \\ -14 \end{bmatrix}$

17. 60 buffets; 600 chairs; 100 tables   **19.** 2340 of the first species, 10,128 of the second species, 224 of the third species   **21.** jeans \$34.50; jacket \$72; sweater \$44; shirt \$21.75   **23.** $\begin{bmatrix} 6.43 \\ 26.12 \end{bmatrix}$ **25.** About 1073 metric tons of wheat, about 1431 metric tons of oil   **27.** Gas \$98 million, electric \$123 million   **29.** (a) $\frac{7}{4}$ bushels of yams, $\frac{15}{8} \approx 2$ pigs

(b) 167.5 bushels of yams, $153.75 \approx 154$ pigs   **31.** (a) .40 unit of agriculture, .12 unit of manufacturing, and 3.60 units of households
(b) 848 units of agriculture, 516 units of manufacturing, and 2970 units of households   (c) About 813 units   **33.** (a) .017 unit of manufacturing and .216 unit of energy   (b) 123,725,000 pounds of agriculture, 14,792,000 pounds of manufacturing, 1,488,000 pounds of energy
(c) 195,492,000 pounds of agriculture, 25,933,000 pounds of manufacturing, 13,580,000 pounds of energy   **35.** \$532 million of natural resources, \$481 million of manufacturing, \$805 million of trade and services, \$1185 million of personal consumption

37. (a) $\begin{bmatrix} 1.67 & .56 & .56 \\ .19 & 1.17 & .06 \\ 3.15 & 3.27 & 4.38 \end{bmatrix}$

(b) These multipliers imply that, if the demand for one community's output increases by \$1, then the output of the other community will increase by the amount in the row and column of that matrix. For example, if the demand for Hermitage's output increases by \$1, then output from Sharon will increase by \$.56, from Farrell by \$.06, and from Hermitage by \$4.38.

39. $\begin{bmatrix} 23 \\ 51 \end{bmatrix}, \begin{bmatrix} 13 \\ 30 \end{bmatrix}, \begin{bmatrix} 45 \\ 96 \end{bmatrix}, \begin{bmatrix} 69 \\ 156 \end{bmatrix}, \begin{bmatrix} 87 \\ 194 \end{bmatrix}, \begin{bmatrix} 23 \\ 51 \end{bmatrix}, \begin{bmatrix} 51 \\ 110 \end{bmatrix}, \begin{bmatrix} 45 \\ 102 \end{bmatrix}, \begin{bmatrix} 69 \\ 157 \end{bmatrix}$

41. (a) 3   (b) 3   (c) 5   (d) 3

43. (a) $B = \begin{bmatrix} 0 & 2 & 3 \\ 2 & 0 & 4 \\ 3 & 4 & 0 \end{bmatrix}$ (b) $B^2 = \begin{bmatrix} 13 & 12 & 8 \\ 12 & 20 & 6 \\ 8 & 6 & 25 \end{bmatrix}$ (c) 12   (d) 14

45. (a) $C = \begin{array}{r} \text{Dogs} \\ \text{Rats} \\ \text{Cats} \\ \text{Mice} \end{array} \begin{array}{cccc} \text{Dogs} & \text{Rats} & \text{Cats} & \text{Mice} \\ \begin{bmatrix} 0 & 1 & 1 & 1 \\ 0 & 0 & 0 & 1 \\ 0 & 1 & 0 & 1 \\ 0 & 0 & 0 & 0 \end{bmatrix} \end{array}$

(b) $\begin{bmatrix} 0 & 1 & 0 & 2 \\ 0 & 0 & 0 & 0 \\ 0 & 0 & 0 & 1 \\ 0 & 0 & 0 & 0 \end{bmatrix}$; C^2 gives the number of food sources once removed from the feeder.

Chapter 6 Review Exercises (Page 330)

Refer to Section	6.1	6.2	6.3	6.4	6.5	6.6
For Exercises	1–10	11–16	17–20, 79–86	21–38	39–66	67–78, 87–94

1. $(9, -14)$ **3.** $(2, -2)$ **5.** 100 shares of first stock; 300 shares of second stock   **7.** Inconsistent, no solution   **9.** $(-18, 69, 12)$
11. $(-14, 17, 11)$ **13.** No solution   **15.** $(4, 3, 2)$ **17.** 19 ones; 7 fives; 9 tens   **19.** 5 blankets; 3 rugs; 8 skirts   **21.** 2×2; square

23. 1×4; row   **25.** 2×3 **27.** $\begin{bmatrix} 542.10 & -6.93 & 12,605,900 \\ 52.37 & .53 & 3,616,100 \\ 44.06 & -.21 & 11,227,700 \end{bmatrix}$

29. $\begin{bmatrix} -1 & -2 & 3 \\ -2 & -3 & 0 \\ 0 & -1 & -4 \end{bmatrix}$ **31.** $\begin{bmatrix} 14 & 6 \\ -4 & 4 \\ 13 & 23 \end{bmatrix}$ **33.** Not defined

35. $\begin{bmatrix} 2 & 18 \\ -4 & -12 \\ 7 & 13 \end{bmatrix}$ **37.** $\begin{bmatrix} -6.93 & 12,605,900 \\ .53 & 3,616,100 \\ -.21 & 11,227,700 \end{bmatrix}$;

$\begin{bmatrix} -15.1 & 21,226,200 \\ .51 & 3,397,000 \\ .24 & 14,930,400 \end{bmatrix}$; $\begin{bmatrix} -22.03 & 33,832,100 \\ 1.04 & 7,013,100 \\ .03 & 26,158,100 \end{bmatrix}$

39. $\begin{bmatrix} 14 & 56 \\ -6 & -22 \\ 19 & 79 \end{bmatrix}$ **41.** Not defined   **43.** $\begin{bmatrix} 322 & 420 \\ -126 & -166 \\ 455 & 591 \end{bmatrix}$

45. About 20 head and face injuries; about 12 concussions; about 3 neck injuries; about 55 other injuries

47. (a) $\begin{bmatrix} & \text{Cost} & \text{Earnings} \\ & 61.17 & 1 \\ & 60.50 & .84 \\ & 96.21 & 1.88 \end{bmatrix}$ (b) [100 500 200]

(c) Total cost $55,609; total dividend $896

49. Many correct answers, including $\begin{bmatrix} 1 & 2 \\ 3 & 4 \end{bmatrix}$ **51.** $\begin{bmatrix} -.5 & .2 \\ 0 & .2 \end{bmatrix}$

53. No inverse   **55.** $\begin{bmatrix} \frac{1}{4} & \frac{1}{2} & \frac{1}{2} \\ \frac{1}{4} & -\frac{1}{2} & \frac{1}{2} \\ \frac{1}{12} & -\frac{1}{6} & -\frac{1}{6} \end{bmatrix}$ **57.** No inverse

59. $\begin{bmatrix} -\frac{2}{3} & -\frac{17}{3} & -\frac{14}{3} & -3 \\ \frac{1}{3} & \frac{1}{3} & \frac{1}{3} & 0 \\ -\frac{1}{3} & -\frac{10}{3} & -\frac{7}{3} & -2 \\ 0 & 2 & 1 & 1 \end{bmatrix}$ **61.** $\begin{bmatrix} -\frac{7}{19} & \frac{2}{19} \\ \frac{6}{19} & \frac{1}{19} \end{bmatrix}$

63. $\begin{bmatrix} -\frac{1}{12} & -\frac{1}{4} \\ \frac{5}{12} & \frac{1}{4} \end{bmatrix}$ **65.** $\begin{bmatrix} -1.2 & 1.1 & -.9 \\ .8 & -.4 & .6 \\ -.2 & .1 & .1 \end{bmatrix}$ **67.** $\begin{bmatrix} -5 \\ -3 \end{bmatrix}$

69. $\begin{bmatrix} -22 \\ -18 \\ 15 \end{bmatrix}$ **71.** $(-4, 2)$ **73.** $(4, 2)$ **75.** $(-1, 0, 2)$

77. No inverse; no solution for the system   **79.** 16 liters of the 9%; 24 liters of the 14%   **81.** 30 liters of 40% solution; 10 liters of 60% solution   **83.** 80 bowls; 120 plates   **85.** $12,750 at 8%; $27,250 at 8.5%; $10,000 at 11%

87. (a) $\begin{bmatrix} 1 & -\frac{1}{4} \\ -\frac{1}{2} & 1 \end{bmatrix}$ (b) $\begin{bmatrix} \frac{8}{7} & \frac{2}{7} \\ \frac{4}{7} & \frac{8}{7} \end{bmatrix}$ (c) $\begin{bmatrix} 2800 \\ 2800 \end{bmatrix}$

89. Agriculture $140,909; manufacturing $95,455
91. (a) .4 unit agriculture; .09 unit construction; .4 unit energy; .1 unit manufacturing; .9 unit transportation   (b) 2000 units of agriculture; 600 units of construction; 1700 units of energy; 3700 units of manufacturing; 2500 units of transportation   (c) 29,049 units of agriculture; 9869 units of construction; 52,362 units of energy; 61,520 units of manufacturing; 90,987 units of transportation

93. $\begin{bmatrix} 54 \\ 32 \end{bmatrix}, \begin{bmatrix} 134 \\ 89 \end{bmatrix}, \begin{bmatrix} 172 \\ 113 \end{bmatrix}, \begin{bmatrix} 118 \\ 74 \end{bmatrix}, \begin{bmatrix} 208 \\ 131 \end{bmatrix}$

Case Study 6 Exercises (Page 335)

1. All Stampede Air cities except Lubbock may be reached by a two-flight sequence from San Antonio; all Stampede cities may be reached by a three-flight sequence.
3. The connection between Lubbock and Corpus Christi and the connection between Lubbock and San Antonio take three flights.

5. $B^2 = \begin{bmatrix} 2 & 1 & 1 & 1 & 1 \\ 1 & 1 & 1 & 1 & 0 \\ 1 & 1 & 1 & 1 & 0 \\ 1 & 1 & 1 & 2 & 1 \\ 1 & 0 & 0 & 1 & 4 \end{bmatrix}$; an entry is nonzero whenever there is a two-step sequence between the cities.

Chapter 7

Section 7.1 (Page 343)
1. F   **3.** A   **5.** E
7.   **9.**

11.   **13.**

15.   **17.**

19.   **21.**

23.   **25.**

27. Answers vary.
29.   **31.**

33.

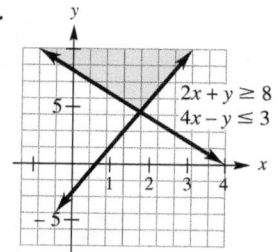

$2x + y \geq 8$
$4x - y \leq 3$

35.

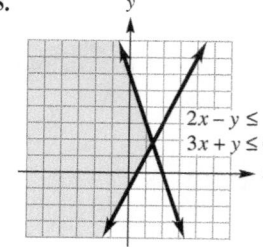

$2x - y \leq 1$
$3x + y \leq 6$

37.

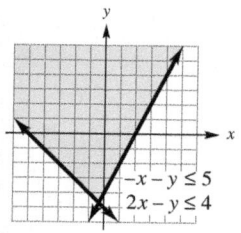

$-x - y \leq 5$
$2x - y \leq 4$

39.

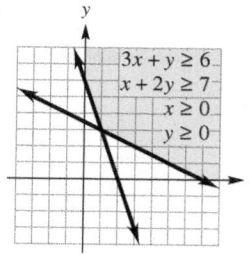

$3x + y \geq 6$
$x + 2y \geq 7$
$x \geq 0$
$y \geq 0$

41.

$-2 \leq x \leq 3$
$-1 \leq y \leq 5$
$2x + y \leq 6$

43.

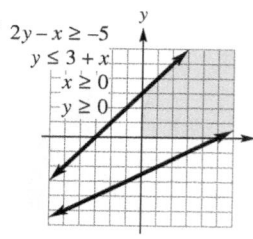

$2y - x \geq -5$
$y \leq 3 + x$
$x \geq 0$
$y \geq 0$

45.

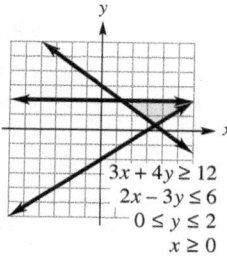

$3x + 4y \geq 12$
$2x - 3y \leq 6$
$0 \leq y \leq 2$
$x \geq 0$

47. $x \geq 0$
$0 \leq y \leq 4$
$4x + 3y \leq 24$

49. $2 < x < 7$
$-1 < y < 3$

51. (a)

Number	Hours Spinning	Hours Dyeing	Hours Weaving
Shawls x	1	1	1
Afghans y	2	1	4
Maximum Number of Hours Available	8	6	14

(b) $x + 2y \leq 8$; $x + y \leq 6$; $x + 4y \leq 14$; $x \geq 0$; $y \geq 0$

(c)

$x + 2y \leq 8$
$x + y \leq 6$
$x + 4y \leq 14$
$x \geq 0$
$y \geq 0$

53.

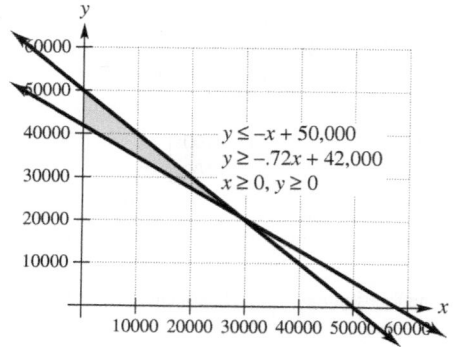

$y \leq -x + 50{,}000$
$y \geq -.72x + 42{,}000$
$x \geq 0, y \geq 0$

55.

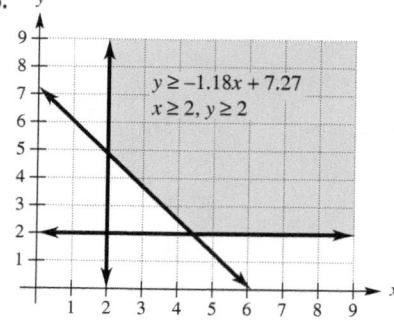

$y \geq -1.18x + 7.27$
$x \geq 2, y \geq 2$

Section 7.2 (Page 351)

1. Maximum of 40 at (5, 10); minimum of 7 at (1, 1)   **3.** Maximum of 6 at (0, 12); minimum of 0 at (0, 0)   **5. (a)** No maximum; minimum of 12 at (12, 0)   **(b)** No maximum; minimum of 18 at (3, 4)
(c) No maximum; minimum of 21 at $\left(\dfrac{13}{2}, 2\right)$
(d) No maximum; minimum of 8 at (0, 8)
7. Maximum of 8.4 at (1.2, 1.2)   **9.** Minimum of 13 at (5, 3)
11. Maximum of 68.75 at $\left(\dfrac{105}{8}, \dfrac{25}{8}\right)$ **13.** No maximum; minimum of 9
15. Maximum of 22; no minimum   **17. (a)** (18, 2)   **(b)** $\left(\dfrac{12}{5}, \dfrac{39}{5}\right)$
(c) No maximum   **19.** Answers vary.

Section 7.3 (Page 356)

1. $8x + 5y \leq 110$, $x \geq 0$, and $y \geq 0$, where x is the number of canoes and y is the number of rowboats   **3.** $250x + 750y \leq 9500$, $x \geq 0$, and $y \geq 0$, where x is the number of radio spots and y is the number of TV ads
5. 12 chain saws; no chippers   **7.** 10 lb deluxe; 40 lb regular
9. 12 shocks; 6 brakes   **11.** 8 radio spots; 10 TV ads
13. 3 Brand X and 2 Brand Z, for a minimum cost of $1.05
15. 800 type 1 and 1600 type 2, for a maximum revenue of $272
17. From warehouse I, ship 60 boxes to San Jose and 250 boxes to Memphis, and from warehouse II, ship 290 boxes to San Jose and none to Memphis, for a minimum cost of $136.70   **19.** $20 million in bonds and $24 million in mutual funds, for maximum interest of $2.24 million
21. 8 humanities, 12 science   **23.** About 53 shares of the ClearBridge Fund   **25.** 100 shares of the Delaware Fund   **27.** (b)   **29.** (c)

Section 7.4 (Page 369)

1. (a) 3   **(b)** s_1, s_2, s_3 **(c)**
$$4x_1 + 2x_2 + s_1 \qquad\qquad = 20$$
$$5x_1 + x_2 \qquad + s_2 \qquad = 50$$
$$2x_1 + 3x_2 \qquad\qquad + s_3 = 25$$

3. (a) 3 **(b)** s_1, s_2, s_3 **(c)**
$$3x_1 - x_2 + 4x_3 + s_1 \qquad\qquad = 95$$
$$7x_1 + 6x_2 + 8x_3 \qquad + s_2 \qquad = 118$$
$$4x_1 + 5x_2 + 10x_3 \qquad\qquad + s_3 = 220$$

5.

x_1	x_2	s_1	s_2	s_3	z	
2	5	1	0	0	0	6
4	1	0	1	0	0	6
5	3	0	0	1	0	15
-5	-1	0	0	0	1	0

7.

x_1	x_2	x_3	s_1	s_2	s_3	z	
1	2	3	1	0	0	0	10
2	1	1	0	1	0	0	8
3	0	4	0	0	1	0	6
-1	-5	-10	0	0	0	1	0

9. 4 in row 2, column 2   **11.** 6 in row 3, column 1

13.

x_1	x_2	x_3	s_1	s_2	z	
-1	0	3	1	-1	0	16
1	1	$\frac{1}{2}$	0	$\frac{1}{2}$	0	20
2	0	$-\frac{1}{2}$	0	$\frac{1}{2}$	1	60

15.

x_1	x_2	x_3	s_1	s_2	s_3	z	
$-\frac{1}{2}$	$\frac{1}{2}$	0	1	$-\frac{1}{2}$	0	0	10
$\frac{3}{2}$	$\frac{1}{2}$	1	0	$\frac{1}{2}$	0	0	50
$-\frac{7}{2}$	$\frac{1}{2}$	0	0	$-\frac{3}{2}$	1	0	50
2	0	0	0	1	0	1	100

17. (a) Basic: x_3, s_2, z; nonbasic: x_1, x_2, s_1 **(b)** $x_1 = 0, x_2 = 0,$
$x_3 = 16, s_1 = 0, s_2 = 29, z = 11$ **(c)** Not a maximum
19. (a) Basic: x_1, x_2, s_2, z; nonbasic: x_3, s_1, s_3 **(b)** $x_1 = 6, x_2 = 13,$
$x_3 = 0, s_1 = 0, s_2 = 21, s_3 = 0, z = 18$ **(c)** Maximum
21. Maximum is 30 when $x_1 = 0, x_2 = 10, s_1 = 0, s_2 = 0,$ and $s_3 = 16.$
23. Maximum is 8 when $x_1 = 4, x_2 = 0, s_1 = 8, s_2 = 2,$ and $s_3 = 0.$
25. No maximum   **27.** No maximum   **29.** Maximum is 34 when
$x_1 = 17, x_2 = 0, x_3 = 0, s_1 = 0,$ and $s_2 = 14$ or when $x_1 = 0, x_2 = 17,$
$x_3 = 0, s_1 = 0,$ and $s_2 = 14.$ **31.** Maximum is 26,000 when
$x_1 = 60, x_2 = 40, x_3 = 0, s_1 = 0, s_2 = 80,$ and $s_3 = 0.$
33. Maximum is 64 when $x_1 = 28, x_2 = 16, x_3 = 0, s_1 = 0, s_2 = 28,$ and
$s_3 = 0.$ **35.** Maximum is 250 when $x_1 = 0, x_2 = 0, x_3 = 0, x_4 = 50,$
$s_1 = 0,$ and $s_2 = 50.$ **37. (a)** Maximum is 24 when $x_1 = 12, x_2 = 0,$
$x_3 = 0, s_1 = 0,$ and $s_2 = 6.$ **(b)** Maximum is 24 when $x_1 = 0, x_2 = 12,$
$x_3 = 0, s_1 = 0,$ and $s_2 = 18.$ **(c)** The unique maximum value of z is 24,
but this occurs at two different basic feasible solutions.

Section 7.5 (Page 375)

1.

x_1	x_2	s_1	s_2	s_3	
2	1	1	0	0	90
1	2	0	1	0	80
1	1	0	0	1	50
-12	-10	0	0	0	0

where x_1 is the number of Siamese cats and x_2 is the number of
Persian cats.

3.

x_1	x_2	x_3	x_4	s_1	s_2	s_3	
0	0	.375	.625	1	0	0	500
0	.75	.5	.375	0	1	0	600
1	.25	.125	0	0	0	1	300
-90	-70	-60	-50	0	0	0	0

where x_1 is the number of kilograms of P, x_2 is the number of kilograms of Q,
x_3 is the number of kilograms of R, and x_4 is the number of kilograms of S.
5. (a) Make no 1-speed or 3-speed bicycles; make 2295 10-speed bicycles;
maximum profit is $55,080 **(b)** 5280 units of aluminum are unused; all
the steel is used.

7. (a) 12 minutes to the sports segment, 9 minutes to the news segment, and
6 minutes to the weather segment for a maximum of 1.32 million viewers.
(b) $s_1 = 0$ means that all of the 27 available minutes were used; $s_2 = 0$
means that sports had exactly twice as much as the weather; $s_3 = 0$ means
that the sports and the weather had a total time exactly twice the time of the
news.   **9. (a)** 300 Japanese maple trees and 300 tri-color beech trees
are sold, for a maximum profit of $255,000. **(b)** There are 200 unused
hours of delivering to the client.   **11.** 4 radio ads, 6 TV ads, and no
newspaper ads, for a maximum exposure of 64,800 people
13. (a) 22 fund-raising parties, no mailings, and 3 dinner parties, for a
maximum of $6,200,000 **(b)** Answers vary.   **15.** 3 hours running,
4 hours biking, and 8 hours walking, for a maximum calorie expenditure
of 6313 calories   **17. (a)** (3) **(b)** (4) **(c)** (3)   **19.** The breeder
should raise 40 Siamese and 10 Persian cats, for a maximum gross income
of $580.   **21.** 163.6 kilograms of food P, none of Q, 1090.9 kilograms
of R, 145.5 kilograms of S; maximum is 87,454.5

Section 7.6 (Page 385)

1.
$$\begin{bmatrix} 3 & 1 & 0 \\ -4 & 10 & 3 \\ 5 & 7 & 6 \end{bmatrix}$$
3.
$$\begin{bmatrix} 3 & 4 \\ 0 & 17 \\ 14 & 8 \\ -5 & -6 \\ 3 & 1 \end{bmatrix}$$

5. Maximize $z = 4x_1 + 6x_2$
   subject to $3x_1 - x_2 \le 3$
            $x_1 + 2x_2 \le 5$
            $x_1 \ge 0, x_2 \ge 0.$

7. Maximize $z = 18x_1 + 15x_2 + 20x_3$
   subject to $x_1 + 4x_2 + 5x_3 \le 2$
            $7x_1 + x_2 + 3x_3 \le 8$
            $x_1 \ge 0, x_2 \ge 0, x_3 \ge 0.$

9. Maximize $z = 18x_1 + 20x_2$
   subject to $7x_1 + 4x_2 \le 5$
            $6x_1 + 5x_2 \le 1$
            $8x_1 + 10x_2 \le 3$
            $x_1 \ge 0, x_2 \ge 0.$

11. Maximize $z = 5x_1 + 4x_2 + 15x_3$
   subject to $x_1 + x_2 + 2x_3 \le 8$
            $x_1 + x_2 + x_3 \le 9$
            $x_1 \qquad + 3x_3 \le 3$
            $x_1 \ge 0, x_3 \ge 0, x_3 \ge 0.$

13. $y_1 = 0, y_2 = 4, y_3 = 0$; minimum is 4.   **15.** $y_1 = 4, y_2 = 0,$
$y_3 = \frac{7}{3}$; minimum is 39.   **17.** $y_1 = 0, y_2 = 100, y_3 = 0$;
minimum is 100.   **19.** $y_1 = 0, y_2 = 12, y_3 = 0$; minimum is 12.
21. $y_1 = 0, y_2 = 0, y_3 = 2$; minimum is 4.   **23.** $y_1 = 10, y_2 = 10,$
$y_3 = 0$; minimum is 320.   **25.** $y_1 = 0, y_2 = 0, y_3 = 4$; minimum is 4.
27. 4 servings of A and 2 servings of B, for a minimum cost of $1.76
29. 28 units of regular beer and 14 units of light beer, for a minimum cost
of $1,680,000   **31. (a)**
33. (a) Minimize $w = 200y_1 + 600y_2 + 90y_3$
     subject to $y_1 + 4y_2 \qquad \ge 1$
             $2y_1 + 3y_2 + y_3 \ge 1.5$
             $y_1 \ge 0, y_2 \ge 0, y_3 \ge 0.$
(b) $y_1 = .6, y_2 = .1, y_3 = 0, w = 180$ **(c)** $186 **(d)** $179

Section 7.7 (Page 396)

1. (a) Maximize $z = -5x_1 + 4x_2 - 2x_3$
     subject to $-2x_1 + 5x_3 - s_1 \qquad = 8$
             $4x_1 - x_2 + 3x_3 \qquad + s_2 = 12$
             $x_1 \ge 0, x_2 \ge 0, x_3 \ge 0, s_1 \ge 0, s_2 \ge 0.$

(b)

x_1	x_2	x_3	s_1	s_2	
0	−2	5	−1	0	8
4	−1	3	0	1	12
5	−4	2	0	0	0

3. (a) Maximize $z = 2x_1 - 3x_2 + 4x_3$
subject to $x_1 + x_2 + x_3 + s_1 \qquad\qquad = 100$
$x_1 + x_2 + x_3 \qquad - s_2 \qquad = 75$
$x_1 + x_2 \qquad\qquad - s_3 = 27$
$x_1 \geq 0, x_2 \geq 0, x_3 \geq 0, s_1 \geq 0, s_2 \geq 0, s_3 \geq 0.$

(b)

x_1	x_2	x_3	s_1	s_2	s_3	
1	1	1	1	0	0	100
1	1	1	0	−1	0	75
1	1	0	0	0	−1	27
−2	3	−4	0	0	0	0

5. Maximize $z = -2y_1 - 5y_2 + 3y_3$
subject to $y_1 + 2y_2 + 3y_3 \geq 115$
$2y_1 + y_2 + y_3 \leq 200$
$y_1 \qquad + y_3 \geq 50$
$y_1 \geq 0, y_2 \geq 0, y_3 \geq 0.$

y_1	y_2	y_3	s_1	s_2	s_3	
1	2	3	−1	0	0	115
2	1	1	0	1	0	200
1	0	1	0	0	−1	50
2	5	−3	0	0	0	0

7. Maximize $z = -10y_1 - 8y_2 - 15y_3$
subject to $y_1 + y_2 + y_3 \geq 12$
$5y_1 + 4y_2 + 9y_3 \geq 48$
$y_1 \geq 0, y_2 \geq 0, y_3 \geq 0.$

y_1	y_2	y_3	s_1	s_2	
1	1	1	−1	0	12
5	4	9	0	−1	48
10	8	15	0	0	0

9. Maximum is 480 when $x_1 = 40$ and $x_2 = 0$.   **11.** Maximum is 114 when $x_1 = 38, x_2 = 0$, and $x_3 = 0$.   **13.** Maximum is 90 when $x_1 = 12$ and $x_2 = 3$ or when $x_1 = 0$ and $x_2 = 9$.   **15.** Minimum is 40 when $y_1 = 0$ and $y_2 = 20$.   **17.** Maximum is $133\frac{1}{3}$ when $x_1 = 33\frac{1}{3}$ and $x_2 = 16\frac{2}{3}$.   **19.** Minimum is 512 when $y_1 = 6$ and $y_2 = 8$.
21. Maximum is 112 when $x_1 = 0, x_2 = 36$, and $x_3 = 16$.
23. Maximum is 346 when $x_1 = 27, x_2 = 0$, and $x_3 = 73$.
25. Minimum is −600 when $y_1 = 0, y_2 = 0$, and $y_3 = 200$.
27. Minimum is 96 when $y_1 = 0, y_2 = 12$, and $y_3 = 0$.

29.

y_1	y_2	y_3	s_1	s_2	s_3	s_4	
1	1	1	−1	0	0	0	10
1	1	1	0	1	0	0	15
1	−$\frac{1}{4}$	0	0	0	−1	0	0
−1	0	1	0	0	0	−1	0
.30	.09	.27	0	0	0	0	0

31.

y_1	y_2	y_3	y_4	s_1	s_2	s_3	s_4	s_5	s_6	
1	1	0	0	−1	0	0	0	0	0	32
1	1	0	0	0	1	0	0	0	0	32
0	0	1	1	0	0	−1	0	0	0	20
0	0	1	1	0	0	0	1	0	0	20
1	0	1	0	0	0	0	0	1	0	25
0	1	0	1	0	0	0	0	0	1	30
14	12	22	10	0	0	0	0	0	0	0

33. Ship 200 barrels of oil from supplier S_1 to distributor D_1; ship 2800 barrels of oil from supplier S_2 to distributor D_1; ship 2800 barrels of oil from supplier S_1 to distributor D_2; ship 2200 barrels of oil from supplier S_2 to distributor D_2. Minimum cost is $180,400.   **35.** Use 1000 lb of bluegrass, 2400 lb of rye, and 1600 lb of Bermuda, for a minimum cost of $560.   **37.** Allot $3,000,000 in commercial loans and $22,000,000 in home loans, for a maximum return of $2,940,000   **39.** Make 32 units of regular beer and 10 units of light beer, for a minimum cost of $1,632,000.
41. $1\frac{2}{3}$ ounces of ingredient I, $6\frac{2}{3}$ ounces of ingredient II, and $1\frac{2}{3}$ ounces of ingredient III produce a minimum cost of $1.55 per barrel.
43. 22 from W_1 to D_1, 10 from W_2 to D_1, none from W_1 to D_2, and 20 from W_2 to D_2, for a minimum cost of $628.

Chapter 7 Review Exercises (Page 400)

Refer to Section	7.1	7.2	7.3	7.4	7.5	7.6	7.7
For Exercises	1–10	11–16	17–18	19–32, 37	33–36, 57–59	38–46, 51–52, 61–62	47–50, 53–56, 63–64

1.

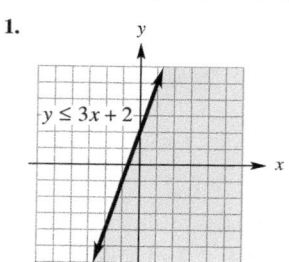

$y \leq 3x + 2$

3.

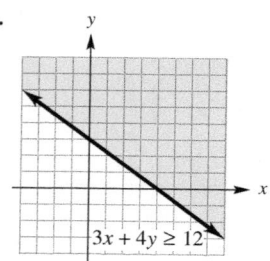

$3x + 4y \geq 12$

5.

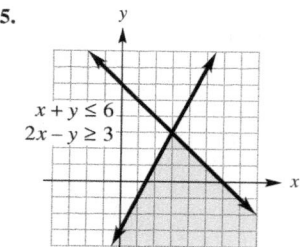

$x + y \leq 6$
$2x - y \geq 3$

7.

$2 \leq x \leq 5$
$1 \leq y \leq 6$
$x - y \leq 3$

9. Let x represent the number of summary reports, and let y represent the number of inference reports. Then

$$2x + 4y \leq 15$$
$$1.5x + 2y \leq 9$$
$$x \geq 0, y \geq 0.$$

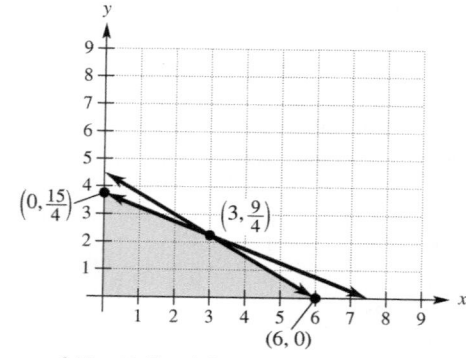

$\left(0, \frac{15}{4}\right)$ $\left(3, \frac{9}{4}\right)$ $(6, 0)$

11. Maximum of 46 at $(6, 7)$; minimum of 10 at $(2, 1)$
13. Maximum of 30 when $x = 5$ and $y = 0$ **15.** Minimum of 40 when $x = 0$ and $y = 20$ **17.** She should complete 3 summary projects and 2.25 inference projects for a maximum profit of $3187.5.
19. Donald should buy 400 shares from the BlackRock fund for a minimum risk of 5280.

21. (a)
$$x_1 + x_2 + x_3 + s_1 \qquad\qquad = 100$$
$$2x_1 + 3x_2 \qquad\qquad + s_2 \qquad = 500$$
$$x_1 \qquad + 2x_3 \qquad\qquad + s_3 = 350$$

(b)

x_1	x_2	x_3	s_1	s_2	s_3	
1	1	1	1	0	0	100
2	3	0	0	1	0	500
1	0	2	0	0	1	350
−5	−6	−3	0	0	0	0

23. (a)
$$x_1 + x_2 + x_3 + s_1 \qquad\qquad = 90$$
$$2x_1 + 5x_2 + x_3 \qquad + s_2 \qquad = 120$$
$$x_1 + 3x_2 \qquad\qquad + s_3 = 80$$

(b)

x_1	x_2	x_3	s_1	s_2	s_3	
1	1	1	1	0	0	90
2	5	1	0	1	0	120
1	3	0	0	0	1	80
−1	−8	−2	0	0	0	0

25. Maximum is 80 when $x_1 = 16, x_2 = 0, x_3 = 0, s_1 = 12$, and $s_2 = 0$.
27. Maximum is 35 when $x_1 = 5, x_2 = 0, x_3 = 5, s_1 = 35, s_2 = 0$, and $s_3 = 0$.   **29.** Maximum of 600 when $x_1 = 0, x_2 = 100$, and $x_3 = 0$
31. Maximum of 225 when $x_1 = 0, x_2 = \frac{15}{2}$, and $x_3 = \frac{165}{2}$
33. (a) Let $x_1 = $ number of item A, $x_2 = $ number of item B, and $x_3 = $ number of item C.   **(b)** $z = 4x_1 + 3x_2 + 3x_3$
(c) $2x_1 + 3x_2 + 6x_3 \le 1200$
$$x_1 + 2x_2 + 2x_3 \le 800$$
$$2x_1 + 2x_2 + 4x_3 \le 500$$
$$x_1 \ge 0, x_2 \ge 0, x_3 \ge 0$$
35. (a) Let $x_1 = $ number of gallons of Fruity wine and $x_2 = $ number of gallons of Crystal wine.   **(b)** $z = 12x_1 + 15x_2$
(c) $2x_1 + x_2 \le 110$
$$2x_1 + 3x_2 \le 125$$
$$2x_1 + x_2 \le 90$$
$$x_1 \ge 0, x_2 \ge 0$$
37. When there are more than 2 variables.   **39.** Any standard minimization problem   **41.** Minimum of 172 at (5, 7, 3, 0, 0, 0)
43. Minimum of 640 at (7, 2, 0, 0)   **45.** Minimum of 170 when $y_1 = 0$ and $y_2 = 17$

47.

5	10	1	0	120
10	15	0	−1	200
−20	−30	0	0	0

49.

1	1	2	−1	0	0	0	48
1	1	0	0	1	0	0	12
0	0	1	0	0	−1	0	10
3	0	1	0	0	0	−1	30
12	20	−8	0	0	0	0	0

51. Minimum of 427 at (8, 17, 25, 0, 0, 0)   **53.** Maximum is 480 when $x_1 = 24$ and $x_2 = 0$.   **55.** Minimum is 40 when $y_1 = 10$ and $y_2 = 0$.
57. Get 250 of A and none of B or C for maximum profit of $1000.
59. Make 17.5 gal of Crystal and 36.25 gal of Fruity, for a maximum profit of $697.50.   **61.** Produce 660 cases of corn, no beans, and 340 cases of carrots, for a minimum cost of $15,100.   **63.** Use 1,060,000 kilograms for whole tomatoes and 80,000 kilograms for sauce, for a minimum cost of $4,500,000.

Case Study 7 Exercises (Page 404)

1. The answer in 100-gram units is 0.243037 unit of feta cheese, 2.35749 units of lettuce, 0.3125 unit of salad dressing, and 1.08698 units of tomato. Converting into kitchen units gives approximately $\frac{1}{6}$ cup feta cheese, $4\frac{1}{4}$ cups lettuce, $\frac{1}{8}$ cup salad dressing, and $\frac{7}{8}$ of a tomato.

Chapter 8

Section 8.1 (Page 412)
1. False   **3.** True   **5.** True   **7.** True   **9.** False
11. Answers vary.   **13.** $\subseteq$ **15.** $\not\subseteq$ **17.** $\subseteq$ **19.** $\subseteq$
21. 8   **23.** 128   **25.** $\{x | x$ is an integer ≤ 0 or $\ge 8\}$
27. Answers vary.   **29.** $\cap$ **31.** $\cap$ **33.** $\cup$ **35.** $\cup$
37. $\{b, 1, 3\}$ **39.** $\{d, e, f, 4, 5, 6\}$ **41.** $\{e, 4, 6\}$ **43.** $\{a, b, c, d, 1, 2, 3, 5\}$ **45.** All students not taking this course.   **47.** All students taking both accounting and philosophy.   **49.** C and D, A and E, C and E, D and E **51.** $\{$Ford, First Solar$\}$ **53.** $\{$Ford$\}$ **55.** $M \cap E$ is the set of all male employed applicants.   **57.** $M' \cup S'$ is the set of all female or married applicants.   **59.** $\{$Television, Magazines$\}$ **61.** $\varnothing$
63. $F = \{$Comcast, Direct TV, Dish Network, Time Warner$\}$
65. $H = \{$Dish Network, Time Warner, Verizon, Cox$\}$
67. $F \cup G = \{$Comcast, Direct TV, Dish Network, Time Warner$\}$
69. $I' = \{$Verizon, Cox$\}$ **71.** $\{$Soybeans, Rice, Cotton$\}$
73. $\{$Wheat, Corn, Soybeans, Rice, Cotton$\}$

Section 8.2 (Page 419)
1.

3.

5.

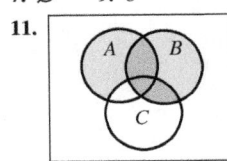

7. $\varnothing$ **9.** 8
11.

13.

15.

17. 18%   **19. (a)** 105   **(b)** 39   **(c)** 15   **(d)** 3   **21. (a)** 227
(b) 182   **(c)** 27   **23. (a)** 54   **(b)** 17   **(c)** 10   **(d)** 7   **(e)** 15
(f) 3   **(g)** 12   **(h)** 1   **25. (a)** 308,000   **(b)** 227,000   **(c)** 92,000
(d) 113,000   **27. (a)** 23,682 thousand   **(b)** 75,161 thousand
(c) 14,399 thousand   **(d)** 11,404 thousand   **29.** Answers vary.
31. 9   **33.** 27
35.

37.

39.

41.

43.

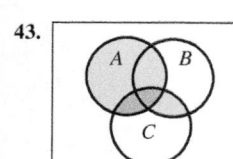

45. The complement of *A* intersect *B* equals the union of the complement of *A* and the complement of *B*.   **47.** *A* union (*B* intersect *C*) equals (*A* union *B*) intersect (*A* union *C*).

Section 8.3 (Page 430)

1. Answers vary.   **3.** {January, February, March, . . . , December}
5. {0, 1, 2, . . . , 80}   **7.** {go ahead, cancel}   **9.** {Q_1, Q_2, Q_3, Q_4}
11. Answers vary.   **13.** No   **15.** Yes   **17.** No
19. *S* = {C&K, C&L, C&J, C&T, C&N, K&L, K&J, K&T, K&N, L&J, L&T, L&N, J&T, J&N, T&N}   **(a)** {C&T, K&T, L&T, J&T, T&N}
(b) {C&J, C&N, J&N}   **21.** *S* = {forest sage & rag painting, forest sage & colorwash, evergreen & rag painting, evergreen & colorwash, opaque & rag painting, opaque & colorwash}
(a) $\frac{1}{2}$ **(b)** $\frac{2}{3}$ **23.** *S* = {10′ & beige, 10′ & forest green, 10′ & rust, 12′ & beige, 12′ & forest green, 12′ & rust}   **(a)** $\frac{1}{6}$ **(b)** $\frac{1}{2}$ **(c)** $\frac{1}{3}$
25. $\frac{1}{2}$ **27.** $\frac{1}{3}$ **29.** *S* = {male beagle, male boxer, male collie, male Labrador, female beagle, female boxer, female collie, female Labrador}
31. $\frac{1}{2}$ **33.** $\frac{1}{8}$ **35.** $\frac{3}{4}$ **37.** $\frac{646}{4690} \approx .1377$
39. (a) $\frac{191}{1974} \approx .0968$ **(b)** $\frac{168}{1974} \approx .0851$ **(c)** $\frac{603}{1974} \approx .3055$
41. (a) The person is not overweight.   **(b)** The person has a family history of heart disease and is overweight.   **(c)** The person smokes or is not overweight.
43. (a) $\frac{4}{2826} \approx .0014$ **(b)** $\frac{1278}{2826} \approx .4522$ **(c)** $\frac{1479}{2826} \approx .5234$
45. Possible   **47.** Not possible   **49.** Not possible

Section 8.4 (Page 438)

1. $\frac{20}{38} = \frac{10}{19}$ **3.** $\frac{28}{38} = \frac{14}{19}$ **5.** $\frac{5}{38}$ **7.** $\frac{12}{38} = \frac{6}{19}$ **9. (a)** $\frac{5}{36}$
(b) $\frac{1}{9}$ **(c)** $\frac{1}{12}$ **(d)** 0   **11. (a)** $\frac{5}{18}$ **(b)** $\frac{5}{12}$ **(c)** $\frac{1}{3}$ **13.** $\frac{1}{3}$
15. (a) $\frac{1}{2}$ **(b)** $\frac{2}{5}$ **(c)** $\frac{3}{10}$ **17. (a)** .62 **(b)** .32 **(c)** .11 **(d)** .81
19. (a) .699 **(b)** .374 **(c)** .301 **(d)** .728   **21. (a)** .266 **(b)** .432
(c) .809   **23.** 1:5   **25.** 2:1   **27. (a)** 1:4 **(b)** 8:7 **(c)** 4:11
29. 2:7   **31.** 21:79   **33.** 6:94   **35.** $\frac{43}{50}$ **37.** $\frac{6}{25}$
39. (a) Answers vary, but should be close to .2778   **(b)** Answers vary, but should be close to .4167   **41. (a)** Answers vary, but should be close to .0463 **(b)** Answers vary, but should be close to .2963   **43.** About .8369   **45.** About .2269   **47.** About .7311   **49.** .12   **51.** .08
53. .60   **55.** About .7552   **57.** About .3462   **59. (a)** .961
(b) .491 **(c)** .509 **(d)** .505 **(e)** .004 **(f)** .544

Section 8.5 (Page 450)

1. $\frac{1}{3}$ **3.** 1   **5.** $\frac{1}{6}$ **7.** $\frac{4}{17}$ **9.** .012   **11.** Answers vary.
13. Answers vary.   **15.** No   **17.** Yes   **19.** No, yes
21. About .537   **23.** About .256   **25.** About .6882
27. About .3424   **29.** About .0517   **31.** About .1858   **33.** .527
35. .042   **37.** .857   **39.** Dependent   **41.** *P*(*C*) = .0800, *P*(*D*) = .0050, *P*(*C* ∩ *D*) = .0004, *P*(*C*|*D*) = .08; yes; independent
43. .05   **45.** About .8107   **47.** About .4111   **49.** About .0621
51. About .0352   **53.** About .5409   **55.** .4955   **57.** .999985
59. (a) 3 backups   **(b)** Answers vary.   **61.** Dependent or "No"

Section 8.6 (Page 457)

1. $\frac{1}{3}$ **3.** .0488   **5.** .5122   **7.** .4706   **9.** About .6
11. About .264   **13.** About .505   **15.** About .4874
17. About .488   **19.** (c)   **21.** .519   **23.** About .418
25. About .350   **27.** About .560   **29.** About .518
31. About .376   **33.** About .865

Chapter 8 Review Exercises (Page 459)

Refer to Section	8.1	8.2	8.3	8.4	8.5	8.6
For Exercises	1–23	24–30	31–44	45–55, 63–78	56–62, 63–78	79–83

1. False   **3.** False   **5.** True   **7.** True   **9.** {New Year's Day, Martin Luther King Jr.'s Birthday, Presidents' Day, Memorial Day, Independence Day, Labor Day, Columbus Day, Veterans' Day, Thanksgiving, Christmas}   **11.** {1, 2, 3, 4}   **13.** {$B_1, B_2, B_3, B_6, B_{12}$}
15. {*A, C, E*}   **17.** {$A, B_3, B_6, B_{12}, C, D, E$}   **19.** Female students older than 22   **21.** Females or students with a GPA > 3.5
23. Nonfinance majors who are 22 or younger

25.

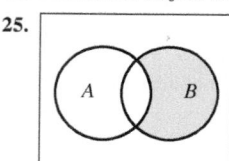

27. 5   **29.** 44   **31.** {1, 2, 3, 4, 5, 6}   **33.** {(Rock, Rock), (Rock, Pop), (Rock, Alternative), (Pop, Rock), (Pop, Pop), (Pop, Alternative), (Alternative, Rock), (Alternative, Pop), (Alternative, Alternative)}
35. {(Dell, Epson), (Dell, HP), (Gateway, Epson), (Gateway, HP), (HP, Epson), (HP, HP)}   **37.** *E*′ ∩ *F*′ or (*E* ∪ *F*)′   **39.** A probability cannot be > 1.   **41.** Answers vary.   **43.** .2271   **45.** .0392
47. About .7504   **49.** About .0733   **51.** About .0846
53. About .8729   **55.** About .0698   **57.** About .8692

59.

	N_2	T_2
N_1	N_1N_2	N_1T_2
T_1	T_1N_2	T_1T_2

61. $\frac{1}{2}$ **63.** $\frac{5}{36} \approx .139$ **65.** $\frac{5}{18} \approx .278$ **67.** $\frac{1}{3}$ **69.** .79
71. .66   **73.** .7   **75.** Answers vary.
77. (a) $\frac{1}{40}$ **(b)** 471:29   **79.** $\frac{19}{22}$ **81.** $\frac{1}{3}$ **83.** .0646
85. .271   **87.** .625   **89.** .690   **91.** No. Answers vary.
93. About .2779   **95.** About .0906   **97.** About .6194
99. About .4957

Case Study 8 Exercises (Page 463)

1. .001   **3.** .331

Chapter 9

Section 9.1 (Page 471)

1.

Number of boys	0	1	2	3	4
P(*x*)	.063	.25	.375	.25	.063

3.

Number of Queens	0	1	2	3
P(*x*)	.7826	.2042	.0130	.0002

5.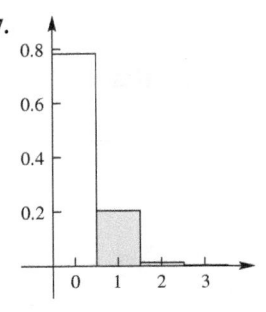

7.

9. 4   **11.** 5.4   **13.** 2.7   **15.** 2.5   **17.** $-\dfrac{1}{19} \approx -.05$

19. −$.50   **21.** −$.97   **23.** −$1.67   **25.** 1.1319

27. Not valid, cannot have a probability <0.

29. Valid.   **31.** .15   **33.** .25

35. Many correct answers, including .15, .15.

37. $4550   **39.** .4111

41.

Account Number	Expected Value	Existing Volume + Expected Value of Potential	Class
3	2000	22,000	C
4	1000	51,000	B
5	25,000	30,000	C
6	60,000	60,000	A
7	16,000	46,000	B

43. (a) Drug A $217, Drug B $229   (b) Drug A

45. (a) £550,000   (b) £618,000

Section 9.2 (Page 484)

1. 12   **3.** 56   **5.** 8   **7.** 24   **9.** 84   **11.** 1716

13. 6,375,600   **15.** 240,240   **17.** 8568   **19.** 40,116,600

21. $\dfrac{24}{0}$ is undefined.   **23.** (a) 8   (b) 64   **25.** 576

27. 1 billion in theory; however, some numbers will never be used (such as those beginning with 000); yes.   **29.** 1 billion   **31.** 120

33. (a) 160; 8,000,000   (b) Some, such as 800, 900, etc., are reserved.

35. 1600   **37.** Answers vary.   **39.** 95,040   **41.** 12,144

43. 863,040   **45.** 272   **47.** (a) 210   (b) 210   **49.** 330

51. Answers vary.   **53.** (a) 9   (b) 6   (c) 3, yes   **55.** (a) 8568

(b) 56   (c) 3360   (d) 8512   **57.** (a) 210   (b) 7980

59. (a) 1,120,529,256   (b) 806,781,064,320   **61.** 81

63. Not possible, 4 initials   **65.** (a) 10   (b) 0   (c) 1   (d) 10

(e) 30   (f) 15   (g) 0   **67.** 3,247,943,160   **69.** 5.524×10^{26}

71. (a) 2520   (b) 840   (c) 5040   **73.** (a) 479,001,600   (b) 6

(c) 27,720

Section 9.3 (Page 491)

1. .422   **3.** $\dfrac{5}{8}$ **5.** $\dfrac{5}{28}$ **7.** .00005   **9.** .0163   **11.** .5630

13. 1326   **15.** .851   **17.** .765   **19.** .941   **21.** Answers vary.

23. exactly .1396   **25.** (a) 8.9×10^{-10} (b) 1.2×10^{-12}

27. 3.26×10^{-17} **29.** (a) .0322   (b) .2418   (c) .7582

31. (a) .0015   (b) .0033   (c) .3576   **33.** $1 - \dfrac{_{365}P_{100}}{(365)^{100}} \approx 1$

35. .0031   **37.** .3083   **39.** We obtained the following answers— yours should be similar: (a) .0399   (b) .5191   (c) .0226

Section 9.4 (Page 497)

1. About .2001   **3.** About .000006   **5.** About .999994

7. About .0011   **9.** About .000003   **11.** About .999997

13. $\dfrac{1}{32}$ **15.** $\dfrac{13}{16}$ **17.** Answers vary.   **19.** About .0197

21. About .0057   **23.** About .0039   **25.** About .1817   **27.** 270

29. .247   **31.** .193   **33.** .350   **35.** 3.85   **37.** About .9093

39. 33   **41.** About .2811   **43.** 23

Section 9.5 (Page 506)

1. Yes   **3.** Yes   **5.** No   **7.** No   **9.** No   **11.** No

13. Not a transition diagram   **15.** $\begin{bmatrix} .6 & .20 & .20 \\ .9 & .02 & .08 \\ .4 & 0 & .6 \end{bmatrix}$ **17.** Yes

19. Yes   **21.** No   **23.** $\left[\dfrac{19}{64}, \dfrac{45}{64}\right]$ **25.** $\left[\dfrac{3}{11}, \dfrac{8}{11}\right]$

27. [.4633, .1683, .3684]   **29.** [.4872, .2583, .2545]

31. $A^2 = \begin{bmatrix} .23 & .21 & .24 & .17 & .15 \\ .26 & .18 & .26 & .16 & .14 \\ .23 & .18 & .24 & .19 & .16 \\ .19 & .19 & .27 & .18 & .17 \\ .17 & .2 & .26 & .19 & .18 \end{bmatrix}$

$A^3 = \begin{bmatrix} .226 & .192 & .249 & .177 & .156 \\ .222 & .196 & .252 & .174 & .156 \\ .219 & .189 & .256 & .177 & .159 \\ .213 & .192 & .252 & .181 & .162 \\ .213 & .189 & .252 & .183 & .163 \end{bmatrix}$

$A^4 = \begin{bmatrix} .2205 & .1916 & .2523 & .1774 & .1582 \\ .2206 & .1922 & .2512 & .1778 & .1582 \\ .2182 & .1920 & .2525 & .1781 & .1592 \\ .2183 & .1909 & .2526 & .1787 & .1595 \\ .2176 & .1906 & .2533 & .1787 & .1598 \end{bmatrix}$

$A^5 = \begin{bmatrix} .21932 & .19167 & .25227 & .17795 & .15879 \\ .21956 & .19152 & .25226 & .17794 & .15872 \\ .21905 & .19152 & .25227 & .17818 & .15898 \\ .21880 & .19144 & .25251 & .17817 & .15908 \\ .21857 & .19148 & .25253 & .17824 & .15918 \end{bmatrix}$; .17794

33. (a) $\begin{bmatrix} .9 & .10 \\ .3 & .70 \end{bmatrix}$ (b) [.51, .49]   (c) [.75, .25]   **35.** [.802, .198]

37. $\left[\dfrac{1}{4}, \dfrac{1}{2}, \dfrac{1}{4}\right]$ **39.** (a) [.576, .421, .004]   (b) [.473, .526, .002]

41. (a) [42,500   5000   2500]   (b) [37,125   8750   4125]

(c) [33,281   11,513   5206]   (d) [.475   .373   .152]

43. (a) About .203   (b) .286

45. (a)
$\begin{matrix} & 0 & 1 & 2 \\ 0 & \begin{bmatrix} .4 \\ .4 \\ 0 \end{bmatrix} & \begin{matrix} .3 \\ .3 \\ .5 \end{matrix} & \begin{matrix} .3 \\ .3 \\ .5 \end{matrix} \end{matrix}$
(b)
$\begin{matrix} & 0 & 1 & 2 \\ 0 & \begin{bmatrix} .28 \\ .28 \\ .2 \end{bmatrix} & \begin{matrix} .36 \\ .36 \\ .4 \end{matrix} & \begin{matrix} .36 \\ .36 \\ .4 \end{matrix} \end{matrix}$

(c) .36   **47.** [0   0   .102273   .897727]

Section 9.6 (Page 511)

1. (a) Coast   (b) Highway   (c) Highway; $38,000   (d) Coast

3. (a) Do not upgrade.   (b) Upgrade.   (c) Do not upgrade; $10,060.

5. (a)
	Fails	Doesn't Fail
Overhaul	−$8600	−$2600
Don't Overhaul	−$6000	$0

(b) Don't overhaul the machine.

7. (a)
	No Rain	Rain
Rent tent	$2500	$1500
Do not rent tent	$3000	$0

(b) Rent tent because expected value is $2100.   **9.** Environment, 15.3

Chapter 9 Review Exercises (Page 514)

Refer to Section	9.1	9.2	9.3	9.4	9.5	9.6
For Exercises	1–12, 46, 47	13–21, 31–32	22–30	33–37, 48	38–43	44–45

1. (a) **(b)** 1.1

3. (a) 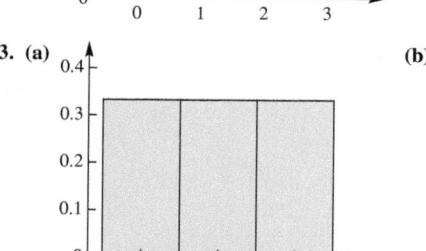 **(b)** 0

5. 1.15764   **7. (a)**

x	0	1	2
$P(x)$	$\frac{7}{15}$	$\frac{7}{15}$	$\frac{1}{15}$

(b) .6

9. \$1.29   **11.** .15   **13.** 40,320   **15.** 220   **17.** 427,518,000
19. (a) 14,905,800   **(b)** 14,905,800   **21.** Answers vary.
23. .059   **25.** .995   **27.** .018   **29.** .218

31. (a) $1, n, \dfrac{n(n-1)}{2}, 1$ **(b)** $_nC_0 + {_nC_1} + {_nC_2} + \cdots + {_nC_n}$

33.

x	0	1	2	3	4	5	6	7
$P(x)$	0.0001	0.0013	0.0115	0.0577	0.1730	0.3115	0.3115	0.1335

$E(x) = 5.25$

35. (a) About .3907   **(b)** About .2118   **(c)** About .9997
37. (a)

x	0	1	2	3	4	5
$P(x)$	.0086	.0682	.2168	.3449	.2743	.0873

(b) 3.07   **39.** No   **41.** Yes   **43. (a)** [.1515, .5635, .2850]
(b) [.1526, .5183, .3290]   **(c)** [.1509, .4697, .3795]
45. (a) Active learning   **(b)** Active learning   **(c)** Lecture, 17.5
(d) Active learning, 48   **47. (c)**

Case Study 9 Exercises (Page 518)
1. +.2031

3.

x	$P(x)$
0	.30832
1	.43273
2	.21264
3	.04325
4	.00306

5. \$.19438

Chapter 10

Section 10.1 (Page 524)

1.

Interval	Frequency
0–.9	11
1.0–1.9	15
2.0–2.9	3
3.0–3.9	4
4.0–4.9	2
5.0–5.9	4
6.0–6.9	0
7.0–7.9	0
8.0–8.9	1

3.

Interval	Frequency
−5.00–(−.01)	2
0–4.99	30
5.00–9.99	6
10.00–14.99	1
15.00–19.99	0
20.00–24.99	1

5. Answers vary, but one way to create the intervals appears here.

Interval	Frequency
0–29	12
30–59	3
60–89	10
90–119	2
120–149	0
150–179	1
180–209	2

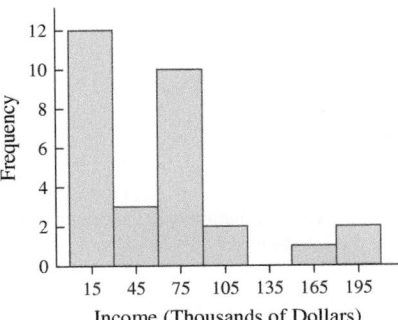

7. Answers vary, but one way to create the intervals appears here.

Interval	Frequency
0–49	5
50–99	8
100–149	10
150–199	4
200–249	2
250–299	0
300–349	1

9. Answers vary, but one way to create the intervals appears here.

Interval	Frequency
50–54	3
55–59	15
60–64	6
65–69	5
70–74	1

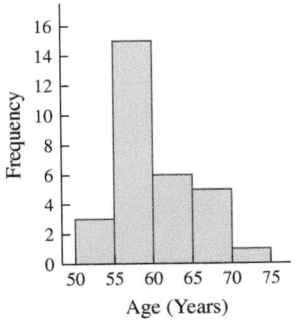

11.

Stem	Leaves
0	13444556899
1	122333344777889
2	046
3	0157
4	56
5	4666
6	
7	
8	7

Units: 8|7 = 8.7 million

13.

Stem	Leaves
0	0011111
0	22223
0	444
0	666777
0	8888
1	01
1	
1	5
1	
1	
1	8
2	0

Units: 2|0 = $200

15.

Stem	Leaves
0	33444
0	55567789
1	001112334
1	55667
2	22
2	
3	2

Units: 3|2 = $320

17.

Stem	Leaves
5	0
5	23
5	55
5	6677
5	888899999
6	0111
6	3
6	455
6	667
6	
7	
7	2

Units: 7|2 = 72 years

19.

Stem	Leaves
8	111
8	222333
8	4444555
8	66667777
8	8888899999
9	000000001111
9	2222

Units: 9|2 = 92%

21. Uniform **23.** Left skewed **25. (a)** Right skewed **(b)** 8
(c) 10 **27. (a)** Right skewed **(b)** 13 **(c)** 5
29. (a) Right skewed **(b)** 6 **(c)** 6

Section 10.2 (Page 533)
1. $27,955 **3.** 4.8 **5.** 10.3 **7.** 21.2 **9.** 14.8
11. $33,679 **13.** 98.5 **15.** 2 **17.** 65, 71 **19.** No mode
21. Answers vary. **23.** $\bar{x} = 19.45$; 10.0–19.9
25. (a) $1091.5 million **(b)** $852 million **27. (a)** $508.25 million
(b) $454.5 million **29. (a)** $8880.25; $9593.25 **(b)** 2007
31. $\bar{x} = 49.6$; median = 48.5 **33.** Right skewed; median = $624.5
35. (a) Right skewed **(b)** Median = 22.5%

Section 10.3 (Page 542)
1. Answers vary. **3.** 31.5; 12.26 **5.** 5.0; 1.65 **7.** 7.9; 2.87
9. 2.1; .86 **11.** 45.2 **13.** $\bar{x} = 75.08825$; $s = 72.425$
15. $\frac{3}{4}$ **17.** $\frac{5}{9}$ **19.** 93.75% **21.** 11.1%
23. $\bar{x} \approx 255.2857$; $s \approx 17.3$ **25.** $\bar{x} \approx 1785.4286$; $s \approx 311.4$
27. Cross-training **29.** $\bar{x} = 60.5$; $s = 52.1$
31. (a) $s^2 = 14.8$; $s = 3.8$ **(b)** 10
33. (a) $\frac{1}{3}, 2, -\frac{1}{3}, 0, \frac{5}{3}, \frac{7}{3}, 1, \frac{4}{3}, \frac{7}{3}, \frac{2}{3}$
(b) 2.1, 2.6, 1.5, 2.6, 2.5, .6, 1, 2.1, .6, 1.2 **(c)** 1.13 **(d)** 1.68
(e) $-2.15, 4.41$; the process is out of control.
35. $\bar{x} = 80.17$, $s = 12.2$ **37.** Answers vary.

Section 10.4 (Page 555)
1. The mean **3.** Answers vary. **5.** 45.99% **7.** 16.64%
9. 7.7% **11.** 47.35% **13.** 91.20% **15.** 1.64 or 1.65
17. -1.04 **19.** .5; .5 **21.** .889; .997 **23.** .3821 **25.** .5762
27. .3156 **29.** .2004 **31.** .4452 **33.** .9370 **35.** .0179
37. .0726 **39.** 45.2 mph **41.** 24.17% **43.** Answers vary.
45. 665 units **47.** 190 units **49.** 15.87% **51.** Minimum = 27.0,
$Q_1 = 32.6, Q_2 = 41.35, Q_3 = 57.8$, maximum = 66.5

53.

Pepsi Revenue (Billions of Dollars)

55.

Revenue (Billions of Dollars)

Pepsi has greater variability among its annual revenue amounts.
57. Minimum = 5.3, $Q_1 = 13.2, Q_2 = 16.3, Q_3 = 25.0$,
maximum = 32.8

59.

Education Expenditures (Billions of Dollars)

61. Answers vary, but estimates are: Hospital: $Q_1 \approx 2.2$,
$Q_2 \approx 3.1, Q_3 \approx 4.5$; Highway: $Q_1 \approx 2.4, Q_2 \approx 3.3, Q_3 \approx 3.9$.
63. Police protection; The distance from minimum to maximum is greater
and the distance from Q_1 to Q_3 also is greater.

Section 10.5 (Page 561)
1. The number of trials and the probability of success on each trial
3. (a) .1964 **(b)** .1974 **5. (a)** .0021 **(b)** .0030
7. .0240 **9.** .9463 **11.** .0956 **13.** .7291 **15.** .1841
17. (a) .0238 **(b)** .6808 **19.** .1112 **21.** .9842
23. (a) .0005 **(b)** .001 **(c)** .0000 **25.** 370
27. .0268 **29.** .0018 **31. (a)** .0764 **(b)** .121
(c) Yes; the probability of such a result is .0049.

Chapter 10 Review Exercises (Page 564)

Refer to Section	10.1	10.2	10.3	10.4	10.6
For Exercises	1–4, 9, 28	5–8, 10–18	19–26, 39–40	27, 29, 30–33, 35–38, 41–50	34, 51–54

1. Answers vary, but one way to create the intervals appears here.

Interval	Frequency
0–9.9	23
10.0–19.9	11
20.0–29.9	2
30.0–39.9	2
40.0–49.9	0
50.0–59.9	1
60.0–69.9	1

Revenue (Billions of Dollars)

3.

Stem	Leaves
0	122223344444444557889
1	0000112356789
2	49
3	3
4	0
5	8
6	6

Units: 6|6 = 66 billion dollars

5. $16.48 billion; $7.4 billion **7.** $1137 million; $749.5 million
9. Answers vary. **11.** 42.5 hours; 40, 50 hours **13.** 0–499
15. Right skewed **17.** Normal **19.** Answers vary.

21. Range $= 54$; $s = 15.8$ **23.** $s = 1465.4$ **25.** Mean $= 1.776$, $s = .41$ **27.** Answers vary.   **29.** .4115   **31.** .9620   **33.** 1.41   **35.** .0096   **37.** .1357   **39. (a)** Mean $= 93.8$, $s = 69.7$ (69.8 depending on rounding)   **(b)** Nissan   **41.** Minimum $= 22$, $Q_1 = 26$, $Q_2 = 66.5$, $Q_3 = 141$, maximum $= 214$

43.

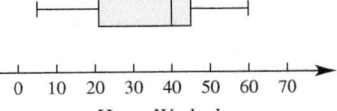

Number of Vehicles
(Thousands)

45. Minimum $= 5$, $Q_1 = 21$, $Q_2 = 40$, $Q_3 = 45$, maximum $= 60$

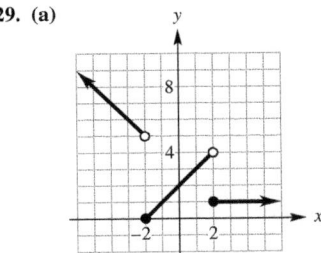

Hours Worked

47. .1357   **49.** .5675   **51.** .0681   **53.** .8810

Case Study 10 Exercises (Page 567)
1. 1.2697; 15.24   **3.** 1.2433; 14.92   **5.** 4.6841; 16.23
7. 4.5071; 15.61   **9.** (−.99, 31.47)

Chapter 11

Section 11.1 (Page 578)
1. (a) 8 **(b)** 0   **3. (a)** 4 **(b)** 2   **5. (a)** Does not exist **(b)** 2
7. (a) Does not exist **(b)** 2   **9.** Answers vary.   **11.** 1
13. 0   **15.** 3   **17.** 5   **19.** Does not exist   **21.** 15
23. $\dfrac{5}{2}$ **25.** 5   **27.** $\dfrac{7}{4}$

29. (a)

y

8

4

−2   2   x

(b) Does not exist   **(c)** 3   **(d)** Does not exist   **31.** 0
33. $\dfrac{19}{31}$ **35.** 10   **37.** 7   **39.** $\dfrac{1}{2}$ **41.** Does not exist
43. $\sqrt{6}$ **45.** Does not exist   **47.** $-\dfrac{1}{9}$ **49.** $\dfrac{1}{10}$
51. $\dfrac{1}{2\sqrt{5}}$ or $\dfrac{\sqrt{5}}{10}$ **53. (a)** 13.125 **(b)** 68.25 **(c)** 68.25
55. (a) $4.00 **(b)** $1.15 **(c)** $0.58   **57. (a)** 87,000 employees
(b) 88,000 employees **(c)** Does not exist   **59. (a)** About 1,000,000 people **(b)** About −5,000,000 people **(c)** Between 2001 and 2002

Section 11.2 (Page 589)
1. 3   **3.** −2   **5.** 6   **7.** 0   **9. (a)** 0 **(b)** 1 **(c)** −1
(d) −1   **11. (a)** 1 **(b)** 0 **(c)** ∞ **(d)** −∞   **13.** 0   **15.** 1
17. −9   **19.** $\dfrac{1}{4}$

21.

y

10
8
6
4
2

−10−8−6−4−2   2 4 6 8 10   x

−2
−4
−6
−8
−10

(a) 5 **(b)** 0 **(c)** Does not exist   **23. (a)** ∞ **(b)** ∞ **(c)** −∞
25. −∞   **27.** ∞   **29.** ∞ and 0   **31.** −10 and −10
33. ∞ and −∞   **35.** −1   **37.** 0   **39.** 1   **41.** 0
43. $\dfrac{10}{3}$ **45.** 0   **47.** −2   **49.** $\dfrac{4}{5}$ **51.** 0   **53.** 15   **55.** 1
57. −1   **59. (a)** $20 **(b)** $20 **(c)** $20 **(d)** $50 **(e)** $60
(f) Does not exist   **(g)** $8 per thousand gallons   **(h)** $10
61. (a) $3,000 **(b)** $1,000 **(c)** Does not exist **(d)** 3 **(e)** 12
63. (a) $5 **(b)** $5 **(c)** $7 **(d)** $7 **(e)** $15 **(f)** $5 **(g)** $5
(h) $7 **(i)** Does not exist **(j)** $15   **65. (a)** $65 **(b)** $11
(c) $5   **67. (a)** About 64.68 **(b)** 71.8; answers vary (how significant are 7 teeth?)

Section 11.3 (Page 600)
1. 8   **3.** 2   **5.** $\dfrac{1}{4}$ **7.** $-\dfrac{1}{3}$
9. (a) 1; from catalog distributions of 10,000 to 20,000, sales will have an average increase of $1000 for each additional 1000 catalogs distributed.
(b) $\dfrac{3}{5}$; from catalog distributions of 20,000 to 30,000, sales will have an average increase of $600 for each additional 1000 catalogs distributed.
(c) $\dfrac{2}{5}$; from catalog distributions of 30,000 to 40,000, sales will have an average increase of $400 for each additional 1000 catalogs distributed.
(d) As more catalogs are distributed, sales increase at a smaller and smaller rate.   **(e)** Answers vary   **11. (a)** 9 to 10 **(b)** 9 to 10
(c) 7 to 9   **13. (a)** $4 billion/year **(b)** − $2.5 billion/year
(c) $1.4 billion/year   **15. (a)** About 815,000 employees/billion dollars
(b) About 368,000 employees/billion dollars **(c)** About 485,000 employees/billion dollars   **17.** Answers vary   **19.** 22 ft/sec   **21.** 66 ft/sec
23. 6 ft/sec   **25. (a)** 5 ft/sec **(b)** 2 ft/sec **(c)** 3 ft/sec
(d) 5 ft/sec **(e) (i)** 3 ft/sec; **(ii)** 2.5 ft/sec
(f) (i) 5 ft/sec; **(ii)** 4 ft/sec   **27. (a)** $a^2 + 2ah + h^2 - a - h - 1$
(b) $2a + h - 1$ **(c)** 9   **29. (a)** $a^3 + 3a^2h + 3ah^2 + h^3$
(b) $3a^2 + 3ah + h^2$ **(c)** 75   **31. (a)** $5998 per unit
(b) $6000 per unit **(c)** $5998 **(d)** Answers vary.
33. (a) 6% per day **(b)** 7% per day   **35. (a)** 6000 degrees/year
(b) 2000 degrees/year

37. (a)   100

0   6

−20

(b) About 81.51 kilojoules per hour per hour   **(c)** About 18.81 kilojoules per hour per hour   **(d)** At approximately $t = 1.3$ hours

Section 11.4 (Page 615)
1. $f'(x) = 8$; 8; 8; 8   **3.** $f'(x) = -8x + 11$; −5; 11; 35
5. $f'(x) = 3x^2$; 12; 0; 27   **7.** $f'(x) = \dfrac{2}{x^2}$; $\dfrac{1}{2}$; undefined; $\dfrac{2}{9}$

9. $f'(x) = \dfrac{1}{\sqrt{x}}, \dfrac{1}{\sqrt{2}}$; undefined; undefined   **11.** $y = \dfrac{1}{6}x + \dfrac{3}{2}$

13. $y = -\dfrac{1}{4}x - 1$ **15. (a)** 4   **(b)** $y = 4x - 1$ **17. (a)** $-\dfrac{7}{9}$

(b) $y = -\dfrac{7}{9}x + \dfrac{14}{3}$ **19. (a)** $\dfrac{5}{6}$ **(b)** $y = \dfrac{5}{6}x + \dfrac{15}{2}$

21. (a) x_5 **(b)** x_4 **(c)** x_3 **(d)** x_2
23. Here is one of many possible graphs:

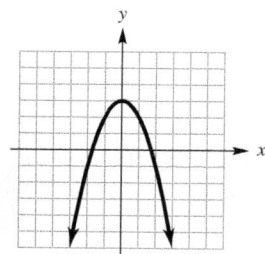

25. 45 min, 3 hrs   **27. (a)** is distance;   **(b)** is velocity.
29. $-6; 6$ **31.** $-5; -3; 0; 2; 4$ **33.** Seven seconds after it is
dropped, the stone hits the ocean and its velocity at that instant is -224 ft/s.
35. (a) °F per foot   **(b)** Negative. As elevation increases, temperatures
are expected to decrease.   **37. (a)** If the interest rate on your mortgage
is 5%, your monthly payment will be $1610.46.   **(b)** If the interest rate
you can get on your mortgage increases from 5% to 6%, your monthly
payment will increase by approximately $183.37.   **39. (a)** If the
interest rate on your mortgage is 5%, the amount you can afford to borrow
is $223,537.94.   **(b)** If the interest rate you can get on your mortgage
increases from 5% to 6%, the amount you can afford to borrow decreases
by $25,449.21.   **41.** 1000; the population is increasing at a rate of 1000
shellfish per time unit. 570; the population is increasing more slowly at 570
shellfish per time unit. 250; the population is increasing at a much slower
rate of 250 shellfish per time unit.   **43. (a)** About 4.427; 11.986; 32.452
(b) The rate is increasing.   **45.** $g'(14) \simeq 1.049$. In 2014, the number
of licensed drivers will increase by approximately 1.049 million in the next
year.

47. (a)   **(b)**

(c) The graphs appear identical, which suggests that $f'(x) = g(x)$.
49. (d)

Section 11.5 (Page 628)

1. $f'(x) = 8x - 3$ **3.** $y' = 6x^2 + 6x - 6$
5. $g'(x) = 4x^3 + 9x^2 - 8$ **7.** $f'(x) = 9x^5 - 2x^{-.5}$
9. $y' = -22.5x^{1/2} + 3.8x^9 + 1$ **11.** $y' = 36t^{1/2} + 2t^{-1/2}$
13. $y' = 4x^{-1/2} + \dfrac{9}{2}x^{-1/4}$ **15.** $g'(x) = -30x^{-6} + 2x^{-2}$
17. $y' = -20x^{-3} - 24x^{-5} + 3$ **19.** $f'(t) = \dfrac{4}{t^2} - \dfrac{16}{t^3}$
21. $y' = -48x^{-5} + 21x^{-4} - 6x^{-2}$
23. $g'(x) = \dfrac{-5}{2}x^{-3/2} - \dfrac{7}{2}x^{-1/2} + 101$
25. $y' = \dfrac{-21}{2}x^{-5/2} - 4x^{-3/2} + 3x^2$ **27.** $y' = \dfrac{-19}{4}x^{-5/4}$
29. $y' = \dfrac{-8}{3}t^{-2/3}$ **31.** $\dfrac{dy}{dx} = -40x^{-6} + 36x^{-5} + 36x^3$
33. $-\dfrac{9}{2}x^{-3/2} - 3x^{-5/2}$ or $-\dfrac{9}{2x^{3/2}} - \dfrac{3}{x^{5/2}}$ **35.** -26 **37.** $\dfrac{11}{16}$

39. (b)   **41.** $0; y = 0$ **43.** $7; y = 7x - 3$ **45. (a)** $2.96
(b) $56.60   **(c)** $296.44   **(d)** $596.38   **47. (a)** 2010
(b) 127.45   **49. (a)** $R'(x) = .1216x + 1.4284$
(b) $2.0364 hundred million   **(c)** $2.2796 hundred million
51. (a) $16 per table   **(b)** $15.998 or $16   **(c)** The marginal revenue
found in part (a) approximates the actual revenue from the sale of the
1001st item found in part (b).   **53. (a)** $-2p + 5$ **(b)** -19; demand is
decreasing at the rate of about 19 items per $1 increase in price.
55. (a) $14,000/violin   **(b)** $4000/violin   **(c)** 0   **57. (a)** 30
(b) 0   **(c)** -10 **59. (a)** For such an individual, the cost of $100,000
in life insurance is $94.87 and adding an additional $1,000 in coverage
would increase the cost by approximately $0.71.   **(b)** For such an
individual, the cost of $1,000,000 in life insurance is $533.48 and adding
an additional $1,000 in coverage would increase the cost by approximately
$0.40.   **61. (a)** In 2014, the percentage of the population that is age
0–17 years is estimated to be 24.02% and to decrease by approximately
.05% in the next year.   **(b)** In 2024, the percentage of the population
that is age 0–17 years is estimated to be 23.64% and to decrease by
approximately .03% in the next year.   **63. (a)** Negative. Generally, we
expect the winning time to decrease over time.   **(b)** $-.0304$ seconds/year
(c) $-.0005$ seconds/year   **65. (a)** About -16.4 index points/year

(b) About -2.4 index points/year   **67. (a)** $\dfrac{dV}{dr} = 160\pi r$

(b) 640π; the volume of blood is increasing 640π cu mm per mm of
change in the radius.   **(c)** 960π; the volume of blood is increasing
960π cu mm per mm of change in the radius.   **(d)** 1280π; the volume
of blood is increasing 1280π cu mm per mm of change in the radius.

69. (a) 28.24   **(b)** 26 lb   **(c)** $f'(h) = -\dfrac{175,750}{h^3}$

(d) $f'(65) = -.64$; answers vary.   **71. (a)** $v(t) = 16t + 3$
(b) 3; 83; 163   **73. (a)** $v(t) = 6t^2 + 12t$ **(b)** 0; 210; 720
75. (a) -32 ft per sec; -64 ft per sec   **(b)** In 3 sec   **(c)** -96 ft per sec

77. (a) $(x + h)^n = x^n + n \cdot x^{n-1}h + \dfrac{n(n-1)}{2}x^{n-2}h^2 + \cdots + h^n$

(b) $\dfrac{(x+h)^n - x^n}{h} = n \cdot x^{n-1} + \dfrac{n(n-1)}{2}x^{n-2}h + \cdots + h^{n-1}$

(c) $\lim\limits_{h \to 0} \dfrac{(x+h)^n - x^n}{h} = n \cdot x^{n-1} = y'$

79. (a)–(c) The derivative is negative on $(-\infty, \infty)$.
(d) The graph is always falling.

Section 11.6 (Page 637)

1. $y' = 9x^2 + 4x - 6$ **3.** $y' = 120x^3 - 54x^2 + 10$
5. $y' = 24x^5 - 35x^4 - 20x^3 + 42x^2 + 4x - 6$
7. $y' = 100x^3 + 360x^2 + 288x$ **9.** $y' = 96x^5 + 240x^4 + 144x^3$
11. $y' = \dfrac{-4}{(x-3)^2}$ **13.** $f'(t) = \dfrac{t^2 + 6t - 12}{(t+3)^2}$
15. $g'(x) = \dfrac{-6x^4 - 4x^3 - 12x - 2}{(2x^3 - 2)^2}$ **17.** $y' = \dfrac{x^2 + 6x - 14}{(x+3)^2}$
19. $r'(t) = \dfrac{-3t + 4}{2\sqrt{t}(3t+4)^2}$ **21.** $y' = \dfrac{\dfrac{9\sqrt{x}}{2} + \dfrac{4}{\sqrt{x}}}{x}$ or $\dfrac{9x+8}{2x\sqrt{x}}$
23. $y' = \dfrac{-236}{(4x+11)^2}$ **25.** $f'(p) = \dfrac{264p^2 + 396p - 277}{(4p+3)^2}$
27. $g'(x) = \dfrac{6x^4 + 30x^3 - 27x^2 + 96x + 120}{(3x+9)^2(2x-1)^2}$
29. In the first step, the numerator should be $(x^2 - 1)(2) - (2x + 5)(2x)$.
31. $y = -2x + 9$ **33.** $y = -1.25x + 53.25$

35. (a) $\overline{C}(x) = \dfrac{200 + 75x}{x}$

(b) $\overline{C}(10) = 95$ means that, at a sales level of 1000 hotdogs, the average
cost is $95 per 100 hotdogs (or $.95/hotdog). Similarly, $\overline{C}(50) = 79$.

(c) $\overline{C}'(x) = \dfrac{-200}{x^2}$

(d) $\overline{C}'(10) = -2$ means that, at a sales level of 1000 hotdogs, if an additional 100 hotdogs are sold, the average cost decreases by \$2 per hundred hotdogs. Similarly, $\overline{C}'(50) = -.08$.

37. (a) $\dfrac{999}{(x + 100)^2}$; \$6.94/basket; \$5.10/basket

(b) $\dfrac{10x + 1}{x^2 + 100x}$; \$8.38/basket; \$7.16/basket

(c) $\dfrac{-10x^2 + 2x + 100}{(x^2 + 100x)^2}$; –\$.07/basket per basket; –\$.05/basket per basket

39. (a) $T'(x) = \dfrac{-10x^2 + 50}{(x^2 + 5)^2}$

(b) 2; temperature increasing at 2 degrees per hour **(c)** About 1.1111; temperature increasing at about 1.1111 degrees per hour **(d)** About $-.2041$; temperature decreasing at about .2041 degrees per hour **(e)** About $-.1028$; temperature decreasing at about .1028 degrees per hour **41. (a)** 8.57 min **(b)** 16.36 min **(c)** 6.12 min/(kcal/min) and 2.48 min/(kcal/min); answers vary. **43. (a)** .1173 **(b)** 2.625

45. (a) $M'(x) = \dfrac{12{,}000x}{(x^2 + 75)^2}$

(b) About 2 codes/shift; 5 codes/shift; 6 codes/shift; 5 codes/shift; 1 code/shift **(c)** Answers vary.

Section 11.7 (Page 648)

1. 779   **3.** 259   **5.** $16x + 36$; $16x + 27$

7. $-64x^3 - 96x^2 - 48x - 6$; $-4x^3 + 10$ **9.** $\dfrac{1}{x^2}$; $\dfrac{1}{x^2}$

11. $\sqrt{8x^2 - 6x + 2}$; $8x + 16 - 6\sqrt{x + 2}$
13. If $f(x) = x^5$ and $g(x) = 4x + 3$, then $y = f[g(x)]$.
15. If $(x) = \sqrt{x}$ and $g(x) = 6 + 3x^2$, then $y = f[g(x)]$.

17. If $f(x) = \dfrac{x + 3}{x - 3}$ and $g(x) = \sqrt{x}$, then $y = f[g(x)]$.

19. If $f(x) = x^3 + x + 5$ and $g(x) = x^{1/2} - 3$, then $y = f[g(x)]$.
21. $y' = 35(7x - 12)^4$ **23.** $y' = 112(4x + 3)^3$

25. $y' = -400x(10x^2 + 8)^4$ **27.** $y' = \dfrac{99}{2}(3x + 5)^{1/2}$

29. $y' = -\dfrac{21}{2}(8x + 9)(4x^2 + 9x)^{1/2}$ **31.** $y' = \dfrac{16}{\sqrt{4x + 7}}$

33. $y' = \dfrac{-2x - 4}{\sqrt{x^2 + 4x}}$ **35.** $y' = 2(x + 1)(x - 3) + (x - 3)^2$

37. $y' = 70(x + 3)(2x - 1)^4(x + 2)$ **39.** $y' = \dfrac{(3x + 1)^2(21x + 1)}{2\sqrt{x}}$

41. $y' = \dfrac{-3}{(x - 2)^4}$ **43.** $y' = \dfrac{(2x - 7)(8x + 24)}{(4x - 1)^2}$

45. $y' = \dfrac{-3x^2 - 28x + 5}{(3x + 1)^4}$ **47.** $y' = \dfrac{6x + 8\sqrt{x} + 3}{2x^{1/2}}$

49. (a) -2 **(b)** $-\dfrac{24}{7}$ **51. (d)**

53. $D(c) = \dfrac{-c^2 + 10c - 25}{25} + 500$

55. (a) The time in hours that can be driven on g gallons of gas **(b)** You can drive 120 miles on 4 gallons of gas. **(c)** If you have driven 120 miles, driving 1 more mile will take approximately 1/60 more hours. **(d)** If you have used 4 gallons of gas, using 1 more gallon of gas will allow you to travel approximately 30 more miles. **(e)** $f'(4) = .5$ means that if you have used 4 gallons of gas, using one more gallon of gas will allow you to travel approximately .5 more hours.

57. $C'(x) = \dfrac{(50x - 1)}{2(200 + 25x^2 - x)^{1/2}}$ **59. (a)** $R'(x) = \dfrac{15(250 - 2x)}{(500x - 2x^2)^{1/2}}$

(b) \$19.67; \$8.19; \$.85; -6.19 **(c)** Answers vary.
61. (a) \$20 **(b)** $-\$16$ **63. (a)** $R(x) = x\sqrt{900 - 2x}$

(b) $R'(x) = \dfrac{900 - 3x}{\sqrt{900 - 2x}}$ **(c)** $R'(250) = \$7.50/\text{ticket}$

65. (a) \$1462.33 per percentage point   **(b)** \$1551.57 per percentage point   **(c)** \$1646.19 per percentage point   **67. (a)** \$509.67 per percentage point   **(b)** \$519.52 per percentage point   **(c)** \$539.77 per percentage point   **69.** \$120 per worker

71. (a) $\overline{C}(x) = \dfrac{\sqrt{6x + 5}}{x}$ **(b)** $\overline{C}'(x) = \dfrac{-3x - 5}{x^2\sqrt{6x + 5}}$ **73. (a)** $-.5$

(b) $-\dfrac{1}{54}$ **(c)** About $-.010667$ **(d)** $-\dfrac{1}{128}$

75. (a) $F'(t) = \dfrac{150t}{(8 + t^2)^{3/2}}$ **(b)** About 3.96; 1.34; .36; .09

(c) Answers vary.

Section 11.8 (Page 658)

1. $y' = 5e^{5x}$ **3.** $f'(x) = 10e^{2x}$ **5.** $g'(x) = 28e^{-7x}$
7. $y' = 2xe^{x^2}$ **9.** $f'(x) = x^2e^{x^3/3}$ **11.** $y' = -18xe^{3x^2 + 5}$

13. $y' = \dfrac{-20x + 7}{-10x^2 + 7x}$ **15.** $y' = \dfrac{5}{2(5x + 1)}$

17. $f'(x) = \dfrac{15x^2 + 18x + 5}{(5x + 9)(x^2 + 1)}$ **19.** $y' = \dfrac{-20}{(4 - x)(3x + 8)}$

21. $y' = e^{-3x}(-3x^4 + 4x^3)$ **23.** $y' = e^{-3x}[-18x^2 + 27x - 5]$

25. $y' = \dfrac{3(8x^2 - 1)}{2x(8x^2 - 3)}$ **27.** $y' = \dfrac{-4x^4}{9 - x^4} + \ln(9 - x^4)$

29. $x^3(1 + 4\ln|x|)$

31. $y' = \dfrac{\dfrac{-25}{x} + 10 - 10\ln|x|}{(5 - 2x)^2}$ **33.** $y' = \dfrac{1}{2(x - 3)\sqrt{\ln(x - 3)}}$

35. $y' = \dfrac{xe^x\ln|x| - e^x + 1}{x(\ln|x|)^2}$ **37.** $y' = \dfrac{xe^x + xe^{-x} - e^x + e^{-x}}{x^2}$ or

$\dfrac{e^x(x - 1) + e^{-x}(x + 1)}{x^2}$ **39.** $f'(x) = \dfrac{4e^{3x+2}}{4x - 5} + 3e^{3x+2}\ln(4x - 5)$

41. $y' = \dfrac{2800e^{.4x}}{(7 - 10e^{.4x})^2}$ **43.** $y' = \dfrac{1250e^{-.5x}}{(12 + 5e^{-.5x})^2}$ **45.** $y' = \dfrac{1}{x\ln|x|}$

47. $y' = (\ln 8)\, 8^x$ **49.** $y' = 2(\ln 15) \cdot 15^{2x}$ **51.** $g'(x) = \dfrac{1}{(\ln 10)\, x}$

53. $y = -x + 1$ **55.** $y = 0$ **57.** $\dfrac{1}{8}$

59. (a) About 900 billion per year   **(b)** About 1742 billion per year
61. About \$458 billion; \$76 billion per year   **63. (a)** About 27.1 thousand
(b) About 1.2 thousand   **(c)** Answers vary   **65.** About 7.19 % per year
67. (a) About .7°F per hour   **(b)** About $-.1$°F per hour   **69. (a)** 6393; increasing about 2916 per year   **(b)** 20,807; increasing about 6490 per year   **(c)** 48,771; increasing about 1575 per year   **(d)** The growth rate increases rapidly at first and then gradually decreases to almost 0.
71. (a) 3.857 cm³   **(b)** .973 cm   **(c)** About 214 mo
(d) The tumor is 240 months old; it is increasing in volume at the instantaneous rate of .282 cm³/mo.   **73. (a)** 2000 degrees per year
(b) 1500 degrees per year

75. (a) $\dfrac{dR}{dx} = 100 + \dfrac{50(\ln x - 1)}{(\ln x)^2}$ **(b)** \$112.48

77. (a) It takes about 78.2 months to reach a balance of \$300.   **(b)** Positive
(c) When $A = \$300$, if you want the balance to increase another \$1, it will take approximately 1.4 more months.
79. (a) About 817 cars/hr; -41.2 cars/hr per ft   **(b)** About 522 cars/hr; -20.9 cars/hr per ft   **81. (a)** 2974.15 g   **(b)** 2.75 g/day

(c)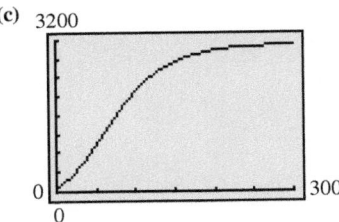

(d)

Weight	Day	Rate
990.9797	50	24.87793
2121.673	100	17.72981
2733.571	150	7.603823
2974.153	200	2.753855
3058.845	250	0.942782
3087.568	300	0.316772

Section 11.9 (Page 667)

1. $x = 0, 2$ **3.** $x = 1$ **5.** $x = -3, 0, 3$ **7.** $x = 0, 6$
9. Yes, no **11.** No, no, yes **13.** Yes, no, yes **15.** Yes, no, yes
17. Yes, no **19.** Continuous everywhere **21.** $x = -4$
23. $x < 2$
25. (a)

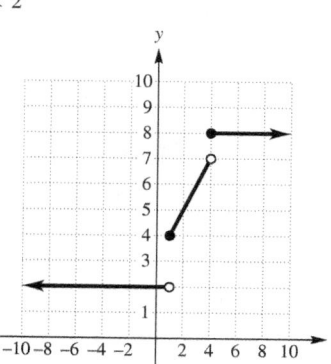

(b) $x = 1, 4$ **27.** $k = 1$ **29. (a)** 7.25% **(b)** 7.25%
(c) 7.25% **(d)** 7.25% **(e)** 6.25% **(f)** Does not exist
(g) $x = 2004, 2009, 2011$ **(h)** $x = 2004, 2009, 2011$
31. Discontinuous at $t = m$; differentiable everywhere *except* $t = m$ and the endpoints
33. (a)

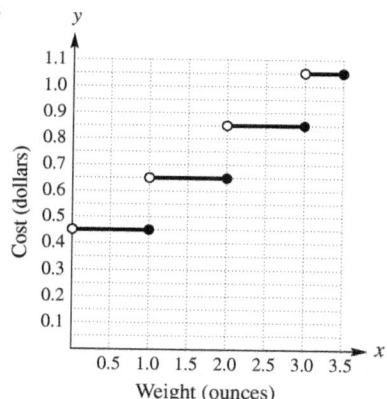

(b) $.45 **(c)** $.65 **(d)** Does not exist **(e)** $.85 **(f)** $.85
(g) $.85 **(h)** $x = 1, 2, 3$ ounces **35. (a)** $88 **(b)** $88
(c) $97.50 **(d)** Does not exist **(e)** $x = 2, 3, 4$ miles
37. $(-5, 7)$ **39.** $(-\infty, -3]$ **41.** $(-6, 0), (4, 8)$
43. (a)

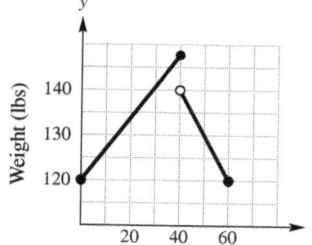

(b) No, at $t = 40$

Chapter 11 Review Exercises (Page 672)

Refer to Section	11.1	11.2	11.3	11.4	11.5	11.6	11.7	11.8	11.9
For Exercises	1–12, 79–80	13–22, 81–82	23–28, 37–38, 83–84	29–36, 86	39–44, 85, 87–88	45–54, 91–92	55–62, 93–96, 99	63–72, 89–90	73–78, 97–98

1. 4; 4; 4 **3.** $-.35$ **5.** 7 **7.** 0 **9.** 8 **11.** $\dfrac{1}{6}$ **13.** 0

15. Does not exist **17.** $-\infty$ **19.** 0 **21.** -3 **23.** $\dfrac{1}{4}$

25. 18 **27.** $-\dfrac{1}{3}$ **29.** $y' = 2$ **31.** $y' = 4x - 1$

33. $-2; y = -2x - 4$ **35.** $\dfrac{2}{9}; y = \dfrac{2}{9}x - \dfrac{2}{9}$

37. (a) -25.33 per dollar **(b)** -16.75 per dollar
(c) -31.12 per dollar **39.** $y' = 12x - 7$ **41.** $y' = 18x^{7/2}$

43. $f'(x) = -6x^{-7} + \dfrac{1}{2}x^{-1/2}$ **45.** $y' = 20t^4 + 27t^2 - 40t$

47. $y' = 40x^{3/4} + 6(5x + 1)x^{-1/4}$ **49.** $f'(x) = \dfrac{-4(x^2 + 8)}{(x^2 - 8)^2}$

51. $y' = \dfrac{-3x + 7 + 36\sqrt{x}}{2\sqrt{x}(3x + 7)^2}$ **53.** $y' = \dfrac{x^2 - 2x}{(x - 1)^2}$

55. $f'(x) = 16(4x - 2)^3$ **57.** $y' = \dfrac{1}{\sqrt{2t - 5}}$

59. $y' = 18x(3x - 4)^2 + 2(3x - 4)^3$

61. $f'(u) = \dfrac{(2u + 3)(6u - 4) - 6(3u^2 - 4u)}{(2u + 3)^4}$ **63.** $y' = -12e^{2x}$

65. $y' = -6x^2e^{-2x^3}$ **67.** $y' = 10xe^{2x} + 5e^{2x}$

69. $y' = \dfrac{2x + 4}{x^2 + 4x - 1}$ **71.** $y' = \dfrac{x - \dfrac{1}{x} - 2x(\ln 6x)}{(x^2 - 1)^2}$

73. None **75.** Yes, no, yes **77.** No, yes, no **79. (a)** $5
(b) Does not exist **81. (a)** $135 **(b)** $135 **(c)** $200
(d) Does not exist **83.** .25% per year **85.** $7,477,000 per year
87. (a) 30.22 youth/100 working-age people; $-.13$ youth/100 working-age people per year **(b)** 30.45 youth/100 working-age people; .20 youth/100 working-age people per year **89.** About 1175 million; 587 million/year
91. (a) $C'(x) = \dfrac{9910}{(2x + 40)^2}$ **(b)** $275.28

93. (a) $R(x) = x\sqrt{25 - .1x}$ **(b)** $R'(x) = \dfrac{25 - .15x}{\sqrt{25 - .1x}}$ **(c)** $360

(d) $2.88 **95. (a)** $x = 250 - 10p^2$ **(b)** $\dfrac{dx}{dp} = -20p$

(c) Demand would decrease by approximately 60 cups.
97. (a) $x = 100$ **(b)** $x = $50, 100 **99. (a)** About 28.13 cm
(b) About 4.34 cm/year **(c)** About 205.52 g **(d)** About 21.19 g/cm
(e) About 91.96 g/year

Case Study 11 Exercises (Page 676)

1. About .452 **3. (a)** About 1.1; about .65 **(b)** $95.14
5. Demand is constant, no matter what the price.

Extended Project (Page 677)

(a) Roll-your-own tobacco, 2153%; pipe tobacco, 157%. Pipe tobacco had a similar percent increase to cigarettes, but roll-your-own tobacco had a dramatically larger increase. **(b)** $q = -1.34p + 364$
(c) $q = -570.99p + 20,301$ **(d)** .08 inelastic; .23 inelastic
(e) .03 inelastic; 2.30 elastic **(f)** At the higher price, demand for cigarettes is inelastic but demand for roll-your-own tobacco is elastic. This may be due to the fact that pipe tobacco is a less expensive substitute product for roll-your-own tobacco. **(g)** Answers vary.

Chapter 12

Section 12.1 (Page 688)

1. Increasing on $(1, \infty)$; decreasing on $(-\infty, 1)$; local minimum of -4 at $x = 1$ **3.** Increasing on $(-\infty, -2)$; decreasing on $(-2, \infty)$; local maximum of 3 at $x = -2$ **5.** Increasing on $(-\infty, -4)$ and $(-2, \infty)$; decreasing on $(-4, -2)$; local maximum of 3 at $x = -4$; local minimum of 1 at $x = -2$ **7.** Increasing on $(-7, -4)$ and $(-2, \infty)$; decreasing on $(-\infty, -7)$ and $(-4, -2)$; local maximum of 3 at $x = -4$; local minima of -2 at $x = -7$ and $x = -2$ **9.** Increasing on $\left(-\infty, -\frac{1}{3}\right)$ and $(2, \infty)$; decreasing on $\left(-\frac{1}{3}, 2\right)$ **11.** Increasing on $(-\infty, -3)$ and $(-3, \infty)$ **13.** Increasing on $(0, \infty)$; decreasing on $(-\infty, 0)$ **15.** Increasing on $(-\infty, -2)$ and $(1, \infty)$; decreasing on $(-2, 1)$ **17.** $-2, -1, 2$ **19.** Local maximum at -2; local minimum at 0   **21.** Local maximum at -3; local minimum at -1 **23.** Local maximum at $\frac{1}{4}$; local minimum at 5   **25.** Local maximum at -2; local minimum at 3   **27.** Local maximum at $x = 0$; local minima at $x = -4, 2$ **29.** Local maximum at 0; $f(0) = 1$; local minimum at $\frac{6}{11}$; $f\left(\frac{6}{11}\right) \approx .7804$ **31.** Local maximum at $\frac{3}{4}$; $f\left(\frac{3}{4}\right) = 4$ **33.** No local extrema   **35.** Local maximum at $x = 1$; $f(1) = \frac{1}{e}$ **37.** Local maximum at $-\frac{1}{e}$; $f\left(-\frac{1}{e}\right) = \frac{1}{e}$; local minimum at $\frac{1}{e}$; $f\left(\frac{1}{e}\right) = -\frac{1}{e}$ **39.** Local minimum at $-\frac{1}{3}$; $f\left(-\frac{1}{3}\right) \approx -2.1226$ **41.** Approximate local minimum: $(-5.5861, -563.4222)$ **43.** Approximate local maxima: $(-18.5239, 5982.7502)$ and $(.3837, 40.9831)$; approximate local minima: $(-2.8304, 11.4750)$ and $(4.9706, -53.7683)$ **45.** Increasing on $(2002, 2004)$, $(2005, 2009)$, $(2010, 2011)$; decreasing on $(2004, 2005)$, $(2009, 2010)$ **47. (a)** 2010 **(b)** 2008   **49. (a)** $(5, 16)$, $(18, 19)$ **(b)** $(0, 5)$, $(16, 18)$, $(19, 23)$ **(c)** 5:00 A.M, 4:00 P.M., 6:00 P.M., 7:00 P.M.   **51. (a)** 343.25 ft **(b)** $t = 9.007$ **(c)** -148 ft/sec   **53.** $x = 44.30$ (2034), with a population of approximately 1.46 billion   **55.** 12.6°C   **57. (a)** 10 **(b)** 500   **59. (a)** $(0, 2.16)$ **(b)** $(2.16, 6)$ **61.** Approximate local minimum at $(4.03, 468.36)$; approximate local maximum at $(15.55, 886.61)$ **63.** Increasing on $(-\infty, 0)$; decreasing on $(0, \infty)$ **65.** 10 min   **67.** After 9 days

69. (a)

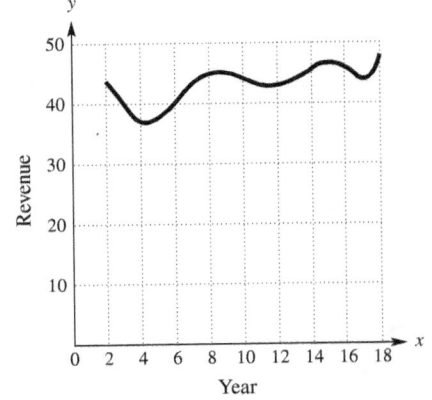

(b) 5   **(c)** $(4.306, 37.072)$, $(8.534, 45.376)$, $(11.561, 43.033)$, $(15.037, 46.981)$, $(17.112, 44.285)$

Section 12.2 (Page 700)

1. $f''(x) = 6x - 12; -12; 0; -30$ **3.** $f''(x) = 12(x + 3)^2; 108; 300; 0$

5. $f''(x) = \dfrac{2}{(1 + x)^3}; 2; \dfrac{2}{27}; -\dfrac{1}{4}$

7. $f''(x) = -\dfrac{(x + 4)^{-3/2}}{4}$ or $-\dfrac{1}{4(x + 4)^{3/2}}; -\dfrac{1}{32}; -\dfrac{1}{4 \cdot 6^{3/2}}; -\dfrac{1}{4}$

9. $f''(x) = \dfrac{2}{9x^{4/3}}$; not defined; $\dfrac{1}{9 \cdot 2^{1/3}}; \dfrac{2}{9(-3)^{4/3}}$

11. $f''(x) = 2e^x; 2; 2e^2; \dfrac{2}{e^3}$ **13.** $f''(x) = 24e^{2x}; 24; 24e^4; \dfrac{24}{e^6}$

15. $f''(x) = \dfrac{-4}{(2x + 1)^2}; -4; \dfrac{-4}{25}$; not defined

17. $f''(x) = \dfrac{2\ln|x| - 3}{x^3}$; not defined; $\dfrac{2\ln 2 - 3}{8}; \dfrac{2\ln 3 - 3}{27}$

19. Answers vary.   **21.** $v(t) = 12t + 5; a(t) = 12;$ $v(0) = 5$ cm/sec; $v(4) = 53$ cm/sec; $a(0) = a(4) = 12$ cm/sec^2 **23.** $v(t) = 9t^2 - 8t + 8; a(t) = 18t - 8; v(0) = 8$ cm/sec; $v(4) = 120$ cm/sec; $a(0) = -8$ cm/sec^2; $a(4) = 64$ cm/ sec^2 **25.** Concave upward on $(0, \infty)$; concave downward on $(-\infty, 0)$; point of inflection at $(0, -5)$ **27.** Concave upward on $\left(-\frac{4}{3}, \infty\right)$; concave downward on $\left(-\infty, -\frac{4}{3}\right)$; point of inflection at $\left(-\frac{4}{3}, \frac{425}{27}\right)$ **29.** Concave upward on $(4, \infty)$; concave downward on $(-\infty, 4)$; no points of inflection   **31.** Concave upward on $(-\infty, -5)$ and $(1, \infty)$; concave downward on $(-5, 1)$; points of inflection at $(-5, -1248)$ and $(1, 0)$ **33.** $(14, 26,688)$ **35.** $(22, 6517.9)$ **37.** No critical numbers; no local extrema   **39.** Critical number $x = 3$; no local extrema   **41.** Local maximum at $x = 0$; local minima at $x = 2$ and $x = -2$ **43.** Local maximum at $x = -2$; local minimum at $x = 2$ **45.** Local maximum at $x = -3$; local minimum at $x = 3$ **47.** No critical numbers; no local extrema   **49.** Local maximum at $x = 2$; local minima at $x = 1$ and $x = 4$; points of inflection at $x = \dfrac{7 + \sqrt{7}}{3}$ and $x = \dfrac{7 - \sqrt{7}}{3}$ **51.** Local minimum at $x = 1$; points of inflection at $x = \dfrac{4}{3}$ and $x = 2$ **53. (a)** E **(b)** C **(c)** A, F **(d)** D **(e)** B **55. (a)** $[1, 12]$ **(b)** \$1.62/week **(c)** \$.32/week   **57. (a)** -96 ft/sec **(b)** -160 ft/sec **(c)** -256 ft/sec **(d)** -32 ft/sec^2 **59.** About \$73,000   **61.** The graph is concave down to the left of the inflection point at approximately $(8.8, 14,141)$ and concave up to the right of it. Hence GDP is increasing at a decreasing rate prior to $x \approx 8.8$ (near the end of 2008) and GDP is increasing at an increasing rate after $x \approx 8.8$.   **63.** Local maximum at $x \approx 6.1$ (early in 2006); local minimum at $x \approx 11.1$ (early in 2011)   **65. (a)** Increase **(b)** The graph is increasing and concave down, which means the population is increasing more and more slowly.   **67. (a)** 100 **(b)** About \$7357.59 **(c)** About \$73.58   **69. (a)** 22.5 days **(b)** 71.19%

Section 12.3 (Page 712)

1. Absolute maximum at $x = 4$; absolute minimum at $x = 1$ **3.** Absolute maximum at $x = -1$; absolute minimum at $x = 1$ **5.** Absolute maximum at $x = -4$; absolute minima at $x = -7$ and $x = -2$ **7.** Absolute maximum at $x = 0$; absolute minima at $x = -3$ and $x = 3$ **9.** Absolute maximum at $x = 6$; absolute minimum at $x = 4$ **11.** Absolute maximum at $x = \sqrt{2}$; absolute minimum at $x = -1$ **13.** Absolute maximum at $x = -3$; absolute minimum at $x = 0$ **15.** Absolute maximum at $x = 0$; absolute minima at $x = -1$ and $x = 1$ **17.** Absolute minimum at $x = 2$ **19.** No absolute extrema   **21.** Absolute minimum at $x = -\dfrac{1}{\sqrt{2}}$ **23.** Absolute maximum at $x = 1$ **25.** Absolute minimum average cost of \$118.75 per wheel when $x = 75$ wheels are produced   **27.** Absolute maximum of 48,537 employees at $x = 11$; absolute minimum of 6,532 employees at $x \approx 2.8$.   **29.** Absolute maximum of \$10,417,300,000 at $x = 9$ (2009); absolute minimum of \$8,485,000,000 at $x = 0$ (2000)   **31. (a)** $R(x) = 400x$ **(b)** $P(x) = 430x - 525,000 - .012x^2$ **(c)** About 17,917 grills; \$3,327,083 profit   **33. (a)** After 12 days **(b)** 50 per ml **(c)** After one day **(d)** 81.365 per ml   **35. (a)** 8 **(b)** 29.43%   **37.** 8 in. by 8 in.   **39.** 4 in. by 4 in. by 2 in.

41. $r = 10$ cm; $h = 10$ cm   **43. (a)** $1200 - 2x$
(b) $A(x) = 1200x - 2x^2$ **(c)** 300 m   **(d)** 180,000 m^2 **45.** $2400
47. About 6.90 in. $\times$ 10.35 in   **49. (a)** $R(x) = 100{,}000x - 100x^2$
(b) 500   **(c)** 25,000,000¢, or $250,000   **51.** 2009   **53.** P is about
1.134 miles from A.   **55.** 6   **57.** 69   **59.** 3333 booklets   **61. (c)**

Section 12.4 (Page 722)

1. -1 **3.** $-x^3/y^3$ **5.** $\dfrac{3x^2}{y^4}$ **7.** $-\dfrac{2y}{5x}$ **9.** $\dfrac{5\sqrt{y}}{2\sqrt{x}}$ **11.** $\dfrac{-10x}{e^y}$

13. $-\dfrac{1}{x}$ **15.** $-\dfrac{3y}{x}$ **17.** $-\dfrac{y}{x \ln x}$ **19.** $-\dfrac{5}{6}$ **21.** $\dfrac{9}{4}$ **23.** 0

25. $-\dfrac{1}{5}$ **27.** $-e$ **29.** $y = 5$ **31.** $y = \dfrac{8}{3}x - \dfrac{2}{3}$

33. $y = -4x + 5$ **35. (a)** $-\dfrac{1}{x}$ **(b)** $-\dfrac{1}{x}$ **(c)** Answers agree.

37. $\dfrac{dq}{dp} = -2$ means that if the price is increased by \$1, the quantity

demanded decreases by approximately 2 tee times.   **39.** $\dfrac{dq}{dp} = -2$

means that if the price is increased by \$1, the quantity demanded decreases

by approximately 2 suites.   **41.** $\dfrac{dq}{dp} \approx -.075$ means that if the price

is increased by \$1, the quantity demanded decreases by approximately

75 drinks.   **43.** $\dfrac{dR}{dn} = 270$ **45.** $\dfrac{dR}{dn} \approx 294$ **47.** $\dfrac{dA}{dt} = -1.8$

means that if one more hour passes, approximately 1.8 mg of drug will be
eliminated from the body.

Section 12.5 (Page 729)

1. 2   **3.** 10   **5.** 1   **7.** 1   **9.** $\dfrac{15}{4}$ **11.** About \$4 billion per year

13. (a) Decrease   **(b)** About $-.047$ **15.** About 37.7 in^2/min
17. About 5655 mm^3/month   **19.** 2.4 yd/sec   **21.** 18 lbs
23. About 12.6 cm^3/min   **25.** About $-.4$ m/hour   **27.** $-\$192$/day
29. $-\$.42$/month   **31.** Violent crimes were increasing by 5 crimes
per 100,000 people per year

Section 12.6 (Page 737)

1. No points of inflection

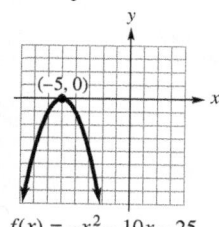

$f(x) = -x^2 - 10x - 25$

3. Point of inflection at $x = \dfrac{1}{3}$

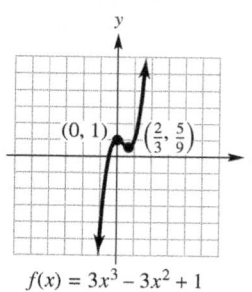

$f(x) = 3x^3 - 3x^2 + 1$

5. Point of inflection at $x = -\dfrac{3}{2}$

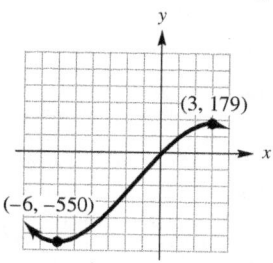

$f(x) = -2x^3 - 9x^2 + 108x - 10$

7. Point of inflection at $x = -\dfrac{7}{12}$

$f(x) = 2x^3 + \dfrac{7}{2}x^2 - 5x + 3$

9. No points of inflection

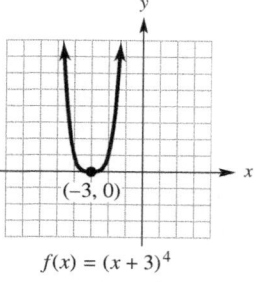

$f(x) = (x + 3)^4$

11. Points of inflection at $x = -\sqrt{3}$
and $x = \sqrt{3}$

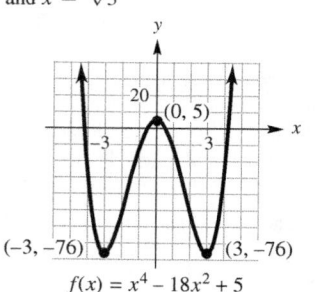

$f(x) = x^4 - 18x^2 + 5$

13. No points of inflection

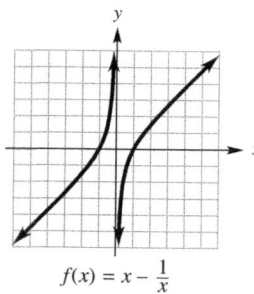

$f(x) = x - \dfrac{1}{x}$

15. No points of inflection

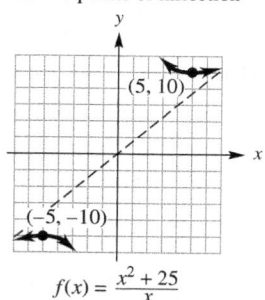

$f(x) = \dfrac{x^2 + 25}{x}$

17. No points of inflection

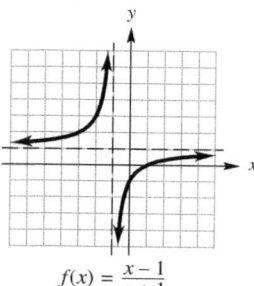

$f(x) = \dfrac{x - 1}{x + 1}$

19. No points of inflection

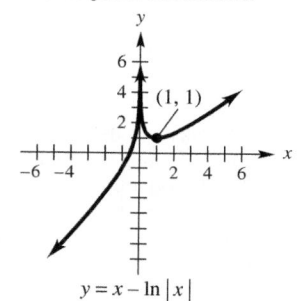

$y = x - \ln |x|$

21. Point of inflection at $x = 2$

$y = xe^{-x}$

23.

25.

27.

29. Smart cards; rate of growth of sales begins to decline at the point of
inflection.   **31.** Local minimum at (3.5, 760.2); no inflection point
33. (a) About 87.3%; 76.5%   **(b)** Negative   **(c)** Positive

(d) The graph is decreasing and concave up. Voter registration is decreasing at a slower and slower rate.   **35.** Local maximum at $(9.8, 3154.7)$; local minimum at $(.7, 531.4)$; inflection point $(5.2, 1843.1)$
37. Local maximum at $(8.9, 1467.2)$; local minima at $(3.7, 1215.7)$ and $(10.1, 1463.0)$; inflection points at $(5.6, 1319.8)$ and $(9.5, 1465.0)$
39. Local minimum at $(5.9, 18.2)$; local maxima at $(.9, 34.6)$ and $(8.1, 20.3)$; inflection points at $(2.8, 27.8)$ and $(7.1, 19.3)$ **41.** Local minimum at $(9, 0)$; local maximum at $(3, 108)$; inflection point at $(6, 54)$
43. Local minimum at $(14.7, 11.7)$; local maximum at $(32.4, 15.2)$; inflection points at $(5.7, 13.1)$ and $(25.0, 13.7)$

Chapter 12 Review Exercises (Page 740)

Refer to Section	12.1	12.2	12.3	12.4	12.5	12.6
For Exercises	1, 5–16, 47–48, 55–56	2, 17–20, 49–50	3, 33–40, 51–54, 57–66	41–46, 67–68	69–74	4, 21–32

1. Answers vary.   **3.** Answers vary.   **5.** Increasing on $\left(-\frac{9}{2}, \infty\right)$; decreasing on $\left(-\infty, -\frac{9}{2}\right)$ **7.** Increasing on $\left(-\infty, -\frac{2}{3}\right)$ and $(1, \infty)$; decreasing on $\left(-\frac{2}{3}, 1\right)$ **9.** Decreasing on $(-\infty, 4)$ and $(4, \infty)$
11. Local maximum of 54 at $x = -2$; local minimum of -71 at $x = 3$
13. Local maximum of 2 at $x = 0$; local minima of $-\frac{1}{3}$ at $x = -1$
and -43 at $x = 3$ **15.** Local maximum of $\frac{3}{e}$ at $x = 1$
17. $f''(x) = 40x^3 - 30x$; 10; -260 **19.** $f''(x) = -20e^{2x}$; $-20e^2$; $\frac{-20}{e^4}$
21. No local extrema; point of inflection at $x = -\frac{1}{12}$; decreasing on $(-\infty, \infty)$; concave upward on $\left(-\infty, -\frac{1}{12}\right)$; concave downward on $\left(-\frac{1}{12}, \infty\right)$

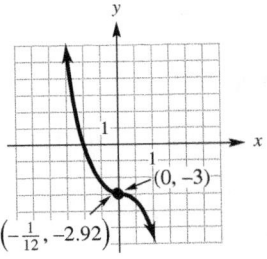

23. Local maximum at $x = 0$; local minima at $x = -1$ and $x = 2$; points of inflection at $x = \frac{1 - \sqrt{7}}{3}$ and $x = \frac{1 + \sqrt{7}}{3}$; increasing on $(-1, 0)$ and $(2, \infty)$; decreasing on $(-\infty, -1)$ and $(0, 2)$; concave upward on $\left(-\infty, \frac{1 - \sqrt{7}}{3}\right)$ and $\left(\frac{1 + \sqrt{7}}{3}, \infty\right)$; concave downward on $\left(\frac{1 - \sqrt{7}}{3}, \frac{1 + \sqrt{7}}{3}\right)$

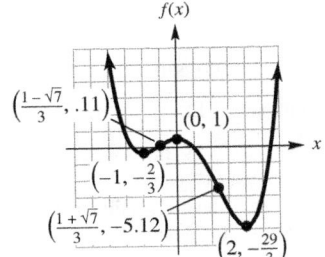

25. No local extrema or points of inflection; increasing on $\left(-\infty, -\frac{1}{2}\right)$; and $\left(-\frac{1}{2}, \infty\right)$; concave upward on $\left(-\infty, -\frac{1}{2}\right)$; concave downward on $\left(-\frac{1}{2}, \infty\right)$

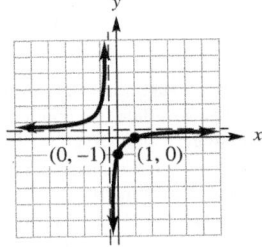

27. Local maximum at $x = \frac{1}{2}$; local minimum at $x = -\frac{2}{3}$; point of inflection at $x = -\frac{1}{12}$; increasing on $\left(-\frac{2}{3}, \frac{1}{2}\right)$; decreasing on $\left(-\infty, -\frac{2}{3}\right)$ and $\left(\frac{1}{2}, \infty\right)$; concave upward on $\left(-\infty, -\frac{1}{12}\right)$; concave downward on $\left(-\frac{1}{12}, \infty\right)$

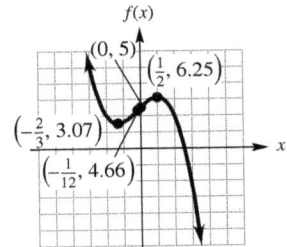

29. Local minimum at $x = 0$; increasing on $(0, \infty)$; decreasing on $(-\infty, 0)$; concave upward on $(-\infty, \infty)$. In the graph, the horizontal lines are 10 units apart.

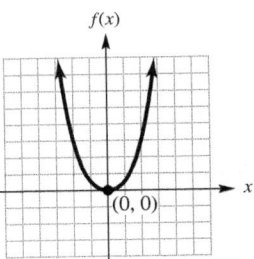

31. Local maximum at $x = -2$; local minimum at $x = 2$; no point of inflection; increasing on $(-\infty, -2)$ and $(2, \infty)$; decreasing on $(-2, 0)$ and $(0, 2)$; concave upward on $(0, \infty)$; concave downward on $(-\infty, 0)$. In the graph, the horizontal lines are 2 units apart.

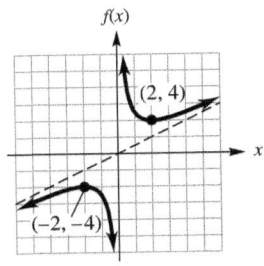

33. Absolute maximum of 10 at $x = 3$; absolute minima of 9 at $x = 2$ and $x = 4$ **35.** Absolute maximum of 11.217 at $x = 3.3$; absolute minimum of $-\dfrac{319}{27}$ at $x = \dfrac{5}{3}$ **37.** Absolute minimum at $x = 1$

39. Absolute maximum at $x = 3$

41. $\dfrac{2 - 10y}{10x - 5}$ **43.** $\dfrac{10 - ye^x}{e^x - 1}$

45. $y = 4x - 3$ **47.** (a) Decreasing (b) Increasing (c) Decreasing
49. (a) Increase (b) The graph is increasing and concave up, which means the population is increasing at a faster and faster rate.
51. (a) 2; 17 (b) Absolute maximum of 17 female senators in 2011; absolute minimum of 0 female senators in 1973   **53.** Absolute maximum of $6,147,000,000$ at $x = 11$ (the start of 2011); absolute minimum of $2,508,750,000$ at $x \approx .5$ (mid-year in 2000)   **55.** (a) Decreasing on $(4.3, 14.1)$ (b) Local maximum $(4.3, 45.6)$; local minimum $(14.1, 32.3)$
57. Absolute maximum of 29% in 2010; absolute minimum of 5.87% in 2000
59. $125 \text{ m} \times 250 \text{ m}$ **61.** $3 \text{ m} \times 3 \text{ m} \times 3 \text{ m}$ **63.** 32 batches
65. 21 batches   **67.** 10   **69.** (a) $-2.2°C/hr$ (b) $5.4°F/hr$
71. \$315/day   **73.** 204 m/min

Case Study 12 Exercises (Page 743)

1. $Z'(m) = -\dfrac{C_1}{m^2} + \dfrac{DC_3}{2}$

3. $D = 3, t = 12, C_1 = 15,000, C_3 = 900, m = \dfrac{10}{3}$

5. $Z(m^+) = Z(4) = \$11,400; Z(m^-) = Z(3) = \$11,300$

Extended Project (Page 744)

(a) 1 month; 4 employees per batch; \$13,000 per month (b) 1 month; 4 employees per batch; \$14,000 per month (c) Answers vary.

Chapter 13

Section 13.1 (Page 753)

1. $F(x)$ and $G(x)$ must differ by a constant.   **3.** Answers vary.

5. $6x^2 + C$ **7.** $2p^4 + C$ **9.** $105x + C$ **11.** $\dfrac{5z^2}{2} - z + C$

13. $\dfrac{z^3}{3} - 2z^2 + 6z + C$ **15.** $\dfrac{x^4}{4} - \dfrac{14x^3}{3} + 11x^2 + 8x + C$

17. $4y^{3/2} + C$ **19.** $\dfrac{12t^{5/2}}{5} + \dfrac{12t^{5/4}}{5} + C$ **21.** $\dfrac{112t^{3/2}}{3} + 4t^{9/2} + C$

23. $-\dfrac{12}{x^2} + C$ **25.** $-\dfrac{1}{2y^2} - 4y^{1/2} + C$ **27.** $-3x^{-2} + 2\ln|x| + C$

29. $\dfrac{4e^{3u}}{3} + C$ **31.** $-\dfrac{15}{4}e^{-.8x} + C$ **33.** $6\ln|x| - 8e^{-.5x} + C$

35. $\ln|t| + \dfrac{t^4}{2} + C$ **37.** $\dfrac{e^{2u}}{2} + 4\ln|u| + C$

39. $\dfrac{25x^3}{3} + 5x^2 + x + C$ **41.** $\dfrac{6x^{7/6}}{7} + \dfrac{3x^{2/3}}{2} + C$ **43.** $f(x) = \dfrac{3x^{5/3}}{5}$

45. (a) $F(x) = 4.71x^2 + 87.14x + 1396.8$ (b) \$3539.92 billion
47. (a) $G(x) = .07x^3 + .18x^2 + 11.38x + 205$ (b) \$317.49 billion

49. $x^3 - 3x^2 + 4x - 40$ **51.** $C(x) = \dfrac{3x^{5/3}}{5} + 5x - 1.2$

53. $C(x) = \dfrac{x^3}{3} - x^2 + 3x + 16$

55. $C(x) = \dfrac{800}{e^{.05x}} + 100x + 276.96$

57. (a) $F(t) = 4300e^{.035t}$ (b) About 7,796,000 background checks
59. (a) $G(x) = 48.28 - 10.2\ln x$
(b) Age 18, 18.8; age 20, 17.7; age 50, 8.4; age 70, 4.9
(c) Answers vary.

Section 13.2 (Page 761)

1. Answers vary.   **3.** $\dfrac{(12x - 1)^3}{12} + C$ **5.** $\dfrac{-5}{3(3t - 6)} + C$

7. $-\dfrac{1}{\sqrt{x^2 + 2x - 4}} + C$ **9.** $\dfrac{2(r^3 + 3)^{3/2}}{9} + C$ **11.** $-\dfrac{4}{5}e^{5k} + C$

13. $\dfrac{e^{2w^4}}{2} + C$ **15.** $\dfrac{e^{4t - t^2}}{2} + C$ **17.** $2e^{\sqrt{y}} + C$

19. $-\dfrac{5\ln|12 + 6x|}{6} + C$ **21.** $\dfrac{1}{2}\ln|e^{2t} + 1| + C$

23. $-\dfrac{1}{8(2x^2 + 8x)^2} + C$ **25.** $\dfrac{5\left(\dfrac{1}{r} + r\right)^2}{2} + C$

27. $(x^3 + 3x)^{1/3} + C$ **29.** $\ln|3x^2 + 7x + 8| + C$

31. $\dfrac{(x^2 + 5)^4}{4} + C$ **33.** $\dfrac{(x^2 + 12x)^{3/2}}{3} + C$ **35.** $\ln|\ln(x)| + C$

37. $\dfrac{10}{3}(u - 1)^{3/2} + 10(u - 1)^{1/2} + C$

39. $\dfrac{2(5t - 1)^{5/2}}{125} + \dfrac{2(5t - 1)^{3/2}}{75} + C$

41. (a) $6\ln(5x^2 + 1) + 10$ (b) Yes
43. (a) $F(x) = 32e^{.092x}$ (b) About \$97 billion
45. (a) $R(x) = 2.7(x^2 + 27,000)^{1/3} - 67.14$ (b) About \$53,633
(c) 459   **47.** (a) $G(x) = .00040674\,[(x - 1970)^{2.4}/2.4 + 1970(x - 1970)^{1.4}/1.4] + 61.298$ (b) About 180,945

Section 13.3 (Page 770)

1. About 149 kWh   **3.** 13,078.2 million short tons   **5.** Answers vary.
7. (a) 44 (b) 50 (c) 55.4   **9.** (a) 8 (b) 10 (c) 10.66
11. (a) 7.39 (b) 14.60 (c) 24.48   **13.** (a) 64 (b) 57
(c) About 51.41   **15.** 12.5   **17.** 228.75   **19.** 90.55   **21.** .294
23. \$808,680.51   **25.** \$47,703.43   **27.** About 536,055.83 trillion BTUs
29. About 1613 feet   **31.** (a) 9 feet (b) At 2 seconds (c) 4 feet ahead
(d) Between 3 and 3.5 seconds

Section 13.4 (Page 782)

1. 60   **3.** 13   **5.** 8   **7.** 138   **9.** $8\dfrac{1}{4}$ **11.** 9.9873

13. $3e^{10} - 3$ **15.** 1.294   **17.** $\dfrac{91}{3}$ **19.** 63.857   **21.** .1509

23. 49   **25.** .3005   **27.** 105.3946   **29.** $\ln\left(\dfrac{108}{37}\right) \approx 1.0712$

31. A loss, $\displaystyle\int_0^2 (6x^2 - 7x - 3)\,dx$ **33.** $\dfrac{8}{3}$ **35.** 2.67   **37.** $\dfrac{64}{3}$

39. 4.75   **41.** 3.7037   **43.** .6667   **45.** 1   **47.** 11.08
49. 19   **51.** (a) \$22,000 (b) \$108,000   **53.** \$4101.27
55. (a) 43,410,000; the number of people between 20 and 30
(b) 308,430,000; the number of people between 0 and 90
(c) 86,260,000 Millennials   **57.** About 183.4 trillion BTUs
59. (a) 363 (b) 167 (c) Decreasing to 0
61. (a) $y' = \ln|x|$ (b) About \$274.4356 billion
63. .811   **65.** .244

Section 13.5 (Page 793)

1. \$280; \$11.67   **3.** \$87.62 billion   **5.** \$2500; \$30,000   **7.** No

9. \$33.327 billion   **11.** About \$503 billion   **13.** $\dfrac{56}{3}$ **15.** $\dfrac{5}{192}$

17. About 1.22   **19.** 325.04   **21.** 4.999   **23.** (a) 8 years
(b) \$147.96 (c) About \$771   **25.** (a) About 10 years
(b) About \$833,622   **27.** (a) 3.02 years (b) About 12.74 trillion gallons
29. (a) About 88.22 gal (b) About 40 hours (c) About 128 gal
(d) About 75.78 hours

31. (a)

Graph showing $D(q) = -\frac{3}{5}q + 10$, point $(5, 7)$, and $S(q) = \frac{7}{5}q$

(b) $(5, 7)$ **(c)** $\$7.50$ **(d)** $\$17.50$ **33.** $\$1999.54$ **35.** $\$38.50$

37. (a)

Graph showing $D(q) = 400 - e^{q/2}$ and $S(q) = e^{q/2} - 1$

(b) $(10.60, 199.50)$ **(c)** $\$1726.63$ **(d)** $\$1726.63$ **39.** $\frac{27}{16}$

41. (a) $\$1600$ **(b)** $\$51,200$ **43. (a)** $P(t) = \frac{25}{8}t^4 - \frac{1}{8}t^5 + 4000$

(b) $67,000$ deer   **(c)** $t = 20$ (year 1925)   **(d)** $104,000$ deer
45. (a) 10 items   **(b)** 10 hours per item

Section 13.6 (Page 797)

1. $-7\ln\left|x + \sqrt{x^2 + 36}\right| + C$ **3.** $\ln\left|\dfrac{x - 3}{x + 3}\right| + C, (x^2 > 9)$

5. $\dfrac{4}{3}\ln\left|\dfrac{3 + \sqrt{9 - x^2}}{x}\right| + C, (0 < x < 3)$

7. $-\dfrac{5x}{3} + \dfrac{5}{9}\ln|3x + 1| + C$ **9.** $-\dfrac{13}{15}\ln\left|\dfrac{x}{3x - 5}\right| + C$

11. $\ln\left|\dfrac{2x - 1}{2x + 1}\right| + C, \left(x^2 > \dfrac{1}{4}\right)$

13. $-3\ln\left|\dfrac{1 + \sqrt{1 - 9x^2}}{3x}\right| + C, \left(0 < x < \dfrac{1}{3}\right)$

15. $\dfrac{15x}{2} - \dfrac{45}{4}\ln|2x + 3| + C$ **17.** $\dfrac{1}{25(5x - 1)} - \dfrac{\ln|5x - 1|}{25} + C$

19. $\dfrac{3x^5}{4}\left(\dfrac{\ln|x|}{5} - \dfrac{1}{25}\right) + C$ **21.** $\dfrac{7}{x}(-\ln|x| - 1) + C$

23. $2xe^{3x} - \dfrac{2e^{3x}}{3} + C$ **25.** $\$10,473.56$ **27.** $12,613$ microbes

Section 13.7 (Page 805)

1. $y = -x^3 + \dfrac{7x^2}{2} + C$ **3.** $y = -3e^{-2x} + C$ **5.** $y = \dfrac{3x^4}{8} + C$

7. $y^2 = x^2 + C$ **9.** $y = Me^{2x^2}$ **11.** $y = Me^{x^4 - x^3}$
13. $y = \sqrt[3]{x + C}$ **15.** $y = Mx$ **17.** $y = 7 + Me^x$
19. $y = Me^{-x} + 1$ **21.** $y = \ln|7e^x + C|$ **23.** $y = x^3 - x^2 + 4$

25. $y^2 = 4\ln|x^3 + 28| + 6$ **27.** $y^2 = \dfrac{2x^3}{3} + 16$ **29.** $y = e^{2.5x^2 + 3x}$

31. $2y^2 - 6y = 7x^2 + 2x - 8$ **33.** Answers vary.
35. (a) 3536 units   **(b)** 6356 units   **37. (a)** $y = 1330e^{.4x}$
(b) About $73,000$ girls   **39. (a)** $y = 4t^2 + 50$ **(b)** $t = 11$ days

41. (a) $\dfrac{dy}{dt} = -.15y$ **(b)** $y = Me^{-.15t}$ **(c)** About 9.2 years

43. About 17.3 years   **45. (a)** $k = .8$ **(b)** 11 people   **(c)** 55 people
(d) 2981 people   **47.** 21.94 items   **49. (a)** $26,075$

(b) $29,974$ **(c)** $29,999$ **51. (a)** $T = 68 + 30.6e^{-.33t}$

(b) $83.8°$ **(c)** 4.5 hours   **(d)** 24.3 hours   **53.** $q = \dfrac{C}{p^2}$

Chapter 13 Review Exercises (Page 809)

Refer to Section	13.1	13.2	13.3	13.4	13.5	13.6	13.7
For Exercises	1–8	9–28, 34	29–33, 56	35–50, 67–68	51–55, 57–66	69–72	73–86

1. $\dfrac{x^3}{3} - 4x^2 - 7x + C$ **3.** $\dfrac{14x^{3/2}}{3} + C$ **5.** $\dfrac{2x^{3/2}}{3} + 9x^{1/3} + C$

7. $3x^{-2} + C$ **9.** $-\dfrac{3e^{2x}}{2} + C$ **11.** $10\ln|x - 3| + C$

13. $y = -\ln|3 - x| + C$ **15.** $\dfrac{3\ln|x^2 - 1|}{2} + C$

17. $-\dfrac{4}{3}(x^3 + 5)^{-3} + C$ **19.** $\ln|2x^2 - 5x| + C$ **21.** $\dfrac{5e^{3x^2}}{6} + C$

23. $-\dfrac{e^{-3x^3}}{9} + C$ **25.** $\dfrac{(\ln x)^6}{2} + C$ **27.** $y = \dfrac{1}{3}(2x + 9)^{\frac{3}{2}} + C$

29. Answers vary.   **31. (a)** 140 **(b)** 148.8 **33.** 28; answers vary.

35. $\dfrac{128}{3}$ **37.** $\dfrac{381}{200}$ **39.** $15\ln 5 \approx 24.1416$ **41.** $.40$

43. 66.907 **45.** 6.313 **47.** 3 **49.** 6.3891

51. $C(x) = 10x - \dfrac{5x^2}{2} + 4$ **53.** $C(x) = (2x - 1)^{3/2} + 145$

55. $45,000$ units   **57.** 26.28 years   **59.** About $\$84$ billion
61. About 2365 billion Japanese yen   **63.** 2.5 years, $\$98,958.33$
65. (a) 916.67 **(b)** 666.67 **67. (a)** $.6321$ **(b)** $.2231$

69. $\ln\left|x + \sqrt{x^2 - 64}\right| + C$ **71.** $3\ln\left|\dfrac{x - 3}{x + 3}\right| + C$ $(x^2 > 9)$

73. $y = \dfrac{x^4}{2} + 3x^2 + 5x + C$ **75.** $y^2 = 3x^2 + 2x + C$

77. $y = -5e^{-x} - 5x + 22$ **79.** $y = 2e^{5x - x^2}$ **81. (a)** $y = 57e^{.0192x}$
(b) About 112 million   **83. (a)** $y = 70 - 43e^{-.05x}$ **(b)** About 66%
85. (a) About $234°$ **(b)** About 3 hrs

Case Study 13 Exercises (Page 813)

1. Answers vary.   **3. (a)** $P(t) = \dfrac{10e^{.07t}}{e^{.07t} + 4}$ **(b)** About 7.0 million;

about 7.8 million   **(c)** About 2020

Chapter 14

Section 14.1 (Page 823)
1. 4; -22; -20; 12 **3.** 3; $\sqrt{33}$; $\sqrt{17}$; 8 **5. (a)** 92 **(b)** -17
(c) 47 **(d)** -44 **7.** All ordered pairs (x, y), where x and y are real
numbers   **9.** All ordered pairs (x, y), where x and y are nonnegative
real numbers   **11.** All ordered triples (u, v, w), where u, v, and w
are real numbers such that $v \neq w$ **13.** $P(l, w) = 2l + 2w$

15. $S(R, i, n) = R\dfrac{(1 + i)^n - 1}{i}$ **17.** $C(x, y, z) = 200x + 100y + 50z$

19. Answers vary.
21.

3D graph with axes z, y, x; values 12, 4, 6 marked.

23.

3D graph with axes z, y, x; values 4, 4 marked; plane $x + y = 4$.

25.

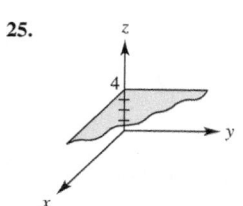

27. $3x + 2y + z = 18$

$3x + 2y + z = 18$

29. $y^2 - x = -z$

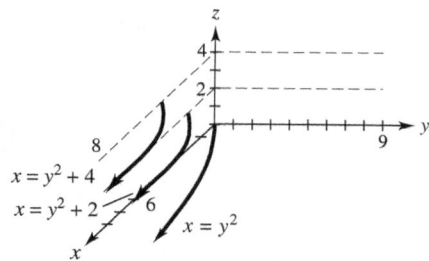

$x = y^2 + 4$

$x = y^2 + 2$

$x = y^2$

31.

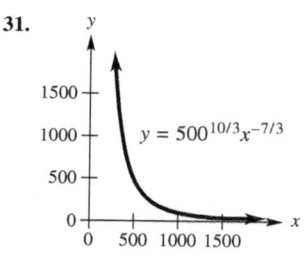

$y = 500^{10/3}x^{-7/3}$

33. z is multipled by $2^{.7}$ (≈ 1.6); z is multiplied by $2^{.3}$ (≈ 1.2); z is doubled. **35.** **(a)** About 1987 **(b)** About 595 **(c)** About 359,768 **37.** **(a)** 73; comfortable **(b)** 77; uncomfortable **39.** 1.14; the IRA grows faster. **41.** **(a)** 1.5 m/sec; 5.5 m/sec **(b)** 1 m/sec **43.** **(a)** About 397 **(b)** Answers vary. **45.** (c) **47.** (e) **49.** (b)

Section 14.2 (Page 833)

1. **(a)** $24x^2 - 8xy$ **(b)** $-4x^2 + 18y$ **(c)** 48 **(d)** -40
3. $f_x(x, y) = -4y; f_y(x, y) = -4x + 18y^2; 4; 178$
5. $f_x = 2e^{2x+y}; f_y = e^{2x+y}; 2e^3; e^{-5}$ **7.** $f_x = \dfrac{2}{e^{x+2y}}; f_y = \dfrac{4}{e^{x+2y}}; 2; \dfrac{4}{e^2}$
9. $f_x = \dfrac{y^3 - x^2 - 6xy^2}{(x^2 + y^3)^2}; f_y = \dfrac{6x^2y - 3xy^2 - 3y^4}{(x^2 + y^3)^2}; -\dfrac{17}{9}; \dfrac{153}{1849} \approx .083$
11. $f_x(x, y) = \dfrac{15x^2y^2}{1 + 5x^3y^2}; f_y(x, y) = \dfrac{10x^3y}{1 + 5x^3y^2}; \dfrac{60}{41}; \dfrac{1920}{2879}$
13. $f_x = 2x^3ye^{2xy} + 2xe^{2xy}; f_y = 2x^3e^{2xy}; -4e^{-4}; -128e^{-24}$
15. $f_{xx} = 8y^2 - 32; f_{yy} = 8x^2; f_{xy} = f_{yx} = 16xy$
17. $h_{xx} = -8y^2; h_{xy} = h_{yx} = -16xy + 14y; h_{yy} = -6 - 8x^2 + 14x$
19. $r_{xx} = \dfrac{12y}{(x + y)^3}; r_{yy} = \dfrac{-12x}{(x + y)^3}; r_{xy} = r_{yx} = \dfrac{6y - 6x}{(x + y)^3}$
21. $z_{xx} = 0; z_{yy} = 4xe^y; z_{xy} = z_{yx} = 4e^y$
23. $r_{xx} = \dfrac{-4}{(2x + y)^2}; r_{yy} = \dfrac{-1}{(2x + y)^2}; r_{xy} = r_{yx} = \dfrac{-2}{(2x + y)^2}$
25. $z_{xx} = \dfrac{1}{x}; z_{yy} = -\dfrac{x}{y^2}; z_{xy} = z_{yx} = \dfrac{1}{y}$ **27.** $\dfrac{1}{2}; -3$
29. $x = -4; y = 2$ **31.** $x = 0, y = 0; x = 3, y = 3$
33. $f_x = 2x; f_y = z; f_z = y + 4z^3; f_{yz} = 1; -2; 1$
35. $f_x = \dfrac{6}{4z + 5}; f_y = -\dfrac{5}{4z + 5}; f_z = \dfrac{4(6x - 5y)}{(4z + 5)^2}; f_{yz} = \dfrac{20}{(4z + 5)^2}$
37. $f_x = \dfrac{2x - 5z^2}{x^2 - 5xz^2 + y^4}; f_y = \dfrac{4y^3}{x^2 - 5xz^2 + y^4};$
$f_z = -\dfrac{10xz}{x^2 - 5xz^2 + y^4}; f_{yz} = \dfrac{40xy^3z}{(x^2 - 5xz^2 + y^4)^2}$

39. 3; 9; answers vary. **41.** **(a)** 80 **(b)** 180 **(c)** 110 **(d)** 360
43. **(a)** \$902,100 **(b)** $f_p(p, i) = 99 - .5i - .005p; f_i(p, i) = -.5p; f_p(p, i)$ gives the rate at which weekly sales are changing per unit change in price when the interest rate remains constant; $f_i(p, i)$ gives the rate at which weekly sales are changing per unit change in interest rate when the price remains constant. **(c)** A weekly sales decrease of \$9700
45. **(a)** \$500 **(b)** \$1100 **47.** **(a)** Fixed costs, that is, the cost when no items have been produced **(b)** $\dfrac{\partial C}{\partial x} = \$600$ is the marginal cost of producing 1 unit of chargers when the production of covers remains constant. $\dfrac{\partial C}{\partial y} = \$120$ is the marginal cost of producing 1 unit of covers when the production of chargers remains constant. **49.** **(a)** About .0112 **(b)** About .0783 **51.** **(a)** $f_x(64, 125) = 1.5625$, the approximate change in production (in thousands of units) for a 1-unit change in labor; $f_y(64, 125) = 1.6$, the approximate change in production (in thousands of units) for a 1-unit change in capital **(b)** An increase of approximately 1563 batteries **(c)** Increasing capital by 1 unit
53. $.7x^{-.3}y^{.3}$, or $\dfrac{.7y^{.3}}{x^{.3}}$; $.3x^{.7}y^{-.7}$, or $\dfrac{.3x^{.7}}{y^{.7}}$ **55.** **(a)** About 5.71
(b) About 6.84 **(c)** $\dfrac{1}{a - v}$ **(d)** $\dfrac{b}{(a - v)^2}$ **57.** **(a)** 62.8% **(b)** 37.0%
(c) $f_n(3, 3, 320) = 2$, meaning that 2% is the rate of change of the probability per additional semester of high school math. $f_a(3, 3, 320) = .078$, which means that .078% is the rate of change of the probability per unit change in SAT score. **59.** **(a)** 4.125 lb **(b)** $\dfrac{\partial f}{\partial n} = \dfrac{n}{4}$, the change in weight loss per unit change in workouts **(c)** An additional loss of about .75 lb
61. **(a)** 28.24 **(b)** $\dfrac{\partial B}{\partial w} = \dfrac{703}{h^2}; \dfrac{\partial B}{\partial h} = \dfrac{-1406w}{h^3}$

Section 14.3 (Page 843)

1. Answers vary. **3.** Local minimum of -22 at $(3, -1)$
5. Local minimum of 2 at $(-2, -2)$ **7.** Saddle point at $\left(-2, \dfrac{5}{3}\right)$
9. Local maximum of 17 at $\left(\dfrac{2}{3}, \dfrac{4}{3}\right)$ **11.** Local minimum of -8
at $(2, -1)$ **13.** Saddle point at $(1, 2)$ **15.** Saddle point at $(0, 0)$; local minimum of -201 at $(6, 18)$ **17.** Saddle point at $(0, 0)$; local minimum of -7.75 at $(4.5, 1.5)$ **19.** Saddle point at $(0, 0)$
21. No local extrema and no saddle points **23.** Local maximum of $\dfrac{9}{8}$ at $(-1, 1)$; saddle point at $(0, 0)$; (a) **25.** Local minima of $-\dfrac{33}{16}$ at $(0, 1)$ and $(0, -1)$; saddle point at $(0, 0)$; (b) **27.** Local maxima of $\dfrac{17}{16}$ at $(1, 0)$ and $(-1, 0)$; local minima of $-\dfrac{15}{16}$ at $(0, 1)$ and $(0, -1)$; saddle points at $(0, 0)$, $(-1, 1)$, $(1, -1)$, $(1, 1)$, and $(-1, -1)$; (e)
29. $x = 4, y = 5; \$59$ **31.** $P(3, 9) = \$627$
33. $C(12, 25) = 2237$ **35.** 3 m $\times$ 3 m $\times$ 3 m
37. 36 in (length) $\times$ 18 in $\times$ 18 in **39.** Length 36 in; radius $36/\pi \approx 11.5$ in **41.** 1000 tons of grade A ore and 2000 tons of grade B ore. **43.** 6 tons of steel, 3 tons of aluminum, \$216,000

Section 14.4 (Page 852)

1. 200 when $x = 10$ and $y = 10$ **3.** $\dfrac{125}{4}$ when $x = 5$ and $y = \dfrac{5}{2}$
5. 28 when $x = 5$ and $y = 3$ **7.** 360 when $x = 20$ and $y = 2$
9. e^{-2} when $x = y = 1$ **11.** $\dfrac{81}{4}$ when $x = \dfrac{3}{2}, y = \dfrac{3}{2}$ and $z = 3$
13. $x = 7, y = 14$ **15.** $x = 34, y = 34, z = 34$ **17.** Answers vary.
19. Answers vary. **21.** $x = 2, y = 4$ **23.** About 166.67 units of labor and 177.78 units of capital **25.** 60 ft $\times$ 60 ft **27.** 50 m $\times$ 50 m
29. Radius 5 in; height 10 in **31.** About 12.91 m $\times$ 12.91 m $\times$ 6.45 m
33. 4 ft $\times$ 4 ft $\times$ 2 ft (height) **35.** **(a)** Let the sides with area xz and

the bottom be made from the free material; this gives the constraint.

It takes $\dfrac{400}{xyz}$ trips to transport the material at a cost of $\left(\dfrac{400}{xyz}\right)(.10)$. The

total cost also includes the material for the ends of the box.

(b) $x = 2$ yd, $y = 1$ yd, $z = .5$ yd

Chapter 14 Review Exercises (Page 855)

Refer to Section	14.1	14.2	14.3	14.4
For Exercises	1–12, 35–36	13–34, 37–38	39–48	49–54

1. 15; 84   **3.** Not defined; -6 **5.** -21; Not defined

7. Answers vary.

9.

11.

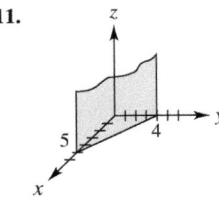

13. **(a)** $-4x + 5y$ **(b)** 3 **(c)** 5   **15.** Answers vary.

17. $f_x = -14xy^3; f_y = 3 - 21x^2y^2$

19. $f_x = \dfrac{3x}{\sqrt{3x^2 + 2y^2}}; f_y = \dfrac{2y}{\sqrt{3x^2 + 2y^2}}$

21. $f_x = \dfrac{-5x^2y - 16xy^4}{(5x + 8y^3)^2}; f_y = \dfrac{-5x^3 + 16x^2y^3}{(5x + 8y^3)^2}$

23. $f_x = 3x^2e^{3y}; f_y = 3x^3e^{3y}$ **25.** $f_x = \dfrac{2x}{x^2 - 4y^3}; f_y = \dfrac{-12y^2}{x^2 - 4y^3}$

27. $f_{xx} = 24xy^2; f_{xy} = 24x^2y - 8$

29. $f_{xx} = \dfrac{10y}{(x - 2y)^3}; f_{xy} = \dfrac{-5x - 10y}{(x - 2y)^3}$ **31.** $f_{xx} = 2e^y; f_{xy} = 2xe^y$

33. $f_{xx} = \dfrac{-2x^2y^2 - 4y}{(2 - x^2y)^2}; f_{xy} = -\dfrac{4x}{(2 - x^2y)^2}$

35. **(a)** \$450 **(b)** \$646 **(c)** \$1030   **37.** **(a)** $\dfrac{1}{2}$ **(b)** 9

39. Local minimum at $(0, 1)$ **41.** Saddle point at $(0, 2)$

43. Local minimum at $\left(1, \dfrac{1}{2}\right)$; saddle point at $\left(-\dfrac{1}{3}, \dfrac{11}{6}\right)$

45. Local minimum at $(0, 0)$

47. **(a)** $x = 11, y = 12$ **(b)** \$431

49. Minimum of 2 when $x = 1$ and $y = -1$ **51.** $\dfrac{160}{3}$ and $\dfrac{80}{3}$

53. Answers vary.

Case Study 14 Exercises (Page 857)

1. The second-derivative test shows that the critical point is a local minimum.   **3.** $y = .01x - 11.08$

Index of Companies, Products, and Agencies

Index of Applications

Physical Science

Social Science

Subject Index

Taken from:
Mathematical Ideas, Twelfth Edition
by Charles D. Miller, Vern E. Heeren, John Hornsby,
Margaret L. Morrow and Jill Van Newenhizen

INTRODUCTION TO LOGIC 3

In the 2007 movie *Shrek the Third*, Shrek searches for the rightful heir to the throne of the Kingdom of Far Far Away, while Prince Charming schemes to gain the throne for himself. The Prince, knowing that Pinocchio's nose grows if he lies, questions Pinocchio.

PRINCE CHARMING: So tell me puppet, where is Shrek?

PINOCCHIO: Well, I don't know where he's not.

PRINCE CHARMING: You're telling me you don't know where Shrek is?

PINOCCHIO: It wouldn't be inaccurate to assume that I couldn't exactly not say that is or isn't almost partially incorrect.

PRINCE CHARMING: So you do know where he is!

PINOCCHIO: On the contrary, I'm possibly more or less not definitely rejecting the idea that in no way, with any amount of uncertainty, that I undeniably do or do not know where he shouldn't probably be. If that indeed wasn't where he isn't. Even if he wasn't not where I knew he was, it could mean. . . .

Unable to contain his frustration with Pinocchio's roundabout answer, one of the Three Little Pigs blurts out that Shrek has gone to search for the rightful heir. The pig was unable to follow Pinocchio's logic, or lack of it. In this chapter, we examine the basics of the study of logic.

3.1 STATEMENTS AND QUANTIFIERS

Statements • Negations • Symbols • Quantifiers • Quantifiers and Number Sets

Statements

Gottfried Leibniz (1646–1716) was a wide-ranging philosopher and a universalist who tried to patch up Catholic–Protestant conflicts. He promoted cultural exchange between Europe and the East. Chinese ideograms led him to search for a universal symbolism. He was an early inventor of **symbolic logic.**

This section introduces the study of **symbolic logic,** which uses letters to represent statements, and symbols for words such as *and, or, not.* Logic is used in the study of the **truth value** (that is, the truth or falsity) of statements with multiple parts. The truth value of such statements depends on their components.

Many kinds of sentences occur in ordinary language, including factual statements, opinions, commands, and questions. Symbolic logic discusses only the type that involves facts. A **statement** is a declarative sentence that is either true or false, but not both simultaneously.

Electronic mail provides a means of communication. $\left.\begin{array}{l}\\ \\\end{array}\right\}$ Statements
$$12 + 6 = 13$$ Each is either true or false.

Access the file.
Did the Saints win the Super Bowl? $\left.\begin{array}{l}\\ \\ \\\end{array}\right\}$ Not statements
Tim Lincecum is a better baseball player than Cliff Lee. Each cannot be identified as being either true or false.
This sentence is false.

Of the sentences that are not statements, the first is a command, and the second is a question. The third is an opinion. "This sentence is false" is a paradox: If we assume it is true, then it is false, and if we assume it is false, then it is true.

A **compound statement** may be formed by combining two or more statements. The statements making up a compound statement are called **component statements.** Various **logical connectives,** or simply **connectives,** such as *and, or, not,* and *if . . . then,* can be used in forming compound statements. (While a statement such as "Today is not Tuesday" does not consist of two component statements, for convenience it is considered compound, because its truth value is determined by noting the truth value of a different statement, "Today is Tuesday.")

▌▌ EXAMPLE 1 Deciding Whether a Statement Is Compound

Decide whether each statement is compound. If so, identify the connective.

(a) Lord Byron wrote sonnets, and the poem exhibits iambic pentameter.

(b) You can pay me now, or you can pay me later.

(c) If he said it, then it must be true.

(d) My pistol was made by Smith and Wesson.

SOLUTION

(a) This statement is compound, because it is made up of the component statements "Lord Byron wrote sonnets" and "the poem exhibits iambic pentameter." The connective is *and*.

(b) The connective here is *or.* The statement is compound.

(c) The connective here is *if . . . then*, discussed in more detail in **Section 3.3.** The statement is compound.

(d) While the word "and" is used in this statement, it is not used as a *logical* connective. It is part of the name of the manufacturer. The statement is not compound. ▄▄▄

Negations

The sentence "Anthony Mansella has a red truck" is a statement. The **negation** of this statement is "Anthony Mansella does not have a red truck." ***The negation of a true statement is false, and the negation of a false statement is true.***

▌▌ **EXAMPLE 2** Forming Negations

Form the negation of each statement.

(a) That city has a mayor.   **(b)** The moon is not a planet.

SOLUTION

(a) To negate this statement, we introduce *not* into the sentence: "That city does not have a mayor."

(b) The negation is "The moon is a planet." ▄▄▄

One way to detect incorrect negations is to check truth values. *A negation must have the opposite truth value from the original statement.*

The next example uses some of the inequality symbols in **Table 1**. In the case of an inequality involving a variable, the negation must have the opposite truth value for *any* replacement of the variable.

```
TEST  LOGIC
1: =
2: ≠
3: >
4: ≥
5: <
6: ≤
```

The TEST menu of the TI-83/84 Plus calculator allows the user to test the truth or falsity of statements involving $=$, $\neq$, $>$, $\geq$, $<$, and $\leq$. If a statement is true, it returns a 1. If it is false, it returns a 0.

Table 1

Symbolism	Meaning	Examples	
$a < b$	a is less than b	$4 < 9$	$\frac{1}{2} < \frac{3}{4}$
$a > b$	a is greater than b	$6 > 2$	$-5 > -11$
$a \leq b$	a is less than or equal to b	$8 \leq 10$	$3 \leq 3$
$a \geq b$	a is greater than or equal to b	$-2 \geq -3$	$-5 \geq -5$

▌▌ **EXAMPLE 3** Negating Inequalities

```
4<9
            1
4>9
            0
```

4 < 9 is true, as indicated by the 1.
4 > 9 is false, as indicated by the 0.

Give a negation of each inequality. Do *not* use a slash symbol.

(a) $x < 9$ **(b)** $7x + 11y \geq 77$

SOLUTION

(a) The negation of "x is less than 9" is "x is *not* less than 9." Because we cannot use "not," which would require writing $x \not< 9$, phrase the negation as "x is greater than or equal to 9," or

$$x \geq 9.$$

(b) The negation, with no slash, is

$$7x + 11y < 77.$$ ▄▄▄

Symbols

The study of logic uses symbols. Statements are represented with letters, such as *p*, *q*, or *r*. Several symbols for connectives are shown in **Table 2**.

Table 2

Connective	Symbol	Type of Statement
and	$\wedge$	Conjunction
or	$\vee$	Disjunction
not	$\sim$	Negation

The symbol $\sim$ represents the connective *not*. If *p* represents the statement "Barack Obama was president in 2009" then $\sim p$ represents "Barack Obama was not president in 2009."

▌▌ **EXAMPLE 4** Translating from Symbols to Words

Let *p* represent "It is 70° today," and let *q* represent "It is Tuesday." Write each symbolic statement in words.

(a) $p \vee q$ **(b)** $\sim p \wedge q$ **(c)** $\sim(p \vee q)$ **(d)** $\sim(p \wedge q)$

SOLUTION

(a) From the table, $\vee$ symbolizes *or*. Thus, $p \vee q$ represents

It is 70° today or it is Tuesday.

(b) It is not 70° today and it is Tuesday.

(c) It is not the case that it is 70° today or it is Tuesday.

(d) It is not the case that it is 70° today and it is Tuesday.   ▌▌▌

The statement in **Example 4(c)** usually is translated as **"Neither *p* nor *q*."**

Quantifiers

Quantifiers are used to indicate *how many* cases of a particular situation exist. The words **all, each, every,** and **no(ne)** are called **universal quantifiers,** while words and phrases such as **some, there exists,** and **(for) at least one** are called **existential quantifiers. *Be careful when forming the negation of a statement involving quantifiers.***
     The negation of a statement must be false if the given statement is true and must be true if the given statement is false, in all possible cases. Consider this statement.

All girls in the group are named Mary.

Many people would write the negation of this statement as "No girls in the group are named Mary" or "All girls in the group are not named Mary." But neither of these is correct. To see why, look at the three groups below.

> *Group I:*   Mary Jane Payne, Mary Meyer, Mary O'Hara
> *Group II:*   Mary Johnson, Lisa Pollak, Margaret Watson
> *Group III:*   Donna Garbarino, Paula Story, Rhonda Alessi, Kim Falgout

These groups contain all possibilities that need to be considered. In Group I, *all* girls are named Mary. In Group II, *some* girls are named Mary (and some are not). In Group III, *no* girls are named Mary. Look at the truth values in **Table 3** on the next page, and keep in mind that "some" means "at least one (and possibly all)."

Aristotle, the first to systematize the logic we use in everyday life, appears above in a detail from the painting *The School of Athens*, by Raphael. He is shown debating a point with his teacher **Plato.**

Table 3

Truth Value as Applied to:	Group I	Group II	Group III
(1) All girls in the group are named Mary. (Given)	T	F	F
(2) No girls in the group are named Mary. (Possible negation)	F	F	T
(3) All girls in the group are not named Mary. (Possible negation)	F	F	T
(4) Some girls in the group are not named Mary. (Possible negation)	F	T	T

Negation (from (1) and (4) in Group III)

The negation of the given statement (1) must have opposite truth values in *all* cases. It can be seen that statements (2) and (3) do not satisfy this condition (for Group II), but statement (4) does. It may be concluded that the correct negation for "All girls in the group are named Mary" is "Some girls in the group are not named Mary." Other ways of stating the negation include the following.

Not all girls in the group are named Mary.

It is not the case that all girls in the group are named Mary.

At least one girl in the group is not named Mary.

Table 4 shows how to find the negation of a statement involving quantifiers.

Table 4 Negations of Quantified Statements

Statement	Negation
All do.	Some do not. (Equivalently: Not all do.)
Some do.	None do. (Equivalently: All do not.)

The negation of the negation of a statement is simply the statement itself. For instance, the negations of the statements in the Negation column are simply the corresponding original statements in the Statement column. As an example, the negation of "Some do not" is "All do."

EXAMPLE 5 Forming Negations of Quantified Statements

Form the negation of each statement.

(a) Some cats have fleas. **(b)** Some cats do not have fleas.

(c) No cats have fleas.

SOLUTION

(a) Because *some* means "at least one," the statement "Some cats have fleas" is really the same as "At least one cat has fleas." The negation of this is

"No cat has fleas."

(b) The statement "Some cats do not have fleas" claims that at least one cat, somewhere, does not have fleas. The negation of this is

"All cats have fleas."

(c) The negation is "Some cats have fleas."

Avoid the incorrect answer "All cats have fleas."

Quantifiers and Number Sets

Earlier we introduced sets of numbers.

Sets of Numbers

Natural or Counting numbers $\{1, 2, 3, 4, \ldots\}$

Whole numbers $\{0, 1, 2, 3, 4, \ldots\}$

Integers $\{\ldots, -3, -2, -1, 0, 1, 2, 3, \ldots\}$

Rational numbers $\left\{\frac{p}{q} \mid p \text{ and } q \text{ are integers, and } q \neq 0\right\}$

(*Examples:* $\frac{3}{5}$, $-\frac{7}{9}$, 5, 0. Any rational number may be expressed as a terminating decimal number, such as 0.25, or a repeating decimal number, such as 0.666 ....)

Real numbers $\{x \mid x \text{ is a number that can be written as a decimal}\}$

Irrational numbers $\{x \mid x \text{ is a real number and } x \text{ cannot be written as a quotient of integers}\}$

(*Examples:* $\sqrt{2}$, $\sqrt[3]{4}$, π. Decimal representations of irrational numbers are neither terminating nor repeating.)

EXAMPLE 6 Deciding Whether Quantified Statements Are True or False

Decide whether each statement involving a quantifier is *true* or *false*.

(a) There exists a whole number that is not a natural number.

(b) Every integer is a natural number.

(c) Every natural number is a rational number.

(d) There exists an irrational number that is not real.

SOLUTION

(a) Because there is such a whole number (it is 0), this statement is true.

(b) This statement is false, because we can find at least one integer that is not a natural number. For example, −1 is an integer but is not a natural number.

(c) Because every natural number can be written as a fraction with denominator 1, this statement is true.

(d) In order to be an irrational number, a number must first be real. Because we cannot give an irrational number that is not real, this statement is false. (Had we been able to find at least one, the statement would have then been true.) ■■■

3.1 EXERCISES

Decide whether each is a statement or is not a statement.

1. February 2, 2009, was a Monday.

2. The ZIP code for Oscar, LA, is 70762.

3. Listen, my children, and you shall hear of the midnight ride of Paul Revere.

4. Yield to oncoming traffic.

5. $5 + 9 \neq 14$ and $4 - 1 = 12$

6. $5 + 9 \neq 12$ or $4 - 2 = 5$

7. Some numbers are positive.

8. Millard Fillmore was president of the United States in 1851.

9. Accidents are the main cause of deaths of children under the age of 7.

10. *The Dark Knight* was the top-grossing movie of 2008.

11. Where are you going tomorrow?

12. Behave yourself and sit down.

13. Kevin "Catfish" McCarthy once took a prolonged continuous shower for 340 hours, 40 minutes.

14. One gallon of milk weighs more than 3 pounds.

Decide whether each statement is compound.

15. I read the *Detroit Free Press*, and I read the *Sacramento Bee*.

16. My brother got married in Copenhagen.

17. Tomorrow is Saturday.

18. Mamie Zwettler is younger than 18 years of age, and so is her friend Emma Lister.

19. Jay Beckenstein's wife loves Ben and Jerry's ice cream.

20. The sign on the back of the car read "Canada or bust!"

21. If Lorri Morgan sells her quota, then Michelle Cook will be happy.

22. If Bobby is a politician, then Mitch is a crook.

Write a negation for each statement.

23. Her aunt's name is Hermione.

24. The flowers are to be watered.

25. Every dog has its day.

26. No rain fell in southern California today.

27. Some books are longer than this book.

28. All students present will get another chance.

29. No computer repairman can play blackjack.

30. Some people have all the luck.

31. Everybody loves somebody sometime.

32. Everyone loves a winner.

Give a negation of each inequality. Do not use a slash symbol.

33. $x > 12$

34. $x < -6$

35. $x \geq 5$

36. $x \leq 19$

37. Try to negate the sentence "The exact number of words in this sentence is ten" and see what happens. Explain the problem that arises.

38. Explain why the negation of "$x > 5$" is not "$x < 5$."

Let p represent the statement "She has green eyes" and let q represent the statement "He is 60 years old." Translate each symbolic compound statement into words.

39. $\sim p$

40. $\sim q$

41. $p \wedge q$

42. $p \vee q$

43. $\sim p \vee q$

44. $p \wedge \sim q$

45. $\sim p \vee \sim q$

46. $\sim p \wedge \sim q$

47. $\sim(\sim p \wedge q)$

48. $\sim(p \vee \sim q)$

Let p represent the statement "Chris collects DVDs" and let q represent the statement "Josh is an art major." Convert each compound statement into symbols.

49. Chris collects DVDs and Josh is not an art major.

50. Chris does not collect DVDs or Josh is not an art major.

51. Chris does not collect DVDs or Josh is an art major.

52. Josh is an art major and Chris does not collect DVDs.

53. Neither Chris collects DVDs nor Josh is an art major.

54. Either Josh is an art major or Chris collects DVDs, and it is not the case that both Josh is an art major and Chris collects DVDs.

55. Incorrect use of quantifiers often is heard in everyday language. Suppose you hear that a local electronics chain is having a 40% off sale, and the radio advertisement states "All items are not available in all stores." Do you think that, literally translated, the ad really means what it says? What do you think is really meant? Explain your answer.

56. Repeat **Exercise 55** for the following: "All people don't have the time to devote to maintaining their vehicles properly."

Refer to the groups of art labeled A, B, and C, and identify by letter the group or groups that are satisfied by the given statements involving quantifiers.

A

B

C

57. All pictures have frames.

58. No picture has a frame.

59. At least one picture does not have a frame.

60. Not every picture has a frame.

61. At least one picture has a frame.

62. No picture does not have a frame.

63. All pictures do not have frames.

64. Not every picture does not have a frame.

Decide whether each statement in Exercises 65–74 involving a quantifier is true *or* false.

65. Every whole number is an integer.

66. Every natural number is an integer.

67. There exists a rational number that is not an integer.

68. There exists an integer that is not a natural number.

69. All rational numbers are real numbers.

70. All irrational numbers are real numbers.

71. Some rational numbers are not integers.

72. Some whole numbers are not rational numbers.

73. Each whole number is a positive number.

74. Each rational number is a positive number.

75. Explain the difference between the following statements.

All students did not pass the test.
Not all students passed the test.

76. The statement "For some real number x, $x^2 \geq 0$" is true. However, your friend does not understand why, because he claims that $x^2 \geq 0$ is true for *all* real numbers x (and not *some*). How would you explain his misconception to him?

77. Write the following statement using "every": There is no one here who has not done that at one time or another.

78. Only one of these statements is true. Which one is it?
A. For some real number x, $x \not< 0$.
B. For all real numbers x, $x^3 > 0$.
C. For all real numbers x less than 0, x^2 is also less than 0.
D. For some real number x, $x^2 < 0$.

3.2 TRUTH TABLES AND EQUIVALENT STATEMENTS

Conjunctions • Disjunctions • Negations • Mathematical Statements • Truth Tables • Alternative Method for Constructing Truth Tables • Equivalent Statements and De Morgan's Laws

Conjunctions

Truth values of component statements are used to find truth values of compound statements. To begin, we must decide on truth values of the **conjunction p and q,** symbolized $p \wedge q$. Here, the connective *and* implies the idea of "both." The following statement is true, because each component statement is true.

Monday immediately follows Sunday and March immediately follows February.

True

On the other hand, the following statement is false, even though part of the statement (Monday immediately follows Sunday) is true.

Monday immediately follows Sunday and March immediately follows January.

False

For the conjunction p ∧ q to be true, both p and q must be true. This result is summarized by a table, called a **truth table,** which shows all four of the possible combinations of truth values for the conjunction *p and q.*

Truth Table for the Conjunction   *p* and *q*

	p and *q*	
p	*q*	*p* ∧ *q*
T	T	T
T	F	F
F	T	F
F	F	F

▮▮ **EXAMPLE 1** Finding the Truth Value of a Conjunction

5>3 and 6<0

        0

The calculator returns a "0" for 5 > 3 *and* 6 < 0, indicating that the statement is false.

Let *p* represent "5 > 3" and let *q* represent "6 < 0." Find the truth value of *p* ∧ *q*.

SOLUTION

Here *p* is true and *q* is false. Looking in the second row of the conjunction truth table shows that *p* ∧ *q* is false. ▮▮▮

In some cases, the logical connective *but* is used in compound statements.

He wants to go to the mountains but she wants to go to the beach.

Here, *but* is used in place of *and* to give a different emphasis to the statement. We consider this statement as we would consider the conjunction using the word *and.* The truth table for the conjunction, given above, would apply.

Disjunctions

In ordinary language, the word *or* can be ambiguous. The expression "this or that" can mean either "this or that or both," or "this or that but not both." For example, consider the following statement.

I will paint the wall or I will paint the ceiling.

This statement probably means: "I will paint the wall or I will paint the ceiling or I will paint both." On the other hand, consider the following statement.

I will drive the Lexus or the BMW to the store.

It probably means "I will drive the Lexus, or I will drive the BMW, but I will not drive both."

The symbol ∨ represents the first *or* described. That is,

p ∨ q   **means**   **"p or q or both."**   Disjunction

With this meaning of *or*, *p* ∨ *q* is called the **inclusive disjunction,** or just the **disjunction** of *p* and *q*. In everyday language, the disjunction implies the idea of "either." For example, consider the following disjunction.

I have a quarter or I have a dime.

It is true whenever I have either a quarter, a dime, or both. The only way this disjunction could be false would be if I had neither coin. ***The disjunction p ∨ q is false only if both component statements are false.***

The calculator returns a "1" for $5 > 3$ *or* $6 < 0$, indicating that the statement is true.

Truth Table for the Disjunction   *p* or *q*

p or *q*

p	*q*	*p* ∨ *q*
T	T	T
T	F	T
F	T	T
F	F	F

▮▮ **EXAMPLE 2**   Finding the Truth Value of a Disjunction

Table 5

Statement	Reason That It Is True
$8 \geq 8$	$8 = 8$
$3 \geq 1$	$3 > 1$
$-5 \leq -3$	$-5 < -3$
$-4 \leq -4$	$-4 = -4$

Let *p* represent "$5 > 3$" and let *q* represent "$6 < 0$." Find the truth value of $p \vee q$.

SOLUTION

Here, as in **Example 1,** *p* is true and *q* is false. The second row of the disjunction truth table shows that $p \vee q$ is true.   ▮▮▮

The symbol $\geq$ is read **"is greater than or equal to,"** while $\leq$ is read **"is less than or equal to."** If *a* and *b* are real numbers, then $a \leq b$ is true if $a < b$ or $a = b$. **Table 5** in the margin shows several statements and the reasons they are true.

Negations

The **negation** of a statement *p*, symbolized **~*p*,** must have the opposite truth value from the statement *p* itself. This leads to the truth table for the negation.

Truth Table for the Negation   not *p*

not *p*

p	~*p*
T	F
F	T

▮▮ **EXAMPLE 3**   Finding the Truth Value of a Compound Statement

Suppose *p* is false, *q* is true, and *r* is false. What is the truth value of the compound statement $\sim p \wedge (q \vee \sim r)$?

SOLUTION

Here parentheses are used to group *q* and ~*r* together. Work first inside the parentheses. Because *r* is false, ~*r* will be true. Because ~*r* is true and *q* is true, find the truth value of $q \vee \sim r$ by looking in the first row of the *or* truth table. This row gives the result T.

Because *p* is false, ~*p* is true, and the final truth value of $\sim p \wedge (q \vee \sim r)$ is found in the top row of the *and* truth table. From the *and* truth table, when ~*p* is true, and $q \vee \sim r$ is true, the statement

$$\sim p \wedge (q \vee \sim r) \quad \text{is true.}$$

We can use a short-cut symbolic method that involves replacing the statements with their truth values, letting T represent a true statement and F represent a false statement.

$$\sim p \wedge (q \vee \sim r)$$
$$\sim F \wedge (T \vee \sim F)$$ Work within parentheses first.
$$T \wedge (T \vee T)$$ ~F gives T.
$$T \wedge T$$ T ∨ T gives T.
The compound statement is true. → T   T ∧ T gives T.   ■■■

Mathematical Statements

We can use truth tables to determine the truth values of compound mathematical statements.

EXAMPLE 4 Deciding Whether a Compound Mathematical Statement Is True or False

Let p represent the statement $3 > 2$, q represent $5 < 4$, and r represent $3 < 8$. Decide whether each statement is *true* or *false*.

(a) $\sim p \wedge \sim q$ **(b)** $\sim(p \wedge q)$ **(c)** $(\sim p \wedge r) \vee (\sim q \wedge \sim p)$

SOLUTION

(a) Because p is true, $\sim p$ is false. By the *and* truth table, if one part of an "and" statement is false, the entire statement is false.

$$\sim p \wedge \sim q \ \text{ is false.}$$

(b) For $\sim(p \wedge q)$, first work within the parentheses. Because p is true and q is false, $p \wedge q$ is false by the *and* truth table. Next, apply the negation. The negation of a false statement is true.

$$\sim(p \wedge q) \ \text{ is true.}$$

(c) Here p is true, q is false, and r is true. This makes $\sim p$ false and $\sim q$ true. By the *and* truth table, $\sim p \wedge r$ is false, and $\sim q \wedge \sim p$ is also false. By the *or* truth table,

$$(\sim p \wedge r) \vee (\sim q \wedge \sim p) \ \text{ is false.}$$
$$\downarrow \qquad\qquad \downarrow$$
$$\text{F} \quad \vee \quad \text{F}$$ (Alternatively, see **Example 8(b)**.)   ■■■

When a quantifier is used with a conjunction or a disjunction, we must be careful in determining the truth value, as shown in the following example.

EXAMPLE 5 Deciding Whether a Quantified Mathematical Statement Is True or False

Decide whether each statement is *true* or *false*.

(a) For some real number x, $x < 5$ and $x > 2$.

(b) For every real number x, $x > 0$ or $x < 1$.

(c) For all real numbers x, $x^2 > 0$.

SOLUTION

(a) Replacing x with 3 (as an example) gives $3 < 5$ and $3 > 2$. Because both $3 < 5$ and $3 > 2$ are true statements, the given statement is true by the *and* truth table. (Remember: *Some* means "at least one.")

not(3>2) and not (5<4)   0

not((3>2) and (5<4))   1

Example 4(a) explains why

$$\sim(3 > 2) \wedge [\sim(5 < 4)]$$

is false. The calculator returns a 0. For a true statement such as

$$\sim[(3 > 2) \wedge (5 < 4)],$$

it returns a 1.

George Boole (1815–1864) grew up in poverty. His father, a London tradesman, gave him his first mathematics lessons and taught him to make optical instruments. Boole was largely self-educated. At 16 he worked in an elementary school and by age 20 had opened his own school. He studied mathematics in his spare time. He died of lung disease at age 49.

Boole's ideas have been used in the design of computers and telephone systems.

(b) No matter which real number might be tried as a replacement for x, at least one of the two statements

$$x > 0, \quad x < 1$$

will be true. Because an "or" statement is true if one or both component statements are true, the entire statement as given is true.

(c) Because the quantifier is a universal quantifier, we need only find one case in which the inequality is false to make the entire statement false. Can we find a real number whose square is not positive (that is, not greater than 0)? Yes, we can—0 is the *only* real number whose square is not positive. This statement is false. ▮▮▮

For Further Thought

Whose Picture Am I Looking At?

Raymond Smullyan is one of today's foremost writers of logic puzzles. This professor of mathematics and philosophy is now retired from Indiana University and has written several books on recreational logic, including *What Is the Name of This Book?*, *The Lady or the Tiger?*, and *Alice in Puzzleland*. The first of these includes the following puzzle, which has been around for many years.

For Group or Individual Investigation

A man is looking at a portrait. Someone asked him, "Whose picture are you looking at?" He replied: "Brothers and sisters, I have none, but this man's father is my father's son. ("This man's father" means, of course, the father of the man in the picture.)
 Whose picture was the man looking at? (The answer is on **page 96.**)

p	q	Compound Statement
T	T	
T	F	
F	T	
F	F	

Truth Tables

In the preceding examples, the truth value for a given statement was found by going back to the basic truth tables. In the long run, it is easier to first create a complete truth table for the given statement itself. Then final truth values can be read directly from this table.

In this book we use the standard format shown in the margin for listing the possible truth values in compound statements involving two component statements.

▮▮ **EXAMPLE 6** Constructing a Truth Table

Consider the statement $(\sim p \wedge q) \vee \sim q$.

(a) Construct a truth table.

(b) Suppose both p and q are true. Find the truth value of the compound statement.

SOLUTION

(a) Begin by listing all possible combinations of truth values for p and q, as above. Then list the truth values of $\sim p$, which are the opposite of those of p, as shown in the table in the margin.

p	q	$\sim p$
T	T	F
T	F	F
F	T	T
F	F	T

Use only the "~p" column and the "q" column, along with the *and* truth table, to find the truth values of ~p ∧ q. List them in a separate column.

p	q	~p	~p ∧ q
T	T	F	F
T	F	F	F
F	T	T	T
F	F	T	F

Next include a column for ~q.

p	q	~p	~p ∧ q	~q
T	T	F	F	F
T	F	F	F	T
F	T	T	T	F
F	F	T	F	T

Finally, make a column for the entire compound statement. To find the truth values, use *or* to combine ~p ∧ q with ~q.

p	q	~p	~p ∧ q	~q	(~p ∧ q) ∨ ~q
T	T	F	F	F	F
T	F	F	F	T	T
F	T	T	T	F	T
F	F	T	F	T	T

(b) Look in the first row of the final truth table above, where both p and q have truth value T. Read across the row to find that the compound statement is false. ▮▮▮

EXAMPLE 7 Constructing a Truth Table

Construct the truth table for $p \land (\sim p \lor \sim q)$.

SOLUTION
Proceed as shown.

p	q	~p	~q	~p ∨ ~q	p ∧ (~p ∨ ~q)
T	T	F	F	F	F
T	F	F	T	T	T
F	T	T	F	T	F
F	F	T	T	T	F

Emilie, Marquise du Châtelet
(1706–1749) participated in the scientific activity of the generation after Newton and Leibniz. Educated in science, music, and literature, she was studying mathematics at the time (1733) she began a long intellectual relationship with the philosopher **François Voltaire** (1694–1778). She and Voltaire competed independently in 1738 for a prize offered by the French Academy on the subject of fire. Although du Châtelet did not win, her dissertation was published by the academy in 1744.

If a compound statement involves three component statements p, q, and r, we will use the following standard format in setting up the truth table.

p	q	r	Compound Statement
T	T	T	
T	T	F	
T	F	T	
T	F	F	
F	T	T	
F	T	F	
F	F	T	
F	F	F	

▮▮▮

▌▌ **EXAMPLE 8** Constructing a Truth Table

Consider the statement $(\sim p \wedge r) \vee (\sim q \wedge \sim p)$.

(a) Construct a truth table.

(b) Suppose p is true, q is false, and r is true. Find the truth value of this statement.

SOLUTION

(a) There are three component statements: p, q, and r. The truth table thus requires eight rows to list all possible combinations of truth values of p, q, and r. The final truth table can be found in much the same way as the ones earlier.

p	q	r	$\sim p$	$\sim p \wedge r$	$\sim q$	$\sim q \wedge \sim p$	$(\sim p \wedge r) \vee (\sim q \wedge \sim p)$
T	T	T	F	F	F	F	F
T	T	F	F	F	F	F	F
T	F	T	F	F	T	F	F
T	F	F	F	F	T	F	F
F	T	T	T	T	F	F	T
F	T	F	T	F	F	F	F
F	F	T	T	T	T	T	T
F	F	F	T	F	T	T	T

(b) By the third row of the truth table in part (a), the compound statement is false. (This is an alternative method for working part (c) of **Example 4**.) ▌▌▌

PROBLEM-SOLVING HINT One strategy for problem solving is to notice a pattern and use inductive reasoning. This strategy is applied in the next example.

▌▌ **EXAMPLE 9** Using Inductive Reasoning

If n is a counting number, and a logical statement is composed of n component statements, how many rows will appear in the truth table for the compound statement?

SOLUTION

To answer this question, we examine some of the earlier truth tables in this section. The truth table for the negation has one statement and two rows. The truth tables for the conjunction and the disjunction have two component statements, and each has four rows. The truth table in **Example 8(a)** has three component statements and eight rows.

Summarizing these in **Table 6** (seen in the margin) reveals a pattern encountered earlier. Inductive reasoning leads us to the conjecture that if a logical statement is composed of n component statements, it will have 2^n rows. This can be proved using more advanced concepts. ▌▌▌

Table 6

Number of Statements	Number of Rows
1	$2 = 2^1$
2	$4 = 2^2$
3	$8 = 2^3$

The result of **Example 9** is reminiscent of the formula for the number of subsets of a set having n elements.

Number of Rows in a Truth Table

A logical statement having n component statements will have 2^n rows in its truth table.

Alternative Method for Constructing Truth Tables

After making a reasonable number of truth tables, some people prefer the shortcut method shown in **Example 10,** which repeats **Examples 6 and 8.**

EXAMPLE 10 Constructing Truth Tables

Construct the truth table for each compound statement.

(a) $(\sim p \wedge q) \vee \sim q$ **(b)** $(\sim p \wedge r) \vee (\sim q \wedge \sim p)$

SOLUTION

(a) Start by inserting truth values for $\sim p$ and for q. Then, use the *and* truth table to obtain the truth values for $\sim p \wedge q$.

p	q	$(\sim p$	$\wedge$	$q)$	$\vee$	$\sim q$
T	T	F		T		
T	F	F		F		
F	T	T		T		
F	F	T		F		

p	q	$(\sim p$	$\wedge$	$q)$	$\vee$	$\sim q$
T	T	F	F	T		
T	F	F	F	F		
F	T	T	T	T		
F	F	T	F	F		

Now disregard the two preliminary columns of truth values for $\sim p$ and for q, and insert truth values for $\sim q$. Finally, use the *or* truth table.

p	q	$(\sim p \wedge q)$	$\vee$	$\sim q$
T	T	F		F
T	F	F		T
F	T	T		F
F	F	F		T

p	q	$(\sim p \wedge q)$	$\vee$	$\sim q$
T	T	F	F	F
T	F	F	T	T
F	T	T	T	F
F	F	F	T	T

These steps can be summarized as follows.

p	q	$(\sim p$	$\wedge$	$q)$	$\vee$	$\sim q$
T	T	F	F	T	F	F
T	F	F	F	F	T	T
F	T	T	T	T	T	F
F	F	T	F	F	T	T
		①	②	①	④	③

> The circled numbers indicate the order in which the various columns of the truth table were found.

(b) Work as follows.

p	q	r	$(\sim p$	$\wedge$	$r)$	$\vee$	$(\sim q$	$\wedge$	$\sim p)$
T	T	T	F	F	T	F	F	F	F
T	T	F	F	F	F	F	F	F	F
T	F	T	F	F	T	F	T	F	F
T	F	F	F	F	F	F	T	F	F
F	T	T	T	T	T	T	F	F	T
F	T	F	T	F	F	F	F	F	T
F	F	T	T	T	T	T	T	T	T
F	F	F	T	F	F	T	T	T	T
			①	②	①	⑤	③	④	③

> The circled numbers indicate the order.

∎∎∎

Equivalent Statements and De Morgan's Laws

Two statements are **equivalent** if they have the same truth value in *every* possible situation. The columns of the two truth tables that were the last to be completed will be the same for equivalent statements.

▌▌ **EXAMPLE 11** Deciding Whether Two Statements Are Equivalent

Are the following two statements equivalent?

$$\sim p \wedge \sim q \quad \text{and} \quad \sim(p \vee q)$$

SOLUTION

Construct a truth table for each statement.

p	q	$\sim p \wedge \sim q$		p	q	$\sim(p \vee q)$
T	T	F		T	T	F
T	F	F		T	F	F
F	T	F		F	T	F
F	F	T		F	F	T

Because the truth values are the same in all cases, as shown in the columns in color, the statements $\sim p \wedge \sim q$ and $\sim(p \vee q)$ are equivalent. Equivalence is written with a three-bar symbol, $\equiv$.

$$\sim p \wedge \sim q \equiv \sim(p \vee q)$$

▌▌▌

In the same way, the statements $\sim p \vee \sim q$ and $\sim(p \wedge q)$ are equivalent. We call these equivalences *De Morgan's laws*.

De Morgan's Laws for Logical Statements

For any statements p and q, the following equivalences are valid.

$$\sim(p \vee q) \equiv \sim p \wedge \sim q \quad \text{and} \quad \sim(p \wedge q) \equiv \sim p \vee \sim q$$

(Compare the logic statements of De Morgan's laws with the set versions on **page 64.**) De Morgan's laws can be used to find the negations of certain compound statements.

▌▌ **EXAMPLE 12** Applying De Morgan's Laws

Find a negation of each statement by applying De Morgan's laws.

(a) I got an A or I got a B.   **(b)** She won't try and he will succeed.

(c) $\sim p \vee (q \wedge \sim p)$

SOLUTION

(a) If p represents "I got an A" and q represents "I got a B," then the compound statement is symbolized $p \vee q$. The negation of $p \vee q$ is $\sim(p \vee q)$. By one of De Morgan's laws, this is equivalent to

$$\sim p \wedge \sim q,$$

or, in words,   **I didn't get an A and I didn't get a B.**

This negation is reasonable—the original statement says that I got either an A or a B. The negation says that I didn't get *either* grade.

(b) From one of De Morgan's laws, $\sim(p \wedge q) \equiv \sim p \vee \sim q$, so the negation becomes

She will try or he won't succeed.

(c) Negate both component statements and change $\vee$ to $\wedge$.

$$\sim[\sim p \vee (q \wedge \sim p)] \equiv p \wedge \sim(q \wedge \sim p)$$

Now apply De Morgan's law again.

$$p \wedge \sim(q \wedge \sim p) \equiv p \wedge (\sim q \vee \sim(\sim p))$$
$$\equiv p \wedge (\sim q \vee p)$$

A truth table will show that the statements

$\sim p \vee (q \wedge \sim p)$ and $p \wedge (\sim q \vee p)$ are negations of each other.   ▮▮▮

3.2 EXERCISES

Use the concepts introduced in this section to answer Exercises 1–6.

1. If q is false, what must be the truth value of the statement $(p \wedge \sim q) \wedge q$?

2. If q is true, what must be the truth value of the statement $q \vee (q \wedge \sim p)$?

3. If the statement $p \wedge q$ is true, and p is true, then q must be _____.

4. If the statement $p \vee q$ is false, and p is false, then q must be _____.

5. If $\sim(p \vee q)$ is true, what must be the truth values of the component statements?

6. If $\sim(p \wedge q)$ is false, what must be the truth values of the component statements?

Let p represent a false statement and let q represent a true statement. Find the truth value of the given compound statement.

7. $\sim p$

8. $\sim q$

9. $p \vee q$

10. $p \wedge q$

11. $p \vee \sim q$

12. $\sim p \wedge q$

13. $\sim p \vee \sim q$

14. $p \wedge \sim q$

15. $\sim(p \wedge \sim q)$

16. $\sim(\sim p \vee \sim q)$

17. $\sim[\sim p \wedge (\sim q \vee p)]$

18. $\sim[(\sim p \wedge \sim q) \vee \sim q]$

19. Is the statement $6 \geq 2$ a conjunction or a disjunction? Why?

20. Why is the statement $8 \geq 3$ true? Why is $5 \geq 5$ true?

Let p represent a true statement, and q and r represent false statements. Find the truth value of the given compound statement.

21. $(p \wedge r) \vee \sim q$

22. $(q \vee \sim r) \wedge p$

23. $p \wedge (q \vee r)$

24. $(\sim p \wedge q) \vee \sim r$

25. $\sim(p \wedge q) \wedge (r \vee \sim q)$

26. $(\sim r \wedge \sim q) \vee (\sim r \wedge q)$

27. $\sim[(\sim p \wedge q) \vee r]$

28. $\sim[r \vee (\sim q \wedge \sim p)]$

29. $\sim[\sim q \vee (r \wedge \sim p)]$

30. What is the only possible case in which the statement $(p \wedge \sim q) \wedge \sim r$ is true?

Let p represent the statement $16 < 8$, let q represent the statement $5 \not> 4$, and let r represent the statement $17 \leq 17$. Find the truth value of the given compound statement.

31. $p \wedge r$

32. $p \vee \sim q$

33. $\sim q \vee \sim r$

34. $\sim p \wedge \sim r$

35. $(p \wedge q) \vee r$

36. $\sim p \vee (\sim r \vee \sim q)$

37. $(\sim r \wedge q) \vee \sim p$

38. $\sim(p \vee \sim q) \vee \sim r$

Give the number of rows in the truth table for each compound statement.

39. $p \vee \sim r$

40. $p \wedge (r \wedge \sim s)$

41. $(\sim p \wedge q) \vee (\sim r \vee \sim s) \wedge r$

42. $[(p \vee q) \wedge (r \wedge s)] \wedge (t \vee \sim p)$

43. $[(\sim p \wedge \sim q) \wedge (\sim r \wedge s \wedge \sim t)] \wedge (\sim u \vee \sim v)$

44. $[(\sim p \wedge \sim q) \vee (\sim r \vee \sim s)]$
       $\vee [(\sim m \wedge \sim n) \wedge (u \wedge \sim v)]$

45. If the truth table for a certain compound statement has 128 rows, how many distinct component statements does it have?

46. Is it possible for the truth table of a compound statement to have exactly 54 rows? Why or why not?

Construct a truth table for each compound statement.

47. $\sim p \wedge q$

48. $\sim p \vee \sim q$

49. $\sim(p \wedge q)$

50. $p \vee \sim q$

51. $(q \vee \sim p) \vee \sim q$

52. $(p \wedge \sim q) \wedge p$

53. $\sim q \wedge (\sim p \vee q)$ **54.** $\sim p \vee (\sim q \wedge \sim p)$

55. $(p \vee \sim q) \wedge (p \wedge q)$

56. $(\sim p \wedge \sim q) \vee (\sim p \vee q)$

57. $(\sim p \wedge q) \wedge r$

58. $r \vee (p \wedge \sim q)$

59. $(\sim p \wedge \sim q) \vee (\sim r \vee \sim p)$

60. $(\sim r \vee \sim p) \wedge (\sim p \vee \sim q)$

61. $\sim(\sim p \wedge \sim q) \vee (\sim r \vee \sim s)$

62. $(\sim r \vee s) \wedge (\sim p \wedge q)$

Use one of De Morgan's laws to write the negation of each statement.

63. You can pay me now or you can pay me later.

64. I am not going or she is going.

65. It is summer and there is no snow.

66. $\frac{1}{2}$ is a positive number and -9 is less than zero.

67. I said yes but she said no.

68. Dan La Chapelle tried to sell the software, but he was unable to do so.

69. $6 - 1 = 5$ and $9 + 13 \neq 7$

70. $8 < 10$ or $5 \neq 2$

71. Prancer or Vixen will lead Santa's reindeer sleigh next Christmas.

72. The lawyer and the client appeared in court.

Identify each statement as true *or* false.

73. For every real number x, $x < 14$ or $x > 6$.

74. For every real number x, $x > 9$ or $x < 9$.

75. There exists an integer n such that $n > 0$ and $n < 0$.

76. For some integer n, $n \geq 3$ and $n \leq 3$.

77. Complete the truth table for *exclusive disjunction*. The symbol $\underline{\vee}$ represents "one or the other is true, but not both."

p	q	$p \underline{\vee} q$
T	T	
T	F	
F	T	
F	F	

Exclusive disjunction

78. Attorneys sometimes use the phrase "and/or." This phrase corresponds to which usage of the word *or:* inclusive or exclusive disjunction?

Decide whether each compound statement is true *or* false. *Remember that* $\underline{\vee}$ *is the* exclusive disjunction of **Exercise 77.**

79. $3 + 1 = 4 \underline{\vee} 2 + 5 = 7$

80. $3 + 1 = 4 \underline{\vee} 2 + 5 = 10$

81. $3 + 1 = 6 \underline{\vee} 2 + 5 = 7$

82. $3 + 1 = 12 \underline{\vee} 2 + 5 = 10$

83. In his book *The Lady or the Tiger and Other Logic Puzzles,* Raymond Smullyan proposes the following problem. It is taken from the classic Frank Stockton short story, in which a prisoner must make a choice between two doors: behind one is a beautiful lady, and behind the other is a hungry tiger.

    What if each door has a sign, and the man knows that only one sign is true?

    The sign on Door 1 reads:

IN THIS ROOM THERE IS A LADY AND
IN THE OTHER ROOM THERE IS A TIGER.

    The sign on Door 2 reads:

IN ONE OF THESE ROOMS THERE IS A LADY AND IN ONE OF THESE ROOMS THERE IS A TIGER.

    With this information, the man is able to choose the correct door. Can you?

84. In Raymond Smullyan's books, he writes about an island in which certain inhabitants are called knights and others are called knaves. Knights always tell the truth, and knaves always lie. Every inhabitant is either a knight or a knave.

    Three inhabitants—A, B, and C—were standing together in a garden. A stranger passed by and asked A, "Are you a knight or a knave?" A answered, but rather indistinctly, so the stranger could not make out what he said. The stranger then asked B, "What did A say?" B replied "A said that he is a knave." At this point, the third inhabitant, C, said, "Don't believe B; he is lying!"

    The question is, what are B and C?

3.3 THE CONDITIONAL AND CIRCUITS

Conditionals • Negation of a Conditional • Circuits

In his April 21, 1989, five-star review of *Field of Dreams*, the *Chicago Sun-Times* movie critic Roger Ebert gave an explanation of why the movie has become an American classic.

There is a speech in this movie about baseball that is so simple and true that it is heartbreaking. And the whole attitude toward the players reflects that attitude. Why do they come back from the great beyond and play in this cornfield? Not to make any kind of vast, earthshattering statement, but simply to hit a few and field a few, and remind us of a good and innocent time.

The photo above was taken in 2007 in Dyersville, Iowa, at the actual scene of the filming. The carving "Ray Loves Annie" in the bleacher seats can be seen in a quick shot during the movie. It has weathered over time.

Conditionals

"If you build it, he will come."
  —The Voice in the movie *Field of Dreams*

Ray Kinsella, an Iowa farmer in the movie *Field of Dreams*, hears a voice from the sky. No one else, including his wife Annie, can hear it. Ray interprets it as a promise that if he builds a baseball field in his cornfield, then the ghost of Shoeless Joe Jackson (a baseball star in the early days of the twentieth century) would come to play on it.

This promise came in the form of a conditional statement. A **conditional** statement is a compound statement that uses the connective *if . . . then.*

> *If* I read for too long, *then* I get tired.
> *If* looks could kill, *then* I would be dead.
> *If* he doesn't get back soon, *then* you should go look for him.

Conditional statements

In each of these conditional statements, the component coming after the word *if* gives a condition (but not necessarily the only condition) under which the statement coming after *then* will be true. For example, "If it is over 90°, then I'll go to the mountains" tells one possible condition under which I will go to the mountains—if the temperature is over 90°.

The conditional is written with an arrow, so "if p, then q" is symbolized as follows.

$$p \rightarrow q \qquad \text{If } p, \text{then } q.$$

We read $p \rightarrow q$ as "**p implies q**" or "**if p, then q.**" In the conditional $p \rightarrow q$, the statement p is the **antecedent,** while q is the **consequent.**

The conditional connective may not always be explicitly stated. That is, it may be "hidden" in an everyday expression. For example, consider the following statement.

Big girls don't cry.

It can be written in *if . . . then* form as

If you're a big girl, *then* you don't cry.

As another example, consider this statement.

It is difficult to study when you are distracted.

It can be written

If you are distracted, *then* it is difficult to study.

In the quotation "If you build it, he will come" from the movie *Field of Dreams*, the word "then" is not stated but understood from the context of the statement. "You build it" is the antecedent, and "he will come" is the consequent.

The conditional truth table is a little harder to define than the tables in the previous section. To see how to define the conditional truth table, we analyze a statement made by a politician, Senator Laura Kennedy.

If I am elected, then taxes will go down.

There are four possible combinations of truth values for the two component statements. Let p represent "I am elected," and let q represent "Taxes will go down."

$\sqrt[3]{250}$ 90° (0, −3)

θ 45.5 ÷ 2⁻¹ ∞

$x = (4+8)−3$ |a|

$y = −x + 2$ ¼

10^2 ≥ $f(x) =$

The importance of **symbols** was emphasized by the American philosopher-logician **Charles Sanders Peirce** (1839–1914), who asserted the nature of humans as symbol-using or sign-using organisms. Symbolic notation is half of mathematics, Bertrand Russell once said.

You Lie! (or Do You?) Granted, the T for Case 3 is less obvious than the F for Case 2. However, the laws of symbolic logic permit only one of two truth values. Since no lie can be established in Case 3, we give the senator the benefit of the doubt. Likewise, *any* conditional statement is declared to be true whenever its antecedent is false.

As we analyze the four possibilities, it is helpful to think in terms of the following: "Did Senator Laura Kennedy lie?" If she lied, then the conditional statement is considered false. If she did not lie, then the conditional statement is considered true.

Possibility	Elected?	Taxes Go Down?	
1	Yes	Yes	p is T, q is T.
2	Yes	No	p is T, q is F.
3	No	Yes	p is F, q is T.
4	No	No	p is F, q is F.

The four possibilities are as follows.

1. In the first case assume that the senator was elected and taxes did go down (p is T, q is T). The senator told the truth, so place T in the first row of the truth table. (We do not claim that taxes went down *because* she was elected. It is possible that she had nothing to do with it at all.)

2. In the second case assume that the senator was elected and taxes did not go down (p is T, q is F). Then the senator did not tell the truth (that is, she lied). So we put F in the second row of the truth table.

3. In the third case assume that the senator was defeated, but taxes went down anyway (p is F, q is T). The senator did not lie. She only promised a tax reduction if she were elected. She said nothing about what would happen if she were not elected. In fact, her campaign promise gives no information about what would happen if she lost. Because we cannot say that the senator lied, place T in the third row of the truth table. (See the margin note.)

4. In the last case assume that the senator was defeated and taxes did not go down (p is F, q is F). We cannot blame her, because she only promised to reduce taxes if elected. Thus, T goes in the last row of the truth table.

The completed truth table for the conditional is defined as follows.

Truth Table for the Conditional   If p, then q

If p, then q

p	q	$p \rightarrow q$
T	T	T
T	F	F
F	T	T
F	F	T

The use of the conditional connective in no way implies a cause-and-effect relationship. Any two statements may have an arrow placed between them to create a compound statement. Consider this example.

If I pass mathematics, then the sun will rise the next day.

It is true, because the consequent is true. (See the special characteristics following **Example 1** on the next page.) There is, however, no cause-and-effect connection between my passing mathematics and the rising of the sun. The sun will rise no matter what grade I get.

▮▮ **EXAMPLE 1** Finding the Truth Value of a Conditional

Given that p, q, and r are all false, find the truth value of the statement.

$$(p \rightarrow \sim q) \rightarrow (\sim r \rightarrow q)$$

```
PROGRAM:SIGN
: Input A
: If A>0
: Then
: Disp "POSITIVE"
  :
  :
```

```
PROGRAM:SIGN
  :
: Else
: Disp "NOT POSITIVE"
: End
  :
```

```
prgmSIGN
?3
POSITIVE
                Done
```

```
prgmSIGN
?-5
NOT POSITIVE
                Done
```

Conditional statements are useful in writing programs. The short program in the first two screens determines whether a number is positive. Notice the lines that begin with *If* and *Then*.

SOLUTION

Using the short-cut method explained in **Example 3** of the previous section, we can replace p, q, and r with F (since each is false) and proceed as before, using the negation and conditional truth tables as necessary.

$$
\begin{array}{ccc}
(p \rightarrow \sim q) & \rightarrow & (\sim r \rightarrow q) \\
(F \rightarrow \sim F) & \rightarrow & (\sim F \rightarrow F) \\
(F \rightarrow T) & \rightarrow & (T \rightarrow F) \qquad \text{Use the negation truth table.} \\
T & \rightarrow & F \qquad\quad \text{Use the conditional truth table.} \\
& F &
\end{array}
$$

The statement $(p \rightarrow \sim q) \rightarrow (\sim r \rightarrow q)$ is false when p, q, and r are all false. ▮▮▮

Special Characteristics of Conditional Statements

1. $p \rightarrow q$ is false only when the antecedent is *true* and the consequent is *false*.

2. If the antecedent is *false*, then $p \rightarrow q$ is automatically *true*.

3. If the consequent is *true*, then $p \rightarrow q$ is automatically *true*.

▮▮ **EXAMPLE 2** Determining Whether a Conditional Is True or False

Write *true* or *false* for each statement. Here T represents a true statement, and F represents a false statement.

(a) $T \rightarrow (7 = 3)$ **(b)** $(8 < 2) \rightarrow F$ **(c)** $(4 \neq 3 + 1) \rightarrow T$

SOLUTION

(a) Because the antecedent is true, while the consequent, $7 = 3$, is false, the given statement is false by the first point mentioned above.

(b) The antecedent is false, so the given statement is true by the second observation.

(c) The consequent is true, making the statement true by the third characteristic of conditional statements. ▮▮▮

▮▮ **EXAMPLE 3** Constructing Truth Tables

Construct a truth table for each statement.

(a) $(\sim p \rightarrow \sim q) \rightarrow (\sim p \wedge q)$ **(b)** $(p \rightarrow q) \rightarrow (\sim p \vee q)$

SOLUTION

(a) Insert the truth values of $\sim p$ and $\sim q$. Find the truth values of $\sim p \rightarrow \sim q$.

p	q	$\sim p$	$\sim q$	$\sim p \rightarrow \sim q$
T	T	F	F	T
T	F	F	T	T
F	T	T	F	F
F	F	T	T	T

Next use $\sim p$ and q to find the truth values of $\sim p \wedge q$.

p	q	$\sim p$	$\sim q$	$\sim p \rightarrow \sim q$	$\sim p \wedge q$
T	T	F	F	T	F
T	F	F	T	T	F
F	T	T	F	F	T
F	F	T	T	T	F

Now find the truth values of $(\sim p \rightarrow \sim q) \rightarrow (\sim p \wedge q)$.

p	q	$\sim p$	$\sim q$	$\sim p \rightarrow \sim q$	$\sim p \wedge q$	$(\sim p \rightarrow \sim q) \rightarrow (\sim p \wedge q)$
T	T	F	F	T	F	F
T	F	F	T	T	F	F
F	T	T	F	F	T	T
F	F	T	T	T	F	F

(b) For $(p \rightarrow q) \rightarrow (\sim p \vee q)$, go through steps similar to the ones above.

p	q	$p \rightarrow q$	$\sim p$	$\sim p \vee q$	$(p \rightarrow q) \rightarrow (\sim p \vee q)$
T	T	T	F	T	T
T	F	F	F	F	T
F	T	T	T	T	T
F	F	T	T	T	T

▮▮▮

As the truth table in **Example 3(b)** shows, the statement

$$(p \rightarrow q) \rightarrow (\sim p \vee q)$$

is always true, no matter what the truth values of the components. Such a statement is called a **tautology.** Several other examples of tautologies (as can be checked by forming truth tables) are

$$p \vee \sim p, \quad p \rightarrow p, \quad \text{and} \quad (\sim p \vee \sim q) \rightarrow \sim(p \wedge q). \quad \text{Tautologies}$$

The truth tables in **Example 3** also could have been found by the alternative method shown in **Section 3.2.**

Negation of a Conditional

Suppose that someone makes the following conditional statement.

"If it rains, then I take my umbrella."

When will the person have lied to you? The only case in which you would have been misled is when it rains *and* the person does *not* take the umbrella. Letting p represent "it rains" and q represent "I take my umbrella," you might suspect that the symbolic statement

$$p \wedge \sim q$$

is a candidate for the negation of $p \rightarrow q$. This would imply that

$$\sim(p \rightarrow q) \equiv p \wedge \sim q.$$

This is indeed the case, as the following truth table indicates.

p	q	$p \rightarrow q$	$\sim(p \rightarrow q)$	$\sim q$	$p \wedge \sim q$
T	T	T	F	F	F
T	F	F	T	T	T
F	T	T	F	F	F
F	F	T	F	T	F

↑ ≡ ↑

In the 1959 Disney short film *Donald in Mathmagicland,* Donald Duck, dressed as Alice from Lewis Carroll's *Through the Looking Glass,* is attacked by a "none-too-friendly group of chess pieces." Logic and **chess** have been paired for centuries. Most scholars agree that chess dates back at least 1500 years, coming from Northern India and Afghanistan following trade routes through Persia.

Good chess players rely on memory, imagination, determination, and inspiration. They are pattern thinkers that use long-established sets of consequences and probabilities.

In the end, logic does not necessarily dictate the final outcome of any chess game, for if it did, humans would not stand a chance when playing faceless, number-crunching computers.
© Disney Enterprises, Inc.

Sources: www.imdb.com, Walter A. Smart.

Negation of $p \to q$

The negation of $p \to q$ is $p \wedge {\sim}q$.

Because

$$\sim(p \to q) \equiv p \wedge {\sim}q,$$

by negating each expression we have

$$\sim[\sim(p \to q)] \equiv \sim(p \wedge {\sim}q).$$

The left side of the above equivalence is $p \to q$, and one of De Morgan's laws can be applied to the right side.

$$p \to q \equiv {\sim}p \vee {\sim}({\sim}q)$$
$$p \to q \equiv {\sim}p \vee q$$

This final row indicates that a conditional may be written as a disjunction.

Writing a Conditional as a Disjunction

$p \to q$ is equivalent to ${\sim}p \vee q$.

▮▮ EXAMPLE 4 Determining Negations

Determine the negation of each statement.

(a) If you build it, he will come.   **(b)** All dogs have fleas.

> Do not try to negate a conditional with another conditional.

SOLUTION

(a) If b represents "you build it" and q represents "he will come," then the given statement can be symbolized by $b \to q$. The negation of $b \to q$, as shown earlier, is $b \wedge {\sim}q$, so the negation of the statement is

> You build it and he will not come.

(b) First, we must restate the given statement in *if . . . then* form.

> If it is a dog, then it has fleas.

Based on our earlier discussion, the negation is

> It is a dog and it does not have fleas.   ▮▮▮

As seen in **Example 4,** the negation of a conditional statement is written as a conjunction.

▮▮ EXAMPLE 5 Determining Statements Equivalent to Conditionals

Write each conditional as an equivalent statement without using *if . . . then.*

(a) If the Indians win the pennant, then Johnny will go to the World Series.

(b) If it's Borden's, it's got to be good.

SOLUTION

(a) Because the conditional $p \to q$ is equivalent to ${\sim}p \vee q$, let p represent "The Indians win the pennant" and q represent "Johnny will go to the World Series." Restate the conditional as

> The Indians do not win the pennant or Johnny will go to the World Series.

(b) If p represents "it's Borden's" and if q represents "it's got to be good," the conditional may be restated as

It's not Borden's or it's got to be good. ▋▋▋

Circuits

Figure 1

One of the first nonmathematical applications of symbolic logic was seen in the master's thesis of Claude Shannon in 1937. Shannon showed how logic could be used to design electrical circuits. His work was immediately used by computer designers. Then in the developmental stage, computers could be simplified and built for less money using the ideas of Shannon.

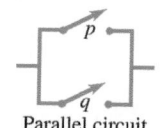

Series circuit

Figure 2

To see how Shannon's ideas work, look at the electrical switch shown in **Figure 1.** We assume that current will flow through this switch when it is closed and not when it is open.

Figure 2 shows two switches connected in *series*. In such a circuit, current will flow only when both switches are closed. Note how closely a series circuit corresponds to the conjunction $p \wedge q$. We know that $p \wedge q$ is true only when both p and q are true.

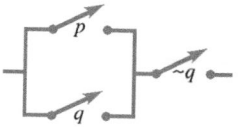

Parallel circuit

Figure 3

A circuit corresponding to the disjunction $p \vee q$ can be found by drawing a *parallel* circuit, as in **Figure 3.** Here, current flows if either p or q is closed or if both p and q are closed.

The circuit in **Figure 4** corresponds to the statement $(p \vee q) \wedge \sim q$, which is a compound statement involving both a conjunction and a disjunction.

Simplifying an electrical circuit depends on the idea of equivalent statements from **Section 3.2.** Recall that two statements are equivalent if they have the same truth table final column. The symbol ≡ is used to indicate that the two statements are equivalent. Some equivalent statements are shown in the following box.

Figure 4

Equivalent Statements Used to Simplify Circuits

$$p \vee (q \wedge r) \equiv (p \vee q) \wedge (p \vee r) \qquad p \vee p \equiv p$$
$$p \wedge (q \vee r) \equiv (p \wedge q) \vee (p \wedge r) \qquad p \wedge p \equiv p$$
$$p \to q \equiv \sim q \to \sim p \qquad \sim(p \wedge q) \equiv \sim p \vee \sim q$$
$$p \to q \equiv \sim p \vee q \qquad \sim(p \vee q) \equiv \sim p \wedge \sim q$$

If T represents any true statement and F represents any false statement, then

$$p \vee T \equiv T \qquad p \vee \sim p \equiv T$$
$$p \wedge F \equiv F \qquad p \wedge \sim p \equiv F.$$

Circuits can be used as models of compound statements, with a closed switch corresponding to T, while an open switch corresponds to F.

▋▋ **EXAMPLE 6** Simplifying a Circuit

Simplify the circuit of **Figure 5.**

Figure 5

SOLUTION

At the top of **Figure 5,** p and q are connected in series, and at the bottom, p and r are connected in series. These are interpreted as the compound statements $p \wedge q$ and $p \wedge r$, respectively. These two conjunctions are connected in parallel, as indicated by the figure treated as a whole.

Write the disjunction of the two conjunctions.

$$(p \wedge q) \vee (p \wedge r)$$

Figure 6

(Think of the two switches labeled "p" as being controlled by the same lever.) By one of the pairs of equivalent statements in the preceding box,

$$(p \wedge q) \vee (p \wedge r) \equiv p \wedge (q \vee r),$$

which has the circuit of **Figure 6.** This circuit is logically equivalent to the one in **Figure 5,** and yet it contains only three switches instead of four—which might well lead to a large savings in manufacturing costs. ▮▮▮

▮▮ **EXAMPLE 7** Drawing a Circuit for a Conditional Statement

Draw a circuit for $p \rightarrow (q \wedge \sim r)$.

SOLUTION

From the list of equivalent statements in the box, $p \rightarrow q$ is equivalent to $\sim p \vee q$. This equivalence gives $p \rightarrow (q \wedge \sim r) \equiv \sim p \vee (q \wedge \sim r)$, which has the circuit diagram in **Figure 7.** ▮▮▮

Figure 7

3.3 EXERCISES

Rewrite each statement using the if . . . then *connective. Rearrange the wording or add words as necessary.*

1. You can believe it if you see it on the Internet.

2. It must be alive if it is breathing.

3. Every integer divisible by 10 is divisible by 5.

4. All perfect square integers have units digit 0, 1, 4, 5, 6, or 9.

5. All Marines love boot camp.

6. Every picture tells a story.

7. No pandas live in Idaho.

8. No guinea pigs are scholars.

9. An opium eater cannot have self-command.

10. Running Bear loves Little White Dove.

Decide whether each statement is true *or* false.

11. If the antecedent of a conditional statement is false, the conditional statement is true.

12. If the consequent of a conditional statement is true, the conditional statement is true.

13. If q is true, then $(p \wedge q) \rightarrow q$ is true.

14. If p is true, then $\sim p \rightarrow (q \vee r)$ is true.

15. The negation of "If pigs fly, I'll believe it" is "If pigs don't fly, I won't believe it."

16. The statements "If it flies, then it's a bird" and "It does not fly or it's a bird" are logically equivalent.

17. Given that $\sim p$ is true and q is false, the conditional $p \rightarrow q$ is true.

18. Given that $\sim p$ is false and q is false, the conditional $p \rightarrow q$ is true.

19. Explain why the statement "If $3 = 5$, then $4 = 6$" is true.

20. In a few sentences, explain how to determine the truth value of a conditional statement.

Tell whether each conditional is true (T) *or* false (F).

21. $T \rightarrow (7 < 3)$

22. $F \rightarrow (4 \neq 8)$

23. $F \rightarrow (5 \neq 5)$

24. $(8 \geq 8) \rightarrow F$

25. $(5^2 \neq 25) \rightarrow (8 - 8 = 16)$

26. $(5 = 12 - 7) \rightarrow (9 > 0)$

Let s represent "She has a bird for a pet," let p represent "he trains dogs," and let m represent "they raise alpacas." Express each compound statement in words.

27. $\sim m \rightarrow p$ **28.** $p \rightarrow \sim m$

29. $s \rightarrow (m \wedge p)$ **30.** $(s \wedge p) \rightarrow m$

31. $\sim p \rightarrow (\sim m \vee s)$ **32.** $(\sim s \vee \sim m) \rightarrow \sim p$

Let b represent "I ride my bike," let s represent "it snows," and let p represent "the play is cancelled." Write each compound statement in symbols.

33. If I ride my bike, then the play is cancelled.

34. If it snows, then I ride my bike.

35. If the play is cancelled, then it does not snow.

36. If I do not ride my bike, then it does not snow.

37. The play is cancelled, and if it snows then I do not ride my bike.

38. I ride my bike, or if the play is cancelled then it snows.

39. It snows if the play is cancelled.

40. I'll ride my bike if it doesn't snow.

Find the truth value of each statement. Assume that p and r are false, and q is true.

41. $\sim r \rightarrow q$ **42.** $\sim p \rightarrow \sim r$

43. $q \rightarrow p$ **44.** $\sim r \rightarrow p$

45. $p \rightarrow q$ **46.** $\sim q \rightarrow r$

47. $\sim p \rightarrow (q \wedge r)$

48. $(\sim r \vee p) \rightarrow p$

49. $\sim q \rightarrow (p \wedge r)$

50. $(\sim p \wedge \sim q) \rightarrow (p \wedge \sim r)$

51. $(p \rightarrow \sim q) \rightarrow (\sim p \wedge \sim r)$

52. $(p \rightarrow \sim q) \wedge (p \rightarrow r)$

53. Explain why, if we know that p is true, we also know that

$$[r \vee (p \vee s)] \rightarrow (p \vee q)$$

is true, even if we are not given the truth values of q, r, and s.

54. Construct a true statement involving a conditional, a conjunction, a disjunction, and a negation (not necessarily in that order), that consists of component statements p, q, and r, with all of these component statements false.

Construct a truth table for each statement. Identify any tautologies.

55. $\sim q \rightarrow p$

56. $p \rightarrow \sim q$

57. $(\sim p \rightarrow q) \rightarrow p$

58. $(\sim q \rightarrow \sim p) \rightarrow \sim q$

59. $(p \vee q) \rightarrow (q \vee p)$

60. $(p \wedge q) \rightarrow (p \vee q)$

61. $(\sim p \rightarrow \sim q) \rightarrow (p \wedge q)$

62. $r \rightarrow (p \wedge \sim q)$

63. $[(r \vee p) \wedge \sim q] \rightarrow p$

64. $[(r \wedge p) \wedge (p \wedge q)] \rightarrow p$

65. $(\sim r \rightarrow s) \vee (p \rightarrow \sim q)$

66. $(\sim p \wedge \sim q) \rightarrow (s \rightarrow r)$

67. What is the minimum number of Fs that must appear in the final column of a truth table for us to be assured that the statement is not a tautology?

68. If all truth values in the final column of a truth table are F, how can we easily transform the statement into a tautology?

Write the negation of each statement. Remember that the negation of $p \rightarrow q$ is $p \wedge \sim q$.

69. If that is an authentic Rolex watch, I'll be surprised.

70. If Minnie Ripperton reaches that note, she will shatter glass.

71. If the English measures are not converted to metric measures, then the spacecraft will crash on the surface of Saturn.

72. If you say "I do," then you'll be happy for the rest of your life.

73. "If you want to be happy for the rest of your life, never make a pretty woman your wife." *Jimmy Soul*

74. "If loving you is wrong, I don't want to be right." *Luther Ingram*

Write each statement as an equivalent statement that does not use the if . . . then *connective. Remember that*

$$p \rightarrow q \quad is \ equivalent \ to \quad \sim p \vee q.$$

75. If you give your plants tender, loving care, they flourish.

76. If the check is in the mail, I will buy you lunch.

77. If she doesn't, he will.

78. If I say "black," she says "white."

79. All residents of Pensacola are residents of Florida.

80. All women were once girls.

Use truth tables to decide which of the pairs of statements are equivalent.

81. $p \rightarrow q$; $\sim p \vee q$

82. $\sim(p \rightarrow q)$; $p \wedge \sim q$

83. $p \rightarrow q$; $\sim q \rightarrow \sim p$

84. $q \rightarrow p$; $\sim p \rightarrow \sim q$

85. $p \wedge \sim q$; $\sim q \rightarrow \sim p$

86. $p \rightarrow q$; $q \rightarrow p$

87. $p \rightarrow \sim q$; $\sim p \vee \sim q$

88. $\sim p \wedge q$; $\sim p \rightarrow q$

89. $q \rightarrow \sim p$; $p \rightarrow \sim q$

90. $\sim p \rightarrow q$; $p \vee q$

Write a logical statement representing each of the following circuits. Simplify each circuit when possible.

91.

92.

93.

94.

95.

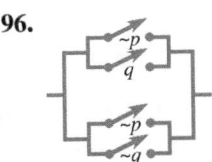

96.

Draw circuits representing the following statements as they are given. Simplify if possible.

97. $p \wedge (q \vee \sim p)$ **98.** $(\sim p \wedge \sim q) \wedge \sim r$

99. $(p \vee q) \wedge (\sim p \wedge \sim q)$

100. $(\sim q \wedge \sim p) \vee (\sim p \vee q)$

101. $[(p \vee q) \wedge r] \wedge \sim p$

102. $[(\sim p \wedge \sim r) \vee \sim q] \wedge (\sim p \wedge r)$

103. $\sim q \rightarrow (\sim p \rightarrow q)$ **104.** $\sim p \rightarrow (\sim p \vee \sim q)$

105. Refer to **Figures 5 and 6** in **Example 6.** Suppose the cost of the use of one switch for an hour is $0.06. By using the circuit in **Figure 6** rather than the circuit in **Figure 5,** what is the savings for a year of 365 days, assuming that the circuit is in continuous use?

106. Explain why the circuit shown will always have exactly one open switch. What does this circuit simplify to?

■ ‖ ‖ ‖ ‖ ‖ ■ **3.4 THE CONDITIONAL AND RELATED STATEMENTS**

Converse, Inverse, and Contrapositive • Alternative Forms of "If p, then q"
• Biconditionals • Summary of Truth Tables

Converse, Inverse, and Contrapositive

Many mathematical properties and theorems are stated in *if . . . then* form. Any conditional statement $p \rightarrow q$ is made up of an antecedent p and a consequent q. If they are interchanged, negated, or both, a new conditional statement is formed. Suppose that we begin with a conditional statement.

If you stay, then I go.   Conditional Statement

By interchanging the antecedent ("you stay") and the consequent ("I go"), we obtain a new conditional statement.

If I go, then you stay.   Converse

This new conditional is called the **converse** of the given conditional statement.

By negating both the antecedent and the consequent, we obtain the **inverse** of the given conditional statement.

If you do not stay, then I do not go.   Inverse

If the antecedent and the consequent are both interchanged *and* negated, the **contrapositive** of the given conditional statement is formed.

If I do not go, then you do not stay.   Contrapositive

These three related statements for the conditional $p \rightarrow q$ are summarized below. (***The inverse is the contrapositive of the converse.***)

Alfred North Whitehead (1861–1947) and Bertrand Russell worked together on *Principia Mathematica*. During that time, Whitehead was teaching mathematics at Cambridge University and had written *Universal Algebra*. In 1910 he went to the University of London, exploring not only the philosophical basis of science but also the "aims of education" (as he called one of his books). It was as a philosopher that he was invited to Harvard University in 1924. Whitehead died at the age of 86 in Cambridge, Massachusetts.

Related Conditional Statements		
Conditional Statement	$p \rightarrow q$	(If p, then q.)
Converse	$q \rightarrow p$	(If q, then p.)
Inverse	$\sim p \rightarrow \sim q$	(If not p, then not q.)
Contrapositive	$\sim q \rightarrow \sim p$	(If not q, then not p.)

‖ **EXAMPLE 1** Determining Related Conditional Statements

Determine each of the following, given the conditional statement

If I live in Orlando, then I live in Florida.

(a) the converse   **(b)** the inverse   **(c)** the contrapositive

SOLUTION

(a) Let p represent "I live in Orlando" and q represent "I live in Florida." Then the given statement may be written $p \rightarrow q$. The converse, $q \rightarrow p$, is

If I live in Florida, then I live in Orlando.

Notice that for this statement, the converse is not necessarily true, even though the given statement is true.

(b) The inverse of $p \rightarrow q$ is $\sim p \rightarrow \sim q$. Thus, the inverse is

If I don't live in Orlando, then I don't live in Florida.

Again, this is not necessarily true.

Bertrand Russell (1872–1970) was a student of Whitehead's before they wrote the *Principia*. Like his teacher, Russell turned toward philosophy. His works include a critique of Leibniz, analyses of mind and of matter, and a history of Western thought.

Russell became a public figure because of his involvement in social issues. Deeply aware of human loneliness, he was "passionately desirous of finding ways of diminishing this tragic isolation." During World War I he was an antiwar crusader, and he was imprisoned briefly. Again in the 1960s he championed peace. He wrote many books on social issues, winning the Nobel Prize for Literature in 1950.

(c) The contrapositive, $\sim q \rightarrow \sim p$, is

　　If I don't live in Florida, then I don't live in Orlando.

The contrapositive, like the given conditional statement, is true.　▌▌▌

Example 1 shows that the converse and inverse of a true statement need not be true. They *can* be true, but they need not be. The relationships between the related conditionals are shown in the truth table that follows.

		Conditional	Converse	Inverse	Contrapositive
p	q	$p \rightarrow q$	$q \rightarrow p$	$\sim p \rightarrow \sim q$	$\sim q \rightarrow \sim p$
T	T	T	T	T	T
T	F	F	T	T	F
F	T	T	F	F	T
F	F	T	T	T	T

(Equivalent: Conditional — Contrapositive; Equivalent: Converse — Inverse)

As this truth table shows,

1. ***A conditional statement and its contrapositive always have the same truth values,*** making it possible to replace any statement with its contrapositive without affecting the logical meaning.

2. ***The converse and inverse always have the same truth values.***

Equivalences

A conditional statement and its contrapositive are equivalent. Also, the converse and the inverse are equivalent.

▌▌ **EXAMPLE 2** Determining Related Conditional Statements

For the conditional statement $\sim p \rightarrow q$, write each of the following.

(a) the converse　　**(b)** the inverse　　**(c)** the contrapositive

SOLUTION

(a) The converse of $\sim p \rightarrow q$ is $q \rightarrow \sim p$.

(b) The inverse is $\sim(\sim p) \rightarrow \sim q$, which simplifies to $p \rightarrow \sim q$.

(c) The contrapositive is $\sim q \rightarrow \sim(\sim p)$, which simplifies to $\sim q \rightarrow p$.　▌▌▌

Alternative Forms of "If p, then q"

The conditional statement "if p, then q" can be stated in several other ways in English. Consider this statement.

　　If you go to the outlet mall, then you will find a place to park.

It can also be written as follows.

　　Going to the outlet mall is *sufficient* for finding a place to park.

According to this statement, going to the outlet mall is enough to guarantee finding a place to park. Going to other places, such as schools or office buildings, *might* also guarantee a place to park, but at least we *know* that going to the outlet mall does. Thus, $p \rightarrow q$ can be written "p is sufficient for q." Knowing that p has occurred is sufficient to guarantee that q will also occur.

On the other hand, consider this statement, which has a different meaning.

Having the set on is necessary for watching television. (∗)

Here, we are saying that one condition that is necessary for watching television is that the set be turned on. This may not be enough. The set might be broken, for example. The statement labeled (∗) could be written as

If you watch television, then the set was turned on.

As this example suggests, $p \rightarrow q$ is the same as "q is necessary for p." In other words, if q doesn't happen, then neither will p. Notice how this idea is closely related to the idea of equivalence between a conditional statement and its contrapositive.

Common Translations of $p \rightarrow q$

The conditional $p \rightarrow q$ can be translated in any of the following ways, none of which depends on the truth or falsity of $p \rightarrow q$.

If p, then q.	p is sufficient for q.
If p, q.	q is necessary for p.
p implies q.	All p are q.
p only if q.	q if p.

Example: If you live in Dubuque, then you live in Iowa.   Statement

You live in Iowa if you live in Dubuque.
You live in Dubuque only if you live in Iowa.
Living in Iowa is necessary for living in Dubuque.   Common
Living in Dubuque is sufficient for living in Iowa.   translations
All residents of Dubuque are residents of Iowa.
Being a resident of Dubuque implies residency in Iowa.

▌▌ **EXAMPLE 3** Rewording Conditional Statements

Write each statement in the form "if p, then q."

(a) You'll be sorry if I go.   **(b)** Today is Tuesday only if yesterday was Monday.

(c) All nurses wear white shoes.

SOLUTION

(a) If I go, then you'll be sorry.

(b) If today is Tuesday, then yesterday was Monday.

(c) If you are a nurse, then you wear white shoes.   ▐▐▐

▌▌ **EXAMPLE 4** Translating from Words to Symbols

Let p represent "A triangle is equilateral," and let q represent "A triangle has three sides of equal length." Write each of the following in symbols.

(a) A triangle is equilateral if it has three sides of equal length.

(b) A triangle is equilateral only if it has three sides of equal length.

SOLUTION

(a) $q \rightarrow p$ **(b)** $p \rightarrow q$ ▐▐▐

Biconditionals

The compound statement **p if and only if q** (often abbreviated **p iff q**) is called a **biconditional**. It is symbolized $p \leftrightarrow q$, and is interpreted as the conjunction of the two conditionals $p \rightarrow q$ and $q \rightarrow p$. Using symbols, this conjunction is written $(q \rightarrow p) \wedge (p \rightarrow q)$ so that, by definition,

$$p \leftrightarrow q \equiv (q \rightarrow p) \wedge (p \rightarrow q). \quad \text{Biconditional}$$

The truth table for the biconditional $p \leftrightarrow q$ can be determined using this definition.

Truth Table for the Biconditional p if and only if q

p if and only if q

p	q	$p \leftrightarrow q$
T	T	T
T	F	F
F	T	F
F	F	T

Principia Mathematica, the title chosen by Whitehead and Russell, was a deliberate reference to *Philosophiae naturalis principia mathematica,* or "mathematical principles of the philosophy of nature," Isaac Newton's epochal work of 1687. Newton's *Principia* pictured a kind of "clockwork universe" that ran via his Law of Gravitation. Newton independently invented the calculus, unaware that Leibniz had published his own formulation of it earlier.

A biconditional is true when both component statements have the same truth value. It is false when they have different truth values.

■ ■ EXAMPLE 5 Determining Whether Biconditionals Are True or False

Determine whether each biconditional statement is *true* or *false*.

(a) $6 + 8 = 14$ if and only if $11 + 5 = 16$

(b) $6 = 5$ if and only if $12 \neq 12$

(c) $5 + 2 = 10$ if and only if $17 + 19 = 36$

SOLUTION

(a) Both $6 + 8 = 14$ and $11 + 5 = 16$ are true. By the truth table for the biconditional, this biconditional is true.

(b) Both component statements are false, so by the last line of the truth table for the biconditional, this biconditional statement is true.

(c) Because the first component ($5 + 2 = 10$) is false, and the second is true, this biconditional statement is false. ■■■

Summary of Truth Tables

Truth tables have been derived for several important types of compound statements.

Summary of Basic Truth Tables

   1. $\sim p$, the **negation** of p, has truth value opposite that of p.

   2. $p \wedge q$, the **conjunction,** is true only when both p and q are true.

   3. $p \vee q$, the **disjunction,** is false only when both p and q are false.

   4. $p \rightarrow q$, the **conditional,** is false only when p is true and q is false.

   5. $p \leftrightarrow q$, the **biconditional,** is true only when both p and q have the same truth value.

3.4 EXERCISES

For each given conditional statement (or statement that can be written as a conditional), write (**a**) *the converse,* (**b**) *the inverse, and* (**c**) *the contrapositive in if . . . then form. In some of the exercises, it may be helpful to first restate the given statement in if . . . then form.*

1. If beauty were a minute, then you would be an hour.

2. If you lead, then I will follow.

3. If it ain't broke, don't fix it.

4. If I had a nickel for each time that happened, I would be rich.

5. Walking in front of a moving car is dangerous to your health. *If you walk in front of a moving car, then it's dangerous to your health*

6. Milk contains calcium.

7. Birds of a feather flock together. *If they are birds of a feather, then they flock together*

8. A rolling stone gathers no moss.

9. If you build it, then he will come.

10. Where there's smoke, there's fire.

11. $p \rightarrow \sim q$

12. $\sim p \rightarrow q$

13. $\sim p \rightarrow \sim q$

14. $\sim q \rightarrow \sim p$

15. $p \rightarrow (q \lor r)$ (*Hint:* Use one of De Morgan's laws as necessary.)

16. $(r \lor \sim q) \rightarrow p$ (*Hint:* Use one of De Morgan's laws as necessary.)

17. Discuss the equivalences that exist among a given conditional statement, its converse, its inverse, and its contrapositive.

18. State the contrapositive of "If the square of a natural number is even, then the natural number is even." The two statements must have the same truth value. Use several examples and inductive reasoning to decide whether both are true or both are false.

Write each statement in the form "if p, then q."

19. If it is muddy, I'll wear my galoshes.

20. If I finish studying, I'll go to the party.

21. "19 is positive" implies that 19 + 1 is positive.

22. "Today is Wednesday" implies that yesterday was Tuesday.

23. All integers are rational numbers.

24. All whole numbers are integers.

25. Doing logic puzzles is sufficient for driving me crazy.

26. Being in Kalamazoo is sufficient for being in Michigan.

27. A day's growth of beard is necessary for Jeff Marsalis to shave.

28. Being an environmentalist is necessary for being elected.

29. I can go from Boardwalk to Baltic Avenue only if I pass GO.

30. The principal will hire more teachers only if the school board approves.

31. No whole numbers are not integers.

32. No integers are irrational numbers.

33. The Nationals will win the pennant when their pitching improves.

34. Sarah will be a liberal when pigs fly.

35. A rectangle is a parallelogram with a right angle.

36. A parallelogram is a four-sided figure with opposite sides parallel.

37. A triangle with two perpendicular sides is a right triangle.

38. A square is a rectangle with two adjacent sides equal.

39. The square of a two-digit number whose units digit is 5 will end in 25.

40. An integer whose units digit is 0 or 5 is divisible by 5.

41. One of the following statements is not equivalent to all the others. Which one is it?
    A. *r* only if *s*.
    B. *r* implies *s*.
    C. If *r*, then *s*.
    D. *r* is necessary for *s*.

42. Many students have difficulty interpreting *necessary* and *sufficient*. Use the statement "Being in Vancouver is sufficient for being in North America" to explain why "*p* is sufficient for *q*" translates as "if *p*, then *q*."

43. Use the statement "To be an integer, it is necessary that a number be rational" to explain why "*p* is necessary for *q*" translates as "if *q*, then *p*."

44. Explain why the statement "A week has eight days if and only if October has forty days" is true.

Identify each statement as true *or* false.

45. $6 = 9 - 3$ if and only if $8 + 2 = 10$.

46. $3 + 1 \neq 7$ if and only if $8 \neq 8$.

47. $8 + 7 \neq 15$ if and only if $3 \times 5 \neq 8$.

48. $6 \times 2 = 18$ if and only if $9 + 7 \neq 16$.

49. George H. W. Bush was president if and only if George W. Bush was not president.

50. Burger King sells Big Macs if and only if Apple manufactures Ipods.

Two statements that can both be true about the same object are **consistent.** *For example, "It is green" and "It weighs 60 pounds" are consistent statements. Statements that cannot both be true about the same object are called* **contrary.** *"It is a Nissan" and "It is a Mazda" are contrary. In Exercises 51–56, label each pair of statements as either* contrary *or* consistent.

51. Michael Jackson is alive. Michael Jackson is dead.

52. Barack Obama is a Democrat. Barack Obama is a Republican.

53. That animal has four legs. That same animal is a cat.

54. That book is nonfiction. That book costs more than $150.

55. This number is a whole number. This same number is irrational.

56. This number is positive. This same number is a natural number.

57. This number is an integer. This same number is a rational number.

58. This number is a whole number. This same number is a negative number.

59. Make up two statements that are consistent.

60. Make up two statements that are contrary.

3.5 ANALYZING ARGUMENTS WITH EULER DIAGRAMS

Logical Arguments • Arguments with Universal Quantifiers • Arguments with Existential Quantifiers

Leonhard Euler (1707–1783) won the Academy prize and edged out du Châtelet and Voltaire. That was a minor achievement, as was the invention of "Euler circles" (which antedated Venn diagrams). Euler was the most prolific mathematician of his generation despite blindness that forced him to dictate from memory.

Logical Arguments

With inductive reasoning we observe patterns to solve problems. Now we study how deductive reasoning may be used to determine whether logical arguments are valid or invalid.

A logical argument is made up of **premises** (assumptions, laws, rules, widely held ideas, or observations) and a **conclusion.** Recall that *deductive* reasoning involves drawing specific conclusions from given general premises. When reasoning from the premises of an argument to obtain a conclusion, we want the argument to be valid.

> **Valid and Invalid Arguments**
>
> An argument is **valid** if the fact that all the premises are true forces the conclusion to be true. An argument that is not valid is **invalid.** It is called a **fallacy.**

"Valid" and "true" do not have the same meaning—an argument can be valid even though the conclusion is false. (See Example 4.)

Arguments with Universal Quantifiers

Several techniques can be used to check whether an argument is valid. One such technique is based on **Euler diagrams.**

Leonhard Euler (pronounced "Oiler") was one of the greatest mathematicians who ever lived. He is immortalized in mathematics history with the important irrational number *e*, named in his honor. This number appears throughout mathematics, and is discussed in **Chapters 6 and 8.**

Figure 8

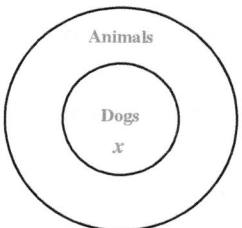

x represents Dotty.

Figure 9

▮▮ **EXAMPLE 1** Using an Euler Diagram to Determine Validity

Is the following argument valid?

> All dogs are animals.
> Dotty is a dog.
> _____
> Dotty is an animal.

SOLUTION

To begin, draw regions to represent the first premise. Because all dogs are animals, the region for "dogs" goes inside the region for "animals," as in **Figure 8.**

The second premise, "Dotty is a dog," suggests that "Dotty" would go inside the region representing "dogs." Let *x* represent "Dotty." **Figure 9** shows that "Dotty" is also inside the region for "animals." If both premises are true, the conclusion that Dotty is an animal must be true also. The argument is valid. ▮▮▮

▮▮ **EXAMPLE 2** Using an Euler Diagram to Determine Validity

Is the following argument valid?

> All rainy days are cloudy.
> Today is not cloudy.
> _____
> Today is not rainy.

SOLUTION

In **Figure 10,** the region for "rainy days" is drawn entirely inside the region for "cloudy days." Since "Today is *not* cloudy," place an *x* for "today" *outside* the region for "cloudy days." See **Figure 11.** Placing the *x* outside the region for "cloudy days" forces it also to be outside the region for "rainy days." Thus, if the two premises are true, then it is also true that today is not rainy. The argument is valid.

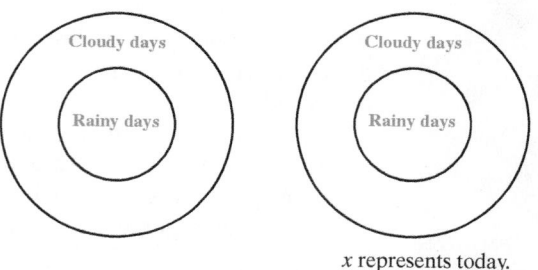

Figure 10

x represents today.

Figure 11 ▮▮▮

▮▮ **EXAMPLE 3** Using an Euler Diagram to Determine Validity

Is the following argument valid?

> All magnolia trees have green leaves.
> That plant has green leaves.
> _____
> That plant is a magnolia tree.

SOLUTION

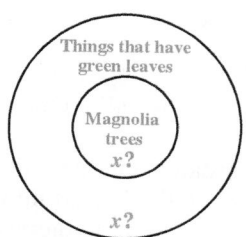

Figure 12

The region for "magnolia trees" goes entirely inside the region for "things that have green leaves." See **Figure 12.** The *x* that represents "that plant" must go inside the region for "things that have green leaves," but can go either inside or outside the region for "magnolia trees." Even if the premises are true, we are not forced to accept the conclusion as true. This argument is invalid. It is a fallacy. ▮▮▮

▍▍ **EXAMPLE 4** Using an Euler Diagram to Determine Validity

Is the following argument valid?

All expensive things are desirable.
All desirable things make you feel good.
All things that make you feel good make you live longer.

All expensive things make you live longer.

SOLUTION

A diagram for the argument is given in **Figure 13.**
If each premise is true, then the conclusion must be true because the region for "expensive things" lies completely within the region for "things that make you live longer." Thus, the argument is valid. (This argument is an example of the fact that a *valid* argument need *not* have a true conclusion.)

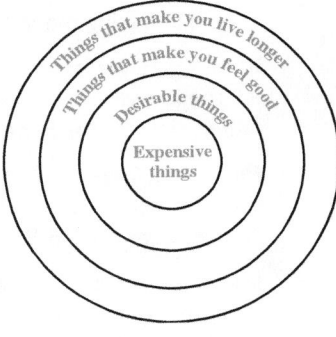

Figure 13 ▍▍▍

Arguments with Existential Quantifiers

▍▍ **EXAMPLE 5** Using an Euler Diagram to Determine Validity

Is the following argument valid?

Some students go to the beach for Spring Break.
I am a student.

I go to the beach for Spring Break.

SOLUTION

The first premise is sketched in **Figure 14,** where some (but not necessarily *all*) students go to the beach. There are two possibilities for *I*, as shown in **Figure 15.** One possibility is that *I* go to the beach. The other is that *I* don't. Since the truth of the premises does not force the conclusion to be true, the argument is invalid. ▍▍▍

Figure 14

Figure 15

For Further Thought

Discussions in everyday conversation, politics, and advertising provide a nearly endless stream of examples of **fallacies**—arguments exhibiting illogical reasoning. There are many general forms of fallacies, and we now present descriptions and examples of some of the more common ones. (Much of this list is adapted from the excellent web page Mission: Critical, A Project of the Institute of Teaching and Learning, San Jose State University, www.sjsu.edu/depts/itl/graphics.)

1. **Circular Reasoning** (also called *Begging the Question*) In circular reasoning, the person making the argument assumes to be true what he is trying to prove.

   Husband: What makes you say that this dress makes you look fat?

   Wife: Because it does.

   Here the wife makes her case by stating what she wants to prove.

2. **False Dilemma** (also called the *Either-Or Fallacy,* or the *Black and White Fallacy*) Presenting two options with the assumption that they are contradictions (that is, the truth of one implies the falsity of the other) when in fact they are not, is the basis of a common fallacy.

   Politician: America: Love it or leave it.

   This argument implies only two choices. It is possible that someone may love America and yet leave, while someone else may not love America and yet stay.

   (continued)

For Further Thought (cont.)

3. **Loaded Question and Complex Claims** This fallacy involves one person asking a question or making a statement that is constructed in such a way as to obtain an answer in which the responder agrees to something with which he does not actually agree.

   Teenager Beth to her father: I hope you enjoyed embarrassing me in front of my friends.

   If Beth gets the expected response "No, I didn't enjoy it," the answer allows Beth to interpret that while her father didn't enjoy it, he did indeed embarrass her.

4. *Post Hoc* **Reasoning** An argument that is based on the false belief that if event A preceded event B, then A must have caused B is called *post hoc* reasoning.

   Johnny: I wore my Hawaiian shirt while watching all three playoff games, and my team won all three games. So I am going to wear that shirt every time I watch them.

   The fact that Johnny put the same shirt on before each game has nothing to do with the outcomes of the games.

5. **Red Herring** (also called *Smoke Screen*, or *Wild Goose Chase*) This fallacy involves introducing an irrelevant topic to divert attention away from the original topic, allowing the person making the argument to seemingly prevail.

   (From the movie *Field of Dreams*, in a scene where Annie and Beulah are arguing at a town meeting about the banning of books)

   Beulah: I say smut and filth like this has no place in our schools.... The so-called novels of Terence Mann endorse promiscuity, godlessness, the mongrelization of the races, and disrespect to high-ranking officers of the United States army. And that is why school boards across the country have been banning his books since 1969.
   Annie: Excuse me, madam. Terence Mann was a warm and gentle voice of reason in a time of great madness. He coined the phrase "Make love, not war."... He was talking about peace, and love, and understanding ...
   Beulah: Oh yeah, well your husband plowed under his corn and built a baseball field ... the weirdo....
   Annie: Now there's an intelligent response.

   While most of the people in the audience agreed that Annie's husband Ray was doing strange things, those things had nothing to do with banning books.

6. **Shifting the Burden of Proof** A person making a claim usually is required to support that claim. In this fallacy, if the claim is difficult to support, that person turns the burden of proof of that claim over to someone else.

   Employee: You accuse me of embezzling money? That's ridiculous.
   Employer: Well, until you can prove otherwise, you will just have to accept it as true.

   If money has been disappearing, it is up to the employer to prove that this employee is guilty. The burden of proof is on the employer, but he is insinuating that the employee must prove that he is not the one taking the money.

7. **Straw Man** This fallacy involves creating a false image (like a scarecrow, or straw man) of someone else's position in an argument.

   Dan Quayle: I have as much experience in the Congress as Jack Kennedy did when he sought the presidency.
   Lloyd Bentsen: Senator, I served with Jack Kennedy. I knew Jack Kennedy. Jack Kennedy was a friend of mine. And Senator, you're no Jack Kennedy.
   Dan Quayle: That was really uncalled for, Senator.
   Lloyd Bentsen: You're the one that was making the comparison, Senator.

   While this was the defining moment of the 1988 vice-presidential debate, Bentsen expertly used the straw man fallacy. Quayle did not compare himself or his accomplishments to those of Kennedy, but merely stated that he had spent as much time in Congress as Kennedy had when the latter ran for president.

For Group or Individual Investigation

Use the Internet to investigate the following additional logical fallacies.

Appeal to Authority	Appeal to Common	Common Practice
Two Wrongs	Belief	Wishful Thinking
Appeal to Fear	Indirect Consequences	Appeal to Pity
Appeal to Prejudice	Appeal to Loyalty	Appeal to Vanity
Guilt by Association	Appeal to Spite	Hasty Generalization
	Slippery Slope	

3.5 EXERCISES

Decide whether each argument is valid *or* invalid.

1. All amusement parks have thrill rides.
   Universal Orlando is an amusement park.
   Universal Orlando has thrill rides.

2. All disc jockeys play music.
   Phlash Phelps is a disc jockey.
   Phlash Phelps plays music.

3. All politicians lie, cheat, and steal.
   That man lies, cheats, and steals.
   That man is a politician.

4. All Southerners speak with an accent.
   Bill Leonard speaks with an accent.
   Bill Leonard is a Southerner.

5. All dogs love to bury bones.
   Puddles does not love to bury bones.
   Puddles is not a dog.

6. All vice-presidents use cell phones.
   Bob DeBiasio does not use a cell phone.
   Bob DeBiasio is not a vice-president.

7. All residents of Minnesota know how to live in freezing temperatures.
   Jessica Rockswold knows how to live in freezing temperatures.
   Jessica Rockswold lives in Minnesota.

8. All people who apply for a loan must pay for a title search.
   Kurt Massey paid for a title search.
   Kurt Massey applied for a loan.

9. Some dinosaurs were plant eaters.
   Danny was a plant eater.
   Danny was a dinosaur.

10. Some philosophers are absent minded.
    Nicole Mallon is a philosopher.
    Nicole Mallon is absent minded.

11. Some nurses wear blue uniforms.
    Dee Boyle is a nurse.
    Dee Boyle wears a blue uniform.

12. Some trucks have sound systems.
    Some trucks have gun racks.
    Some trucks with sound systems have gun racks.

13. Refer to **Example 3.** If the second premise and the conclusion were interchanged, would the argument then be valid?

14. Refer to **Example 4.** Give a different conclusion than the one given there so that the argument is still valid.

Construct a valid argument based on the Euler diagram shown.

15.
16.

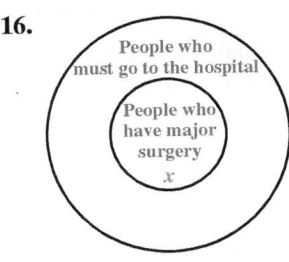

x represents Natalie Graham   *x* represents Mark Robinson

As mentioned in the text, an argument can have a true conclusion yet be invalid. In these exercises, each argument has a true conclusion. Identify each argument as valid *or* invalid.

17. All birds fly.
    All planes fly.
    A bird is not a plane.

18. All cars have tires.
    All tires are rubber.
    All cars have rubber.

19. All chickens have beaks.
    All hens are chickens.
    All hens have beaks.

20. All chickens have beaks.
    All birds have beaks.
    All chickens are birds.

21. Little Rock is northeast of Texarkana.
    Little Rock is northeast of Austin.
    Texarkana is northeast of Austin.

22. Veracruz is south of Tampico.
    Tampico is south of Monterrey.
    Veracruz is south of Monterrey.

23. No whole numbers are negative.
    −3 is negative.
    −3 is not a whole number.

24. A scalene triangle has a longest side.
    A scalene triangle has a largest angle.
    The largest angle in a scalene triangle is opposite the longest side.

In Exercises 25–30, the premises marked A, B, *and* C *are followed by several possible conclusions. Take each conclusion in turn, and check whether the resulting argument is valid or invalid.*

A. *All people who drive contribute to air pollution.*

B. *All people who contribute to air pollution make life a little worse.*

C. *Some people who live in a suburb make life a little worse.*

25. Some people who live in a suburb contribute to air pollution.

26. Some people who live in a suburb drive.

27. Suburban residents never drive.

28. Some people who contribute to air pollution live in a suburb.

29. Some people who make life a little worse live in a suburb.

30. All people who drive make life a little worse.

EXTENSION   Logic Problems and Sudoku

How to Solve Logic Problems • How to Solve Sudoku

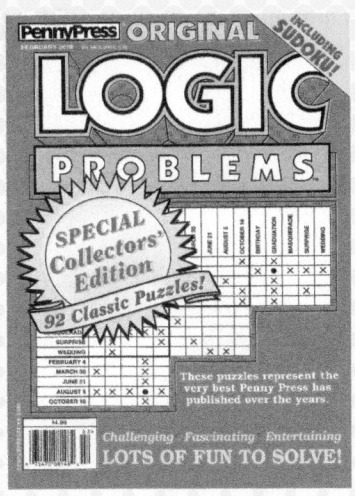

Logic problems, which are based on deductive reasoning, appear in periodicals such as *Original Logic Problems, World-Class Logic Problems,* and *England's Best Logic Problems* (all PennyPress), and *Logic Puzzles* (Dell). The following explanation on solving such problems appeared in the February 2010 issue of *Original Logic Problems.*

How to Solve Logic Problems   Solving logic problems is entertaining and challenging. All the information you need to solve a logic problem is given in the introduction and clues, and in illustrations, when provided. If you've never solved a logic problem before, our sample should help you get started. Fill in the Sample Solving Chart as you follow our explanation. We use a "•" to signify "Yes" and an "X" to signify "No."

Sample Logic Problem
Five couples were married last week, each on a different weekday. From the information provided, determine the woman (one is Cathy) and man (one is Paul) who make up each couple, as well as the day on which each couple was married.

1. Anne was married on Monday, but not to Wally.

2. Stan's wedding was on Wednesday. Rob was married on Friday, but not to Ida.

3. Vern (who married Fran) was married the day after Eve.

Sample Solving Chart:	PAUL	ROB	STAN	VERN	WALLY	MONDAY	TUESDAY	WEDNESDAY	THURSDAY	FRIDAY
ANNE										
CATHY										
EVE										
FRAN										
IDA										
MONDAY										
TUESDAY										
WEDNESDAY										
THURSDAY										
FRIDAY										

1	PAUL	ROB	STAN	VERN	WALLY	MONDAY	TUESDAY	WEDNESDAY	THURSDAY	FRIDAY
ANNE	X	X			X	•	X	X	X	X
CATHY						X				
EVE						X				
FRAN						X				
IDA		X				X				X
MONDAY	X	X								
TUESDAY	X	X								
WEDNESDAY	X	X	•	X	X					
THURSDAY	X	X								
FRIDAY	X	•	X	X	X					

Explanation

Anne was married Mon. (1), so put a "•" at the intersection of Anne and Mon. Put "X"s in all the other days in Anne's row and all the other names in the Mon. column. (Whenever you establish a relationship, as we did here, be sure to place "X"s at the intersections of all relationships that become impossible as a result.) Anne wasn't married to Wally (1), so put an "X" at the intersection of Anne and Wally. Stan's wedding was Wed. (2), so put a "•" at the intersection of Stan and Wed. (Don't forget the "X"s.) Stan didn't marry Anne, who was married Mon., so put an "X" at the intersection of Anne and Stan. Rob was married Fri., but not to Ida (2), so put a "•" at the intersection of Rob and Fri., and "X"s at the intersections of Rob and Ida and Ida and Fri. Rob also didn't marry Anne, who was married Mon., so put an "X" at the intersection of Anne and Rob. Now your chart should look like **chart 1.**

Vern married Fran (3), so put a "•" at the intersection of Vern and Fran. This leaves Anne's only possible husband as Paul, so put a "•" at the intersection of Anne and Paul and Paul and Mon. Vern and Fran's wedding was the day after Eve's (3), which wasn't Mon. [Anne], so Vern's wasn't Tue. It must have been Thu. [see chart], so Eve's was Wed. (3). Put "•"s at the intersections of Vern and Thu., Fran and Thu., and Eve and Wed. Now your chart should look like **chart 2.**

2	PAUL	ROB	STAN	VERN	WALLY	MONDAY	TUESDAY	WEDNESDAY	THURSDAY	FRIDAY
ANNE	•	X	X	X	X	•	X	X	X	X
CATHY	X			X		X		X	X	
EVE	X			X		X	X	•	X	X
FRAN	X	X	X	•	X	X	X	X	X	•
IDA	X	X		X		X		X	X	X
MONDAY	•	X	X	X	X
TUESDAY	X	X	X	X	
WEDNESDAY	X	X	•	X	X
THURSDAY	X	X	X	•	X
FRIDAY	X	•	X	X	X

3	PAUL	ROB	STAN	VERN	WALLY	MONDAY	TUESDAY	WEDNESDAY	THURSDAY	FRIDAY
ANNE	•	X	X	X	X	•	X	X	X	X
CATHY	X	•	X	X	X	X	X	X	X	•
EVE	X	X	•	X	X	X	X	•	X	X
FRAN	X	X	X	•	X	X	X	X	•	X
IDA	X	X	X	X	•	X	•	X	X	X
MONDAY	•	X	X	X	X
TUESDAY	X	X	X	X	•
WEDNESDAY	X	X	•	X	X
THURSDAY	X	X	X	•	X
FRIDAY	X	•	X	X	X

The chart shows that Cathy was married Fri., Ida was married Tue., and Wally was married Tue. Ida married Wally, and Cathy's wedding was Fri., so she married Rob. After this information is filled in, Eve could only have married Stan. You've completed the puzzle, and your chart should now look like **chart 3.**

In summary: Anne and Paul, Mon.; Cathy and Rob, Fri.; Eve and Stan, Wed.; Fran and Vern, Thu.; Ida and Wally, Tue.

In some problems, it may be necessary to make a logical guess based on facts you've established. When you do, always look for clues or other facts that disprove it. If you find that your guess is incorrect, eliminate it as a possibility.

How to Solve Sudoku Sudoku is a simple game that has gained great popularity in the United States during the past few years. It is believed that the game originated as Number Place in the United States over 25 years ago, but gained in popularity only after it became a sensation in Japan, where it was renamed Sudoku, meaning "single number." (*Source: Sudoku #13*, 2005, Platinum Magazine Group.)

There is only one rule in Sudoku: **"Fill in the grid so that every row, every column, and every 3 × 3 box contains the digits 1 through 9."** This involves scanning the given digits, marking up the grid, and analyzing. Here is a sample Sudoku.

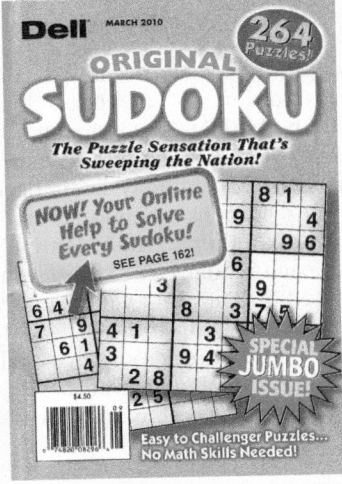

			7	3	2			
8	4		1				9	
					8	2	1	
		9		8	7			5
2	8		4		1		6	3
1			5	6		9		
5	3	8						9
	9				2		1	4
				7	5	6		

9	1	7	3	2	8	4	5	6
8	4	2	1	5	6	3	9	7
6	5	3	7	4	9	8	2	1
3	6	9	2	8	7	1	4	5
2	8	5	4	9	1	7	6	3
1	7	4	5	6	3	9	8	2
5	3	8	6	1	4	2	7	9
7	9	6	8	3	2	5	1	4
4	2	1	9	7	5	6	3	8

Given Form   **Solved Form**

You can find Sudoku puzzles and solving strategies online at www.sudoku.org.uk and at www.pennydellsudokusolver.com.

EXTENSION EXERCISES

Follow the guidelines to solve each logic problem, which appeared in the February 2010 issue of Original Logic Problems, *published by PennyPress.*

1. **Breath Taking** As part of a weekly tradition, Drew and four of his friends met for lunch at Aristotle's Grill. Each person enjoyed a different lunch special, but when it came time for the post-meal conversation, the five quickly realized that they were all in need of a mint or two. Luckily, each person had a container of mints on his or her person. No two friends had the same brand of mint (one is Inti-mints), and no two friends had mints with the same flavor. A few seconds later they were all ready to talk, but they agreed that next week, they'll be a little more careful about what they order for lunch! From the information provided, can you determine the meal enjoyed by each friend, as well as the brand and flavor of mint each person used afterward?

(a) The friend who had garlic shrimp ate a couple of orange-flavored mints (which weren't Fresh Air mints). The person who ordered the spanakopita isn't the one who had wintergreen-flavored TKO mints.

(b) The friend who ate French onion soup followed it with a few Liplickers mints. Nash (who didn't have the spearmint-flavored mints) didn't order garlic shrimp.

(c) Neither Nash nor Xerxes is the one who ate a tuna-salad sandwich. The friend who had a buffalo-chicken sandwich isn't the one who freshened his or her breath with spearmint-flavored mints.

(d) One friend had a couple of cinnamon-flavored Deltoids mints. The Liplickers mints were vanilla-flavored.

(e) Ilse (who ate a buffalo-chicken sandwich) didn't have wintergreen-flavored mints. Neither Uma nor Xerxes is the friend who had a couple of Fresh Air mints.

2. **Kings of Hearts** Although the exact origins of the holiday are murky, the tradition of Valentine's Day probably harkens back to the Middle Ages, when it was better known as the feast of Saint Valentine. Couples exchanged gifts on this February holiday even back then, and no one gave more expensive and elaborate valentines than the royalty of that time. One Valentine's Day, each of four kings, each whom ruled a different small kingdom, gave his queen a different valuable gift. It just goes to show that love (or at least the idea of it) stands the test of time! From the information provided, can you determine the king and queen of each kingdom, as well as the gift each king gave his wife for the feast of Saint Valentine?

(a) King Jacobus didn't give his queen a platinum crown.

(b) Neither the jeweled scepter nor the platinum crown was the gift given to Queen Meyla (who was married to either King Kevrick or King Vermond).

(c) Queen Dejah (who was married to either King Fedris or King Jacobus) wasn't the ruler of Undervale.

(d) King Kevrick wasn't the ruler of the Dalelands.

(e) Neither the platinum crown nor the set of velvet robes was the gift given by King Vermond.

(f) The queen of Undervale (who was married to either King Fedris or King Jacobus) was given a golden throne by her husband.

(g) Queen Tilnara wasn't given a jeweled scepter by her husband. Queen Aasta ruled Hightop.

		AASTA	DEJAH	MEYLA	TILNARA	DALELANDS	HIGHTOP	SHADOW COAST	UNDERVALE	GOLDEN THRONE	JEWELED SCEPTER	PLATINUM CROWN	VELVET ROBES
		QUEEN				KINGDOM				GIFT			
KING	FEDRIS												
	JACOBUS												
	KEVRICK												
	VERMOND												
GIFT	GOLDEN THRONE												
	JEWELED SCEPTER												
	PLATINUM CROWN												
	VELVET ROBES												
KINGDOM	DALELANDS												
	HIGHTOP												
	SHADOW COAST												
	UNDERVALE												

3. *New Year's Revelations* Lucy and four of her friends met at the Golden Panda for dinner one evening in January. Much to their surprise, they had wandered in to the restaurant during a celebration of the Chinese New Year. Luckily for the five, this meant a discount on their meals and a free session with the mysterious medium Madame Wau Pei. The five friends had their fortunes told, one at a time. Each person told the mystic the date and year of his or her birth and learned that, according to Chinese astrology, each friend's birth year is designated by a different animal. Also, each of the five was told that he or she has a different lucky element. Before leaving the restaurant, the five friends compared their predictions, noticing that all of them had a long journey in their future—the trip back home! From the information provided, determine the order in which the five friends had their fortunes told, the year in which each person was born, and each person's lucky element.

(a) Toni was the third person to get her fortune told. The person whose lucky element is wood was the last person to see the fortune-teller.

(b) Earl (whose lucky element is fire) had his fortune told immediately before the person who was born in the Year of the Rooster. The fourth person to visit the fortune-teller was born in the Year of the Dragon.

(c) The person born in the Year of the Ox had his or her fortune told at some point before the one whose lucky element is metal. Ivana was born in the Year of the Horse.

(d) The person whose lucky element is water (who was born in the Year of the Cow) wasn't the first person to have his or her fortune told.

(e) The person whose lucky element is earth had his or her fortune told exactly two after Philip.

		EARL	IVANA	LUCY	PHILIP	TONI	COW	DRAGON	HORSE	OX	ROOSTER	EARTH	FIRE	METAL	WATER	WOOD
		FRIEND					YEAR					ELEMENT				
ORDER	FIRST															
	SECOND															
	THIRD															
	FOURTH															
	FIFTH															
ELEMENT	EARTH															
	FIRE															
	METAL															
	WATER															
	WOOD															
YEAR	COW															
	DRAGON															
	HORSE															
	OX															
	ROOSTER															

4. *Barn Again* For as long as I can remember, I've dreamed of owning my own bed-and-breakfast, and it looks like my dream is about to come true! We'd like our inn to be distinctive, so my husband and I have decided to purchase a barn and convert it into unique living quarters. We viewed five barns recently, each of which had once served a different purpose. My husband and I visited each barn with a different contractor, each of whom gave us a different estimate ($50,000, $60,000, $70,000, $80,000, or $100,000) for the conversion. Each barn has a different feature that makes it appealing (one has a functioning hoist), but we still haven't decided which one to buy—we're starting to go a little haywire! From the information provided, determine the contractor who visited each barn with us and the special feature of each structure, as well as the estimate given for the renovation of each barn.

(a) The apple barn (which has distinctive octagonal windows) will cost exactly $20,000 less to convert than the barn we visited with a Bill's Building representative. The estimate for renovating the hay barn is higher than the estimate for converting the potato barn.

(b) The barn we visited with the person from AB Contracting (which isn't the barn that has fabulous heavy beams) will cost more to renovate than the barn we viewed with the contractor from Pine Valley but exactly $10,000 less to convert than the horse barn.

(c) The estimates for converting the apple barn and the barn with lovely board-and-batten siding are the lowest and highest estimates, in some order.

(d) The barn we visited with the contractor from Dekker Ltd. will cost exactly $20,000 more to renovate than the barn with insulation worth preserving.

(e) The old dairy barn will cost more to renovate than the one we visited with the representative from Vander Estates.

		APPLE	DAIRY	HAY	HORSE	POTATO	BEAMS	HOIST	INSULATION	SIDING	WINDOWS	$50,000	$60,000	$70,000	$80,000	$100,000
		BARN					FEATURE					ESTIMATE				
CONTRACTOR	AB CONTRACTING															
	BILL'S BUILDING															
	DEKKER LTD.															
	PINE VALLEY															
	VANDER ESTATES															
ESTIMATE	$50,000															
	$60,000															
	$70,000															
	$80,000															
	$100,000															
FEATURE	BEAMS															
	HOIST															
	INSULATION															
	SIDING															
	WINDOWS															

Solve each Sudoku, which appeared in Dell Original Sudoku, *March 2010, Penny Publications. (They are categorized according to difficulty level.)*

5. Easy

	4		1	6	8			5
		9		5			2	8
	6		9					4
		4	7		9			
	3	8		4		2	9	
			2		3	8		
2					1		6	
9	7			2		5		
4			6	9	5		7	

6. Easy

2		3			8	1	4	
	7		6	2	4			
	8			3				7
8	4	7	2			6		
			8		6			
	1				9	4	8	2
7				6			2	
		9	5	7		1		
	6	9	3			5		4

7. Medium

8	3		6					1
	1			4			5	6
		6			8			
		7	1				3	8
		1		2		4		
5	4				6	1		
			5			7		
9	8			7			1	
6					1		2	3

8. Medium

			4	5		6		
4	5					3		9
	6	1			3			8
5	8				1		6	
		9		3		2		
	4		9				1	7
8			1			7	3	
1		5					9	2
		6		7	2			

9. Hard

	1			2				4
4		9			1		7	
		8				9		
	3		6				2	
7				3				9
	9				8		5	
		2				4		
	8		2			6		5
9				8			3	

10. Hard

	2			9		6	7	
	5	6						
			6		4			5
	6	9						1
			3	6	9			
8						9	4	
1			4		7			
						4	2	
	4	8		2			3	

3.6 ANALYZING ARGUMENTS WITH TRUTH TABLES

Truth Tables (Two Premises) • Valid and Invalid Argument Forms • Truth Tables (More Than Two Premises) • Arguments of Lewis Carroll

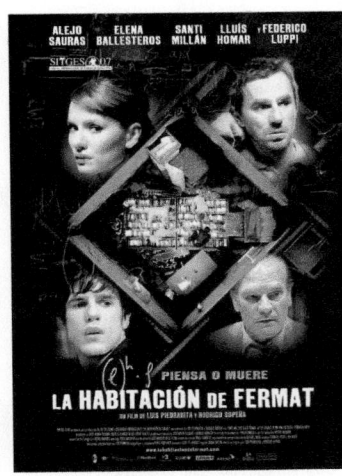

In the 2007 Spanish film *La Habitacion de Fermat (Fermat's Room)*, four mathematicians are invited to dinner, only to discover that the room in which they are meeting is designed to eventually crush them as walls creep in closer and closer. The only way for them to delay the inevitable is to answer enigmas, questions, puzzles, problems, and riddles that they are receiving on a cell phone.

One of the enigmas deals with a hermetically sealed room that contains a single light bulb. There are three switches outside the room, and only one of the switches controls the bulb. You are allowed to push any or all of the buttons as many times as you wish before you enter the room, but once you enter you cannot return to the switches outside. How can you determine which one controls the bulb? (The answer is on **page 126.**)

Truth Tables (Two Premises)

In **Section 3.5** we used Euler diagrams to test the validity of arguments. While Euler diagrams often work well for simple arguments, difficulties can develop with more complex ones, because Euler diagrams require a sketch showing every possible case. In complex arguments, it is hard to be sure that all cases have been considered.

In deciding whether to use Euler diagrams to test the validity of an argument, look for quantifiers such as "all," "some," or "no." These words often indicate arguments best tested by Euler diagrams. If these words are absent, it may be better to use truth tables to test the validity of an argument.

As an example of this method, consider the following argument:

> If the floor is dirty, then I must mop it.
> The floor is dirty.
> _____
> I must mop it.

To test the validity of this argument, we begin by identifying the *component* statements found in the argument. They are "the floor is dirty" and "I must mop it." We assign the letters p and q to represent these statements:

p represents "the floor is dirty";

q represents "I must mop it."

Now we write the two premises and the conclusion in symbols.

> Premise 1: $p \rightarrow q$
> Premise 2: p
> _____
> Conclusion: q

To decide if this argument is valid, we must determine whether the conjunction of both premises implies the conclusion for all possible cases of truth values for p and q. Therefore, write the conjunction of the premises as the antecedent of a conditional statement, and the conclusion as the consequent.

$$[(p \rightarrow q) \quad \wedge \quad p] \quad \rightarrow \quad q$$

$$\uparrow \qquad \uparrow \qquad \uparrow \qquad \uparrow \qquad \uparrow$$

premise   and   premise   implies   conclusion

Finally, construct the truth table for this conditional statement, as shown below.

p	q	$p \rightarrow q$	$(p \rightarrow q) \wedge p$	$[(p \rightarrow q) \wedge p] \rightarrow q$
T	T	T	T	T
T	F	F	F	T
F	T	T	F	T
F	F	T	F	T

Because the final column, shown in color, indicates that the conditional statement that represents the argument is true for all possible truth values of p and q, the statement is a tautology. Thus, the argument is valid.

Answer to the Light Bulb question on
page 125.

Label the switches 1, 2, and 3. Turn switch 1 on and leave it on for several minutes. Then turn switch 1 off, turn switch 2 on, and then immediately enter the room. If the bulb is on, then you know that switch 2 controls it. If the bulb is off, touch it to see if it is still warm. If it is, then switch 1 controls it. If the bulb is not warm, then switch 3 controls it.

The pattern of the argument in the floor-mopping example

$$p \rightarrow q$$
$$\underline{p}$$
$$q$$

is called **modus ponens,** or the *law of detachment*.

To test the validity of an argument using a truth table, follow the steps in the box.

Testing the Validity of an Argument with a Truth Table

Step 1 Assign a letter to represent each component statement in the argument.

Step 2 Express each premise and the conclusion symbolically.

Step 3 Form the symbolic statement of the entire argument by writing the *conjunction* of *all* the premises as the antecedent of a conditional statement, and the conclusion of the argument as the consequent.

Step 4 Complete the truth table for the conditional statement formed in Step 3. If it is a tautology, then the argument is valid; otherwise, it is invalid.

▮▮ **EXAMPLE 1** Using a Truth Table to Determine Validity

Determine whether the argument is *valid* or *invalid*.

If my check arrives in time, I'll register for the fall semester.
I've registered for the fall semester.

My check arrived in time.

SOLUTION

Let p represent "my check arrives (arrived) in time" and let q represent "I'll register (I've registered) for the fall semester." The argument can be written as follows.

$$p \rightarrow q$$
$$\underline{q}$$
$$p$$

To test for validity, construct a truth table for the statement $[(p \rightarrow q) \land q] \rightarrow p$.

p	q	$p \rightarrow q$	$(p \rightarrow q) \land q$	$[(p \rightarrow q) \land q] \rightarrow p$
T	T	T	T	T
T	F	F	F	T
F	T	T	T	F
F	F	T	F	T

The third row of the final column of the truth table shows F, and this is enough to conclude that the argument is invalid. ▮▮▮

If a conditional and its converse were logically equivalent, then an argument of the type found in **Example 1** would be valid. Because a conditional and its converse are *not* equivalent, the argument is an example of what is sometimes called the **fallacy of the converse.**

▮▮ **EXAMPLE 2** Using a Truth Table to Determine Validity

Determine whether the argument is *valid* or *invalid*.

If a man could be in two places at one time, I'd be with you.
I am not with you.

A man can't be in two places at one time.

SOLUTION

If p represents "a man could be in two places at one time" and q represents "I'd be with you," the argument is written as follows.

$$\begin{array}{c} p \rightarrow q \\ \sim q \\ \hline \sim p \end{array}$$

The symbolic statement of the entire argument is as follows.

$$[(p \rightarrow q) \wedge \sim q] \rightarrow \sim p$$

The truth table for this argument indicates a tautology, and the argument is valid.

p	q	$p \rightarrow q$	$\sim q$	$(p \rightarrow q) \wedge \sim q$	$\sim p$	$[(p \rightarrow q) \wedge \sim q] \rightarrow \sim p$
T	T	T	F	F	F	T
T	F	F	T	F	F	T
F	T	T	F	F	T	T
F	F	T	T	T	T	T

The pattern of reasoning of this example is called **modus tollens,** or the *law of contraposition*, or *indirect reasoning*. ▮▮▮

With reasoning similar to that used to name the fallacy of the converse, the fallacy

$$\begin{array}{c} p \rightarrow q \\ \sim p \\ \hline \sim q \end{array}$$

is called the **fallacy of the inverse.** An example of such a fallacy is "If it rains, I get wet. It doesn't rain. Therefore, I don't get wet."

▌▌ EXAMPLE 3 Using a Truth Table to Determine Validity

Determine whether the argument is *valid* or *invalid*.

> I'll buy a car or I'll take a vacation.
> I won't buy a car.
> _____
> I'll take a vacation.

SOLUTION

If p represents "I'll buy a car" and q represents "I'll take a vacation," the argument is symbolized as follows.

$$\begin{array}{c} p \vee q \\ \sim p \\ \hline q \end{array}$$

We must set up a truth table for the statement $[(p \vee q) \wedge \sim p] \rightarrow q$.

p	q	$p \vee q$	$\sim p$	$(p \vee q) \wedge \sim p$	$[(p \vee q) \wedge \sim p] \rightarrow q$
T	T	T	F	F	T
T	F	T	F	F	T
F	T	T	T	T	T
F	F	F	T	F	T

The statement is a tautology and the argument is valid. Any argument of this form is valid by the law of **disjunctive syllogism.** ▮▮▮

▐▐ **EXAMPLE 4** Using a Truth Table to Determine Validity

Determine whether the argument is *valid* or *invalid*.

> If it squeaks, then I use WD-40.
> If I use WD-40, then I must go to the hardware store.
> If it squeaks, then I must go to the hardware store.

SOLUTION

Let p represent "it squeaks," let q represent "I use WD-40," and let r represent "I must go to the hardware store." The argument takes on the following general form.

$$p \to q$$
$$q \to r$$
$$\overline{ p \to r }$$

Make a truth table for this statement, which requires eight rows.

$$[(p \to q) \land (q \to r)] \to (p \to r)$$

p	q	r	$p \to q$	$q \to r$	$p \to r$	$(p \to q) \land (q \to r)$	$[(p \to q) \land (q \to r)] \to (p \to r)$
T	T	T	T	T	T	T	T
T	T	F	T	F	F	F	T
T	F	T	F	T	T	F	T
T	F	F	F	T	F	F	T
F	T	T	T	T	T	T	T
F	T	F	T	F	T	F	T
F	F	T	T	T	T	T	T
F	F	F	T	T	T	T	T

This argument is valid because the final statement is a tautology. This pattern of argument is called **reasoning by transitivity,** or the *law of hypothetical syllogism.* ▓▓▓

Valid and Invalid Argument Forms

A summary of the valid and invalid forms of argument presented so far in this section follows.

In a scene near the beginning of the 1974 film *Monty Python and the Holy Grail*, an amazing application of **poor logic** leads to the apparent demise of a supposed witch. Some peasants have forced a young woman to wear a nose made of wood. The convoluted argument they make is this: Witches and wood are both burned, and because witches are made of wood, and wood floats, and ducks also float, if she weighs the same as a duck, then she is made of wood and, therefore, is a witch!

Valid Argument Forms

Modus Ponens	Modus Tollens	Disjunctive Syllogism	Reasoning by Transitivity
$p \to q$	$p \to q$	$p \lor q$	$p \to q$
p	$\sim q$	$\sim p$	$q \to r$
$\overline{q}$	$\overline{\sim p}$	$\overline{q}$	$\overline{p \to r}$

Invalid Argument Forms (Fallacies)

Fallacy of the Converse	Fallacy of the Inverse
$p \to q$	$p \to q$
q	$\sim p$
$\overline{p}$	$\overline{\sim q}$

Truth Tables (More Than Two Premises)

When an argument contains more than two premises, it is necessary to determine the truth values of the conjunction of *all* of them. *If at least one premise in a conjunction of several premises is false, then the entire conjunction is false.*

■ EXAMPLE 5 | Using a Truth Table to Determine Validity

Determine whether the argument is *valid* or *invalid*.

If Eddie goes to town, then Mabel stays at home. If Mabel does not stay at home, then Rita will cook. Rita will not cook. Therefore, Eddie does not go to town.

SOLUTION

In an argument written in this manner, the premises are given first, and the conclusion is the statement that follows the word "Therefore." Let p represent "Eddie goes to town," let q represent "Mabel stays at home," and let r represent "Rita will cook."

$$p \rightarrow q$$
$$\sim q \rightarrow r$$
$$\underline{\sim r}$$
$$\sim p$$

To test validity, set up a truth table for this statement.

$$[(p \rightarrow q) \wedge (\sim q \rightarrow r) \wedge \sim r] \rightarrow \sim p$$

p	q	r	$p \rightarrow q$	$\sim q$	$\sim q \rightarrow r$	$\sim r$	$(p \rightarrow q) \wedge (\sim q \rightarrow r) \wedge \sim r$	$\sim p$	$[(p \rightarrow q) \wedge (\sim q \rightarrow r) \wedge \sim r] \rightarrow \sim p$
T	T	T	T	F	T	F	F	F	T
T	T	F	T	F	T	T	T	F	F
T	F	T	F	T	T	F	F	F	T
T	F	F	F	T	F	T	F	F	T
F	T	T	T	F	T	F	F	T	T
F	T	F	T	F	T	T	T	T	T
F	F	T	T	T	T	F	F	T	T
F	F	F	T	T	F	T	F	T	T

Because the final column does not contain all Ts, the statement is not a tautology. The argument is invalid.   ■■■

Arguments of Lewis Carroll

Consider the following verse, which has been around for many years.

For want of a nail, the shoe was lost. For want of a shoe, the horse was lost. For want of a horse, the rider was lost. For want of a rider, the battle was lost. For want of a battle, the war was lost.
    Therefore, for want of a nail, the war was lost.

Each line of the verse may be written as an *if . . . then* statement. For example, the first line may be restated as "if a nail is lost, then the shoe is lost." The conclusion, "for want of a nail, the war was lost," follows from the premises, because repeated use of the law of transitivity applies. Arguments such as the one used by Lewis Carroll in the next example often take on a similar form.

Alice in the Forest of Forgetfulness
When Alice entered the Forest of Forgetfulness, she often forgot what day of the week it was. She encountered a Lion and a Unicorn, two strange creatures. The Lion lies on Mondays, Tuesdays, and Wednesdays and tells the truth on the other days of the week. The Unicorn, on the other hand, lies on Thursdays, Fridays, and Saturdays, but tells the truth on the other days of the week.

One day Alice met the Lion and the Unicorn resting under a tree. They made the following statements:

Lion: Yesterday was one of my lying days.
Unicorn: Yesterday was one of my lying days, too.

From these two statements, Alice was able to deduce the day of the week. What day was it? (The answer is on **page 133**.)

(Adapted from a problem in Raymond Smullyan's *What Is the Name of This Book?*)

EXAMPLE 6 Supplying a Conclusion to Assure Validity

Supply a conclusion that yields a valid argument for the following premises.

> Babies are illogical.
> Nobody is despised who can manage a crocodile.
> Illogical persons are despised.

SOLUTION
First, write each premise in the form *if . . . then. . . .*

> If you are a baby, then you are illogical.
> If you can manage a crocodile, then you are not despised.
> If you are illogical, then you are despised.

Let p be "you are a baby," let q be "you are logical," let r be "you can manage a crocodile," and let s be "you are despised." The statements can be written symbolically.

$$p \to \sim q$$
$$r \to \sim s$$
$$\sim q \to s$$

Begin with any letter that appears only once. Here p appears only once. Using the contrapositive of $r \to \sim s$, which is $s \to \sim r$, rearrange the statements as follows.

$$p \to \sim q$$
$$\sim q \to s$$
$$s \to \sim r$$

From the three statements, repeated use of reasoning by transitivity gives the conclusion

$$p \to \sim r, \quad \text{which leads to a valid argument.}$$

In words, the conclusion is "If you are a baby, then you cannot manage a crocodile," or, as Lewis Carroll would have written it, "Babies cannot manage crocodiles." ■■■

3.6 EXERCISES

Each argument is either valid by one of the forms of valid arguments discussed in this section, or it is a fallacy by one of the forms of invalid arguments discussed. (See the summary boxes.) Decide whether the argument is valid *or a* fallacy, *and give the form that applies.*

1. If James Taylor comes to town, then I will go to the concert.
If I go to the concert, then I'll call in sick for work.
___
If James Taylor comes to town, then I'll call in sick for work.

2. If you use binoculars, then you get a glimpse of the space shuttle.
If you get a glimpse of the space shuttle, then you'll be amazed.
___
If you use binoculars, then you'll be amazed.

3. If Julie Nhem works hard enough, she will get a promotion.
Julie Nhem works hard enough.
___
She gets a promotion.

4. If Andrew Noble sells his quota, he'll get a bonus.
Andrew Noble sells his quota.
___
He gets a bonus.

5. If he doesn't have to get up at 3:00 A.M., he's ecstatic.
He's ecstatic.
___
He doesn't have to get up at 3:00 A.M.

6. If she buys another pair of shoes, her closet will overflow.
Her closet will overflow.
___
She buys another pair of shoes.

7. If Mariano Rivera pitches, the Yankees win.
The Yankees do not win.
_____

Mariano Rivera does not pitch.

8. If Nelson Dida plays, the opponent gets shut out.
The opponent does not get shut out.
_____

Nelson Dida does not play.

9. "If we evolved a race of Isaac Newtons, that would not be progress." (quote from Aldous Huxley)
We have not evolved a race of Isaac Newtons.
_____

That is progress.

10. "If I have seen farther than others, it is because I stood on the shoulders of giants." (quote from Sir Isaac Newton)
I have not seen farther than others.
_____

I have not stood on the shoulders of giants.

11. She uses e-commerce or she pays by credit card.
She does not pay by credit card.
_____

She uses e-commerce.

12. Mia kicks or Drew passes.
Drew does not pass.
_____

Mia kicks.

Use a truth table to determine whether the argument is valid *or* invalid.

13. $p \lor q$
p
_____

$\sim q$

14. $p \land \sim q$
p
_____

$\sim q$

15. $\sim p \to \sim q$
q
_____

p

16. $p \lor \sim q$
p
_____

$\sim q$

17. $p \to q$
$q \to p$
_____

$p \land q$

18. $\sim p \to q$
p
_____

$\sim q$

19. $p \to \sim q$
q
_____

$\sim p$

20. $p \to \sim q$
$\sim p$
_____

$\sim q$

21. $(p \land q) \lor (p \lor q)$
q
_____

p

22. $(p \to q) \land (q \to p)$
p
_____

$p \lor q$

23. $(\sim p \lor q) \land (\sim p \to q)$
p
_____

$\sim q$

24. $(r \land p) \to (r \lor q)$
$q \land p$
_____

$r \lor p$

25. $(\sim p \land r) \to (p \lor q)$
$\sim r \to p$
_____

$q \to r$

26. $(p \to \sim q) \lor (q \to \sim r)$
$p \lor \sim r$
_____

$r \to p$

27. Earlier we showed how to analyze arguments using Euler diagrams. Refer to **Example 4** in this section, restate each premise and the conclusion using a quantifier, and then draw an Euler diagram to illustrate the relationship.

28. Explain in a few sentences how to determine the statement for which a truth table will be constructed so that the arguments that follow in **Exercises 29–38** can be analyzed for validity.

Determine whether each argument is valid *or* invalid.

29. Joey loves to watch movies. If Terry likes to jog, then Joey does not love to watch movies. If Terry does not like to jog, then Carrie drives a school bus. Therefore, Carrie drives a school bus.

30. If Hurricane Gustave hit that grove of trees, then the trees are devastated. People plant trees when disasters strike and the trees are not devastated. Therefore, if people plant trees when disasters strike, then Hurricane Gustave did not hit that grove of trees.

31. If the social networking craze continues, then downloading music will remain popular. American Girl dolls are favorites or downloading music will remain popular. American Girl dolls are not favorites. Therefore, the social networking craze does not continue.

32. Carrie Underwood sings or Joe Jonas is not a teen idol. If Joe Jonas is not a teen idol, then Jennifer Hudson does not win a Grammy. Jennifer Hudson wins a Grammy. Therefore, Carrie Underwood does not sing.

33. The Dolphins will be in the playoffs if and only if Chad leads the league in passing. Tony coaches the Dolphins or Chad leads the league in passing. Tony does not coach the Dolphins. Therefore, the Dolphins will not be in the playoffs.

34. If I've got you under my skin, then you are deep in the heart of me. If you are deep in the heart of me, then you are not really a part of me. You are deep in the heart of me or you are really a part of me. Therefore, if I've got you under my skin, then you are really a part of me.

35. If Dr. Hardy is a department chairman, then he lives in Atlanta. He lives in Atlanta and his first name is Larry. Therefore, if his first name is not Larry, then he is not a department chairman.

36. If I were your woman and you were my man, then I'd never stop loving you. I've stopped loving you. Therefore, I am not your woman or you are not my man.

37. All men are created equal. All people who are created equal are women. Therefore, all men are women.

38. All men are mortal. Socrates is a man. Therefore, Socrates is mortal.

39. Suppose that you ask a stranger for the time and you get the following response:

"If I tell you the time, then we'll start chatting. If we start chatting, then you'll want to meet me at a truck stop. If we meet at a truck stop, then we'll discuss my family. If we discuss my family, then you'll find out that my daughter is available for marriage. If you find out that she is available for marriage, then you'll want to marry her. If you want to marry her, then my life will be miserable since I don't want my daughter married to some fool who can't afford a $10 watch."

Use reasoning by transitivity to draw a valid conclusion.

40. Molly Riggs made the following observation: "If I want to determine whether an argument leading to the statement

$$[(p \rightarrow q) \land \sim q] \rightarrow \sim p$$

is valid, I only need to consider the lines of the truth table which lead to T for the column headed $(p \rightarrow q) \land \sim q$." Molly was very perceptive. Can you explain why her observation was correct?

In the arguments used by Lewis Carroll, it is helpful to restate a premise in if . . . then *form in order to more easily identify a valid conclusion. The following premises come from Lewis Carroll. Write each premise in* if . . . then *form.*

41. All my poultry are ducks.

42. None of your sons can do logic.

43. Guinea pigs are hopelessly ignorant of music.

44. No teetotalers are pawnbrokers.

45. No teachable kitten has green eyes.

46. Opium-eaters have no self-command.

47. I have not filed any of them that I can read.

48. All of them written on blue paper are filed.

Exercises 49–54 involve premises from Lewis Carroll. Write each premise in symbols, and then in the final part, give a conclusion that yields a valid argument.

49. Let *p* be "it is a duck," *q* be "it is my poultry," *r* be "one is an officer," and *s* be "one is willing to waltz."

   (a) No ducks are willing to waltz.

   (b) No officers ever decline to waltz.

   (c) All my poultry are ducks.

   (d) Give a conclusion that yields a valid argument.

50. Let *p* be "one is able to do logic," *q* be "one is fit to serve on a jury," *r* be "one is sane," and *s* be "he is your son."

   (a) Everyone who is sane can do logic.

   (b) No lunatics are fit to serve on a jury.

   (c) None of your sons can do logic.

   (d) Give a conclusion that yields a valid argument.

51. Let *p* be "one is honest," *q* be "one is a pawnbroker," *r* be "one is a promise-breaker," *s* be "one is trustworthy," *t* be "one is very communicative," and *u* be "one is a wine-drinker."

   (a) Promise-breakers are untrustworthy.

   (b) Wine-drinkers are very communicative.

   (c) A person who keeps a promise is honest.

   (d) No teetotalers are pawnbrokers. (*Hint:* Assume "teetotaler" is the opposite of "wine-drinker.")

   (e) One can always trust a very communicative person.

   (f) Give a conclusion that yields a valid argument.

52. Let *p* be "it is a guinea pig," *q* be "it is hopelessly ignorant of music," *r* be "it keeps silent while the *Moonlight Sonata* is being played," and *s* be "it appreciates Beethoven."

   (a) Nobody who really appreciates Beethoven fails to keep silent while the *Moonlight Sonata* is being played.

   (b) Guinea pigs are hopelessly ignorant of music.

   (c) No one who is hopelessly ignorant of music ever keeps silent while the *Moonlight Sonata* is being played.

   (d) Give a conclusion that yields a valid argument.

53. Let p be "it begins with 'Dear Sir'," q be "it is crossed," r be "it is dated," s be "it is filed," t be "it is in black ink," u be "it is in the third person," v be "I can read it," w be "it is on blue paper," x be "it is on one sheet," and y be "it is written by Brown."

(a) All the dated letters are written on blue paper.

(b) None of them are in black ink, except those that are written in the third person.

(c) I have not filed any of them that I can read.

(d) None of them that are written on one sheet are undated.

(e) All of them that are not crossed are in black ink.

(f) All of them written by Brown begin with "Dear Sir."

(g) All of them written on blue paper are filed.

(h) None of them written on more than one sheet are crossed.

(i) None of them that begin with "Dear Sir" are written in the third person.

(j) Give a conclusion that yields a valid argument.

54. Let p be "he is going to a party," q be "he brushes his hair," r be "he has self-command," s be "he looks fascinating," t be "he is an opium-eater," u be "he is tidy," and v be "he wears white kid gloves."

(a) No one who is going to a party ever fails to brush his hair.

(b) No one looks fascinating if he is untidy.

(c) Opium-eaters have no self-command.

(d) Everyone who has brushed his hair looks fascinating.

(e) No one wears white kid gloves unless he is going to a party. (*Hint:* "a unless b" $\equiv \sim b \rightarrow a$.)

(f) A man is always untidy if he has no self-command.

(g) Give a conclusion that yields a valid argument.

Answer to Alice in the Forest of Forgetfulness problem on **page 130:**

The only days the Lion can say, "I lied yesterday" are Mondays and Thursdays. The only days the Unicorn can say "I lied yesterday" are Thursdays and Sundays. Therefore the only day they can both say that is Thursday.

COLLABORATIVE INVESTIGATION

Logic Problems and Sudoku Revisited

Logic problems and Sudoku were first discussed in the **Extension** on **pages 120–124.** The problems here require more time and reasoning skills than the ones appearing in the **Extension.** They are taken from *Original Logic Problems*, February 2010, and *Dell Original Sudoku*, March 2010.

The class may wish to divide up into groups and see which group can solve these problems fastest.

EXERCISES

Note: As an exception to our usual style, answers to these Collaborative Investigation Exercises are given in the back of the book.

1. *Out to Launch* The National Space Association has scheduled five rockets for launch early next year. Each rocket (including the *Penchant*) will take off in a different month (January through May) on a different date (the 1st through the 5th). Each rocket will launch from a different site (including the San Simeon Launch Center) and engage in a different mission. For fans of the space program, next year will be a real blast! From the information provided, determine the month and date of the launch of the rocket from each launch site, as well as each rocket's mission.

(a) The date of the May launch is numbered exactly two lower than the date of the Willard Island launch. None of the rockets will launch on February 1. The mission to test a new propulsion system won't be launching in January.

(b) The *Liberty* and the rocket that will blast off in April will launch from Cape Carnival and Willard Island in some order. Neither the rocket on a mission to measure magnetic fields (which won't launch on the 1st of a month) nor the Willard Island rocket will blast off on the 3rd of a month.

(c) The *Bravura* will launch the month after the rocket that will blast off on the 4th of a month (which will launch later than the rocket that will land on the moon). The *Liberty* won't blast off on the 2nd of a month.

(d) The rocket that will launch from Cape Carnival won't be testing a new propulsion system. The *Twilight*'s mission (which isn't the mission to repair a satellite) won't begin on the 5th of a month.

(e) The rocket on a mission to investigate strange radiation will launch at some point earlier in the year than the *Liberty* (which won't be repairing a satellite) but at some point later in the year than the vessel that will blast off from the Vandyke Facility.

(f) The rocket that will blast off from Eddings Air Force Base will launch on a lower-numbered date than the one that will launch in March (which won't be testing a new propulsion system), which will blast off on a lower-numbered date than the *Falconer*.

2. *Super Challenger Puzzle* To solve the following Super Challenger puzzle, place a number into every box so that each row across, each column down, each small 16-box square (there are 16 of these), and each of the two diagonals contains each number from 1 to 16. No number may appear more than once in any one row or column, in either diagonal, or within any small 16-box square.

CHAPTER 3 TEST

Write a negation for each statement.

1. $6 - 3 = 3$

2. All men are created equal.

3. Some members of the class went on the field trip.

4. If that's the way you feel, then I will accept it.

5. She applied and got a student loan.

Let p represent "You will love me" and let q represent "I will love you." Write each statement in symbols.

6. If you won't love me, then I will love you.

7. I will love you if you will love me.

8. I won't love you if and only if you won't love me.

Using the same statements as for Exercises 6–8, write each of the following in words.

9. $\sim p \wedge q$

10. $\sim(p \vee \sim q)$

In each of the following, assume that p is true and that q and r are false. Find the truth value of each statement.

11. $\sim q \wedge \sim r$

12. $r \vee (p \wedge \sim q)$

13. $r \rightarrow (s \vee r)$ (The truth value of the statement s is unknown.)

14. $p \leftrightarrow (p \rightarrow q)$

15. Explain in your own words why, if p is a statement, the biconditional $p \leftrightarrow \sim p$ must be false.

16. State the necessary conditions for each of the following.
   (a) a conditional statement to be false
   (b) a conjunction to be true
   (c) a disjunction to be false

Construct a truth table for each of the following.

17. $p \wedge (\sim p \vee q)$

18. $\sim(p \wedge q) \rightarrow (\sim p \vee \sim q)$

Decide whether each statement is true *or* false.

19. Some negative integers are whole numbers.

20. All irrational numbers are real numbers.

Write each conditional statement in if . . . then *form.*

21. All integers are rational numbers.

22. Being a rhombus is sufficient for a polygon to be a quadrilateral.

23. Being divisible by 2 is necessary for a number to be divisible by 4.

24. She digs dinosaur bones only if she is a paleontologist.

For each statement, write **(a)** *the converse,* **(b)** *the inverse, and* **(c)** *the contrapositive.*

25. If a picture paints a thousand words, the graph will help me understand it.

26. $\sim p \rightarrow (q \wedge r)$ (Use one of De Morgan's laws as necessary.)

27. Use an Euler diagram to determine whether the argument is *valid* or *invalid.*

All members of that athletic club save money.
Don O'Neal is a member of that athletic club.

Don O'Neal saves money.

28. Match each argument in parts (a)–(d) in the next column with the law that justifies its validity, or the fallacy of which it is an example, in choices A–F.

A. Modus ponens
B. Modus tollens
C. Reasoning by transitivity
D. Disjunctive syllogism
E. Fallacy of the converse
F. Fallacy of the inverse

(a) If he eats liver, then he'll eat anything.
He eats liver.

He'll eat anything.

(b) If you use your seat belt, you will be safer.
You don't use your seat belt.

You won't be safer.

(c) If I hear *Mr. Bojangles*, I think of her.
If I think of her, I smile.

If I hear *Mr. Bojangles*, I smile.

(d) She sings or she dances.
She does not sing.

She dances.

Use a truth table to determine whether each argument is valid *or* invalid.

29. If I write a check, it will bounce. If the bank guarantees it, then it does not bounce. The bank guarantees it. Therefore, I don't write a check.

30. $\sim p \rightarrow \sim q$
$q \rightarrow p$
$p \vee q$

ANSWERS TO SELECTED EXERCISES

CHAPTER 3 INTRODUCTION TO LOGIC

3.1 Exercises *(pages 88–90)*

1. statement **3.** not a statement **5.** statement
7. statement **9.** statement **11.** not a statement
13. statement **15.** compound **17.** not compound
19. not compound **21.** compound **23.** Her aunt's
name is not Hermione. **25.** At least one dog does not
have its day. **27.** No book is longer than this book.
29. At least one computer repairman can play blackjack.
31. Someone does not love somebody sometime.
33. $x \leq 12$ **35.** $x < 5$ **37.** Answers will vary.
39. She does not have green eyes. **41.** She has green
eyes and he is 60 years old. **43.** She does not have green
eyes or he is 60 years old. **45.** She does not have green
eyes or he is not 60 years old. **47.** It is not the case that
she does not have green eyes and he is 60 years old.
49. $p \wedge \sim q$ **51.** $\sim p \vee q$ **53.** $\sim(p \vee q)$ or,
equivalently, $\sim p \wedge \sim q$ **55.** Answers will vary.
57. C **59.** A, B **61.** A, C **63.** B **65.** true
67. true **69.** true **71.** true **73.** false **75.** Answers
will vary. **77.** Every person here has done that at one
time or another.

3.2 Exercises *(pages 99–100)*

1. false **3.** true **5.** They must both be false. **7.** T
9. T **11.** F **13.** T **15.** T **17.** T **19.** It is a
disjunction, because it means "$6 > 2$ or $6 = 2$." **21.** T
23. F **25.** T **27.** T **29.** F **31.** F **33.** T **35.** T
37. T **39.** 4 **41.** 16 **43.** 128 **45.** seven **47.** FFTF
49. FTTT **51.** TTTT **53.** FFFT **55.** TFFF
57. FFFFTFFF **59.** FTFTTTTT
61. TTTTTTTTTTTFTTT **63.** You can't pay me now
and you can't pay me later. **65.** It is not summer or
there is snow. **67.** I did not say yes or she did not say
no. **69.** $6 - 1 \neq 5$ or $9 + 13 = 7$ **71.** Neither Prancer
nor Vixen will lead Santa's reindeer sleigh next Christmas.
73. T **75.** F **77.**

p	q	$p \veebar q$
T	T	F
T	F	T
F	T	T
F	F	F

79. F **81.** T **83.** The lady is behind Door 2. *Reasoning*:
Suppose that the sign on Door 1 is true. Then the sign on
Door 2 would also be true, but this is impossible. So the
sign on Door 2 must be true, and the sign on Door 1 must
be false. Because the sign on Door 1 says the lady is in
Room 1, and this is false, the lady must be behind Door 2.

3.3 Exercises *(pages 107–109)*

1. If you see it on the Internet, then you can believe it.
3. If an integer is divisible by 10, then it is divisible by 5.
5. If the soldier is a marine, then the soldier loves boot
camp. **7.** If it is a panda, then it does not live in Idaho.
9. If it is an opium-eater, then it has no self-command.
11. true **13.** true **15.** false **17.** true **19.** Answers
will vary. **21.** F **23.** T **25.** T **27.** If they do not raise
alpacas, then he trains dogs. **29.** If she has a bird for a
pet, then they raise alpacas and he trains dogs. **31.** If he
does not train dogs, then they do not raise alpacas or she
has a bird for a pet. **33.** $b \rightarrow p$ **35.** $p \rightarrow \sim s$
37. $p \wedge (s \rightarrow \sim b)$ **39.** $p \rightarrow s$ **41.** T **43.** F
45. T **47.** F **49.** T **51.** T **53.** Answers will vary.
55. TTTF **57.** TTFT **59.** TTTT; tautology **61.** TFTF
63. TTTTTTFT **65.** TTTFTTTTTTTTTTTT
67. one **69.** That is an authentic Rolex watch and I am
not surprised. **71.** The English measures are not
converted to metric measures and the spacecraft does not
crash on the surface of Saturn. **73.** You want to be
happy for the rest of your life and you make a pretty
woman your wife. **75.** You do not give your plants
tender, loving care or they flourish. **77.** She does or he
will. **79.** The person is not a resident of Pensacola or is
a resident of Florida. **81.** equivalent **83.** equivalent
85. not equivalent **87.** equivalent **89.** equivalent
91. $(p \wedge q) \vee (p \wedge \sim q)$; The statement simplifies to p.
93. $p \vee (\sim q \wedge r)$ **95.** $\sim p \vee (p \vee q)$; The statement
simplifies to T.

97. The statement simplifies to $p \wedge q$.

99. The statement simplifies to F.

101. The statement simplifies to $(r \wedge \sim p) \wedge q$.

103. The statement simplifies to $p \vee q$.

105. $525.60

3.4 Exercises *(pages 114–115)*

1. (a) If you were an hour, then beauty would be a minute. **(b)** If beauty were not a minute, then you would not be an hour. **(c)** If you were not an hour, then beauty would not be a minute. **3. (a)** If you don't fix it, then it ain't broke. **(b)** If it's broke, then fix it. **(c)** If you fix it, then it's broke. **5. (a)** If it is dangerous to your health, then you walk in front of a moving car. **(b)** If you do not walk in front of a moving car, then it is not dangerous to your health. **(c)** If it is not dangerous to your health, then you do not walk in front of a moving car. **7. (a)** If they flock together, then they are birds of a feather. **(b)** If they are not birds of a feather, then they do not flock together. **(c)** If they do not flock together, then they are not birds of a feather. **9. (a)** If he comes, then you built it. **(b)** If you don't build it, then he won't come. **(c)** If he doesn't come, then you didn't build it. **11. (a)** $\sim q \rightarrow p$ **(b)** $\sim p \rightarrow q$ **(c)** $q \rightarrow \sim p$ **13. (a)** $\sim q \rightarrow \sim p$ **(b)** $p \rightarrow q$ **(c)** $q \rightarrow p$ **15. (a)** $(q \vee r) \rightarrow p$ **(b)** $\sim p \rightarrow (\sim q \wedge \sim r)$ **(c)** $(\sim q \wedge \sim r) \rightarrow \sim p$ **17.** Answers will vary. **19.** If it is muddy, then I'll wear my galoshes. **21.** If 19 is positive, then $19 + 1$ is positive. **23.** If a number is an integer, then it is a rational number. **25.** If I do logic puzzles, then I am driven crazy. **27.** If Jeff Marsalis is to shave, then he must have a day's growth of beard. **29.** If I go from Boardwalk to Baltic Avenue, then I pass GO. **31.** If a number is a whole number, then it is an integer. **33.** If their pitching improves, then the Nationals will win the pennant. **35.** If the figure is a rectangle, then it is a parallelogram with a right angle. **37.** If a triangle has two perpendicular sides, then it is a right triangle. **39.** If a two-digit number whose units digit is 5 is squared, then the square will end in 25.

41. D **43.** Answers will vary. **45.** true **47.** false **49.** false **51.** contrary **53.** consistent **55.** contrary **57.** consistent **59.** Answers will vary. One example is: That man is Otis Taylor. That man sells books.

3.5 Exercises *(pages 119–120)*

1. valid **3.** invalid **5.** valid **7.** invalid **9.** invalid **11.** invalid **13.** yes **15.** All people with blue eyes have blond hair.
Natalie Graham does not have blond hair.
Natalie Graham does not have blue eyes.
17. invalid **19.** valid **21.** invalid **23.** valid **25.** invalid **27.** invalid **29.** valid

Extension Exercises *(pages 122–124)*

1. Drew, spanakopita, Fresh Air, spearmint; Ilse, buffalo-chicken sandwich, Deltoids, cinnamon; Nash, French onion soup, Liplickers, vanilla; Uma, tuna-salad sandwich, TKO, wintergreen; Xerxes, garlic shrimp, Inti-mints, orange **3.** 1st, Earl, Ox, fire; 2nd, Philip, Rooster, metal; 3rd, Toni, Cow, water; 4th, Lucy, Dragon, earth; 5th, Ivana, Horse, wood

5.
7	4	2	1	6	8	9	3	5
3	1	9	4	5	7	6	2	8
8	6	5	9	3	2	7	1	4
6	2	4	7	8	9	1	5	3
1	3	8	5	4	6	2	9	7
5	9	7	2	1	3	8	4	6
2	5	3	8	7	1	4	6	9
9	7	6	3	2	4	5	8	1
4	8	1	6	9	5	3	7	2

7.
8	3	9	6	5	7	2	4	1
7	1	2	9	4	3	8	5	6
4	5	6	2	1	8	3	7	9
2	6	7	1	9	4	5	3	8
3	9	1	8	2	5	4	6	7
5	4	8	7	3	6	1	9	2
1	2	3	5	6	9	7	8	4
9	8	4	3	7	2	6	1	5
6	7	5	4	8	1	9	2	3

9.
6	1	7	9	2	3	5	8	4
4	5	9	8	6	1	2	7	3
3	2	8	4	5	7	9	6	1
8	3	5	6	4	9	1	2	7
7	6	1	5	3	2	8	4	9
2	9	4	7	1	8	3	5	6
5	7	2	3	9	6	4	1	8
1	8	3	2	7	4	6	9	5
9	4	6	1	8	5	7	3	2

3.6 Exercises *(pages 130–133)*

1. valid by reasoning by transitivity **3.** valid by modus ponens **5.** fallacy by fallacy of the converse **7.** valid by modus tollens **9.** fallacy by fallacy of the inverse **11.** valid by disjunctive syllogism **13.** invalid **15.** valid **17.** invalid **19.** valid **21.** invalid **23.** invalid **25.** invalid

27. Every time something squeaks, I use WD-40.
Every time I use WD-40, I go to the hardware store.
Every time something squeaks, I go to the hardware store.

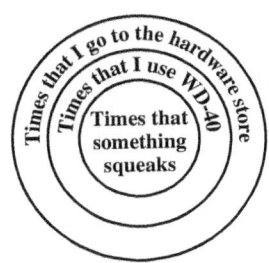

29. valid   **31.** invalid   **33.** invalid   **35.** valid
37. valid   **39.** If I tell you the time, then my life will be
miserable.   **41.** If it is my poultry, then it is a duck.
43. If it is a guinea pig, then it is hopelessly ignorant of
music.   **45.** If it is a teachable kitten, then it does not
have green eyes.   **47.** If I can read it, then I have not
filed it.   **49. (a)** $p \rightarrow \sim s$ **(b)** $r \rightarrow s$ **(c)** $q \rightarrow p$
(d) None of my poultry are officers.   **51. (a)** $r \rightarrow \sim s$
(b) $u \rightarrow t$ **(c)** $\sim r \rightarrow p$ **(d)** $\sim u \rightarrow \sim q$ **(e)** $t \rightarrow s$
(f) All pawnbrokers are honest.   **53. (a)** $r \rightarrow w$
(b) $\sim u \rightarrow \sim t$ **(c)** $v \rightarrow \sim s$ **(d)** $x \rightarrow r$ **(e)** $\sim q \rightarrow t$
(f) $y \rightarrow p$ **(g)** $w \rightarrow s$ **(h)** $\sim x \rightarrow \sim q$ **(i)** $p \rightarrow \sim u$
(j) I can't read any of Brown's letters.

Collaborative Investigation *(pages 134–135)*
1. Jan. 1, Vandyke Facility, *Penchant*, repair satellite;
Feb. 5, San Simeon Launch Center, *Falconer*, investigate
radiation; Mar. 3, Cape Carnival, *Liberty*, land on moon;
Apr. 4, Willard Island, *Twilight*, test propulsion; May 2,
Eddings Air Force Base, *Bravura*, measure magnetic
fields

2.

⑤	10	11	4	1	6	14	2	16	7	12	8	15	9	13	③
12	⑮	7	3	8	4	9	13	2	11	5	1	16	10	⑭	6
13	8	⑥	14	11	16	10	7	9	15	3	4	5	①	12	2
9	1	2	⑯	5	3	12	15	6	14	10	13	⑪	4	7	8
11	13	9	10	②	14	16	3	1	12	8	⑥	7	15	4	5
7	6	16	2	12	⑩	15	4	13	5	⑨	11	1	3	8	14
1	4	15	12	6	8	⑪	5	3	⑯	7	14	9	2	10	13
3	14	8	5	13	9	7	①	④	2	15	10	12	6	16	11
4	7	5	11	14	12	3	⑩	⑧	6	2	15	13	16	1	9
15	16	1	9	7	5	②	11	10	③	13	12	14	8	6	4
2	12	10	6	9	⑬	4	8	11	1	⑭	16	3	5	15	7
14	3	13	8	⑮	1	6	16	5	9	4	⑦	2	12	11	10
10	9	14	⑦	16	2	8	12	15	13	6	3	④	11	5	1
6	2	⑫	15	4	11	5	14	7	8	1	9	10	⑬	3	16
16	⑤	4	13	3	7	1	6	12	10	11	2	8	14	⑨	15
⑧	11	3	1	10	15	13	9	14	4	16	5	6	7	2	⑫

Chapter 3 Test *(pages 135–136)*
1. $6 - 3 \neq 3$ **2.** Some men are not created equal.
3. No members of the class went on the field trip.
4. That's the way you feel and I won't accept it.
5. She did not apply or did not get a student loan.
6. $\sim p \rightarrow q$ **7.** $p \rightarrow q$ **8.** $\sim q \leftrightarrow \sim p$ **9.** You won't love
me and I will love you.   **10.** It is not the case that you
will love me or I will not love you. (Equivalently: You
won't love me and I will love you.)   **11.** T   **12.** T
13. T   **14.** F   **15.** Answers will vary.   **16. (a)** The
antecedent must be true and the consequent must be
false.   **(b)** Both component statements must be true.
(c) Both component statements must be false.
17. TFFF   **18.** TTTT (tautology)   **19.** false   **20.** true
Wording may vary in the answers for Exercises 21–25.
21. If the number is an integer, then it is a rational
number.   **22.** If a polygon is a rhombus, then it is a
quadrilateral.   **23.** If a number is divisible by 4, then it is
divisible by 2.   **24.** If she digs dinosaur bones, then she is
a paleontologist.   **25. (a)** If the graph helps me
understand it, then a picture paints a thousand words.
(b) If a picture doesn't paint a thousand words, then the
graph won't help me understand it.   **(c)** If the graph
doesn't help me understand it, then a picture doesn't
paint a thousand words.   **26. (a)** $(q \wedge r) \rightarrow \sim p$
(b) $p \rightarrow (\sim q \vee \sim r)$ **(c)** $(\sim q \vee \sim r) \rightarrow p$ **27.** valid
28. (a) A   **(b)** F   **(c)** C   **(d)** D   **29.** valid   **30.** invalid

COMPOUND AMOUNT

If P dollars is deposited for n time periods at a compound interest rate i per period, the **compound amount** A is

$$A = P(1 + i)^n.$$

Consider an ordinary annuity of n payments of R dollars each at the end of consecutive interest periods with interest compounded at a rate of i per period. The **future value** S of the annuity is:

$$S = R\left[\frac{(1 + i)^n - 1}{i}\right].$$

The **present value** P of the annuity is:

$$P = R\left[\frac{1 - (1 + i)^{-n}}{i}\right].$$

The **matrix** version of the elimination method uses the following **matrix row operations** to obtain the augmented matrix of an equivalent system. They correspond to using elementary row operations on a system of equations.

1. Interchange any two rows.
2. Multiply each element of a row by a nonzero constant.
3. Replace a row by the sum of itself and a constant multiple of another row in the matrix.

UNION RULE

For any events E and F from a sample space S.

$$P(E \cup F) = P(E) + P(F) - P(E \cap F).$$

PROPERTIES OF PROBABILITY

Let S be a sample space consisting of n distinct outcomes $s_1, s_2, \ldots, s_n$. An acceptable probability assignment consists of assigning to each outcome s_1 a number p_1 (the probability of s_1) according to these rules.

1. The probability of each outcome is a number between 0 and 1.

$$0 \le p_1 \le 1, \quad 0 \le p_2 \le 1, \quad \ldots, \quad 0 \le p_n \le 1.$$

2. The sum of the probabilities of all possible outcomes is 1.

$$p_1 + p_2 + p_3 + \cdots + p_n = 1.$$

BAYES' FORMULA

For any events E and $F_1, F_2, \ldots, F_n$, from a sample space S, where $F_1 \cup F_2 \ldots \cup F_n = S$,

$$P(F_i|E) = \frac{P(F_i) \cdot P(E|F_i)}{P(F_1) \cdot P(E|F_1) + \cdots + P(F_n) \cdot P(E|F_n)}.$$

PERMUTATIONS

The number of permutations of n elements taken r at a time, where $r \leq n$, is

$$_nP_r = \frac{n!}{(n - r)!}.$$

COMBINATIONS

The number of combinations of n elements taken r at a time, where $r \leq n$, is

$$_nC_r = \binom{n}{r} = \frac{n!}{(n - r)!r!}.$$

BINOMIAL PROBABILITY

If p is the probability of success in a single trial of a binomial experiment, the probability of x successes and $n - x$ failures in n independent repeated trials of the experiment is

$$_nC_r p^x (1 - p)^{n-x}.$$

MEAN

The mean of the n numbers, $x_1, x_2, x_3, \ldots, x_n$, is

$$\bar{x} = \frac{x_1 + x_2 + \cdots + x_n}{n} = \frac{\Sigma(x)}{n}.$$

SAMPLE STANDARD DEVIATION

The standard deviation of a sample of n numbers, $x_1, x_2, x_3, \ldots, x_n$, with mean $\bar{x}$, is

$$s = \sqrt{\frac{\Sigma(x - \bar{x})^2}{n - 1}}.$$

BINOMIAL DISTRIBUTION

Suppose an experiment is a series of n independent repeated trials, where the probability of a success in a single trial is always p. Let x be the number of successes in the n trials. Then the probability that exactly x successes will occur in n trials is given by

$$_nC_r p^x (1 - p)^{n-x}.$$

The mean μ and variance σ^2 of a binomial distribution are, respectively,

$$\mu = np \quad \text{and} \quad \sigma^2 = np(1 - p).$$

The standard deviation is

$$\sigma = \sqrt{np(1 - p)}.$$

The **derivative** of the function f is the function denoted f' whose value at the number x is defined to be the number

$$f'(x) = \lim_{h \to 0} \frac{f(x + h) - f(x)}{h},$$

provided this limit exists.

RULES FOR DERIVATIVES

Assume all indicated derivatives exist.

Constant Function   If $f(x) = k$, where k is any real number, then

$$f'(x) = 0.$$

Power Rule   If $f(x) = x^n$, for any real number n, then

$$f'(x) = n \cdot x^{n-1}.$$

Constant Times a Function   Let k be a real number. Then the derivative of $y = k \cdot f(x)$ is

$$y' = k \cdot f'(x).$$

Sum or Difference Rule   If $y = f(x) \pm g(x)$, then

$$y' = f'(x) \pm g'(x).$$

Product Rule   If $f(x) = g(x) \cdot k(x)$, then

$$f'(x) = g(x) \cdot k'(x) + k(x) \cdot g'(x).$$

Quotient Rule   If $f(x) = \dfrac{g(x)}{k(x)}$, and $k(x) \neq 0$, then

$$f'(x) = \frac{k(x) \cdot g'(x) - g(x) \cdot k'(x)}{[k(x)]^2}.$$

Chain Rule   Let $y = f[g(x)]$. Then

$$y' = f'[g(x)] \cdot g'(x).$$

Chain Rule (Alternative Form)   If y is a function of u, say $y = f(u)$, and if u is a function of x, say $u = g(x)$, then $y = f[g(x)]$, and

$$\frac{dy}{dx} = \frac{dy}{du} \cdot \frac{du}{dx}.$$

Generalized Power Rule   Let u be a function of x, and let $y = u^n$ for any real number n. Then

$$y' = n \cdot u^{n-1} \cdot u'.$$

Exponential Function   If $y = e^{g(x)}$, then

$$y' = g'(x) \cdot e^{g(x)}.$$

Natural Logarithmic Function   If $y = \ln |g(x)|$, then

$$y' = \frac{g'(x)}{g(x)}.$$

FIRST DERIVATIVE TEST

Assume that $a < c < b$ and that c is the only critical number for a function f in the interval $[a, b]$. Assume that f is differentiable for all x in $[a, b]$ except possibly at $x = c$.

1. If $f'(a) > 0$ and $f'(b) < 0$, then there is a local maximum at c.
2. If $f'(a) < 0$ and $f'(b) > 0$, then there is a local minimum at c.
3. If $f'(a)$ and $f'(b)$ are both positive, or both negative, then there is no local extremum at c.

SECOND DERIVATIVE TEST

Let c be a critical number of the function f such that $f'(c) = 0$ and $f''(x)$ exists for all x in some open interval containing c.

1. If $f''(c) > 0$, then f has a local minimum at c.
2. If $f''(c) < 0$, then f has a local maximum at c.
3. If $f''(c) = 0$, then this test gives no information; use the first derivative test.

BASIC INTEGRALS

$$\int x^n \, dx = \frac{1}{n+1} x^{n+1} + C \qquad (\text{if } n \neq -1)$$

$$\int e^{kx} \, dx = \frac{1}{k} e^{kx} + C \qquad (\text{if } k \text{ is any real number, } k \neq 0)$$

$$\int \frac{a}{x} \, dx = a \ln |x| + C \qquad (\text{if } x \neq 0)$$

SUBSTITUTION METHOD

Form of the Integral | *Form of the Antiderivative*

1. $\int [u(x)]^n \cdot u'(x) \, dx, \, n \neq -1$ \qquad $\dfrac{[u(x)]^{n+1}}{n+1} + C$

2. $\int e^{u(x)} \cdot u'(x) \, dx$ \qquad $e^{u(x)} + C$

3. $\int \dfrac{u'(x) \, dx}{u(x)}$ \qquad $\ln |u(x)| + C$

TEST FOR LOCAL EXTREMA

Suppose $f(x, y)$ is a function such that f_{xx}, f_{yy}, f_{xy} all exist. Let (a, b) be a critical point for which

$$f_x(a, b) = 0 \quad \text{and} \quad f_y(a, b) = 0.$$

Let M be the number defined by

$$M = f_{xx}(a, b) \cdot f_{yy}(a, b) - [f_{xy}(a, b)]^2.$$

1. If $M > 0$ and $f_{xx}(a, b) < 0$, then f has a local maximum at (a, b).
2. If $M > 0$, and $f_{xx}(a, b) > 0$, then f has a local minimum at (a, b).
3. If $M < 0$, then f has a saddle point at (a, b).
4. If $M = 0$, the test gives no information.